A Guide to the Common Sea Fishes of Southern Africa

TO TANYA AND PETER

A GUIDE TO THE COMMON SEA FISHES OF SOUTHERN AFRICA

Rudy van der Elst

Edited by Peter Borchert

STRUIK

About the author

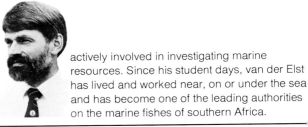

Rudy van der Elst was born in Holland and came to South Africa in 1959. He holds an MSc from Natal University and is Senior Research Officer at the Oceanographic Research Institute in Durban, where he is actively involved in investigating marine resources. Since his student days, van der Elst has lived and worked near, on or under the sea and has become one of the leading authorities on the marine fishes of southern Africa.

Publisher's note:
While every attempt has been made to supply accurate information at the time of going to press, the Publisher cannot accept liability for outdated information. It is advisable for anglers to keep abreast of the current fishing regulations and restrictions for their region.

Struik Publishers (a member of
The Struik Group (Pty) Ltd)
Cornelis Struik House
80 McKenzie Street
Cape Town 8001

Reg. no.: 63/00203/07

First published in hardcover 1981
Second edition 1988
First published in softcover 1985
Second edition 1990
Third edition 1993

Designer: Neville Poulter, Cape Town
Line illustrations: Nadaraj Kistnasamy Nayager, Durban
Lithographic reproduction and photoset by Studiographix (Pty) Ltd, Cape Town
Printed and bound by Kyodo Printing Co (Singapore) Pte Ltd

ISBN 0 86977 464 6 (hardcover)
ISBN 1 86825 394 5 (softcover)

Photographic Credits With a few exceptions, the colour photographs reproduced in this book were taken by the author. Those who kindly made material available from their own collections were: Dr Jack Randall, *Chaetodon kleinii* p. 166, *C. vagabundus* p. 173, *Periopthalmus koelreuteri* p. 202, *Grammistes sexlineatus* p. 203, *Plectorhincus playfairi* p. 207, *P. schotaf* p. 208, *Labroides dimidiatus* p. 230, *Upeneus vittatus* p. 264, *Pomacanthus imperator* (juvenile) p. 279, *P. semicirculatus* (juvenile) p. 280, *Anthias squamipinnis* p. 283; Tony Thorpe, *Pteromylaeus bovinus* p. 60, *Alectis indicus* p. 134, *Carangoides ferdau* p. 138, *C. fulvoguttatus* p. 139; Dr Phil Heemstra, *Epinephelus tukula* p. 327; George Begg, *Lutjanus argentimaculatus* p. 243; Oceanographic Research Institute, *Carcharhinus brevipinna* p. 36, *Galeocerdo cuvier* p. 42, *Taeniura melanospilos* p. 53, *Carcharodon carcharias* p. 56, *Rhinoptera javanica* p. 61, *Raja alba* p. 65, *Poroderma africanum* p. 72, *Squatina africana* p. 78, *Acanthurus triostegus* p. 114; Simon Chater, *Megalaspis cordyla* p. 152, *Trachinotus africanus* p. 158, *Chirocentrus dorab* p. 179, *Scomber japonicus* p. 302, *Argyrops filamentosus* p. 334, *A. spinifer* p. 335; Elinor Bullen, *Thunnus obesus* p. 307; Ernst Röhe, *Merluccius capensis* p. 255; Nat Kistnasamy, *Caesio teres* p. 131, *Atrobucca nibe* p. 291. Copyright for the abovementioned photographs remains with the owners.

CONTENTS

ACKNOWLEDGEMENTS

There are literally thousands of anglers in southern Africa who have given unselfishly of their time, expertise and prize catches to satisfy the marine biologists who perpetually plague them for specimens. To all I'd like to say a big 'thank you'.

I am indeed grateful to the late Professor Margaret Smith, doyenne of ichthyology in southern Africa, for the support she gave me. Much initial encouragement to embark on this project came from Peter Adams, who also put me in touch with my publishers.

Several experts generously provided advice and information: namely Dr Jerry Allen and Dr Paddy Berry (both of the Western Australian Museum), Mike Brokensha (Natal Parks Board), Dr Tony de Freitas of the Oceanographic Research Institute (O.R.I.), Dr Allan Heydorn (National Research Institute for Oceanology), Charles Joubert (O.R.I.), Tony Thorpe (S.A. Anglers' Union) and Dr John E. Randall (Bernice P. Bishop Museum, Hawaii). In particular, the comments of Dr 'Butch' Hulley (S.A. Museum) and Dr John Wallace (P.E. Museum) have been invaluable.

Additional constructive comments on the first edition were gratefully received from Roy Bros (Fisheries Development Corporation), Pat Garratt (O.R.I.), Dr Phil Heemstra (J.L.B. Smith Institute), Dr John Randall, Prof. Margaret Smith, Dr W. Smith-Vaniz (Academy of Natural Sciences, Philadelphia), and Tony Thorpe.

Numerous anglers, colleagues and friends assisted in the collection of fish for photographs, often under trying conditions. In particular I offer my sincere thanks to the following: Michael Chater, Billy Clark, Robert Cooper, Nick de Kok, Jeff Gaisford, Pat Garratt, Christo Herrer, Louis Knobel, Christian Smith, Francois Stemmett, Jack and Tony Thorpe, Barry Rose and Paul White. Special efforts were made by Hennie Crous of the Sea Fisheries Research Institute and by my colleague Simon Chater; these were immensely appreciated.

The generous help of Len Jones, his wife Jessica and Mark Roxburgh in providing spearfishing records and specimens is much appreciated.

Dr 'Jack' Randall's spontaneous response to my last-minute plea for photographic aid is acknowledged with gratitude.

I am grateful to Maureen Smith for her help and encouragement at various stages of production. Others who have helped me in numerous tasks are George Begg, Marilyn Joubert, Logan Naiker and Frances Hanekom.

I am particularly grateful to the tireless assistance of both Lorna Cameron and Franki Adkin in typing and proofreading respectively.

I am indebted to my colleagues at O.R.I. for much support and particularly to our director, Prof. Alan Bowmaker for his advice and sustained enthusiasm. To the former chairman of the South African Association for Marine Biological Research, Bob Levitt, and his board, I express my appreciation for permitting me to publish this book and for allowing me access to library and computer facilities.

I would like to thank Ian Porter and Phil Evers of the University of Natal Electron Microscope Unit for their invaluable aid. Thanks are also due to Dr Walter Fischer of the Food and Agricultural Organization (F.A.O.) of the United Nations for permission to use certain drawings from the organization's *Illustrated Identification Guide to Fishes.*

For the first edition, Peter Borchert and Neville Poulter acted as editor and designer respectively, while Kevin McRae contributed much to the second edition. Their dedication and enthusiasm contributed much to this book.

The excellent line drawings by Nat Kistnasamy, together with his expert knowledge of sharks, have given an added dimension to the introductory pages and are greatly appreciated.

Special recognition is due to the late Tony Thorpe who was a wealth of knowledge about South African angling and an ichthyologist extraordinary. I should like to pay a most sincere tribute to him and his very fine son, Jack, both having helped me so much with this book and in various research programmes. Their presence is sadly missed.

Finally, I would like to thank my wife, Charmaine, for the tremendous enthusiasm and support that she has given me.

INTRODUCTION

Oceans probably represent the most important life-support system on earth. Their influence on climate, oxygen levels and the cycling of nutrients is critical to the survival of life as we know it. In addition to these physical processes, man himself is becoming increasingly dependent on the sea's natural resources, its animal, vegetable and mineral wealth, to secure his future on this planet.

Exploration for minerals, such as oil beneath the sea-bed and manganese nodules on the bottom, is comparatively recent, but already the levels of exploitation are intense. On the other hand, man has used the ocean's renewable resources, its fish and other animals as well as plants, from the earliest times. Such harvesting by humans has, until this century, made little impact on the abundance of marine organisms. Even as recently as the 1930s, the total world catch of fish and shellfish was less than 20 million tons a year. But with the improved technology of fishing gear, echo-sounders used to locate shoals and advanced freezing techniques, this catch increased more than twofold over the following few decades to reach some 70 million tons in 1970. Since then catches have levelled, though human populations have continued to spiral. This increased pressure on marine food resources has had a dramatic effect. A number of fish species have been pushed to the limit of their recuperative powers and some even beyond, as manifested by the collapse of several major fisheries throughout the world.

Regrettably, such examples of marine mismanagement are not rare and that they happen clearly illustrates not only man's expanding need for protein, but also his greed and, possibly most significantly, his ignorance of the delicate fabric of marine life and food webs. Only when the biological processes that govern life in the oceans are properly understood can real progress be made towards optimal and sustained exploitation of the sea.

Much work in this field has already been undertaken by marine researchers worldwide, but this knowledge is of limited value if retained only by a few select scientists. Certainly, it is the obligation of every scientist to publish his or her findings, but too often such literature lies hidden on the shelves and in the stackrooms of institutional libraries. It is of equal, indeed, possibly of greater importance to reach the 'end user', in this case, the fisherman himself. For whether his interest is food or gamefish, commercial gain or recreation, it is only through his personal involvement and well-informed attitudes that marine fisheries can be managed with a responsibility that will not only ensure a high yield of protein for generations to come, but also provide a great many people with endless hours of sheer good sport.

As a guide, this book is intended to help people identify fishes they may see or catch. But it is also intended to help establish a rapport between science and anyone with an interest in the sea and its fishes. To this end, innumerable scientific papers and original research reports were consulted. Hopefully it will broaden the knowledge of many fishermen and, more generally, stimulate an awareness of the fascinating diversity of fish inhabiting the coastal waters of southern Africa. As our coastline is bordered by two oceans and embraces both tropical and temperate waters, many of the fishes encountered here have a far wider world distribution and the information in this book could well prove useful along the shores of other countries.

Care has been taken to include all those species caught by anglers and spearfishermen or seen by scuba divers and other underwater enthusiasts. In all, 316 marine and estuarine species belonging to 99 families are described. Though substantial, this volume does not pretend to be a complete and definitive treatise on the marine fishes of southern Africa and should a reader come across a fish not described here, it is suggested that *Smiths' Sea Fishes* be consulted. If the identity of a fish still remains obscure, the nearest museum should be contacted, or the J.L.B. Smith Institute in Grahamstown, or the Oceanographic Research Institute in Durban.

HOW TO USE THIS BOOK

This book has been specifially designed to provide easy access to any of the 316 species described. It is divided in two: **Part I** (pages 23 to 79) deals with the cartilaginous fishes – the sharks, rays or skates and guitarfishes or sandsharks – while **Part II** (pages 80 to 381) covers the bony fishes. Within these divisions, the more conventional system of arranging books of this nature into evolutionary or phylogenic order has been forsaken in favour of grouping all the families discussed in strict alphabetical order. Where more than one species is described for a family, these too are listed in alphabetical order. For users familiar with these scientific names, this guide is as easy to use as a dictionary, while readers who may know fish only by their common names will find the areas of interest to them via the comprehensive and cross-referenced index beginning on page 394.

Should the reader wish to identify a fish that is unknown to him, the illustrated family introductions between pages 27 and 32 for cartilaginous fishes and 84 and 112 for bony fishes should be consulted. By paging through either of these sections he should be able to select the line drawing that most closely resembles the animal at hand. The accompanying text should confirm his choice, and the cross-reference provided will take him directly to the correct species entries. The advantage of this straightforward, visual system is obvious, for, once the reader has made his selection he does not have to consult the index to find the appropriate species.

Another unique feature is the single page presentation of each species which incorporates a full colour plate. All information on a particular fish is given on that page, succinctly presented in sections. The following information on some of these sections will provide useful background to the reader.

IDENTIFYING FEATURES

Most information presented under this heading is self-explanatory but a few comments are relevant.

1. The number of spines and rays in the dorsal and anal fins is often characteristic and therefore useful in identification. The number of spines can be determined by counting the unsegmented, rigid fin supports. Rays on the other hand are usually much more flexible and have a segmented appearance. In many species the last fin ray may be branched and care must be taken not to count this twice.
2. A gill raker count is also often necessary to establish the correct identity of a species. In this book, the total number of rakers on the entire first gill arch is recorded, except in a few clearly noted cases where only the lower part of the first gill arch is considered. Such counts must be interpreted with care, however, as in many fish, rakers undergo considerable changes with growth. It should be noted that only those rakers that are longer than they are wide are normally counted.
3. Teeth may be diagnostic, especially in sharks, where the tooth formula is most helpful. For example, a tooth count of $\frac{12 - 1 - 12}{10 \text{ or } 11 - 2 - 10 \text{ or } 11}$ means 25 teeth in the upper jaw of which one is central and flanked by 12 on either side. The lower jaw, therefore, has two central teeth with 10 or 11 on either side.
4. In many bony fishes, a careful scale count may be necessary to confirm identity. This is always taken along the lateral line, or at least along the full length of each flank. Should the scales be indistinct, dry the fish in tissue paper and project a beam of light from the tail region along each flank.
5. For the benefit of readers wanting additional taxonomic information on a particular species, the relevant code number of each fish has been given for reference to *Smiths' Sea Fishes*.

DISTRIBUTION

The areas coloured blue on each map illustrate the fish's local and worldwide distribution. On the local map, the grey area indicates the extent of the continental shelf. Obviously individual reports of occurrences and catches outside the accepted range, cannot be accommodated on a map of this scale.

Furthermore, the absence, in several cases, of a fish from an area where it could logically be expected to occur, may well reflect a lack of published information rather than a break in its distribution.

NATURAL HISTORY

Wherever possible, the information in this section has been obtained from studies and observations of local specimens. However, in some cases details have been included from research conducted elsewhere. While in most cases such information would be compatible with southern African populations, there may be instances where there are slight differences.

CAPTURE

The latest lists of angling and spearfishing records have been consulted, but obviously some records will in time be broken. Nevertheless, these figures provide a useful guide as to the upper range of a species' weight.

SPECIFIC CATCH RESTRICTIONS

Where restrictions are based on a fish's size, the total length is usually given, but wherever length is not qualified it may be taken to refer to fork length.

SIMILAR SPECIES

Some fish may prove rather difficult to identify, especially if species of similar appearance also occur in the region. For this reason a section is included which emphasizes those features of the fish that will immediately distinguish it from all others and are thus most likely to lead to a positive identification.

GRAPH

Weight, length and age relationships are graphically portrayed in this book. In many cases these curves are based on the statistics of thousands of specimens and provide a good overall average value of weight and age for certain length.

Whereas the age curve of bony fishes (coloured blue when included) is usually based on analysis of otoliths or scales, that of cartilaginous fishes is based on embryonic growth rate during gestation. From such knowledge it is theoretically possible to predict growth during the course of the animal's life. Though rather 'coarse', this technique remains one of the most useful methods of estimating growth in cartilaginous fishes.

On the lower axis of the graph, length is given in centimetres. To estimate the weight of a fish at a certain length, the corresponding value opposite the black curve must be read off the left axis. Should this value be less than the actual weight of the specimen it can be assumed that it has enjoyed good health or that it may be 'ripe' with milt or roe. If the converse applies, the fish may well be in a poor, possibly post-spawning condition. Age can be similarly determined by reading the blue curve across to the right axis. It is not possible, however, to relate weight directly to age without first calculating the length.

Terminology

Finally, although care has been taken to minimize the use of technical words, in some cases it has not been possible to avoid scientific terminology. Most of these terms are explained in the glossary beginning on page 383 and in some instances, especially in these introductory pages, drawings serve to further illustrate these concepts.

THE SEAS OF SOUTHERN AFRICA

Numerous factors govern the dispersal of fishes in the coastal waters of southern Africa. Certainly one of the major influences on the presence and abundance of fishes is the availability of food. But fishes feed on fishes, other animals and plants, all making up the intricate web of life in the sea. As with plants and animals on land, life in the oceans is primarily governed by physical and chemical parameters which, acting in concert, create specific marine 'climates'. Of these parameters, the most influential are probably ocean currents, temperature, salinity, light and tidal action.

Ocean currents

Flowing like great rivers through and around the main body of the oceans, currents traverse the seas. In terms of the dispersal of fishes, these colossal movements of water are of great importance, for, not only do they carry passively drifting eggs and fry to distant shores, but they also distribute waters of varying temperatures and salinities.

The movement of the ocean currents is far from random and is largely determined by earth rotation and prevailing winds. Generally, the basins of all oceans display similar circulatory patterns; in the southern hemisphere water moves anti-clockwise, while in the north it moves clockwise. Where these circulating waters flow alongside continents they are known as boundary currents. Two such currents influence the southern African coast. Flowing southward along the East Coast is the Indian Ocean's western boundary current, while along the West Coast the eastern boundary current of the Atlantic Ocean flows northwards. From the accompanying map, it is immediately apparent that these currents, the Agulhas and Benguela respectively, push tropical water south and temperate water north.

The mighty Agulhas Current transports more water than any other boundary current in the world. It has its 'source' in the South Equatorial Current flowing down the East African coast. This considerable body of water streams southwards until bisected by Madagascar. South of the island, these branches re-join and, strengthened by water recycled in the southern Indian Ocean, meander down the East Coast of southern Africa. Moving at speeds of 0,5 - 3,5 km/h this current is sometimes as close as two kilometres from the shore while at others, the centre of flow can be as much as 50 km out to sea. Its strength varies seasonally and in summer penetration is greatest, when its warm waters may reach as far south as Cape Point. During winter, and particularly during south-westerly winds, intermittent movements of cool water occur in the very narrow zone between the Agulhas Current and the shore, but flowing in the opposite direction. Known as the Inshore Counter Current, this phenomenon probably plays a vital role in the penetration of fishes from the Cape to Natal, the most famous of these winter migrations being the annual 'sardine run'.

The Benguela Current bathes the West Coast in cool Antarctic water. It is less defined than the Agulhas and generally moves northwards along the coast at an average velocity of 0,8 - 1,1 km/h varying from season to season. Water movements close to the West Coast shore tend to move in sympathy with the prevailing winds, which blow northwards for much of the year. These south easterlies blow parallel to the coast and are generated by the high pressure systems that dominate the offshore Cape waters during summer.

Temperature

Fish, with the exception of some tuna, are cold-blooded animals and in most instances their body temperature differs from that of the water surrounding them by less than one degree. Consequently, water temperature influences their metabolism and plays a controlling role in such processes as growth, digestion, reproduction and swimming speed. Though most species have evolved their physiology to suit a specific temperature range, their eggs or larvae may often require a completely different temperature regime to ensure development. This often necessitates long and arduous migrations by some fishes to suitable spawning grounds, while ocean currents also play a role in the transportation of eggs and larvae to regions more conducive to their development.

Although waters closer to the tropics tend to become warmer, startling differences can occur at similar latitudes. This phenomenon, directly attributable to the influence of ocean currents, is well illustrated by the mean water temperature at Sodwana Bay which is twice as high as that of Luderitz at the same latitude, but on the opposite coast. Where the Agulhas and Benguela currents meet off the southern tip of Africa, the relatively large temperature difference within a limited area results in a significant 'subtraction zone', in effect an almost impenetrable barrier to the distribution of East and West Coast species. Thus, the fishes and other marine life of southern Africa show a marked difference from the limited numbers of a great many species populating the warmer East Coast waters to the vast shoals of relatively few species off the Atlantic seaboard. The great diversity of fish in the coastal waters washed by the Indian Ocean is again influenced by temperature. Warmer waters generally include a wider range of habitats and life cycles are usually shorter. Foodwebs are more complex therefore and hence these regions are suited to a greater variety of organisms.

The actions and effects of the wind, currents and earth rotation are, however, not only confined to surface waters; frequently these elements act together to force water downwards. Also, when water cools, it becomes denser and therefore heavier. In Arctic and Antarctic regions, surface waters may occasionally cool to such an extent that their increased density makes them heavier than the water beneath and they sink. Both processes result in a counter-movement of deeper waters to the surface, which carries with it huge concentrations of nutrient salts that have accumulated in the ocean abyss. Where this phenomenon, termed upwelling, takes place, great blooms of phytoplankton occur, stimulated by the presence of nutrients and light. These prolific growths are the food for filter-feeding zooplankton which in turn attract vast shoals of anchovies, pilchards and other pelagic species – a fact well understood and exploited by fishermen.

However, vertical movement of water is often inhibited

Ocean Currents

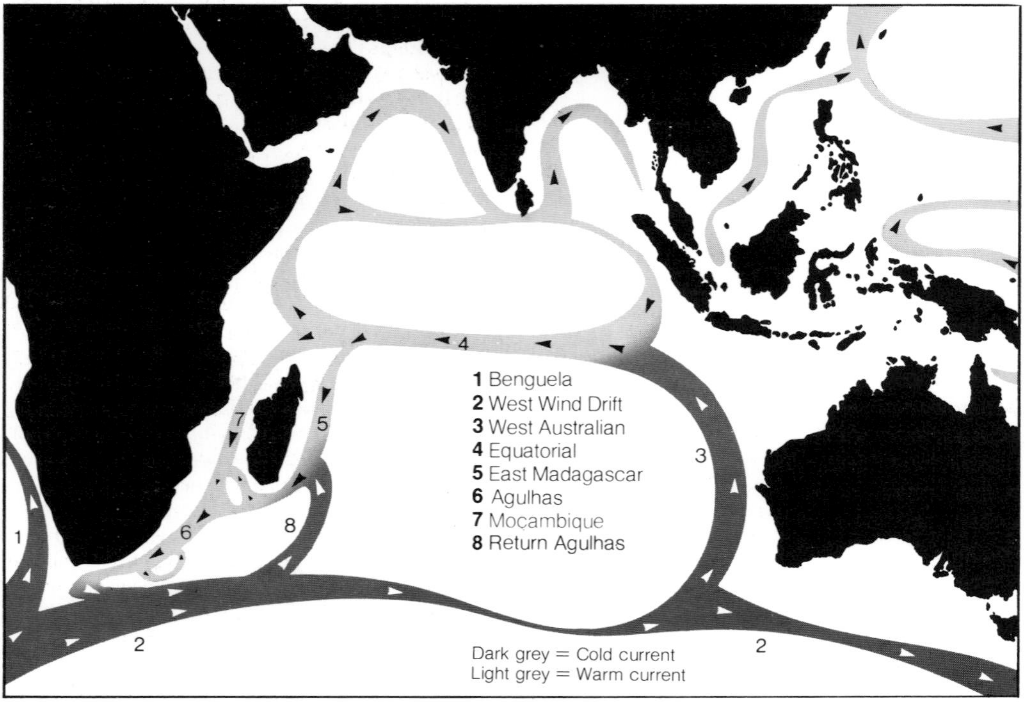

by yet another temperature phenomenon. Over much of the world's oceans a distinct layer of warmer surface water overlies a much cooler, deeper layer. Differences in density preclude mixing, and the interface, known as the thermocline, often creates a formidable temperature barrier that few fishes penetrate.

Average monthly temperatures
(surface coastal waters)

1 Sodwana; **2** Richards Bay; **3** Durban;
4 East London; **5** Port Elizabeth;
6 False Bay; **7** Cape Town; **8** Lamberts Bay.

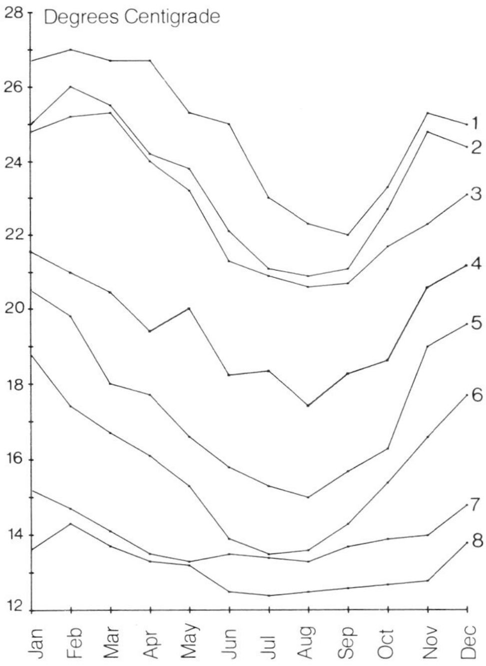

Salinity
The constant cycle of rainfall flowing off the continents and into the seas has, over aeons, leached vast amounts of salts and minerals from the land mass. These salts have become increasingly concentrated in seawater and much of the world's oceans presently contains 35 parts of salt for every 1 000 parts of water. This salinity is expressed in scientific terms as 35‰. Marine fishes have evolved to cope with such salinity, but the majority are highly intolerant of salinity changes (stenohaline) and can only survive concentrations of salt within a range of 34-35‰. There are of course several estuarine species which can tolerate salinities down to 1 and as high as 70‰ (euryhaline), as was shown during Lake St Lucia's hypersaline conditions of 1970.

Generally, salinity fluctuations in the open ocean are minimal, though not unimportant, whereas salinities in coastal waters may fluctuate periodically as a result of heavy rainfall and flooding rivers. When this happens, most stenohaline fish will move away from the affected area only returning when optimal conditions have been re-established.

Fishes experience two major effects when salinities change, one physical and the other chemical. The physical impact results from the change in water density that accompanies salinity fluctuations. Thus a Zambezi shark swimming into the less dense, fresh water of a river system will, on average, find its body 2,6 percent heavier. Whereas some fish could adjust to this change simply by additional inflation of the swim bladder, species that lack such a device, including the Zambezi shark will simply have to swim somewhat more energetically to avoid sinking to the bottom.

The chemical impact of salinity is more complex. Placed in a salt solution that is more concentrated than the salts in its own body fluids (a *hypertonic* environment), a fish will experience a constant inflow of salts into its body, together with a considerable loss of water. Unless counter-balanced, this process of osmosis would result in complete dehydration and death. To achieve the necessary equilibrium, the fish has to actively 'pump' salts from its body via the kidneys and special salt cells located in the gills, while dehydration is prevented by the simultaneous intake of water through the mouth. For the fish suddenly placed in a *hypotonic* environment, the opposite must take place; body salt must be conserved and excess water eliminated to maintain an internal chemical balance.

It is interesting to note that the salt content of bony fishes is lower than that of cartilaginous fishes (sharks and rays). This disparity occurs because sharks are able to accumulate urea salts derived from body waste.

Light
Carbohydrates are the first link in all foodwebs; they are the basic fuels on which all animals, whether on land or in the sea, depend. The prime source of carbohydrates is plant-life and therefore, the proliferation of animals is directly related to the abundance of plants. Plants are the only life forms able to convert the simple compounds of carbon dioxide and water into complex organic matter by the process of photosynthesis, which, as the name implies, is dependent on the presence of light. In the oceans such a primary food source is provided mainly by phytoplankton and, to a lesser extent, by the seaweeds growing in coastal waters.

Although the seas have a vast surface area capable of absorbing light, actual penetration is minimal and with increasing depth, both the intensity and quality of light decreases rapidly. It has been calculated that even in the clearest oceanic water, almost 60 per cent of the total light input is absorbed in the first metre, and about

80 per cent in the first ten metres. Obviously light penetration is also directly related to water clarity and in more turbid coastal waters as much as 90 per cent may be lost in the first metre. It goes without saying, therefore, that the silt poured into the sea by flooding rivers each rainy season must have a detrimental impact on primary productivity.

The total amount of phytoplankton far exceeds that of inshore algae, and provides a food resource that supports immense shoals of pelagic, filter-feeding organisms. Coastal seaweeds, nevertheless, play a vital role in providing energy for many herbivorous fish and invertebrates inhabiting the shallower inshore waters. These primary consumers therefore represent an important link in the overall foodweb as they provide prey for many other species.

Tides

All round the world, regular flows of water surge up the shore and, just as regularly, recede to expose shallow reefs, sandy beaches, mudflats and sandbars. This tidal cycle usually occurs twice each day and is the result of gravitational forces exerted by the moon and sun, as well as by centrifugal forces created by the earth's 'spin'. Tides, not to be confused with currents, vary in frequency and amplitude, with some shores, notably those in northern Europe and America, experiencing a tidal range of as much as 15 m. In southern Africa such extremes are rarely experienced and the range is usually between 1,2 and 2,5 m.

In general, the effect of tides on the habits of most fishes is not very important. Obvious exceptions are those species living in the littoral and estuarine zones. Such fish are usually either small or 'flat' bottom-dwellers, for example juvenile fish, soles or skates, which must migrate with the tides to avoid being stranded. Some species, such as those that feed on intertidal organisms, frequently have feeding periods geared to the tidal cycle. Others are known to regulate their spawning according to the tides, relying on the ebb to carry their progeny out to sea.

FISH AND THEIR DISTRIBUTION

The coastline of southern Africa is almost unequalled in its variety of geography, seas and climate. From tropical Moçambique in the east to the much colder shores of Namibia in the west, widely divergent environments occur, each offering a suitable habitat for numerous different species. Numerous indeed, for approximately 2 200 species have been identified from this region. Nearly 13 per cent of these are possibly endemic – that is, they are restricted to this area.

Fishes are highly mobile creatures but there is a strong tendency for species to inhabit certain zones. The largest of these, the *abyssal zone,* comprises the sub-surface waters of all oceans, occasionally to depths of 10 000 m. Though large in volume, fauna is not particularly prolific mainly because of insufficient light penetration and lack of shelter. Here, in cold, still waters, fishes, sometimes of bizarre design, live a specialized life in total darkness. Many tend to be scaleless and black, with only rudimentary eyes. Enormous jaws bearing large teeth, as well as rows of luminous organs, assist these fish in their hunt for food.

Oceanic surface waters constitute the *pelagic zone.* Though less in volume than the ocean depths, this region has the greatest surface area and its usually crystal clear waters ensure maximum light penetration. Consequently, fish life is often dense, especially where the upwelling of rich nutrients results in prolific blooms of phytoplankton. Herring-like fishes (e.g. pilchards) as well as their predators, tuna, mackerel, dolphinfish and several others are common here. It is interesting to note that most of these inhabitants of offshore surface waters tend to be uniform in shape and pattern, largely because of their relatively static environment. Many are torpedo-shaped, darkly coloured on top and with silvery-white undersides, a two-tone colour scheme which forms an integral part of their defence strategy. Since the surface of the sea is silvery when viewed from underwater and blue-green from above, these fish are inconspicuous to predators whether above or below.

While the greatest mass of fish is found in the pelagic zone, the greatest diversity is undoubtedly found in the *coastal zone* which embraces the waters covering the continental shelf, arbitrarily defined as extending down to the 200 m contour. The majority of the inhabitants of this region dwell close to the shore, in the *littoral zone.* It is for these inshore areas, where most anglers' catches are made, that this book has its greatest application. Here too, fishes display an amazing variety of form and colour. This is mainly determined by the different habitats embraced by the coastal zone; coral reefs, rocky shores with tidal pools, offshore reefs, sandy beaches and estuaries.

Coral reefs

Confined almost exclusively to Moçambique and the marine reserves off Zululand and Natal, the majority of fish encountered here are of tropical origin. A feature characterizing these warmer coastal waters worldwide is the exceptional range of species found. Coral reefs in southern Africa are no exception, the abundant shelter and food they provide encouraging a great multitude of colourful and variously shaped fishes. Such colours are often spectacular and rival those of the surrounding corals, sponges and other creatures. Coral reef inhabitants include butterflyfish, clownfish, painted surgeon and emperor angelfish.

Rocky shores

Although less spectacular than coral reefs in terms of the colour and diversity of inhabitants, rocky shores also offer a suitable habitat for a number of important species. In addition to providing shelter, rocky outcrops tend to accumulate decaying organic matter such as tufts of dislodged seaweed. This increases the primary food supply of the area and, as a result, sessile organisms such as mussels, oysters and redbait proliferate, thereby providing an energy resource and attracting numerous carnivorous fishes. Many of the fishes living along rocky shores are juveniles using these rich habitats as nursery areas. Fish encountered include the blenny, strepie, blacktail and galjoen.

Offshore reefs

Scattered over much of the continental shelf are rocky reefs ranging from steep pinnacles to vast flat areas. These provide shelter and food for large numbers of fish, many of which are resident, that is, present throughout the year. Obviously the type of fish encountered depends largely on the depth of the reef. For example, on very deep reefs, with minimal light penetration and no growth of seaweed, herbivores are absent and most inhabitants are dull coloured and have enlarged eyes better suited to low light levels. Conversely, in shallower waters there is a progressive increase in colour variation and in the number of herbivores. Fish common over deeper reefs are the scorpionfishes, cavebass and blueskin.

Sandy beaches

Long stretches of sandy beach, interspersed only occasionally by rocky promontories, are a feature of much of the southern African coastline. Here, relentless wave action often creates considerable turbulence. The fish inhabiting these regions are largely bottom-dwellers, feeding on burrowing crustaceans or other slow-swimming species. Many have developed special refinements for foraging in the sandy substrate; for example, the ability to separate tiny food organisms from fine sand before the food is swallowed. Several species have, with evolution, acquired a mouth on the underside, while the water intake for breathing has evolved on the upper surface. In this way, sand, which would damage the fine structure of the gills is not inhaled. The largespot pompano, sandsharks, stingrays and white steenbras are representative of the fish fauna along sandy shores.

Estuaries

Many of the fish encountered in other environments may be equally at home in estuaries, at least for a specific part of their life-cycle. It is well known that estuaries act as nutrient traps for the rivers that feed them and, consequently, these regions become enriched and increased productivity results. This, together with safe refuge from a number of predators, makes estuaries ideal nursery areas for many species.

Although fry, and sometimes post-spawning adults, immigrate into estuarine systems, very few species actually spawn in this environment. Granted, a small minority of species do spend their entire lives in estuaries, but the belief that these environments represent vast breeding grounds is totally untrue.

Estuarine environments are highly unstable, with sudden or drastic changes always possible. With each tidal cycle, for example, there may be rapid and immense fluctuations in salinity, temperature, turbidity and hence light-penetration. The average water depth, often no more than a few metres, results in great differences between day and night temperatures. Thus, while many animals would undoubtedly benefit from rich and sheltered estuarine environments, it is only those adapted to endure such harsh physical fluctuations that are successful.

It should be added that the estuary is also a fragile environment, easily disturbed by man's agricultural and industrial development. Regrettably, too many of southern Africa's estuaries have already been grossly mismanaged and siltation, pollution and agricultural encroachment have all taken their toll. Unless these harmful processes can be halted and reversed, the future stock of river bream, mullet and other species that depend on these areas, are at risk.

Clearly many of the zones discussed have no fixed boundaries and obviously fish range freely throughout them. The larger predators, for instance, will travel long distances in pursuit of food-fish, thereby passing through a variety of different habitats. But even among predators there are distinct preferences. Some, such as the kob and the Zambezi shark, which hunt mainly by smell and vibration, prefer turbid water and often hunt at night. Others, including yellowtail, garrick, elf and king mackerel, depend on their acute eyesight to catch prey and therefore require clean water and daylight.

THE LIFE CYCLES OF FISH

Fish hatch or develop from eggs, but in most cases, several intermediate stages take place before adulthood is reached and the cycle is repeated. While some species pass through only a few of these stages, others may have numerous, different life phases, some of them so removed from the form of the mature adult, that the relationship is hard to credit. For example, the larval stage of the springer closely resembles the young eel, only the forked tail revealing its true identity. The juveniles of surgeonfishes, too, are so removed from the adult form that they were once named as a separate genus, *Acronurus*. To add to this confusion, it is known that the life-cycles of bony fishes are fundamentally different to those of cartilaginous fishes.

The main phases in the life cycle of fish are explained on page 15.

MARINE FOOD ORGANISMS

The accompanying illustration shows some of the important components of the foodweb of marine fishes. Smaller animals such as the crab zoea, copepod, krill and isopod are presented larger than life and are, therefore, out of proportion to larger creatures such as the rock lobster and octopus.

1 squid; **2** polychaete worm; **3** crab zoea; **4** rock lobster; **5** krill; **6** mysid; **7** phyllosoma; **8** crab megalopa; **9** copepod; **10** ascidian; **11** amphipod; **12** shrimp; **13** gastropod mollusc; **14** brittlestar; **15** sand dollar; **16** sea urchin; **17** cuttlefish; **18** hermit crab; **19** bivalve mollusc; **20** swimming crab; **21** barnacle; **22** sponge; **23** octopus; **24** stomatopod (mantis shrimp); **25** isopod; **26** mole crab; **27** mud-prawn; **28** tube worm.

Egg phase

Once fertilized, the egg represents the starting point of any fish's life.

Bony fishes In most instances the egg is externally fertilized, usually by a simple mixing of the male and female reproductive products in the surrounding water. The egg is then passively transported by ocean currents to distant nursery areas, or cemented to some submarine object by the parent fish. In both cases, embryonic development is quite rapid and the larval fish may emerge within 36 hours, though in eggs attached to the substrate this may take a little longer.

Cartilaginous fishes Here the egg is fertilized internally, sperm being transmitted into the female by means of the male's claspers. In some groups, the egg is then encapsulated into a 'mermaid's purse' and attached by the mother to some suitable underwater object (oviparous). In others, the encapsulated embryo is retained within the mother's uterus where it also soon hatches (ovoviviparous), while yet others merely have free eggs in the uterus, eventually giving birth to well-developed young (viviparous).

Larval phase

This phase is reached as soon as the embryo becomes self-sustaining, but usually before it has assumed the characteristics of the adult. In several cases larvae do not occur, and the embryo develops directly into the juvenile.

Bony fishes In most cases the large yolk sac is now progressively used up and the passively drifting larvae begin to feed on minute planktonic organisms. This phase may last for several months until these young metamorphose into juveniles that usually, but not always, resemble adults. In species where the eggs have been deposited on the sea-bed, larval life is sacrificed in favour of a lengthy embryonic stage, thereby ensuring that the young are particularly well developed and able to cope with the reef environment immediately on hatching.

Cartilaginous fishes The larval phase in this group is either absent or strongly reduced and is certainly never subjected to the harsh conditions of the open sea. The embryo may develop into an egg capsule or within the mother's uterus and in most instances there is a very substantial yolk supply on which the developing young can feed for months, if not years. In the case of viviparous and ovoviviparous species, the young, living freely in the uterus, most closely resemble larvae as they are nourished on fluids secreted by the mother while some even feed on unfertilized eggs and other embryos. In oviparous cartilaginous fishes the developing embryo is also nourished by yolk, but usually hatches at a less developed stage.

Typical life cycles

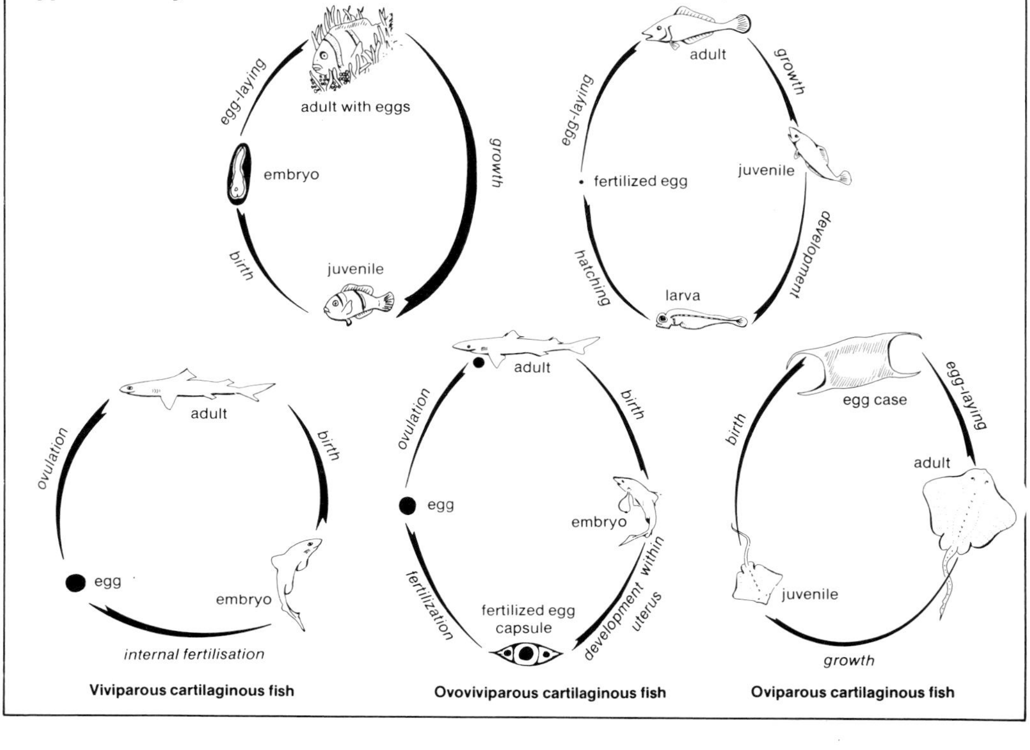

Juvenile phase

During this part of a fish's life, when it usually resembles the adult, the juvenile actively forages for food and gradually grows through adolescence into adulthood.

Bony fishes Very often the juveniles of a certain species will congregate in specific regions known as nursery areas, where the abundant supply of food and shelter ensures a maximum survival rate. Estuaries are perhaps the best-known nursery areas, but of equal if not greater importance are sheltered reefs and quiet bays. During the juvenile phase of some species, considerable changes in body colour and proportions may occur, ultimately resulting in the recognizable adult form.

Cartilaginous fishes The juveniles of these fishes are always proportionately much larger at birth than bony fishes, some measuring one third the length of their parents. As a result they are better able to cope with the environment and are less dependent on nurseries. Nevertheless, many juvenile sharks congregate in certain areas, apparently often to escape their cannibalistic parents. Although some changes in body proportions occur during this growth period, most cartilaginous juveniles closely resemble adults.

Adult phase

Once sexual maturity has been attained, the adult or reproductive phase of a fish's life commences with the development of ovaries, testes and, occasionally, secondary sexual characteristics. Triggered by phenomena including fluctuating water temperatures, daylight hours and salinity, the fish now enters its breeding period, which in many cases has a distinct annual cycle. Unlike most other vertebrate animals, fishes continue to grow after reaching sexual maturity and in many instances their ultimate size is probably only limited by their life span.

Bony fishes It usually takes from one to four years to attain sexual maturity. After this some fish may claim territories, while others may congregate into shoals, as a prelude to their spawning season. In the majority of cases, external fertilization occurs and hence vast quantities of eggs are shed to guarantee a high success rate. Clearly the more eggs produced, the greater the species' future abundance. The actual number of eggs released depends also on body size and hence older, larger fish make a greater contribution to future generations than recently matured individuals.

Cartilaginous fishes A period of up to ten years may be required before sexual maturity is attained. These fishes may then form pairs, or group into small shoals as a prelude to copulation. The number of young produced is normally directly related to the gestation period, with short-term pregnancies producing more pups. The overall size of female sharks usually does not have any great influence on their carrying capacity.

Cartilaginous fishes not only produce fewer young than bony fishes but their growth rates are also much slower.

THE EVOLUTION OF FISH

This chart is a hypothetical and schematic representation of the evolutionary pathways and relationships between some of the fishes appearing in this book. It is largely based on fossil records which are, in many cases, incomplete.

At the base of the chart is a geologic time-scale against which the evolution of fishes can be partly measured. Notice how the cartilaginous fishes are no older than the bony fishes, but have remained relatively unchanged for some 200 million years. By contrast, the bony fishes have diversified comparatively recently, especially the Perciformes, or spined fishes, to which the majority of modern fishes belong.

(Based on Nikolsky, 1965, and Greenwood *et al,* 1966)

1 Ordovician
2 Silurian
3 Devonian
4 Carboniferous
5 Permian
6 Triassic
7 Jurassic
8 Cretaceous
9 Tertiary
10 Quaternary

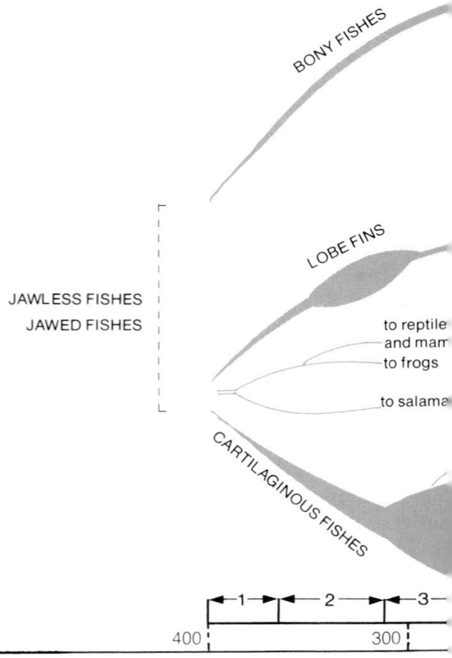

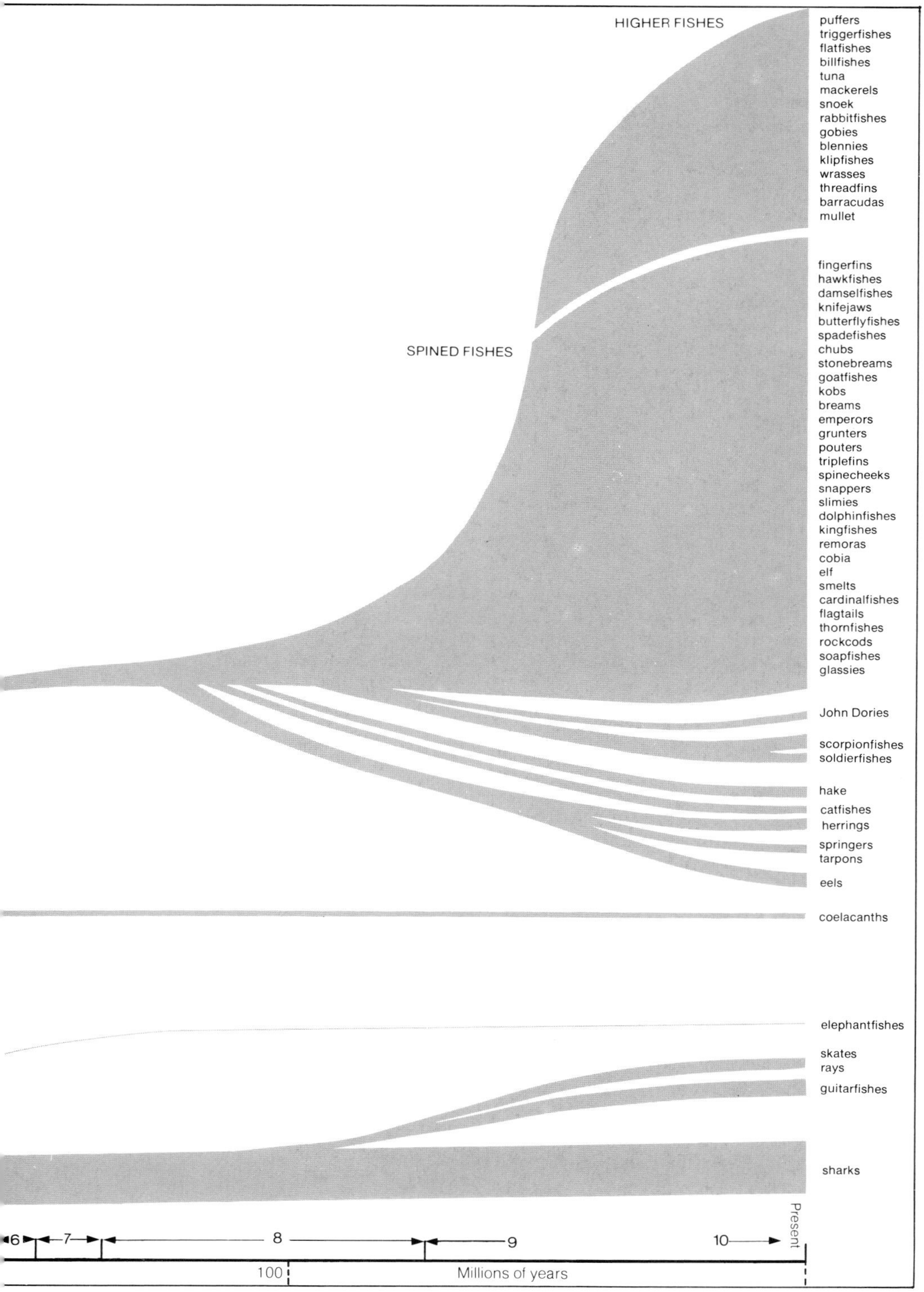
HIGHER FISHES
puffers
triggerfishes
flatfishes
billfishes
tuna
mackerels
snoek
rabbitfishes
gobies
blennies
klipfishes
wrasses
threadfins
barracudas
mullet
SPINED FISHES
fingerfins
hawkfishes
damselfishes
knifejaws
butterflyfishes
spadefishes
chubs
stonebreams
goatfishes
kobs
breams
emperors
grunters
pouters
triplefins
spinecheeks
snappers
slimies
dolphinfishes
kingfishes
remoras
cobia
elf
smelts
cardinalfishes
flagtails
thornfishes
rockcods
soapfishes
glassies
John Dories
scorpionfishes
soldierfishes
hake
catfishes
herrings
springers
tarpons
eels
coelacanths
elephantfishes
skates
rays
guitarfishes
sharks
Present
6
7
8
9
10
100
Millions of years

THE NAMING OF FISH

There can be few coastal fishes for which fishermen and anglers have not coined a name, and there are a great number which have a range of vernacular names that differ virtually from hamlet to hamlet. The red stumpnose (*Chrysoblephus gibbiceps*) provides a good example (see page 341). Though such names are often colourful and historically fascinating, they frequently lead to confusion and misinterpretation. For this reason Professor Margaret Smith has published an official list of common names. While not necessarily discarding the use of popular local names, this list should go a long way towards removing ambiguity in the naming of fish, without having to resort to scientific names.

The most precise system of naming fishes is, of course, by means of their scientific classification. Here fishes are grouped into a number of distinct categories, in some ways not unlike our own address system, but based instead on evolutionary, genetic and natural characteristics. There are seven standard categories: kingdom, phylum, class, order, family, genus and species which, in our analogy of the address, can be likened to continent, country, province, town, suburb, street and house number respectively. Moving from the largest and most inclusive, the kingdom, the divisions become more and more exclusive until the species is reached, a name appropriate only to a group of fish that are to all intents and purposes, identical. To avoid any possible confusion the genus or generic name always precedes the specific name, thus giving rise to the so-called binominal system of nomenclature.

Throughout this book, the scientific name of each species described is followed by that of the author or scientist who first described it. Some of these names are placed in brackets, a convention which indicates that this author initially applied a different name to the fish. Where no brackets occur the author's original name has remained unchanged.

CONSERVATION

Few words evoke more discord amongst fishermen than the term conservation. To many it represents no more than a host of autocratic rules and regulations designed to rob them of their catch and their sport. In many instances they may well be right. Conservation for conservation's sake can never be justified.

Sea fish represent a natural and renewable resource that shows remarkable resilience to exploitation. These fish are available for man to use, now and in the future. Armed with scientific facts to ensure an intelligent approach to exploitation, there is no reason why good catches should not continue.

Yet why do catches of some species continue to decline? The answer is straightforward: every fish stock has its limits. If, in a virgin fishery, the number of participating fishermen (effort) increases, then it can be expected that with time their daily catches (catch per unit effort, CPUE) will gradually diminish. This is a result of the inability of that stock to yield what is demanded of it and the catch having to be divided amongst more fishermen. Despite the decrease of CPUE there is nevertheless an initial increase in the *total* catch of fish. This increase, however, may also gradually reduce as more and more fishermen participate, until a point is reached where, in spite of an increase in fishing effort, the total catch is not increased. This point is known as the maximum sustainable yield (MSY) of a stock and it provides a simple yet valuable yardstick against which to assess future catches. The objective of conservation should, therefore, be to ensure that the level of fishing effort does not exceed that at MSY. Ideally it should be maintained just below this level, and there are a number

SUMMARY OF NON-COMMERCIAL FISHING REGULATIONS IN THE CAPE

	LICENCE	DAILY BAG LIMIT	SIZE LIMIT
ANGLING	No	Refer linefish table	Refer species entries and linefish table
SPEARFISHING	No	Refer linefish table	Refer species entries and linefish table
GRAINING	No	—	Refer species entry
LIVE SPECIMEN COLLECTING	Yes		
NETTING	Yes		
ALIKREUKEL	No	10	6,35 cm across broadest part
ARMADILLO (Baby's Cradle)	No	6	None
BLOODWORM	No	5	None
CLAM	No	8	None
CRAB *(Scylla serrata)*	No	2	11,43 cm across broadest part of carapace

of methods that can be employed to achieve this. For example, the setting of catch quotas, limiting the issue of licences and proclaiming closed seasons, all effectively reduce fishing effort.

Fishermen naturally resist these measures, and understandably so, particularly among the commercial fishermen who depend on their catches for economic survival. The recreational angler, however, is largely motivated by the thrill of landing a prize catch and consequently he can derive additional benefit from the quality of angling, rather than the absolute quantity. It has been calculated that the annual increase in angling in southern Africa exceeds that of population growth. Already 300 000 fishing reels are sold in South Africa annually and by the year 2 000 this country's population will have almost doubled. Consequently, to maintain even the present quality of fishing, there will have to be three to four times as many fish available for capture by the turn of the century. Regulations should therefore not be evaluated in the short term but should be considered a necessary prerequisite for continued good angling far into the future.

Fishery biologists cannot perform miracles, and the time has arrived where each and every fisherman must contribute towards the wellbeing of the resource. The very least any angler should do is to make his catch records available for scientific analysis. The South African National Committee for Oceanographic Research in association with the Sea Fisheries Research Institute and Oceanographic Research Institute have introduced a programme based on such analyses, and anglers may have noticed an increasing demand for their records. These catch details are crucial to the study of fish population dynamics and will never be used to incriminate the over-zealous angler. In fact the Oceanographic Research Institute in Durban, and all other similar research bodies, specifically undertakes to guarantee that anglers' catches remain confidential. In return, the angler submitting catch records is entitled to be informed of latest developments and he should insist that the fishery biologist provides him with a reasonable amount of feedback.

Yet another research programme that invites the active participation of anglers is the Oceanographic Research Institute nationwide Tagging Programme. This exciting project has already enlisted the support of 1 500 anglers who tagged 15 000 fish during the past three years. Each angler has a stake in the project and receives full computerized details if his fish is recaught by another fisherman. Moreover, he is contributing to the science, and wellbeing, of his favourite pastime.

Further information about both these worthwhile research projects can be obtained from: The Records Officer, Oceanographic Research Institute, P.O. Box 10712, Marine Parade 4056.

Sea Fisheries Act

Rules and regulations pertaining to the capture of fish in South African waters are promulgated on a national basis under the Sea Fisheries Act by the Department of Agriculture and Fisheries. Provincial ordinances control the capture of fish in most estuaries and along the Natal beaches, while Namibia and Transkei have their own parallel legislation. Although the measures applicable to specific species have been described in this book it is always advisable to remain acquainted with current, updated legislation.

To inform the angler of the most important rules and regulations pertaining to the capture of marine organisms in South Africa, the following tables have been included.

PERMITTED METHOD OF CAPTURE	CLOSED SEASON	OTHER
No jigging with unbaited hooks	Refer linefish table	—
Not with Scuba or artificial lights	Refer linefish table	—
Not with Scuba or artificial lights	None	—
SPECIFIC PERMITS ISSUED FOR SCIENTIFIC PURPOSES ONLY		
SPECIFIC PERMITS REQUIRED		
Implement with flat blade not wider than 38 mm	None	Measured through a ring
Screwdriver may be used	None	—
Implement with flat blade not wider than 38 mm	None	—
By hand	None	—
By hand or baited hook	None	Not with eggs

	LICENCE	DAILY BAG LIMIT	SIZE LIMIT
CRAB (other)	No	15	None
ROCK LOBSTER (East Coast or Natal Lobster)	No	5	57,15 mm carapace length
ROCK LOBSTER (Cape Spiny Lobster)	Yes	4	80 mm carapace length
LIMPETS	No	15	None
MUD & SAND PRAWNS	No	50	None
MUSSELS (black & on rocks)	No	25	None
MUSSELS (white & in sand)	No	50	35 mm
OCTOPUS	No	2	None
OYSTER	No	25	51 mm
PERLEMOEN (Abalone)	Yes	4	114 mm
PERIWINKLE	No	50	None
RAZOR CLAM (Pencil Bait)	No	20	None
REDBAIT	No	2 kg (without shell)	None
SCALLOPS	No	10	None
SIFFIE (Venus ear)	No	10	32 mm
SEA URCHIN	No	20	None
WORMS	No	20	None

SUMMARY OF NON-COMMERCIAL FISHING REGULATIONS IN NATAL

ANGLING	No	Refer linefish table	Refer species entries and linefish table
SPEARFISHING	Yes	Refer linefish table	Each fish 2 kg minimum. Refer species entries and linefish table
GRAINING	Yes	None	Refer species entry
LIVE SPECIMEN COLLECTING	Yes for tanks only		
NETTING	Yes		
BAIT	Yes	3 crayfish; 6 crabs (not swimming); 30 mud & sand prawns; 20 mussels; 25 limpets; 30 sea lice; 1 octopus	Crayfish: 65 mm carapace length, 22 mm 2nd abdominal segment length
CRAB (swimming)	Yes	6	125 mm across broadest part of carapace
CRAB (other)	Yes	10	None
CRAYFISH	Yes	8	65 mm carapace length; 22 mm 2nd abdominal segment length
LIMPETS	Yes	25	None
MUD & SAND PRAWNS	Yes	50 of either	None
MUSSELS	Yes	50	None – but all are included in bag
OCTOPUS	Yes	2	None
OYSTERS	Yes	8 doz.	None – but all are included in bag
PRAWNS	Yes	None	None
REDBAIT	No	2 kg (without shell)	None
SEA LICE (mole crab)	Yes	30	None
SEA URCHIN	No	25	None
SQUID	Yes	None	None
WORMS (marine)	—	—	—

PERMITTED METHOD OF CAPTURE	CLOSED SEASON	OTHER
By hand or baited hook	None	Not with eggs
By hand or baited hook; not with Scuba	1 Nov-31 Jan	Not with eggs
By hand or baited hook; not with Scuba	1 July-31 Oct	Not with eggs; not to be caught at night
Implement with flat blade not wider than 38 mm	None	—
Approved pump, not by digging	None	—
Implement with flat blade not wider than 38 mm	None	—
Not with spade, fork or plough	None	Measured through a ring
By hand, gaff or jigging	None	—
Implement with flat blade not wider than 38 mm	1 Dec-15 Jan	Measured through a ring
Implement with flat blade not wider than 38 mm	1 Aug-31 Oct	Measured through a ring
By hand	None	—
By hand	None	—
By hand, knife or bait-hook	None	—
By hand	None	—
By hand or screwdriver	None	Measured through a ring
By hand	None	—
Implement with flat blade not wider than 38 mm	None	—

No jigging with unbaited hooks	Refer linefish table	—
Not within 25 m of bathers; not with Scuba	Refer linefish table	Not permitted: ray, skate, sandshark, sunfish, sawfish, brindle/potato bass, wrasse, parrotfish
Spear with 5 or fewer prongs	None	Restricted to sole & mullet
SPECIFIC COLLECTING PERMITS ISSUED ON REQUEST		
SPECIFIC LICENCES ISSUED ON APPLICATION		
Refer to specific sections below	Crayfish: 1 Nov-29 Feb	No crabs or crayfish with eggs
By hand, baited hooks or approved trap	None	Not with eggs
By hand, baited hooks or approved trap	None	Not with eggs
By hand, baited hooks or approved trap Not from boat or floating object; or with Scuba	1 Nov-29 Feb	Not with eggs
Implement no bigger than 12 mm wide and 100 mm long	1 Nov-29 Feb	Only to be taken on crayfish or bait licences
Approved pump; not by digging	None	
Implement no bigger than 12 mm wide & 100 mm long	None	
Gaff with hook no bigger than 5/0	None	
Implement with blade no wider than 40 mm; length no more than 1 m. Not with diving equipment	None	
Drag, hoop or dip nets of prescribed dimensions	None	
With knife, leaving base of animal intact	None	
Triangular net not longer than 610 mm per side	None	
By hand	None	
Dip & hoop net of prescribed dimensions	None	
Not permitted	—	

NOTE:
Natal: Temporary and Annual Licences may be obtained from the Natal Fisheries Licensing Board, P/B 15, Congella 4013
Cape: Permits may be obtained from the Director, Dept. Nature Conservation, P/B 9066, Cape Town 8000

SUMMARY OF LINEFISH REGULATIONS

South Africa boasts an extensive coastline, a wide variety of marine habitats and an enviable diversity of fish species. Unfortunately not all fish occur in great abundance, therefore the growth in the number of fishermen cannot be sustained without management. Such management is based on research undertaken by several institutes and is in accordance with recommendations made by th South African Marine Linefish Management Association (SAMLMA).

A new set of regulations came into effect at the end of 1992. All species are now grouped into five distinct management categorie depending on the species' own status and the needs of different types of fishermen. This retains flexibility of control. For instance should there be a sudden drop in the abundance of a certain species, it can be shifted to a more protective category. Conversely benefits of management can be freely passed on to fishermen should the fish regain their abundance, simply by changing the classification. For the first time, a group of fish has been reserved for recreational anglers only and may not be sold. Size limits for ke species will still apply.

These fishery regulations are flexible and may change from time to time. For latest details and legal considerations, please contac your local fisheries officer or consult the relevant government gazette.

CATEGORIES

Critical (5 species): Fish in dire need of protection; depleted by more than 50% of original stock.
Restricted (>13 species): Fish in need of management because of reduced abundance and vulnerable lifestyle.
Exploitable (>25 species): Fish that can sustain commercial, recreational and subsistence harvesting.
Recreational (>30 species): Fish of primary benefit t recreational anglers and not likely to sustain commercia exploitation.
Bait (>20 species): Fish primarily used as bait with littl commercial or recreational linefish value.

	A OPEN	B REGULATED	C PROTECTED	D SEASONAL	E SIZE LIMIT	TOTAL
	billfish carpenter cartilaginous fishes (sharks) geelbek hake lizardfish maasbanker mackerel mullet/harder sandsoldier/red tjor-tjor snoek (Cape) steentjie strepie tuna yellowtail	All other species not listed in A, C or D	baardman bronze bream Cape knifejaw dageraad elf/shad Englishman galjoen garrick/leervis janbruin milkfish musselcracker poenskop red steenbras red stumpnose river bream Roman Scotsman seventyfour slinger soldier/santer spotted rockcod squid/tjokka white-edged rockcod yellow-belly rockcod	elf/shad* galjoen seventyfour* red steenbras*	15 cm: strepie 20 cm: blacktail Cape stumpnose white stumpnose 22 cm: hottentot 25 cm: dageraad Natal stumpnose poenskop Roman red steenbras red stumpnose river bream Scotsman seventyfour silverfish slinger soldier/santer 30 cm: elf/shad spotted rockcod white-edged rockcod yellowbelly rockcod 35 cm: galjoen 40 cm: geelbek kob musselcracker spotted grunter squaretail kob white steenbras 60 cm: snoek (Cape) 70 cm: garrick/leervis	catch per person per day
SPORT ANGLER	Unlimited	10 per person per day	5 per person per day in total Squid: 20 per person per day	*Closed from 1.9 to 30.11 Galjoen – closed from 15.10 to 8.2	Applicable	No more than a total of 10 of B + C Squid: 20 per person per day
SPEARFISHERMAN	Unlimited	10 per person per day	5 per person per day in total Squid: 20 per person per day	*Closed from 1.9 to 30.11 Galjoen – closed from 15.10 to 28.2	Applicable	No more than a total of 10 of B + C Squid: 20 per person per day
SEMI-COMMERCIAL	Unlimited	Unlimited	5 per person per day in total No galjoen Squid: Closed from 1.12 to 15.1 for certain fishermen	*Closed from 1.9 to 30.11 No galjoen	Applicable	No more than a total of 5 of C Catch stats compulsory
COMMERCIAL	Unlimited	Unlimited	Unlimited No galjoen Squid: Closed from 1.12 to 15.1 for certain fishermen	*Closed from 1.9 to 30.11 No galjoen	Applicable	Limited by licence not catch. Catch stats compulsory

SHARKS The following control measures are applicable to the catching of sharks:

1. No person shall carry on any boat a shark gill net or any other netting for the use of shark fishing, unless such person is in possession of a permit issued by the Chief Director of Fisheries.
2. Soupfin shark must be landed in a whole state.
3. Other sharks may be de-headed, gutted and the tail cut off at sea, but such offal shall not be returned to the sea.

TUNA The following control measures are applicable to the catching of tuna:

1. The minimum weight for yellowfin tuna is 3,2 kg.
2. The minimum weight for bluefin tuna is 6,4 kg.
3. The minimum weight for bigeye tuna is 3,2 kg.

PART I

THE CARTILAGINOUS FISHES

CARTILAGINOUS FISHES

An illustrated outline

The cartilaginous fishes include sharks, rays, guitarfishes and sawfishes, known collectively as elasmobranchs, and chimaeras. These marine vertebrates are similar to the bony fishes in general design and anatomy, but they do have a number of most distinctive characteristics which eliminate confusion.

Most significant of these is the structure of the skeleton which, unlike that of bony fishes, is not composed of bony tissue but of cartilage. In areas that bear great stress, as in the jaws and backbone, this cartilage is provided with additional rigidity by an overlying mosaic of bony plates. True bone is not entirely lacking, however, but is confined to the dentine of the teeth, the spines and, in the few instances where they occur, the scales.

Other skeletal differences occur in the jaws. The upper jaw is derived from a distinctly different part of the skull than that in bony fishes and both jaws are covered with bands of teeth which are being continuously replaced. This is especially evident in many of the sharks; as the functional teeth wear or break, so those next in line move forward to take their place in a continuing folding process over the jaws. These teeth are in fact identical in structure to the dermal denticles of the skin (see electron microscope magnifications on page 25).

The large, thick fins of cartilaginous fishes, too, are different from those of bony fishes and except for the dorsal fins of chimaeras, are rigid. With the exception of the spiny dogfish and chimaeras, fin spines are lacking and, though rays are not visible, the fins are supported and stiffened internally by hundreds of hair-like, horny filaments.

All cartilaginous fishes are carnivorous, but their prey can vary from the large fish and marine mammals that make up the diet of the bigger pelagic sharks, to the mussels and crustaceans eaten by the more sluggish, bottom-dwelling rays and guitarfishes.

Most elasmobranchs, especially the sharks, have an exceptionally well-developed sense of smell, certainly superior to their eyesight. In fact, the largest part of the brain is devoted to the olfactory senses. These fishes are also acutely sensitive to vibrations which are received by the nerve cells of the lateral line system. Together these highly developed senses play a central role in the hunting strategy of these animals, enabling them to track down prey even in very turbid waters.

While some rays and sharks are elaborately patterned, most cartilaginous fishes, particularly sharks, tend to be rather drab and dull-coloured, usually in overall shades of brown or grey. The identification of these animals on the basis of colour is often difficult, therefore, and is complicated by their tendency to haemorrhage extensively when captured. Sharks are more clearly distinguished by characteristics such as their size and especially the relative positions of their fins, as well as the shape of the caudal fin and the shape of the head. The type of teeth, especially the tooth formula (explained in the introductory section *How to use this book),* is often highly diagnostic.

Anatomy of a shark

1 nostril; **2** eye; **3** brain; **4** spiracle; **5** nerve cord; **6** vertebrae; **7** muscles; **8** testis; **9** first dorsal fin; **10** dorsal spine; **11** second dorsal fin; **12** caudal fin; **13** muscles;

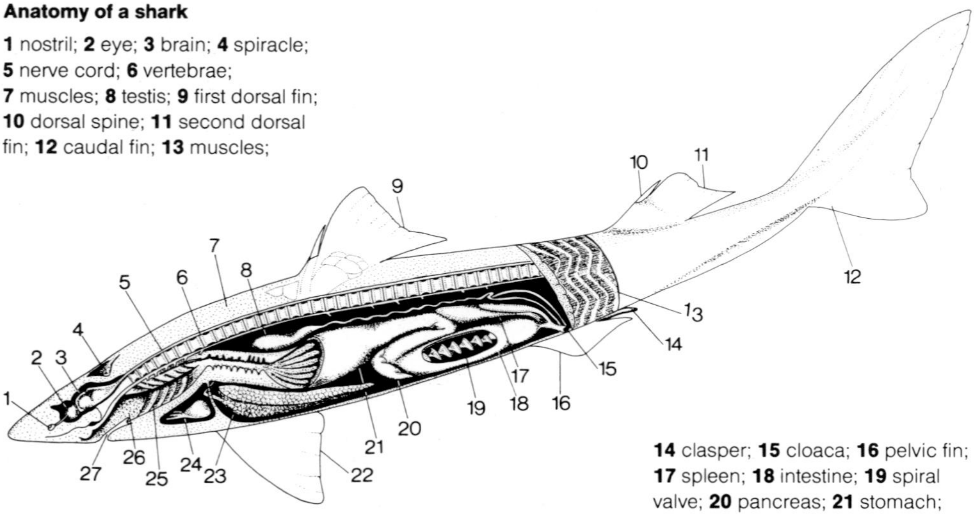

14 clasper; **15** cloaca; **16** pelvic fin; **17** spleen; **18** intestine; **19** spiral valve; **20** pancreas; **21** stomach; **22** pectoral fin; **23** liver; **24** heart; **25** gills; **26** pharynx; **27** mouth.

Rays and guitarfishes

Obvious external differences prevent confusion between rays and sharks. Of these, the position of the gill openings and the arrangement of the pectoral fins is most characteristic. Rays have their gill openings located on the underside of the head as opposed to the lateral gill slits of sharks, and their pectoral fins are enlarged into the typical flattened disc. In true sharks the pectoral fins never extend forward of the gill openings. Guitarfishes are more shark-like in general shape, but they too have gill slits opening on the underside and much enlarged pectoral fins which give them their distinctive shovel-shaped heads.

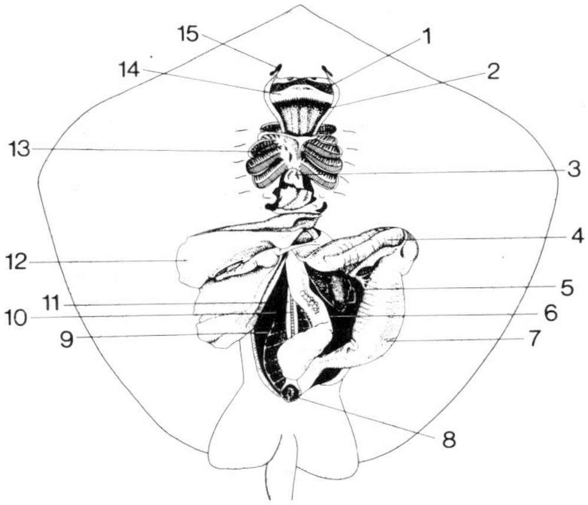

Internal anatomy of a stingray
1 teeth; **2** gullet; **3** heart; **4** stomach; **5** liver; **6** ovary; **7** spiral valve; **8** cloaca; **9** kidney; **10** spinal cord; **11** uterus; **12** liver; **13** gills; **14** buccal flap; **15** nostril.

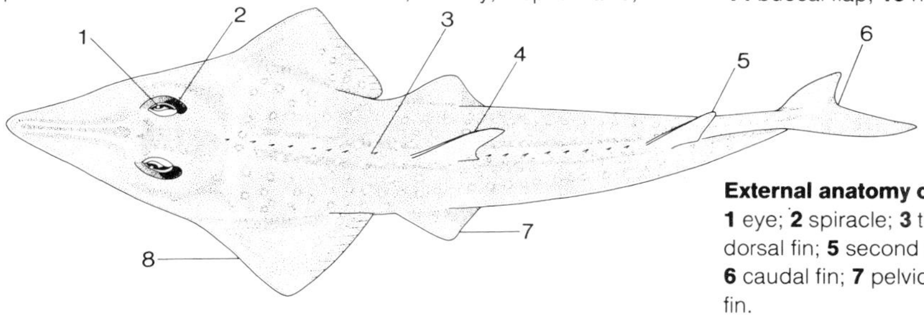

External anatomy of a guitarfish
1 eye; **2** spiracle; **3** tubercles; **4** first dorsal fin; **5** second dorsal fin; **6** caudal fin; **7** pelvic fin; **8** pectoral fin.

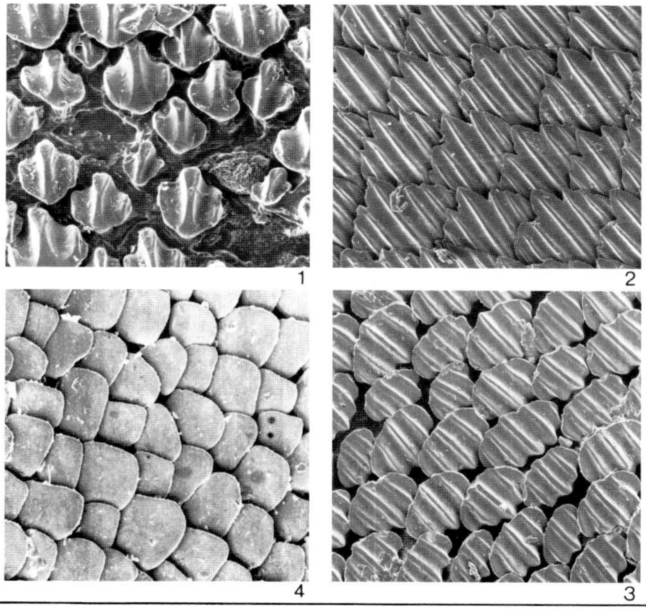

Skin types

Cartilaginous fishes lack the 'typical' scales of bony fishes. Their skin is nevertheless very rough and abrasive and shark skin, known commercially as shagreen, has wide application and is still used in primitive societies as a 'sandpaper' and to make non-slip handles for knives, spears and other tools. The four skin types here magnified are from *Galeocerdo cuvier* **1**, *Carcharhinus obscurus* **2**, *C. plumbeus* **3** and *Rhinobatos annulatus* **4**. Although these outgrowths display an overlapping pattern and look superficially similar to the scales of bony fishes they are, in fact, fundamentally different. Shark 'scales' are tooth-like and each has a central core overlaid with dentine and coated with enamel.

Teeth

Although variations occur, the teeth of most cartilaginous fishes usually fall into four categories and provide a reliable clue as to feeding habits. The great white and many grey sharks have triangular, heavily serrated teeth **1** suited to cutting and tearing. Slanted, cockscomb teeth **2** like those of the tiger shark are similarly adapted, while the triple-cusped, pointed teeth **3** of ragged-tooth sharks are more suited to grasping and piercing. The rounded teeth of rays and guitar-fishes **4** provide a mill-like grinding mechanism well able to crush molluscs and crustaceans.

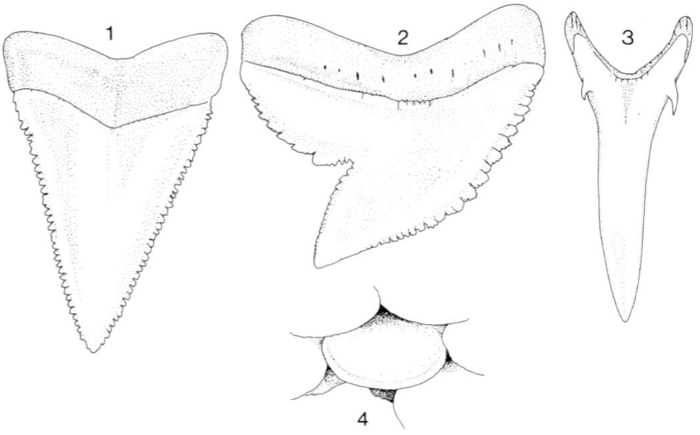

Jaw mechanism

The teeth of many pelagic sharks are not always obvious as the lower jaw can fit snugly into the upper, providing an almost unbroken profile to the streamlined head. However, when the mouth is opened wide, the movable upper jaw appears to 'dislocate' and is thrust forward, the teeth being well presented in the process. This ability is put to good effect when attacking prey, but sharks often flex their jaws when not feeding. Such 'yawning' is not clearly understood.

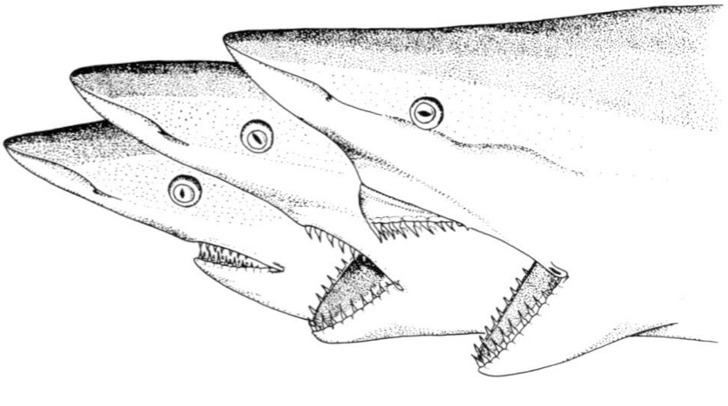

Tail shapes

Forward movement in sharks is the function of the tail. The shape of the caudal fin is, therefore, indicative of swimming ability. The swiftest, the mackerel sharks, have great sickle-shaped tail fins **1**, while those of most grey and thresher sharks **2 & 3** are also robust and capable of propelling these fishes at considerable speed. The caudal fins of spiny dogfish and cigar sharks **4 & 5** are not as powerful, but the lower lobe is well developed and demonstrates pelagic habits. The lower lobe is reduced in more sluggish sharks such as the ragged-tooth and houndsharks **6**, while in the bottom-dwelling, slow-swimming frill and catsharks **7 & 8** the lower lobe is almost entirely lacking.

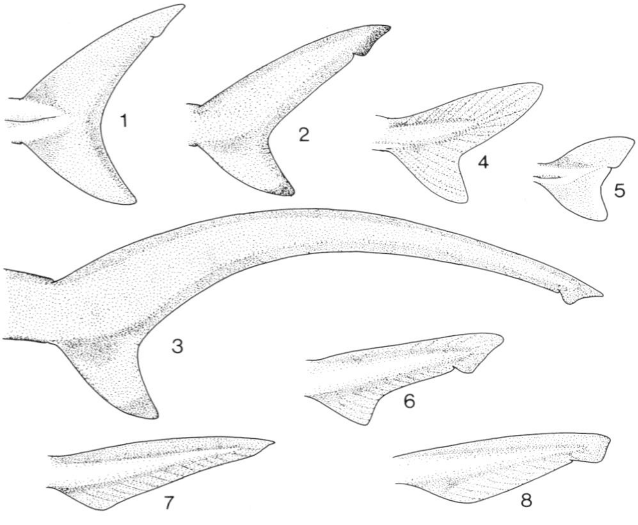

CALLORHINCHIDAE
Elephantfishes

See page 33 for species description

The Callorhinchidae belong to the Chimaeriform fishes, once numerous and diverse, but now mostly extinct. Of the four species known in this family, only one occurs in southern African waters. In many ways, the anatomy of the elephantfishes is similar to that of sharks, but the belief that they share a common ancestor is questionable.

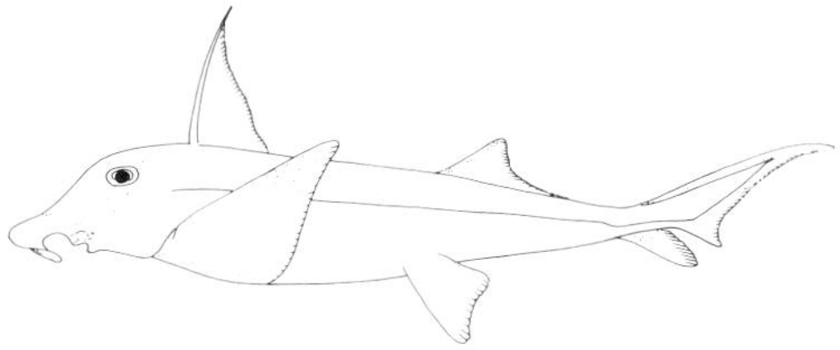

Their curious shape and anatomy makes them easily identifiable. Elephantfishes are smooth-bodied and scaleless, and have a trunk-like, flexible snout, which is believed to serve a sensory function. A single gill plate covers the four gill openings, and there are no spiracles, water for respiration being taken in through the nostrils. The first of two dorsal fins can be erected, and has a spine. The teeth in the underslung mouth are fused into bony plates. Like sharks, elephantfishes have a spiral valve instead of a true stomach, a cartilaginous skeleton and no rib cage. The anal and urinogenital openings, however, are separate, and not combined into a cloaca. The large pectoral fins, unlike those of sharks, are movable, and play a part in locomotion. Adult males have clasping organs on the head and pelvic fins, with which the female is held during copulation. Following internal fertilization, the females deposit one or two brown egg capsules on the sea-bed.

CARCHARHINIDAE
Requiem or grey sharks

See pages 34 to 47 for species descriptions

Carcharhinidae are the most 'typical' of modern sharks, and representative species occur in all oceans. The family includes more than 85 species of which at least 36 frequent southern African waters. The genus *Carcharhinus* is the largest single group of modern sharks, and includes many of the commonly known species that inhabit tropical seas.

Requiem sharks have two spineless dorsal fins, the first of which is positioned in front of the pelvics. There are five gill slits on either side of the body, and the fifth opens directly above, or behind, the origin of the pectoral fins. Nasal barbels are absent, and most species have an internal, or external, nictitating membrane covering the eyes.

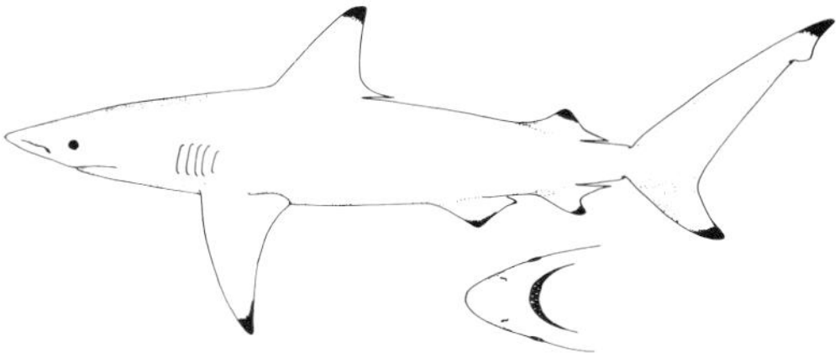

With a few exceptions, the jaws are large and armed with an awesome set of serrated, triangular teeth, This feature makes large requiem sharks potentially very dangerous to bathers and skin-divers.

Most Carcharhinidae are open-water fish, but many will make use of inshore gullies to come right into the surf zone in pursuit of food. Though requiem sharks are not generally tolerant of low salinities, at least one species, the Zambezi shark, has adjusted to life in both salt and fresh water.

Fertilization takes place internally, and female Carcharhinidae produce live young after gestation periods which range from six months to two years. Growth is rather slow and it may take a decade or more for these sharks to attain sexual maturity.

DASYATIDAE
Stingrays

See pages 48 to 53 for species descriptions

There are about 89 species in this family, which occur in marine, brackish and, occasionally, fresh waters throughout the world.In southern Africa there are at least 16 species, many of which are common in shallow water and estuaries. Stingrays are bottom-dwellers, and often lie partially buried under the sand or soft mud. This, coupled with their brown or mottled body colouration and markings, makes them inconspicuous even in very clear water.

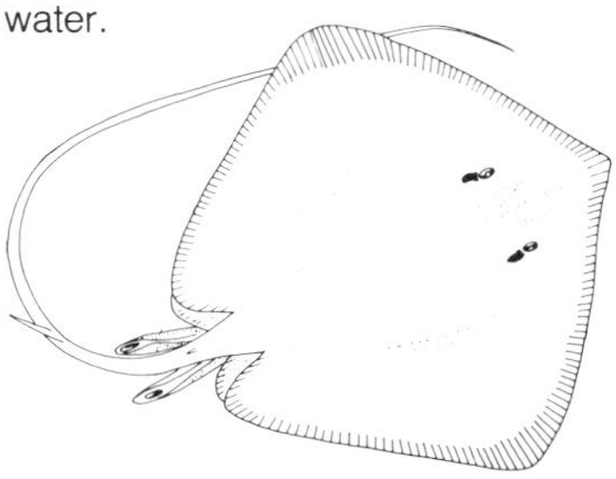

An obvious anatomical feature in most species is the long, slender, whip-like tail which has one or several sharp, serrated, poisonous spines near its base. The butterflyray and a few other species, however, have very short tails and provide a striking contrast. When caught or molested, the stingray lashes with its tail and the spines often inflict very painful wounds. Lacerations should be treated seriously, and a doctor should be consulted. A highly effective and immediate treatment, however, is the immersion of the wound in water, as hot as the victim can stand, for at least half an hour. This tends to destroy the powerful protein toxin.

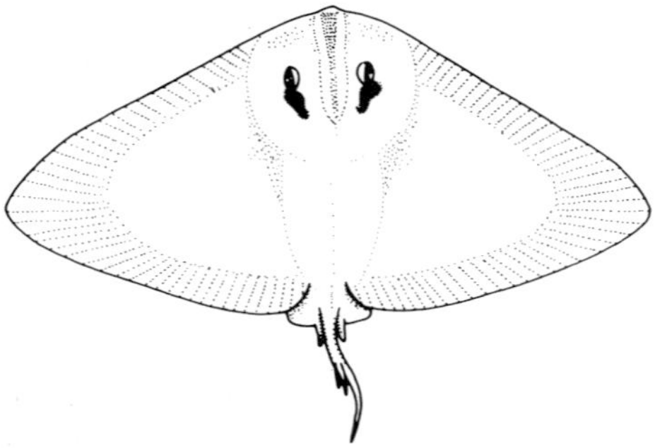

Aside from the long tail, the body is usually rounded or disc-shaped, and is very flattened, consisting primarily of greatly enlarged pectoral fins, which are partially fused to the fleshy pelvic fins. The mouth and gill slits are on the underside, and water for respiration is taken in through spiracles located on the upper surface of the head. There are no dorsal fins, and all but one rare species lack a caudal fin. The smooth skin may have patches of rough tubercles.
The females are fertilized internally and bear litters of as many as ten live young.

HETERONTIDAE
Bullhead sharks

See page 54 for species description

These curious sharks have only eight representative species worldwide, one being found off South Africa. Though generally shark-like in appearance, their most distinguishing feature is the pre-

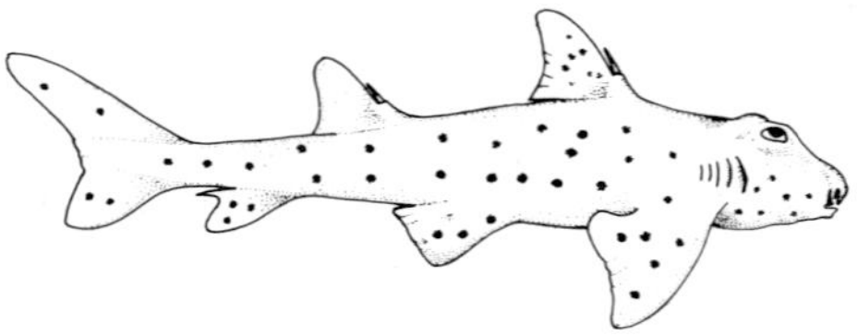

sence of an anal fin as well as two dorsal fin spines. The snout is noticeably blunt, with a terminal mouth, large ridges over the eyes, and five gill slits that decrease in size posteriorly. Bullsharks are confined to the warmer coastal waters of the Indian and Pacific Oceans, where they forage at night on the bottom in search of invertebrate prey. These oviparous sharks are known to lay their eggs in specific nesting sites.

HEXANCHIDAE
Cowsharks

See page 55 for species description

This is a family of rather primitive, elongate and stout sharks that enjoys a wide distribution throughout the world's temperate oceans. Unique to this family is the presence of six or seven pairs of gill slits, where most other cartilaginous fishes have five. There is only one dorsal fin, usually positioned far back on the body, and without any fin spines. The mouth is located underneath the throat and, in most cases, armed with formidable comb-like teeth. Their diet consists mostly of other fishes, and, in some cases, cowsharks may be potentially dangerous to bathers. All the females

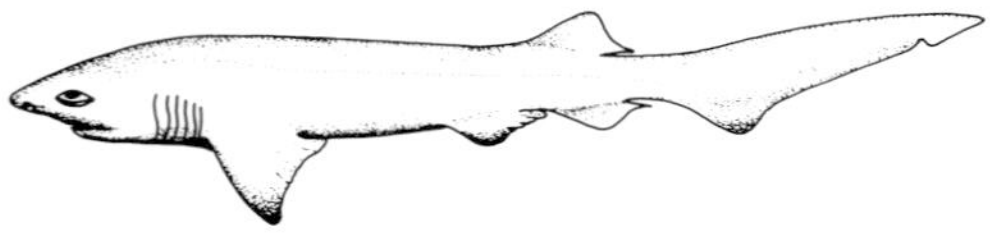

are ovoviviparous, and may produce many young each season. Cowsharks are invariably large, and generally prefer deep water, though some are important to commercial and sport fisherman in shallower waters.

LAMNIDAE
Mackerel sharks

See page 56 for species description

There are several species in this family, of which at least four occur in southern African waters. Lamnidae include the mako and porbeagle sharks, but the most feared member is the 'great white'.
The mackerel sharks are powerful pelagic predators, found throughout the tropical and cooler waters of all oceans. Their stout, forked caudal fins, with a single keel on each side of the peduncle, manifest their considerable swimming prowess. Other identifying characteristics include the absence of nictitating eyelids; minute spiracles (these are completely lacking in some species); and a first

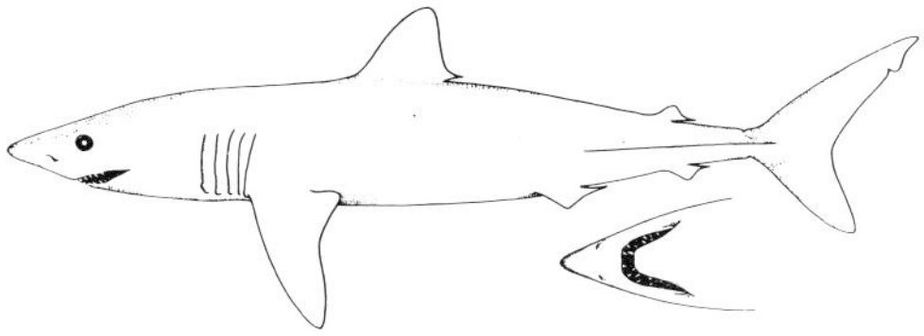

dorsal fin that originates from a point in line with, or just behind, the inner edge of the pectorals. There are five gill slits on each side of the body, the fifth being situated in front of the pectoral fin.
These sharks have received a great deal of publicity in the mass media, which has led to their being popularly regarded as 'man-eaters'. Though they are without doubt formidable fish, the natural food of large mackerel sharks certainly does not normally include humans. Marine mammals, especially seals and dolphins, are an important food source, and not surprisingly, therefore, they are frequently found near seal colonies or whaling stations. This affinity for warm-blooded animals, however, may make them potentially more dangerous to man than any other group of sharks.
The females produce live young, but further details of the life cycle are unknown.

MOBULIDAE
Mantas

See page 57 for species description

Although less than ten species belong to this family, all are equally distinctive with their very wide, angular bodies and well-defined heads from which a pair of cephalic fins or horns project forwards.

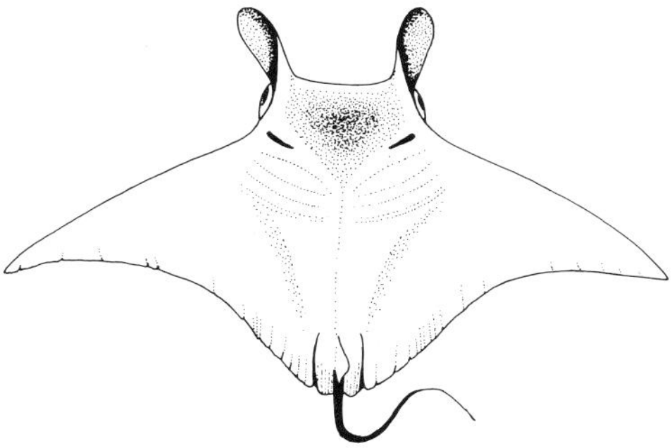

These harmless fishes can attain enormous sizes, possibly in excess of two tonnes. Mantas frequent the warmer parts of all oceans, and usually occur in small groups, feeding on minute planktonic animals that are filtered from the water. The ovoviviparous females produce a milky uterine fluid that nourishes the embryos.

MYLIOBATIDAE
Eaglerays

See pages 58 to 61 for species descriptions

This family comprises 25 species which are found mainly in tropical and sub tropical seas. At least four are common to southern African waters. With the exception of the mantas, eaglerays are the only rays to have abandoned bottom-living for a pelagic existence in the midwater region. Occasionally they even burst from the surface in brief 'flights'.

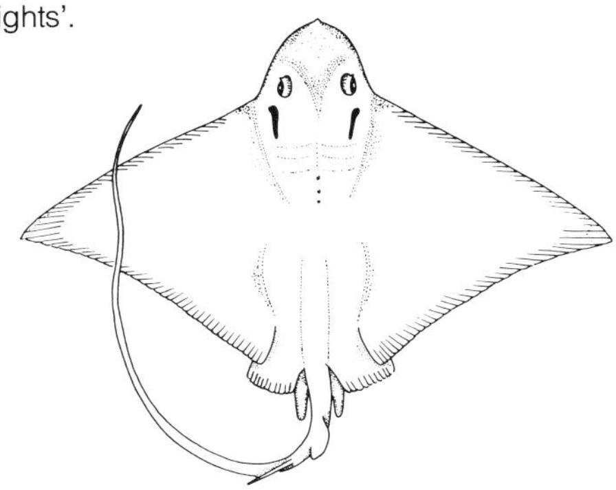

These flattened fishes have a distinct head which is raised above the body and positioned in front of the enlarged and pointed pectoral fins. Unlike the bottom-dwelling stingrays, eaglerays have their eyes and spiracles located at the sides of the head rather than on top. The position of the eyes undoubtedly gives these animals wide lateral vision – a useful adaptation to their pelagic habits. The whip-like tail is distinct from the smooth-skinned body, and carries a small dorsal fin plus one or more poisonous, barbed spines at its base. As with the stingrays, these spines can cause severe and very painful wounds, which should be treated similarly (see page 28). The spines of all rays are barbed along their sides, and recent observations suggest that, once firmly lodged in a victim, these spines cannot be withdrawn and are shed. It is not known whether spines lost in this manner can be replaced.
Females are fertilized internally and bear litters of live young.

ODONTASPIDIDAE
Ragged-tooth sharks

See page 62 for species description

Of the four species in this family two are found in southern African waters. One, the spotted ragged-tooth, is common and widely distributed.
These sharks have two spineless dorsal fins, the

first not much larger than the second. There are five gill slits on each side of the body, the fifth opening directly before the origin of the pectoral fin. The eyes have no nictitating lower eyelids. The mouth has numerous rows of long, awl-shaped teeth in each jaw.

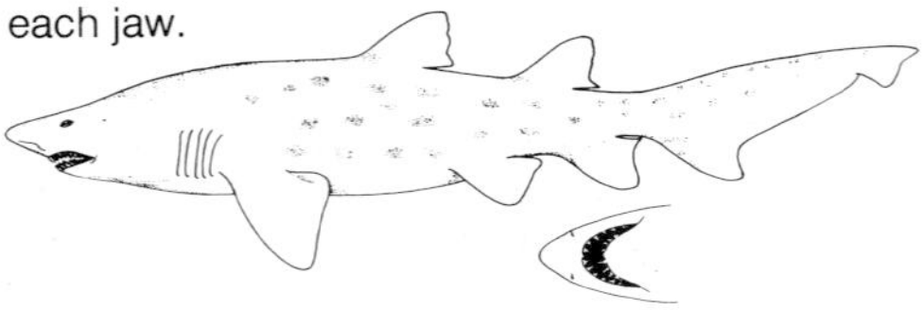

Although potentially dangerous to man, these sharks should not be classed as 'man-eaters'. Their fearsome, sharply pointed teeth are more suited to grasping than cutting, and their diet consists mainly of small fish, sharks and squid which can be swallowed whole.

Ragged-tooth sharks are known to congregate at specific localities during summer, possibly as a prelude to breeding. Reproduction is unique. Following internal fertilization, the eggs remain in the uterus where they hatch and continue to develop as free-swimming embryos. These as-yet-unborn 'baby sharks' receive their nourishment by feeding on other eggs as well as on fellow embryos. All sharks have two uteri, but in ragged-tooth species only the right ovary is functional.

ORECTOLOBIDAE
Carpet sharks

See page 63 for species description

Most of the 25 species in this family occur in the tropical Indo-Pacific region, with at least four representatives in southern African waters.

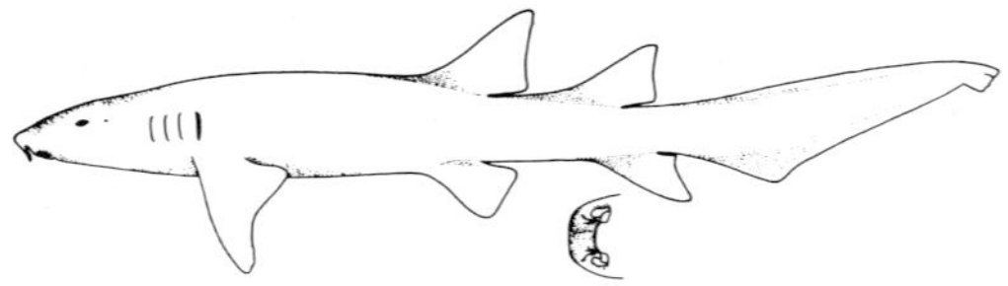

These sluggish, bottom-living sharks have a number of unique anatomical features: the nostrils are connected to the ventral mouth by two deep external grooves; distinct nasal barbels occur; the fourth and fifth gill slits are often close together, and open behind the origin of the pectoral fin; and the first dorsal fin is placed well back towards the tail. The lower lobe of the caudal fin is much reduced or even absent. The upper lobe, however, is long, and extends backwards, giving these fishes a somewhat flattened dorsal profile.

Some species lay eggs, but others bear live young after the egg cases have been retained and hatched within the uterus.

Although carpet sharks are widely distributed, nowhere are they very common, and their natural history has consequently remained obscure.

PRISTIDAE
Sawfishes

See page 64 for species description

This family includes at least six species which are distributed throughout tropical marine, estuarine and, occasionally, freshwater regions. There are three representatives in southern African waters, two of which can attain lengths of 600 cm.

The sawfishes are unmistakable, as they have long, narrow snouts formidably set along each side with numerous equal-sized, pointed teeth, which have blunt front and sharp rear cutting edges. This 'saw' is used to forage for food in mud or sand on the sea-bed, and also to slash at prey, usually shoals of small fish. Aside from the unique saw, members of this family exhibit features of both the true shark and the guitarfish or sand-shark. The body is elongate and shark-like, with

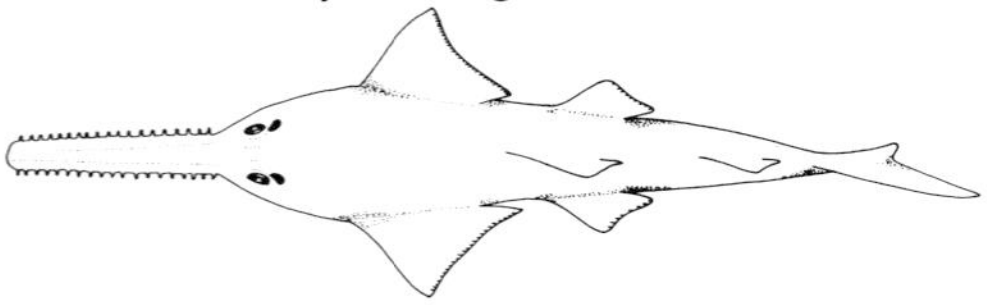

two dorsal fins, a caudal, and separate pectoral and pelvic fins. The pectoral fins, which are only partially attached to the body, are large and extend backwards from the head rather like those of the guitarfish. Gill slits occur on the underside of the head on both sides of the body, just behind the mouth.

Reproduction is viviparous and large, pregnant females frequently enter estuaries to give birth.

RAJIDAE
Skates

See page 65 for species description

This cosmopolitan and largest of the batoid families embraces more than 200 species world-wide, with at least 23 of these found in southern Africa. All are confined to a benthic existence, usually over sand or muddy bottoms, and never in association with coral reefs. Skates range widely, and may be encountered from shallow coastal or estuarine waters to depths exceeding 1000 m.

Members of this family are easily recognized by

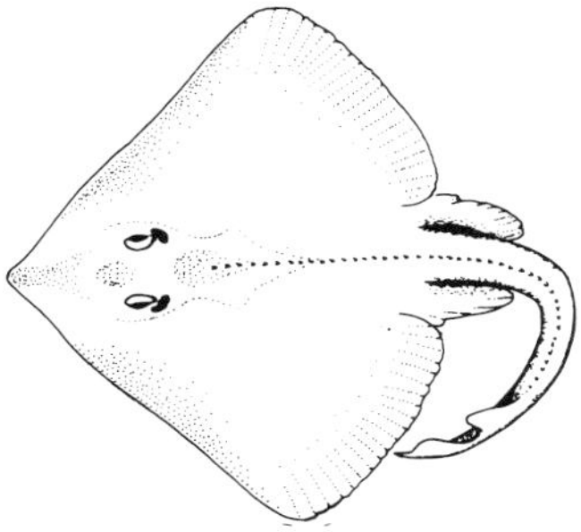

their angular, disc-shaped bodies which are about 1,3-1,4 times longer than wide. Paired spiracles occur close behind the eyes, and there are usually several rows of strong teeth in the jaws. Most have a distinctly pointed snout, two dorsal fins, a small caudal fin and a stocky tail, often with fleshy lateral projections. The sharp spines and whip-like tail, common of stingrays, are not found in Rajidae. All skates are oviparous, and the males often have very large claspers. Skate egg cases that are washed ashore are sometimes known as 'mermaid's purses'.

Some skates possess small electric organs. Most are a fine food source in the form of 'skate wings'.

RHINOBATIDAE

Guitarfishes or sandsharks

See pages 66 to 68 for species descriptions

Each of the approximately 52 members of this family is marine, and representative species may be found in all oceans. At least seven species of guitarfish occur in southern African waters.

Fish belonging to this family are most distinctive, and exhibit features of both sharks and stingrays.

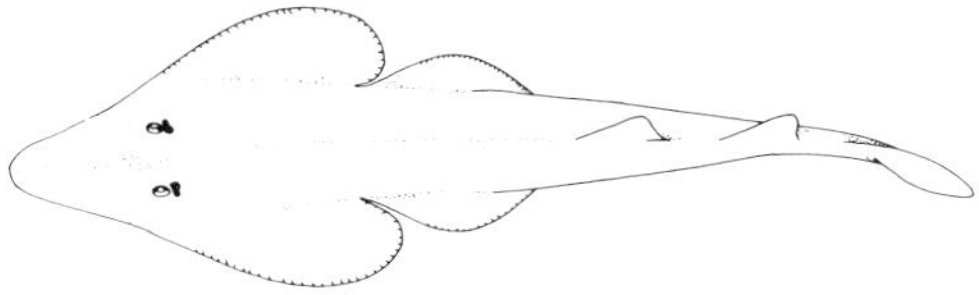

The forward part of the body, including the head, pointed snout and large pectoral fins, is flattened and shovel- or wedge-shaped. The tail is stout and forms an integral part of the body. There are two distinct dorsal fins, and the pelvic fins are separate from the pectorals. A row of small, closely set, dermal denticles forms a ridge along the midline of the back. The mouth and gill slits open ventrally. The dorsally positioned eyes are an indication of this family's bottom-dwelling habits. The spiracles also represent a successful adaptation to a muddy, turbid environment because, being situated on top of the head, they enable clear water to be drawn in for respiration. Guitarfishes prey mostly on shellfish. During summer, females give birth to a number of live young.

SCYLIORHINIDAE

Catsharks

See pages 69 to 74 for species descriptions

The catshark family has some 58 species distributed throughout the temperate and tropical regions of all oceans. They are relatively small sharks, and most adults are less than one metre long. At least 13 species occur in southern African waters, and many have distinct and colourful markings.

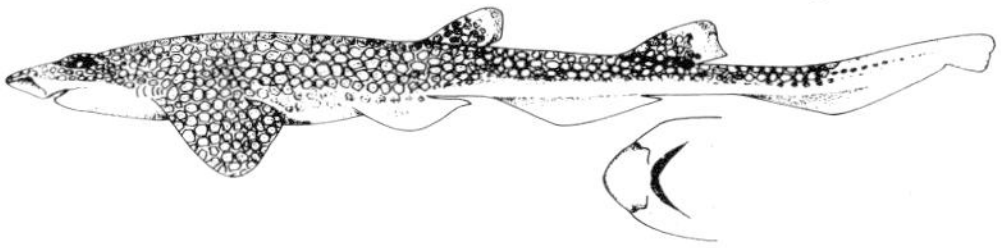

Catsharks are noticeably elongate, and their small, spineless dorsal fins occur well back towards the tail. The position of the fifth gill slit is either directly above, or behind, the origin of the pectoral fin. The nictitating eyelids are poorly developed, and spiracles occur just behind the eyes.

These sluggish, bottom-living sharks are found in both coastal and deep, oceanic waters.

Following internal fertilization, the females produce a number of egg cases, which are attached by tendrils submarine objects. The embryos hatch after 3-6 weeks.

SPHYRNIDAE

Hammerhead sharks

See page 75 for species description

There are about nine species in this tropical family, of which three occur in southern African waters.

These sharks are easily identified by the lateral extensions of the head into the well-known hammer shape. The tip of each 'wing' of the hammer bears an eye. Apart from this feature, the members of this family are very similar to the requiem sharks. The significance of the hammer-shaped head, with its lateral eyes, is not fully understood, but, undoubtedly, it gives these sharks a wide field of vision. It is likely, therefore, that sight plays a greater role in hunting than for most sharks. Although large, hammerheads have fairly small mouths, and their diet consists mainly of squid and small fish. Fertilization is internal, and the females give birth to 15-35 live pups. The gestation period is less than a year, a relatively short pregnancy when compared with most cartilaginous fishes.

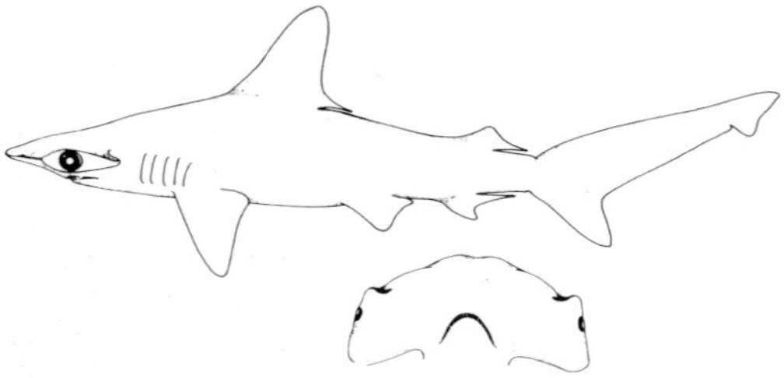

Fertilization is internal, and the females give birth to 15-35 live pups. The gestation period is less than a year, a relatively short pregnancy when compared with most cartilaginous fishes.

SQUALIDAE
Dogfish sharks

See pages 76 and 77 for species descriptions

Squalidae comprise numerous species, mostly rather small, and armed with one or two sharp dorsal spines. There are 25 species representing the family in southern African waters, and four belong to the genus *Squalus* (spiny dogfish).

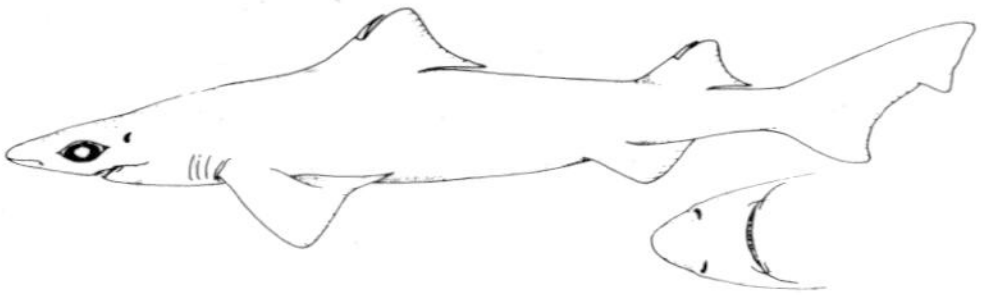

There has been considerable confusion in the classification of Squalidae, mainly because some species have, with evolution, lost their spines.

The spiny dogfishes, however, may be broadly categorized into four groups, which, although they vary in detail, occur throughout the world. The most common variation lies in the number of vertebrae. These sharks range widely from the surf zone to depths of 500 m or more. Some of the deep-water dogfishes have light-emitting organs. A number of species are exploited commercially. The ovoviviparous females give birth to live young.

SQUATINIDAE
Angelsharks

See page 78 for species description

Though resembling guitarfishes, the angelsharks are nevertheless true sharks, with ventral gill slits that extend partially up the sides of the head, and enlarged pectoral fins that lie along the body, but are not fully fused to it. There are two spineless dorsals, but no anal fins.

There are about 12 species in this family, all confined to a bottom existence, usually over muddy banks, but also to great depths. Angelsharks occur primarily in the Atlantic and eastern Pacific Oceans, and only one species is found in the Indian Ocean.

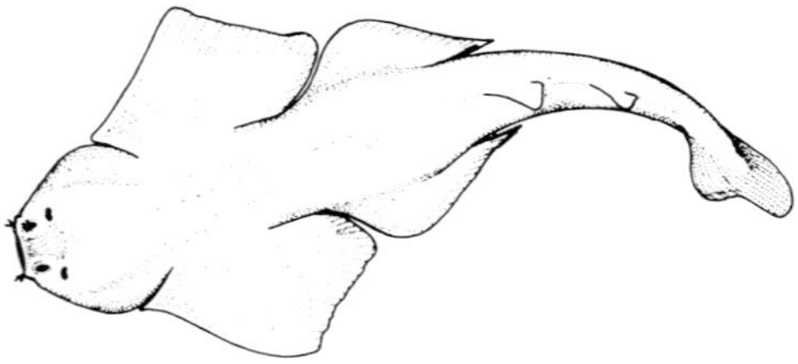

TORPEDINIDAE
Electric rays

See page 79 for species description

This worldwide family includes at least 35 species, three occurring in southern African waters.

Once shocked by the powerful electric organs, there can be no doubt that a member of this family has been encountered! The body is more circular and fleshy than other rays, and the stocky tail carries two dorsal fins in addition to the well-developed caudal fin.

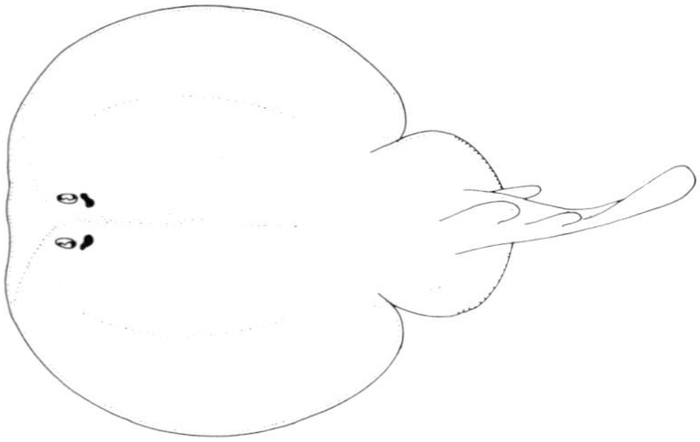

In this rather sedentary family, the large pectoral muscles are modified into electric organs. The cells of this highly specialized muscle tissue can store electric energy in chemical form. Release of this energy is controlled by an intricate nerve network, which can bring about a synchronized discharge of as much as 75 volts. The pectoral fins, therefore, have no function in locomotion, and electric rays swim by lashing clumsily from side to side with their stumpy tails. This is in direct contrast to other skates and rays, which are propelled by undulations of the pectoral fins.

Reproduction is ovoviviparous, and females give birth to a maximum of 30 young in any one season. Embryonic development involves three distinct body phases: shark-like; stingray-like; and finally the characteristic, almost circular form.

Callorhinchus capensis

Dumeril, 1865

Common names SA – elephantfish. Elsewhere – ratfish, plownose chimaera

[Smith 34□1]

IDENTIFYING FEATURES

COLOUR, SHAPE AND SIZE

This most unusually shaped fish has a steep forehead, long, pointed tail (almost half the body length) and a curious, trunk-like lobe projecting downwards from the tip of the snout. The overall body colour is silver, sometimes with a mother-of-pearl sheen along the back. Can attain 100 cm.

EXTERNAL ANATOMY

The elephantfish has no scales and its skin is exceptionally smooth. Aside from a single stout spine in the erectile dorsal, the fins are spineless and the paired pectorals are very large. The teeth of the underslung mouth are fused to form three hard plates, two in the upper jaw and one in the lower. The gill slits occur on the underside and are fused into a single opening. The lateral line system is conspicuous and includes several branches on the head. Mature males have a stalked knob on the forehead and distinct, elongate claspers positioned just before the pelvic fins.

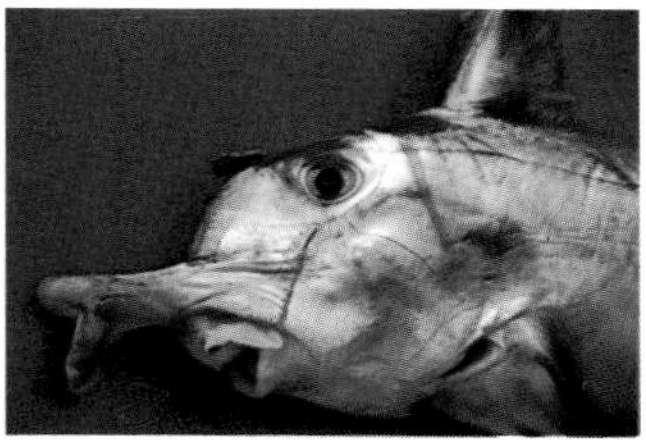

Close-up of male head showing stalked knob.

NATURAL HISTORY

The elephantfish is a curious, invariably solitary, and fairly common bottom-dwelling species, found in shallow water and to depths of 200 m. This primitive animal has a cartilaginous skeleton and has remained relatively unchanged for some 100 million years. The lateral line system resembles those of both sharks and bony fishes, and comprises a series of sensory cells situated in a distinct groove or canal. Additional sensory information, believed to be tactile, is received through the peculiar snout. Water for respiration is taken in through nostrils and not the mouth, as is the case with bony fishes. The diet of this sluggish fish includes brittlestars, crabs, shrimps and molluscs, as well as several species of slow-swimming fish. Breeding takes place during summer and females undergo internal fertilization before depositing two pointed, brown, egg cases on the sea-bed.

DISTRIBUTION

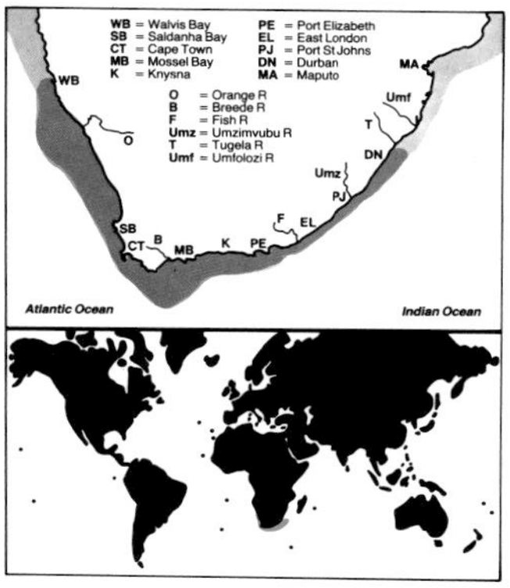

CAPTURE

The elephantfish is often caught in trawl or beach seine nets and occasionally also hooked by sport fishermen. It is of moderate commercial and angling importance, being increasingly marketed as a substitute for kingklip fillets. Though the flesh is palatable, this fish is invariably rejected because of its odd shape. In time to come this prejudice may well be overcome as marine resources are more widely exploited to meet a growing demand for protein. The 'pen', or first dorsal spine, of this fish is said by fishermen to cause a painful slow-healing wound. It is rarely landed by spearfishermen.

SA angling record – 6,0 kg.

SA spearfishing record – 3,6 kg.

SPECIFIC CATCH RESTRICTIONS

None.

NAME DERIVATION

Callorhinchus, hard-skinned snout; *capensis,* of the Cape. Elephantfish, a reference to its peculiar, lobed snout.

SIMILAR SPECIES

Chimaera monstrosa and other related chimaeras have much longer second dorsals and lack the fleshy snout projection.

Carcharhinus albimarginatus

(Rüppell, 1837)
Common name Worldwide – silvertip shark
[Smith 9□1]

IDENTIFYING FEATURES

COLOUR, SHAPE AND SIZE

This is a large and rather slender-bodied shark with a moderately long and rounded snout. The body colours and fin markings are most distinctive. The overall dorsal colour is grey, but live specimens have a distinctly coppery-brown hue. The underside is white. All fins have a white tip or outer edge, and this is especially conspicuous in the first dorsal, pectoral, pelvic and caudal fins. Seen underwater, these bright-white edges are even more noticeable, and it is known that these colour patterns exist in both juvenile and adult silvertip sharks. Can attain 275 cm.

EXTERNAL ANATOMY

The fins are well developed, especially the pectorals, which appear proportionately slightly longer and more falcate than those of most other requiem sharks. The dorsal fin is moderately high, and slightly rounded at its tip. Along the back, between the two dorsal fins, there is always a distinct, dermal ridge. Large teeth occur in both jaws, those in the upper jaw being very finely serrate, triangular, and progressively more slanted towards the outer edges of the jaw. Usual tooth count = $\frac{13 - 1 \text{ or } 2 - 13}{12 - 1 \text{ or } 2 - 12}$.

NATURAL HISTORY

This is an inquisitive and often bold shark of the open ocean, especially around oceanic islands or associated with ships at sea. The silvertip appears as at home near the surface as it does in the depths of the ocean; some have been reported to venture deeper than 600 m. The natural diet of this shark consists of a wide variety of fish, comprising both surface species such as flyingfish and small tuna, and bottom-dwelling fishes such as soles and lanternfishes. The viviparous females produce litters of about six pups, though a maximum of 11 pups has been recorded. These juveniles are born during midsummer, after a one year gestation period. Each measures 70-80 cm. Young sharks may spend their first years close to shore, occasionally over shallower coral reefs or in atoll lagoons. Sexual maturity is attained some years later when males are about 170 cm and females 200 cm in length. While no attacks on humans have yet been attributed to this species, it is, nevertheless, potentially dangerous, and should be handled with circumspection.

DISTRIBUTION

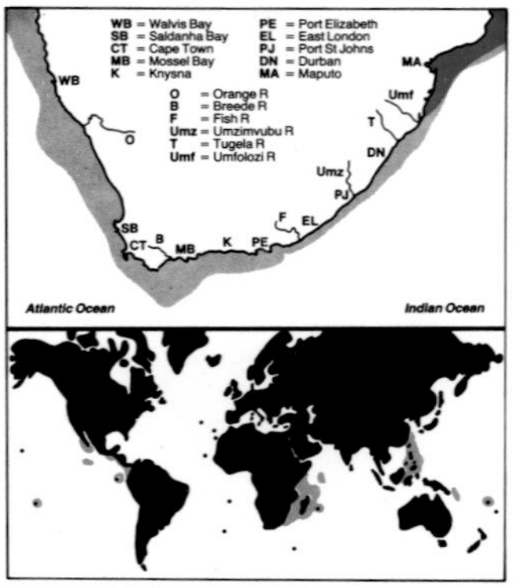

CAPTURE

The silvertip is quite often hooked from commercial pleasure craft off Moçambique and northern Natal. It is usually the first fish around a stationary boat and often boldly inspects divers in open ocean waters. The silvertip shark is edible.

SPECIFIC CATCH RESTRICTIONS

None.

NAME DERIVATION

Carcharhinus, an ancient name meaning jagged shark, a reference to its rasp-like skin; *albimarginatus* white-edged. Silvertip shark, a reference to the white fin tips.

SIMILAR SPECIES

The oceanic whitetip shark *(C. longimanus),* has much longer, lobe-like pectoral and dorsal fins, and a black-tipped anal fin that almost touches the lower tail. The white-tipped reef shark *(Triaenodon obesus)* is a bottom-or cave-dwelling shark with a stockier body, a first dorsal fin located further back (opposite midpoint between pectoral and pelvic fins) and a second dorsal that is distinctly longer than that of either the silvertip or oceanic whitetip.

Typical teeth: lower (left); upper (right).

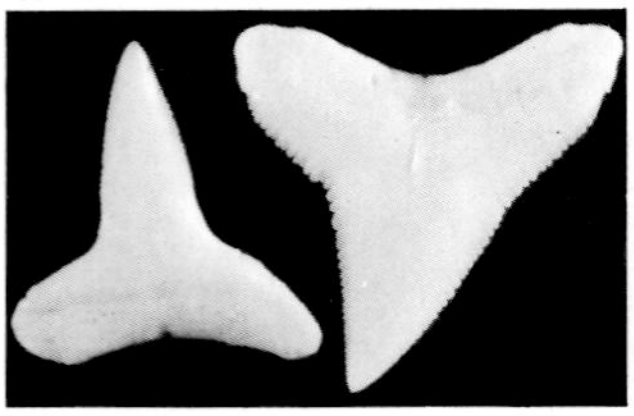

Carcharhinus brachyurus

(Günther, 1870)

Common names Worldwide – copper shark, bronze whaler, narrow-tooth shark

[Smith 9□5]

IDENTIFYING FEATURES

COLOUR, SHAPE AND SIZE

The body is stocky and, though this is not always obvious, slightly arched above the gill slits, giving the head a depressed appearance. A coppery sheen extends along the top and sides of the body, but dead specimens are generally browny-grey with a pale underside. The tips of the pectoral and pelvic fins range from dusky to black. Can attain 300 cm.

EXTERNAL ANATOMY

The fins are well developed and the caudal fin has a bulge near the base of the front edge. Most copper sharks are smooth backed, but some may have an indistinct interdorsal ridge. The pointed teeth are triangular and rather slender, with those of the upper jaw being serrated and outward slanting. Usual tooth count = $\frac{15 - 1 - 15}{15 - 1 - 15}$.

DISTRIBUTION

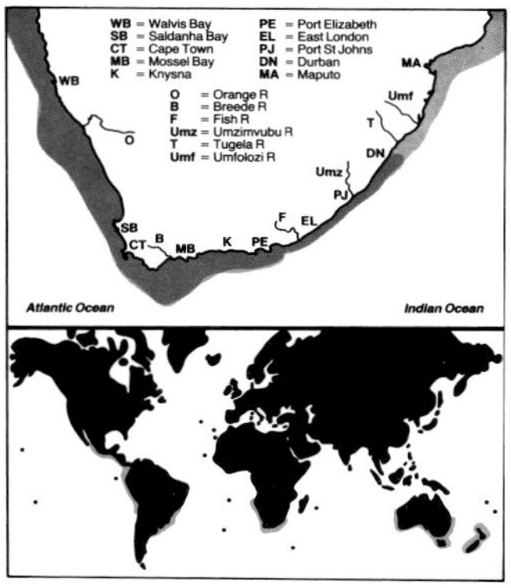

NATURAL HISTORY

The copper shark favours temperate to cooler waters and though it is primarily a shallow-water species, it has occasionally been recorded at depths of 100 m. During winter, large numbers are known to follow sardine shoals along the southern Natal coast, though few have been noted north of Durban.

Despite the many copper sharks that take advantage of the abundant and easy food sources that these shoals offer, this species usually feeds near the bottom, its diet consisting mainly of slow-swimming fish such as gurnard and sole. Small sharks, skates and squid, however, are also eaten.

Females are fertilized internally and the young are born live in litters of 13-20 and are 60-70 cm long at birth. Sexual maturity is reached at an age of about five years and a length of approximately 230 cm. Though the copper shark is potentially dangerous to man, few attacks have been attributed to the species.

Typical teeth: lower (left); upper (right).

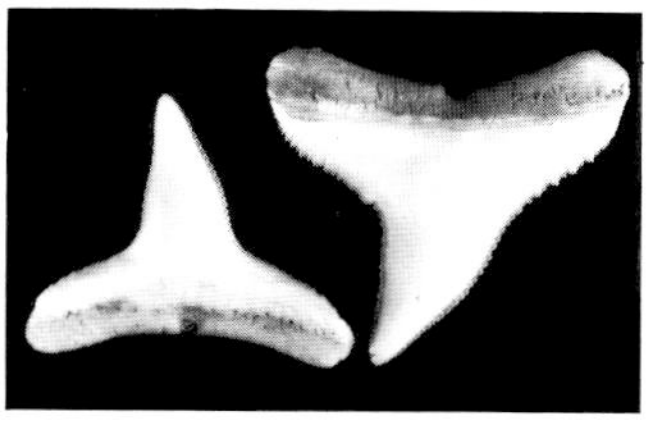

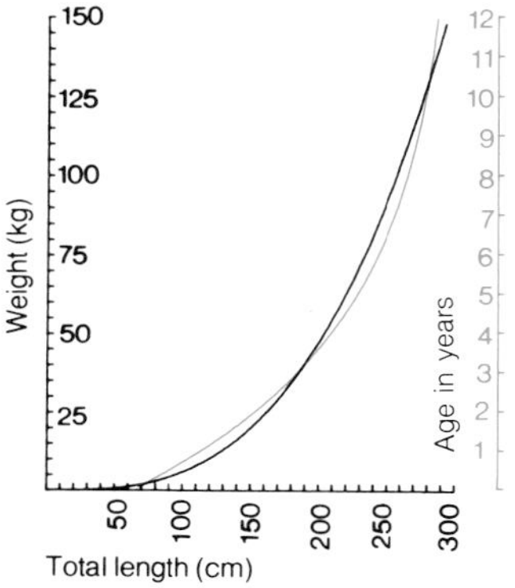

CAPTURE

This fine angling fish makes good eating and is often landed by shore anglers in Namibia, the Cape and Transkei, especially during the sardine run. Large specimens are occasionally caught in Natal's shark nets.

SA angling record – 192,0 kg.

SA spearfishing record – 71,2 kg.

SPECIFIC CATCH RESTRICTIONS

None.

NAME DERIVATION

Carcharhinus, an ancient name meaning jagged shark, a reference to the rasp-like skin; *brachyurus,* short-bodied. Copper shark, a reference to the body colour. Bronze whaler, a reference to its alleged habit of feeding on whale carcasses, especially in Australian waters.

SIMILAR SPECIES

Though easily confused with *C. obscurus, C. limbatus, C. brevipinna* and *C. plumbeus,* the distinctive upper tooth shape, absence of pronounced body markings and little or no dorsal ridge should confirm the identity of *C. brachyurus.*

Carcharhinus brevipinna

(Müller & Henle, 1839)
Common names Worldwide – spinner shark, long-nosed grey shark
[Smith 9□6]

IDENTIFYING FEATURES

COLOUR, SHAPE AND SIZE

This is a large, slender-bodied shark, with a long, pointed snout and rather small eyes. The overall body colouration is grey or brownish-grey above, and white below, often with a paler narrow band along each flank. The fins of specimens exceeding 130 cm are characteristically marked: the tips of both dorsals, pectorals, anal and lower caudal are distinctly black. There is some variability in this, however, as occasional specimens lack the black tip to the first dorsal and upper pectoral fins. Some specimens have also been recorded with a black-tipped pelvic fin, though this is most unusual. Juveniles are more difficult to identify as they have virtually no marks on their fins.

EXTERNAL ANATOMY

The arrangement of fins is typical of the requiem sharks, except that the first dorsal is somewhat smaller and located well back – its origin usually directly above, or just behind, the rear tips of the pectoral fins. There is no dermal ridge between the dorsal fins. The teeth of spinner sharks are quite small and distinctive in shape, being triangular, but with pointed, upright cusps. It is noticeable that, although its upper and lower jaw teeth are similar in shape, it is only the upper teeth that have a sharply serrated edge.
Usual tooth count = $\frac{16 - 2 - 16}{16 - 1 - 16}$.

NATURAL HISTORY

This is a common shark of coastal waters. It may venture into quite shallow water, and is often the shark most commonly netted off Natal's beaches by the Natal Sharks Board. The spinner shark appears to prefer the shallows,

Typical teeth: lower (left); upper (right).

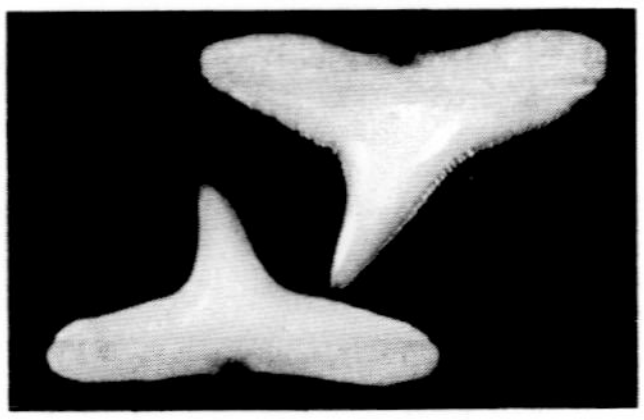

none having been recorded deeper than 75 m. This active predator preys on a variety of midwater shoaling fishes such as small tuna, kob, mullet, kingfishes, sardines, lizardfishes and small sharks. Squid and cuttlefish are also eaten, and most of the food is swallowed whole because this shark lacks typical cutting dentition. Part of its feeding strategy appears to involve dashing full-speed into a shoal of fish, and thereafter breaking the surface, often spinning in mid-air. Adult females occur off the Natal coast throughout the year, but males are common only during summer. Sexual maturity is attained at about 180 cm for males and 210 cm for females. The gestation period is one year, and the viviparous females produce litters of 6-15 young during autumn. Spinner sharks are about 60 cm long when born, and often move into shallow water off sandy beaches just afterwards. Young spinner sharks are known to undertake considerable migrations. This shark does not pose a major threat to bathers, but it should be handled with caution.

DISTRIBUTION

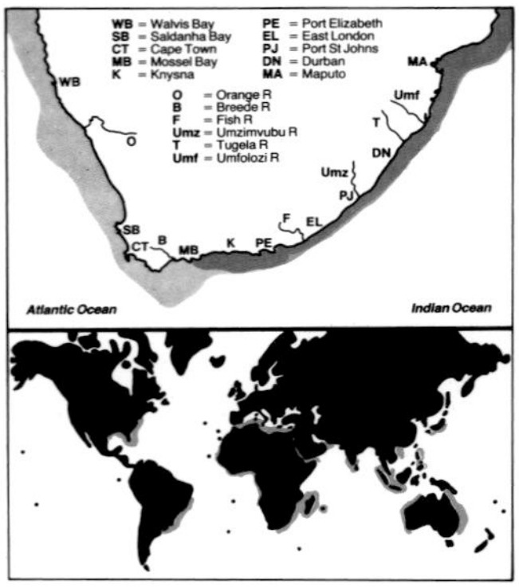

CAPTURE

Juvenile spinner sharks are caught by shore anglers, and adults are trapped in shark nets. Spinner sharks are edible, and the fins are suitable for sharkfin soup.
SA angling record – 122,5 kg.

SPECIFIC CATCH RESTRICTIONS

None.

SIMILAR SPECIES

The conspicuous, black colouration on specific fins is usually sufficient to positively identify a spinner shark. The blacktail reef shark (*C. wheeleri*) has the entire rear edge of the tail fin blackened, while the blackspot shark (*C. sealei*) has only the second dorsal fin black.

Carcharhinus leucas

(Valenciennes, 1839)
Common names SA – Zambezi shark, river shark. Elsewhere – bull shark
[Smith 9□9]

IDENTIFYING FEATURES

COLOUR, SHAPE AND SIZE
This robust-bodied shark has a rounded, blunt snout. The colour of the body is predominantly grey with a pale to white underside. Juveniles have black tips to their fins; these fade with age. Attains 320 cm.
EXTERNAL ANATOMY
The pointed fins are well developed and there is no interdorsal ridge. This species is frequently confused with the Java shark *(C. amboinensis),* but can be distinguished by the relative heights of the dorsal fins. (The ratio between the vertical heights of the first and second dorsals is greater than 3,2:1 for the Java shark, but less than 3,2:1 for the Zambezi). Teeth in the upper jaw are upright, strongly serrated, triangular and broad at their bases, while in the lower jaw they are more slender and pointed.
Usual tooth count = $\frac{13-2-13}{12-2-12}$

DISTRIBUTION

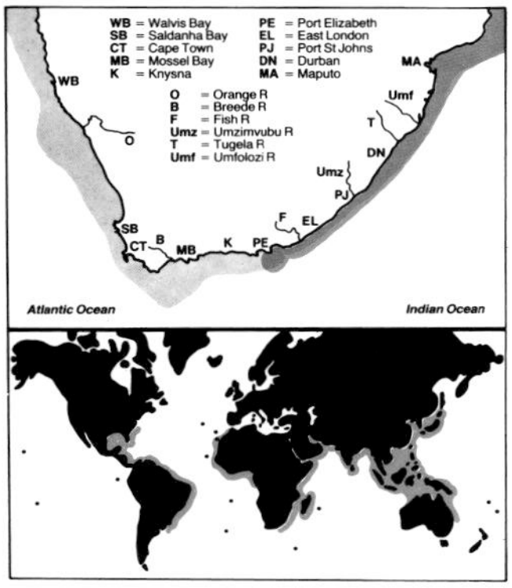

NATURAL HISTORY

This shark is remarkable for its ability to live in fresh water for indefinite periods. It has been recorded hundreds of kilometres upstream in large rivers such as the Zambezi and lake Nicaragua in Central America. This freshwater tolerance gives the Zambezi shark the advantage of feeding in areas where there are fewer large predators. It feeds in muddy water. Bony fish, especially mullet and spotted grunter, comprise 50 per cent of the diet. Small sharks, skates, dolphins, turtles, small mammals and crabs, however, have also been found in the stomachs of captured specimens. Aside from freshwater habitats, this sluggish shark is generally confined to coastal waters, river mouths and estuaries such as St Lucia and Richards Bay. These also serve as nursery areas for the young which are born live in summer after a gestation period of approximately one year. The average litter size is 11 or 12. Juveniles are about 50 cm long at birth and are often seen 'spinning' out of the water, apparently in an attempt to rid themselves of external parasites. Sexual maturity is attained after about six years at a length of 250 cm. The Zambezi shark has been responsible for several, sometimes fatal, attacks on bathers along the East Coast of southern Africa.

Typical teeth: lower (left); upper (right).

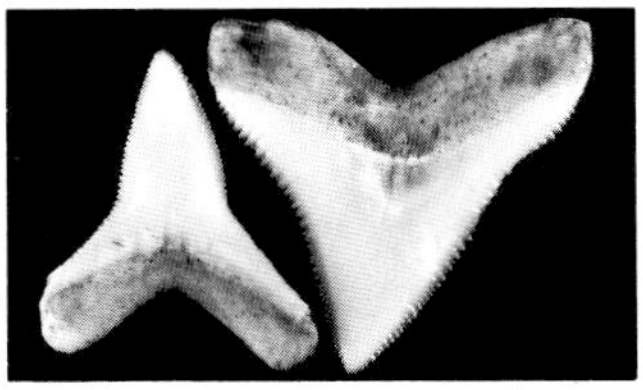

CAPTURE

Though not commercially important, this species makes good eating. It is caught at river mouths by shore anglers using live bait, whole mullet or grunter heads. Its inshore habits make it particularly vulnerable to the gill nets protecting most of Natal's beaches. It thrives in captivity and some have lived in Durban's Seaworld for 15 years.
SA angling record – 304,0 kg.
SA spearfishing record – 34,0 kg.

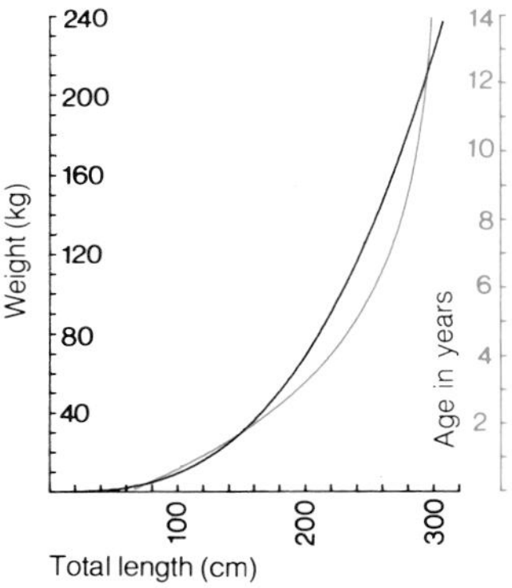

SPECIFIC CATCH RESTRICTIONS

None.

NAME DERIVATION

Carcharhinus, an ancient name meaning jagged shark, a reference to its rasp-like skin; *leucas,* white, Zambezi shark, a reference to one of the river systems it freely enters.

Carcharhinus limbatus

(Muller & Henle, 1839)
Common name Worldwide – blacktip or blackfin shark
[Smith 9□10]

IDENTIFYING FEATURES

COLOUR, SHAPE AND SIZE

This shark is somewhat elongate and has a distinctly pointed snout. The body colour is generally grey with a pale underside and all fins, with the exception of the anal, are black tipped. These markings, which are especially noticeable on the pectoral fins of this young specimen, fade with age. Most specimens have a distinct, dark band along each side, ending in a point over the origin of the pelvics. Can attain 250 cm.

EXTERNAL ANATOMY

The fins are well developed and pointed, especially the first dorsal which, compared with other members of the genus, is relatively tall and narrow. There is no interdorsal ridge. The finely serrated teeth of the upper jaw are erect, pointed and narrow, but set on broad bases. The teeth of the lower jaw are similar. but slightly smaller and tend to curve inwards. Usual tooth count = $\frac{15 - 2 - 15}{15 - 1 - 15}$.

Typical teeth: lower (left); upper (right).

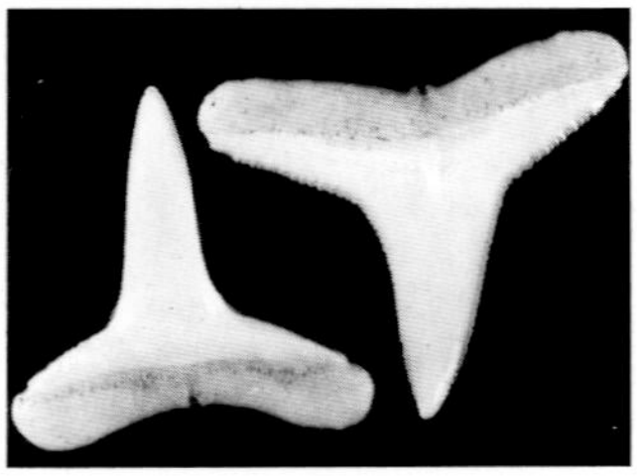

DISTRIBUTION

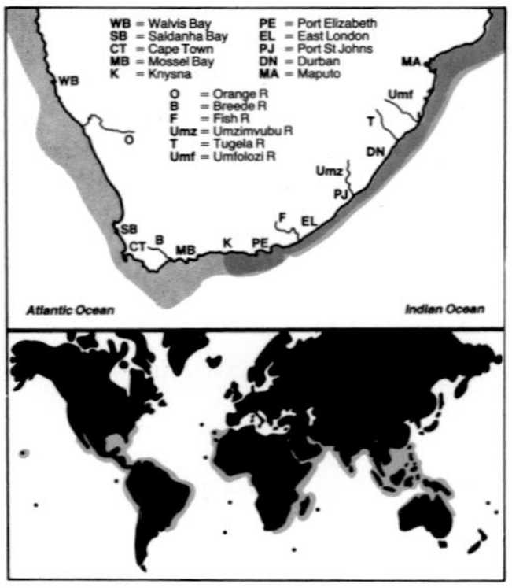

NATURAL HISTORY

This fast and sometimes aggressive predator generally hunts in the mid-water region of inshore areas. It can withstand short periods of reduced salinity and may, therefore, be encountered near river mouths and estuaries. The diet consists largely of bony fish including fast gamefish, the juveniles of the other shark species, stingrays, cuttlefish and crayfish. During summer, pregnant females move to specific nursery areas where they give birth to 6-8 young. The gestation period is 11-12 months and each pup is some 60 cm long at birth. Sexual maturity is reached after four years at an approximate length of 180 cm. The blacktip shark is potentially dangerous to bathers – it is frequently seen by spearfishermen and has been known to harass those with catches.

CAPTURE

The blacktip shark readily takes live or dead bait and is a fine, gamely fighting sport fish which makes good eating. It is commonly caught in Natal's shark nets.
SA angling record – 129,5 kg.
SA spearfishing record – 27,0 kg.

SPECIFIC CATCH RESTRICTIONS

None.

NAME DERIVATION

Carcharhinus, an ancient name meaning jagged shark, a reference to its rasp-like skin; *limbatus,* edged. Blacktip, an obvious reference to the colour of the fin tips.

SIMILAR SPECIES

The blacktip is most easily confused with the spinner shark *(C. brevipinna),* which has a longer snout, smaller eyes, plain pelvics but black tips to the anal.

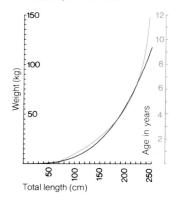

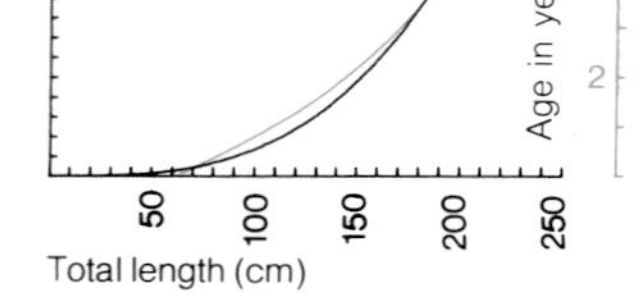

Carcharhinus obscurus

(Lesueur, 1818)

Common names Worldwide – dusky shark, ridgeback grey shark [Smith 9□14]

IDENTIFYING FEATURES

COLOUR, SHAPE AND SIZE

This shark has a robust body, slightly flattened head and a moderately pointed snout. The general body colour is dusky grey with slightly darker fin tips and a white underside. The tips of the pectoral and pelvic fins are quite dark in young specimens. Can attain 350 cm.

EXTERNAL ANATOMY

The fins are well developed and the pointed first dorsal originates just behind the level of the pectoral base. A characteristic feature of the dusky shark is the distinct interdorsal ridge. The teeth of the upper jaw are triangular, serrated and have a slight, backward slant. Those of the lower jaw are similar in shape, but smaller. Usual tooth count = $\frac{14 \text{ or } 15 - 2 - 14 \text{ or } 15}{14 - 1 - 14}$

DISTRIBUTION

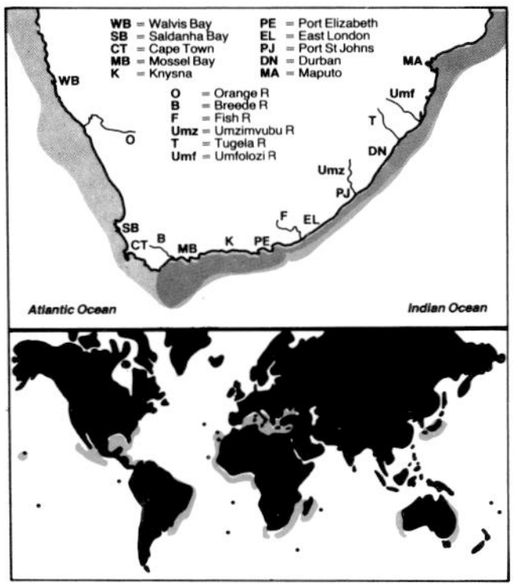

NATURAL HISTORY

The dusky shark is an offshore predator, especially in the Agulhas Current region, where adults are often seen following ships. It is intolerant of low salinities and is, therefore, rarely found in estuaries. At least 75 per cent of the diet comprises a wide variety of bony fish. Juvenile sharks, crabs, crayfish, octopus and squid have also been found in the stomachs of landed specimens. The gestation period has not been accurately determined, but females move close inshore along the Natal coast during spring and summer to give birth to litters of about ten juveniles, each weighing 4,5 kg. These young sharks migrate down the coast as far as Mossel Bay before taking an as-yet-unidentified route to join the parent stock several years later. Sexual maturity is reached at 11-13 years. The size of dusky shark populations is normally regulated by other large predatory sharks, but as many of these have been eliminated by Natal's anti-shark nets, the number of juvenile duskies in that region has increased in recent years. Small dusky sharks are known to feed in packs, and adults are potentially dangerous to man.

Typical teeth: lower (left); upper (right).

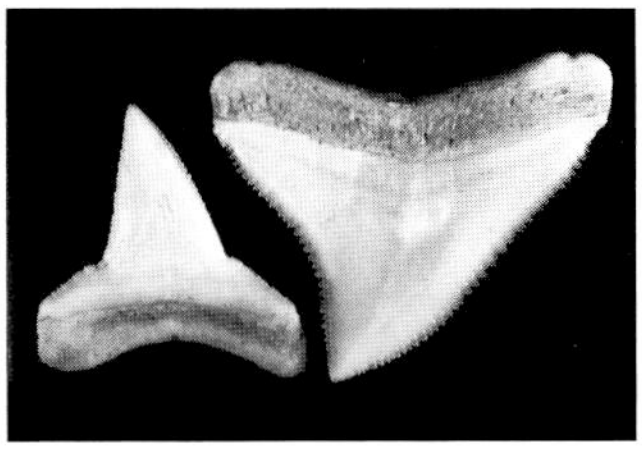

CAPTURE

This shark is not of commercial importance, though the young are caught by shore and ski-boat anglers using almost any bait. The flesh of this shark makes excellent eating.

All-Africa angling record – 116,6 kg.
SA angling record – 326,6 kg.
SA spearfishing record – 26,4 kg.

SPECIFIC CATCH RESTRICTIONS

None.

NAME DERIVATION

Carcharhinus, an ancient name meaning jagged shark, a reference to its rasp-like skin; *obscurus,* dusky. Dusky, a reference to its body colour. Ridgeback, a reference to the interdorsal ridge.

SIMILAR SPECIES

Though closely resembling numerous similar sharks, the dorsal ridge, absence of distinct markings and nearly erect upper teeth distinguish the dusky from the rest. The sandbar *(C. plumbeus)* has a higher dorsal.

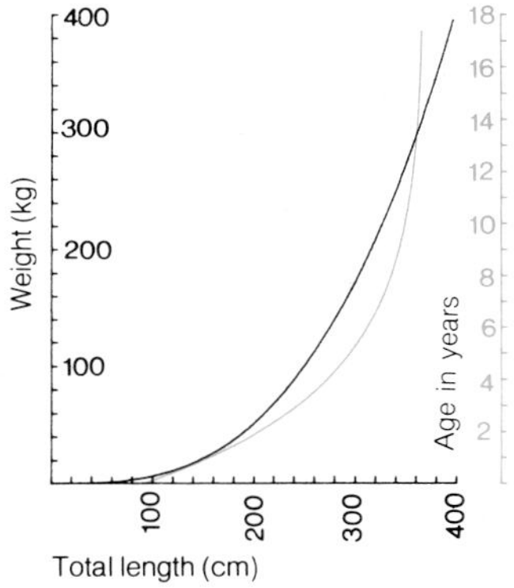

Carcharhinus plumbeus

(Nardo, 1827)
Common name Worldwide – sandbar shark
[Smith 9□15]

IDENTIFYING FEATURES

COLOUR, SHAPE AND SIZE
This medium-sized, rather stocky shark has a bluntly rounded snout and quite large fins. The body colour of the sandbar is different from most other requiem sharks in that it is considerably lighter and usually more brownish-grey overall. Furthermore, none of the fins has distinctive marks or colour patterns, except in smaller specimens, where the outer margins of fins may be slightly dusky. Attains 220 cm, but may grow to 250 cm in the Atlantic.
EXTERNAL ANATOMY
The fins are most distinctive, especially the very high first dorsal which is twice the length of the snout. This is set far forward with its origin directly over the pectoral fin base. The other fins are typical of most other requiem sharks. Along the back there is always a distinct dorsal ridge, while the jaws are well armed with large teeth. Those in the upper jaw are triangular but slightly slanted in shape, and have fine serrations on their cutting edges. Usual tooth count = $\frac{14-1 \text{ or } 2-14}{14-1-14}$.

NATURAL HISTORY

This widely distributed shark is most commonly encountered in the world's warmer coastal waters, predominantly over sandy or muddy offshore banks that have formed opposite large river mouths and estuaries. Adults seldom venture into the nearshore surf zone, though many specimens have been reported from protective shark nets, as well as longline and trawl catches, in comparatively shallow water. Others have also been caught off oceanic islands, possibly indicating a wider range of habitat preference. Nevertheless, it would appear that the sandbar lives close to the bottom, where it feeds on a variety of small prey such as eels, soles, small fishes, octopuses, squid, prawns and other invertebrates. Most of the prey is swallowed whole, despite the formidable cutting teeth. This species matures at a rather small size; 160 cm for males and 170 cm for females. Reproduction is viviparous, and the sex ratio of embryos is 1:1. Litters comprising about eight young are born during midsummer, after a gestation period of approximately one year. While newborn young are not commonly caught, two- or three-year-old juveniles do periodically appear in anglers' catches during summer. Considerable numbers have been caught at Richards Bay, and as far south as Port St Johns.

Typical teeth: lower (left); upper (right).

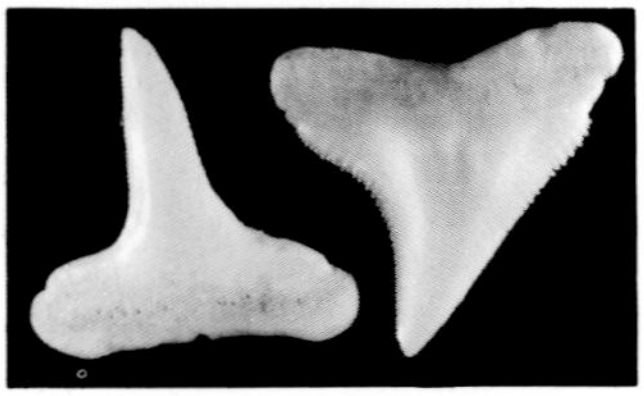

SPECIFIC CATCH RESTRICTIONS

None.

CAPTURE

Young sandbars are occasionally caught by rock and surf anglers especially at Richards Bay. This species is edible.
World angling record – 96,6 kg.
SA angling record – 150,0kg.
SA spearfishing record – vacant.

DISTRIBUTION

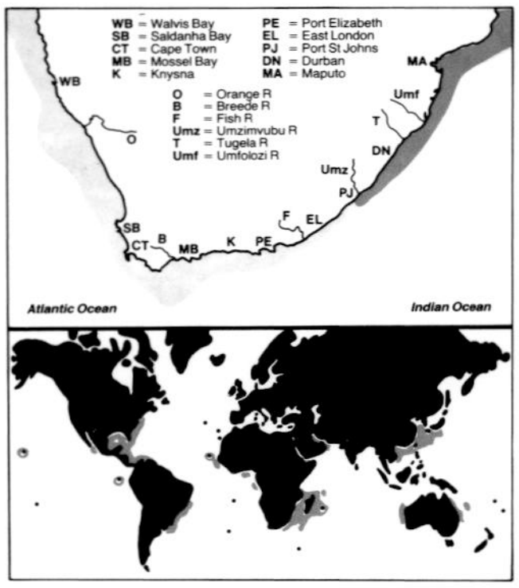

NAME DERIVATION

Carcharhinus, an ancient name meaning jagged shark, a reference to its rasp-like skin; *plumbeus,* lead-like. Sandbar shark, a reference to its common occurrence on nearshore sandbanks.

SIMILAR SPECIES

This species is readily distinguished from all other requiem sharks by its high dorsal fin which is situated well forward, pale body colour, and tooth shape. The pale colouration makes this fish most distinctive when viewed underwater.

Carcharhinus sealei

(Pietschmann, 1913)
Common name Worldwide – blackspot shark
[Smith 9□16]

IDENTIFYING FEATURES

COLOUR, SHAPE AND SIZE
This small, slender shark has a pointed snout and is readily identified by the conspicuous jet-black tip of the second dorsal fin. The overall body colour, including the fins, is khaki-grey, with a pale underside. Can attain 100 cm.

EXTERNAL ANATOMY
The fins are well developed and while in most cases the back is smooth, a faint interdorsal ridge may sometimes be present. Individual muscle blocks may be seen through the skin along the sides of the body. (These are obvious in the photograph as faint chevron-like markings along the flanks). The nostrils, on the underside of the snout, have a distinct lobe in front. The teeth of the upper jaw are triangular, but slanted outwards and strongly serrated. Those of the lower jaw are much smaller, pointed and only microscopically serrated, if at all. Usual tooth count = $\frac{12 - 2 - 12}{12 - 1 - 12}$.

DISTRIBUTION

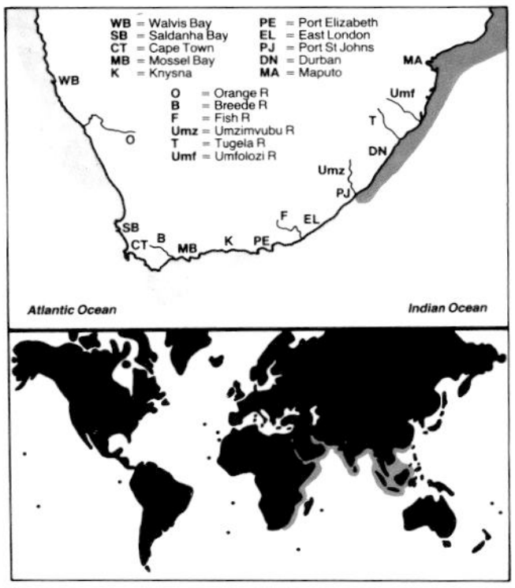

NATURAL HISTORY

This small, non-aggressive species lives in coastal waters to depths of 40 m. It is not generally found near river mouths and is probably intolerant of low salinities. Though present throughout the year, it is more abundant during summer. Blackspot sharks usually feed near the sea-bed, where they prey mainly on slower fish, prawns and squid. During spring, females give birth to one or two young after a nine-month gestation period. Each newly born pup is about 40 cm long. Sexual maturity is reached at a length of 75 cm. As a species, blackspot sharks are considered too small to be dangerous to man.

Typical teeth: lower (left); upper (right).

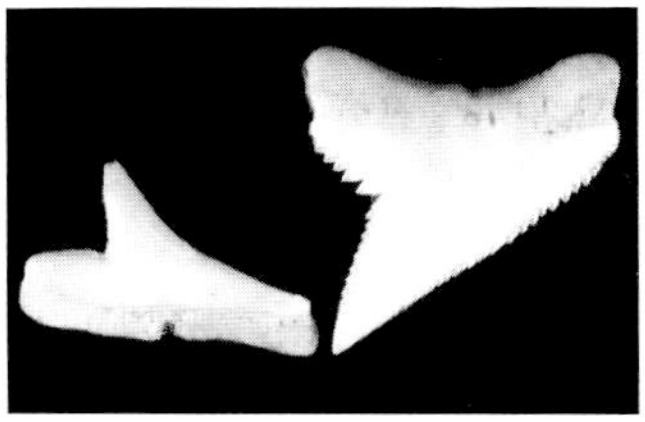

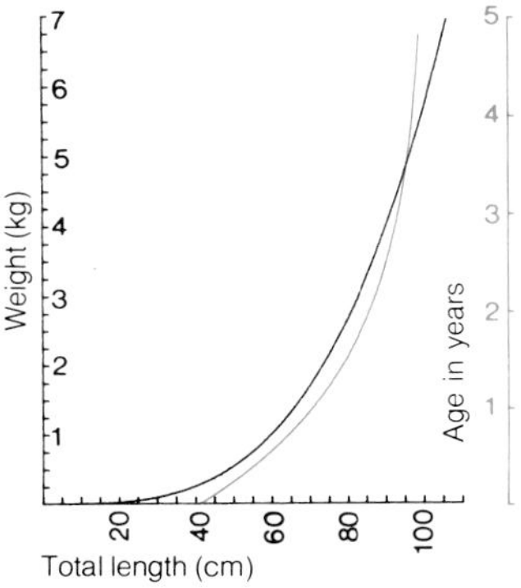

CAPTURE

The blackspot shark is quite commonly caught by shore anglers on a variety of baits, but it is more noted for the quality of its flesh than for its fighting abilities. It is rarely speared.
SA angling record – 6,5 kg.
SA spearfishing record – 4,4 kg.

SPECIFIC CATCH RESTRICTIONS

None.

NAME DERIVATION

Carcharhinus, an ancient name meaning jagged shark, a reference to its rasp-like skin; *sealei,* after Alvin Seale, a former ichthyologist at Hawaii's famous Bishop Museum. Blackspot, a reference to the distinctive mark on the second dorsal fin.

SIMILAR SPECIES

While there are other sharks with black fin-tips, none has only the second dorsal black.

Galeocerdo cuvier

(Peron & Lesueur, 1822)
Common name Worldwide – tiger shark
[Smith 9□19]

IDENTIFYING FEATURES

COLOUR, SHAPE AND SIZE
This very large, blunt-snouted and robust shark has numerous grey bars running down the upper sides. These are particularly evident in juveniles but fade considerably in adults. The largest tiger shark to be accurately measured was a 550 cm specimen caught off Cuba, but there is a photographic record of a 740 cm female tiger shark landed in Indo-China.
EXTERNAL ANATOMY
In adults, the first dorsal fin originates directly above the pectoral axil and is linked to the second, much smaller, dorsal by means of an interdorsal ridge. The upper lobe of the caudal fin has a long, thin, tapering tip and each side of the slender caudal peduncle bears a distinct keel. Spiracles are present and the eyes have internal nictitating eyelids. The distinctive, cockscomb-shaped teeth are strongly serrated and set in very wide jaws. Usual tooth count = $\frac{\text{10 or 11 - 1 - 10 or 11}}{\text{11 - 1 - 11}}$.

DISTRIBUTION

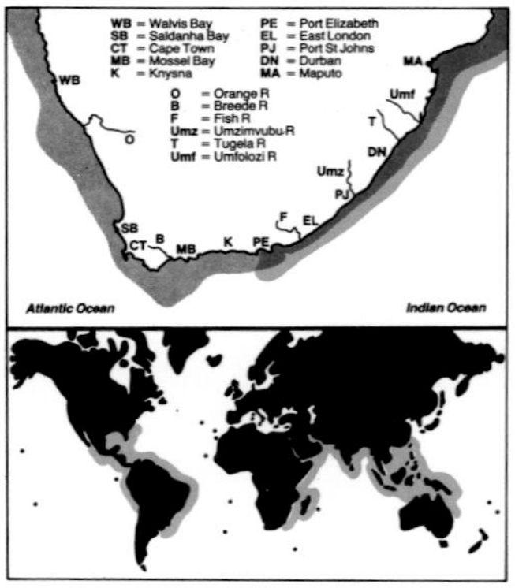

NATURAL HISTORY

The tiger shark is a solitary predator widespread throughout all tropical regions. It frequently enters

Typical teeth: lower (left); upper (right).

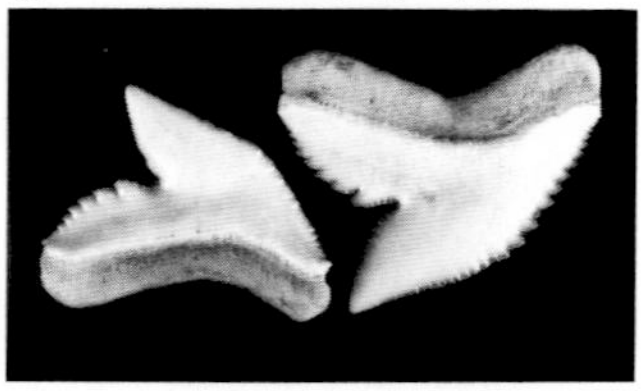

shallow coastal waters and often lurks in the vicinity of large river mouths. The inshore environment provides a rich and varied food source which well suits the scavenging habits of this shark. The diet includes sharks, bony fish, birds, turtles, seals and dolphins to crayfish, crabs and squid. 'Food' also includes anything from plastic bags and tin cans to the remains of livestock and humans. Much of this garbage is taken in harbours and near large rivers when these flood into the sea following inland rains. Despite its voracious habits, the tiger shark is a relatively sluggish species and is capable, like bony fish and the ragged-tooth shark, of pumping water over the gills for respiration. This enables it to swim at slower speeds than most sharks which have to keep a constantly faster 'pace' to maintain an adequate flow of water over the gills. Sexual maturity is attained at a length of about 290 cm in males and 340 cm in females. The size of litters varies considerably from 23-46. Each pup measures about 100 cm in length at birth. There is no doubt about the tiger shark's potential danger to man.

CAPTURE

Not many tiger sharks are caught from the shore, and only from Durban's breakwater are occasional landings made.
Ski-boat anglers quite often hook this fish, but because it is often enormous, most are never landed. Its flesh is palatable and the liver is rich in vitamin A.
World angling record – 807,0kg.
All-Africa angling record – 469,0 kg.
SA angling record – 469,0 kg.

SPECIFIC CATCH RESTRICTIONS

None.

NAME DERIVATION

Galeocerdo, a weasel-like shark; *cuvier,* named after the famous ichthyologist, Cuvier.

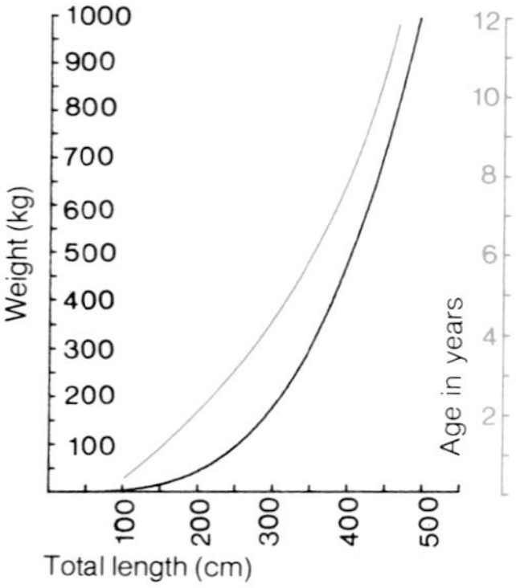

Galeorhinus galeus

(Linnaeus, 1758)
Common names SA – soupfin shark, vaalhaai. Elsewhere – soupfin shark, tope
[Smith 9□20]

IDENTIFYING FEATURES

COLOUR, SHAPE AND SIZE
This elongate shark has a pointed, translucent snout. The general body colour is grey and the underside is pale to white. Can attain 170 cm

EXTERNAL ANATOMY
The fins are smaller than those of most other sharks and there is no interdorsal ridge. Small spiracles are situated just behind the eyes. The teeth are small, triangular and slanted, with several coarse serrations on the outer edge of their bases. Tooth counts vary, but are usually $\frac{34-40}{31-36}$.

DISTRIBUTION

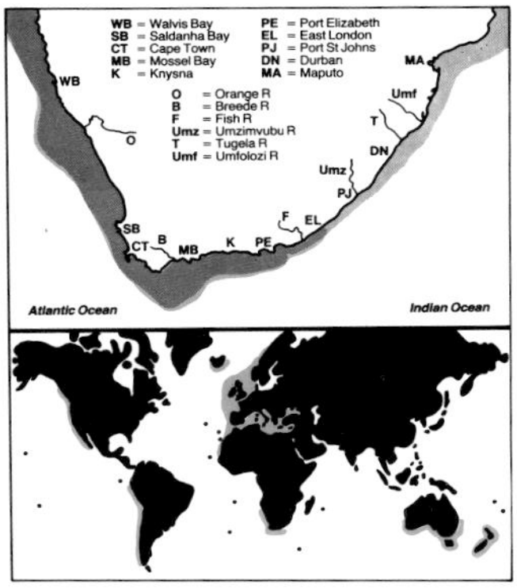

NATURAL HISTORY

The soupfin shark abounds in Cape waters and occurs to depths of 100 m. Young specimens are particularly common in shallow waters near the shore, but as a species, this shark is intolerant of low salinities and does not enter estuaries. It is generally sluggish and is usually found near the sea-bed where its prey comprises, almost exclusively, bottom-living fishes such as sole, hake and gurnard. Occasionally, however, the soupfin shark feeds more actively in the midwater region when baitfish and squid are plentiful. The soupfin shark is one of the few species in southern African waters that occurs in sufficient numbers to be fished commercially. Ironically, however, no local biologist has studied this shark in depth and consequently little is known of its life history or habits. Sexual maturity is attained after approximately ten years at a length of 130 cm and, if its biology is taken to be similar to that of the Australian soupfin shark, females bear 30-40 live young after a two-year gestation period.

Typical teeth: lower (left); upper (right).

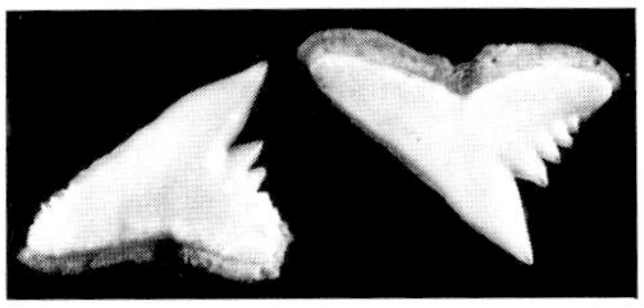

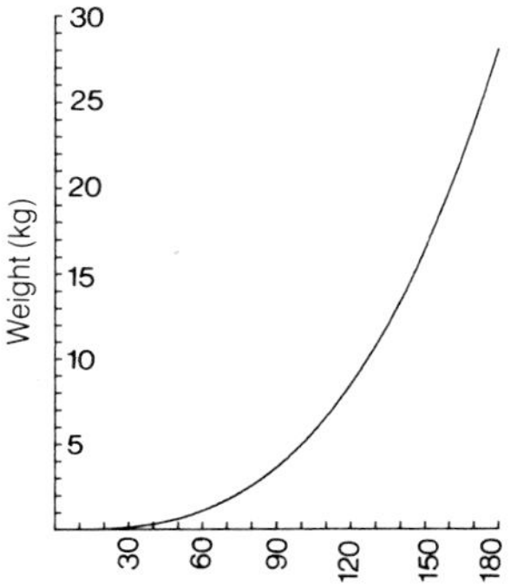

CAPTURE

In many parts of the world this species is extensively fished on a commercial scale, previously for its vitamin-A-rich liver oil, but now mainly for its flesh and fins. Part of the small South African catch is used to make fish biltong or jerky. It is caught mainly on handlines and in bottom trawls.
World angling record – 32,5 kg.
SA angling record – 32,5 kg.
SA spearfishing record – vacant.

SPECIFIC CATCH RESTRICTIONS

None.

NAME DERIVATION

Galeorhinus, weasel-like shark, a reference to the pointed snout; *galeus,* weasel. Soupfin shark, a reference to its exploitation in the Far East for sharkfin soup. Vaalhaai, Afrikaans meaning 'drab' shark, a reference to its dull grey colour.

Mustelus mosis

Hemprich & Ehrenberg, 1899
Common name Worldwide - hardnose houndshark
[Smith 9□26]

IDENTIFYING FEATURES

COLOUR, SHAPE AND SIZE

This slender-bodied shark has a short head that appears distinctly flattened so that the mouth is not easily visible in side view. The greyish or tan-coloured body lacks any spots or markings, although the trailing edges of the first dorsal and caudal fins are noticeably paler. Older specimens can have several points of excessive calcification in the skull, which may be externally visible as hard lumps. Can attain 150 cm.

EXTERNAL ANATOMY

Though an interdorsal ridge is present, it is not as distinct as in some species. The fins are well developed, and the first dorsal originates behind the level of the pectorals. The noticeably large second dorsal precedes the anal fin. Each jaw bears 55 rows of small, flat teeth arranged in a pavement fashion. The large eliptical eyes are often noticeably green. The identification of this genus is receiving further study at the JLB Smith Institute of Ichthyology.

NATURAL HISTORY

This sluggish, bottom-living shark frequents coastal waters, but also occurs to considerable depths. As is indicated by the strong, crushing teeth, this hardnose houndshark feeds on crustaceans such as crabs and small crayfish. Sometimes squid and small fish are also eaten. Young are born during the summer, after a one-year gestation period, and litters consist of about 13 juveniles measuring 23-30 cm each. Though newly born houndsharks are common in the surf zone, it is probable that many move to deeper water, where they grow to sexual maturity at a length of about 90 cm.

DISTRIBUTION

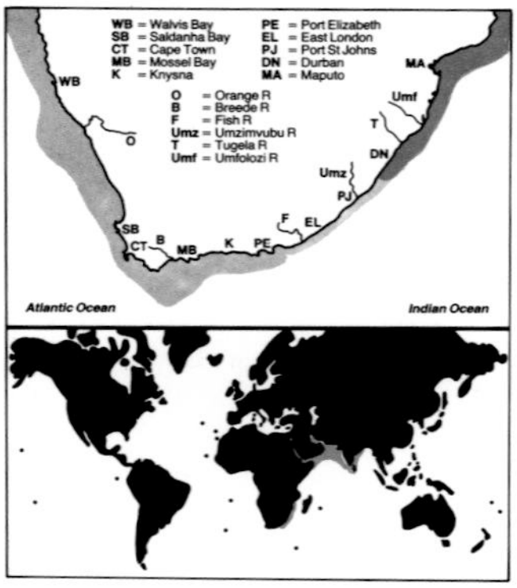

CAPTURE

The hardnose houndshark takes most fish baits, and is frequently caught by shore and ski-boat anglers throughout the year, but especially during autumn. Its flesh makes good eating, but this shark is not valued for its sporting potential, and it has no spearfishing importance. It is occasionally caught in trawl nets.

SA angling record - vacant.

SA spearfishing record - 6,2 kg.

SPECIFIC CATCH RESTRICTIONS

None.

NAME DERIVATION

Mustelus, weasel; *mosis,* meaning obscure. Hardnose houndshark, a reference to its rather dog-like head.

SIMILAR SPECIES

This is the only houndshark species found off Natal and Zululand. The similar whitespotted houndshark (*Mustelus palumbes*), found only along the Cape coast, is grey, with small, white spots on the upper body.

Detail of pavement teeth.

Mustelus mustelus

(Linnaeus, 1758)
Common names Worldwide - smoothhound or houndshark
[Smith 9□27]

IDENTIFYING FEATURES

COLOUR, SHAPE AND SIZE
This is the largest of the houndsharks, and has a rather slender body with a long, but blunt snout and somewhat flattened head. The general body colour is greyish-brown above, with many (but not all) specimens showing distinct, black spots on the upper flanks. The underside is much paler, and sometimes even appears white. Can attain 160 cm.
EXTERNAL ANATOMY
The fins of this shark, as in other houndsharks, are large and well developed, especially the second dorsal, which is almost the size of the first dorsal and considerably larger than the anal fin. The caudal fin is also large and has a distinct notch towards its tip. The mouth is located ventrally, and each jaw is set with numerous rows of pavement-like teeth, with the lower teeth showing very slight cusp development. There are also denticles on the roof of the mouth and on the tongue, though these are confined to the front of the mouth on this species. Viewed from underneath, the space between the nostrils is seen to be wide. The eyes are large and usually green.

NATURAL HISTORY

This is a common shark of Cape waters, being especially abundant along the shallow, sandy beaches of False Bay and areas of the southern Cape. It is not confined to the shallows, however, and smoothhounds have been captured in nets to depths of 350 m. Most of their time is spent lying on, or sluggishly swimming close to, the bottom; a fact indicated by their diet which consists mainly of bottom-dwelling invertebrates. These include crabs, crayfish, slipper crayfish, hermit crabs, squid and octopuses. A variety of fish species, including eels, have also been found in their stomachs. While the smoothhound is a viviparous species, the pregnant females show considerable development of a primitive placenta which nourishes the pups.
A maximum of 15 young, each measuring about 40 cm, are born after a gestation period of approximately one year .

DISTRIBUTION

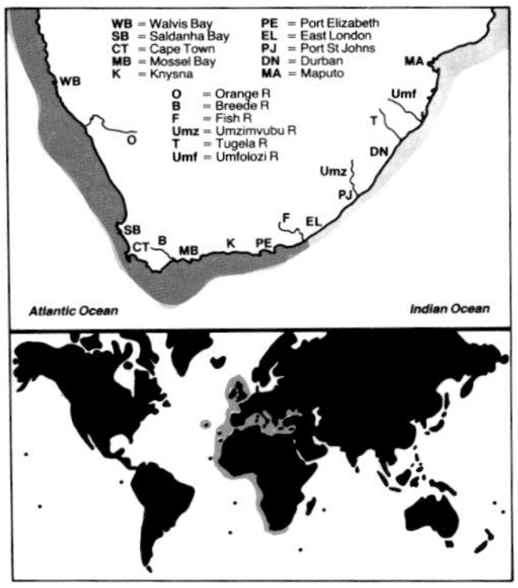

SPECIFIC CATCH RESTRICTIONS

None.

CAPTURE

Most smoothhounds are caught during shore-based angling tournaments off the Cape, though occasional catches have also been reported by trawlers operating further offshore. Though seldom eaten in this region, the smoothhound represents a considerable fresh and processed fish resource in Europe. Its value there is varied, and includes dried and salted fish as well as oil products.
SA angling record - 27,0 kg.

NAME DERIVATION

Mustelus, weasel. Smoothhound, a reference to the absence of spines and dog-like features of the head.

SIMILAR SPECIES

Houndhsarks are difficult to distinguish from each other without much detailed measurement, counting of vertebrae, and study. The isolated, black spots of this species are most distinctive, but, unfortunately, not always present. However, its abundance in Cape waters west of the Fish River should help to avoid confusion with the hardnose houndshark of the east coast *(M. mosis).* The absence of white spots on its body clearly distinguishes it from the whitespotted houndshark *(M. palumbes),* while the molar teeth and much less dense, black markings, help to avoid confusion with the spotted gullyshark *(T. megalopterus).*

Detail of pavement teeth.

Rhizoprionodon acutus

(Rüppell, 1837)
Common name Worldwide – milkshark
[Smith 9□33]

IDENTIFYING FEATURES

COLOUR, SHAPE AND SIZE

This shark has an elongate head with a protruding, almost translucent snout. The overall body colour is grey, fading to a white underside. There is an obvious black edge to the upper lobe of the caudal fin.
Can attain 100 cm.

EXTERNAL ANATOMY

The fins are well developed, with the second dorsal beginning well behind the origin of the anal fin. There is no dorsal ridge and spiracles are absent. The small, sharp, triangular teeth are not serrated. Teeth in the upper jaw have cusps which slant outwards, while those of the lower jaw are more erect and pointed. Usual tooth count = $\frac{12-1-12}{11-2-11}$

DISTRIBUTION

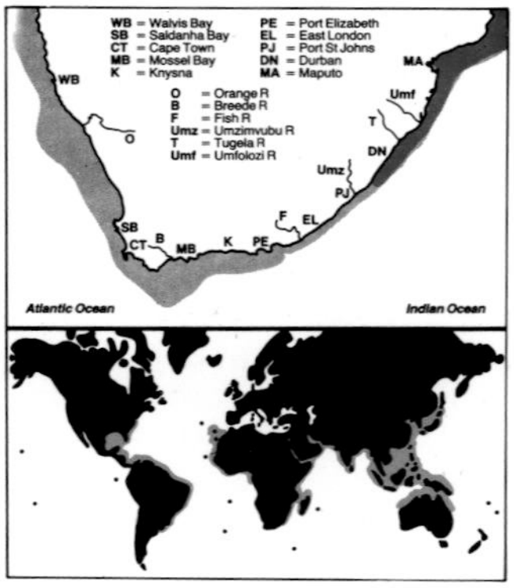

NATURAL HISTORY

The milkshark is one of the most common East Coast cartilaginous fishes and it is especially abundant during summer off the beaches of northern and central Natal. It often enters the surf zone, is usually found in midwater or near the bottom and occasionally encountered in estuaries. It is not tolerant of low salinities. Its diet includes small fish, squid, crabs and prawns. Aside from normal yearly fluctuations, this species, like the dusky shark, has increased in numbers in recent years owing to reduced predation by larger shark species which have been decimated by Natal's shark nets. After a gestation period of approximately a year, 3-6 young are born during summer. Birth length is 30-35 cm and sexual maturity is attained some two years later at length of about 70 cm.

CAPTURE

The milkshark is easily hooked on most dead baits and is often caught together with juvenile dusky sharks. Notwithstanding its palatable flesh, nowhere is it of commercial or spearfishing importance.
SA angling record – 6,8 kg.
SA spearfishing record – vacant.

SPECIFIC CATCH RESTRICTIONS

None.

NAME DERIVATION

Rhizoprionodon, teeth with serrated roots; *acutus,* sharp. Milkshark, a reference to the belief amongst some Indians that eating this shark's flesh improves the milk production of breast-feeding mothers.

SIMILAR SPECIES

The positioning of its second dorsal, and its other features, distinguish *R. acutus* from other sharks.

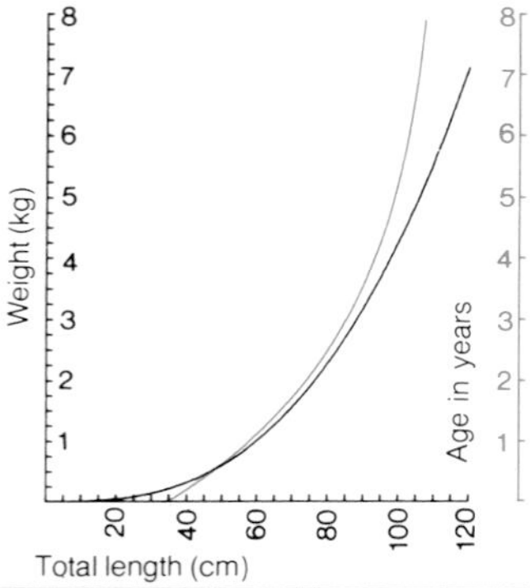

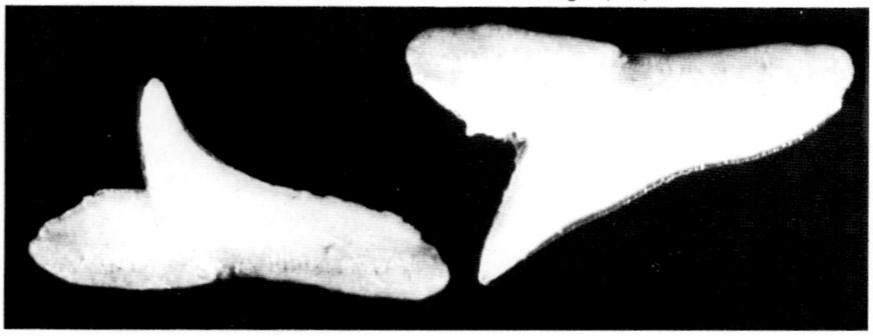

Typical teeth: lower (left); upper (right).

Triakis megalopterus

(Smith, 1839)
Common names Worldwide – spotted gullyshark, sharptooth houndshark, sweet William
[Smith 9□36]

IDENTIFYING FEATURES

COLOUR, SHAPE AND SIZE

This robust shark has a large, blunt and fleshy snout. The overall body colour is dark grey and the underside is pale. Irregular, black 'inkspots' cover the flanks and dorsal surface, while paler spots occur on the underside of the pectoral and pelvic fins. Most spotted gullysharks are not as densely spotted as the specimen shown here. Can attain 170 cm.

EXTERNAL ANATOMY

The fins of the spotted gullyshark are noticeably large and rounded, especially the pectorals. The second dorsal is more than half the height of the first dorsal, while the lower lobe of the caudal fin is small but distinct. There is no dorsal ridge. Numerous rows of teeth, arranged in pavement fashion, are set in the jaws of the large, wide mouth. Individual teeth are small and rounded at their base, but each has a single, short, but strongly pointed cusp. Many specimens appear to be loose-skinned and there are noticeable lip-like folds around the mouth. Also characteristic is the deep, diagonal groove on either side of the snout.

NATURAL HISTORY

The spotted gullyshark is common off the sandy shores of the southern and western Cape, especially near rocks or gullies in shallow bays. The structure and arrangement of teeth is specialized and well able to cope with a varied diet that includes bony fish and small sharks as well as crabs and other crustaceans. The sharp points of the teeth are more suited to grasping free-swimming prey, while the broad base and pavement arrangement provide a grinding mechanism for crushing hard-shelled animals. During summer this species congregates into shoals, especially in False Bay; many of the females are pregnant. Females are ovoviviparous and, though records are scant, it would appear that litters average ten pups. Sexual maturity is attained between 120-140 cm in males and 130-150 cm in females.

DISTRIBUTION

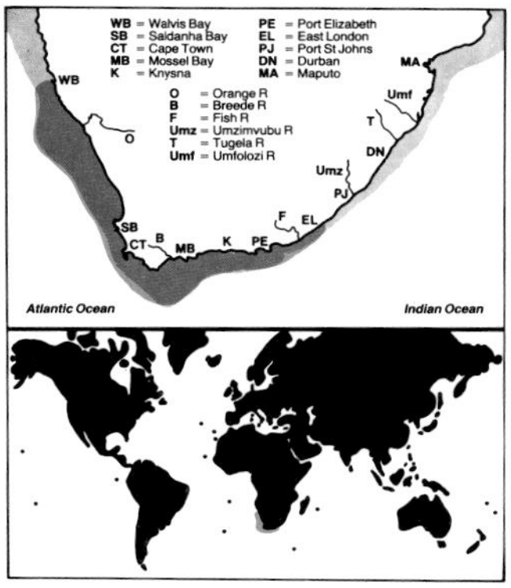

SPECIFIC CATCH RESTRICTIONS

None.

CAPTURE

This species is very commonly caught by rock and surf anglers and, though not a great fighting fish, most specimens are large enough to give fishermen a good struggle. The flesh is edible, but not popular and rather than leaving carcasses to rot, fishermen should help to ensure the future abundance of these and similar sharks by returning their catches to the water unharmed.
SA angling record – 40,0 kg.
SA spearfishing record – vacant.

NAME DERIVATION

Triakis, three pointed, a description more accurate of the teeth of other species of this genus; *megalopterus,* large finned. Spotted gullyshark, a reference to its markings and inshore habits.

SIMILAR SPECIES

While the specimens with fewer black spots are occasionally confused with the smoothhound *(M. mustelus),* the cusped teeth are distinctive of this species.

Detail of pavement teeth.

Dasyatis pastinaca

(Linnaeus, 1758)
Common name Worldwide – blue stingray
[Smith 30□3]

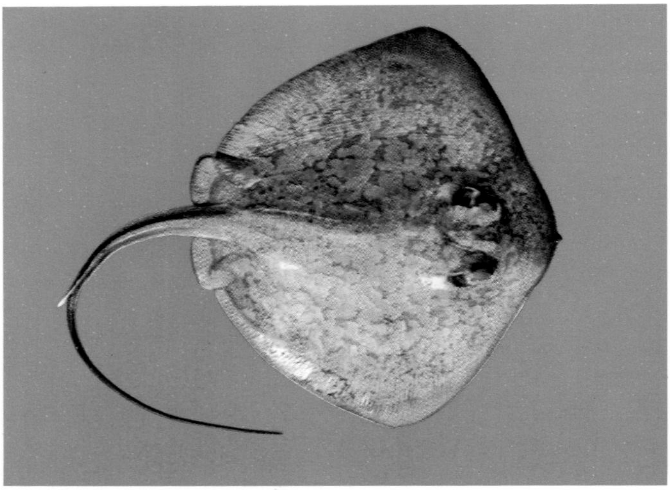

IDENTIFYING FEATURES

COLOUR, SHAPE AND SIZE
This beautiful ray has extensive slate blue reticulations running across the brown dorsal surface. The underside is pale. The body, with its slightly rounded snout, is disc-shaped and is 1,2 times wider than it is long. The undamaged tail measures 1,4 times the disc length. Can attain a disc width of 75 cm.

EXTERNAL ANATOMY
The blue stingray has a smooth skin devoid of rough tubercles. There is no dorsal fin and the fleshy pelvics are partially fused to the pectoral fins. The tail usually has one stout, serrated spine. The spiracles are larger than the eyes and occur on the upper surface of the head. The mouth is on the underside, and has $\frac{28-38}{28-43}$ teeth arranged in pavement fashion, and a central projection in the upper jaw which fits into a depression in the lower jaw. There are also five fleshy papillae on the floor of the mouth.

DISTRIBUTION

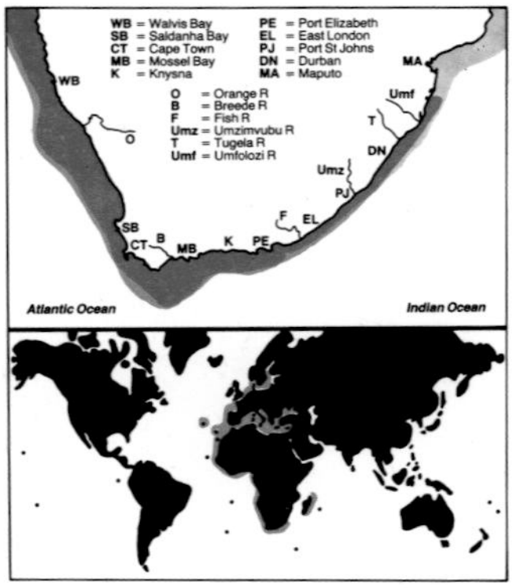

NATURAL HISTORY

The blue stingray is a common coastal species that occurs along sandy beaches throughout the year, July to October marking its peak abundance. It rarely enters estuaries. As with all Dasyatidae, the spiracles are situated on the top of the head which facilitates the drawing in of clean water for respiration when feeding in mud or sand. The diet consists mainly of bottom-living organisms such as mole-crabs (sea lice), crabs, marine worms and slow-swimming, bottom-dwelling fish. The strong teeth are well able to crush very hard food items. Sexual maturity is reached at a disc width of about 45 cm in males and 50-55 cm in females. After a one-year gestation period 1-4 young are born live, each with a disc width of 13-17 cm. Although this species is not aggressive towards man, the sharp, poisonous spine on the tail can inflict painful wounds which should be treated by immersion in very hot water to counteract the powerful protein toxin.

CAPTURE

This is one of the most commonly caught rays and it is usually landed along sandy beaches, often at night. Sardine tends to be the most effective bait. Though edible, the flesh is not popular and most blue stingrays landed are released unharmed. Occasionally this ray is caught in trawl nets at depths of up to 50 m.
SA angling record – 24,5 kg.

SPECIFIC CATCH RESTRICTIONS

Spearfishing of this species is illegal in Natal.

NAME DERIVATION

Dasyatis, from *Dasybatus,* a shaggy or rough skate; *pastinaca,* a parsnip or turnip, (an obscure reference, but probably derived from *pasternaque,* a French common name for a stingray with violet markings similar to those on a turnip). Blue stingray, a reference to its blue colouration.
Note: D. pastinaca is known as the common stingray in European waters, but its colours and patterns are distinct from those of local stocks and the two 'varieties' may yet be described as separate species.

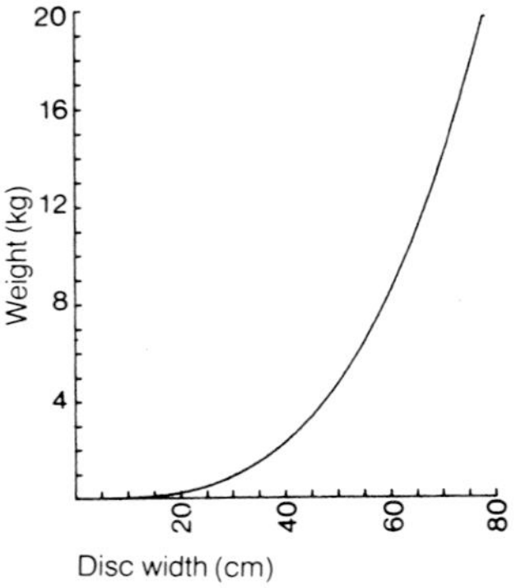

Gymnura natalensis

(Gilchrist & Thompson, 1911)
Common names Worldwide – butterflyray, diamondray or backwater butterflyray
[Smith 30□7]

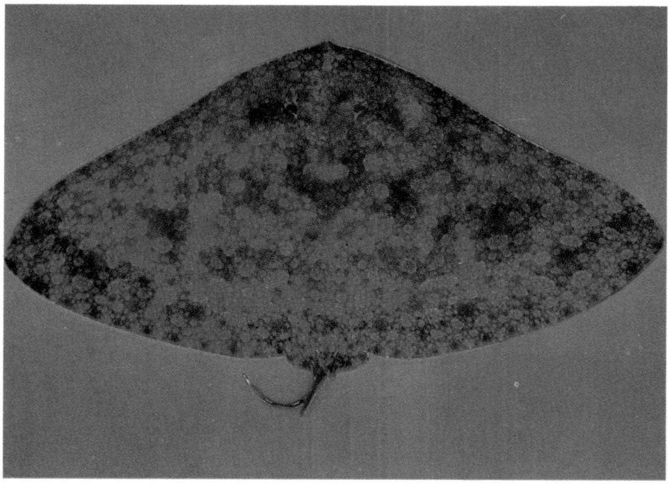

IDENTIFYING FEATURES

COLOUR, SHAPE AND SIZE

The body of this fish is diamond-shaped and is twice as wide as it is long. The tail is one third of the disc length. A small point may project forwards from the snout. The general body colour is grey, olive-green or brown, and usually mottled. The underside is pale. Attains a 250 cm disc width.

EXTERNAL ANATOMY

The butterflyray is smooth-bodied and there are no tubercles on the back or between the eyes. The pectoral fins are very wide, the pelvics are fleshy and there is no dorsal fin. The tail has one or two sharp, serrated spines at its base. The ventral mouth has $\frac{68-93}{70-93}$ rows of teeth arranged in pavement fashion and there is a notch in the middle of the lower jaw. Both spiracles open upwards and have small tentacles at their posterior corners.

Detail of teeth.

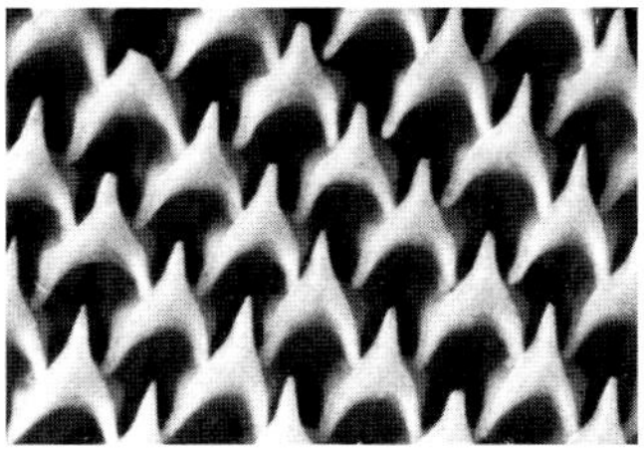

DISTRIBUTION

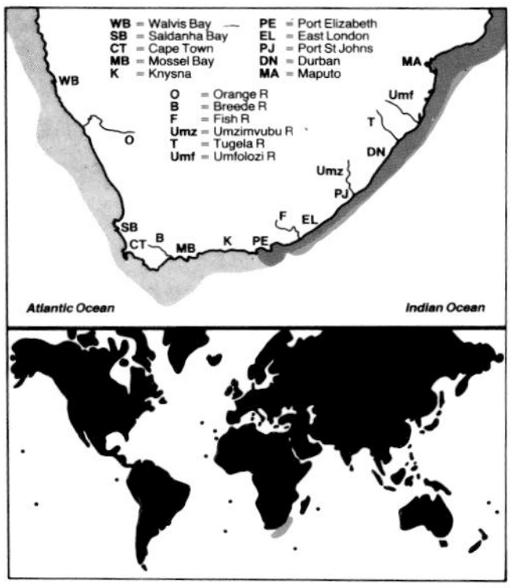

NATURAL HISTORY

The butterflyray is common year-round off shallow, sandy beaches, as well as over offshore banks to depths of 75 m. December and January mark its period of peak abundance. Though normally solitary, large shoals have been spotted often comprising animals of one sex. Single butterflyrays are generally confined to the sea-bed where they may hide below the sand or mud, but shoals often move in the midwater region. This predator feeds mainly on bottom-living fish such as soles, but other species, including sardines, are also eaten. Mole crabs (sea lice), marine worms and crabs supplement the diet, hard-shelled prey being crushed by the strong teeth. Sexual maturity is attained at a disc width of approximately 100 cm in males and 150 cm in females. Pregnant females have been recorded from January to August and litters of 2-9 young are born after a gestation period of one year. At birth, each of the young rays has a disc width of about 35 cm and can weigh as much as 0,5 kg. Females produce uterine 'milk' to feed the developing embryo during pregnancy.

CAPTURE

The butterflyray is commonly caught by shore anglers using a variety of baits, but, being one of the largest of the rays, it is rarely landed without a fierce struggle. Its flesh is edible, but not popular and landed specimens are usually released. Large butterflyrays are sometimes caught in Natal's shark nets.

SA angling record – 90,0 kg.

SPECIFIC CATCH RESTRICTIONS

Spearfishing of this species is illegal in Natal.

NAME DERIVATION

Gymnura, naked tail; *natalensis,* of Natal. Butterflyray, a reference to its extended, wing-like pectoral fins.

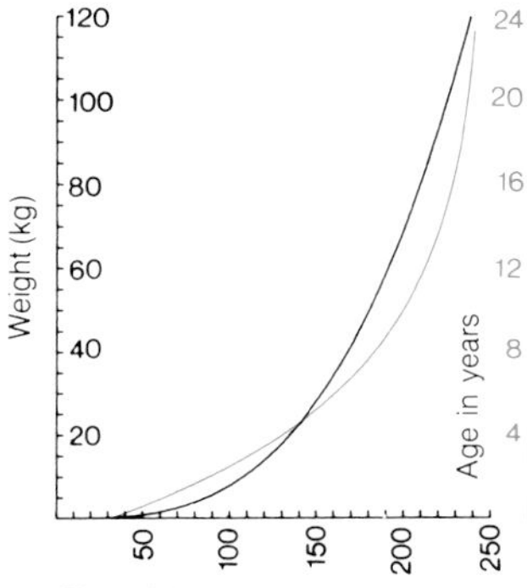

Himantura gerrardi

(Gray, 1851)

Common names SA – sharpnose or brown stingray. Elsewhere – pointed-nosed stingray
[Smith 30□9]

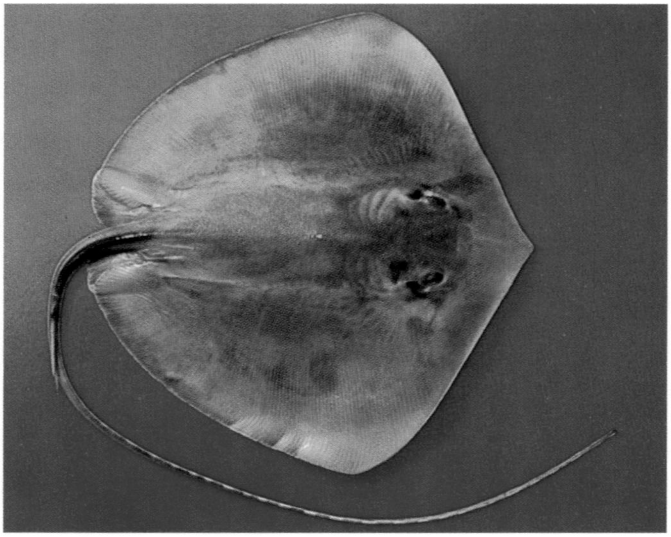

IDENTIFYING FEATURES

COLOUR, SHAPE AND SIZE

The disc-shaped body is about as long as it is wide, and the tail, if undamaged, is 1,9-2,4 times longer than the disc. The snout is distinctly pointed. The overall colour is light brown, though juveniles may have darker crossbands. The underside is pale. Disc width can reach 90 cm.

EXTERNAL ANATOMY

The skin is smooth, except for a wide band of closely spaced tubercles along the back. There is no dorsal fin, and the pelvic fins are small and virtually fused to the large pectorals. The tail has one or two serrated spines at its base. The mouth is situated on the underside and has $\frac{22-34}{28-40}$ diagonal rows of teeth arranged in pavement fashion. Four fleshy papillae project from the floor of the mouth. The gill slits open ventrally, and the spiracles open on top of the head.

DISTRIBUTION

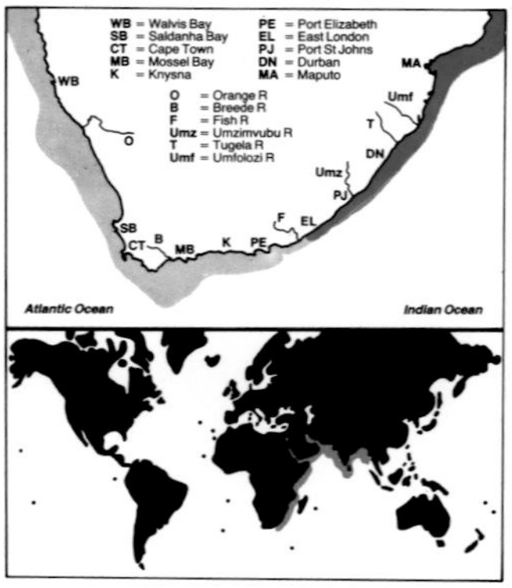

NATURAL HISTORY

This coastal species occurs along the sandy surf zone in muddy estuaries and river mouths, and on offshore banks, to depths of 50 m. It is tolerant of low salinities, and life in its muddy and often-turbulent, bottom habitat is made possible by the upward-facing spiracles, through which clean water can be inhaled. Though common throughout the year, peak abundance is reached during December and January. The sharpnose stingray is known to be ovoviviparous, and to breed off the Natal coast during summer. After a one-year gestation period, females bear at least two live young. Sexual maturity is attained at a disc width of 60-70 cm. Though this species is not aggressive towards man, the poisonous spines of the tail can cause severe lacerations, which should be treated immediately by immersion in hot water to reduce the effect of the protein toxin.

CAPTURE

Shore anglers frequently catch this ray on a variety of baits, and, once hooked, it puts up a fierce fight. It is also caught in trawl and beach seine nets. Though the flesh makes excellent eating, it is not popular, and many sharpnose stingrays are returned to the water unharmed. SA angling record – 34,0 kg.

SPECIFIC CATCH RESTRICTIONS

Spearfishing of this species is illegal in Natal.

Detail of pavement teeth.

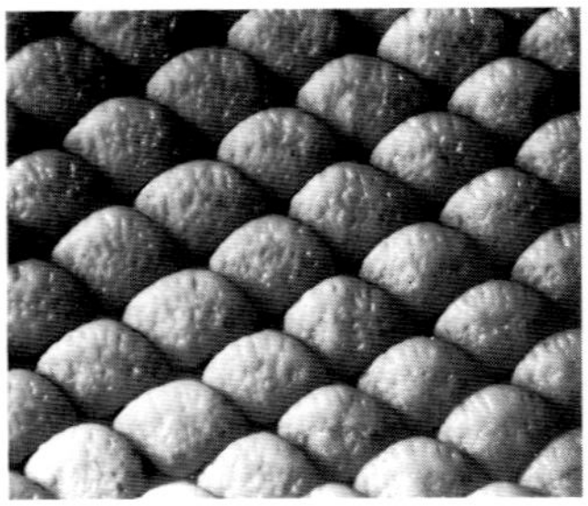

NAME DERIVATION

Himantura, thong-like tail; *gerrardi,* presumably named after Gerrard – obscure. Sharpnose stingray, a reference to the pointed snout.

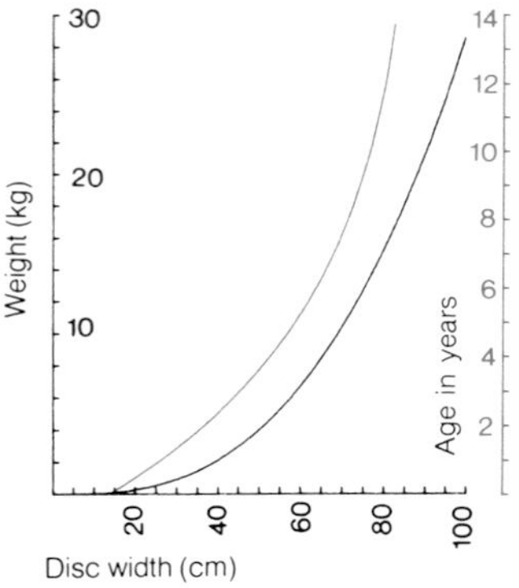

Himantura uarnak

(Forsskål, 1775)

Common names SA – honeycomb, marbled or leopard stingray. Elsewhere – coachwhip ray.
[Smith 30□10]

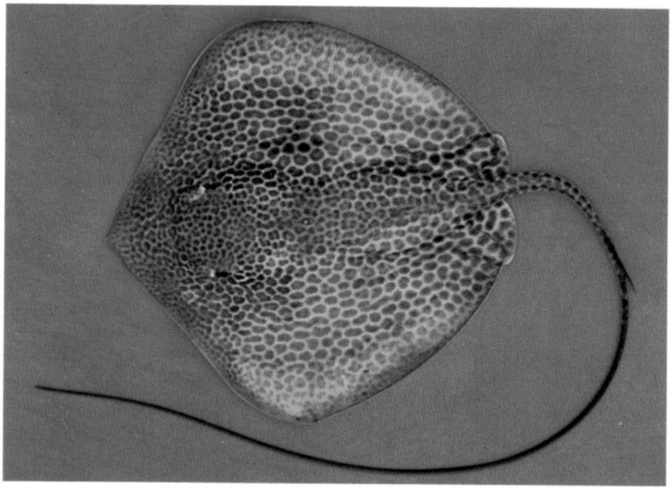

IDENTIFYING FEATURES

COLOUR, SHAPE AND SIZE

The overall colour of the upper body is brown or black with a distinct pattern of spots or marble-like reticulations. The underside is whitish. The disc-shaped body is slightly wider than it is long and the snout is pointed. The tail, if undamaged, is 2,6 to 3 times longer than the body. Can attain a disc width of 200 cm.

EXTERNAL ANATOMY

A row of small tubercles occurs on the back and between the eyes. There is no dorsal fin, the small pelvic fins are almost fused to the large pectorals and the tail has 1-3 stout spines near its thick base. The ventral mouth has $\frac{26-40}{27-44}$ rows of teeth arranged in pavement fashion. There are also four fleshy papillae on the floor of the mouth.

DISTRIBUTION

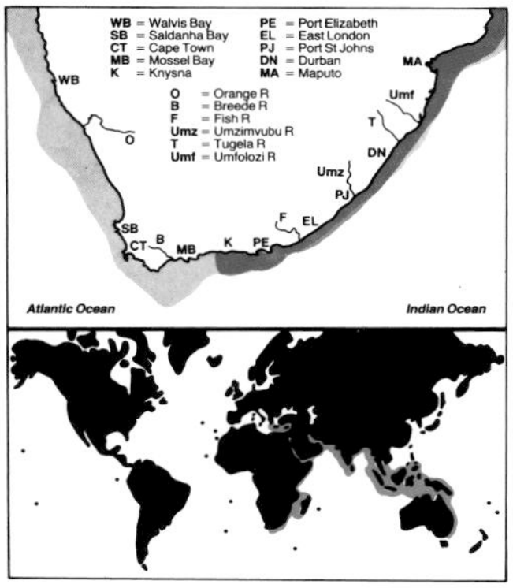

NATURAL HISTORY

This coastal species shows considerable tolerance to low salinities and freely enters estuaries. It also frequents shallow bays and the surf zone and has been recorded on offshore banks down to 50 m. December and January mark its period of peak abundance, though it occurs throughout the year. Respiration in its often-turbid habitat is facilitated by the large spiracles situated on top of the head behind the eyes and through which clean water is inhaled. The strong, crushing teeth make short work of bivalve molluscs, crabs and prawns that constitute the honeycomb stingray's diet. Tube worms are also occasionally eaten. Sexual maturity is attained at a disc-width of 100 cm which corresponds to an age of 4-5 years. During summer 3-5 young, each with a disc width of 20 cm, are born live after a one-year gestation period. Though this species is not aggressive towards man, the sharp, poisonous spines can inflict painful wounds which should be treated by immersion in very hot water to reduce the effect of the protein toxin.

Detail of pavement teeth.

CAPTURE

The honeycomb stingray is frequently caught by shore fishermen and boat anglers in estuaries. A variety of baits can be used. The flesh is palatable, but not highly esteemed and landed specimens are usually returned to the water unharmed.
SA angling record – 117,9 kg.

SPECIFIC CATCH RESTRICTIONS

Spearfishing of this species is illegal in Natal.

NAME DERIVATION

Himantura, thong-like tail; *uarnak,* of Arabic origin, a reference to the body patterns. Honeycomb, marbled or leopard stingray, references to the reticulated body pattern.

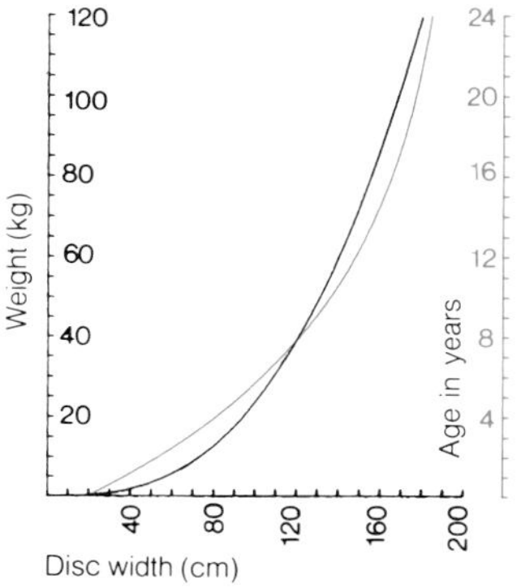

Taeniura lymma

(Forsskål, 1775)
Common name Worldwide – bluespotted ribbontail
[Smith 30□13]

IDENTIFYING FEATURES

COLOUR, SHAPE AND SIZE

The disc-like body of this attractive stingray is ovoid in shape and usually 1,2 times longer than wide. The tail is rather fleshy, and only a little longer than the disc length. The upper-body colouration is most striking, with numerous bright-blue spots on an otherwise yellowish-brown background. These spots are edged in black, and tend to become smaller and more numerous towards the edges of the disc. There are two equally bright-blue lines along the tail as far back as the spine. The underside is white. Can attain 200 cm but most have a less than 80 cm disc width.

EXTERNAL ANATOMY

This smooth-bodied ray has a single row of fine tubercles along the mid-back, and several rows directly over the gill chambers. The eyes are prominent, and located just in front of well-developed spiracles. Two fleshy and roundly angular pelvic fins lie on either side of the thick tail base. An important feature is the fleshy fold of skin that runs along the length of the tail from its spine to the tip. The mouth, located on the underside, is rather small, and bears 15-24 rows of pavement teeth in each jaw.

NATURAL HISTORY

This is a tropical stingray confined to shallow, sandy regions and coastal lagoons. Bluespotted ribbontails are not infrequently seen lying on the white sand close to the inside edges of coral reefs in the St Lucia Marine Reserve. Some seek shelter by hiding just below the sand with only their bulbous eyes projecting. While this stingray is not an abundant species, good numbers visit South African waters during the summer months. Details of breeding in this species are poorly documented, though it is known to be viviparous. The small mouth indicates its preference for small food, which is known to include small shrimps, crabs, burrowing worms, and also hermit crabs that are associated with the reef environment. Despite its beauty and soft, velvety skin, the bluespotted ribbontail carries one or two sharp tail spines that can cause lacerations to careless hands.

Close-up of head.

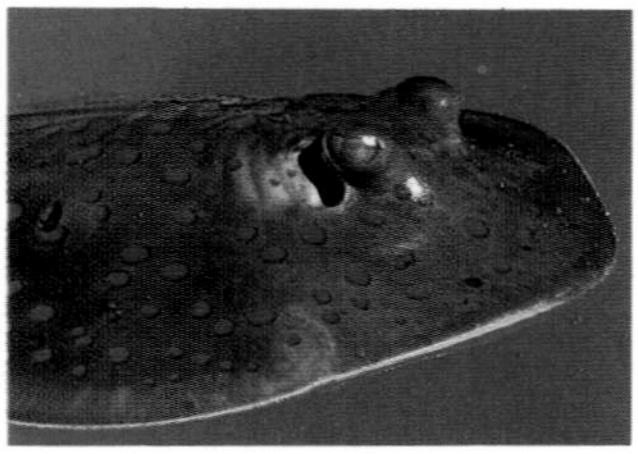

DISTRIBUTION

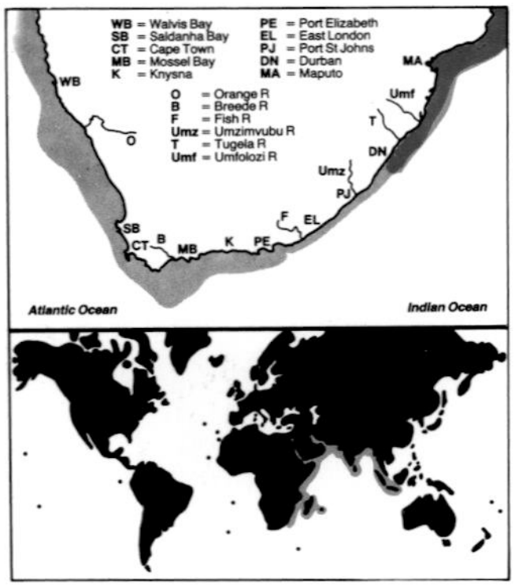

CAPTURE

Though seldom, if ever, caught on hook and line, skin and scuba divers are often treated to a sighting of this species when diving at Sodwana. Presumably it is edible. SA angling record – 2,8 kg.

SPECIFIC CATCH RESTRICTIONS

Spearfishing of this species is illegal in Natal.

NAME DERIVATION

Taeniura, a ribbon-like tail; *lymma,* dirty. Bluespotted ribbontail, an obvious reference to the colours, patterns and distinctive, fan-like end to the tail.

SIMILAR SPECIES

Not only are the body-colours and markings distinctive, but the broad-based tail with its ribbon-like tip, and the body-disc that is longer than wide, will serve to distinguish this from all other blue-patterned rays.

Taeniura melanospilos

Bleeker, 1853

Common names Worldwide – round ribbontail, fantail

[Smith 30□14]

IDENTIFYING FEATURES

COLOUR, SHAPE AND SIZE

This is one of the largest stingrays, and has a distinctly circular, disc-shaped body. The round ribbontail is strikingly coloured, with numerous black spots and mottlings overlying a blue-grey background, while the underside is white. The fleshy tail may equal the length of the body, though the specimen pictured here has a much shorter tail – probably as a result of being previously damaged. Can attain 200 cm disc width.

EXTERNAL ANATOMY

This giant stingray has a relatively smooth-skinned body when young, but, as it gets older, it becomes progressively densely covered with small denticles, which make it rough to the touch. A row of small tubercles also develops along the mid-back and tail. The relatively small eyes are quite prominent, set into protective orbits, and separated by a concave interorbital space. Sizeable spiracles lie just behind the eyes, opening laterally. One or more sharp spines may occur on the tail, the base of which is flanked by two fleshy, smooth-skinned pelvic fins. As with most other members of this genus, the tail bears a skin-like fold at its distal end. The mouth has four papillae-like structures on its floor, and there are $\frac{37-46}{39-45}$ transverse rows of small teeth.

NATURAL HISTORY

This species appears to prefer a turbid-water habitat, as it is most commonly found in proximity to river mouths and large estuaries. It is not confined to the shallows, however, and many have been reported from offshore banks, some to depths of 500 m. It is a large and formidable predator which effortlessly glides very close to the sea-bed in search of prey. This is known to include prawns, crabs, several bivalve species, and also smaller, slow-swimming and bottom-living fishes. Too little research has been directed at this species to document its breeding behaviour, though it is known to be viviparous, with pups probably being born during summer. Specimens with a disc width in excess of 1,2 m are known to be sexually mature, though the exact size at which breeding commences is unknown. Few juveniles have been reported.

DISTRIBUTION

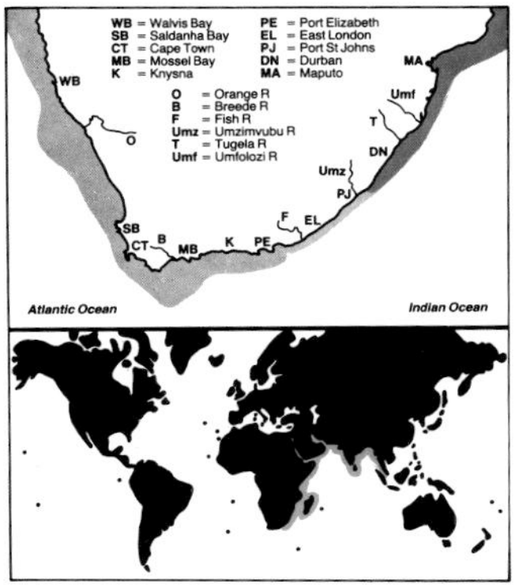

CAPTURE

The great size and enormous strength of this stingray make it a popular, but often elusive, target of competition shore anglers. Most captured round ribbontails originate from prawn trawlers operating over the Tugela, Illovo and other Natal, offshore banks. Though not marketed, it is edible. SA angling record – 153,8 kg.

SPECIFIC CATCH RESTRICTIONS

Spearfishing of this species is illegal in Natal.

NAME DERIVATION

Taeniura, ribbon-like tail; *melanospilos,* black-speckled. Round ribbontail, a reference to the round body disc and ribbon- or fan-like end to the tail.

SIMILAR SPECIES

The combination of the thick, short tail with its ribbon-like fold, absence of a true tail fin, and distinctly rounded body-disc serve to distinguish this ray from any other.

Heterodontus ramalheira

(Smith, 1949)

Common names Whitespotted or Mocambique bullhead shark, Port Jackson shark

[Smith 4□1]

IDENTIFYING FEATURES

COLOUR, SHAPE AND SIZE

This curious shark has a squat, rounded body, pig-like snout and elongated tail. The overall body colour is reddish-brown, extensively scattered with small, white spots. The underside is paler, while the tips of both dorsal fins are distinctly dusky in colour. Can attain 100 cm.

EXTERNAL ANATOMY

The fins of this primitive shark are most pronounced, especially the two dorsal fins, each of which is armed with a thick spine on its leading edge. In contrast to the spiny dogsharks, the bullhead shark does have an anal fin. The caudal fin is large, even though the tail section of this shark is rather slender. The pectorals are also rather large, and positioned just before the level of the first dorsal. There are five pairs of gill slits along the sides of the head, and a rather small mouth located just below the snout, but well in front of the eyes. The teeth are molariform and closely spaced into rows of $\frac{13-13}{10-1-10}$. The medium-sized eyes are set high up on the head and lie below a bony ridge that ends abruptly behind them.

NATURAL HISTORY

Bullhead sharks are generally quite common in the Indo-Pacific region, especially off Australia where the true Port Jackson shark is plentiful. The whitespotted bullhead is much less frequently reported, and then usually from deeper offshore banks between 100 m and 300 m. This is a bottom-dwelling species known to be sluggish and almost certainly nocturnal in habit. It is thought to 'crawl' along the sea-bed in search of food. Its diet includes crabs and, presumably, other bottom-living invertebrates as well. Very little is known of this species' breeding habits, except that it is oviparous, producing a number of egg cases that the female may deposit in a specially prepared 'nest' site. The young of this species have not yet been recorded, but probably take many months to hatch. Despite the sparse records of this shark, it is probably quite common. The fact that it inhabits the edges of deeper reefs, possibly living in caves, makes capture by net improbable. Further research with deeply set longline fishing gear may well throw more light on this fascinating species.

DISTRIBUTION

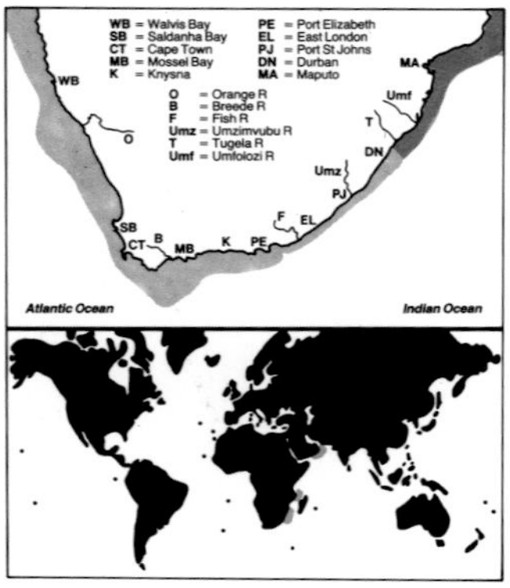

CAPTURE

Virtually all specimens have been caught by offshore trawlers operating off southern Moçambique and the Tugela Banks. It is not considered a food resource. In Australia, some have proved to be most adaptable to life in an aquarium.

SA angling record – vacant.

SPECIFIC CATCH RESTRICTIONS

None.

NAME DERIVATION

Heterodontus, different teeth; *ramalheira,* meaning obscure. Bullhead shark, from its bull-like head shape; Port Jackson shark, a reference to the rather similar species that is commonly found off Port Jackson in Australia.

SIMILAR SPECIES

Bullhead sharks are unmistakeable, especially as they are the only group to possess both spiny dorsal fins and an anal fin. The whitespotted bullhead is probably the only representative of Heterodontidae in the area, and is best recognized by its white spots and first dorsal fin that is positioned directly over the pectorals.

Detail of lower jaw.

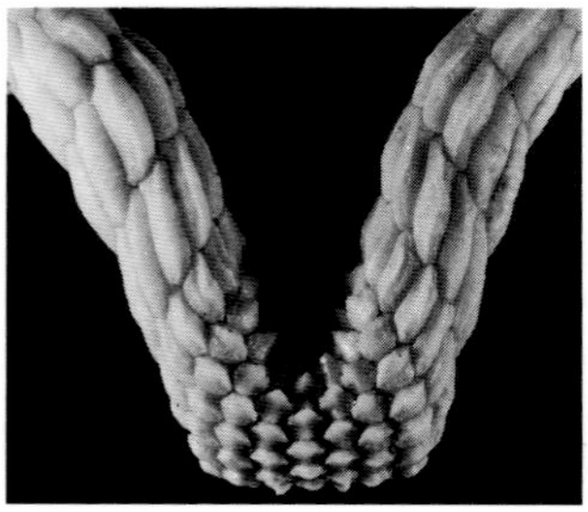

Notorynchus cepedianus

(Peron, 1807)
Common names Worldwide – broadnose sevengill or cowshark [Smith 2□4]

IDENTIFYING FEATURES

COLOUR, SHAPE AND SIZE

This is a very large shark, with a broadly rounded head and blunt snout. The overall body colour is a pale grey or greyish-brown above, with numerous, irregularly scattered, small, black spots. The underside is white. Can attain at least 290 cm.

EXTERNAL ANATOMY

The arrangement of the fins in this and related cowsharks is most distinctive, with a single dorsal set far back on the body. The caudal fin is large, and has a distinct lower lobe. There are seven sizeable gill openings along each side of the head, just before the pectoral fins. The eyes of the cowshark are noticeably small, located far forward on the head and preceding a pair of very small spiracles. The mouth is wide and situated underneath the snout, each jaw being set with quite large, sharp teeth. Those in the lower jaw are rather striking and comb-like in appearance, in contrast to the upper jaw's single-cusped teeth. Usual tooth count = $\frac{7-1-7}{6-1-6}$

NATURAL HISTORY

This primitive shark is a common inhabitant of cooler coastal waters, being found at various places throughout the world, but apparently not in the tropics. It is most frequently encountered off sandy beaches or in shallow bays, where it may pose a moderate threat to bathers and divers. This cowshark is also known to range to depths of at least 50 m. This is a strong shark, which actively hunts for its prey. This consists of a very wide range of fishes, including other sharks, stingrays, eaglerays and some bony fishes. Some are reported to have fed on seals, dolphins and other mammals.

The broadnose sevengill is ovoviviparous, and known to produce large litters, the young being pupped in very shallow water. As many as 80 young, each measuring about 50 cm, may be born to a single female, though surprisingly few of these have been caught or observed. Sexual maturity in adults is attained at a length of 150-180 cm for males and 190-208 cm for females. Females achieve a length considerably greater than that of males.

DISTRIBUTION

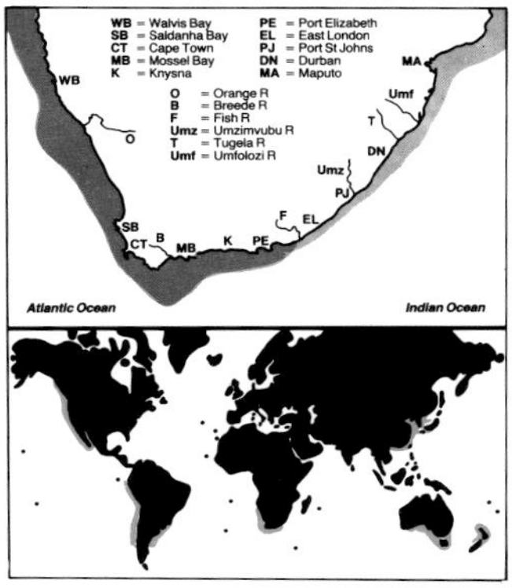

CAPTURE

This species represents a moderate resource in several parts of the world, where it provides food, high quality leather, vitamin A and several other products. In South Africa this shark is only of significance to sport anglers in their winter tournaments around the Cape coast. While readily hooked, this cowshark is not the easiest fish to land, and many rock and surf anglers have fought long battles with this fine angling species. It makes good eating.
SA angling record – 95,0 kg.

NAME DERIVATION

Notorynchus, short snouted; *cepedianus,* meaning obscure. Broadnose sevengill, a reference to its broadly flattened snout and distinctive seven gill openings.

SIMILAR SPECIES

Several other species in this family, often called cowsharks, also resemble the broadnose sevengill. These include the sixgill sharks, such as the giant *Hexanchus griseus,* which are readily distinguished by the difference in the number of gill openings. The sharpnose sevengill shark (*Heptranchas perlo*) is a smaller species, has much larger eyes, a more pointed snout, and generally lacks the black body spots of its close relative.

Typical teeth: lower (left); upper (right).

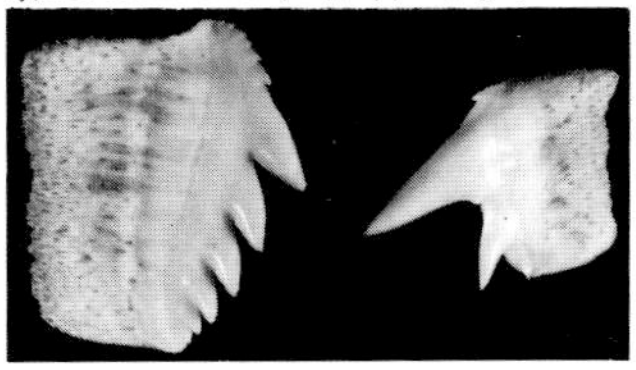

Carcharodon carcharias

(Linnaeus, 1758)

Common names Worldwide – great white shark, blue pointer [Smith 14□1]

IDENTIFYING FEATURES

COLOUR, SHAPE AND SIZE

This very powerful shark has a robust, torpedo-shaped body. The overall colour is blue-grey when the animal is alive, but this rapidly fades to grey after death. The underside is distinctly white and, though the body itself has no obvious markings, the tips of the pectoral fins are black underneath. The largest, reliably recorded great white was 640 cm.

EXTERNAL ANATOMY

The first dorsal fin is large, while the second is much smaller and is situated opposite, but slightly forward of, the small anal fin. The pectoral fins are large and the stout caudal fin is supported by a slightly flattened peduncle with a keel on each side. The pointed snout projects over a huge mouth armed with broad, flattened, triangular teeth that have serrated edges. Usual tooth count = $\frac{13-13}{12-12}$. Serrations may be absent in the teeth of juveniles, and in some very young great whites, the teeth are similar to those of ragged-tooth sharks. The fifth of the five large gill slits on each side of the body extends below, and in front of the pectoral fins.

NATURAL HISTORY

This wide-ranging shark must be one of the largest and most powerful predators on earth, and though some specimens have been recorded in oceanic waters, most appear to be confined to the continental shelf, especially in the case of specimens less than 300 cm in length. Food preference varies somewhat according to size, but the remains of other shark species prevail in the stomach contents of landed specimens. Marine mammals, mostly seals, bony fish and large rays such as mantas, are all important components of the diet. Although the size of sexually mature specimens may vary along the southern African coast, males in excess of 300 cm are usually mature, while females reach maturity at a larger size, probably closer to 400 cm. Young great white sharks are most abundant from July-November along the East Coast and from December to March in Cape waters. Larger specimens occur throughout the year, especially in the Cape. In Natal, however, great whites comprise only about two per cent of the catch in anti-shark nets. The potential danger of these fearsome sharks to bathers and to people in small boats is unquestionable, but it is probable that many attacks have been incorrectly attributed to this species.

DISTRIBUTION

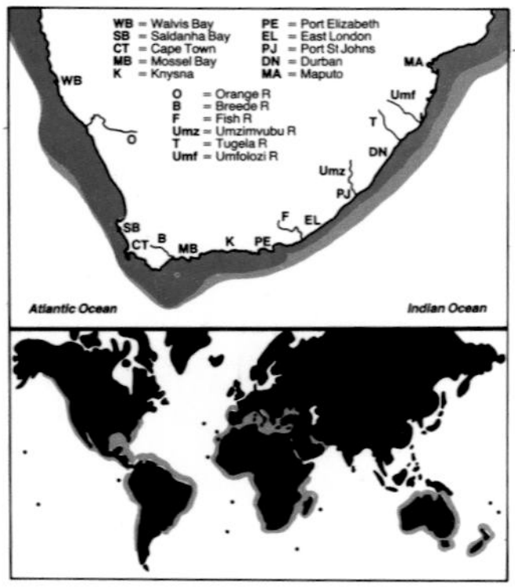

CAPTURE

Few sport anglers can claim to have pitted their skills and strength

Lower tooth (top); upper (bottom).

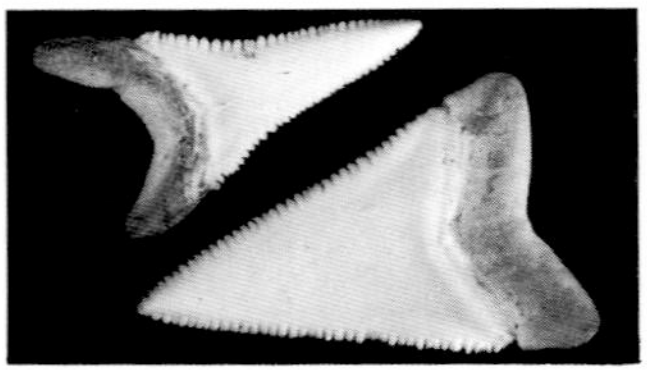

against this species and only a handful have caught great whites in excess of 1 000 lbs. thereby joining the elite '1 000 Club'. Regrettably, however, some fishermen have taken it upon themselves to rid the oceans of these sharks, a practice which must ultimately threaten the balance between predator and prey in specific areas. The flesh is edible and the jaws with their large teeth are of considerable commercial value.

World angling record – 1 208,0 kg.
All-Africa angling record – 753,0 kg.
SA angling record – 753,0 kg.
SA spearfishing record – 127,2 kg.

SPECIFIC CATCH RESTRICTIONS

None.

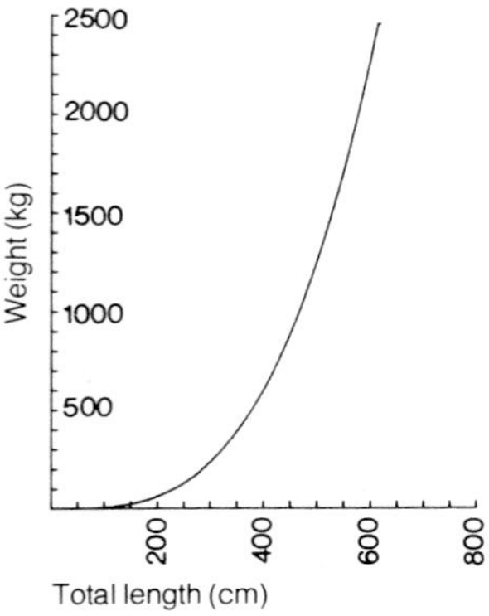

Mobula diabolus

(Shaw, 1804)
Common name devilray
[Smith 29□2]

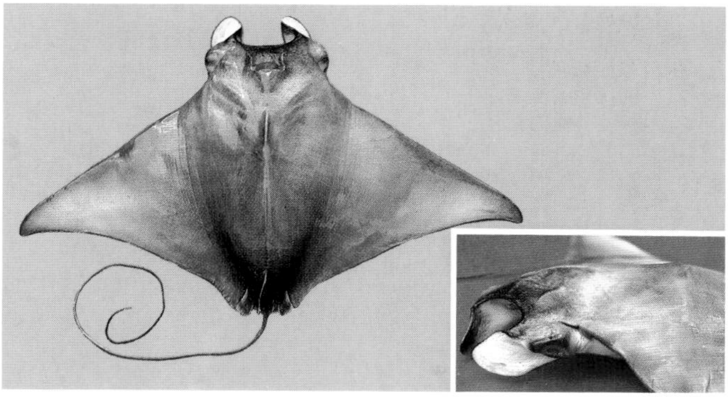

IDENTIFYING FEATURES

COLOUR, SHAPE AND SIZE

The sharply angular, disc-shaped body is 1,7 times wider than it is long, and ends in a thin, whip-like tail that is approximately equal in length to the body width. The colour is grey-brown above, although living specimens seen underwater appear to be a darker blue-black. Can attain 180 cm disc width.

EXTERNAL ANATOMY

The smooth-skinned body with its large, falcate pectoral fins lacks a caudal fin, but does have a relatively large dorsal which is situated far back on the body though not extending beyond the short, fleshy pelvic fins. In front, the large head protrudes somewhat from the rest of the body and bears two distinctive, paddle-like projections. Known as cephalic horns or fins, these structures assist in funneling water and prey into the large mouth that lies between and just below them. In this species, the front of the head is slightly concave in dorsal view. On the underside, and well behind the head, are five pairs of gill openings, their very large size indicative of the great volumes of water that pass through them. Within the gill chamber are large gill arches that carry a series of five sieve-like plates that function in straining food from the water. A small spiracle is located above and just behind each of the large, lateral eyes. The jaws have feeble dentition consisting of a narrow band of $\frac{69-102}{80-126}$ rows of very fine teeth.

NATURAL HISTORY

While the manta ray can attain a much greater size (6,5 m disc width), the habits and behaviour of both the manta and devilray are very similar. Both are common species of warm, coastal waters, usually occurring in small shoals, and mostly found in mid-water. While many have also been seen at the surface. A striking feature for which mantas and devilrays are well known is their ability to leap high out of the water. During such jumps, the ray may cartwheel 'head over tail' numerous times before crashing back to the water surface with a resounding splash that can be heard a long way away. Mantas and devilrays filter-feed zooplankton, much of which includes fish fry, crustacean larvae and small squid, from the water. Enormous quantities of water are passed through the wide mouth and strained through the gill plates as these fish glide along. The ovoviviparous females have special projections in their uterus producing a milky fluid, which nourishes the two young. Devilray pups are born live at 30-40 cm disc width, while sexual maturity in adults is reached at size of less than 100 cm disc width. Manta and devil rays are popular with underwater enthusiasts, often inquisitively approaching to within a few metres. Larger specimens are invariably accompanied by suckerfish and, occasionally, pilotfish.

CAPTURE

Mantas and devilrays have been much maligned in the past, resulting in unnecessary harpooning of these harmless creatures. Today few are killed in South African waters, except those accidentally trapped in Natal's shark nets.
SA angling record – 20,4 kg.

DISTRIBUTION

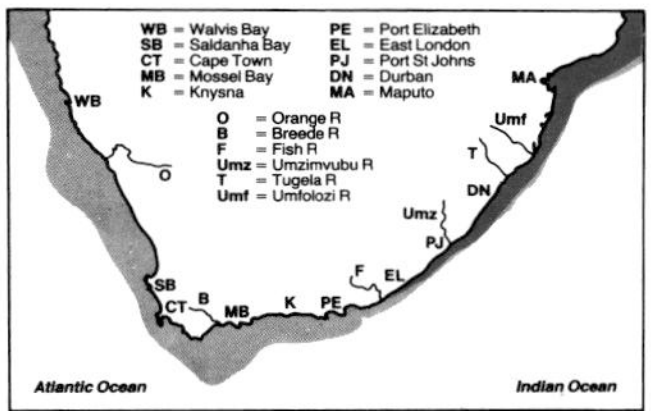

SIMILAR SPECIES

The devilray is distinguished from all other rays by its conspicuous cephalic horns. While it closely resembles the true manta *(Manta birostris),* it can be identified by its mouth, which is located on the underside (terminal in the Manta) and teeth, which are in both jaws (only on the upper jaw in the Manta).

Upper jaw (top); lower jaw (bottom).

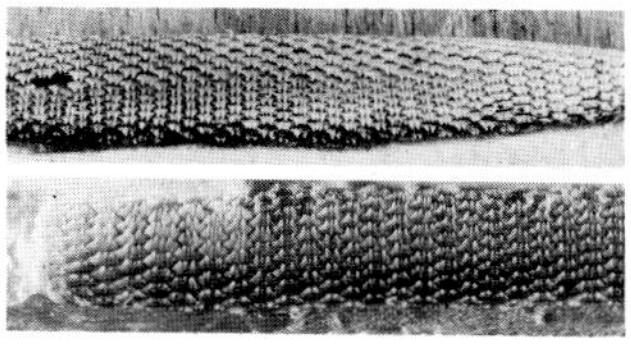

Aetobatus narinari

(Euphrasen, 1790)

Common names Worldwide – spotted eagleray, bonnetray [Smith 28□1]

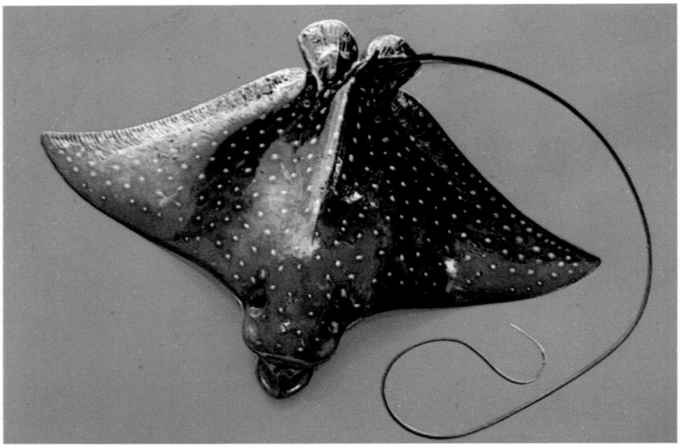

IDENTIFYING FEATURES

COLOUR, SHAPE AND SIZE

The diamond-shaped body, with its pointed 'wings', is much wider than it is long, and the cylindrical tail is 2,7 times longer than the body. The overall body colour is dark brown to black with numerous, but irregular, white spots or rings. The underside is pale. Can attain a disc width of 230 cm.

EXTERNAL ANATOMY

The head is distinctly raised from the body, and the large eyes and wide spiracles are set to the sides. The pelvic fins are fleshy and extend beyond the tip of the small dorsal fin at the base of the tail.The tail also carries 1-3 serrated spines. The jaws of the ventral mouth each have a broad band of teeth arranged in pavement fashion, those of the lower jaw often projecting forward.

DISTRIBUTION

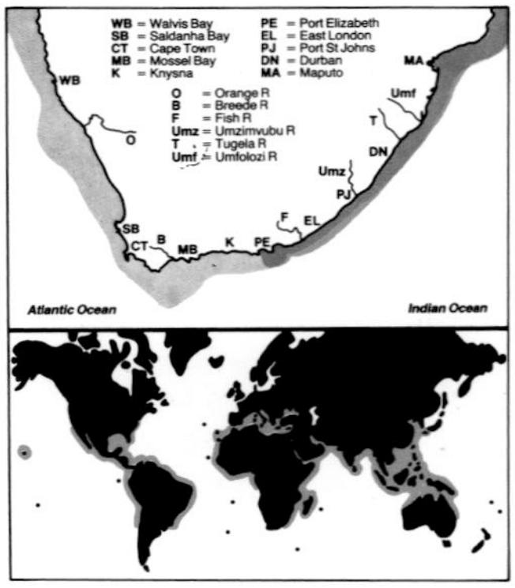

NATURAL HISTORY

The spotted eagleray is one of the largest members of this family and is a coastal species found mainly off Natal during summer. An attractive and graceful fish, it is more free-swimming than most rays and spends much time near the surface or patrolling reefs. Clams, sand mussels, oysters and black rock mussels are carefully selected with the fleshy lips before being crushed by the teeth. Occasionally, prawns, crabs and mole crabs (sea lice) are also eaten. Sexual maturity is attained after 4-6 years at a disc width of 120-150 cm. About four young, each with a disc width of 26 cm, are born live after a gestation period of one year. The spotted eagleray is not aggressive towards man, but if molested is capable of inflicting severe lacerations with its spines. Wounds should be treated by immediate immersion in very hot water for at least 30 minutes to destroy the toxin.

CAPTURE

The spotted eagleray is occasionally caught from piers, sandy beaches and rocky shores, but many anglers have had their tackle stripped by these strong fighters. Although this edible fish takes a variety of baits, fresh fish fillets are best.

SA angling record – 98,0 kg.

SPECIFIC CATCH RESTRICTIONS

Spearfishing of this species is illegal in Natal.

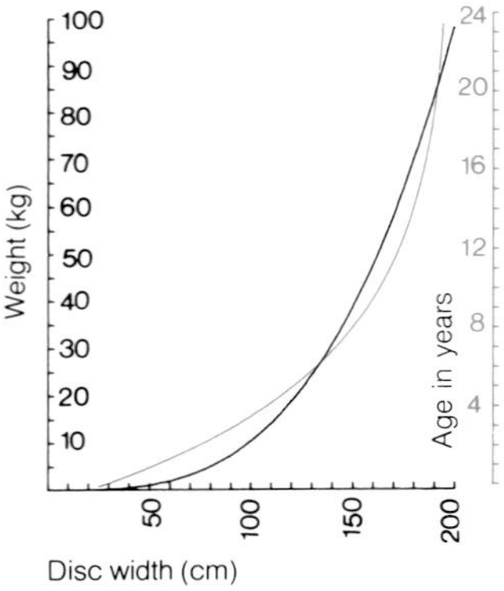

Detail of pavement teeth: lower (left); upper (right).

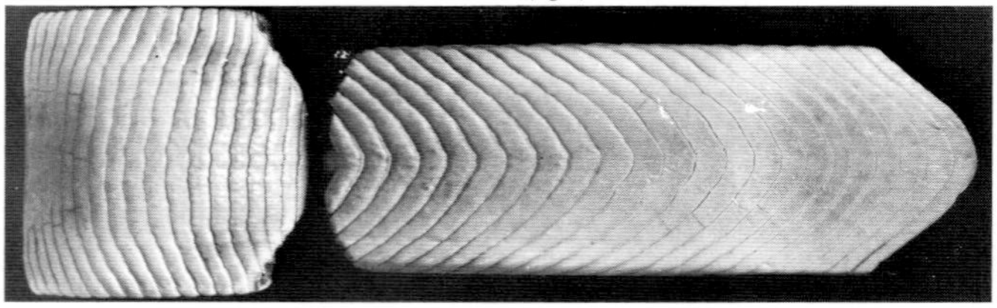

Myliobatus aquila

(Linnaeus, 1758)
Common names Worldwide – eagleray
[Smith 28□2]

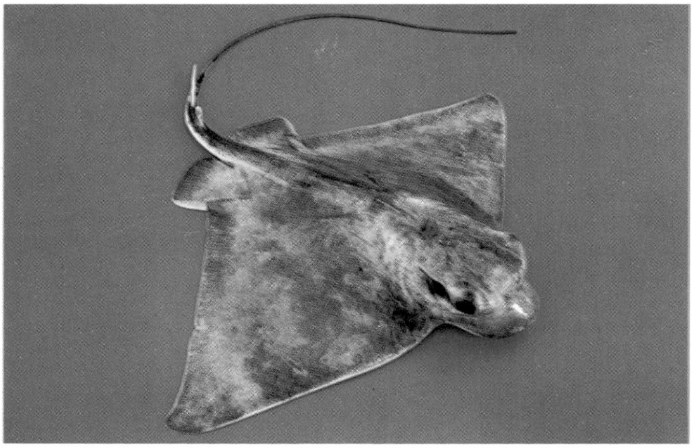

IDENTIFYING FEATURES

COLOUR, SHAPE AND SIZE
The diamond-shaped body is about 1,7 times wider than it is long and the tail is twice the length of the body. The overall body colour is chocolate brown and the underside is pale. Attains a 150 cm disc width.

EXTERNAL ANATOMY
In common with other Myliobatidae this species is smooth-skinned and the head is raised above the level of the body. The eagleray, however, lacks the fleshy snout of the bullray. The large eyes and spiracles occur on the sides of the head and males may develop short 'horns' above the eyes. A small dorsal fin is situated just behind the large fleshy pelvic fins and the long tail has one or two serrated spines near its base. Each jaw of the ventral mouth has seven rows of teeth arranged in pavement fashion.

DISTRIBUTION

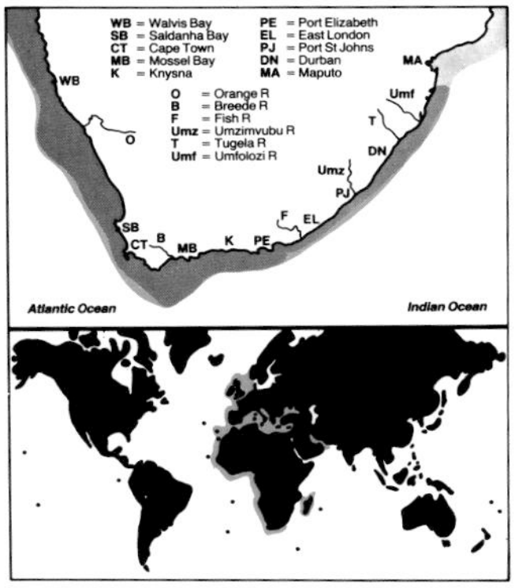

NATURAL HISTORY

The eagleray is a coastal species which frequents sandy shores and freely enters large estuaries. It is most common during summer. This ray is not confined to the bottom and usually swims in groups just below the surface. It even occasionally leaps briefly from the water and, like the giant mantarays, 'pancakes' back with a resounding slap. Favoured food items include sand and rock mussels which are easily crushed with the strong teeth. Crabs, mole crabs (sea lice) and several fish species are also eaten. Sexual maturity is attained at a disc width of 50 cm, with females tending to be larger than males. After a one-year gestation period, females give birth to 3-7 live young in very shallow water. Each newly born eagleray has a disc width of 20-25 cm. Though this species is not aggressive to man, the poisonous spines can cause painful wounds which should be immersed in very hot water to destroy the toxin.

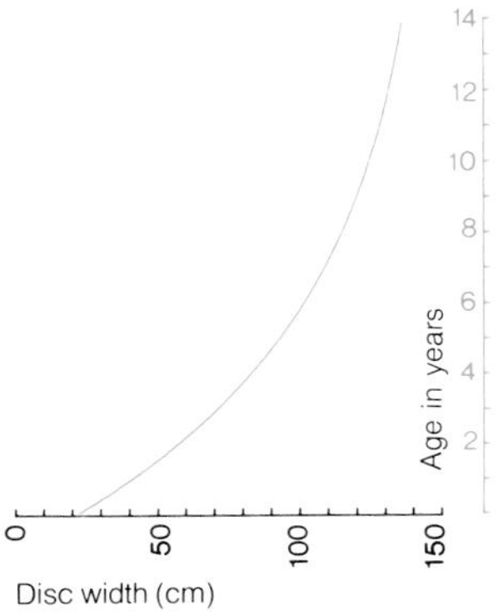

CAPTURE

This ray will take a variety of baits and provides shore fishermen with good sport. Though the flesh makes excellent eating it is not popular and most eaglerays landed are returned to the water alive. More catches are made along the Cape coast than in Natal.
SA angling record – 21,5 kg.

SPECIFIC CATCH RESTRICTIONS

Spearfishing of this species is illegal in Natal.

NAME DERIVATION

Myliobatus, grinding ray; *aquila,* eagle. Eagleray, a reference to the eagle-like, wing-shaped pectoral fins.

SIMILAR SPECIES

There has been much confusion about the common names of this and the next species. While this species has been traditionally known in South Africa as the bullray because of its characteristic, bovine head shape, this is not compatible with scientific nomenclature. Consequently this species should henceforth be known as the eagleray in order to avoid further confusion. It is readily distinguished from similar species by its dorsal fin which is located well behind the pelvics.

Pteromylaeus bovinus

(Saint-Hilaire, 1817)
Common names SA – bullray, duckbill. Worldwide – bullray
[Smith 28□3]

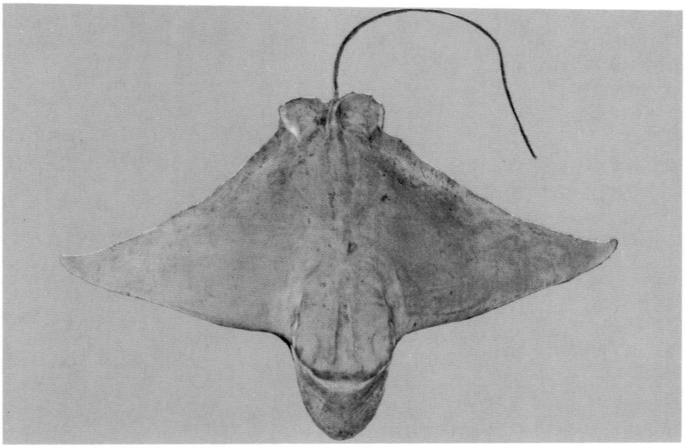

IDENTIFYING FEATURES

COLOUR, SHAPE AND SIZE
The almost diamond-shaped body has a width 1,65 times its length, and the tail is 1,5-1,8 times longer than the body. The head is raised above the level of the body and extends forward into the long, fleshy snout that is characteristic of this species. The overall body colour is brown, and, occasionally, broad crossbars are visible. The underside is pale. Can attain a disc width of 175 cm.

EXTERNAL ANATOMY
The large eyes and wide spiracles are situated on the sides of the prominent head. Adult males develop short 'horns' above the eyes. The small dorsal fin lies between the pelvic fins, which are large and fleshy. The long tail has 1-4 serrated spines at its base. Each jaw of the ventral mouth has seven rows of pavement teeth.

DISTRIBUTION

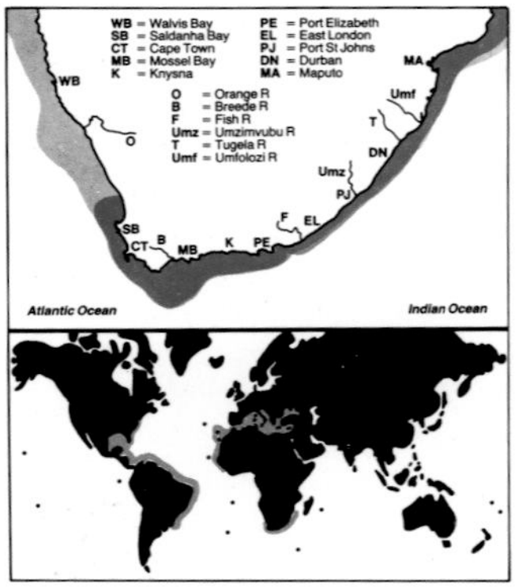

NATURAL HISTORY

This solitary species frequents coastal waters, and reaches peak abundance during summer. It ranges between the surf zone and depths of 30 m, and, being able to tolerate greatly reduced salinities, is also found in estuaries. The bullray is not confined to the bottom, and is often seen on the surface, sometimes leaping from the water in an apparent attempt to rid itself of parasites or suckerfish. The diet is varied, and includes fish, crabs, molluscs, squid and mussels, those with hard shells being ground by the strong teeth. Sexual maturity is attained at a disc width of about 100 cm. After a gestation period of a year, females give live birth to three or four young, each with a disc width of 50 cm. Though this species is not aggressive to man, the poisonous spines can cause painful wounds which should be immersed in very hot water to destroy the toxin.

CAPTURE

Most catches are made along the Natal coast, frequently by shore anglers using a variety of baits. The bullray is well known for its fighting power when hooked. Though of fine eating quality if not too large, it is not a popular table fish, and most anglers prefer to return their catches to the water alive.
SA angling record – 100,0 kg.

SPECIFIC CATCH RESTRICTIONS

Spearfishing of this species is illegal in Natal.

NAME DERIVATION

Pteromylaeus, winged ray; *bovinus,* bovine. Bullray, a reference to the bull-like head – especially in juveniles.

SIMILAR SPECIES

In South Africa, this ray is traditionally known as the duckbill because of its duck-like snout. In order to standardize internationally, it should now be called the bullray.

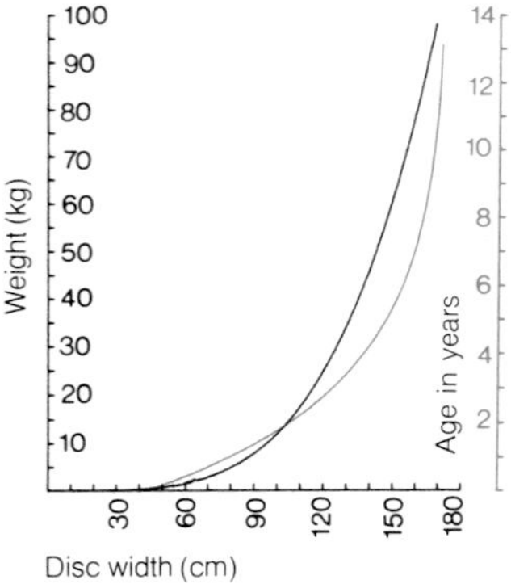

Detail of pavement teeth: lower (left); upper (right). Note how, in the jaws of this old specimen, the constant crushing of shells has worn away the dentition.

Rhinoptera javanica

Müller & Henle 1841
Common names Worldwide – flapnose ray, cownose ray
[Smith 28□4]

IDENTIFYING FEATURES

COLOUR, SHAPE AND SIZE

The diamond-shaped body with its extended, falcate pectoral fins is 1,5-1,6 times wider than long, and typical of the eaglerays. Noticeably different, however, is the broad head, which is deeply concave along its front profile. There is a whip-like tail that extends from the posterior end for a distance approximately equal to body length. This smooth-skinned stingray has a dark-brown or grey upper surface and white underside. Can attain 150 cm disc width.

EXTERNAL ANATOMY

The head of the flapnose ray is not as elevated as that of other eaglerays, though it is most distinctive, with a wide mouth that is covered by a large-bilobed nasal flap. The jaws are covered with transverse rows of pavement teeth, which are usually fused into grinding plates. There are normally seven such rows, but sometimes as many as 10-11 rows may occur. There is a sizeable dorsal fin set well back on the tail base, but not beyond the rear edge of the small, fleshy pelvic fins. There is also at least one sharp spine near the fin base. The eyes are quite large, located far forward on the sides of the head and just in front of two large spiracles that open up and outwards. There are five pairs of medium-sized gill openings on the underside.

NATURAL HISTORY

The flapnose is a summer migrant to the Natal coast, where moderate numbers are angled or netted each year. This is a gregarious species, and underwater observations indicate that sizeable shoals may move close inshore. Unfortunately, this behaviour also renders it vulnerable to capture in Natal's shark nets. Flapnose rays are mostly found in mid-water, reasonably close to shore. Their diet consists mostly of bivalve molluscs which are crushed by the strong pavement teeth. In Japan and other regions, a shoal of flapnose rays can create havoc with the pearl-oyster fisheries. In South African waters, most of the shell diet is foraged from mud banks, quite often within larger estuaries or bays. This viviparous species gives birth to a number of live pups each season, but exact details are still to be discovered.

DISTRIBUTION

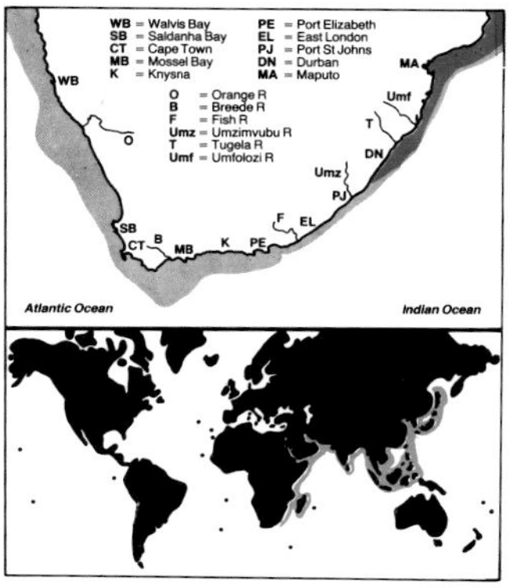

CAPTURE

Though not specifically a target of anglers, flapnose rays are occasionally caught from the shore. Besides Natal's shark nets, beach seines also sometimes trap a shoal of these harmless fish. However, most have been released alive. In the Far East, shoals of up to 500 specimens have reportedly been netted. Though edible, few, if any, are marketed in this country. SA angling record – 12,7 kg.

SPECIFIC CATCH RESTRICTIONS

Spearfishing of this species is illegal in Natal.

NAME DERIVATION

Rhinoptera, snout with eyes; *javanica,* from Java, where the first specimen was reported. Flapnose ray, a reference to the nasal flap that hangs in front of the mouth.

SIMILAR SPECIES

While the flapnose ray can be easily confused with other eaglerays if seen from a distance underwater, landed specimens cannot be confused with any other stingray because of its curious bilobed rostrum. Once thought to be a distinct family, this species is now considered to be a true eagleray.

Detail of pavement teeth: upper (top); lower (bottom).

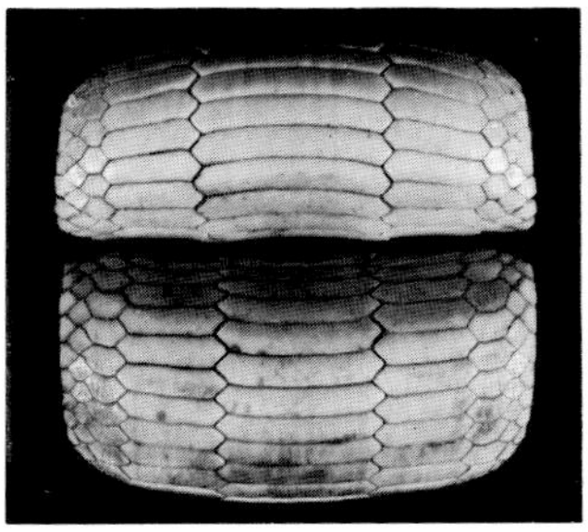

Eugomphodus taurus

(Rafinesque, 1810)

Common names SA – spotted ragged-tooth shark. Elsewhere – grey nurse, sand tiger

[Smith 19□1]

IDENTIFYING FEATURES

COLOUR, SHAPE AND SIZE

This shark is robust, extremely plump-bodied, and has a pointed snout. The overall colour ranges from light brown to grey, with a pale underside. Large, brown spots cover the body, but these may fade with age. Can attain 320 cm.

EXTERNAL ANATOMY

The fins are thick and rounded, and the first dorsal fin originates well behind the posterior edge of the pectorals. Both dorsals and the anal fin are much the same size. The small eyes are situated far foward on the snout. Both jaws carry a double row of long, pointed teeth, most of which are tricuspid. Unlike the serrated, cutting teeth of many members of the Carcharhinidae family, the smooth teeth of the spotted ragged-tooth shark protrude noticeably and are more suited to gripping. Usual tooth count = $\frac{\text{20-21 20-21}}{\text{19-21 19-21}}$.

DISTRIBUTION

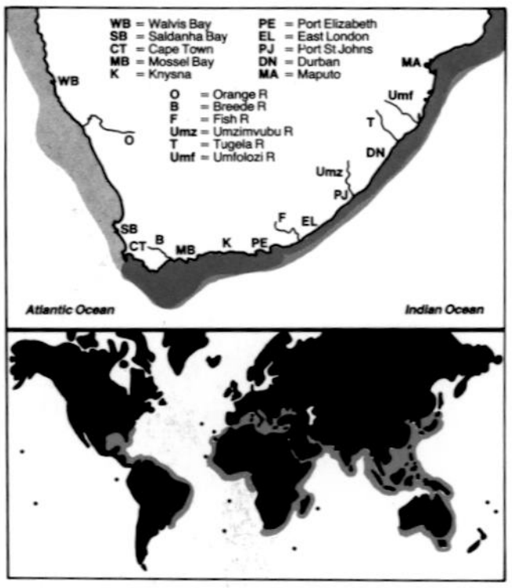

NATURAL HISTORY

The spotted ragged-tooth shark is a sluggish predator which favours shallow reefs, where it often lies in wait for its prey. Its ability to respire like bony fishes, by actively pumping water through the gills, is unusual among sharks, and enables it to remain still for long periods. This shark can also control its buoyancy by gulping air from the surface so that it will not sink below a desired depth. In the eastern Cape, the young of this species often enter estuaries, while in the St Lucia Marine Reserve, seasonal congregations occur during summer, apparently for courtship and mating. Diet consists of bony fish and the juveniles of other sharks, which, owing to the ragged-tooth's non-cutting teeth, are mostly swallowed whole.

Mature females produce numerous eggs, many of which are fertilized, but only two embryos are finally born, as these two feed on the other embryos and the eggs during their free-swimming life in the uterus. The pups are born during winter, and each measures about 100 cm in length. Sexual maturity is attained after five years, at a length of 220 cm.

Though capable of inflicting terrible wounds, this species is not dangerous to man unless provoked. It may, however, harass spearfishermen.

CAPTURE

This shark is a favourite of many shore anglers, and the majority of catches are made from rocky ledges. Live baits are most successful. The species is not of commercial importance.

SA angling record – 216,0 kg.
SA spearfishing record – 165,2 kg.

SPECIFIC CATCH RESTRICTIONS

None.

NAME DERIVATION

Eugomphodus, from the Greek words *eu* meaning good or well, *gomphos* meaning wedge-shaped and *odos* meaning road, i.e. using its wedge-shaped head to plough through the water; *taurus,* bull. Ragged-tooth, a reference to the teeth which leave ragged wounds.

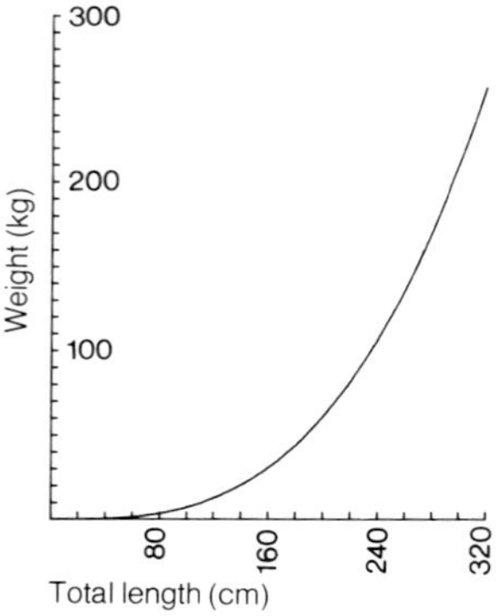

Typical teeth: lower (left); upper (right).

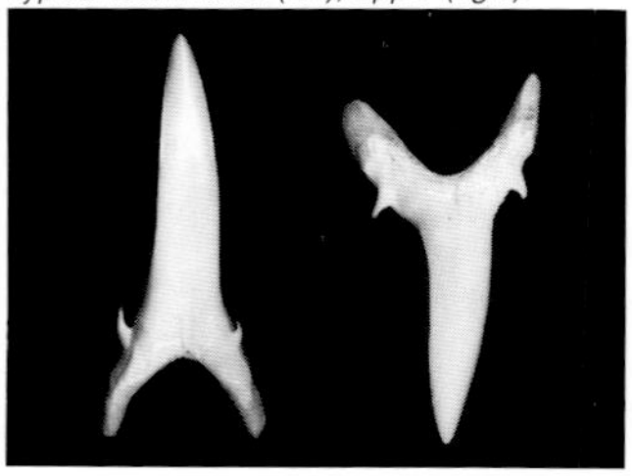

Stegostoma fasciatum

(Hermann, 1783)
Common names Worldwide - zebra shark, leopard shark
[Smith 7□4]

IDENTIFYING FEATURES

COLOUR, SHAPE AND SIZE
The adults of this species have a yellow-brown dorsal surface marked with darker spots, and a pale underside. Juveniles, however, have much bolder colouration and patterns. Body proportions also change with growth, but most distinctive is the elongate shape and very long tail which is about half the total body length. The zebra shark is known to reach 230 cm, though there is an unconfirmed record of 354 cm.

EXTERNAL ANATOMY
The arrangement and structure of the rather fleshy, broadly rounded fins is characteristic. The second dorsal and the anal are small and are positioned close to the caudal fin, which virtually lacks a lower lobe. The origins of the two dorsal fins are not well defined as they merge with the contours of the back. There are a number of distinct longitudinal ridges along the back. The small ventral mouth has tricuspid teeth arranged in 28-33 rows in the upper jaw and 27-34 in the lower. Nasal flaps partially cover the mouth. Around each of the nostrils, which are connected to the mouth by two external grooves, there are several short barbels. These are clearly shown in the close-up photograph. A large and conspicuous spiracle opens just behind each eye.

NATURAL HISTORY

Despite its wide distribution, nowhere does this docile shark occur in great numbers and details of its habits and habitat are sketchy. It is not considered rare, however, and may be found near the bottom in quite shallow water where it feeds on crustaceans, fish and molluscs, especially the black rock mussels found in the Natal region. A number of specimens held in Durban's Seaworld have become exceptionally tame and take food from a diver's hand. Sexual maturity is attained at about 150 cm for males and 170 cm for females. Reproduction is oviparous and a variable number of egg cases are produced, each attached to a submerged object by means of two short tufts of 'hair'. On hatching, the young measure 20-30 cm in length.

DISTRIBUTION

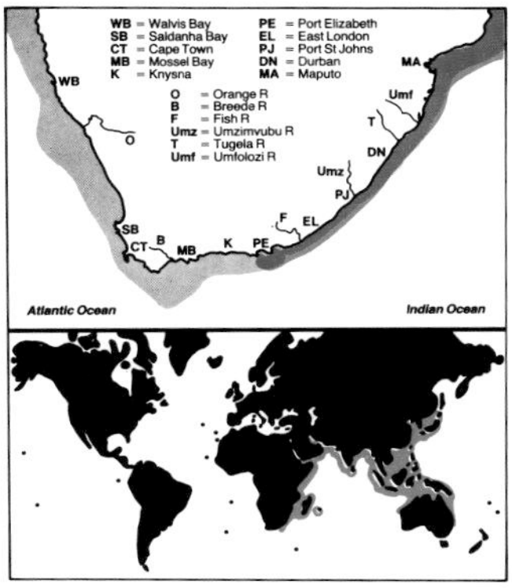

Detail of teeth.

CAPTURE

Both anglers and spearfishermen occasionally land this shark, especially during the warmer summer months. Little is known about its edibility and commercial value.
SA angling record – 34,5 kg.
SA spearfishing record – 50,8 kg.

SPECIFIC CATCH RESTRICTIONS

None.

NAME DERIVATION

Stegostoma, covered mouth; *fasciatum,* banded. Zebra shark, a reference to the zebra-like bands conspicuous in juveniles.

View of mouth showing diagnostic grooves between nostrils and mouth.

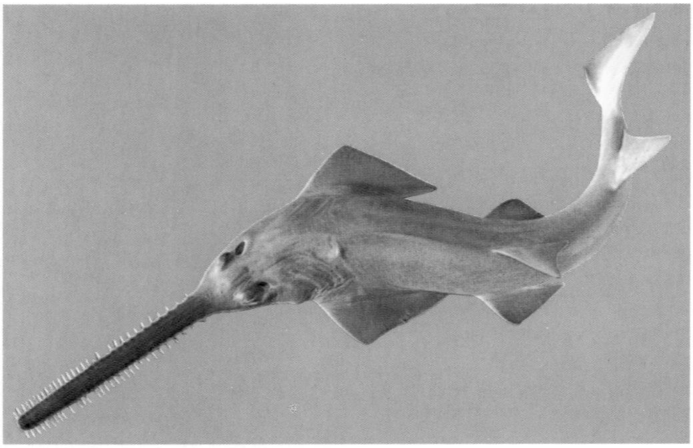

Pristis pectinata

Latham, 1794
Common name Worldwide – largetooth sawfish
[Smith 22□2]

IDENTIFYING FEATURES

COLOUR, SHAPE AND SIZE
The flattened body is khaki above and pale cream below. The conspicuous saw-like snout extends forward from the head for some 30 per cent of the total body length. Can attain 600 cm.

EXTERNAL ANATOMY
There are 24-34 pairs of sharp teeth set in sockets along the saw, the pair nearest the tip pointing slightly downwards. The jaws of the ventral mouth bear small teeth arranged in 7-14 transverse rows, the actual number depending on body size. Although the caudal fin is large it lacks a lower lobe and the pectoral fins are only partly fused to the body. A pair of large spiracles occurs just behind the eyes on top of the head.

DISTRIBUTION

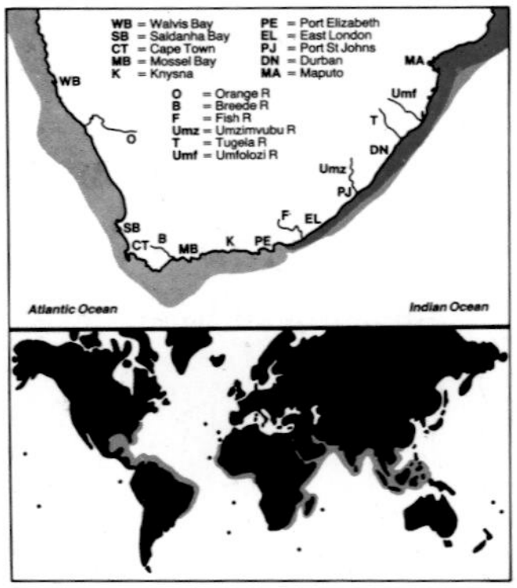

NATURAL HISTORY

This, the largest of the sawfishes, lives mainly in shallow coastal waters. The young are commonly encountered in estuaries and bays which are used as nursery areas. The diet consists of slow-swimming and shoaling fish, especially mullet, which are killed or stunned by side-swipes from the saw. This is evident from scales often found impaled on the teeth and from feeding behaviour observed in Durban's Seaworld. Sawfish can feed in remarkably muddy water where shellfish, such as prawns, clams and crabs, are often dug out from the muddy bottom using the saw. Strictly speaking this fish is not dangerous to man unless provoked or startled by an accidental encounter. During summer, giant, pregnant females often enter Lake St Lucia and Richards Bay in order to pup. Each of the 15-20 young is about 60 cm long at birth.

CAPTURE

Sometimes sawfish are hooked by estuarine anglers, but more often than not these 'catches' are only identified as 'the big one that got away!' Though it is not of commercial value, the flesh makes fine eating. Occasionally specimens become entangled in Natal's shark nets.
World angling record – 403,9 kg.
All-Africa angling record – 275,8 kg.
SA angling record – 275,8 kg.

SPECIFIC CATCH RESTRICTIONS

Spearfishing of this species is illegal in Natal.

NAME DERIVATION

Pristis, an ancient name for one who saws; *pectinata,* comb-toothed. Largetooth sawfish, a reference to the saw with its distinctive, long teeth.

Detail of pavement teeth.

SIMILAR SPECIES

The closely related but rarer smalltooth swordfish *(Pristis microdon)* has only 17-22 saw teeth and a first dorsal placed forward of the pelvics. Recent studies indicate that there may have been a confusion of names, and the species found in southern African waters could, in fact, be *P. zijsron*.

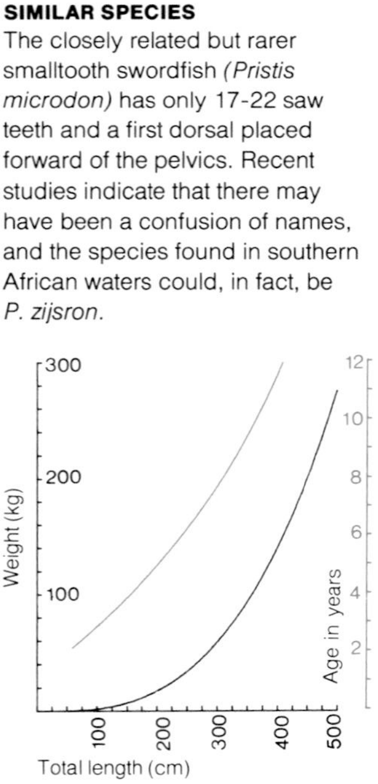

Raja alba

Lacepède, 1803
Common name Worldwide – spearnose skate
[Smith 25□6]

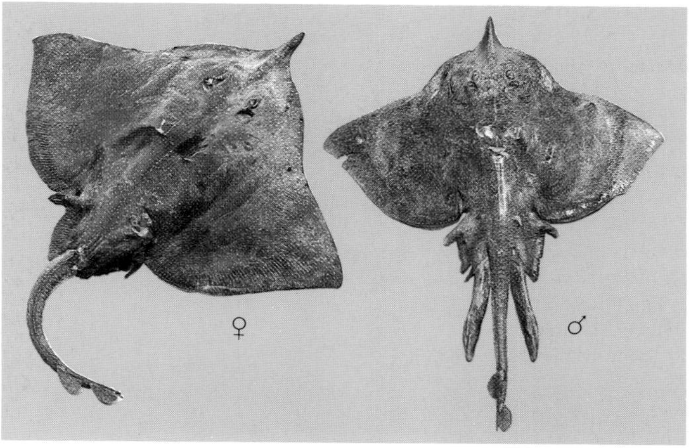

IDENTIFYING FEATURES

COLOUR, SHAPE AND SIZE

The flattened, disc-like body of this and related skates is almost quadrangular in shape. It is about 1,5 times wider than long, with its front end produced into a long, pointed snout, and its thickset tail extending a distance almost equivalent to the disc length. The overall body colour is grey-brown or darker brown as in the specimen shown. While juveniles are uniformly coloured, adults usually display an irregular scattering of whitish spots on their upper surface. The underside is white. Can attain a disc width of 180 cm.

EXTERNAL ANATOMY

The much enlarged pectoral fins are closely fused to the head and trunk, while the small pelvics project backwards as fleshy lobes. The front profile of the head is noticeably undulating, with the long rostral projection or snout being most distinctive. There are two dorsal fins, both set far back on the tail and close to the reduced caudal fin. The upper body surface of the spearnose is smooth, except for a mid-dorsal row of thorns and three well-developed rows of thorns along the tail. The mouth, bears some 40-45 rows of pavement teeth in each jaw. Mature males develop an enormous pair of claspers that can almost reach the first dorsal fins located on the tail.

NATURAL HISTORY

Skates are mostly cool-water fishes, occasionally entering brackish water, but never found in tropical or coral reef environments. The spearnose is no exception, and is commonly found in deeper waters – down to 450 m. Nevertheless, many have also been caught in the shallow surf zone, though it is invariably associated with a sandy or muddy bottom. Here it can forage for the burrowing molluscs, prawns and occasional small fish that it preys on. Spearnose skates are oviparous and the females produce two or more large, quadrangular, mermaid-purse egg capsules. These are attached to underwater plants or similar structures from which the young hatch several months later. The length at birth is about 20 cm while adults mature at about 95 cm. Females grow to a larger size than males.

DISTRIBUTION

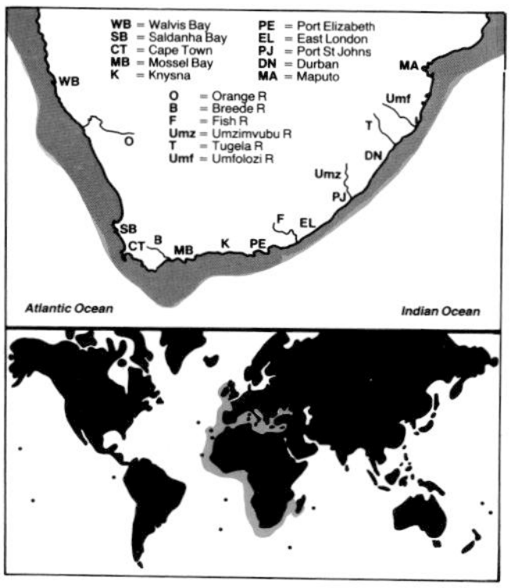

CAPTURE

Most spearnose are caught by offshore trawlers along the Cape and, occasionally, the Natal coast. Skate wings make excellent eating. This giant ray is not infrequently hooked by surf anglers, but most escape due to their enormous size and strength.
SA angling record – 97,5 kg.

SPECIFIC CATCH RESTRICTIONS

Spearfishing of this species is illegal in Natal.

NAME DERIVATION

Raja, from *raia,* the Latin for skate; *alba,* white, a reference to its white body spots. Spearnose skate, a reference to the spear-like snout.

SIMILAR SPECIES

Skates differ from stingrays by the absence of a whip-like tail armed with long spines, and the presence of two dorsal fins. The spearnose can be separated from the other 20 or so skates by its smooth-skinned upper surface, a tail with rows of thorns, and, especially, its pointed snout.

Detail of upper jaw.

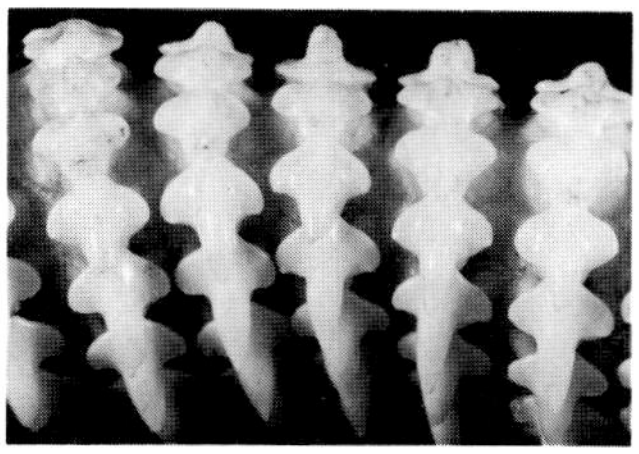

Rhinobatos annulatus

Smith, 1841

Common names Worldwide – lesser guitarfish, lesser sandshark [Smith 27□2]

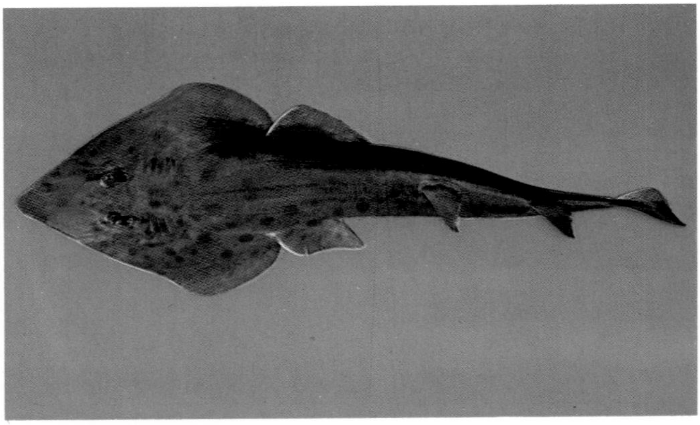

IDENTIFYING FEATURES

COLOUR, SHAPE AND SIZE

This small guitarfish has a depressed, pointed head with a fairly short, broad snout. The body colour ranges from light to dark brown depending on environmental conditions. Spots occur on the upper body surface and these are either well-defined, white rings with brown centres (especially in the Cape), or less distinct, dark-brown spots (most Natal specimens). Attains 120 cm.

EXTERNAL ANATOMY

The body is relatively smooth-skinned. The fins are well developed with the first dorsal starting well behind the origin of the pelvic fins. The caudal fin is small and consists only of an upper lobe. The small eyes are a little larger than the spiracles that lie just behind them. Both the eyes and the spiracles are surrounded by rows of small nodules which also occur before and after the dorsal fins. The small ventral mouth bears tiny teeth set in pavement fashion in diagonal rows: 41-59 in the upper jaw and 46-57 in the lower. These teeth are so minute, however, that a magnifying glass may be needed to see them.

DISTRIBUTION

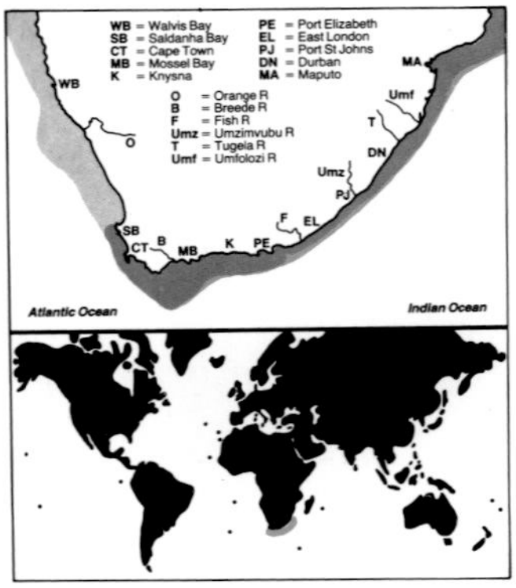

NATURAL HISTORY

This common, shallow-water sandshark favours the surf zone, and although it does not appear to tolerate low salinities, it does occur near estuaries from time to time. Some have been trawled in water to depths of at least 50 m. The lesser guitarfish is rather sluggish and uses its cryptic colouration and camouflage to conceal itself; sometimes it will burrow below the sand, leaving only the spiracles visible. Here it feeds on bottom-living organisms such as crabs, mole crabs (sea lice) and small fish, most of which are crushed by the pavement teeth. Lesser guitarfish are an important source of food for larger sharks. Sexual maturity is attained at 60 cm and females bear litters of 3-8 young during summer.

Electron microscope magnification showing typical arrangement of teeth.

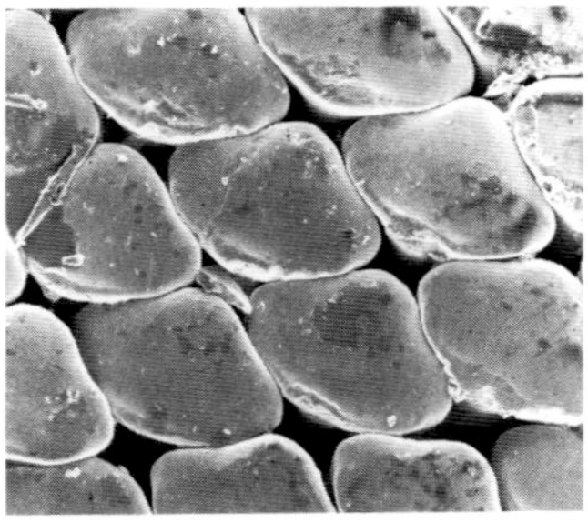

CAPTURE

Lesser guitarfish are caught quite frequently by anglers using a variety of baits set on the bottom. Occasionally specimens are netted by trawlers in the eastern Cape. Though it is a poor fighter, the lesser guitarfish is regarded as a good catch, for its flesh makes excellent eating.

SA angling record – 27,7 kg.

SPECIFIC CATCH RESTRICTIONS

Spearfishing of this species is illegal in Natal.

NAME DERIVATION

Rhinobatos, ray with a broad snout; *annulatus* ringed markings. Lesser guitarfish, a reference to the guitar-shaped body and to its being one of the smaller members of this family.

SIMILAR SPECIES

This is the most common guitarfish in South Africa. Less common but similar species have narrower or broader snouts.

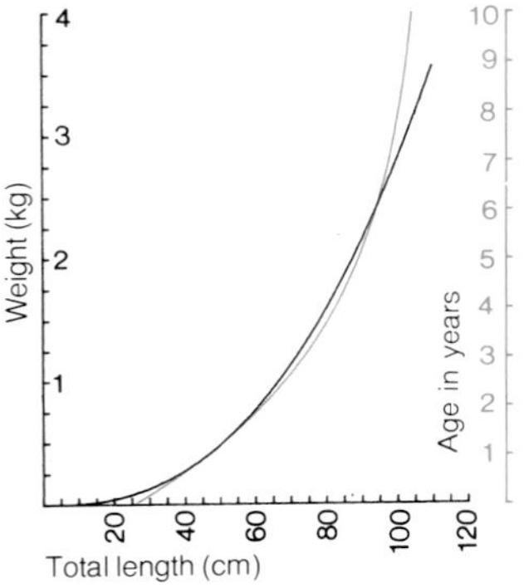

Rhinobatos leucospilus

Norman, 1926

Common names Worldwide – greyspot guitarfish, greyspot sandshark

[Smith 27□5]

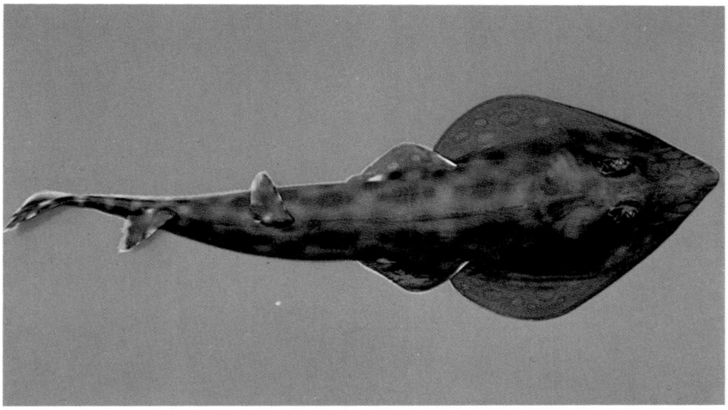

IDENTIFYING FEATURES

COLOUR, SHAPE AND SIZE

This fish has a relatively short, but broad and pointed snout. Its overall body colour is sandy-brown with a number of symmetrically arranged, bluish-grey spots on the pectoral and pelvic fins as well as on the snout. Spots on the dorsal and caudal fins are grey or brown. The underside is pale. Can attain 120 cm.

EXTERNAL ANATOMY

The fins are well developed and the two dorsals are situated far back towards the single-lobed caudal fin. There is a row of some seven small tubercles which extends to in front of the eyes and a similar row of three or four along the inside of each spiracle. These all disappear with age. A further row of about 50 small tubercles runs medially from the spiracles to the first dorsal fin, but none occurs between the dorsal fins. The mouth is situated ventrally and the teeth are arranged in a pavement fashion: 42-51 rows in the upper jaw and 45-58 in the lower.

NATURAL HISTORY

This small species is most commonly found on sandy bottoms and ranges from inshore to depths of 40 m. Some, however, have been trawled to 100 m off the Tugela River. The diet consists of bottom-living organisms such as bivalve and gastropod molluscs, crabs, prawns and occasionally small fish, those items with hard shells being crushed by the strong teeth. Its life history has not been fully investigated, but the species is known to be ovoviviparous and breeding is believed to occur during summer and autumn among specimens that exceed 50 cm. Females bear litters of up to nine young during the summer months, and each pup measures less than 25 cm at birth.

DISTRIBUTION

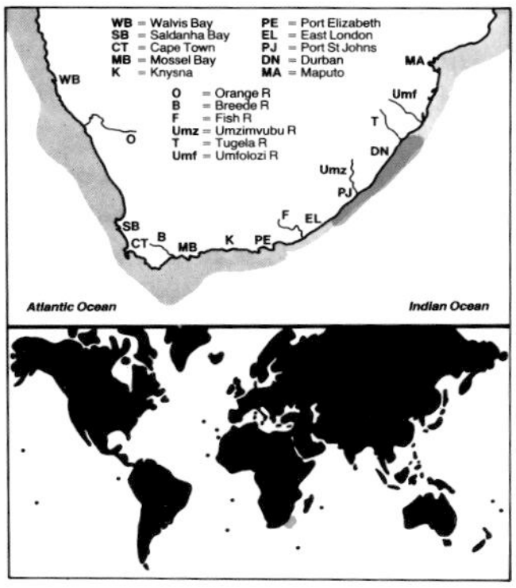

Electron microscope magnification showing typical arrangement of teeth.

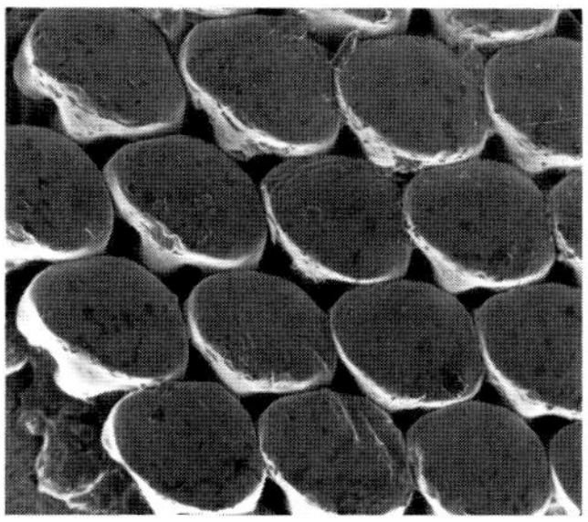

CAPTURE

The greyspot guitarfish is often caught by shore anglers, but most are mistaken for the lesser guitarfish. It will take a wide variety of baits and is a good table fish. It is of no commercial interest.
SA angling record – 6,5 kg.

SPECIFIC CATCH RESTRICTIONS

Spearfishing of this species is illegal in Natal.

NAME DERIVATION

Rhinobatos, ray with a broad snout; *leucospilus,* white spotted. Greyspot guitarfish, a reference to its guitar-shaped body, and grey markings.

SIMILAR SPECIES

Misidentification is impossible because the blue-grey spots are unique to this species.

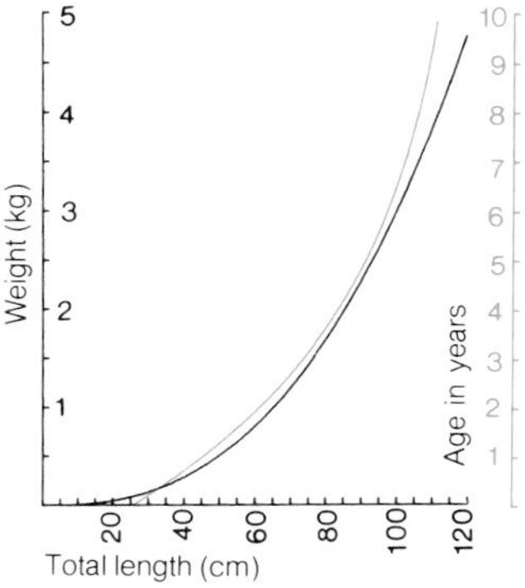

Rhynchobatus djiddensis

(Forsskål, 1775)

Common names SA – giant guitarfish, giant sandshark. Elsewhere – white-spotted shovelnose or shark-ray [Smith 27□7]

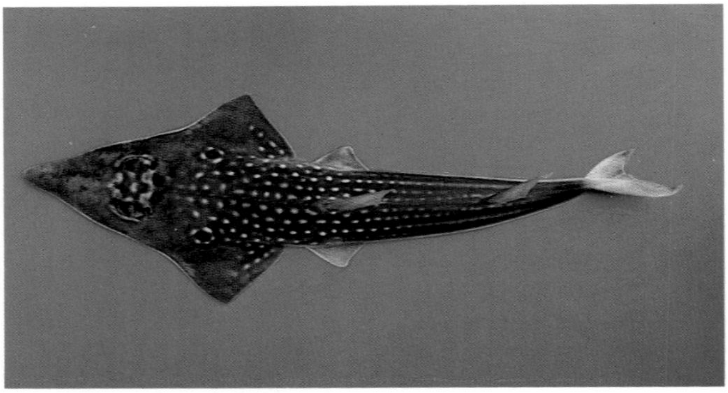

IDENTIFYING FEATURES

COLOUR, SHAPE AND SIZE

This guitarfish belongs to a small sub-family which can be distinguished from other Rhinobatidae by the noticeably elongate snout which makes the head region longer than it is wide. This is especially evident if the giant guitarfish is compared with the previous two species. The overall body colour varies from khaki to dark brown above with a pale cream underside. The upper surface is usually dotted with numerous white spots which are, however, not always evident in living specimens seen underwater. Can attain 300 cm.

EXTERNAL ANATOMY

The fins are well developed with both dorsals being large and triangular, and the caudal deeply forked. The first dorsal fin is located directly above the base of the pelvic fins. The large eyes are situated immediately in front of the wide spiracles. The ventral mouth contains closely spaced teeth set in pavement fashion: 31-41 oblique rows in the upper jaw and 37-48 in the lower.

NATURAL HISTORY

As the common name implies, this is the largest of the guitarfish and it occurs mainly along the sandy shoreline of Natal during summer. Despite its often considerable size, it is especially abundant in the shallow surf zone, although it also occurs along the edges of deeper reefs down to 30 m. The strong jaws and flattened teeth easily crush crabs and bivalve molluscs that are found in these sandy areas. In addition to these hard-shelled animals, small fish are also eaten. Reproduction is ovoviviparous and litters of about four young are born during summer. Each pup measures about 60 cm in length. Sexual maturity is attained at 150 cm.

DISTRIBUTION

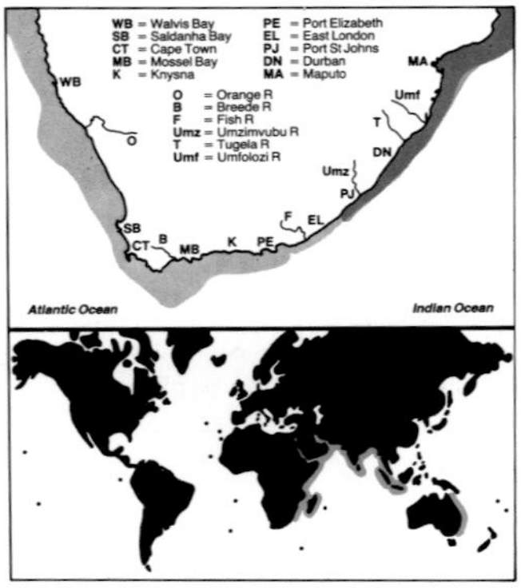

Magnification showing typical arrangement of teeth.

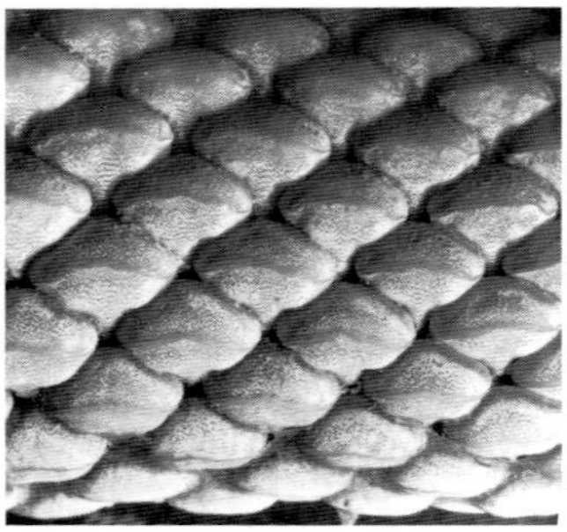

CAPTURE

The giant guitarfish is a favourite target of shore anglers as it invariably puts up a back-breaking fight. Most baits are freely taken, particularly pilchards and crayfish. It has become common practice among fishermen to release these fish unharmed, despite their fine eating quality.

SA angling record – 127,4 kg.

SPECIFIC CATCH RESTRICTIONS

Spearfishing of this species is illegal in Natal.

NAME DERIVATION

Rhynchobatus, ray with a snout; *djiddensis,* named after the original specimen that came from Djeddah in Saudi Arabia. Giant guitarfish, the largest of the guitar-shaped fishes.

SIMILAR SPECIES

This is the only typical guitarfish that has its first dorsal located directly above the pelvics.

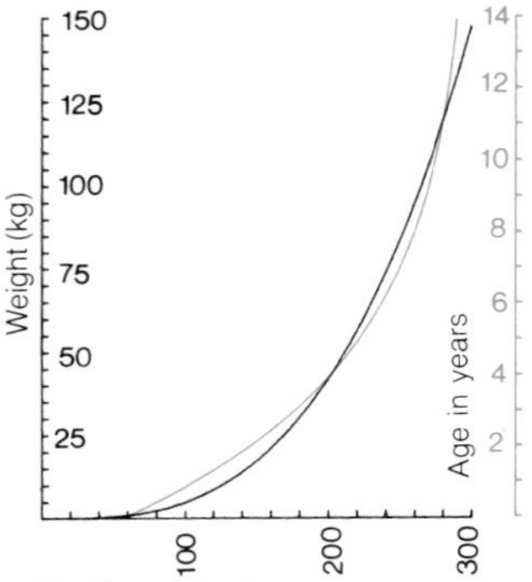

Halaelurus lineatus

Bass, D'Aubrey & Kistnasamy, 1975
Common name SA – banded catshark
[Smith 11□5]

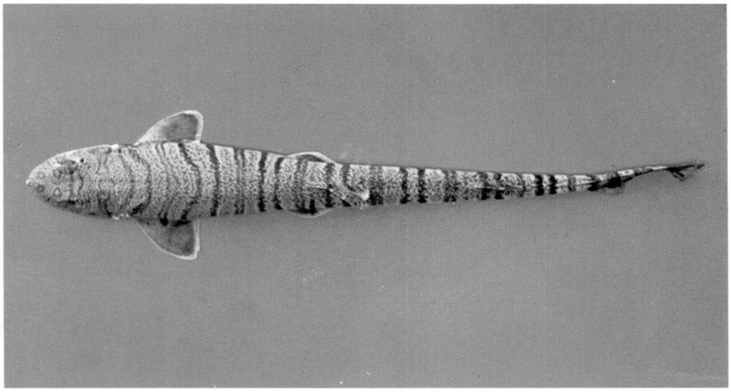

IDENTIFYING FEATURES

COLOUR, SHAPE AND SIZE
This small, elongate shark is easily identified by its characteristic colours and markings – numerous dark-brown saddles on a creamy body. It has an upturned snout which is evident when the fish is viewed from the side. Attains at least 55 cm.

EXTERNAL ANATOMY
The fins are small except for the long but stocky caudal. There is no dorsal ridge. There are many small teeth in both jaws, most being tricuspid and arranged in rows. The eyes have rudimentary nictitating membranes.

DISTRIBUTION

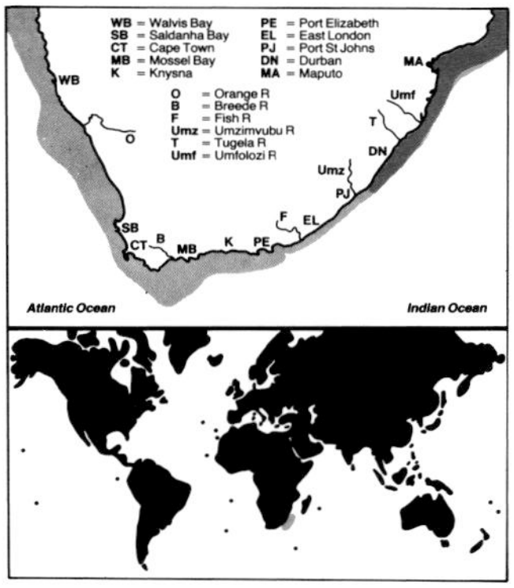

NATURAL HISTORY

The banded catshark is a slow, bottom-dwelling species ranging from the surf zone to depths of 200 m. It does not enter estuaries. Diet consists mainly of the small fish and crustaceans that live on or close to the sea-bed. During winter, females produce up to 16 egg cases which have long, but very thin and weak, tendrils. They are also coated with sticky hairs which help them to adhere to submerged marine vegetation and quite often to Natal's shark nets. When the transparent egg cases are deposited, the developing embryos already measure 3-4 cm and are well advanced, and moving. These embryos can be seen through the egg-case lining and they become progressively more active until hatching 23-36 days later at a length of 8 cm. Sexual maturity is attained at a length of 40 cm, but little else is known of its natural history.

Electron microscope magnification showing typical arrangement of teeth.

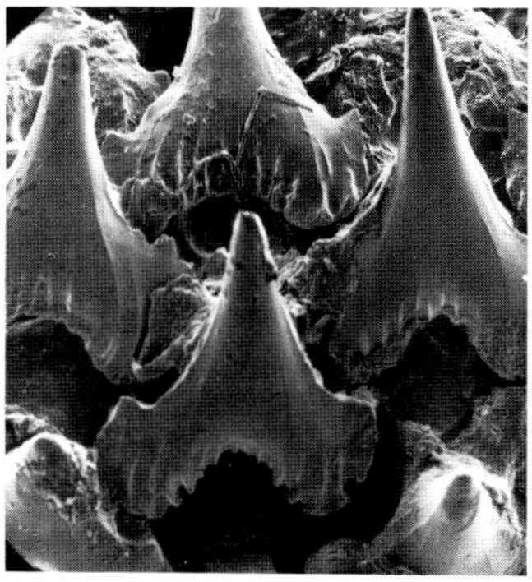

CAPTURE

Though commonly caught by beach anglers and in trawl nets by commercial fishermen, the banded catshark is not generally regarded as a sport fish and is not speared by divers.
SA angling record – 0,8 kg.

SPECIFIC CATCH RESTRICTIONS

None.

NAME DERIVATION

Halaelurus, meaning obscure, but possibly a reference to its being a sea animal with a long tail; *lineatus,* lined. Banded catshark, a reference to its cat-like colours and markings.

SIMILAR SPECIES

With the possible exception of the next species, the banded catshark cannot be confused with any other.

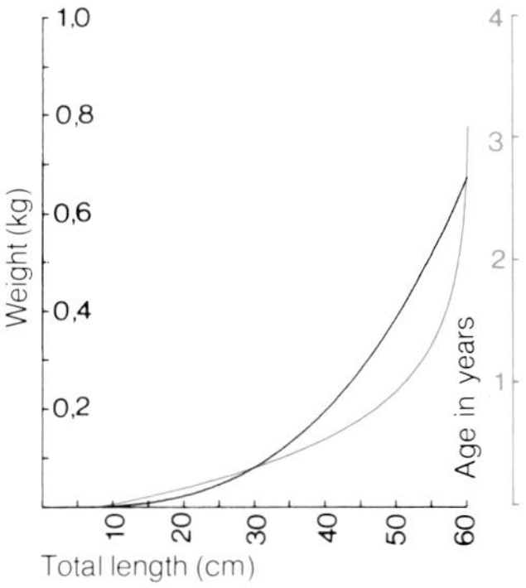

Halaelurus natalensis

(Regan, 1904)
Common name Worldwide – tiger catshark
[Smith 11□7]

IDENTIFYING FEATURES

COLOUR, SHAPE AND SIZE
Like its close relative, the banded catshark (*H. lineatus*), this species is also quite small, with an elongate body and rounded snout that ends in a small, upturned tip. The body colour is yellowish-brown or light grey above, with numerous dark-brown saddles edged in black. The underside is cream coloured. Can attain 47 cm.

EXTERNAL ANATOMY
While the fins of this shark are quite small, they are distinctly longer than those of the banded catshark, especially the dorsal fins. The ventrally situated mouth bears several rows of small, tricuspid teeth in each jaw. Their shape and structure closely resembling that pictured for the banded catshark. There are five gill openings located just before the pectoral fins. Mature males of this species may have knob-like and sharply spiked claspers, as illustrated here.

DISTRIBUTION

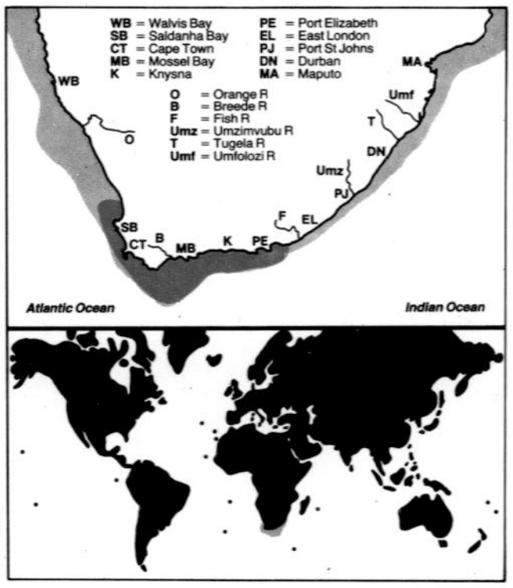

NATURAL HISTORY

This shark, endemic to South Africa, is a common bottom-living shark of the Cape coastal waters. It is frequently caught close to the shore in False Bay and the southern Cape. Further east, it tends to inhabit deeper water, and is often trawled in Algoa Bay. It is a sluggish shark, which forages over the sandy bottom, or around reef perimeters, in search of its prey. This consists of a wide variety of bottom-living organisms, including crabs, shrimps, other crustaceans, small squid, bony fishes and also the juveniles of other sharks. The oviparous females produce up to 11 egg cases each season. The structure of these egg cases is more robust, and with stronger tendrils for attachment, than those of the banded catshark. This may well be of direct benefit to the embryos which are known to hatch in a particularly well-developed stage a month or two later. The adults attain sexual maturity at 37-41 cm. The reason that this Cape species is known as *natalensis* appears to stem from the original specimen, which was poorly labelled, and thought to have been caught off Natal instead of in Algoa Bay.

CAPTURE

Moderate numbers of this shark are caught on line or trawled in deeper water, but nowhere is it considered a cherished catch. It is, however, edible.
SA angling record – vacant.

SPECIFIC CATCH RESTRICTIONS

None.

NAME DERIVATION

Halaelurus, obscure, but possibly derived from the Latin, meaning a sea animal with long tail; *natalensis,* from Natal, a reference to the original specimen, which was incorrectly assumed to have come from Natal. Tiger catshark, a reference to its tiger-like bands, and the cat-like eyes and markings common to most members of this family.

SIMILAR SPECIES

The absence of a groove linking mouth to nostrils, and the lack of elongate nasal barbels are important in determining this genus, and distinguishing the tiger catshark from the puffadder shyshark (*Haploblepharus edwardsii*). The closely related banded catshark has distinctly different patterns, smaller dorsal fins, and a palate that is covered with numerous small denticles.

Magnified details of teeth in lower jaw.

Haploblepharus edwardsii

(Voight, 1832)
Common name Worldwide – puffadder shyshark
[Smith 11□8]

IDENTIFYING FEATURES

COLOUR, SHAPE AND SIZE
This is a small, moderately elongate shark, with a rather robust head and short snout. Like many other catsharks, it has distinctive colours and patterning, consisting of a pale-cream background overlaid with numerous reticulate marks and a number of distinctive dark-brown saddles. These saddles have black outer margins in all specimens. However, Natal specimens have less distinct outer margins to their saddles than the Cape variety illustrated here. Can attain 60 cm.

EXTERNAL ANATOMY
The fins are moderately developed, with the dorsal fins placed far back on the body, the first dorsal originating well behind the level of pelvic origin. The mouth is positioned ventrally, and has several rows of multi-cusped teeth. Males have longer, three-pronged teeth while females have teeth which are shorter and five-pronged. Another unusual feature concerns jaw anatomy; this species has the two halves of the lower jaw joined by a special cartilage instead of connective tissue. This results in a more even distribution of teeth and, presumably, greater jaw-strength.

NATURAL HISTORY

This is a sluggish, bottom-dwelling, endemic shark of cooler waters, where it is most commonly found in the shallows, ranging to depths of 40 m. Off the warmer East Coast this species remains confined to deeper water – down to 130 m – presumably because the water at these depths is usually cooler. Despite its very sluggish behaviour, the puffadder shyshark manages to catch a surprisingly wide range of food, including a variety of small crabs, crayfish, squid and bony fishes – most of a bottom-dwelling type. The oviparous females mature at a length of 45-50 cm, whereafter they may produce one or two slightly furry, brownish egg cases. These mermaid's purses may measure 3,5-5 cm in length, and hatch several months later into 10-cm-long juveniles. These sharks have the curious habit of curling up when disturbed or captured.

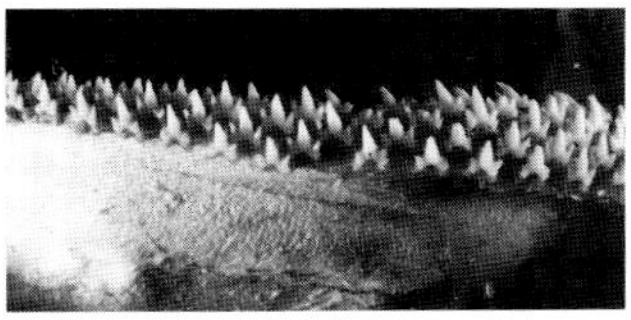

Magnified details of teeth in lower jaw.

DISTRIBUTION

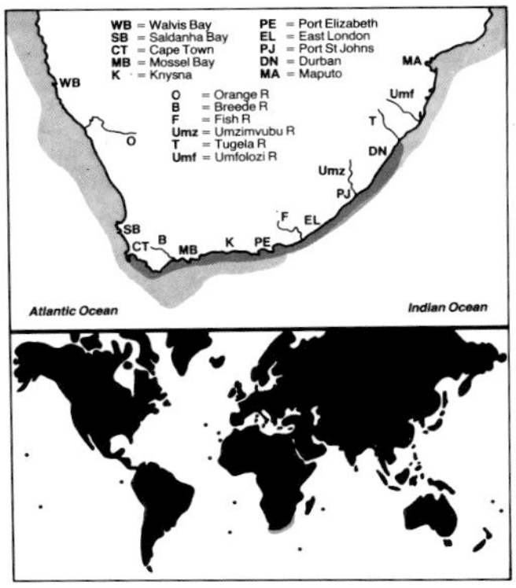

SPECIFIC CATCH RESTRICTIONS

None.

CAPTURE

Most catches are made by boat fishermen in False Bay, though rock and surf anglers around much of the Cape coast east of Cape Point also catch this shark, as do trawlers operating between Mossel Bay and East London. Occasional catches have been reported from Natal. This species is not marketed, though it is undoubtedly edible.
SA angling record – vacant.

NAME DERIVATION

Haploblepharus, single eyelid; *edwardsii,* named after Edwards, a naturalist of the time at which this fish was first named. Puffadder shyshark, a reference to it's puffadder-like colouration, and its habit of curling up after capture, covering its eyes with its tail.

SIMILAR SPECIES

The shysharks can be distinguished from all other catsharks by the presence of a groove that connects the mouth and nostrils. The quecket shark (*Scylliogaleus quecketti*) has a similar groove, but it is plain-coloured and has a first dorsal fin set far forward. The puffadder shyshark can be mistaken for the tiger catshark, though the latter has a pointed snout and more clearly defined saddles. The other two shysharks that occur are either plain-coloured (*H. fuscus*), or lack the dark borders to the brown saddles (*H. pictus*).

Poroderma africanum

(Gmelin, 1789)

Common name – striped catshark

[Smith 11□13]

IDENTIFYING FEATURES

COLOUR, SHAPE AND SIZE

This elongate shark has a broad, flat head region with a blunt snout. Though patterns and colours vary with age and locality, all *Poroderma* species have body markings based on seven longitudinal stripes, one extending along the centre of the back and three parallel stripes on either side. The overall body colour of this catshark, however, tends to be buff or creamy brown with darker, almost black, stripes which become broken towards the tail and lower sides. In adult specimens these dark stripes may have lighter centres. The underside is pale. Can attain 95 cm.

EXTERNAL ANATOMY

Except for the broad, rounded pectorals, the fins are not large. The dorsal fins, however, are distinctive as they are very closely spaced and occur well towards the tail. The first dorsal, in fact, originates behind the level of the pelvic fin axils. Notwithstanding the characteristic arrangement of the fins, the most certain, though not immediately obvious, external identifying feature is the length of the nasal barbels which is less than half the nostril length. These barbels do not reach the mouth. Each jaw is set with several rows of thin, tricuspid teeth.

NATURAL HISTORY

This endemic species is one of the most common catsharks and ranges from inshore to depths of 100 m. The dorsal fins of the striped catshark are small, soft and set well back, indicating its sluggish life-style. This is as opposed to the fins of fast-swimming sharks which tend to be large, rigid and set well forward, as they are used as rudders. The striped catshark spends much of its day lying on the bottom or 'holed up' in a cave. At night, however, activity does increase when it feeds on a variety of bony fish as well as on crabs, crayfish and squid. Sexual maturity is attained at 58-76 cm in males, while the oviparous females mature at 65-72 cm. Each season, two brownish, purse-shaped egg cases are produced which measure 5 cm by 10 cm and have a sticky, hairy surface which adheres to kelp or other submarine vegetation. Young hatch after approximately 5-6 months and each juvenile measures 14-15 cm.

DISTRIBUTION

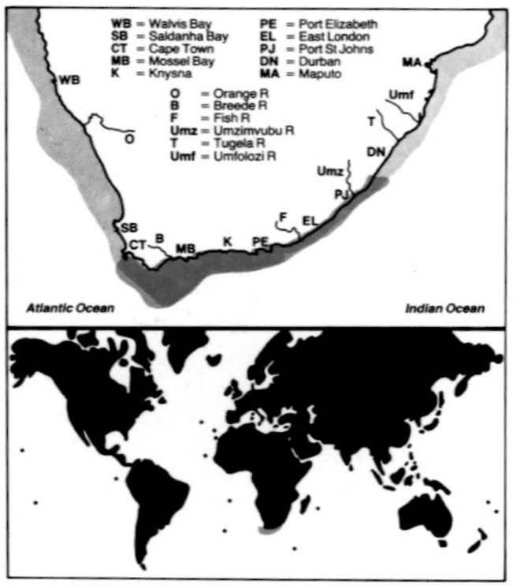

CAPTURE

During summer striped catcharks often congregate into shoals, much to the frustration of rock and surf anglers who regard these easily hooked fish as pests. Large numbers are also caught by trawlers operating in water of 50-100 m. Despite their edibility, few specimens ever reach the market as most are dumped as trash.

SA angling record – 7,9 kg.

SA spearfishing record – vacant.

Detail of typical teeth.

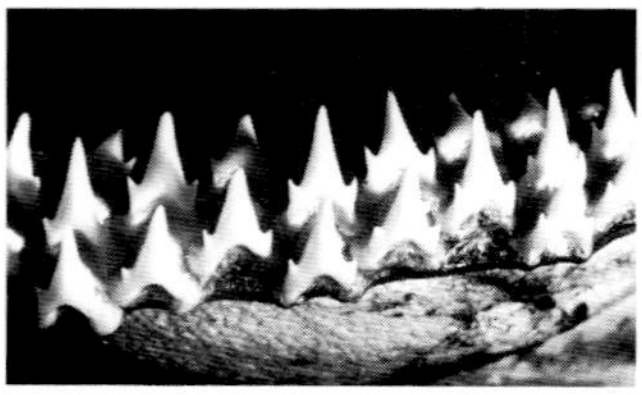

SPECIFIC CATCH RESTRICTIONS

None.

NAME DERIVATION

Poroderma, skin with pores; *africanum*, from Africa. Striped catshark, a reference to the body patterns and an obscure resemblance of some members of the family to cats.

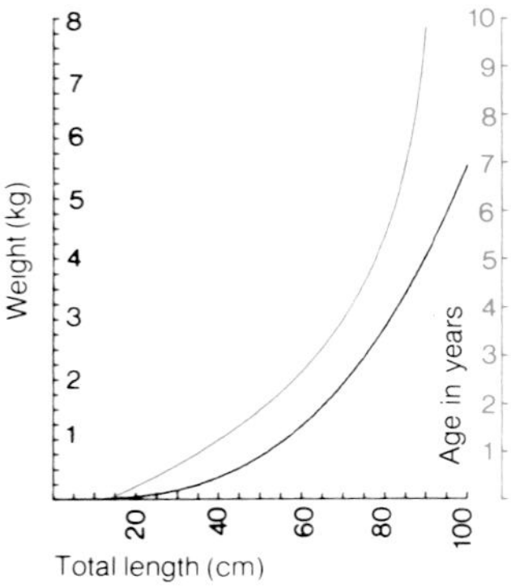

Poroderma marleyi

Fowler, 1934
Common name Worldwide – blackspotted catshark
[Smith 11□14]

IDENTIFYING FEATURES

COLOUR, SHAPE AND SIZE
This somewhat robust and elongate shark has a broad head, blunt snout, and most distinctive colouring. The overall body colour is a creamy grey, overlaid with numerous dark-brown or black spots arranged in longitudinal rows, extending from the tip of snout to the end of tail. The exact positioning of these spots is not consistent between different specimens. The outer edges of all the fins are white, while the underside is a pale-cream colour. Attains 58 cm.

EXTERNAL ANATOMY
Considering the heavy body, the fins of this shark are rather small, and are set far back. The first dorsal fin originates opposite the hind edge of the pelvics, while the anal fin originates behind the axil of the first dorsal. The small mouth is located below the snout, while the jaws extend to behind the level of the eyes. Each jaw carries several rows of smallish, tricuspid teeth, with the central, lower-jaw teeth a little enlarged and single-cusped. This feature may play a role in courtship behaviour. A further striking feature is the pair of nasal barbels that project downward for a distance equal to the nostril length, easily reaching the mouth. The five gill slits are located just above and in front of the pectoral fins, while a small spiracle opens just behind the eye.

NATURAL HISTORY

This attractive, endemic shark is found over sandy bottoms in deeper water off the Transkei and Natal coasts, possibly to a depth of 50 m. Occasional specimens have been caught from beaches, but in general this is not a particularly abundant species. Because of this apparent scarcity, little is known about its life history, and further study is needed. The females are presumed to be oviparous, producing egg-capsules which are attached to the substrate. The diet of this rather sluggish shark consists of bottom-living crustaceans, especially prawns and crabs, as well as other invertebrates and, probably, small fish. This catshark is almost certain to be most active at night.

DISTRIBUTION

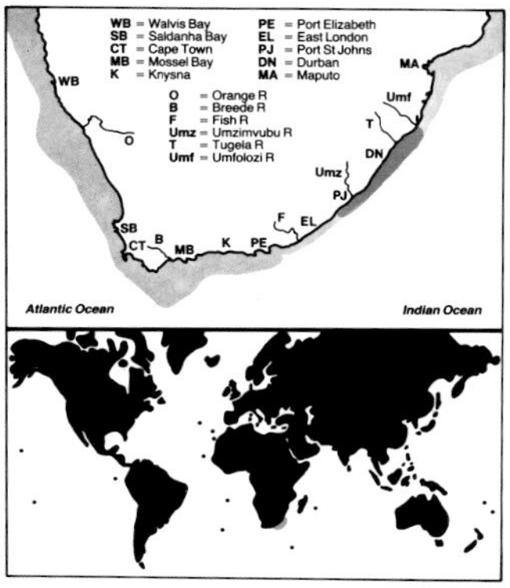

CAPTURE

Though not many blackspotted catsharks have been reported to scientists, quite a few are caught each year, especially by trawlers operating off the Tugela and Mvoti rivers. Numbers have also been taken off the Transkei coast, though few, if any, are ever marketed.
SA angling record – vacant.

SPECIFIC CATCH RESTRICTIONS

None.

NAME DERIVATION

Poroderma, skin with pores; *marleyi*, named in honour of Mr Bell-Marley, the early Natal fisheries officer and dedicated ichthyologist who first collected this species. Blackspotted catshark, a reference to its black markings, common to most members of this family.

SIMILAR SPECIES

The bold spots are a most distinctive feature of the blackspotted catshark, as are the long nasal barbels. The absence of a groove that joins the mouth to the nostrils separates this species from the carpet sharks. This catshark closely resembles the leopard catshark in external anatomy, and it has been postulated that the two are closely related, despite the differences in their body patterns.

Poroderma pantherium

(Smith, 1838)
Common name Worldwide – leopard catshark
[Smith 11□15]

IDENTIFYING FEATURES

COLOUR, SHAPE AND SIZE
This robust and elongate shark has a flattened head and blunt snout. The upper body colouration and patterns are most distinctive, being a cream-coloured background overlaid by leopard-like markings of dark brown. These consist of circles and stripes, mostly arranged in a series of longitudinal bands. This patterning varies from specimen to specimen and between leopard catsharks from various regions; specimens from Algoa tend to have the circle patterns broken up into rosettes. Can attain 84 cm.

EXTERNAL ANATOMY
The rather small fins of this robust shark are positioned far back on the body, especially the first dorsal which originates midway between the levels of the pelvic and anal fins, and not further forward as in other *Poroderma* species. Underneath the snout there is a smallish mouth with jaws that carry several rows of small, tricuspid teeth. In males, the teeth may develop slightly thicker central cusps than in females. A single but lengthy barbel projects downward from the front of each nostril, its length approximately equal to nostril width, but not reaching to the mouth. Five paired gill slits precede the pectoral fins, and there is a small spiracle behind each eye.

NATURAL HISTORY

This is a common species of eastern Cape coastal waters, ranging from the surf zone to depths of at least 250 m. In the southern and western Cape region, this endemic shark appears to be largely restricted to shallower, inshore waters such as False Bay. The leopard catshark is a sluggish species, confined to a sandy bottom, often in proximity to reefs or drop-offs. Here it searches for its food, which consists mostly of small, bottom-living bony fish, as well as crustaceans and squid. Like its close relatives, it feeds mostly at night. Little is known of its reproduction, though it is certain to be oviparous, producing egg cases that are deposited on the sea-bed. The size at birth is probably 10-15 cm, while males of 54-58 cm and females of 58-61 cm are known to be sexually mature.

DISTRIBUTION

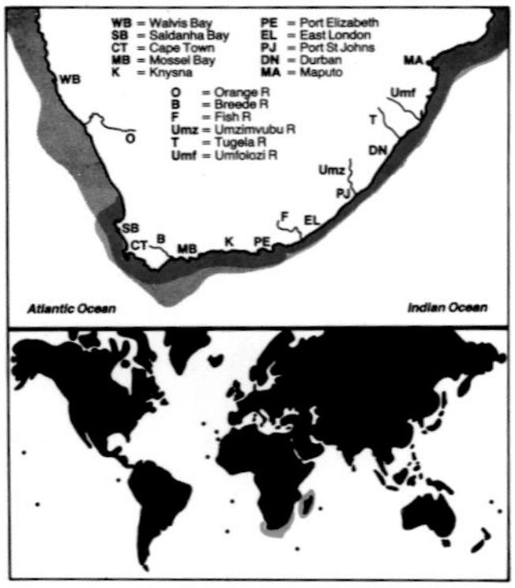

SPECIFIC CATCH RESTRICTIONS

None.

CAPTURE

The leopard catshark is a common, but not necessarily popular, catch with trawlermen and boat anglers. At night, this species appears to move to shallower, surf waters, often resulting in considerable landings by shore anglers. Though edible, it is little, if ever, utilized. SA angling record – 3,2 kg.

NAME DERIVATION

Poroderma, skin with pores; *pantherium,* leopard-like, a reference to its distinctive body patterns. Leopard catshark, derived from its body patterns, and an allusion to the cat-like eyes and patterns of other members of this family.

SIMILAR SPECIES

The striking, leopard-like patterns are most distinctive, and serve to conclusively identify this species. The posterior position of the first dorsal, the length of the nasal barbel, and absence of a groove joining mouth to nostrils are further important features to confirm identity.

Detail of lower jaw.

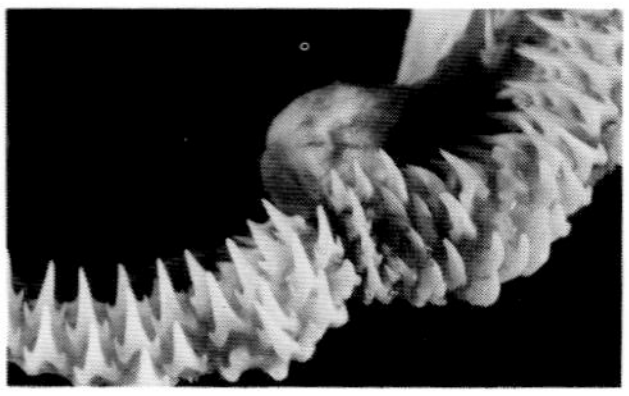

Sphyrna zygaena

(Linnaeus, 1758)

Common name Worldwide – smooth hammerhead shark

[Smith 13□3]

IDENTIFYING FEATURES

COLOUR, SHAPE AND SIZE

This rather slender shark is dusky-grey above with a white underside. The head is flattened and extends forward and sideways to form a large 'hammer', the front edge of which is smoothly curved and lacks the noticeable indentation that distinguishes this species from the other two found in this region – the scalloped hammerhead *(S. lewini)* and the great hammerhead *(S. mokarran).* Can attain 350 cm.

EXTERNAL ANATOMY

The fins are well developed, especially the first dorsal and the caudal, both of which are noticeably large. The back is smooth and lacks a dorsal ridge. A nictitating membrane covers each of the large eyes which are set at the lateral extremities of the hammer. There are no spiracles. The small ventral mouth carries triangular and strongly slanting teeth, the cusps of which are finely serrated.

Usual tooth count = $\frac{14-2-14}{14-1-14}$.

DISTRIBUTION

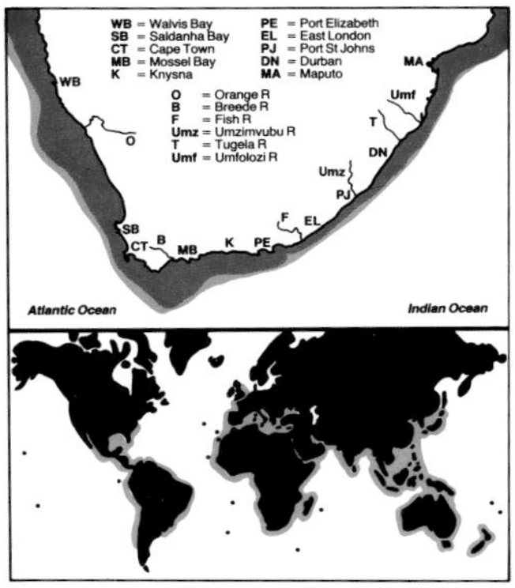

NATURAL HISTORY

This common, pelagic shark is often seen near the surface in large packs, usually quite close to land where it preys mainly on bony fish and squid. The functions of the flattened head are not fully understood, but the eyes, widely separated at each end of the hammer, probably give the fish more accurate vision, an obvious advantage when chasing after fast-moving fish. Seasonal variations in abundance occur and most hammerheads have been caught from February to May. Its danger to bathers has been exaggerated, although it does tend to be 'cheeky' towards spearfishermen and small craft at sea. Most specimens recorded from southern African waters are juveniles, hence their breeding season has not yet been locally established. Sexual maturity is attained at an approximate length of 200-250 cm and, following a six-month gestation period, the females give birth to litters of more than 30 pups. Each juvenile is 60 cm long at birth.

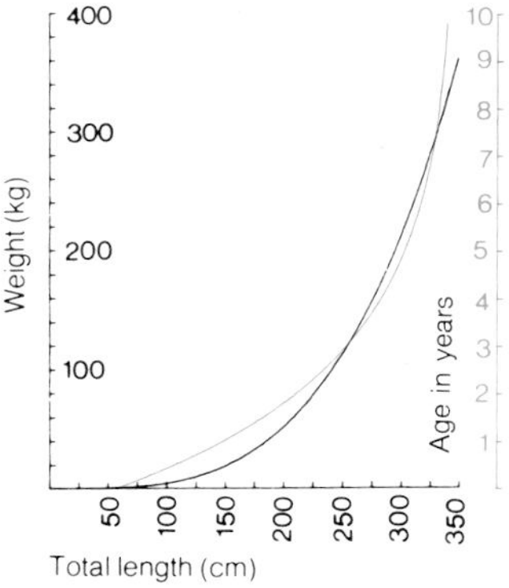

CAPTURE

The smooth hammerhead shark will take a variety of baits and many are caught by anglers from rocky ledges above deep water. It is not commercially important despite its palatable flesh.

SA angling record – 95,2 kg.

SA spearfishing record – 13,8 kg.

SPECIFIC CATCH RESTRICTIONS

None.

Typical teeth: lower (left); upper (right).

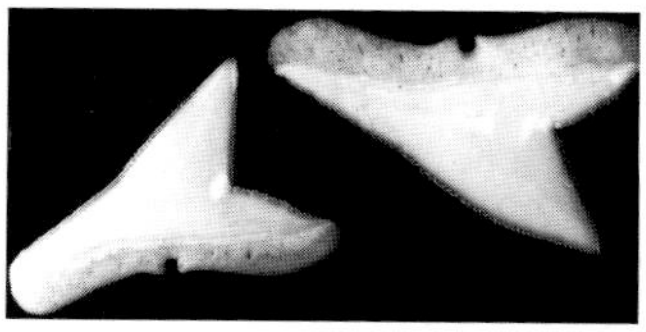

Diagnostic head-shapes of hammerheads in southern African waters.

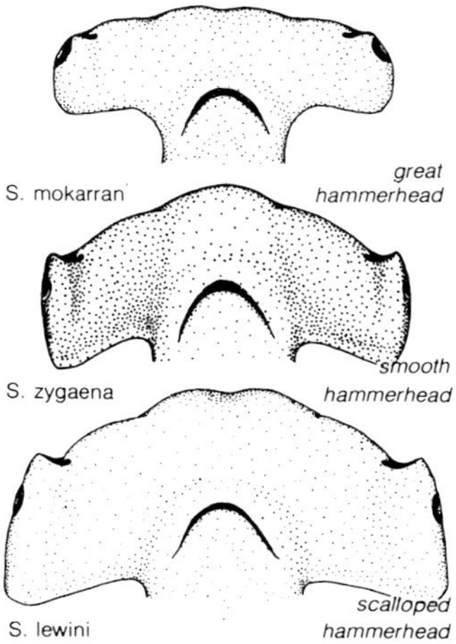

Squalus acanthias
Linnaeus, 1758
Common name Worldwide – spotted spiny dogfish
[Smith 5□24]

IDENTIFYING FEATURES
COLOUR, SHAPE AND SIZE
The elongate body of this shark is brownish-grey above, often with white spots. These are most conspicuous in juveniles but tend to fade with age. The underside is pale. The southern African variety is smaller than those occurring elsewhere with males in local waters attaining a length of 70 cm and females 80 cm.
EXTERNAL ANATOMY
Both dorsal fins are preceded by a sharp spine and the first dorsal is positioned further back than in all other *Squalus* species, usually well behind the pectoral fin. This species has characteristic dermal denticles which change their shape with growth from a thin spike to a tricuspid form. A tiny spiracle is situated just behind each eye. The small teeth are obliquely slanted so as to form a cutting edge, but in males the teeth are slightly more erect and pointed than in females. Usual tooth count = $\frac{13-1-13}{11-1-11}$.

DISTRIBUTION

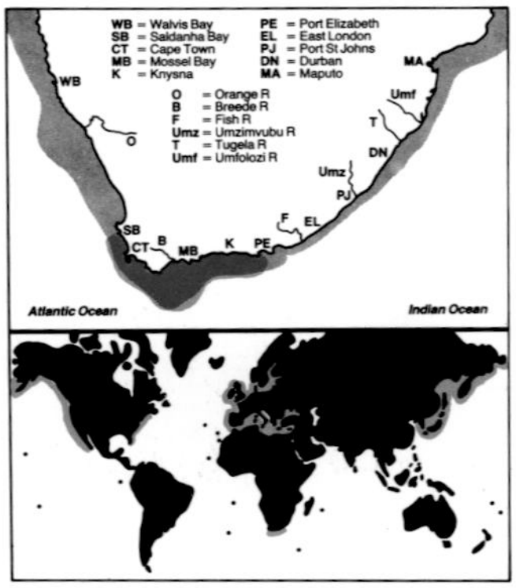

NATURAL HISTORY
This is certainly the most intensely studied shark species in the world and much of its life history has been documented. All first-year zoology or medical students have dissected one during the course of their introduction to animal anatomy. It is a bottom-living species that feeds mainly on the small bony fishes and squid found near the sea-bed, both in shallow water and to depths of over 500 m. The males attain sexual maturity at a length of 50 cm, while females mature at 60 cm. After a gestation period probably lasting two years, females give birth to three or four pups, each with a length of 19-22 cm. The litters of the southern African variety appear to be smaller than those elsewhere. As the spines are strong and sharp, this fish should be handled with care.

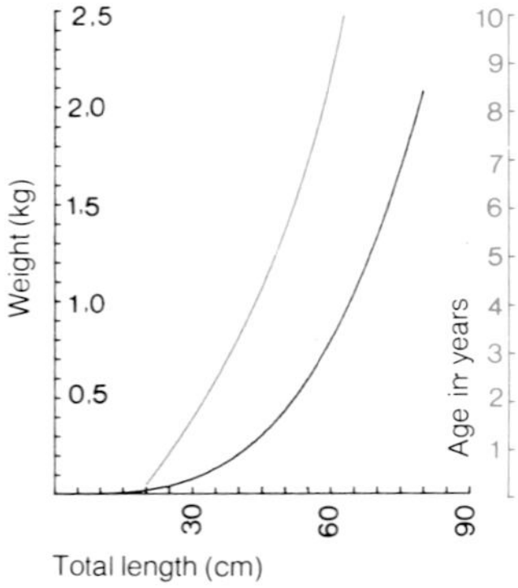

CAPTURE
Commercial exploitation of the spiny dogfish is considerable, particularly in the North Sea where almost the entire catch is destined for the fish-and-chip shops of London. Large numbers are trawled in southern African waters and besides their flesh value, use is also made of the liver and fins for vitamin A and sharkfin soup respectively. Although anglers occasionally hook this species it is not considered a sport fish.
World angling record – 4,6 kg.
SA angling record – vacant.
SA spearfishing record – vacant.

SPECIFIC CATCH RESTRICTIONS
None.

NAME DERIVATION
Squalus, shark; *acanthias,* a spine. Spotted spiny dogfish, a reference to its markings, spines and dog-like head.

SIMILAR SPECIES
There are several dogfish that resemble this species, hence the anatomical description should be carefully evaluated, especially the position of the first dorsal.

Detail of upper and lower jaws.

Squalus megalops

(MacLeay, 1882)
Common name Worldwide – bluntnose spiny dogfish
[Smith 5□26]

IDENTIFYING FEATURES

COLOUR, SHAPE AND SIZE
This elongate shark with its small fins and noticeably large eyes is brown-grey in colour with a white underside. Smaller specimens have white-tipped fins. Unlike other *Squalus* species, there are never white spots on the upper body surface. Males can attain 55 cm and females reach 70 cm.

EXTERNAL ANATOMY
A sharp spine precedes both dorsal fins. Moderate spiracles are present just behind the eyes. The teeth are small and strongly oblique so as to form a cutting edge. Usual tooth count = $\frac{13-1-13}{11-1-11}$.

DISTRIBUTION

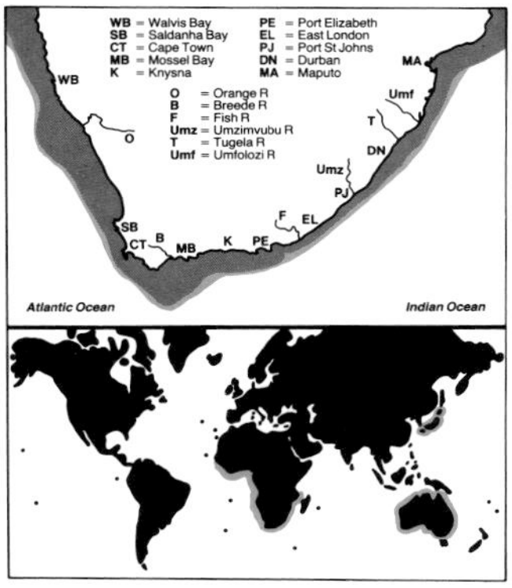

NATURAL HISTORY

This bottom-dwelling, slow-swimming species ranges from the shallows to deep water, but is most abundant from 50-450 m. It often frequents the relatively turbid waters over the continental shelf. Here it feeds primarily on sluggish fish as well as on squid, crustaceans and other bottom-dwelling organisms. During the winter pupping season 2-4 young are born live after a two-year gestation period. Under normal conditions pups measure 23-24 cm at birth. If caught, however, pregnant females often abort their young and these premature pups may measure 18-22 cm. Sexual maturity is attained at a length of 42 cm in males and 55 cm in females. The stout spines may severely lacerate a careless handler.

CAPTURE

This species is mostly caught as a by-catch in the trawling industry and is marketed in a variety of ways. Anglers regularly catch this shark from the shore and many are taken by ski-boaters in the Border region. Though it should be regarded as a good eating fish, it is not popular.
SA angling record – 2,8 kg.
SA spearfishing record – vacant.

SPECIFIC CATCH RESTRICTIONS

None.

NAME DERIVATION

Squalus, shark; *megalops,* large eyes. Bluntnose spiny dogfish, a reference to its short snout, spines and dog-like head.

SIMILAR SPECIES

There are several dogfish that resemble this species, hence the anatomical description should be carefully evaluated, especially the position of the last dorsal. The bluntnose spiny dogfish is easily confused with the closely related longnose spiny dogfish (*S. mitsukurii).* The distinction between the two cannot be made in the field as the extremely subtle differences in the shape of the snout and the pectoral fins, as well as in the structure of the dermal denticles, can only be determined using detailed measuring techniques. *S. megalops* is, however, the more common.

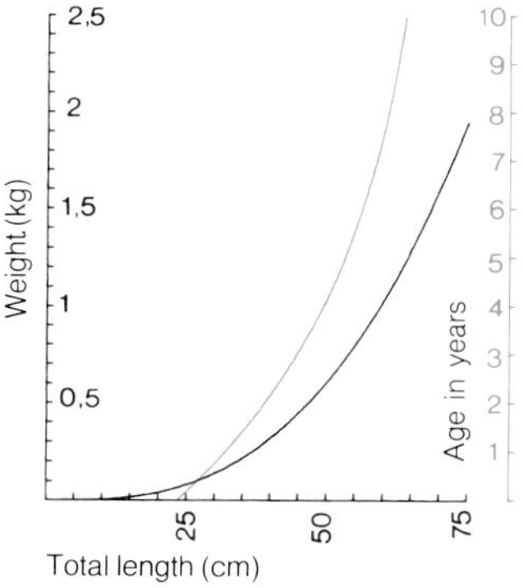

Detail of upper and lower jaws.

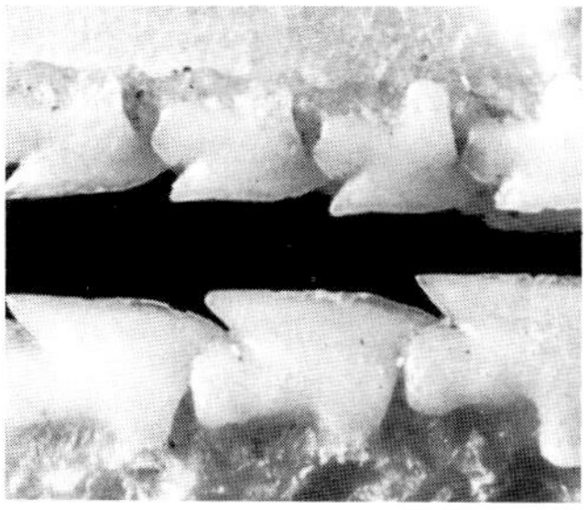

Squatina africana

Regan, 1908

Common name Worldwide - African angelshark

[Smith 21□1]

IDENTIFYING FEATURES

COLOUR, SHAPE AND SIZE

This unusually shaped shark has a flattened body, with a bluntly rounded snout and greatly extended pectorals which give it a quadrangular appearance. The overall body colour is dark brown above, with numerous paler spots and five reticulations. The underside is a pale-cream colour. Can attain 108 cm.

EXTERNAL ANATOMY

The enlarged pectorals are fused to the trunk as in stingrays, skates and guitarfishes, but, significantly, not to the head region. The pelvic fins are also large, and joined to the body, from which a thick tail projects backwards. The two dorsal fins occur far back on the tail, close to the caudal fin. There is no anal fin, and neither are there any spines on the tail or fins, though some short spines may occur on the snout and around the eyes on an otherwise smooth-skinned body. The mouth of the angelshark is situated terminally, and the jaws are set with several rows of very fine, single-cusped teeth. The eyes are located far forward on the upper surface, closely followed by two large spiracles. There are five pairs of gill openings that extend from the sides round to the ventral surface.

NATURAL HISTORY

This is a relatively common cartilaginous fish of east coast waters, occasionally being found along shallow, sandy bays and beaches, especially in water to depths of 400 m. It often occurs in association with offshore banks, such as those opposite the Tugela River. Here it forages on the muddy or sandy bottom in search of its prey, which consists mainly of a variety of small bony fishes as well as cuttlefish, squid, octopuses and prawns. Despite its sluggish appearance, the angleshark is capable of quite sudden bursts of speed, especially when pouncing on prey. Much of the time may also be spent lying still, hidden just below the muddy bottom with only the eyes and spiracles protruding. Some angelsharks are known to be chiefly nocturnal. The female of the species grows to a larger size than the male, and they become sexually mature at about 90 cm and 75 cm respectively. Each season, this ovoviviparous and near-endemic species produces litters of 7-11 pups, each measuring about 30 cm.

DISTRIBUTION

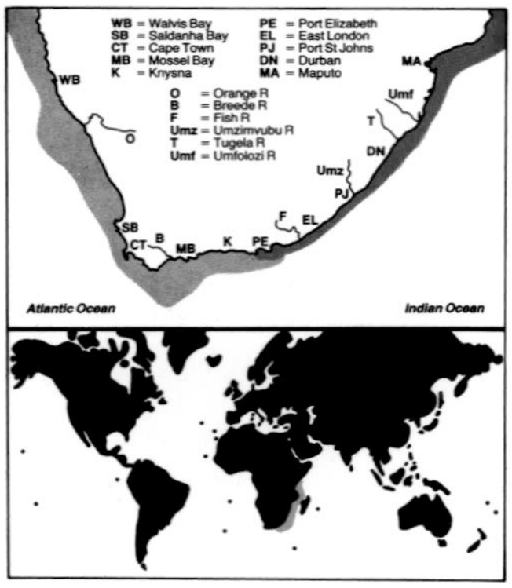

CAPTURE

Most reports of angelsharks have come from trawlermen operating off the Natal coast. Each year, a number are also caught by surf anglers, often in proximity to river mouths, though none have yet been caught in estuaries. None are ever marketed, though it is edible. SA angling record - 10,2 kg.

SPECIFIC CATCH RESTRICTIONS

None.

NAME DERIVATION

Squatina, from the Latin meaning skate, i.e. skate-like shark; *africana,* from Africa. Angelshark, an allusion to the angel-like appearance created by the wing-shaped pectorals.

SIMILAR SPECIES

The African angelshark is the only member of this family found in southern African waters. It is readily distinguished from guitarfishes by its terminal mouth, head that is not fused to the pectoral rays, and dorsal fins that are located far back on the body. While it superficially resembles the bowmouth guitarfish (*Rhina ancylostoma*), the latter is further distinguished by the numerous heavy ridges of large denticles along the back.

Detail of teeth.

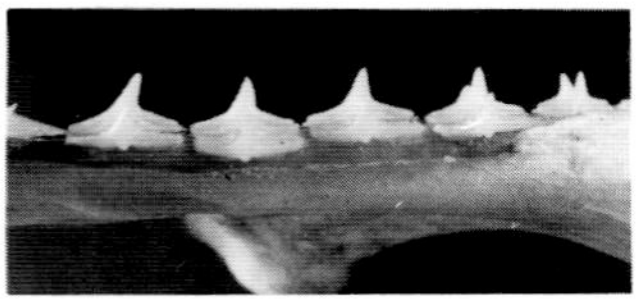

Torpedo sinuspersici

Olfers, 1831
Common name Worldwide – marbled electric ray
[Smith 23□3]

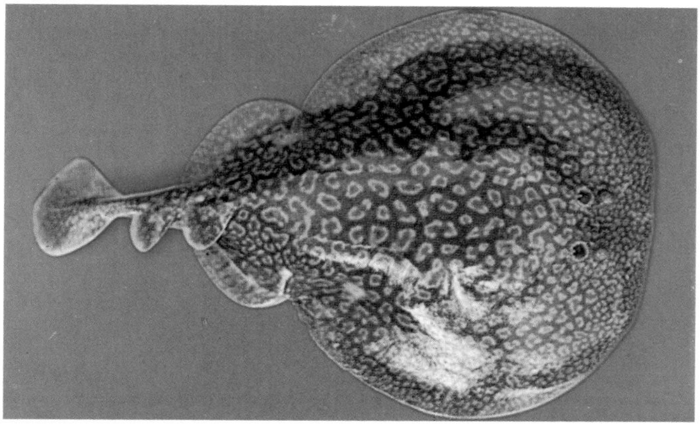

IDENTIFYING FEATURES

COLOUR, SHAPE AND SIZE
The disc-shaped body is almost round and the front edge of large specimens is slightly concave but with a central bulge. The body is mottled overall with numerous irregular blotches. The underside is pale. Attains a disc width of 90 cm.

EXTERNAL ANATOMY
The skin of this fish is very smooth. Two small dorsals occur on the short, stocky tail and the caudal fin is small and rounded. The fleshy and enlarged pelvic fins are partially fused to the pectorals. The eyes are small and just precede the upward facing spiracles which have a number of small tentacles around their edges. The wide, ventral mouth bears small, sharply cusped teeth.

DISTRIBUTION

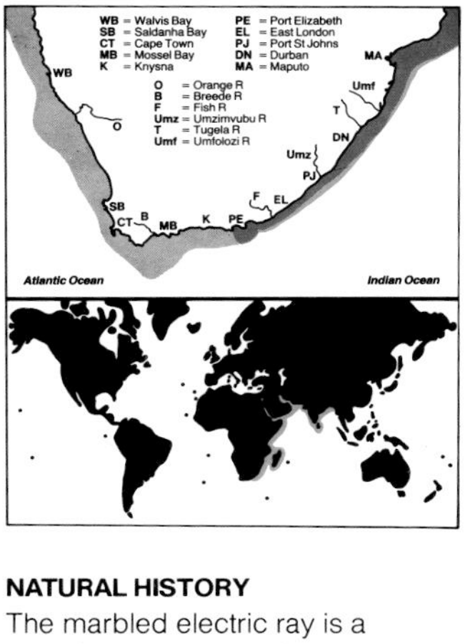

NATURAL HISTORY

The marbled electric ray is a common inhabitant of shallow, sandy areas, but also occurs on offshore banks to depths of 200 m. It is a sluggish, solitary species, confined to the sea-bed and frequently buries itself in the sandy bottom of gullies and estuaries. It reaches peak abundance during summer when females produce 9-22 live young, each measuring about 10 cm in disc width. Sexual maturity in this ovoviviparous species is attained at a disc width of 38-41 cm. As the name implies, this ray can generate powerful shocks from large paired organs in the pectoral fins. This ability to convert nervous energy into electricity is almost certainly used to stun prey which consists primarily of slow-swimming fish. Shocks are also released voluntarily when the ray is molested and many an unsuspecting diver or careless angler has been startled at its 'punch'. Early Romans used the electric ray for 'shock therapy' in the treatment of gout, while the ancient Greeks had an even more bizarre use for these animals; pregnant women were often 'closeted' with them in the belief that the shocks would ease delivery.

CAPTURE

The marbled electric ray is often seen by divers and is occasionally caught by shore anglers using fish bait. The flesh is edible.
SA angling record – 13,0 kg.

SPECIFIC CATCH RESTRICTIONS

Spearfishing of this species is illegal in Natal.

NAME DERIVATION

Torpedo, numbness; *sinuspersici,* a reference to the locality on the Persian Gulf where it was first described. Marbled electric ray, a reference to its colour pattern and electric potential.

SIMILAR SPECIES

Although another four types of electric ray occur in South African waters, this species is the only one with a reticulated pattern on a body disc that is slightly wider than long.

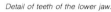

Detail of teeth of the lower jaw.

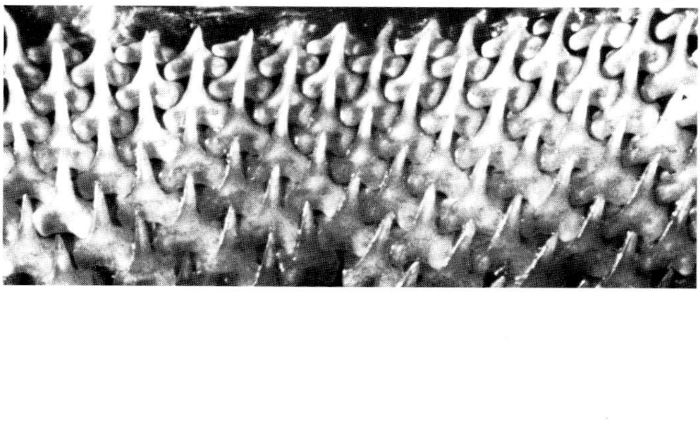

PART II

THE BONY FISHES

BONY FISHES
An illustrated outline

Bony fishes are characterized by a number of features which separate them from the cartilaginous fishes. Most prominent of these are the presence of a true bone skeleton and fins strengthened by bony spines or soft rays. Also diagnostic is the single gill cover on either side of the body which protects the gill chamber. The majority of bony fishes are either completely, or at least partially, covered with scales, although a few families are distinguished by their complete absence, for example, some eels and barbels.

A detailed knowledge of anatomy is not essential to identify most fish and often shape alone will enable the user of this book to pick out the correct group of fish from the line illustrations and descriptions in the introduction to the families beginning on page 84. Colours, too, are often most distinctive, and here the colour photograph in each species description will prove most helpful. In a number of instances, however, especially where the families are large, such as the seabreams (Sparidae) and kingfishes (Carangidae), the differences between species are more subtle. In these cases, characteristics such as the number of dorsal spines or rays, the number of rakers on the first gill arch, the type and number of teeth or even the shape of the swim bladder, can help to pin-point a particular species. For this reason, and to enhance one's understanding of fishes in general, a familiarity with the elementary aspects of fish anatomy can only be of benefit.

External features

1 head length; **2** pre-maxilla (lip); **3** nasal barbel; **4** nostril; **5** eye; **6** first dorsal fin; **7** second dorsal fin; **8** caudal peduncle; **9** caudal fin; **10** body depth; **11** scutes; **12** lateral line; **13** anal fin; **14** detached spines; **15** pectoral fin; **16** pelvic fin; **17** breast; **18** operculum (gill cover); **19** pre-operculum; **20** maxilla (upper jaw); **21** mandible (lower jaw); **22** barbel.

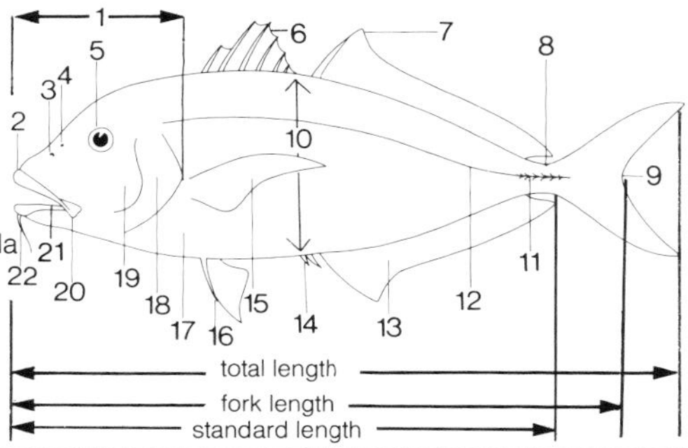

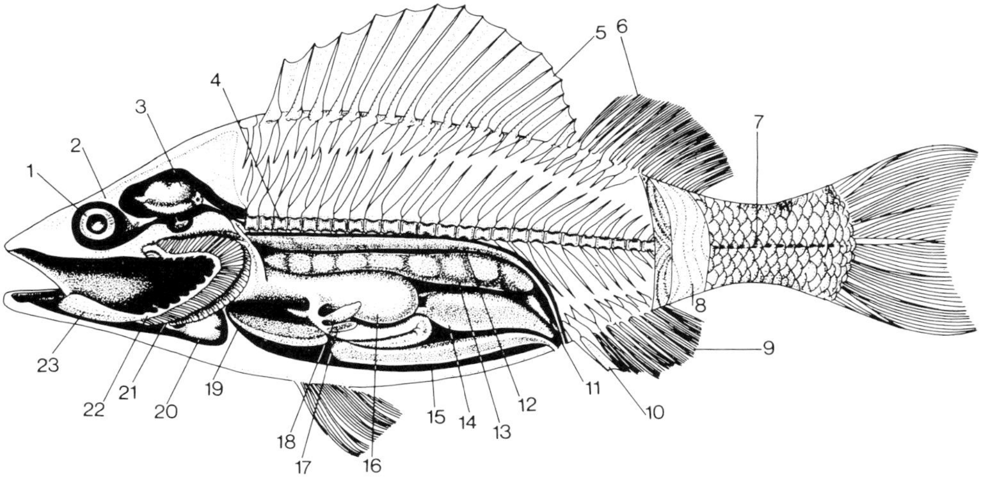

Internal features

1 eye; **2** skull; **3** brain; **4** vertebral column; **5** dorsal spines; **6** dorsal rays; **7** lateral line; **8** muscles; **9** anal rays; **10** anal spines; **11** cloaca (vent or anus); **12** kidney; **13** swim bladder; **14** ovary or testis; **15** intestine; **16** stomach; **17** spleen; **18** pyloric caeca; **19** liver; **20** heart; **21** gills; **22** gill rakers; **23** tongue.

Head profiles showing typical mouth types

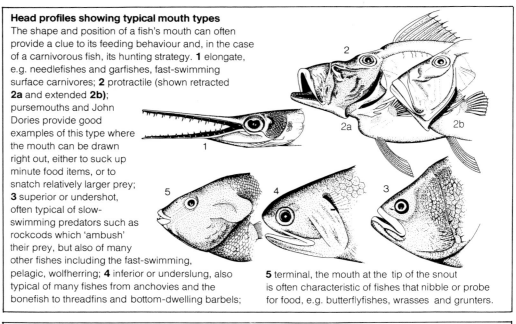

The shape and position of a fish's mouth can often provide a clue to its feeding behaviour and, in the case of a carnivorous fish, its hunting strategy. **1** elongate, e.g. needlefishes and garfishes, fast-swimming surface carnivores; **2** protractile (shown retracted **2a** and extended **2b)**; pursemouths and John Dories provide good examples of this type where the mouth can be drawn right out, either to suck up minute food items, or to snatch relatively larger prey; **3** superior or undershot, often typical of slow-swimming predators such as rockcods which 'ambush' their prey, but also of many other fishes including the fast-swimming, pelagic, wolfherring; **4** inferior or underslung, also typical of many fishes from anchovies and the bonefish to threadfins and bottom-dwelling barbels; **5** terminal, the mouth at the tip of the snout is often characteristic of fishes that nibble or probe for food, e.g. butterflyfishes, wrasses and grunters.

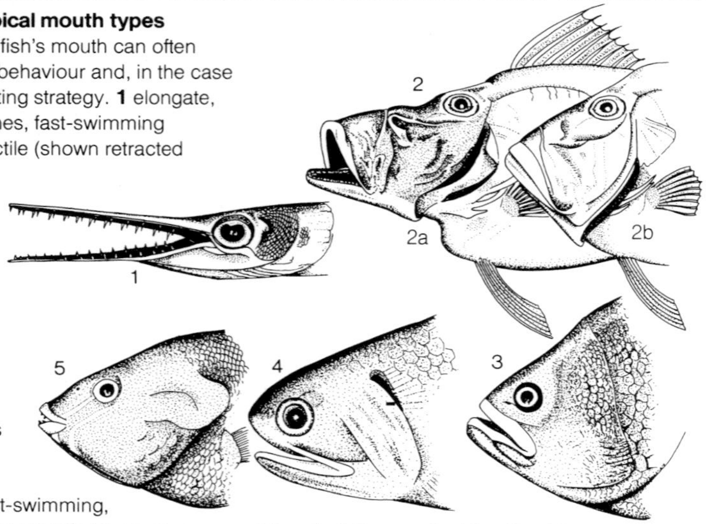

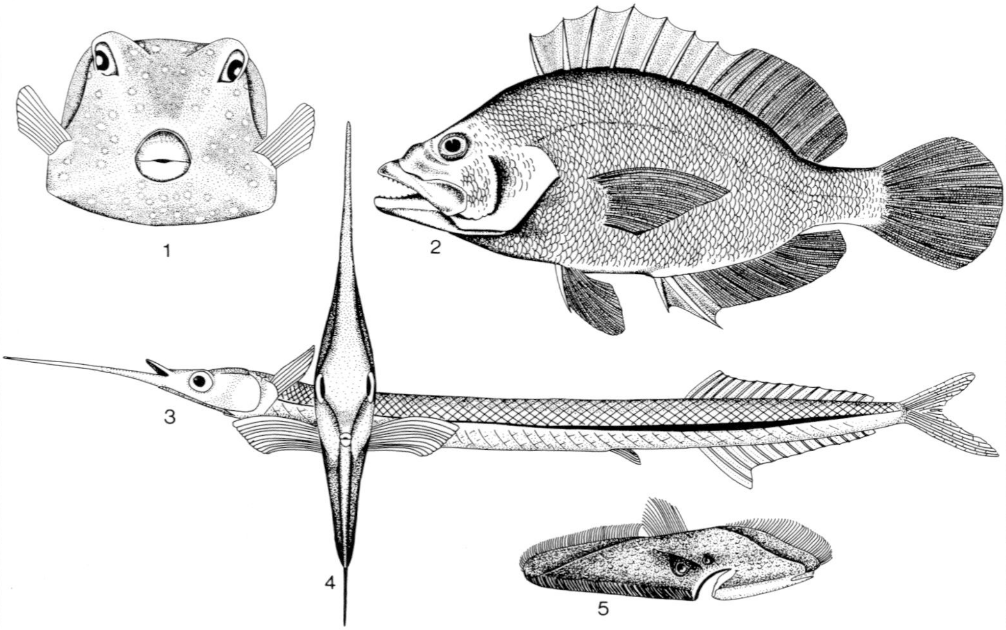

Body shapes

Bony fishes vary greatly in body proportions and the accompanying line drawings serve to illustrate a few of the relative terms used to describe their physical appearance. **1** square in cross-section, e.g. boxfishes and cowfishes; **2** robust, e.g. thick-set fishes such as some seabreams, rockcods and kingfishes; **3** elongate, e.g. halfbeaks, snoek and eels; **4** compressed (that is, flattened from side to side) e.g. John Dories, butterflyfishes, moonfishes and batfishes; **5** flat or depressed, e.g. some bottom-dwellers such as soles and flounders.

Lower jaws showing typical teeth

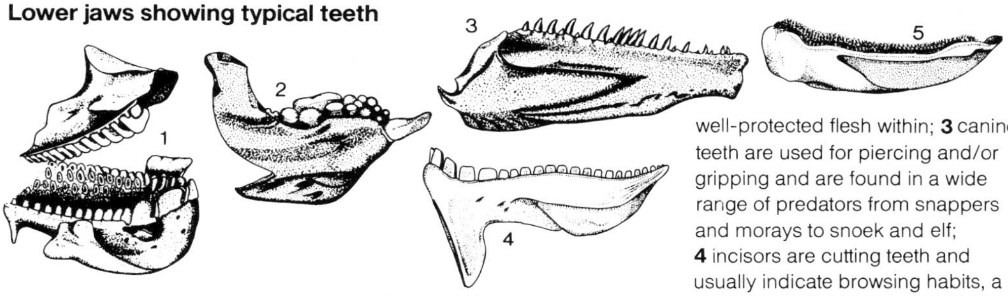

The teeth of a fish usually provide a reliable pointer as to its eating habits. Not all fishes, however, have a totally specialized diet and many therefore have more than one tooth type. Some fishes, filter-feeders such as anchovies, herrings and sardines, may lack teeth altogether. **1** pharyngeal, a grinding mechanism within the gullet, typical of fish such as pompano which eat mussels; **2** molars also indicate a diet of hard-shelled animals which are crushed to reach the well-protected flesh within; **3** canine teeth are used for piercing and/or gripping and are found in a wide range of predators from snappers and morays to snoek and elf; **4** incisors are cutting teeth and usually indicate browsing habits, a good example being provided by the surgeonfishes; **5** villiform, these very fine teeth provide fish such as groupers and rockcods with a 'sandpaper-like' lining to the mouth which is used in conjunction with the powerful jaws to grip prey.

Scales

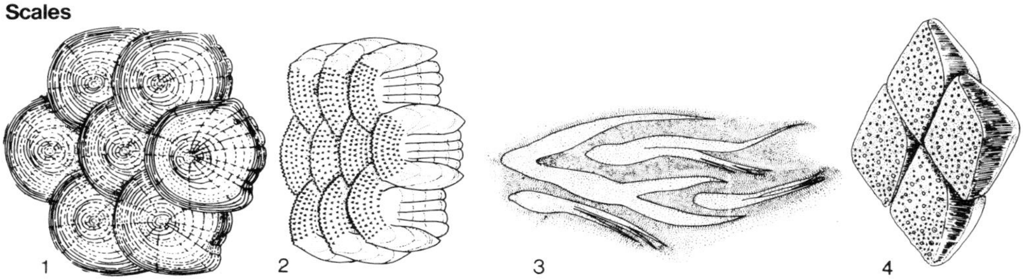

The majority of bony fishes have overlapping scales forming a pattern reminiscent of a tiled roof. Scales, in fact outgrowths of the skin, provide the fish with a flexible covering which together with mucus secreted by glands in the skin form a barrier to bacterial and fungal infection as well as preventing the loss of body fluids. The number of scales of a fish, especially the number of series, usually ranged along the lateral line, is constant and can be diagnostic. Scales vary in shape, however, and also grow with the fish, the 'annual-rings' often proving useful in determining a fish's age and history. Shapes include **1** cycloid (smooth-edged) and **2** ctenoid (rough-edged), while amongst those less frequently found are **3** lanceolate (such scales are sharp and deeply embedded in the skin, e.g. those of marlins) and **4** rhomboid, which do not overlap and form the criss-cross pattern typical of triggerfishes.

Tail shapes

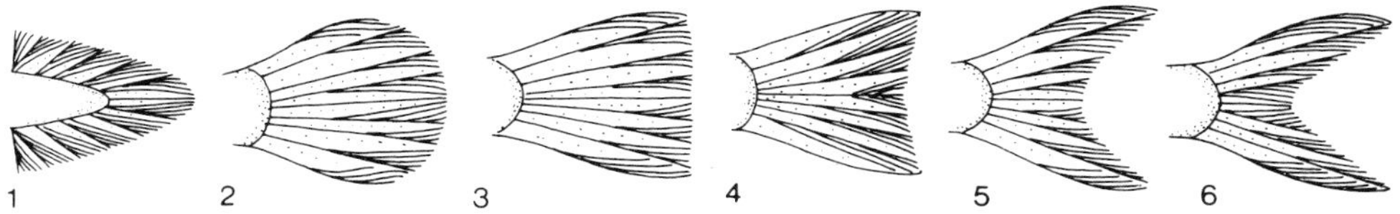

The tail or caudal fin is, in many fishes, the main means of forward propulsion and drives the animal through the water as it is swept from side to side by powerful muscles in the caudal peduncle and the body itself. The shape of the caudal fin taken together with the fish's general body shape, is usually an indication of swimming prowess. Faster, wide-ranging, pelagic fish such as kingfishes, mackerels and tuna have forked tails which are hydrodynamically most efficient. while slower-moving fishes have rounded, truncate or even pointed tails, e.g. kobs and rockcods, grunters and soles, and kingklip and eels respectively **1** pointed; **2** rounded; **3** truncate; **4** emarginate; **5** lunate; **6** forked.

ACANTHURIDAE
Surgeonfishes and unicornfishes

See pages 113 to 116 for species descriptions

Members of this herbivorous family can be found in all tropical seas and of the 50 species that have been identified, about 19 frequent southern African waters.

A diagnostic feature of most surgeonfishes, in fact one that gives them their name, is the sharp, erectile spine on each side of the caudal peduncle. The spines are normally folded into a groove, but when the fish is threatened or alarmed these are lifted and used to slash at the attacker. In unicornfishes these spines take the form of fixed bony plates on either side of the peduncle and there is also a single foward-projecting horn on the forehead.

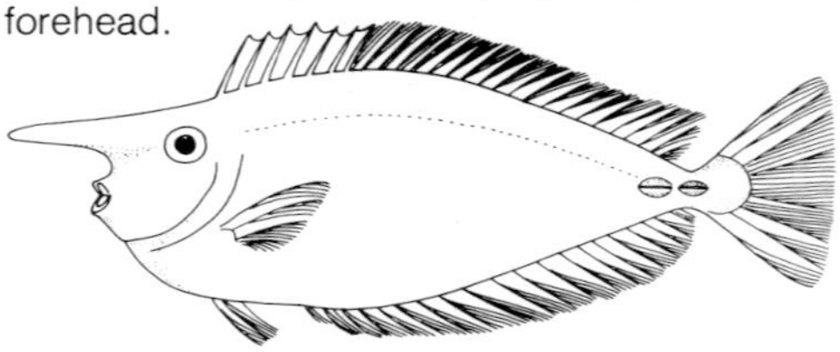

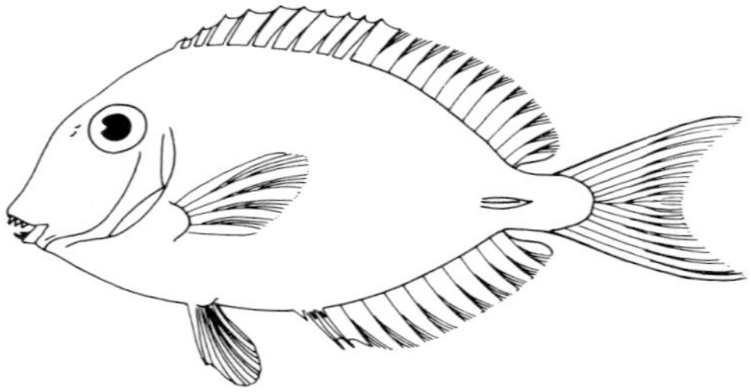

The skin of Acanthuridae is covered with minute ctenoid scales and though a few species are brightly coloured, most are drab and difficult to identify. Many are gregarious and during daylight shoals can be seen grazing on the algae that grow on reefs, especially in shallow water. Both jaws are set with sharp incisors, well suited to cutting and nibbling. The intestines are long and thin-walled, a typical adaptation of vegetarian feeders to a high-bulk, low-calorie diet.

The fry are transparent and almost circular, and differ so much from adults that they were originally thought to belong to a separate group of fishes and were named *Acronurus.*

ALBULIDAE
Bonefish

See page 117 for species description

This family occurs in most tropical seas and brackish water and has, until recently, been considered to comprise a single, worldwide species. Research in Hawaii, however, has shown there to be a number of different species. This highly sophisticated research involves the chemical analysis of body proteins in numerous specimens.

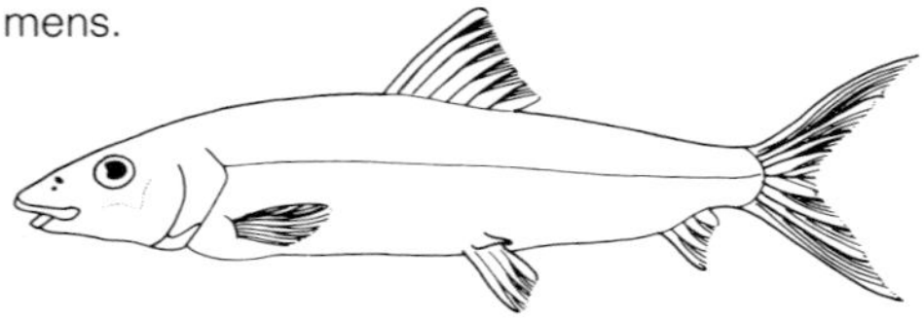

Features which characterize the bonefish include the total absence of spines: the conical, pig-like snout with its underslung mouth; the elongate body covered with brilliant, silvery, cycloid scales; and the distinctive lateral line system, part of which extends on to the upper jaw.

Bonefish favour warm shallows where they move in small groups while foraging for food in the muddy or sandy bottom. The species is regarded as a fine light-tackle game fish and South Africa holds the world record with an 8,6 kg catch off the Zululand coast.

It is probable that the family was ancestral to the eels of today. This belief is supported by the fact that the bonefish passes through a transparent *leptocephalus* larval phase, similar to that of eels.

AMBASSIDAE
Glassies

See pages 118 to 119 for species descriptions

There are only some 30 species in this family, three of which occur in the southern African region.

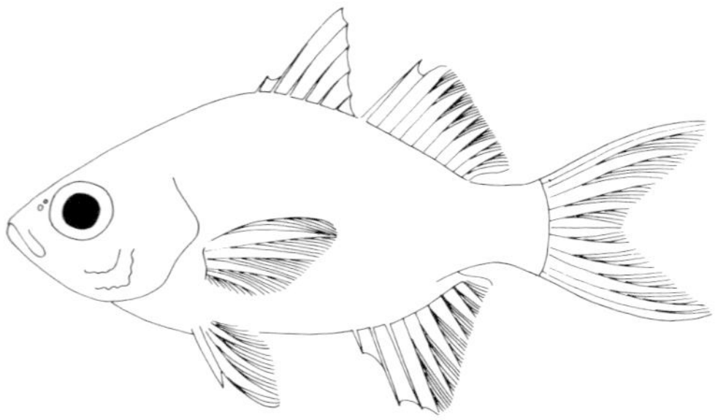

Ambassidae are closely related to the Centropomidae, a group which includes such huge fish as the giant perch *(Lates calcifer),* which can weigh as much as 200 kg and the Nile perch *(L. niloticus),* a freshwater species that is not much smaller. At the other end of the scale, however, is the Indian glassfish *(Chanda ranga),* also a freshwater species, which seldom grows to a length of more than 5 cm.

Glassies are small, carnivorous fish all of which frequent marine or brackish waters. They are silvery, almost transparent, and have cycloid scales, a continuous lateral line and a single dorsal fin with a distinct dip in the mid-body region.

Glassies are shoaling fish and represent one of the few groups of fishes that actually spawn within estuaries. Their great abundance in some coastal lagoons makes them an important source of food for larger predators.

APOGONIDAE
Cardinalfishes

See page 120 for species description

There are at least 200 species of cardinalfishes distributed throughout the tropical waters of the world. Of these, 53 occur off southern Africa, mainly along the East Coast. Though primarily a family of marine reef fish, a few members enter estuaries and some have even adapted to life in the freshwater streams of Pacific Ocean islands.

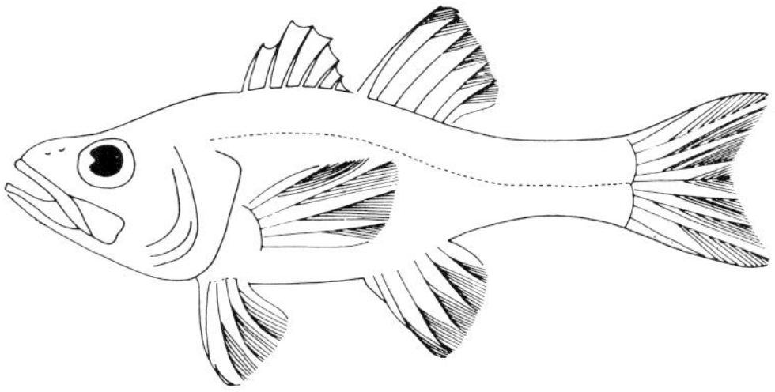

Cardinalfishes are all small, rather elongate and attractively coloured in shades of red. Their bodies are covered with ctenoid scales that are noticeably rough. All species have two separate dorsal fins, the first of 6-8 spines and the second of 8-14 rays. The anal fin has two spines plus 8-18 rays. During the day, these fish remain well hidden in dark recesses, but at night most species congregate into shoals when they forage along the reef for small animals and larvae. The eyes and their pupils are large and effective in low light levels, a useful adaptation to their nocturnal habits. Breeding in many species is unusual because, after egg-laying, the male broods the eggs in his mouth until they are hatched.

Cardinalfishes have no value as a food source, but many species are popular with aquarists and adapt well to a tank environment.

ARIIDAE
Sea catfishes

See page 121 for species description

This large family is the only one of many catfish groups that is primarily marine. Ariidae are distributed throughout tropical and subtropical seas and some are known to enter estuarine and fresh waters. Only three species have been recorded off the southern African coast.

The first dorsal fin and the pectoral fins of all sea catfishes have a large, serrated spine. Though these have no poison glands, each is covered with a highly toxic mucus and wounds can cause the death of the victim. Lacerations from these spines should immediately be treated by immersion of the afflicted part in hot water for at least 30 minutes to destroy the powerful protein toxin. Other characteristics of this family include a forked caudal fin, a small adipose fin, three pairs of barbels around the mouth (none around the nostrils as in other families) and a smooth, scaleless body.

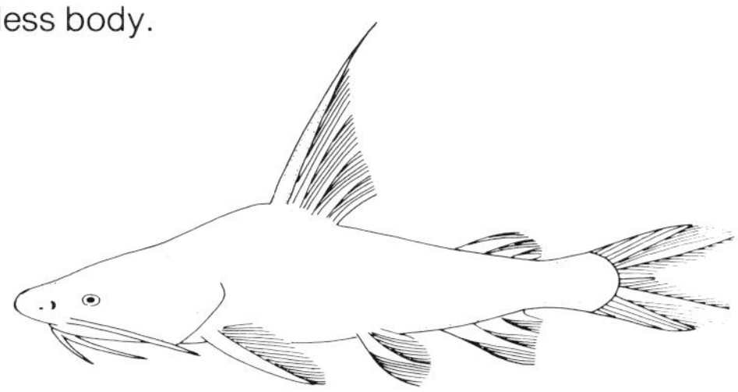

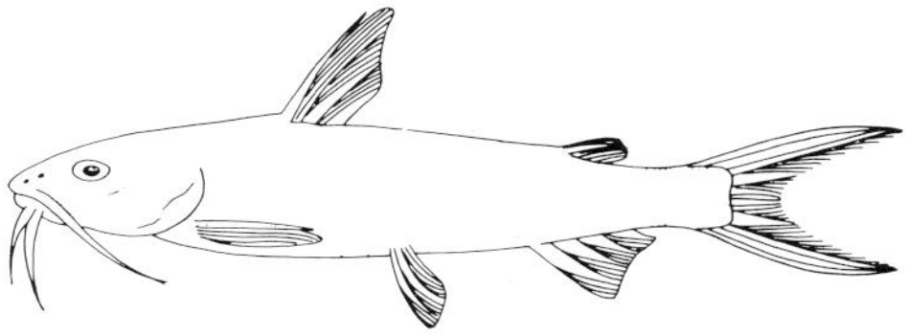

Sea catfishes are able to make certain characteristic sounds by vibrating a thin elastic-like bone in the body cavity. These vibrations are amplified by the adjacent swim bladder which acts as a sound box. Recent research has proved that these noises can be 'heard' by other members of the same species, thereby suggesting a system of sound communication.

Pea-sized eggs are produced by females, and are 'incubated' in the mouths of the males. In some cases 'fathers' have been known to swallow their embryonic progeny and it is uncertain if they are then able to regurgitate the eggs unharmed.

ATHERINIDAE
Silversides

See page 122 and 123 for species descriptions

There are more than 120 species in this large family, but only six occur in southern African waters. Though most Atherinidae are marine fish which inhabit the temperate and subtropical regions of the world's oceans, some species, notably those in Mexico, eastern United States and Australia, are indigenous to fresh water.

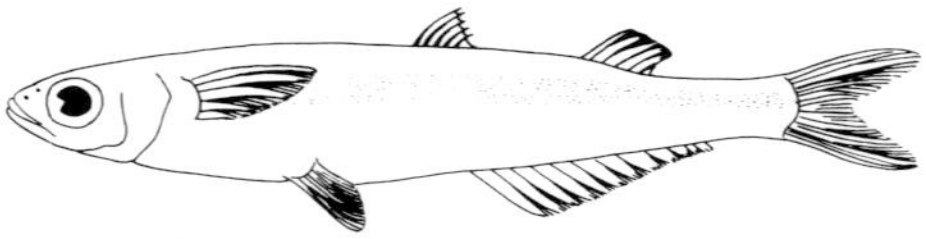

The majority of these small fishes are semi-transparent when alive, but rapidly become more opaque after death with a broad, silvery band along each side. All species lack a lateral line, and though the body is covered with large scales, these are often almost clear and, therefore, difficult to discern. Also characteristic are the two separate dorsal fins and the pelvic fins which are set far back towards the abdomen.

Though the life cycles of very few species have been studied, that of the Californian grunion *(Leuresthes tenuis)* is known to be unique. This particular silverside spawns far up sandy beaches at night during high spring tides. The eggs incubate in the sand well isolated from the water until some future high tide when the young hatch and are carried back into deeper water.

Silversides are extensively preyed on by larger fish as well as by sea birds and in many parts of the world they also represent a valuable human food resource.

BALISTIDAE
Triggerfishes

See pages 124 to 126 for species descriptions

In all there are about 60 species in this tropical family of which 19 have been recorded from southern African waters.

The most obvious identifying characteristic of triggerfishes is the conspicuous and 'trigger-like' first dorsal spine which can be locked into an upright position by the small second spine. This device is used in defence and also to lodge themselves firmly into rock crevices when threatened. The closely related filefishes are very similar in appearance except that the 'trigger' spine is situated directly above the eye. Pelvic fins are either absent or reduced to a single, feeble spine. The eyes can be rotated independently and this wide-ranging vision enables these fishes to keep a sharp lookout for food as well as for danger.

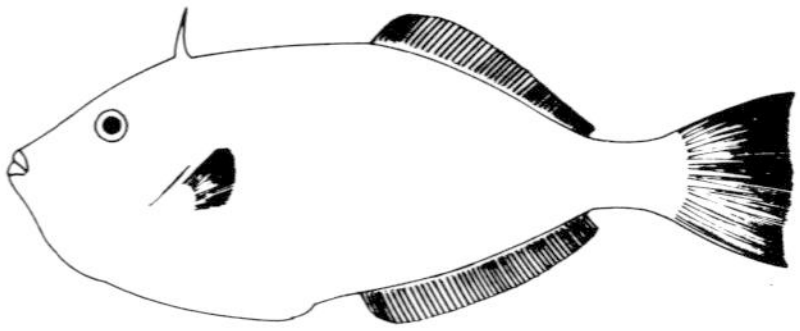

These carnivorous, but also partly herbivorous, fishes occur only in tropical seas and many are especially abundant around reefs where they have been known to cause damage to pearl-oyster beds with their strong crushing teeth. Some species are carriers of ciguatera poison.

BELONIDAE
Needlefishes and garfishes

See pages 127 and 128 for species descriptions

Of the 32 species that occur worldwide, at least four frequent the subtropical and temperate regions of southern Africa's coastal waters. Most needlefishes are marine, but a few freshwater species are known from South America.

Fish in this family can be recognized by their very slender, elongate bodies and large, extended mouths armed with numerous, sharply pointed teeth. The dorsal and anal fins are situated far back and detached finlets are absent.

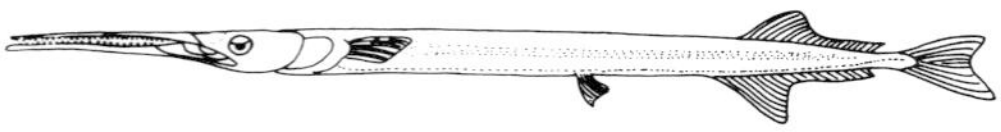

As their streamlined shape would suggest, needlefishes are very fast swimmers. They often break from the water and skitter along the surface, their dorsal, anal and caudal fins sculling rapidly. Occasionally, they even leave the water and dart through the air for short distances. This habit, and the fact that they are attracted by light, makes them a potential hazard to boat fishermen at night. The eggs produced by the females are quite large and have sticky filaments by means of which they attach to floating objects at sea. The very small young of some species resemble twigs floating motionless on the surface.

Despite their green bones and, occasionally, green flesh, needlefishes make excellent eating.

BLENNIIDAE
Blennies

See page 129 for species description

Blenniidae comprise at least 300 species, widely distributed throughout the tropical and subtropical seas. Forty-two species occur along southern African shores, with most being confined to the intertidal zone.

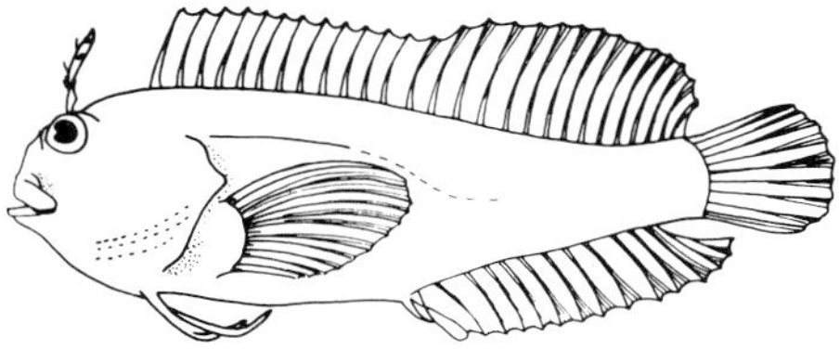

These small, elongate fishes are scaleless, have a blunt, rounded head with prominent eyes, a long dorsal fin with fewer spines than rays, well-developed pectoral fins, short fleshy pelvics and a small mouth with close-set, comb-like teeth. Male blennies may have spongy genital tissue around the cloaca and tentacles above the eyes.

Blennies are rather similar to gobies in looks and habits and, like them, can spend considerable periods out of the water. This is made possible by the ability to store oxygenated water in the gill chamber and to absorb oxygen directly through their mucus-covered bodies. The stout, limb-like pelvic fins are used for 'skipping' short distances over muddy flats. Blennies are endlessly fascinating and many have developed particular living and defence strategies. One species, for example, resembles and mimics the harmless cleaner wrasse, but instead of removing ectoparasites from larger fish as the wrasse does, the blenny takes the opportunity of a quick bite of fin or flesh. Other blennies have poisonous bites and if swallowed by larger fish, these blennies will sink their teeth into the stomach wall of the predator. The result is instant – the toxin causes an immediate spasm of the gut and the blenny is regurgitated.

BOTHIDAE
Left-eye flounders

See page 130 for species description

Of the six families of flatfish described by science, the Bothidae, with 230 members, is the largest. In the southern African region 20 species of this strictly marine family have been recorded, some from temperate West and South Coast waters and others off the more tropical East Coast.

Most flatfish resemble one another superficially in colour, shape and habits, but left-eye flounders do exhibit a few fairly obvious and distinctive features which, if taken together, eliminate confusion. Both eyes occur on the left side of the body, the hind margin of the pre-operculum is entirely free and exposed, the mouth is symmetrical, the dorsal fin originates directly above the eyes, and the pelvic fins are spineless.

Most left-eye flounders are rather small and, despite the excellent flavour of their flesh, only very

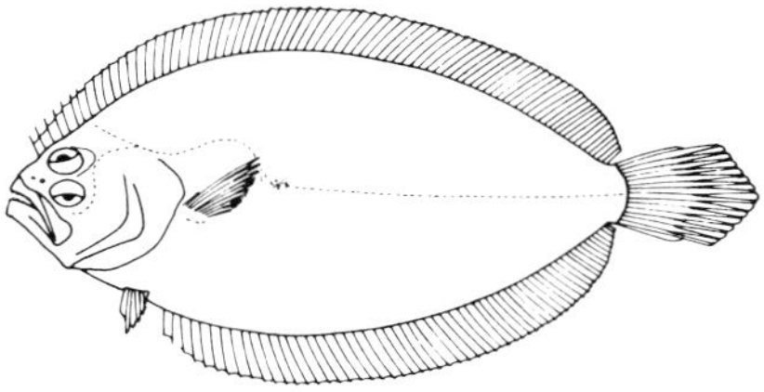

few are of commercial food value. The right-eye flounders (family Pleuronectidae) are, however, much larger and are of great commercial importance, especially to the fishing industries of northern Europe. The giant halibut which can reach a length of 300 cm, is a member of this closely related family.

CAESIONIDAE
Fusiliers

See page 131 for species description

This tropically distributed family comprises some 20 species and is very closely related to the snappers, but may be distinguished by having protrusible upper jaws and maxillae that are clearly exposed. Fusiliers have small, elongate

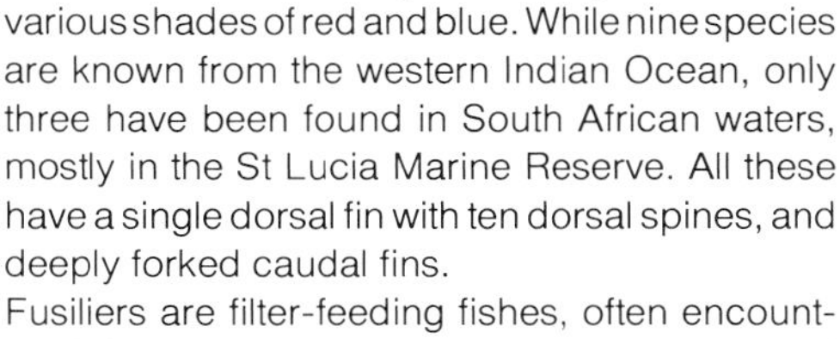

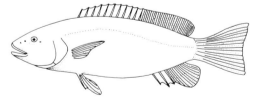

bodies and are usually beautifully coloured in various shades of red and blue. While nine species are known from the western Indian Ocean, only three have been found in South African waters, mostly in the St Lucia Marine Reserve. All these have a single dorsal fin with ten dorsal spines, and deeply forked caudal fins.

Fusiliers are filter-feeding fishes, often encountered in the water column directly over coral reefs.

CARANGIDAE

Kingfishes, yellowtails, pompanos, queenfishes, garrick and rainbow runner

See pages 132 to 161 for species descriptions

More than 140 species of Carangidae inhabit tropical and temperate waters throughout the world and of this large family, approximately 50 members occur off the southern African coast.

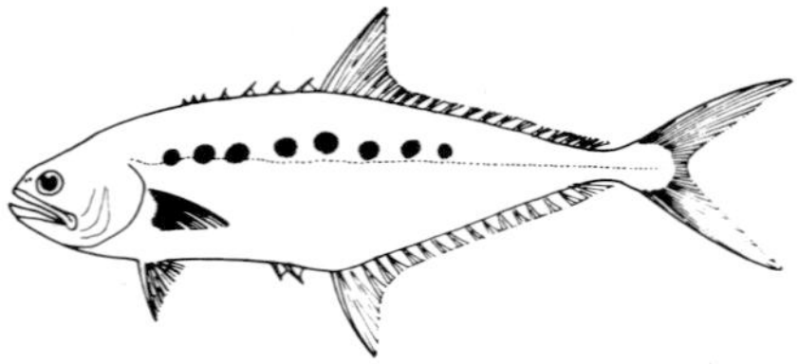

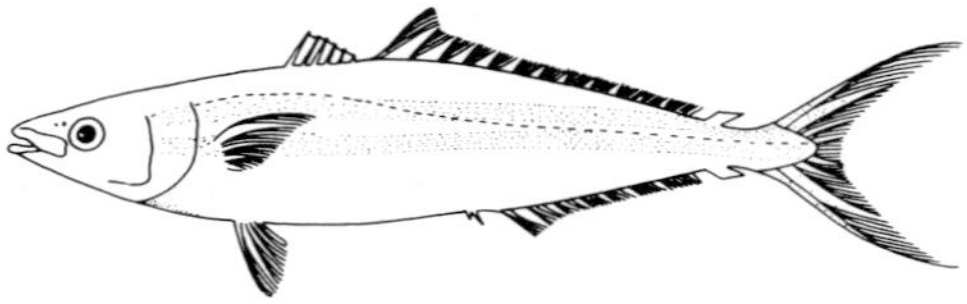

There are no freshwater species and though the juveniles of some frequent estuaries, few adults are known to venture into such low-salinity areas. Shape, colour and size vary greatly within the family, from the large, robust kingfishes to the more elongate and mackerel-shaped queenfishes. Most Carangidae have an iridescent sheen, but this too can range from the silvered appearance of the mirrorfishes to the metallic blues, greens and gold of the rainbow runner.

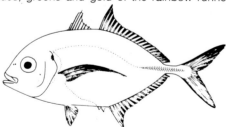

Despite these differences, however, Carangidae exhibit a number of anatomical features which aid their identification. The scales are small and cycloid and, depending on the species, may be absent on the breast. Along the posterior half of the lateral line, a row of scales is often enlarged into scutes which form a keel along both sides of the body. The lateral line itself is distinct and curves markedly around the pectoral fins. The caudal fin is deeply forked and its peduncle slender. There are two detached spines in front of the anal fin.

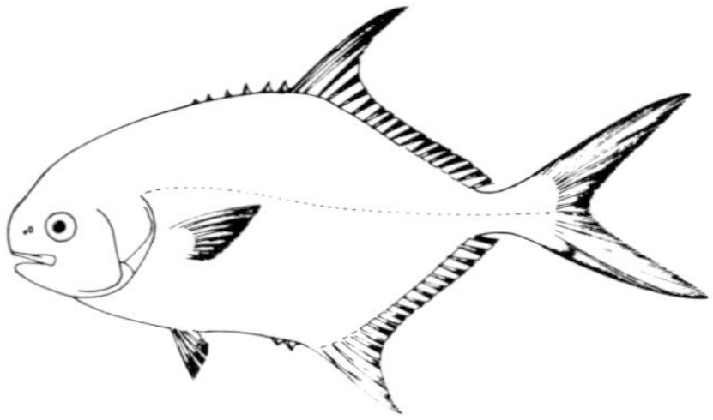

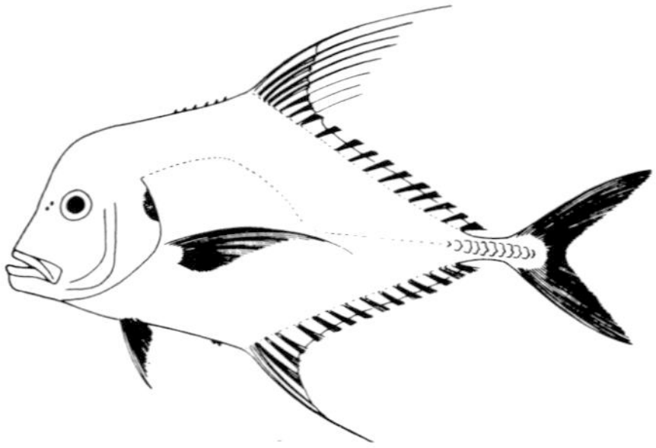

These swift predators generally spawn offshore, and many produce young that are typically banded, possibly as an aid to camouflage when sheltering below jellyfish or other floating objects. Many species are of commercial importance and most are also of great sport-fishing value.

CENTRISCIDAE

Razorfishes and shrimpfishes

See page 162 for species description

Only four species make up this family, all of which are confined to the tropical and subtropical waters of the Indo-Pacific. A single representative of these most curious fishes occurs in southern African waters.

Razorfishes are extremely compressed and the deep body is very elongate and almost entirely encased in bony plates. The small, non-protrusible mouth is located at the end of a tube-like snout. The gill structure differs from that of most other fish as the gill membrane is lobe-shaped rather than filamentous. Unusual as the razorfishes' anatomy is, it is the mode of swimming that is most remarkable, as they almost always swim in a vertical position with the head pointing downwards. The fins and their arrangement have developed accordingly, with the first dorsal spine which is sharp, jointed and movable,

projecting from the 'tail', and the soft dorsal, anal and caudal fins all occuring ventrally.
Centriscidae adapt well to a tank environment and their strange 'life style' understandably makes them very popular with aquarists.

CHAETODONTIDAE
Butterflyfishes

See pages 163 to 175 for species descriptions

There are about 120 species in this colourful family, most of which live in the Indo-Pacific region. At least 24 species occur off the shores of southern Africa, especially around the coral reefs of northern Zululand.

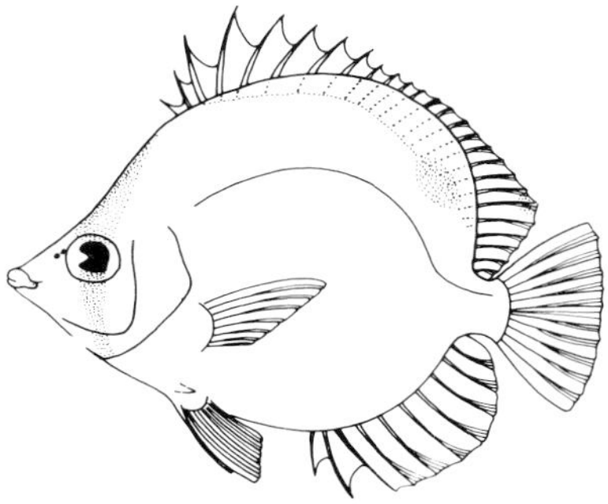

All butterflyfishes have very compressed, disc-shaped bodies covered with small ctenoid scales. The mouth is small, protractile, and set with comb-like teeth, a feeding mechanism which is well suited to retrieving minute animals and plant matter deep within holes and recesses in the reef. In some species the mouth has become specialized to the extent that the entire snout is extended into a tube-like proboscis. The single dorsal and anal fins are densely scaled and often vertically extended, a feature which tends to exaggerate the body depth. Sometimes a dorsal spine or ray forms a long, trailing filament.
Adult Chaetodontidae tend to be herbivorous and live in pairs, while juveniles are usually solitary and occasionally take to pecking external parasites from the bodies of other fishes.
The body colours and patterns are widely varied and often spectacular. Most, however, are variations on spots and crossbands, and it would seem that the body markings displayed by this family have all evolved from a completely barred pattern, with some bars having been lost and only remnants of others remaining as dots. The precise function of these patterns is not clear, but in most cases, especially where larger 'eyespots' are present, these may serve to confuse would-be predators.

CHANIDAE
Milkfish

See page 176 for species description

Though the milkfish is the single representative of this family, its distribution is wide and covers most of the marine and estuarine waters of the Indo-Pacific region. It sometimes even enters fresh waters.

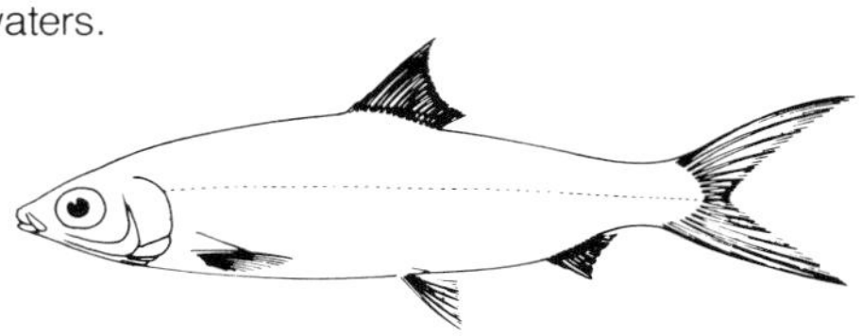

This elongate, silver fish is relatively easy to identify. There is a toothless mouth at the tip of the snout, the eyes are covered with adipose tissue, spines are completely absent, there is a single dorsal fin, and the large pectoral fins each comprise 10-12 rays.
The milkfish is important as a food source in many parts of the world, especially South East Asia. In the Philippines and Indonesia, juvenile milkfish are netted at sea and released in coastal fish-ponds where they feed on plant material until reaching a marketable size.

CHEILODACTYLIDAE
Fingerfins and bank steenbras

See pages 177 and 178 for species descriptions

There are about 17 species in this family world-wide, all are marine and at least some occur in all oceans. Five endemic species are found in southern African waters.

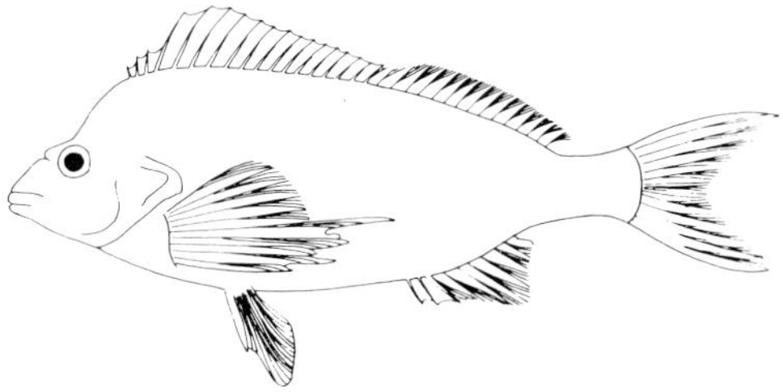

This small family is characterized by enlarged pectoral fins in which 4-7 of the lower rays are separate and fleshy. Though this curious adaptation has been attributed to improving tactile senses, underwater observations confirm that, once extended, these fin rays serve as stabilizing limbs when the fish is 'lying' on the bottom. Each of the species is rather elongate with a small terminal mouth surrounded by fleshy lips. The single dorsal fin has 14-22 spines plus 21-39 rays and the anal fin has 7-19 rays. The palate is toothless.

Fingerfins and bank steenbras, known as morwongs elsewhere in the world, are sluggish, bottom-living species that prefer cooler water. They are generally regarded as good table fish.

CHIROCENTRIDAE
Wolfherrings

See page 179 for species description

Fossil records show that members of this family once reached lengths of 400 cm, but only two species have survived to the present and these seldom reach 100 cm.

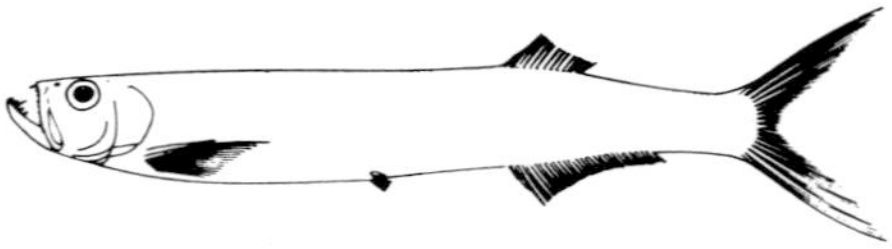

These primitive fishes, believed to be distantly related to the true herrings (Clupeidae), can be easily recognized by the elongate and flattened body, single spineless dorsal fin, deeply forked caudal and enormous, fang-like teeth. The body is covered with minute scales which are easily shed. A vestigial spiral valve, similar to that in sharks, replaces the stomach in the digestive tract.

CIRRHITIDAE
Hawkfishes

See page 180 for species description

Of the some 35 species in this family, most are distributed within the Indo-Pacific region and, owing to their apparent dependence on a coral reef environment, the few representatives in southern African waters are confined to the near-tropical reefs of northern Zululand.

Not a great deal is known about hawkfishes and it is often very difficult to distinguish between species. Sometimes, microscopic examination is needed to identify these differences. These colourful little fishes also resemble scorpionfishes (family Scorpaenidae). Confusion can be avoided, however, as hawkfishes have a single dorsal fin of ten spines plus 11-17 rays often with minute hairy tufts, or cirri, projecting from the membrane which webs the spines. Other characteristics include an anal fin of 5-7 rays, a caudal fin that is never forked and the lack of prominent spines on the head.

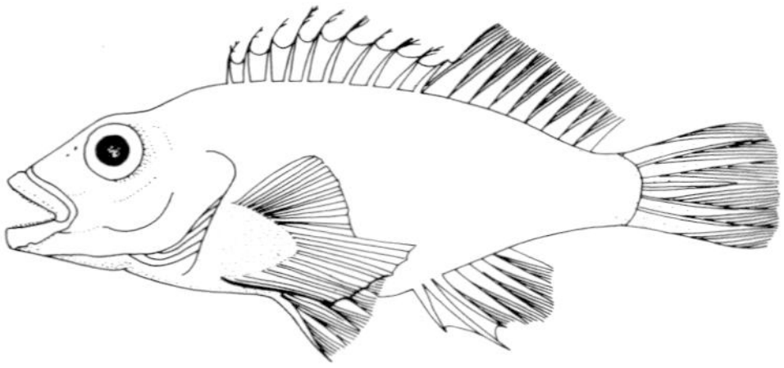

Hawkfishes spend much of their time 'perched' on high vantage-points among the coral heads where they use their stout pectoral fins to stabilize themselves. Periodically, they swim off rather clumsily to forage after small prey they may have detected, but will always return to the same, or some new, lookout.

CLINIDAE
Klipfishes and clinids

See page 181 for species description

The majority of the 175 species in this family frequent the inshore waters of tropical coasts, but the 38 species found in southern Africa favour the more temperate East and South Coast waters.

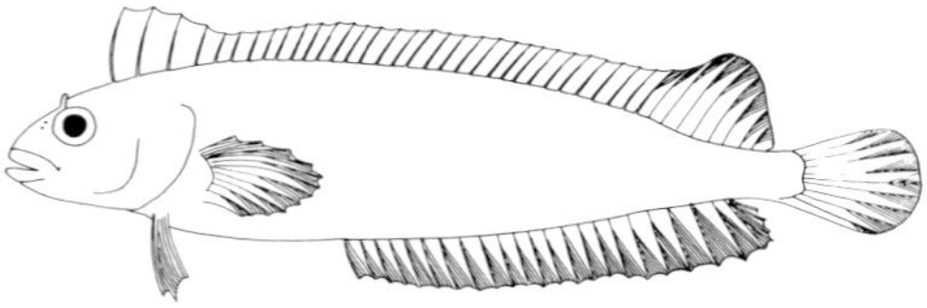

These small, elongate fishes are similar to blennies, but are readily distinguished by the distinct scales that cover the body. Clinidae are further characterized by the long dorsal fin which originates on the head and has more spines than rays. The first three dorsal spines are frequently elevated to form a crest and there may also be tentacles above the eyes. A less obvious, but nevertheless distinctive feature is a fleshy projection from the inner pectoral girdle, only visible if the gill cover is lifted. Unlike the majority of bony fishes, the females of many Clinidae undergo internal fertilization and give birth to live young. Clinids usually frequent kelp beds and stands of eelgrass where their variegated body colours blend well with the surroundings.

CLUPEIDAE
Herrings and sardines

See pages 182 to 185 for species descriptions

Though many close relatives have long been extinct, this primitive family remains prolific with at least 180 species occurring worldwide. There are 13 representatives in southern African waters of which the pilchard is the best known.

Herringfishes have elongate bodies which are round or compressed in cross-section, the mouth is seldom underslung and most species lack a visible lateral line. Thin scales cover the body and are easily shed, except those along the belly which are developed into a sharp, stout and rigid keel. The fins are spineless and there is a single dorsal fin. The gill rakers are long and numerous, a typical feature of filter-feeding fish.

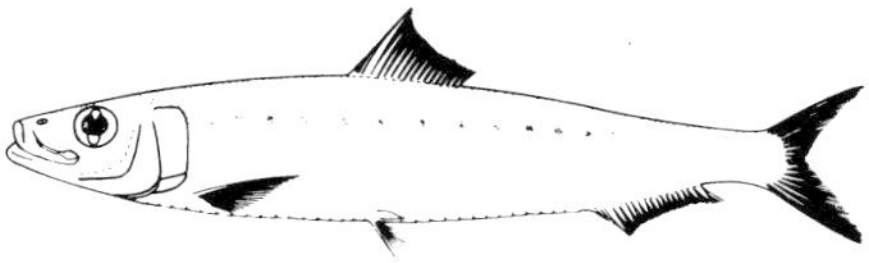

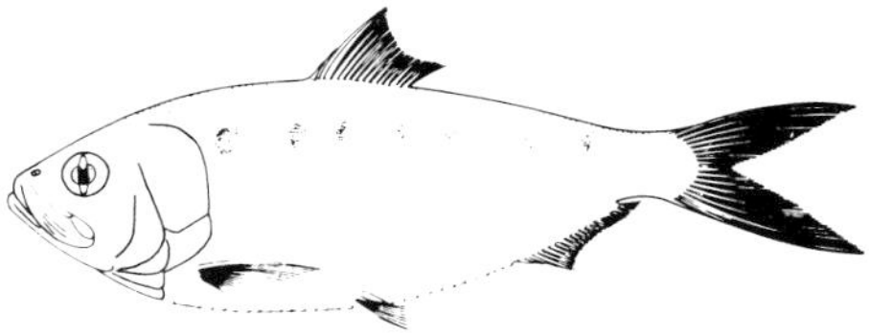

In many parts of the world these fishes gather into vast surface shoals which makes them especially vulnerable to capture. The herring once formed the mainstay of the northern European fishing industry, and the sardine and pilchard have proved equally important in other parts, including South Africa. Without exception, excessive exploitation of these fishes worldwide has led to greatly diminished stocks and most fishing authorities have imposed rigid catch restrictions to allow shoals to recuperate.

CORACINIDAE
Galjoen

See pages 186 and 187 for species descriptions

This family is confined to the coastal waters of Malagasy and southern Africa. Both known species occur locally and are endemic. This, and its great popularity as an angling fish, has led one of these, the Cape galjoen, to be designated as South Africa's national fish.

Galjoen have deep, plump bodies covered with small scales which are not easily shed. The mouth is tiny and set with curved incisors, but lacks strong molars. The rays of both the soft dorsal and anal fins are distinctly longer in front, but taper sharply towards the tail.

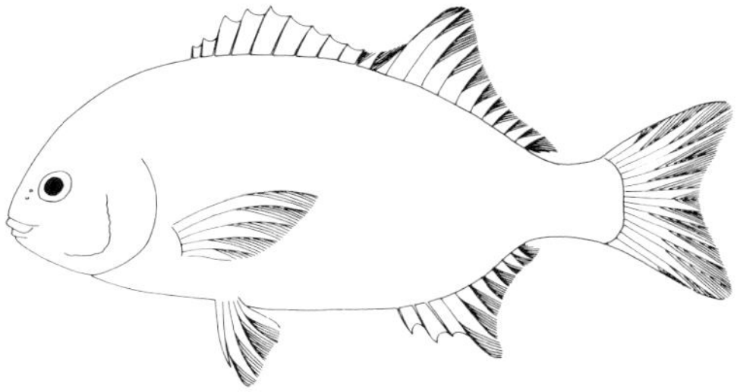

All galjoen prefer the turbulent inshore waters of rocky shorelines and can sometimes even be seen in 'white water' as it surges over the rocks. They are primarily resident fishes and are mostly confined to those inshore regions that suit their mode of life. This has made them vulnerable to over-fishing and it is hoped that the creation of marine reserves along the coast will do much to restore the former abundance of these fish.

CORYPHAENIDAE
Dolphinfishes

See page 188 for species description

There are only two species of dolphinfish, both occurring in tropical and subtropical waters worldwide. Only one has been recorded off the southern African coast.

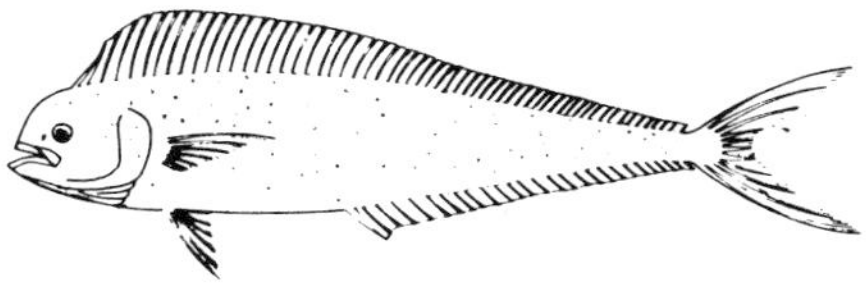

Coryphaenidae are easily recognized by their long, spineless dorsal fins which originate on the head and extend to the caudal peduncle; their deeply forked caudal fins; and their steep, almost vertical head profiles. The most striking feature of these beautiful fishes is, however, the iridescent colour scheme displayed by live specimens.

These agile predators live in open water, but are usually found near floating objects where they feed on small fish sheltering beneath. Spawning occurs in small groups of two or more individuals and the breeding season appears to be prolonged. Dolphinfishes make good eating. They also provide offshore anglers with superb sport, for they are amongst the fastest swimmers in the world, capable of reaching 80 km/h in short dashes.

CYNOGLOSSIDAE
Tonguesoles

See page 189 for species description

About 100 species of tonguesole are distributed

throughout the world, but mainly in tropical regions where they frequent both marine and freshwater environments. Thirteen species occur in the coastal waters of southern Africa.

There should be little difficulty in identifying the members of this family. Like all soles they are asymmetrical and extremely flattened, but the tongue-shaped body of Cynoglossidae is most characteristic. They are further typified by having both eyes on the left side of the body; the pre-operculum hidden beneath the skin; long dorsal and anal fins, both continuous with the caudal fin; the complete absence of pectoral fins; and only one pelvic fin, which is located on the 'eyed' side of the body. Fine teeth occur on the jaws of the asymmetrical mouth. One or more lateral lines are usually distinctly visible.

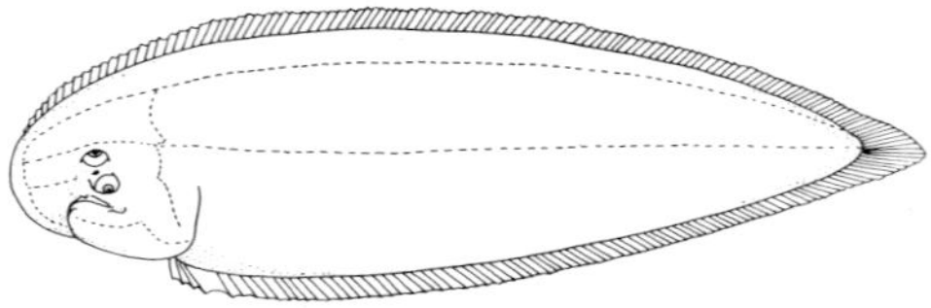

Like all flatfish, Cynoglossidae are sluggish and confined to the sea-bed where their muddy-brown and often mottled colours, together with the habit of virtually burying themselves below the sand, make them most inconspicuous.

Tonguesoles do not grow very large and though most make excellent eating; few species are of commercial value.

DINOPERCIDAE
Cavebass

See page 190 for species description

This small family of only two or three species was, until recently, considered part of the rockcod

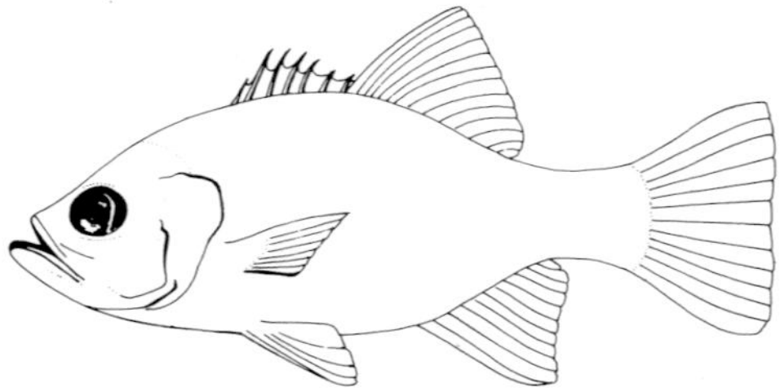

family. However, an anal fin ray count in excess of ten and small scales that extend up to median fins should serve to distinguish these two families. Cavebass have high dorsal and anal fins and a noticeably large eye that facilitates low-light vision in the caves they inhabit. While this family is nowhere abundant, they are nevertheless a popular food fish.

DREPANIDAE
Sicklefishes or concertinafishes

See page 191 for species description

Sicklefishes have deep, strongly compressed bodies with small but highly protusible mouths that point downwards. The fins are well developed, especially the pectoral which is typically sickle-shaped. The body is densely covered in cycloid scales, a feature that distinguishes this family from the closely related Ephippidae.

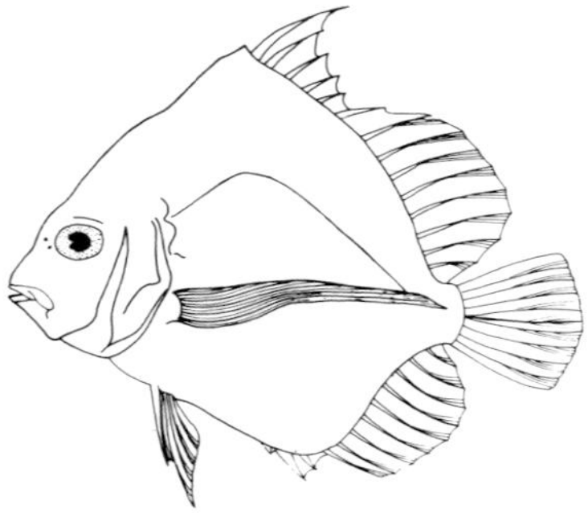

Only two or three species are considered to belong to the Drepanidae, all of Indo-Pacific distribution and exceedingly similar in appearance. Sicklefishes may occur in shoals, feed on animals that burrow in muddy bottoms and represent a moderate food resource in some regions.

ECHENEIDAE
Suckerfishes or remoras

See page 192 for species description

Suckerfish are distributed throughout the oceans of the world and of the seven or eight species in the family, six frequent southern African waters.

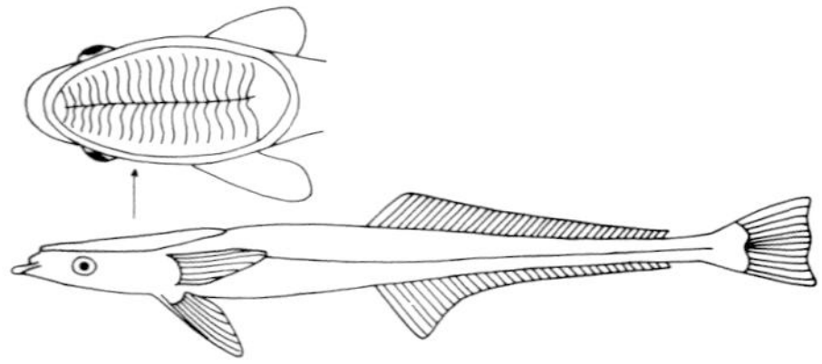

All Echeneidae have their dorsal spines modified to form a powerful sucking disc and this feature alone makes them quite distinct from any other group of fishes. The inside of the sucker reveals

chevron-like grooves or laminae, their number being characteristic and a good basis for the identification of individual species. Remoras use the disk to adhere firmly to large fish and in this way 'hitchhike' from one feeding ground to the next.
Echeneidae associate in this manner with a number of marine animals including sharks, rays, turtles, whales, dolphins and large bony fish, the type of 'host' normally being specific to particular suckerfish species.
Remoras vary greatly in size and while some attain a length of 100 cm, others do not exceed 17 cm. Certain of these smaller species have adapted to life inside the gill covers of large marlin and, being confined to this dark environment, have virtually lost all skin pigmentation.

ELOPIDAE
Springers

See page 193 for species description

Most of the fishes closely related to the Elopidae have long since been extinct and only a single genus with about five species exists today, all of which are confined to tropical and subtropical regions. One representative occurs in southern African waters.

Springers are slender fish and their spineless fins include a single soft dorsal and deeply forked caudal. Numerous cycloid scales cover the body. The terminal mouth has finely-toothed jaws. Some 27-35 bony rays support the lower margin of the gill covers. Elopidae are primitive fish and exhibit a number of primordial features including a reduced heart, a simple lateral line, spineless fins and juveniles that resemble eel larvae or *leptocephali.* Springers are fierce predators and will frequently enter brackish and even fresh water to feed.

ENGRAULIDAE
Anchovies

See pages 194 and 195 for species descriptions

This family of 110 or more species worldwide is primarily marine, but does also include a few freshwater representatives. There are at least six species of Engraulidae in southern African waters.
These small fishes can be immediately recognized by the prominent snout and underslung mouth. All have elongate bodies but, depending on the species, they may either be compressed or nearly round in cross-section. Most, however, taper to a slender tail and have an underside that is invariably edged with a row of sharp scutes which form a ventral keel. Thin cycloid scales cover the body, and these are easily shed. Though the fins are spineless, a single sharp scute may precede the small dorsal fin positioned at the midpoint of the back. No lateral line is visible, but many species have a distinctly bright, silver band along each flank. Very fine teeth may occur in the jaws. The gill arches have numerous elongate rakers.

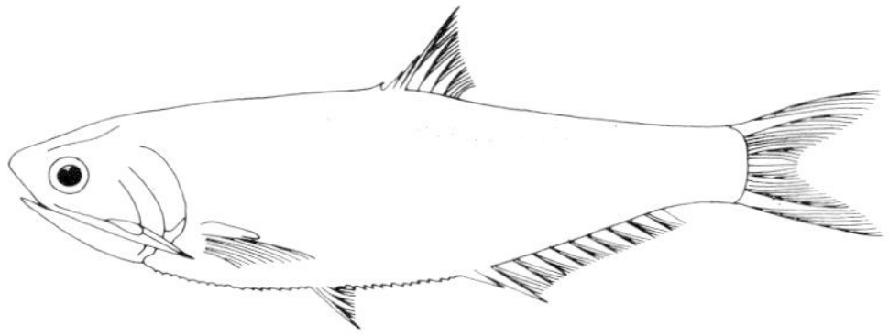

Most anchovy species prefer regions where nutrient upwelling creates a great abundance of food. As a result, immense shoals may congregate during certain seasons and these concentrations of fish are often of great commercial value, especially as the catch is suitable for both fresh consumption and for processing into other products. Throughout the world, heavy, and often uncontrolled, exploitation has often led to drastically diminished levels of abundance.

EPHIPPIDAE
Spadefishes and batfishes

See pages 196 and 197 for species descriptions

Members of this family are distributed throughout tropical and subtropical regions. Both types that frequent the East Coast waters of southern Africa are described in this book. Some biologists include the concertinafishes in this family, as they are unquestionably very closely related.
Ephippidae have deep, almost circular bodies and in some species, notably the batfishes, the dorsal and anal fins are very enlarged and greatly exaggerate the appearance of depth. Other characteristics include a small terminal mouth, three spines in the anal fin, the presence of pelvic fins and, in most cases, a distinct break between the spines and rays comprising the dorsal fin.
Adults are often rather drab, but the young, which usually shelter amongst aquatic vegetation or

below floating objects at sea, often have more contrasting colours with vertically barred patterns which probably provide an effective camouflage.

GEMPYLIDAE
Snoek
See page 198 for species description

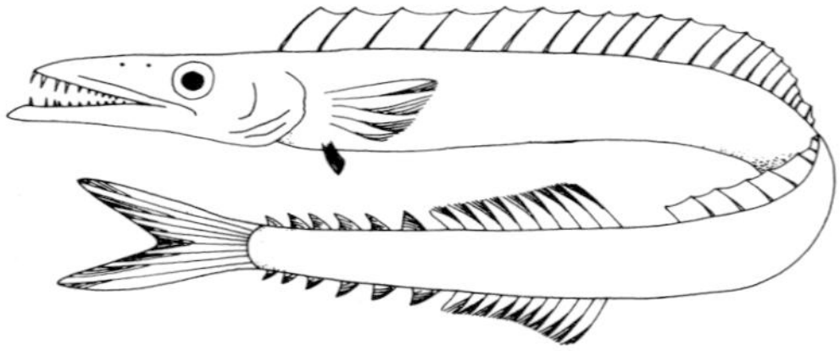

This widely distributed family includes some 20 species, five of which occur in southern African waters. Also known as snake mackerels, these powerful, fast-swimming fishes range over vast stretches of ocean, often at considerable depths. All snoek are elongate and streamlined and have an extremely long dorsal fin made up of spines and rays which often also include detached finlets. The caudal fin is forked, but lacks the lateral keels of the peduncle, common to the true mackerels (family Scombridae). Pectoral fins are located low on the body and the pelvics are either reduced or absent. The large mouth has many sharp, fang-like teeth and both the upper and lower, jutting, jaws are concealed by the preorbital bone.
Gempylidae are voracious predators which hunt in large packs, and during their feeding frenzies large numbers may be caught, usually by commercial boat fishermen using handlines.

GERREIDAE
Pursemouths
See pages 199 and 200 for species descriptions
These small to medium-sized, silvery fishes occur in all shallow, warm seas, often in brackish water. Of the 40 species described, six occur in southern African waters.
Pursemouths are distinguished by the protractile mouth which, when 'pursed', extends downwards into a tube through which small food particles are sucked up. Well-defined scales occur on both head and body and fins include a long single dorsal with spines and rays, long pointed pectorals and a forked caudal. In all species the preoperculum is not serrated.

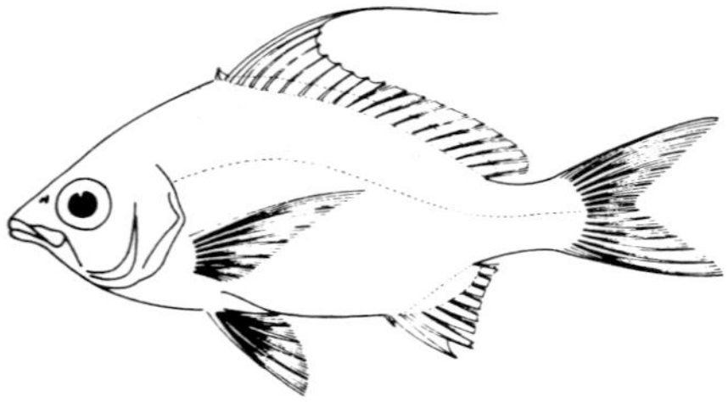

Known elsewhere as majorras these fish are frequently used as bait for larger fish, but in tropical regions they are often of considerable importance as a food source for humans.

GOBIIDAE
Gobies
See pages 201 and 202 for species descriptions
Gobies occur mostly in tropical and subtropical regions and constitute the largest single family of marine fishes. In all, there are about 1600 species of which 107 occur in local waters. Some species also frequent fresh water and on several oceanic islands gobies are the most abundant freshwater species.

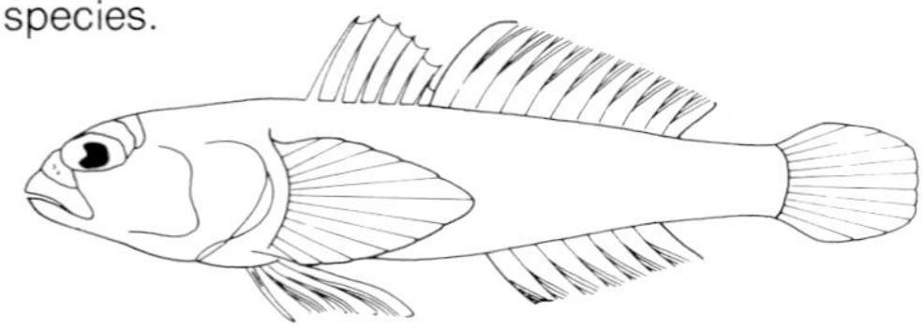

Most gobies are small, only one species attains 50 cm in length. One tiny stream dweller from the Philippines, *Pandaka pygmaea,* measures only 12 mm when fully grown and reaches sexual maturity at a mere 6 mm. All Gobiidae have elongate bodies with a bluntly rounded head. The pelvic fins are particularly well developed and are fused to form a sucking disc. The dorsal fin is usually in two parts, the first of 2-8 spines and the second comprising rays only.
Together with the blennies and clinids, these carnivorous fishes form the largest component of

small fish fauna on most reefs. Some live in close association with shrimps, sponges and sea urchins, while others can live out of water for extended periods because of their ability to absorb oxygen directly from air and to store oxygenated water in the gill chamber.

GRAMMISTIDAE
Striped rockcods or soapfishes
See page 203 for species description
Grammistidae are found in all oceans and of the 18 species known, four occur in southern African waters. Few members of this reef-dwelling family exceed 25 cm.

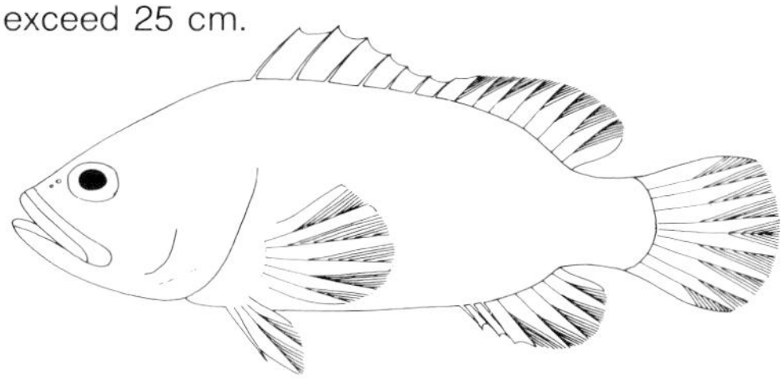

These fishes were once thought to be part of the true rockcod family (Serranidae) and they continue to be known by the same common name. Despite the close similarity, however, Grammistidae can be distinguished by their fewer dorsal spines (usually less than nine) a greater distinction between the spinous dorsal and soft dorsal fins, and pelvic fins that are located just before the level of the pectoral fins. Some species lack anal spines.
The skin of all species exudes a thick mucus that forms a soapy substance containing a toxin called grammistin. The ability to produce this poison when under attack from a predator or when handled, undoubtedly forms an effective defence mechanism. It certainly renders their flesh inedible to humans.

HAEMULIDAE
Grunters and rubberlips
See pages 204 to 215 for species descriptions
This large family is mainly marine, with some species entering brackish regions and a few inhabiting fresh water. Of the 120 species described, representatives occur in all oceans, especially in the tropics. A total of 19 species has been recorded in southern African waters, some in considerable abundance.
Though the perch-like Haemulidae superficially resemble several other families, they have a number of distinctive characteristics. Scales cover the head except for the snout, lips and chin. Two or more pores are located on the chin. When the mouth is closed, the tip of the upper jaw is concealed. The fins are exceptionally spiny (the second anal spine is particularly stout) and the single dorsal fin has 9-15 spines plus 12-26 rays. Teeth are mostly small, arranged in bands, and are never enlarged into canines. There are no teeth on the roof of the mouth. The edge of the pre-operculum is sharply serrated.

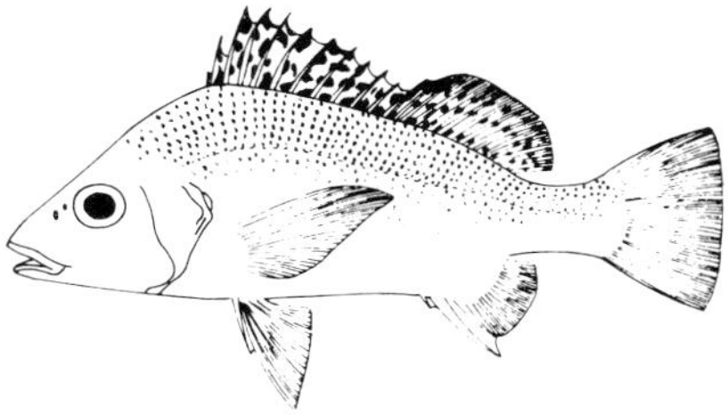

Grunters are perhaps most easily distinguished from rubberlips by the noisy grunting sound they emit after capture. Rubberlips on the other hand, are a little more robust and, as their common name suggests, they have noticeably thick lips. All Haemulidae are very palatable and are important food fishes.

HEMIRAMPHIDAE
Halfbeaks
See page 216 for species description
This is a large family with well over 80 recorded species occurring throughout the oceans of the world, and also from freshwater areas. Some 13 species have been recorded from southern African waters, eight of which are halfbeaks.

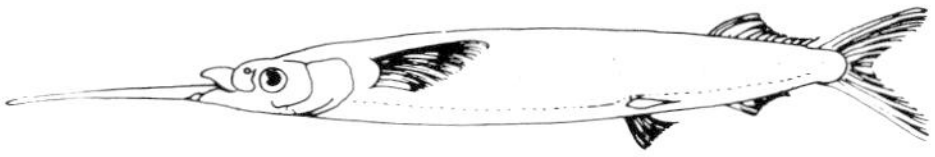

The jaws of halfbeaks are most distinctive, as the lower jaw is greatly extended beyond the upper. Halfbeaks are vegetarian fishes and this highly specialized feeding mechanism enables them to manoeuvre long, filamentous plant matter until it lies the length of the lower beak. It is then systematically drawn into the mouth, chewed and swallowed in a single 'conveyor-belt' operation.
Flyingfishes are closely related to halfbeaks, and similar in colour, shape and size, but lack the beak of their close relatives. Whereas the halfbeaks have short pectoral and pelvic fins, in flyingfishes

these are very enlarged to form wings which enable these fishes to burst from the surface in brief 'flights'. In a series of rapidly succeeding glides these fishes can cover almost a kilometre, undoubtedly a very useful ability when escaping from predators.

All Hemiramphidae are covered with large, silvery, cycloid scales, the mouth is small and has very fine teeth, there are no detached finlets and the lower lobe of the caudal fin is usually larger than the upper.

Most species are oviparous and the females lay large, sticky eggs which adhere to aquatic vegetation. There is, however, one freshwater halfbeak in which fertilization is internal and live young are produced.

Hemiramphidae are strictly surface fishes, and an important food source for gamefish.

HOLOCENTRIDAE
Soldierfishes and squirrelfishes

See pages 217 and 218 for species descriptions

Some 70 species occur throughout tropical waters, at least 13 of which are found off the southern African coast. While most fishes in the order Beryciformes are deep-sea dwellers, the Holocentridae range between the shoreline and a depth of 100 m, where they are usually found close to the sea-bed.

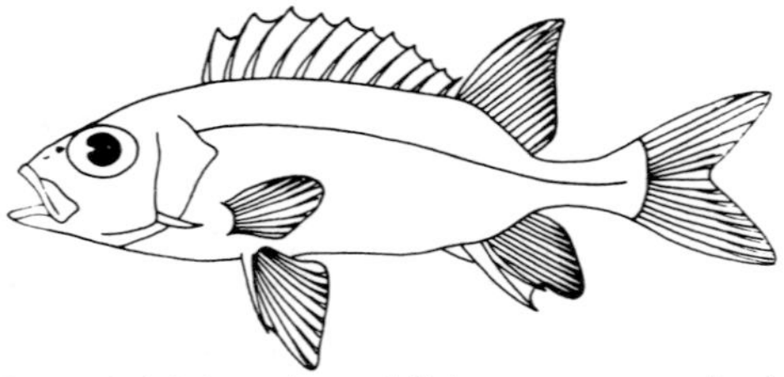

These brightly coloured fishes are exceedingly spiny, and rough to the touch. The body is covered with ctenoid scales and the gill covers and the pre-operculum are strongly serrated. On either side of the body there is also a distinctive, large and poisonous spine projecting backwards from the gill cover. Each of the pelvic fins has a large spine, and the second anal spine is particularly sturdy and sharp. The rays of both the dorsal and anal fins are usually longer than the spines preceding them.

Soldierfishes spend much of the day hidden in caves and crevices in reefs, but at night they become more active when they forage for food. Holocentridae are called squirrelfish in some parts of the world; an apt name, not only in terms of their reddish colour and relatively large eyes, but also their wary habits and the fact that they live in holes. Notwithstanding the prominent spines, these fishes make fair eating.

ISTIOPHORIDAE
Billfishes

See pages 219 to 222 for species descriptions

This family of truly spectacular, oceanic gamefishes includes about ten species which are cosmopolitan in tropical regions. Seven billfish species have been recorded from southern African waters.

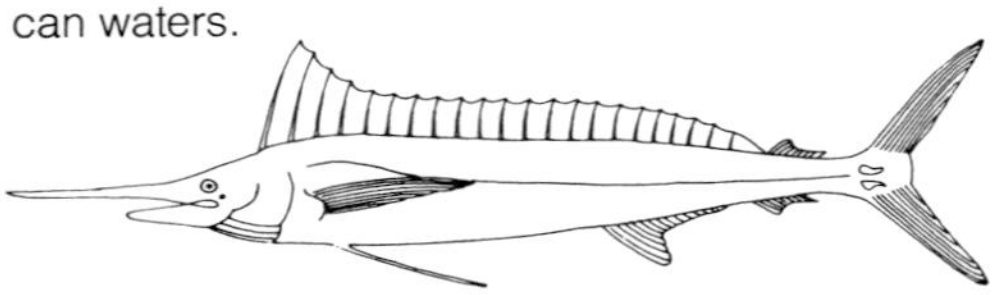

Many of these fishes are large and robust, but without exception they are beautifully streamlined. Their most obvious characteristic is the upper jaw which is greatly elongate, sharply pointed and used to slash at prey. The dorsal fin is very tall and often extends along the greater part of the back. When the fish is swimming at speed the fin folds back into a groove to further improve the hydrodynamics of the body. Other features include thin, elongate pelvic fins, double anal fins and two keels on either side of the caudal peduncle. Thin, lance-like scales cover the body, but are well embedded in the skin. Billfishes should not be confused with the swordfish (family Xiphiidae) which lacks pelvic fins, has a short dorsal fin base and a single keel on each side of the peduncle. These wide-ranging pelagic predators are noted for their strength, speed and endurance and have provided many deep-sea game-fishermen with titanic struggles. Besides being the subject of many 'fishing stories' billfishes are also highly prized as a source of food.

KUHLIIDAE
Flagtails

See page 223 for species description

Kuhliidae comprise a small family of about 12 species which are found in marine and fresh waters throughout the Indo-Pacific. Two species occur off the southern African coast, both of which have compressed, silvery bodies which are noticeably deep in front, and covered with large ctenoid scales. The fins are well developed and spiny, while two further spines occur on each operculum. Both the dorsal and anal fins fold back into sheaths.

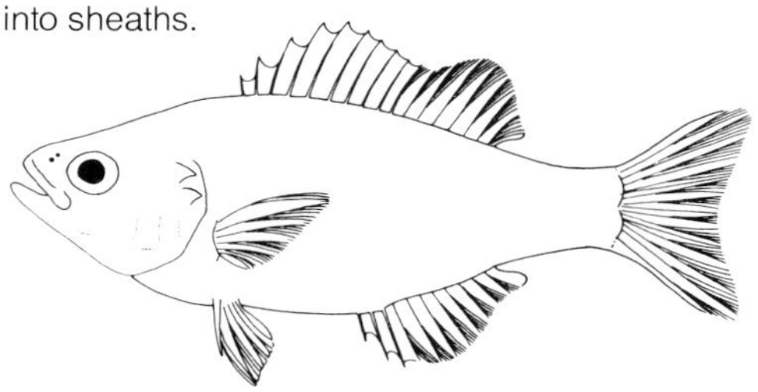

Flagtails are confined to shallow reefs and tidal pools and though edible, most are too small for human consumption. Kuhliidae are related to the North American freshwater sunfishes (family Centrarchidae) which include the black basses so highly regarded by inland anglers.

KYPHOSIDAE
Chubs

See page 224 for species description

Kyphosidae comprise 31 species of which three occur in southern African waters. These plump fishes are exclusively marine, mostly tropical, and representatives occur in all oceans.

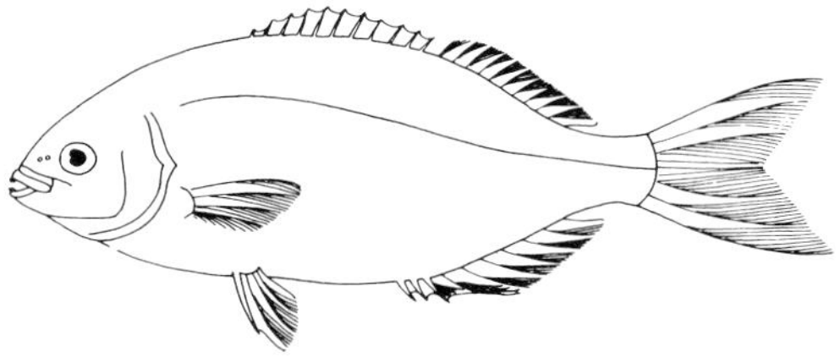

Fine ctenoid scales cover the body. The mouth is small and each jaw is set with a single row of long incisors. In many species the teeth are loosely attached and movable. These fishes do not have molar teeth, but on the palate and tongue, fine, villiform teeth occur which are used to rasp away vegetable matter.

Algae-covered reefs and rocky headlands are the favoured haunts of the herbivorous chubs. Though edible, most are not esteemed as food fish.

LABRIDAE
Wrasses

See pages 225 to 233 for species descriptions

This very large family is one of the most diversified of all fish groups, with species ranging in size from a few centimetres to three metres. The majority of wrasses frequent tropical and subtropical regions and of the 400 species described about 68 have been recorded from southern African waters.

Wrasses are elongate, slightly compressed fish and most are beautifully coloured. They have moderately protractile mouths with distinct and often projecting teeth which gives them a characteristic profile. Further back within the gullet are grinding plates for crushing hard-shelled prey.

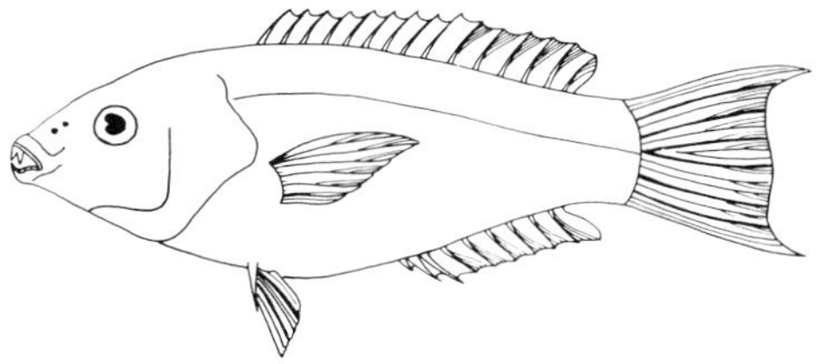

Cycloid scales cover the body and the lateral line is frequently interrupted or abruptly down-turned. Wrasses are particularly active during daylight while at night many 'sleep' in sheltered nooks and crannies along the reef. Reproduction is complex and frequently involves sex reversal, associated with striking changes in colour and pattern. This has created many taxonomic problems. Juveniles are usually very different to larger fish, which in turn pass through a primary (immature and adolescent) phase to a terminal (sexually mature) phase. The terminal males are larger and more strikingly coloured than the other phases.

Several of the larger species are fine angling fish and their flesh generally is wholesome. There have, however, been reports of ciguatera poisoning from these fishes in some tropical regions.

LEIOGNATHIDAE
Slimies and soapies

See pages 234 to 236 for species descriptions

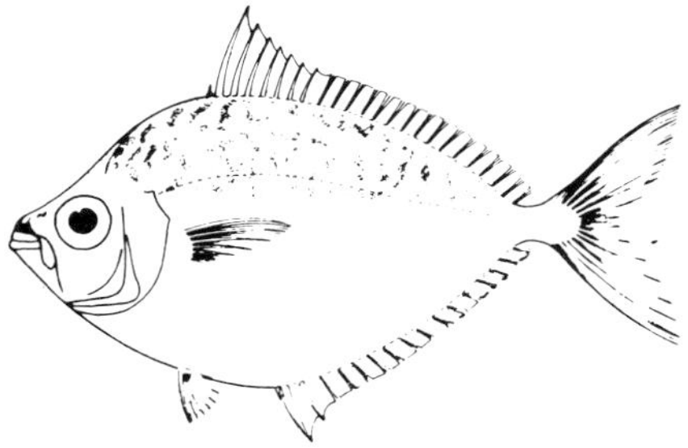

These curious fishes are mainly tropical and confined to marine and brackish waters in the Indo-Pacific region. One species, however, has successfully populated the Mediterranean Sea, obviously using the man-made Suez Canal to extend its distribution from the Red Sea. There are at least 18 species in the family of which five have been recorded from southern African waters.

Leiognathidae are greatly compressed, covered with small, thin scales and, as their common name suggests, they are generally coated with a layer of slimy mucus. The mouth is highly protractile and extends forward into a long tube during feeding. There are bony ridges on top of the head and the spines of the single dorsal fin are somewhat elevated.

These small, shoaling fishes are important as a source of protein in many eastern countries and, because of their abundance, are also probably important as 'fodder' for larger marine predators.

LETHRINIDAE

Emperors, large-eye breams and scavengers

See pages 237 to 240 for species descriptions

This family has a wide Indo-Pacific distribution with most of the 26 species known occurring along the East African coast. One species, however, is found along the Atlantic coastline. The large-eye breams (previously Pentapodidae) are now also considered part of this family.

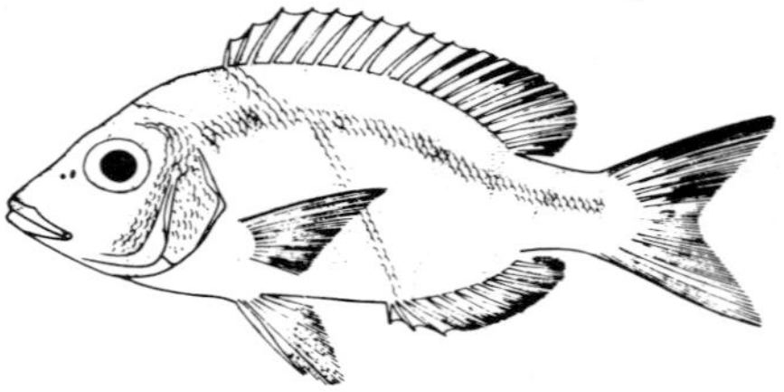

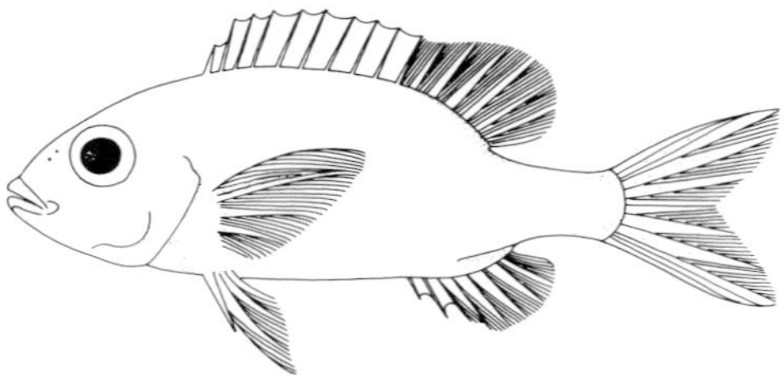

These perch-like fishes have few distinctive anatomical features. They have pointed heads with thick, fleshy lips surrounding the mouth, and the entire snout region is naked. The pre-operculum is not serrated. The dorsal fin is continuous and consists of ten spines plus eight or nine rays, and the caudal fin is usually forked. Emperors are frequently grey or brown in colour and overlaid with a variety of coloured markings. When seen underwater, however, these colours are not conspicuous and they only become apparent after capture, or some other trauma.

Emperors are found near coral and rocky reefs but normally swim in the midwater region above these outcrops. Their excellent flesh makes them an important protein resource, especially in the tropical regions where they are most abundant.

LOBOTIDAE

Tripletail

See page 241 for species description

This one-species family is confined to tropical and subtropical waters. The tripletail *(Lobotes surinamensis)* is famous for its erratic appearances at the mouths of large rivers such as the Amazon in South America, the Ganges in India and, in southern Africa, the Tugela.

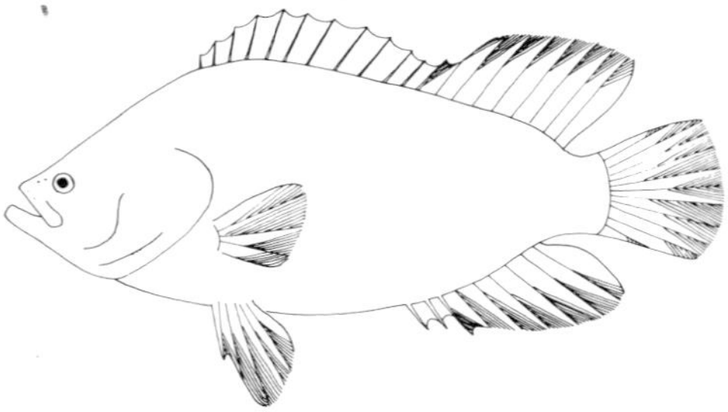

The common name of these deep-bodied, robust fishes derives from their large, rounded dorsal and anal fins which, together with the caudal fin, give the tail region a tri-lobed appearance. Other characteristic features include large, well-developed scales, a serrated pre-operculum and bands of fine teeth in each jaw. There are no teeth on the roof of the mouth.

Juvenile tripletails have developed an effective defence strategy; by drifting sideways with the current they resemble floating leaves and thus often escape the attentions of would-be predators. Though edible, tripletails are never plentiful enough to constitute a regular food source.

LUTJANIDAE

Snappers, kaakap and jobfish

See pages 242 to 252 for species descriptions

The Lutjanidae are a large family of about 100 carnivorous species which are distributed throughout the oceans of the world. They are common in the Pacific Ocean and some species have been artificially introduced to the Hawaiian Islands. There are 24 representatives in southern African waters. All are brightly coloured and vary from yellow, through red, to blue. They also often have blotches, stripes or other patterns.

Members of this perch-like family, with their oblong, compressed bodies, continuous dorsal fins and three anal spines, superficially resemble several other groups of fishes. There are, however, a number of anatomical features which, in conjunction, specifically distinguish this family from others. The upper jaw slips beneath the pre-orbital bone and there are several rows of teeth in the jaws and on the roof of the mouth. Many species may also have an outer pair of large canines, but molars are never present. The front of the head is naked, though several series of scales do occur on the pre-operculum.

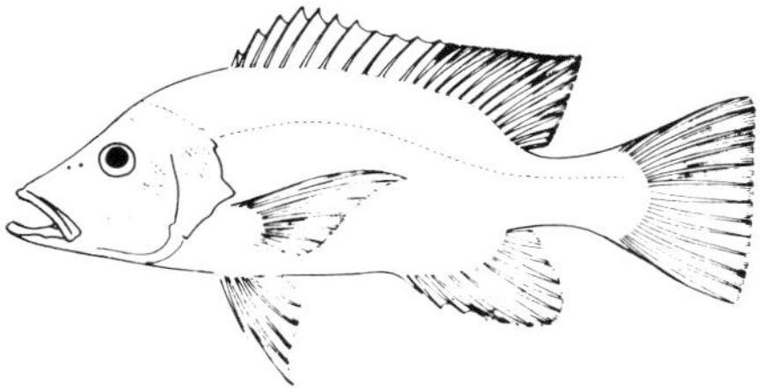

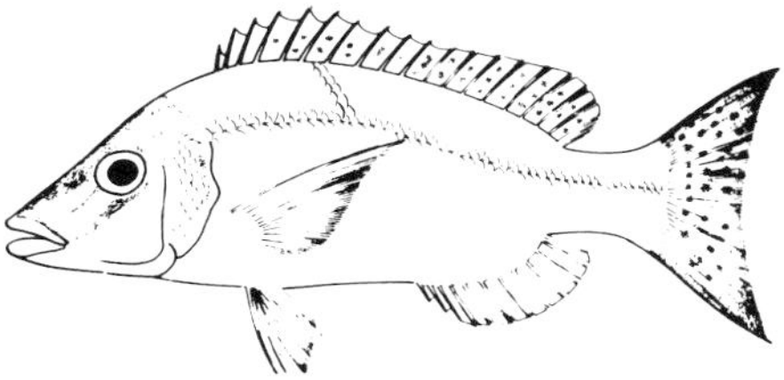

Many snappers are shoaling species and though some enter brackish water, they are primarily marine fish inhabiting shallow reefs where they prey on small fish and crustaceans. The majority of Lutjanidae produce large eggs which are dispersed by ocean currents. The young frequently do not resemble the adults and may undergo several metamorphic changes before adopting mature colouration.

Snappers are highly regarded by sport anglers and most are valuable commercially as food. Under certain environmental conditions, however, and in more tropical regions, these fishes may be responsible for occasional outbreaks of ciguatera poisoning.

MEGALOPIDAE
Tarpons

See page 253 for species description

This primitive family has only two living representatives, one in Atlantic waters and the other in the Indo-Pacific. Whereas *Tarpon atlanticus* attains 220 cm and is one of the world's legendary sport fish, the Indo-Pacific tarpon, whose range includes the East Coast of South Africa, is much smaller and less spectacular.

Tarpons can be recognized by their single, spineless dorsal fin (the last ray of which is filamentous), a slightly upward-facing mouth, large scales and the presence of a lateral line. These silvery fishes superficially resemble herrings in shape, but confusion is unlikely as tarpons never have a sharp keel along the belly.

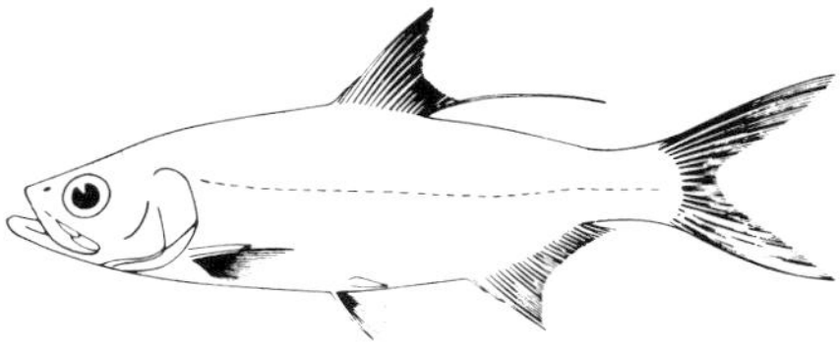

Megalopidae are most common in shallow, coastal and, especially, estuarine waters. They are tolerant of low salinities and some are known to navigate small rivers and streams. In this manner, tarpons frequently make their way to freshwater lakes and lagoons virtually isolated from the sea. These spectacular angling fish are edible and most are eaten fresh, or dried and salted.

MENIDAE
Moonfish

See page 254 for species description

This family consists of a single, widespread Indo-Pacific species. Its range includes the East Coast of southern Africa where it frequents deeper waters, usually near coral reefs.

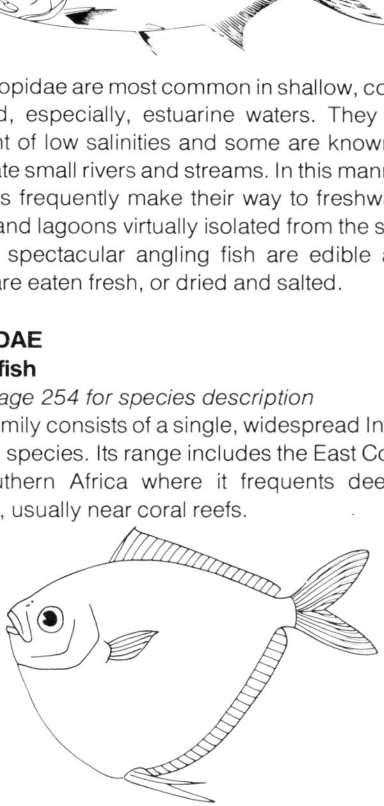

This curious, disc-shaped fish lacks spines and adults have elongate pelvic rays. The protractile mouth opens upwards and bears minute teeth in each jaw.

The moonfish is a shoaling species and represents a considerable food resource in India, where it is caught in traps and wind-dried.

MERLUCCIIDAE
Hakes

See page 255 for species description

Merlucciidae occur mainly in the Atlantic and eastern Pacific oceans, and of the 15-20 species known, five may be found in southern African waters. The family is closely related to the Gadidae, or true cods, well known as food fishes in the northern hemisphere. Hakes are strictly marine in habit and generally live close to the sea-bed in deep water.

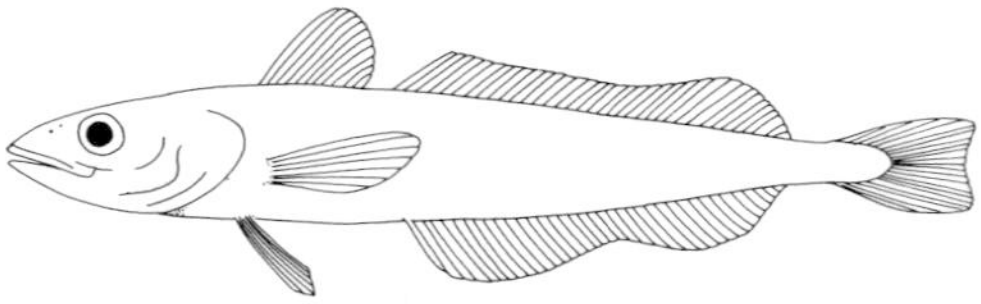

As with all cod-like fishes, hakes are elongate and usually have very long dorsal and anal fins. They are best distinguished by their clearly separate first and second dorsal and anal fins. The caudal fin, too, is separate and does not join the dorsal or anal fins. Also characteristic is the large mouth set with well-developed teeth, and the undershot lower jaw. The gill openings are wide and extend above the level of the pectoral fins. All cod-like fishes have their pelvic fins located well forward and in front of the pectorals, a feature which is particularly noticeable in hakes.

Hake stocks along the West Coast of southern Africa are considerable and if the current level of trawling is carefully controlled, this resource will provide a continued and significant supply of protein for human consumption.

MONODACTYLIDAE
Moonies or kitefishes

See page 256 for species description

Of the five species described in this family at least one occurs off the coast of West Africa, while the others are more widely distributed throughout the Indo-Pacific. Two species occur in southern African waters. Moonies are marine dwellers, but can tolerate brackish and low-salinity conditions.

Monodactylidae are strongly compressed and have very deep, almost diamond-shaped bodies. Also characteristic are the small ctenoid scales which typically extend onto the fins, the long-based anal and dorsal fins and the small mouth bearing fine teeth.

These small, shoaling fishes adapt successfully to aquaria and can even adjust to completely fresh

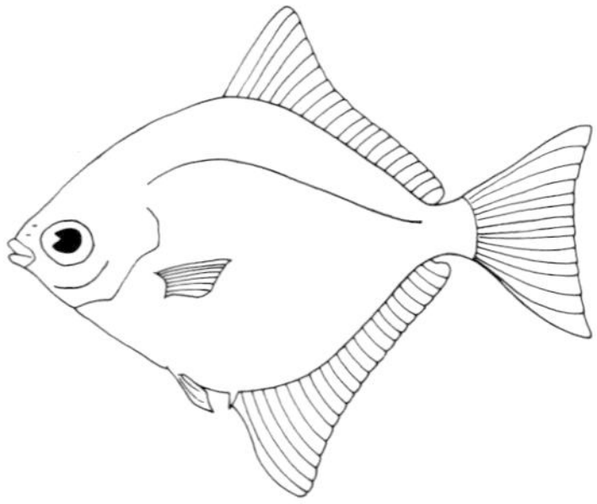

water. Though not locally exploited, in some tropical countries moonies have limited value as a food resource.

MUGILIDAE
Mullets

See pages 257 to 260 for species descriptions

These predominantly warm-water shoaling fishes favour inshore shallows and estuaries, and some are tolerant of fresh water. About 100 species of mullet have been described, but there is much overlapping and many different species names

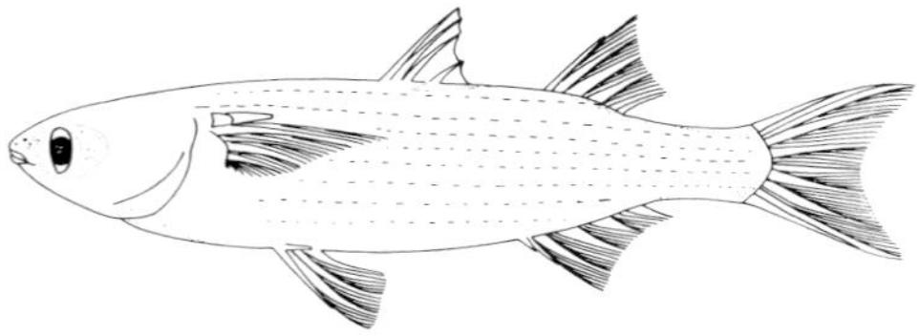

are no doubt synonymous. At least 15 members of this widely distributed family have been recorded from southern African waters.

Mugilidae are elongate, silvery fishes with broad, flattened heads and blunt snouts. The small terminal mouth may or may not bear teeth. There is no lateral line. Two well-separated dorsal fins occur and the pectoral fins are placed high on the sides of the body. A strong, muscular gizzard replaces a true stomach in the alimentary system. Mullet feed on the bottom where they pick up mouthfuls of mud; tiny food items are strained out by the long, sieve-like gill rakers and the indigestible residue is ejected back into the water. The fact that these fish feed on matter low down in the food chain, which they readily assimilate and convert into protein, has made them a favourite choice for aquaculture, or fish farming. Many species are already of considerable economic value, especially in the Middle and Far East.

Mullet are strong swimmers, given to spectacular leaps. Though seldom enticed by baits or lures, if hooked, these fish will provide the angler with good sport.

MULLIDAE
Goatfishes

See pages 261 to 264 for species descriptions

There are about 30 species of goatfish worldwide and 13 have been recorded from southern African waters. Most are found in tropical or subtropical regions and all are marine.

Goatfishes are often brightly coloured and easily identified by the two long barbels projecting from the chin. Other characteristics include a flattened underside, two separate dorsal fins - the first of 6-8 spines and the second of one spine plus eight rays - and a forked caudal.

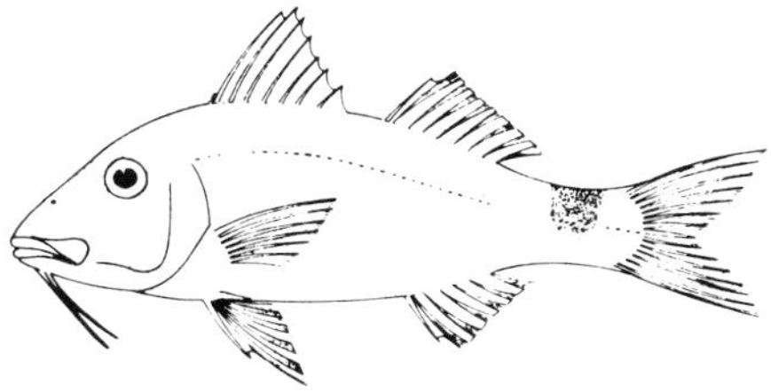

Mullidae are bottom-living fishes that use their sensory barbels to probe the sea-bed for small crustaceans and other invertebrates.

Though not regarded as sport fishes, the members of this family will readily take small baits. They make excellent eating and in the Far East constitute an important food source.

MURAENESOCIDAE
Pike congers

See page 265 for species description

This family of eels comprises about seven species worldwide, only one of which occurs in southern African waters. Pike congers are mainly inhabitants of shallow coastal waters, but some will venture to considerable depths while others will, on occasion, enter estuaries.

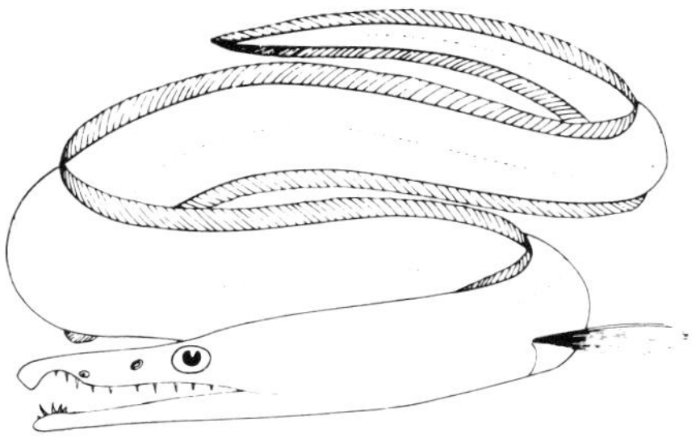

These very elongate, scaleless fishes have well-developed pectoral fins, but no pelvics. In addition to a row of large, strong teeth in each jaw, there is also a row of fang-like teeth on the roof of the mouth. Other features include the large eyes covered with a thin layer of skin, two large and separate gill slits which open low down on the body just before the pectoral fins, and the vent which opens well behind the pectorals.

As with all eels, the life cycle includes a transparent larval stage. In some species these glass-like *leptocephali* may measure 20 cm.

Though not exploited locally, pike congers make excellent eating. In the Far East they are caught at night on both handlines and longlines and are marketed fresh or processed into fishballs.

MURAENIDAE
Moray eels

See pages 266 to 268 for species descriptions

Muraenidae comprise some 180-200 members distributed throughout tropical and subtropical regions worldwide. About 33 species have been recorded from southern African waters. These eels are fairly abundant around rocky and coral reefs, where they tend to lurk in caves or other dark recesses.

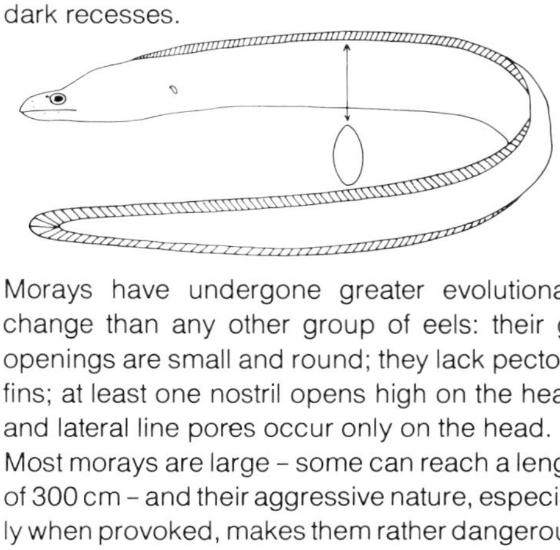

Morays have undergone greater evolutionary change than any other group of eels: their gill openings are small and round; they lack pectoral fins; at least one nostril opens high on the head; and lateral line pores occur only on the head.

Most morays are large - some can reach a length of 300 cm - and their aggressive nature, especially when provoked, makes them rather dangerous. Adults are usually brightly coloured and intricately patterned, but, as with all eels, juveniles pass through a *leptocephalus* larval stage during which they are completely transparent.

Though most Muraenidae make excellent eating, in tropical regions, cases of ciguatera poisoning have been reliably traced to these eels.

NEMIPTERIDAE
Spinecheeks

See page 269 for species description

This large family is closely related to the snappers (family Lutjanidae) and comprises numerous small to medium-sized species. Most belong to the genus *Nemipterus,* a tropical group of fishes known as butterfly breams. But the members of another, smaller genus, *Scolopsis,* are more common in southern African waters. Spinecheeks are mostly brightly coloured, elegant fishes which are most abundant among inshore coral heads.

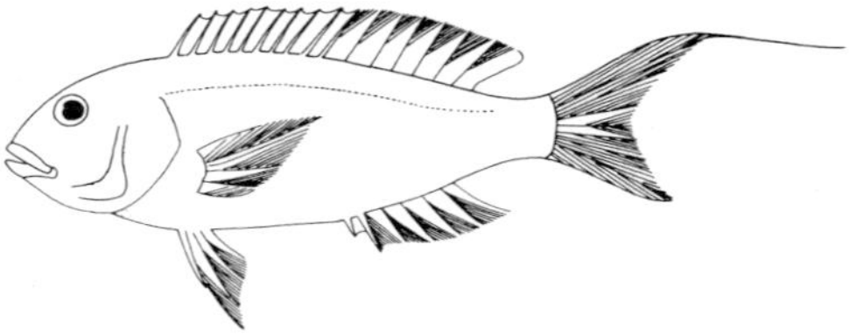

In all Nemipteridae the fins are well developed; the dorsal fin has ten spines plus 8-11 rays, while the anal fin has three spines plus 6-8 rays. The upper lobe of the caudal fin may be filamentous. Though lacking in *Nemipterus* species, and only poorly developed in the members of other genera, a characteristic feature of *Scolopsis* is the stout, backward pointing spine that occurs just below each eye.
Spinecheeks are edible, but few are large enough or sufficiently abundant to be of significant value as a food resource.

OPHIDIIDAE
Cuskeels, brotulas and kingklip
See page 270 for species description
Of the 135 species in this family, 110 belong to the subfamily Brotulinae, while the remainder form the subfamily Ophidiinae. Members of both groups are distributed through temperate and tropical waters around the world and ten species are known to occur off southern Africa.

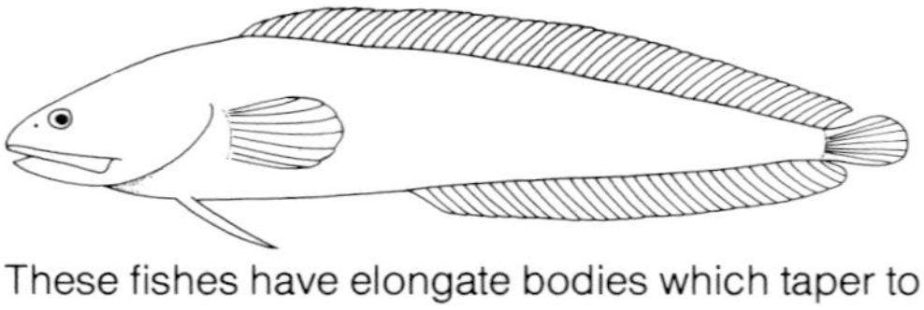

These fishes have elongate bodies which taper to a pointed tail where the dorsal, anal and caudal fins join to form a single continuous fin. When present, the pelvic fins are located well forward on the body, below the gills. The head region is the broadest part of the body and the terminal, or slightly underslung mouth may be protrusible. Scales are normally very small, but may be completely absent. In most species a lateral line is present.

Brotulinae are generally deep-water marine fishes and some species have been dredged from the 7-km-deep Sunda Trench off Java – the deepest record of captured fish. Other members of the subfamily, however, have adapted to fresh water, with some species found in Cuba being blind, cave-dwellers. The kingklip, found in the deeper coastal waters of southern Africa, is a member of the Ophidiinae and is one of the largest members of the entire family.
Ophidiidae include some of the finest quality table fishes and in many parts of the world the members of this family are trawled commercially.

OPLEGNATHIDAE
Knifejaws
See pages 271 and 272 for species descriptions
Oplegnathidae comprise a single genus of four or more species, and though distributed throughout the warmer waters of the world, they are particularly common around Australia, Japan, Hawaii and the Galapagos Islands. Three species occur off southern Africa and can be found on most inshore reefs along the East Coast.

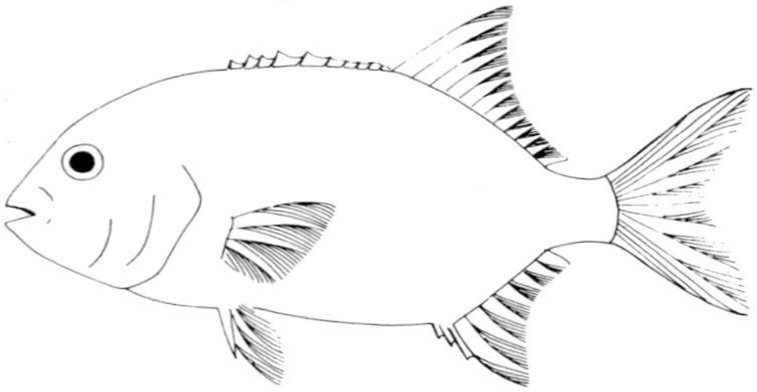

The identity of knifejaws is immediately apparent as they all have a parrot-like beak consisting of fused, projecting teeth. Also characteristic are the small, tightly adhering, tough scales. Colour, however, can be confusing as Oplegnathidae have an inherent ability to change colour. Juveniles differ markedly from adults as their teeth are separate. This, together with their completely different body colouration, previously resulted in juveniles being identified as distinct and separate species.
Knifejaws make excellent eating, but anglers have little success in tempting them with bait as their natural food consists of encrusting organisms such as barnacles and limpets prised from rocks.

OSTRACIIDAE
Boxfishes, cowfishes or trunkfishes
See page 273 for species description
Of the 37 members in this unusual family, at least

ten have been recorded from southern African waters. Boxfishes are primarily inhabitants of tropical regions, all are marine and representatives occur in each of the oceans.

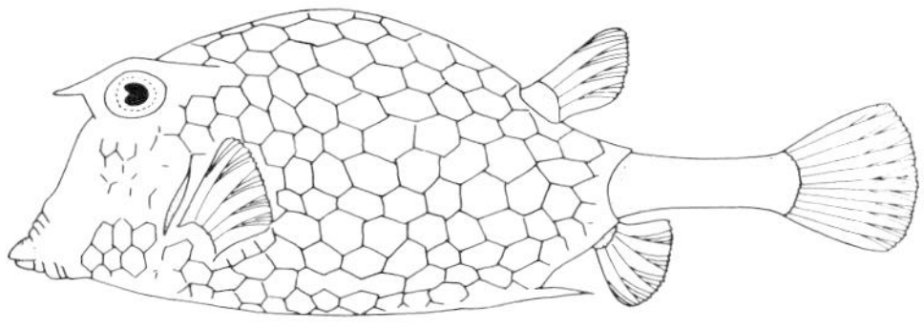

Ostraciidae are easily recognized by the fused, bony plates which enclose the body in a rigid armour much like the shell of a turtle. The only openings in the hard outer case are those making provision for the gills, eyes, small protrusible mouth, vent, and the movement of the fins. The dorsal fin lacks spines and the entire pelvic girdle, together with its associated fins, is absent. Sharp spines may project from the 'corners' of the body. When feeding, boxfishes often 'stand' on their heads and squirt a fine jet of water into the sand. This uncovers minute plants and animals which are then sucked into the mouth. Not surprisingly, in view of their heavy armour, these fishes are poor swimmers. What they lack in speed, however, they make up in manoeuvrability, and by whirling opposing fins against one another, boxfishes move deftly in and out of small spaces.

In addition to their armour and sharp spines, the defence strategy of these curious fishes includes the ability to exude a toxic substance when frightened or molested. This poison is sometimes powerful enough to kill nearby fish and, ironically, sometimes even the boxfish itself. The members of this family are not recommended for human consumption.

PEMPHERIDAE
Sweepers

See page 274 for species description

Approximately 25 species have been described in this family with at least four frequenting southern African waters. Whereas these small fishes are most common in the Indo-Pacific, a few species also occur in the western Atlantic Ocean.

Sweepers are sometimes known as helicopter-fishes, a name which aptly describes their deep bodies and long, narrow hindquarters. The upper jaw does not reach beyond the centre of the large eyes and the smooth pre-operculum lacks serra-

tions. Also distinctive is the short-based dorsal fin which originates before the mid-point of the body. In most species the mouth opens upwards.

This shallow-water family is largely nocturnal and, in addition to the large eyes, many sweepers have luminous organs on the body. Juveniles may occur in dense shoals which 'hang' beneath coral or rocky overhangs. Pempheridae are edible and adapt successfully to aquaria.

PLATYCEPHALIDAE
Flatheads

See page 275 for species description

Except for a single species occuring off West Africa, the members of this family are confined to the Indo-Pacific. Many species have been described, at least 11 of which have been recorded in southern African waters. Though flatheads are largely marine, a few species inhabit estuaries.

Flatheads are elongate, sometimes almost cylindrical in cross-section and, as the common and scientific names infer, the head region is strongly depressed. Numerous ridges occur on the head as well as several stout spines. These sharp

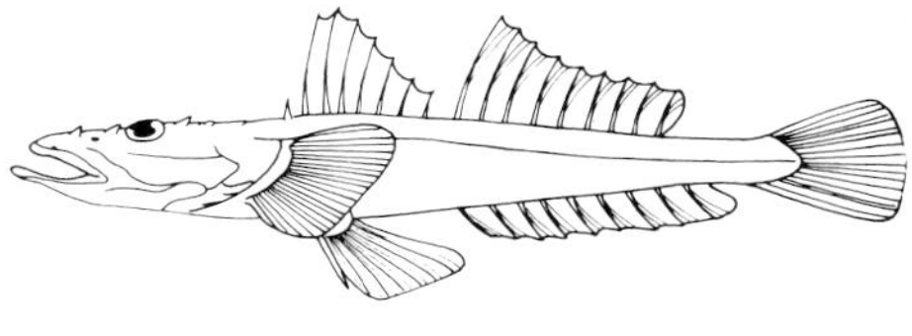

projections undoubtedly deter prospective predators. The lower jaw is undershot. The fins and their arrangement are characteristic: the two dorsals are closely spaced; the anal is spineless; and the pelvics are widely separated and located behind the rather large pectorals which lack loose rays.

Flatheads are bottom-dwelling fishes and many species bury themselves just below the sand or mud. Hidden in this way, they wait for prey such as small fish and crustaceans to come within easy grasp.

Most Platycephalidae make fine eating.

PLOTOSIDAE
Eel-catfishes and eel-barbels

See pages 276 and 277 for species descriptions

In all, there are some 2 000 species of catfishes belonging to about 31 families. Most, however, are freshwater species and only the Ariidae and this family have marine representatives. Of the 25-30 eel-catfishes that have been described, all are confined to the Indo-Pacific and about half are marine. Only two Plotosidae frequent southern African waters.

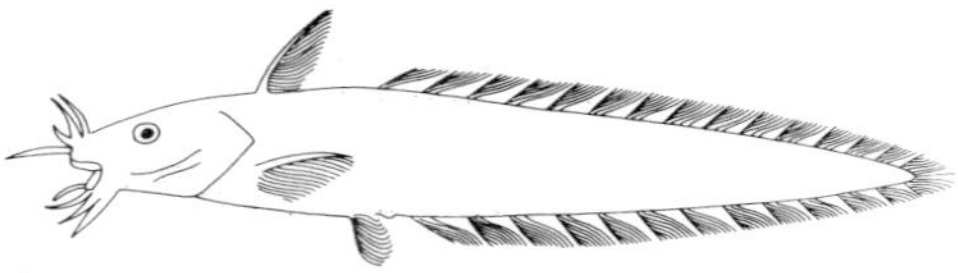

The members of this family are often quite brightly marked, and are easily distinguished from other catfishes by their pointed tails and continuous dorsal, caudal and anal fins. The eel-like body is completely scaleless. Each of the pectoral fins and the first dorsal fin has a single, stout spine which is coated with glandular epidermal cells containing a powerful venom. Wounds from these spines can be excruciatingly painful and should be treated medically. An immediate and effective treatment, however, is the immersion of the afflicted part in very hot water for at least thirty minutes.

Some eel-catfishes are known to build and guard nests during the spawning season and a few freshwater species protect and care for their young.

Despite the highly toxic spines, the flesh of Plotosidae makes excellent eating.

POLYNEMIDAE
Threadfins

See page 278 for species description

This family of 35 species is very widely distributed in tropical and subtropical regions. Most are marine, but some also frequent estuaries and fresh water. At least three species occur in southern African waters.

Being closely related to the Mugilidae, threadfins superficially resemble mullets. Polynemidae, however, exhibit a number of features which prevent confusion. A large, transparent snout projects above the underslung mouth which bears small teeth. The two dorsal fins are separate and the caudal fin is deeply forked. Characteristic too, are the pectoral fins, each comprising two distinct regions, the lower of 4-7 detached rays and the upper of normal, webbed rays. The pelvic fins are located further back, on the belly. Adipose tissue covers the eyes.

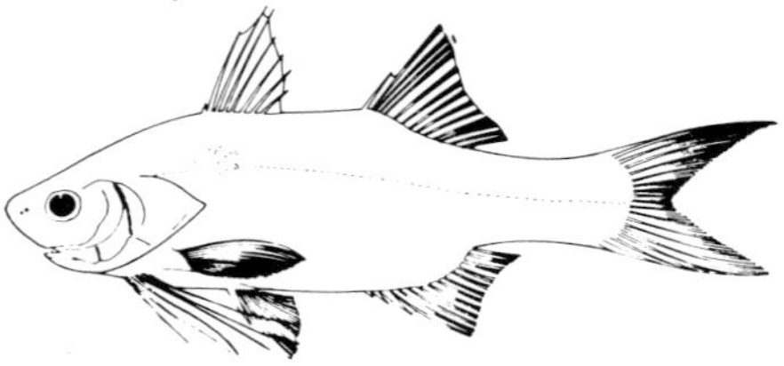

In certain localities, threadfins are sometimes very abundant and good commercial catches are netted in beach seines. Some species are popular with anglers and are of fine eating quality.

POMACANTHIDAE
Angelfishes

See pages 279 to 281 for species descriptions

Members of this tropical family occur worldwide and of the 80 species known, at least 11 occur in southern African waters. Pomacanthidae occur primarily around coral reefs, though one local

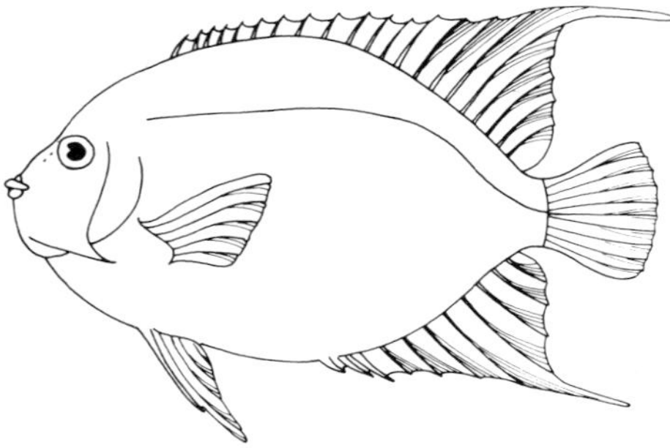

species, *Pomacanthus striatus,* is equally at home on rocky reefs.

The angelfishes are without exception beautifully coloured and patterned and were previously often included with the Chaetodontidae. Confusion is avoided, however, as angelfishes are easily distinguished by the pronounced sharp spine projecting backwards from each operculum. Their compressed bodies are covered with very small, tough scales which are not easily shed. Rows of fine, brush-like teeth are set in both jaws of the terminal mouth. The fins are well developed with strong spines, and the enlarged dorsal rays give these fishes the appearance of being bigger than they are.

Several angelfishes undergo sex reversal and in a

number of species the polygamous males have harems of four or more females. Eggs may be deposited in a sheltered place on the reef, but with some species they are free-floating and widely distributed by ocean currents. In most cases the juvenile form is strikingly different from the adult and this can lead to confusion and sometimes incorrect identification.

POMACENTRIDAE
Damselfishes

See pages 282 to 285 for species descriptions

This very large Indo-Pacific family has about 300 members, all of which are marine. At least 45 species are known to occur in southern African waters. Ichthyologists have struggled for years to finalize the taxonomy of damselfishes, a task made especially difficult by the complex colour and pattern differences between members.

These small coral fishes have deep, compressed bodies covered with large, distinct scales. The jaws of the small terminal mouth are set with incisors. Though the lateral line is clearly visible in most species, it is often incomplete or interrupted. The fins include a single dorsal of 9-14 strong spines plus 11-18 rays; the spiny section usually has a longer base than the soft section. The anal fin has two spines.

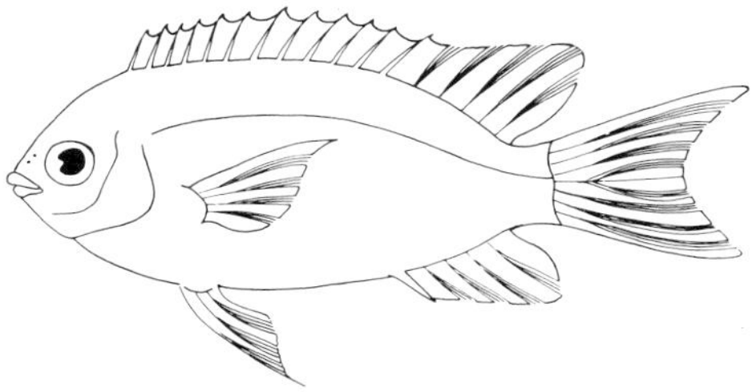

It is likely that more behavioural studies have been conducted on Pomacentridae than any other group of marine fish. A great deal of this research, however, has involved specimens in captivity and it is not certain whether the findings are valid for naturally occurring fish. Most damselfishes lay their eggs on a specially selected site and this nest is aggressively protected against would-be predators. During the hatching process the male fans the eggs with his fins, causing a constant, oxygen-rich current over the nest site. This habit is particularly evident in the anemonefishes of the genus *Amphiprion* and can be easily observed as they will breed successfully in domestic aquaria.

POMATOMIDAE
Elf or shad

See page 286 for species description

Only the cosmopolitan elf belongs to this family. This fish is exclusively marine and frequents subtropical and temperate waters.

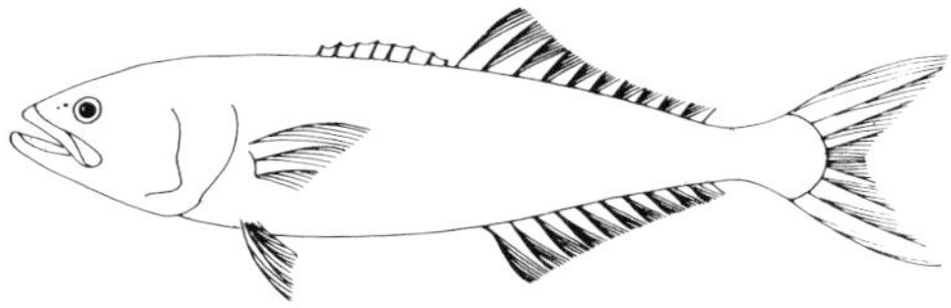

Pomatomidae have elongate, compressed bodies, covered with small scales which extend onto the soft dorsal and anal fins. Both jaws of the wide mouth bear a single row of exceptionally sharp teeth. The two dorsal fins are barely separated, the first comprising short spines, and the second slightly larger rays. The caudal fin is forked, and the anal fin has two spines. A dark blotch occurs at the base of the pectoral fins.

These powerful predators are renowned for their fierce aggression, both when attacking shoals of food-fish and when pouncing on the angler's bait. It is alleged that elf occurring in United States waters have such a bloodlust that they will actually kill more fish than they can eat. Eaten fresh, elf is a superb table fish, and amongst southern Africa's finest angling species. Elf were at one time under severe pressure through over-fishing, but following successful conservation measures, they are once again fairly abundant.

RACHYCENTRIDAE
Cobia or prodigal son

See page 287 for species description

The single species in this family is distributed throughout Atlantic and Indo-Pacific waters. Though this fish is nowhere uncommon, its erratic and unexpected appearance at specific localities has, in southern Africa, earned it the name of 'prodigal son'.

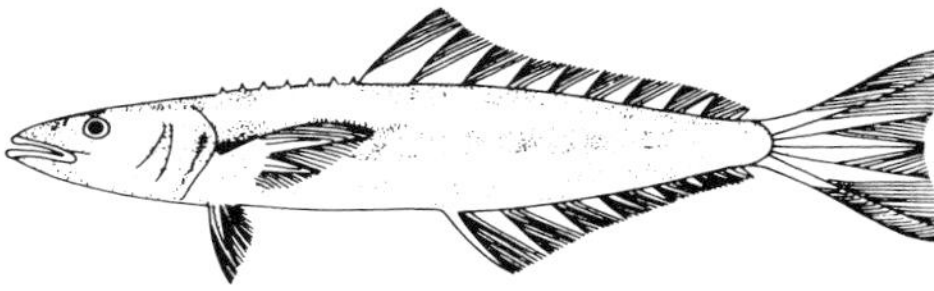

The cobia is elongate and has a depressed head. Some 6-9 short dorsal spines precede a long second dorsal fin, and the equally long anal fin has two or three spines plus 22-28 rays. The alternating dark and light stripes along the body create a striking resemblance to suckerfishes (family Echeneidae), but confusion is unlikely as the cobia lacks a sucking disc and has a forked caudal fin. Their superficial similarity, however, provides a good example of protective mimicry as the cobia enjoys relative safety from would-be predators by frequently moving in close association with sharks which presumably accept it as a suckerfish.

The cobia is an excellent gamefish and is of good eating quality.

SCIAENIDAE

Kobs, geelbek, drums and croakers

See pages 288 to 294 for species descriptions

There are at least 100 species in this family of large and often voracious predators. They frequent marine, brackish and fresh waters throughout the world and at least six species occur off the southern African coast.

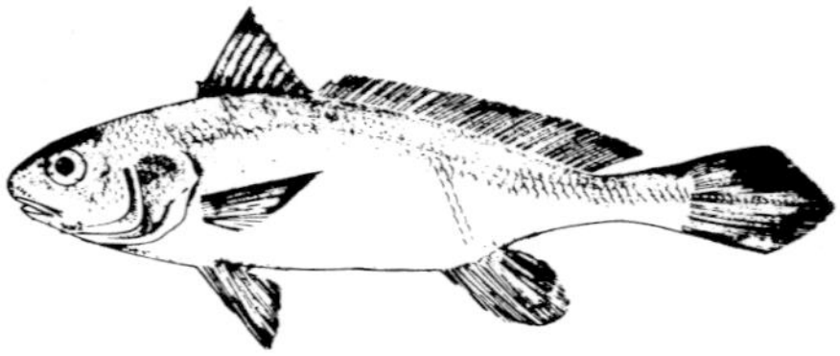

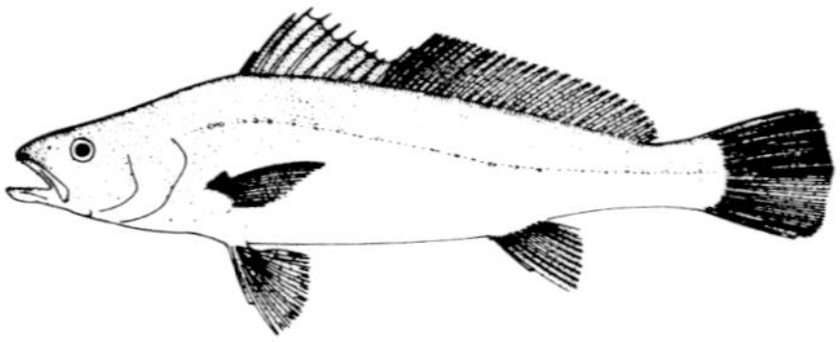

Sciaenidae are generally rather drab, dull-coloured fish, but all are elongate, rather robust and have a number of characteristic features. These include a dorsal fin that is almost completely divided into two; a caudal fin that is usually truncate or rounded; one or two spines in the anal fin; a conspicuous lateral line that extends onto the tail; and both cycloid and ctenoid scales that, in most species, cover the head and body respectively. A few of the bottom-feeding species have one or more sensory barbels on their chins, and virtually all have a large, simple airbladder with numerous small branches. The otoliths, or ear-stones, are very big and their shape is characteristic of individual species.

Those Sciaenidae that have adopted bottom-dwelling habits have become highly specialized in coping with their muddy and often murky environment. The lateral line system is particularly well developed and, in conjunction with the sensory barbels on the snout, has made these fishes less dependent on sight for hunting. Certain abdominal muscles attach to the air bladder and when these are flexed and relaxed, drumming sounds are produced – hence such common names as croaker and drum. This phenomenon is especially evident in males and is thought to be linked to courtship and territorial displays, or even to a means of general communication.

Esteemed by sport and commercial fishermen. Sciaenidae are abundant in warm, shallow waters, especially where major rivers enter the oceans.

SCOMBERESOCIDAE

Sauries

See page 295 for species description

Though similar to the needlefishes and halfbeaks, sauries can be immediately distinguished by the

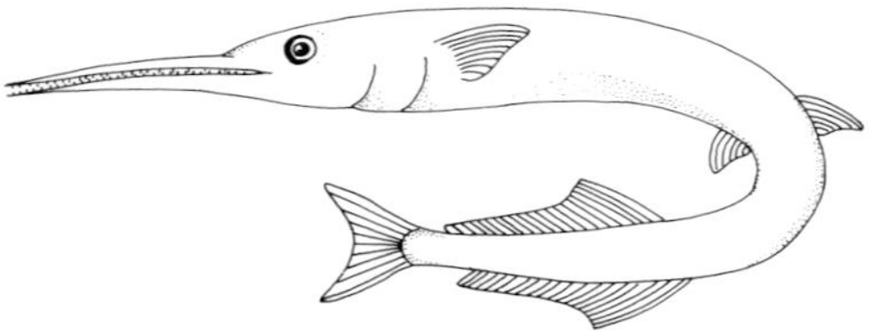

presence of detached dorsal and anal finlets and jaws that do not measure more than the head length. These elongate and cylindrical-bodied fishes of open ocean waters have only four member species, two of which occur off South African shores. The circumglobal sauries are not of great commercial importance, but do represent an important source of food for the larger gamefishes such as tuna.

SCOMBRIDAE

Mackerels and tuna

See pages 296 to 307 for species descriptions

There are about 45 species in this family worldwide. Of these, 24 occur in southern African waters. All are powerful, torpedo-shaped fishes with pointed snouts, tapered tails and strong, forked caudal fins. A number of anatomical features characterize all mackerels and tuna: the two dorsal fins fold back into a groove when the fish swims at speed; a series of small, detached finlets is located behind the dorsal and the anal fins; scales are cycloid, very small and, in many species, restricted to a corselet around the front half of the body; and a slender caudal peduncle is flanked on either side with 1-3 keels.

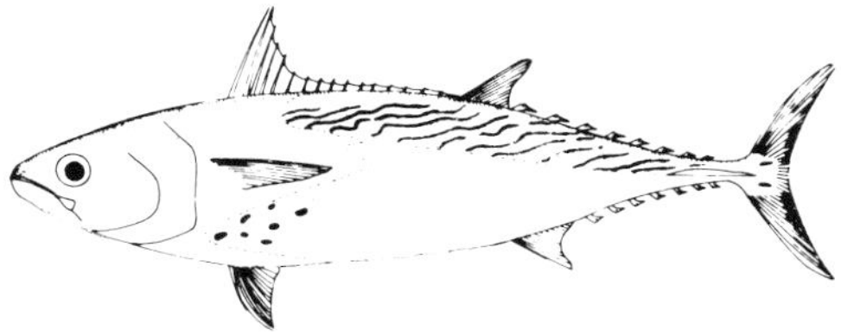

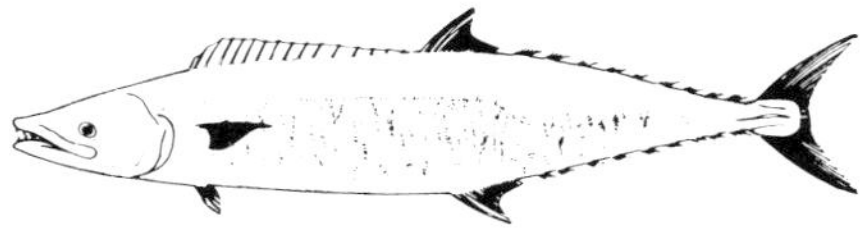

Scombridae, particularly tunas, undertake immensely wide-ranging migrations and can truly be termed 'nomads of the sea'. These are among the fastest swimmers in the world and their streamlined bodies are close to the limits of hydrodynamic refinement. As these fishes are heavier than water and lack an air bladder, and because large quantities of water have to pass over their gills to ensure a constant and adequate supply of oxygen, tuna cannot stop swimming. If they did they would sink and suffocate. Their energy requirements are great, therefore, and some species eat up to 25 per cent of their body weight daily. A few Scombridae have body temperatures that exceed the ambient temperature of the surrounding water.

Most mackerel and tuna are fierce predators and a number have very sharp teeth. Others have only fine teeth, but all are hunters. Their acute eyesight, as with raptors such as eagles and hawks, is binocular and stereoscopic. This optical refinement enables them to judge distances very accurately, a distinct advantage when pursuing prey.

Extensive breeding grounds occur worldwide, but the precise spawning localities of many species remain unknown. It is well known that tuna and mackerel favour slightly warmer waters, and predictions of their abundance can often be made by analysing water temperatures.

Most Scombridae are fine eating fish and many species are also much sought after by deep-sea anglers and spearfishermen.

SCORPAENIDAE

Scorpionfishes and stonefishes

See pages 308 to 312 for species descriptions

This large family has at least 330 members and includes some of the most venomous fishes known. Scorpaenidae are widely distributed in tropical, subtropical and temperate waters worldwide. Some 46 species have been recorded off southern Africa. There has been considerable disagreement concerning the taxonomy of Scorpaenidae, but ichthyologists now include the stonefishes (family Synancejidae) in this family.

Many scorpionfishes are brightly coloured, usually in variegated browns, reds and greys. Their overall shaggy, maned appearance, resulting from the numerous fin spines, as well as from the ridges and spines on the head and gill covers, is unmistakable. Most species have ctenoid scales covering the body, but some are naked. There is a single dorsal fin, and in many scorpionfishes the pectoral fins are particularly well developed.

Poisonous species have hollow dorsal, anal and pelvic spines. When pressure is placed on these spines, the sacs at their bases release venom which is injected into the victim in the manner of a hypodermic syringe. Wounds are excruciatingly painful and must be treated medically. Immersion of the afflicted part in water, as hot as the victim can stand, however, will help to neutralize the powerful protein toxin.

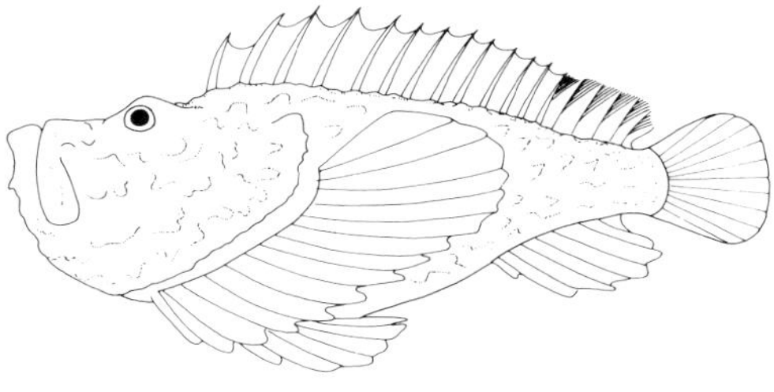

Though one or two species reportedly produce eggs in large gelatinous 'balloons', most scorpionfishes bear live young.

Scorpionfishes often occur at considerable depths and, notwithstanding their venom and somewhat grotesque appearance, many are edible and in some regions are trawled commercially.

Stonefishes are squat and scaleless, usually with

fleshy pectoral fins and warty skin. The mouth usually opens upwards and the eyes are located on top of the head.

SCORPIDIDAE
Stonebreams

See page 313 for species description

This family has about 11 members worldwide, but only one occurs in southern African waters. This sole representative is, however, most prolific. There is some debate concerning the taxonomic status of Scorpididae and scientists frequently group the family with either the Coracinidae or the Kyphosidae.

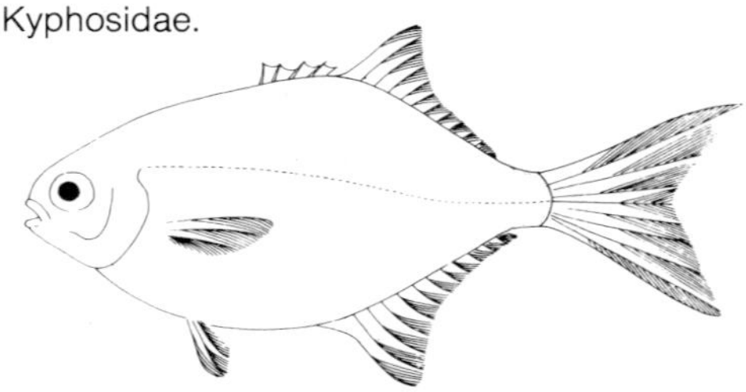

Stonebreams have short dorsal and anal spines, but the well-developed second dorsal and anal fins give these fish a noticeably deep-bodied appearance. The small mouth bears fine villiform teeth in each jaw. Incisors are never present. The pelvic fins are located well behind the pectorals. Most Scorpididae are drab in colour.

Stonebreams are plant feeders and live close inshore, usually in the shallowest part of the surf zone. They have a curious, yet most effective adaptation to their vegetarian habits: the gut is lined with a black membrane which prevents light from penetrating the translucent flesh of the belly. If light was to penetrate the gut lining, chlorophyll in the half-digested vegetable matter in the stomach would remain active. The oxygen released as a by-product of this reaction would literally cause the fish to 'blow up'.

Despite the unpleasant smell when being gutted, stonebreams make excellent eating.

SERRANIDAE
Rockcods and seabasses

See pages 314 to 328 for species descriptions

This large family has more than 320 representatives worldwide, most occurring in tropical and subtropical regions. The majority is marine, but a few are freshwater species. At least 70 species are likely to be found in southern African waters.

Rockcods are robust, attractive fishes which dis-

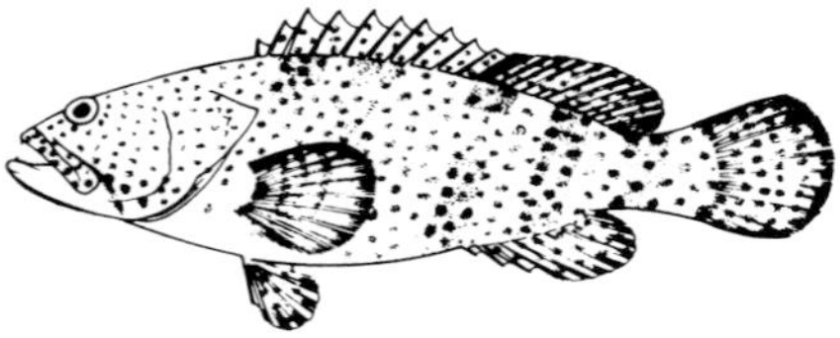

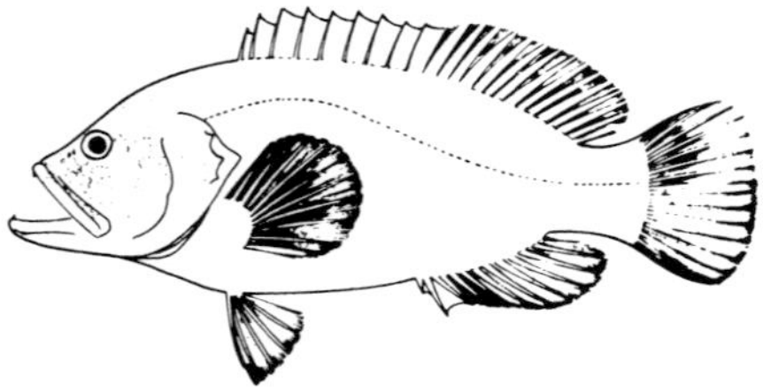

play remarkable diversity in their colours, body markings and size. All have three short spines on the gill covers; a main, central spine with one above and one below. This feature is diagnostic as a number of close relatives can be distinguished by the lack of the lowest of these spines. The caudal fin is either rounded or truncate and, only rarely, lunate. The pelvic fins, each comprising one spine plus five rays, originate below and behind the pectoral fin bases. Scales are always visible and may be either ctenoid or cycloid.

Serranidae are an important group of carnivorous fishes and though some do not exceed 10 cm, others attain 300 cm and may often be the dominant predator species on a reef. Most, if not all, rockcods are hermaphroditic with individuals starting life as females and changing into males when older. In some cases sex reversal takes place on demand. For example, where there is a predominance of females with no males to fertilize them, the dominant female will change sex.

Throughout the world, rockcods are regarded as excellent food fishes.

SIGANIDAE
Rabbitfishes

See page 329 for species description

Though rabbitfishes are essentially Indo-Pacific in distribution, some species have invaded the eastern Mediterranean via the Suez Canal. A total of ten species has been described, two of which are known to occur in southern African waters.

These somewhat elongate and evenly rounded fishes are closely related to the surgeonfishes (family Acanthuridae). Siganidae, however, may be recognized by their distinctive pelvic fins, both of which comprise two spines separated by three rays. The single dorsal fin has 13 exceptionally strong spines plus ten rays, while the anal fin has seven spines plus nine rays. All spines have a deep lateral groove and are exceptionally toxic. Stab wounds are very painful, but the poison can be neutralized by immersion of the afflicted part in very hot water for at least thirty minutes.

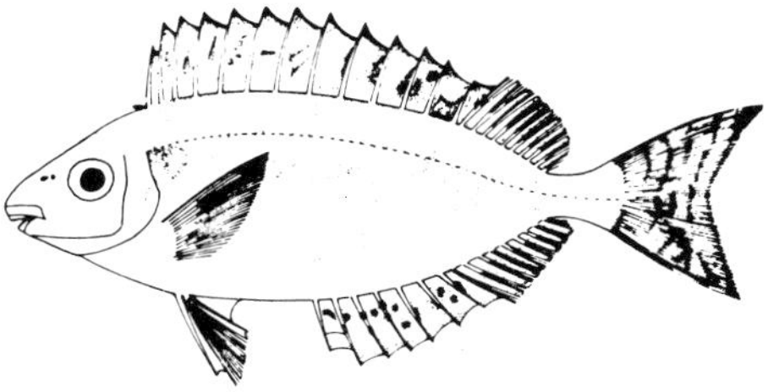

All rabbitfishes are herbivorous and the jaws of the small terminal mouth are set with a row of incisors well suited to grazing algae from reefs. In several countries in the Far East, Siganidae are cultivated in ponds or rice paddies and are generally considered an important protein source.

SILLAGINIDAE
Sillagos or smelts

See page 330 for species description

All six members of this Indo-Pacific family are confined to marine or estuarine waters. Three species may be encountered along the southern African coastline.

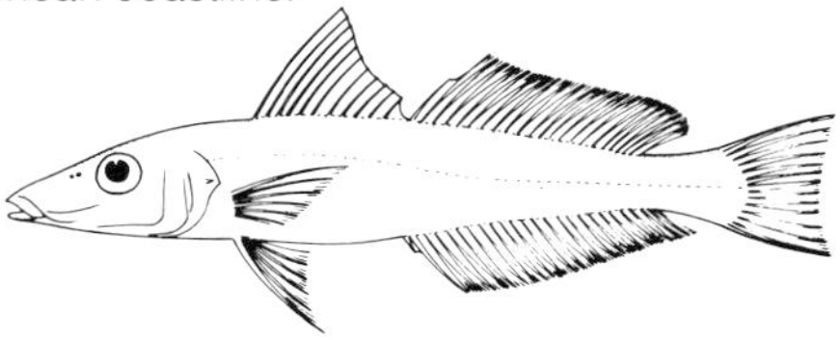

Sillagos are small, elongate, silvery fishes which, though superficially similar to a few other families, have a number of distinctive features. The two dorsal fins are very closely set, the first comprising 9-12 spines and the second 16-26 rays. The anal fin has two spines plus 15-27 rays. The mouth is small and set with fine teeth.
Known as whitings in other parts of the world, the members of this family are of considerable commercial value, especially in Australia where they are highly esteemed as food-fishes.

SOLEIDAE
Soles

See pages 331 to 332 for species descriptions

Soleidae comprise the second largest of the six Pleuronectiform families and representative species may be found in temperate and tropical waters worldwide. Several soles are common in estuaries and some are known to be endemic to freshwater. About 13 species have been recorded off southern Africa.

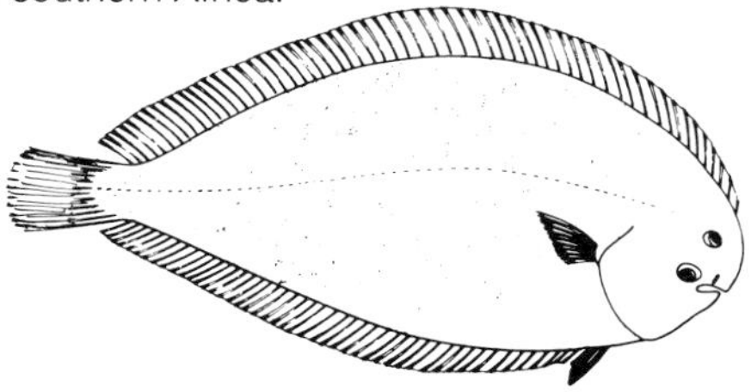

Soles are right-eyed flatfishes, that is, both eyes are located on the right side of the body. The dorsal fin extends from above the eyes to the tail and may be fused to the caudal fin. The margin of the pre-operculum is embedded beneath the skin and is not free. Pectoral fins are sometimes lacking, but when present, the right fin is usually longer than the left. The small mouth is asymmetrical and the minute, villiform teeth are usually better developed on the blind or left side.
Soles are sluggish bottom-dwelling fishes and the defence strategy of most, centres on their drab, sandy colouration and their habit of burrowing just beneath the sand. The zebra sole *(Zebrias zebra)*, however, has poison glands at the base of each fin ray. If attacked, the toxin released is powerful enough to force the predator to release its prey immediately.
The delicate flesh of most soles makes them highly prized throughout the world as table fish of the finest quality.

SPARIDAE
Seabreams, stumpnoses, reds, steenbras, musselcrackers and porgies

See pages 333 to 370 for species descriptions

About 100 species belong to this family with at least some occurring in all but the coldest marine waters. Their centre of distribution, however, appears to be the southern African region where at least 41 species occur, about 25 of which are endemic. Sparidae are one of the most important groups of angling and food fishes in southern Africa and range in habitat from shallow estuaries to deeper, offshore reefs.
These perch-like fishes are characterized by a number of anatomical features. Most are deep-bodied, with large heads, steep foreheads and jaws that do not extend beyond a point in line with

the centre of the eyes. The mouth is small in relation to the body size, and teeth may be conical, incisors or molars. (In some species two, or even all three types may be present). The palate is usually toothless. Spines are prominent in the well-developed fins and the first few spines of the dorsal fin are long in some species. All Sparidae have well-formed scales on the body and on the pre-operculum, but none on the snout. A lateral line is always visible.

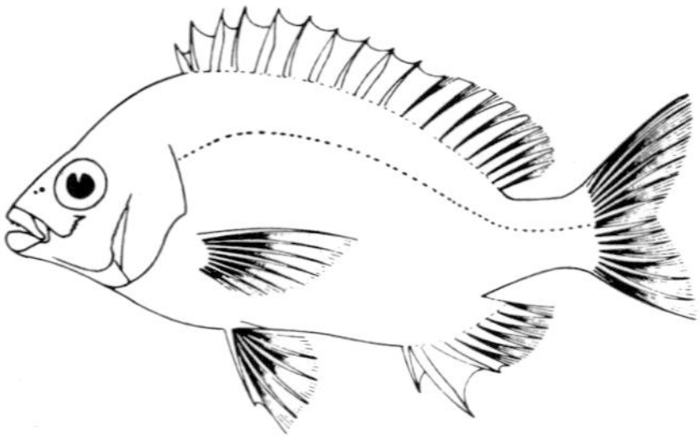

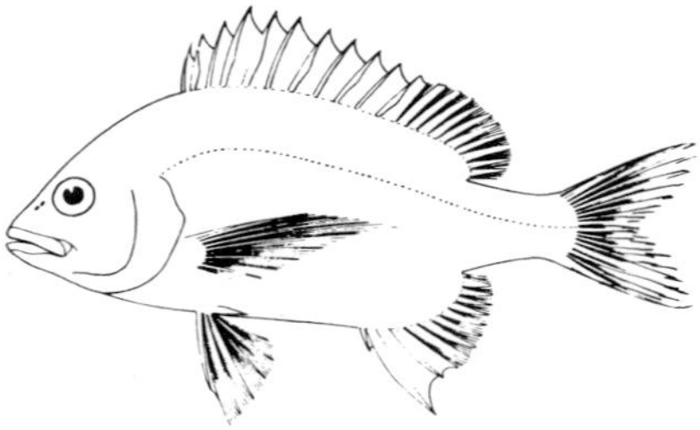

Depending on the species, diet may be carnivorous, herbivorous or omnivorous, those Sparidae with strong molar teeth usually feeding on hard-shelled crustaceans and molluscs. A feature of this family is the capacity of many species either to change sex or to be hermaphroditic at some stage of their life. All Sparidae are fine eating fish and many species are prime targets for anglers and spearfishermen.

SPHYRAENIDAE
Barracudas

See pages 371 and 372 for species descriptions

Many fishes throughout the world are popularly called 'barracuda', but none can be mistaken for the true members of this family of superb gamefishes. There are about 20 species of Sphyraenidae, and while most abundant in tropical or subtropical waters, representatives occur worldwide. In all, ten species have been recorded from southern African waters, some as far south as the eastern Cape.

Barracudas have elongate, streamlined bodies. Their two dorsal fins are widely separated, the first comprising five spines, and the second one spine plus nine rays. Most obvious, however, is the enormous mouth which opens wide to reveal a formidable set of fang-like teeth in each jaw.

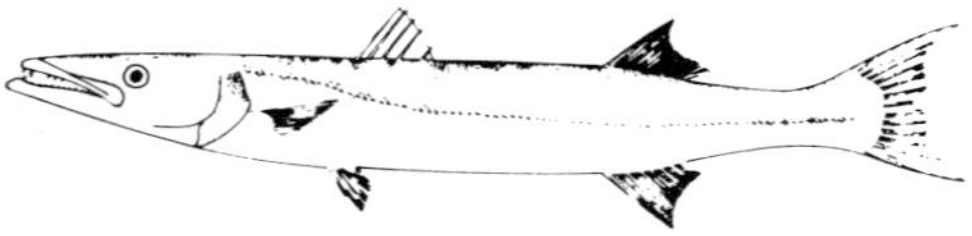

Gill rakers are absent in most species, but when present are usually reduced to a single raker located in the axil of the first arch. The lateral line is conspicuous and well developed.

Their body shape, size and fearsomely armed, widely gaping jaws manifest the voracious, feeding and hunting habits of these fishes. Barracuda are certainly dominant predators of reef fishes and occasionally have been held responsible for attacks on bathers and divers.

Popular with anglers and spearfishermen alike, some of these powerful, hard-fighting fishes reach a length of 180 cm. Their flesh makes reasonable eating, though in certain tropical regions it has been responsible for confirmed cases of ciguatera poisoning.

SYNODONTIDAE
Lizardfishes

See page 373 for species description

The lizardfish family is exclusively marine and representatives can be found in all oceans. Approximately 34 species have been described, nine occurring in southern African waters. All are bottom-living fishes, often found at considerable depths.

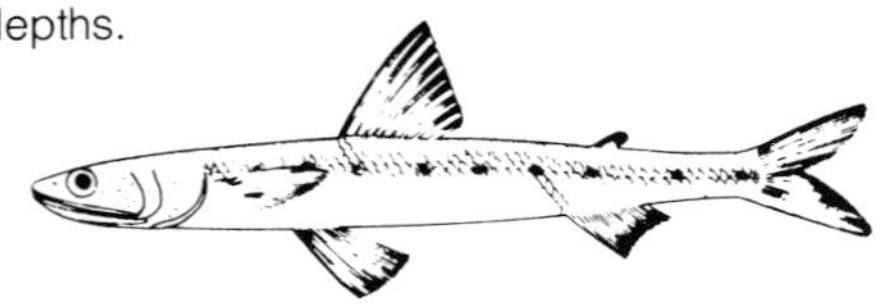

These elongate fishes have depressed heads, and the entire body is covered with scales, none being noticeably enlarged. There is a single dorsal fin of 9-14 rays, followed by a small adipose fin. The anal fin has 8-16 rays, and the caudal fin is distinctly forked. Both jaws are armed with several rows of sharply pointed teeth. The large mouth is, in fact, a well-designed trap, as the teeth can be depressed inwards, thus allowing prey to enter the mouth, but not to escape.

Though most are returned to the water by anglers,

lizardfishes make good eating and are of commercial importance in some regions.

TERAPONIDAE
Thornfishes

See page 374 for species description

Though there are some freshwater species, thornfishes are largely confined to the coastal marine and estuarine waters of the Indo-Pacific region. There are at least 37 species in the family, three occurring in the southern African region.

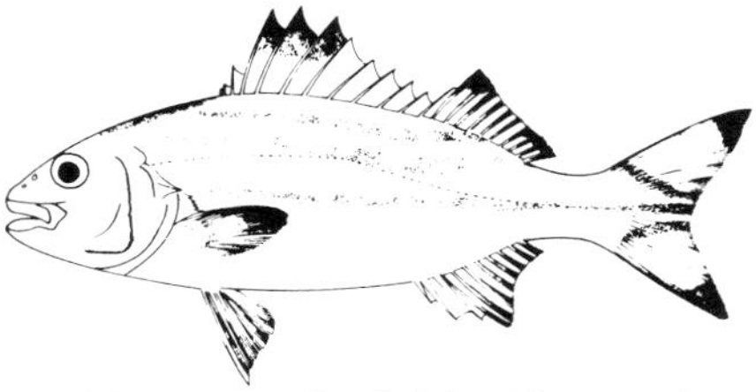

Teraponidae are small, slightly oblong and compressed, and have one or two very distinct spines on each gill cover. The fins include a single dorsal comprising 12-14 spines plus 8-14 rays; an anal of three spines plus 7-12 rays; and pelvics located below and behind the pectoral bases. All thornfishes are covered with small scales, and most species have dark, longitudinal bands along each of their flanks.

Many Teraponidae feed on a variety of organisms, often in exceptionally shallow water. The diet of these aggressive little fishes may even include scales which are fearlessly pecked from their victims, usually fish much bigger than themselves.

TETRAODONTIDAE
Blaasops, puffers and tobies

See pages 375 to 377 for species descriptions

This tropical and subtropical family has some 120 representatives worldwide. Though primarily marine, a few inhabit freshwater regions and are found in large river systems such as the Congo in central Africa. Most species are small, including the approximately 30 described from southern African waters.

As the scientific name implies, these fishes have four teeth, but these are fused into a solid beak. Their rounded bodies are naked, except for reduced, spiky scales scattered irregularly on the back, flanks and belly. The common name too, is appropriate, as puffers are able to pump water, or air from the surface, into a separate branch of the gut. In so doing, these fishes can inflate themselves to a remarkable degree and hence become too large for many would-be predators. Fin spines are absent and the single dorsal and anal fins usually have 7-12 rays each.

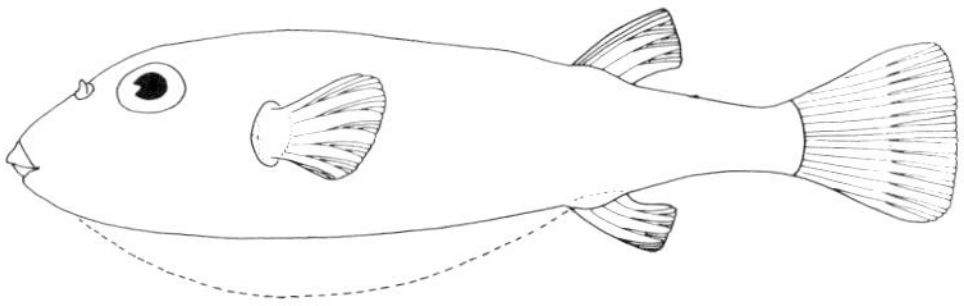

These fishes are highly specialized, and their lack of spines, reduced scales and fins, internal anatomy and skeleton, as well as the well-developed nasal structures, place these and other Tetraodontiformes high on the evolutionary ladder.

Puffers are also well known for their extremely toxic skin and viscera which, if eaten, can prove fatal to humans. The flesh, however, is free from poison and, in Japan, is regarded as a delicacy.

TRICHIURIDAE
Cutlassfishes

See page 379 for species description

These fishes are distantly related to the mackerels, tunas and Cape snoek. Representatives may be found in all oceans, ranging from the tropics to more temperate regions.Cutlassfishes often occur to considerable depths. Of the 17 or more species described, six are known to frequent southern African waters.

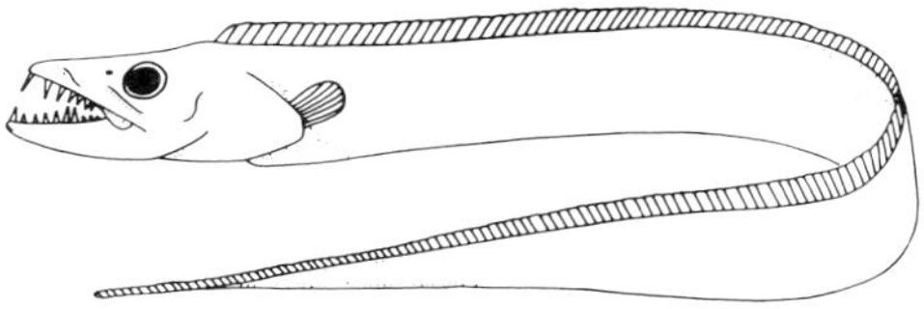

Their scaleless, and exceptionally elongate, ribbon-like bodies carry very long dorsal and anal fins comprising both spines and rays. The caudal fin may be pointed or forked and the pectoral fins are located low on the body. The pelvic fins are either reduced or totally absent. Large, fang-like teeth are conspicuous in both jaws. Most cutlassfishes are bright silvery overall.

Trichiuridae are usually very gregarious and huge shoals are frequently netted by trawlers. Their flesh makes good eating and in some regions of the world cutlassfishes have considerable commercial importance.

TRIGLIDAE
Gurnards
See page 378 for species description

This family is distributed throughout tropical and temperate waters worldwide, and of the 90-100 species known, seven have been recorded off southern Africa.

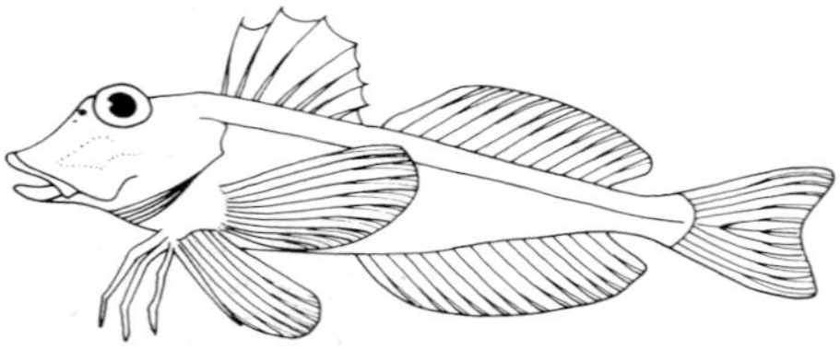

Triglidae are bottom-living fishes, recognized by the armour of spiky, bony plates which shields part of the body, especially the head. In a number of species, barbels and forward-pointing spines on the head add further to their 'thorny' appearance. These elongate, tapering fishes have two dorsal fins and large well-developed pectoral fins with several of the lower rays being detached and enlarged into feelers. All have small mouths with very fine teeth.

Gurnards range considerably in size and some are known to attain 100 cm in length. Their bottom-feeding habits are aided by the pectoral feelers, used to probe the sand or mud for food. Many gurnards are caught in commercial trawl nets and in some fishing ports these fishes represent a significant proportion of the overall catch. Triglidae make excellent eating and many species are highly esteemed as table fish.

ZANCLIDAE
Moorish idol
See page 380 for species description

Previously, this single species family was considered to belong to the Acanthuridae on the basis of their very similar juvenile stages. However, the deeper body, elongate dorsal fin spines and absence of a caudal fin spine place this fish in its own family. Bristle-like teeth occur in the mouth, while a short spike may develop over each eye. Zanclidae are found over tropical, Indo-Pacific coral reefs and are valued as aquarium fishes.

ZEIDAE
John Dories
See page 381 for species description

Zeidae are found in all oceans, where they inhabit the deeper waters of the continental shelf. Nine species frequent southern African waters. The taxonomy of these curious, rather primitive fishes is in a state of flux and a number of groups included may yet be placed in their own distinct families.

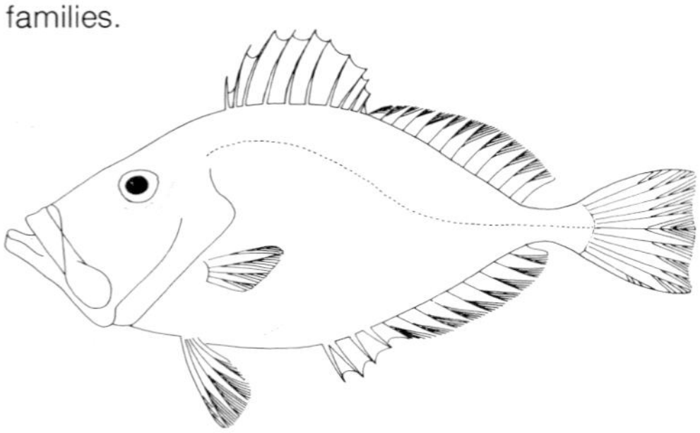

John Dories are unmistakable with their deep, compressed and almost scaleless bodies, protractile mouths and well-formed, spiny fins. Most species also have spiny, bony plates at the bases of their dorsal and anal fins and along the abdomen. They are normally plain-coloured fishes, but some have a large, round spot on each flank. Despite their chunky appearance, these fishes are successful predators. Their hunting strategy is based on their extraordinarily protractile jaws rather than their swimming prowess and when prey wanders within range the telescopic mouth extends forward rapidly to snatch the unsuspecting victim.

Zeidae are often very common in deep-water trawling grounds and on occasion they can comprise the bulk of a fisherman's catch. Though excellent table fish the John Dories' unusual, almost mournful features deter many people from sampling these fish.

Acanthurus leucosternon

Bennett, 1832

Common names SA - painted surgeon. Elsewhere - powder-blue surgeon

[Smith 243□3]

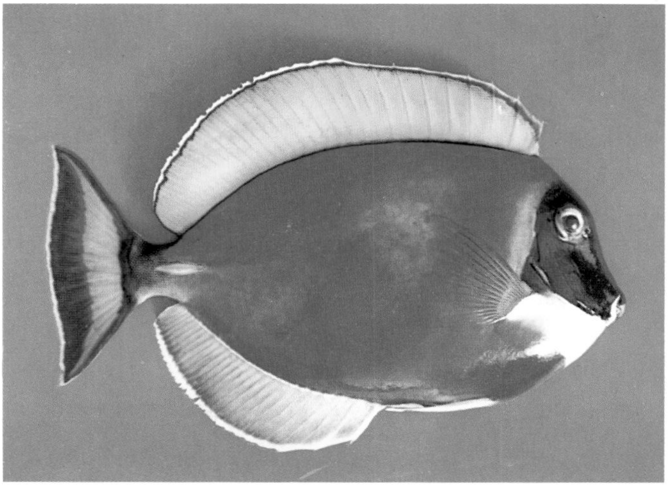

IDENTIFYING FEATURES

COLOUR, SHAPE AND SIZE

The strongly compressed, oval-shaped body of the painted surgeon is predominantly blue, with a black head and white chin. A short, bright-yellow stripe marks the sheath of the caudal spine. The dorsal fin is bright yellow and the anal and pelvic fins are white. The pectoral fins are translucent yellow. A white panel is reversed out of the black caudal fin. Can attain 23 cm.

EXTERNAL ANATOMY

Like all typical surgeonfish the painted surgeon is armed with an erectile, lancet-like spine on either side of the caudal peduncle. Numerous fine, but rough, ctenoid scales cover the thick skin. The fins are well developed and include a single dorsal of nine spines plus 28-30 rays, an anal of three spines plus 24-28 rays and a slightly emarginate caudal. The small mouth protrudes marginally and has a single row of incisors in each jaw. The rakers on the first gill arch are very short. The lateral line is not distinct.

NATURAL HISTORY

This beautiful little fish is virtually confined to coral reefs and is frequently found in very shallow water. It is most active during the day, but once disturbed will take shelter in holes and cracks in the reefs. If molested, the painted surgeon, like other surgeonfishes, will often raise its scalpel-sharp spines and lash from side to side with its tail. It is capable, in this manner, of lacerating both potential predators and careless handlers quite severely. Diet consists mainly of algae, including green, brown, coralline and red seaweeds, for which the fish's cutting incisors are well suited. Tiny gastropods, mollusc eggs and crustaceans also form part of the diet and are rasped away from the rocky bottom. Though generally solitary or paired, small shoals gather over reefs during the breeding season to partake in courtship displays before shedding eggs and sperm into the sea. The pelagic and semi-transparent young are widely dispersed by ocean currents.

DISTRIBUTION

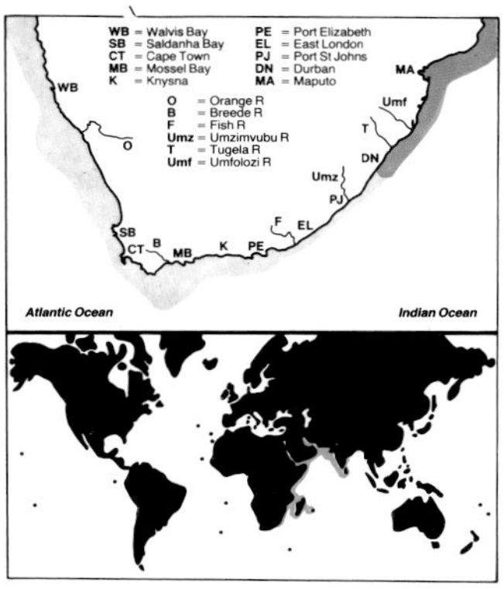

CAPTURE

The painted surgeon's colourful appearance makes it a prized aquarium specimen but, though edible, it is seldom caught for food. It will thrive in captivity if given adequate shelter and careful attention is paid to its varied diet.

SPECIFIC CATCH RESTRICTIONS

None.

NAME DERIVATION

Acanthurus, thorned; *leucosternon,* white chest. Painted surgeon, a reference to its vivid primary colours and scalpel-like spine each side of the caudal peduncle.

SIMILAR SPECIES

The distinctive colouration precludes confusion with any other species.

Acanthurus triostegus

(Linnaeus, 1758)
Common names SA - convict surgeon. Elsewhere - banded surgeon
[Smith 243□11]

IDENTIFYING FEATURES

COLOUR, SHAPE AND SIZE

The overall body colour of this strongly compressed, oval-shaped fish is pale green, with five or six black, vertical bands on each flank, the first passing through the eye. The underside is white and the fins yellowish-green. These colours darken shortly after capture when they more closely resemble nocturnal colouration. Some specimens have several black spots on the fins and body. Can attain 27 cm.

EXTERNAL ANATOMY

Numerous minute, but tough, ctenoid scales cover the body. The fins are well developed and include a single dorsal of nine or ten spines plus 21-25 rays, an anal of three spines plus 19-22 rays and a truncate caudal fin that has a short, erectile spine on either side of the peduncle. The small terminal mouth bears a row of strong incisors at the front of each jaw. The rakers of the first gill arch are short.

NATURAL HISTORY

The convict surgeon is one of the most common of the Acanthuridae, but is generally confined to shallow inshore reefs and rock pools as the growth of its algal food supply is dependent on light penetration. It is also frequently found in harbours where sheltered wharfs and jetties provide ideal surfaces for the growth of vegetable matter. Unlike the painted surgeon, this species is gregarious, and shoals ranging in size from a few to thousands of fish may be seen feeding on a variety of red, green and thread-like seaweeds, which, being of low energy content, are grazed continuously throughout the day. In contrast to many other vegetarian fishes, the convict surgeon can digest its food completely. Sexual maturity is attained at a length of 10 cm and breeding is known to be correlated with periods of full moon during late winter and spring. Spawning occurs in shoals and the transparent, pelagic juveniles are distributed by ocean currents.

DISTRIBUTION

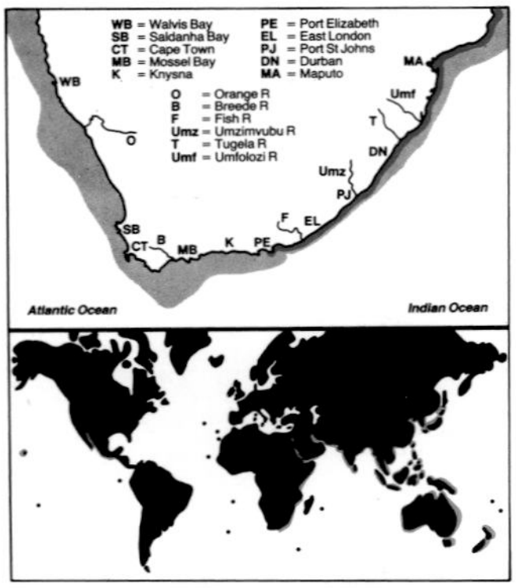

CAPTURE

The convict surgeon is easily and frequently caught by aquarium enthusiasts, but will survive in captivity only if provided with a regular supply of fresh seaweed. This can be ensured by a frequent exchange of algae-covered rocks from intertidal pools. Alternatively, algae may grow in the tank if provided with natural light.

SPECIFIC CATCH RESTRICTIONS

None.

NAME DERIVATION

Acanthurus, thorned; *triostegus,* triple-covered. Convict surgeon, a reference to the convict-like markings and sharp, scalpel-like spines either side of the caudal peduncle.

SIMILAR SPECIES

This is the only surgeonfish in our waters with vertical black bars.

Acanthurus xanthopterus

Valenciennes, 1835
Common names SA – yellowfin or blue surgeon. Elsewhere – yellowfin surgeon
[Smith 243□12]

IDENTIFYING FEATURES

COLOUR, SHAPE AND SIZE

This largest of the surgeonfishes has a typically compressed and oval-shaped body which is attractively, but quite variably, coloured. Most dead specimens are a purplish-brown overall, though living specimens frequently appear to be a lighter blue-grey. There may also be some irregular blue or grey lines on the body, and about four blue lines on the otherwise yellowish-brown dorsal and anal fins. The caudal-fin base is noticeably paler, while the distal ends of both pectorals and pelvics are yellow. Can attain 65 cm.

EXTERNAL ANATOMY

The finely scaled body bears well-developed fins, including a continuous dorsal of 11 spines and 25-27 rays, an anal of three spines and 23-25 rays, and a distinctly concave caudal fin. In larger specimens, this tail becomes almost lunate, and the depth of the fork may equal 20 per cent of the standard body length. As in other Acanthuridae, there is a lancet-like spine on the caudal peduncle, which, in this species, is known to grow longer with age. The terminal mouth bears a row of close-set, spatula-like teeth, and the first gill arch is set with 16-24 rakers.

NATURAL HISTORY

This common surgeon of warm coastal bays and lagoons is primarily confined to shallow coral and rocky reefs. It is frequently sighted by divers over reefs in the St Lucia Marine Reserve, but appears equally abundant elsewhere, such as Limestone Reef in Durban and Aliwal Shoal further south. Its large size makes it conspicuous, and shoals of up to 20 individuals can often be seen foraging over the flat tops of reefs where there is adequate plant growth. This species is also more inclined than other surgeonfishes to move away from the reefs and range over sandy or rubble substrates. The diet of the yellowfin surgeon comprises seaweeds, including those short-tufted algae that may grow on sandy or muddy bottoms, away from the reef. Little is known of the yellowfin surgeon's breeding behaviour, though it probably spawns in small groups in proximity to the reef. The larvae are of the spiky *acronurus* type and distributed by ocean currents.

DISTRIBUTION

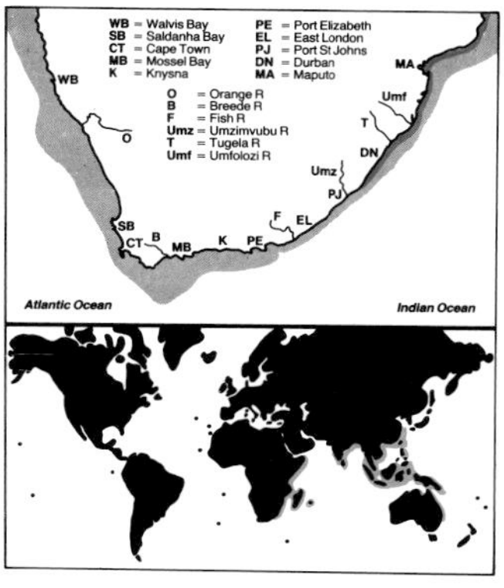

SPECIFIC CATCH RESTRICTIONS

None.

CAPTURE

The yellowfin surgeon readily takes a bait, and is probably the only surgeonfish that does so. Though edible, it is not marketed and seldom specifically fished for. In the Far East, moderate numbers are caught as a by-catch in nets and fishtraps.
SA angling record – 0,8 kg.
SA spearfishing record – 3,4 kg.

NAME DERIVATION

Acanthurus, thorned; *xanthopterus,* yellow finned. Yellowfin surgeon, a reference to its yellow-coloured fins and the scalpel-like spine on each side of the peduncle.

SIMILAR SPECIES

Surgeonfishes may require detailed measurements to confirm identification. The yellowfin surgeon is reasonably distinct, however, because of its large size, blue body with yellow fins, and lunate tail.

Naso unicornis

(Forsskål, 1775)

Common names SA – longhorn unicorn. Elsewhere – longsnouted or brown unicorn

[Smith 243□30]

IDENTIFYING FEATURES

COLOUR, SHAPE AND SIZE

Most unicorn fishes can be immediately recognized by the horn-like structure located on the forehead, and *Naso unicornis* is no exception. However, confusion can sometimes occur because the horn only develops with age and may be less conspicuous in juveniles and female fish. The body of the longhorn unicorn is rather elongate and is also strongly compressed. Though colouration is somewhat variable, most specimens are dark-olive or brownish overall, often with mottled upper flanks. The dorsal and anal fins, and sometimes the caudal, are attractively patterned with irregular orange stripes. Surrounding each of the spines on the caudal peduncle is a bright blue blotch. Occasionally the lips are also blue. Can attain 70 cm.

EXTERNAL ANATOMY

Arranged along the distinct lateral line are numerous series of very fine scales. The well-developed fins have prominent spines. The single dorsal comprises five or six spines plus 27-30 rays and extends from the top of the head to the caudal peduncle. The anal fin is also very long and comprises two spines plus 26-29 rays, while the large caudal fin is noticeably emarginate, often with elongate outer rays. Two scalpel-like spines occur on each side of the caudal peduncle, a typical feature of the family. Unlike the erectile spines of the surgeonfishes, however, those of *Naso* species are fixed and located on bony plates. Each spine has a sharply curved edge which points forward. The small terminal mouth is set with a single row of compressed teeth in each jaw. There are approximately 13 short rakers on the first gill arch.

DISTRIBUTION

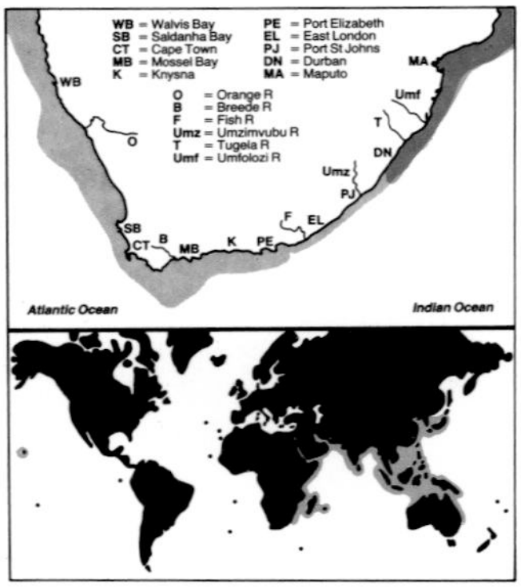

NATURAL HISTORY

This curious fish is confined to shallow-water reefs and may be quite abundant in places. The longhorn unicorn is a herbivore and feeds on a variety of seaweeds, which are continuously cropped into short tufts. It is basically diurnal in habit and certainly most of its feeding takes place during daylight. The breeding biology of this species is not fully understood, but as with other Acanthuridae, the fry are circular, almost transparent and widely distributed by ocean currents. Unicorn fishes in the St Lucia Marine Reserve are generally much larger than those occurring elsewhere in southern Africa.

CAPTURE

Longhorn unicorns are only very rarely tempted by bait, but because they are easily approached underwater, quite a number are shot by spearfishermen. Though edible, few people find the flesh of this species palatable.

SA angling record – 0,8 kg.

SA spearfishing record – 3,4 kg.

SPECIFIC CATCH RESTRICTIONS

None.

NAME DERIVATION

Naso, long nosed; *unicornis,* single-horned. Longhorn unicorn, a reference to the horn-like process on the forehead (it is particularly well developed in this species) and to the obvious analogy with the mythical unicorn.

SIMILAR SPECIES

The presence of two blue, bony plates armed with spines is distinctive of this species.

Albula vulpes

(Forsskål, 1775)
Common name Worldwide – bonefish
[Smith 38□1]

IDENTIFYING FEATURES

COLOUR, SHAPE AND SIZE
This brilliantly silver fish has an elongate body which is almost cylindrical in cross-section. The snout is long and cone-shaped. The fins are dusky and translucent, and the bases of the pectoral fins are bright yellow. Attains 100 cm.

EXTERNAL ANATOMY
Except for the naked head region, the body is covered with well-developed, cycloid scales arranged in 62-73 series along the lateral line. The spineless dorsal and anal fins are situated far back on the body, and have 15-19 and 7-9 soft rays respectively. The small, underslung mouth has five rows of fine, villiform teeth in each jaw, and there are numerous crushing teeth in the gullet. A flap of tissue occurs on the chin, just before the gill openings. There are 8-11 stubby rakers on the first gill arch. The eyes are extensively covered with adipose tissue.

DISTRIBUTION

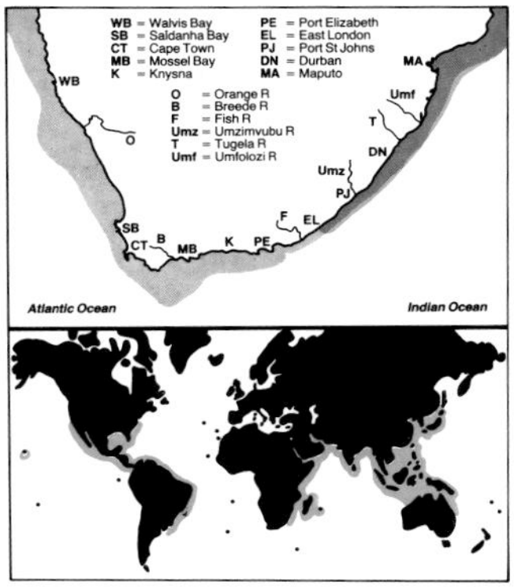

NATURAL HISTORY

This fish frequents muddy and sandy bottoms, sometimes in very shallow water, and occurs either singly or in small groups. Though intolerant of low salinities, bonefish are often caught near small river mouths at high tide. The underslung mouth makes it easier to feed on small crabs, crackershrimps, worms and molluscs, all of which are sucked from the muddy bottom and crushed with the molar-like, pharyngeal teeth. Although it prefers the shallows spawning takes place in deeper water, and breeding fish are encountered all year round. The young pass through an eel-like, transparent *leptocephalus* phase before changing into the adult form at a length of 6 cm. Sexual maturity is reached after one to two years at a length of 25-30 cm.

CAPTURE

Though timid, the bonefish is renowned among light-tackle anglers for its fighting ability rather than for its eating quality, which is impaired by many small bones. Almost any small bait will tempt it, and most catches are made at night, particularly from the beaches of Zululand. The bonefish makes excellent marlin bait, as its firm body and torpedo shape are well suited to trolling.
World angling record – 8,61 kg.
SA angling record – 8,61 kg.
SA spearfishing record – 4,6 kg.

SPECIFIC CATCH RESTRICTIONS

None.

NAME DERIVATION

Albula, white; *vulpes,* fox. Bonefish, a reference to the numerous bones.

SIMILAR SPECIES

The bonefish, like the ladyfish, tarpon and milkfish, lacks fin spines, but it can be distinguished from these three by having an underslung mouth. What was previously considered to be a single species worldwide has now been proven to comprise five different species. Hence this species may in future be known as *Albula glossodonta.* The differences between these species are based on detailed differences in the jaw structure.

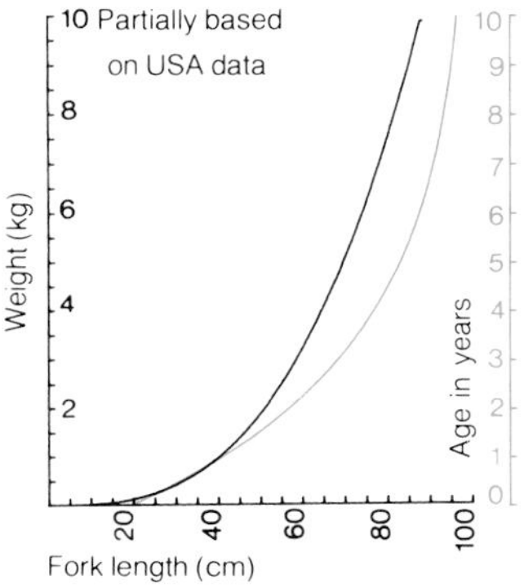

Ambassis natalensis

Gilchrist & Thompson, 1908
Common name Worldwide – slender glassy
[Smith 163□2]

IDENTIFYING FEATURES

COLOUR, SHAPE AND SIZE

This small, oblong fish often has an almost translucent appearance, especially when seen underwater. The general body colour, however, is dusky or yellowish with a distinct, silver, lateral band that has a mother-of-pearl sheen. The slender glassy seldom exceeds 7 cm.

EXTERNAL ANATOMY

The slender glassy is covered with distinctly cycloid scales arranged in some 27-29 series along the conspicuous lateral line. The dorsal and anal fins have strong spines and, significantly, 9-11 scales precede the dorsal fin. The single dorsal fin consists of one forward-pointing spine followed by eight normal spines plus 9-11 rays, while the anal fin consists of three spines plus 9-11 rays. The caudal fin is forked. The mouth is upward-sloping and carries bands of fine teeth in each jaw. The first gill arch has 29 rakers and the pre-operculum is sharply serrated.

DISTRIBUTION

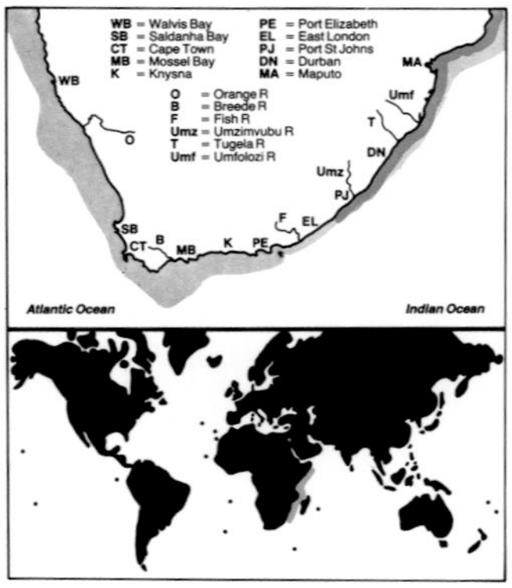

NATURAL HISTORY

This shoaling fish inhabits shallow, coastal waters, bays and lagoons and is tolerant of low salinities. It is the most common of the glassies, and is especially abundant in Natal's larger estuaries and harbours. It is not an active swimming fish and dense shoals may be seen 'hanging' below jetties and along wharfs, where they feed in the midwater region. Small planktonic crustaceans, particularly copepods, are filtered from water passing over the gills by the long rakers. Specimens reach sexual maturity at a length of 4-5 cm and spawning occurs in estuaries throughout the year with a peak from August to December. The fry are not widely distributed and the entire life cycle of this species can, therefore, occur within the estuarine environment.

CAPTURE

Many anglers regard this species as excellent bait and large numbers can be captured with relative ease in small nets. Shoals, however, are often a nuisance to seine netters as, instead of passing harmlessly through the mesh, the slender glassies tend to snag the strands with their sharp dorsal spines and very soon the net is clogged. Aquarists maintain glassies in marine or freshwater tanks with success.

Note: The slender glassy makes an excellent subject for nature study classes and for biological research as it is easily caught and thrives in captivity. Pollution studies undertaken by the CSIR often make use of this species to detect lethal toxins discharged at sea.

SPECIFIC CATCH RESTRICTIONS

None.

NAME DERIVATION

Ambassis, completely dried; *natalensis,* of Natal. Slender glassy, a slender fish which appears semi-transparent when viewed underwater.

SIMILAR SPECIES

Glassies are quite tricky to identify and microscopic examination is essential. The slender glassy is best distinguished by its continuous lateral line and 9-11 predorsal scales. The related longspine glassy *(A. productus)* has about 14 predorsal scales.

Ambassis productus

Cuvier, 1828
Common name Worldwide – longspine glassy
[Smith 163□3]

IDENTIFYING FEATURES

COLOUR, SHAPE AND SIZE
This small, oblong fish often has an almost translucent appearance, especially when seen underwater. The general body colour, however, is dusky or yellowish, with a distinct, silver, lateral band that has a mother-of-pearl sheen. The longspine glassy is the largest member of the Ambassidae and can attain 15 cm.

EXTERNAL ANATOMY
The body is well covered with distinctly cycloid scales arranged in series along the conspicuous and smoothly curved lateral line. Fourteen easily visible rows of scales lie before the first dorsal fin. The double dorsal consists of seven prominent spines and 9-10 rays, the anal has three prominent spines and 9-11 rays, and the caudal fin is forked. Banks of fine teeth occur in both jaws of the upward-slanting mouth. The edge of the pre-operculum is strongly serrated, and the first gill arch carries 28-33 conspicuous gill rakers.

DISTRIBUTION

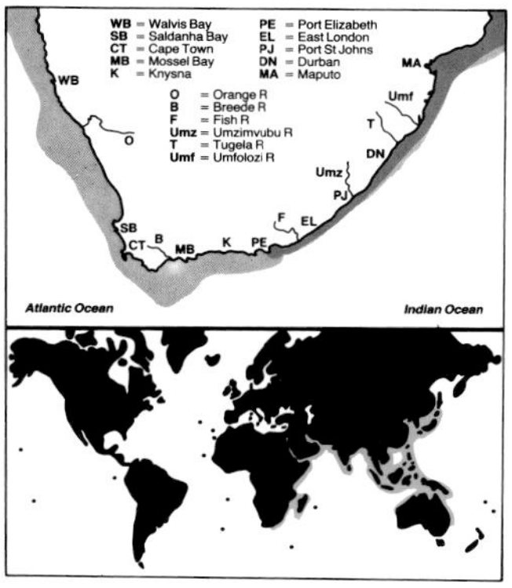

NATURAL HISTORY

This coast-hugging species can adapt to fresh water, and, though it is nowhere abundant, small shoals inhabit most Natal estuaries. The longspine glassy is not an active fish, and often remains motionless in mid-water for long periods. This habit of 'hanging in suspension' enables it to feed almost exclusively on planktonic crustaceans such as copepods, mysids and small shrimps, which are filtered from the water by the long gill rakers. Marine worms, fish fry and fish eggs, however, are also occasionally taken in this manner. The longspine glassy's inactivity would seem to make it particularly vulnerable to predators, but this danger is somewhat offset by its inconspicuous, translucent body, and shoaling habits. Sexual maturity is attained at a length of 5-7,5 cm and spawning occurs within estuarine systems. Little else is known of the breeding cycle.

CAPTURE

Though not an angling fish, this species is of great value as bait, and, in parts of the East, it is salt-dried and eaten.The longspine glassy is popular with marine aquarists, especially as it can adapt to fresh water, and thrives in captivity.

SPECIFIC CATCH RESTRICTIONS

None.

NAME DERIVATION

Ambassis, completely dried; *productus,* a reference to the 'produced' or lengthened spines. Longspine glassy, a reference to the rather long spines, and its translucent appearance when viewed underwater.

SIMILAR SPECIES

The three South African glassies are all rather similar, though this species is easily identified by its 14 pre-dorsal scales, and continuous lateral line.

Apogon thermalis

Cuvier, 1829

Common names SA – masked cardinal. Elsewhere – barcheeked cardinalfish

[Smith 175□26]

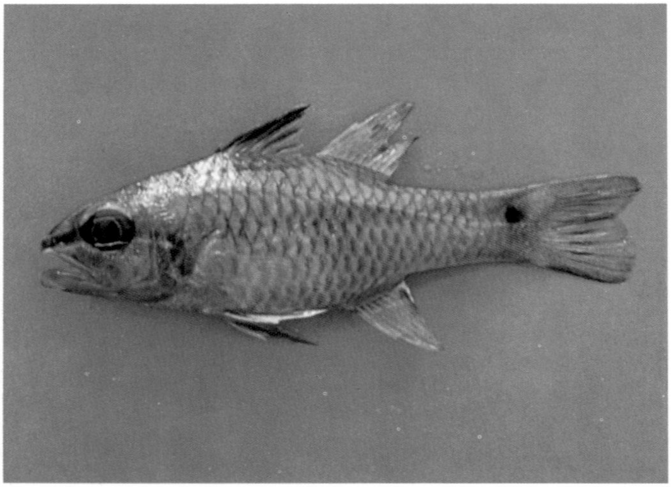

IDENTIFYING FEATURES

COLOUR, SHAPE AND SIZE

The general body colour of this small but robust fish is golden-red with black shading covering part of the first dorsal fin. The most noticeable marking, however, is the black band running from the tip of the snout, through the eye, as far as the gill covers. There is also a black blotch on either side of the caudal peduncle. Can attain 8 cm.

EXTERNAL ANATOMY

The distinctly ctenoid scales are arranged in 22-25 series along the lateral line. The fins are well developed and include a double dorsal of six spines followed by one spine plus nine rays, an anal of two spines and eight or nine rays, and a slightly forked caudal. The large, downward-sloping mouth bears only villiform teeth. The large eyes have black pupils and are situated directly above the angle of the jaw.

DISTRIBUTION

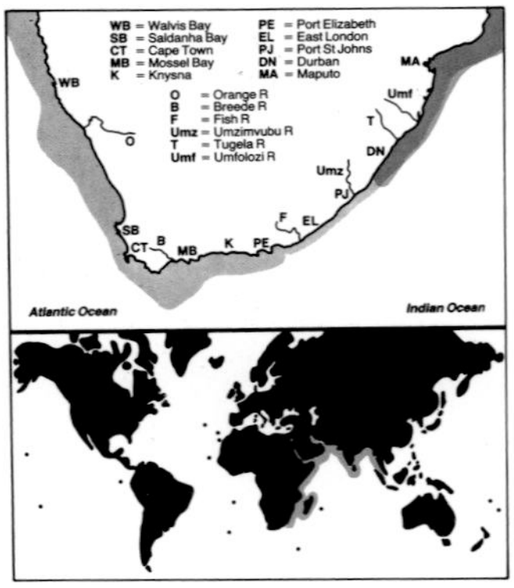

NATURAL HISTORY

As with many Apogonidae, the masked cardinal inhabits coral and rocky regions. Most of the daylight hours are spent hidden in holes or under rocks, but at night, these fish become more active foraging for small crabs, shrimps and larval fish. The large mouth, however, also allows the capture of relatively big prey. Unlike other members of the family, which may form shoals, this species tends to be solitary or paired and may permanently inhabit a certain territory. An unusual feature of this slow-swimming fish is the use of the pectoral fins instead of the caudal fin for forward propulsion.

Breeding, too, is unusual as the male carries the fertilized eggs in his large mouth until they hatch. The precise function of this habit is not clear, but undoubtedly the eggs are protected in this manner against both predators and the elements. The male may also build and guard the breeding nest.

CAPTURE

The masked cardinal is of no interest to anglers, but certainly makes a good aquarium species, and is readily caught in almost any rock pool or shallow reef. To ensure its survival in captivity, however, it is essential to provide a dark hiding place in the tank.

All freshly caught cardinalfishes should be very carefully handled as males may be carrying eggs in their mouths. Often these are regurgitated during the trauma of capture, but if this can be avoided, the aquarist stands a chance of the young being successfully hatched in the tank.

SPECIFIC CATCH RESTRICTIONS

None.

NAME DERIVATION

Apogon, without a beard; *thermalis,* pertaining to heat. Masked cardinal, a reference to the black eyeband or mask, and the red body, reminiscent of the colour of a cardinal's cassock.

SIMILAR SPECIES

This is the only cardinalfish which has six dorsal spines, a black stripe on the snout and a dot on the caudal peduncle. Other cardinal species are more difficult to identify and usually require careful examination.

Galeichthys feliceps

(Valenciennes, 1840)
Common name Worldwide - white seacatfish.
[Smith 59□3]

IDENTIFYING FEATURES

COLOUR, SHAPE AND SIZE
This robust fish has an elongate body with a depressed head. It is dusky-brown overall, but darker above and white below. All fins are dark to black, but the barbels are pale. Can attain 55 cm.

EXTERNAL ANATOMY
The lateral line is conspicuous along the scaleless body and the smooth skin is coated with mucus. The primitive fins include two separate dorsals. The first has one spine plus seven rays, while the second is a fleshy lobe. The anal fin has 17-20 rays. Both pectoral fins have spines, which, like the dorsal spine, are strongly serrated and covered with toxic mucous tissue. The broad, underslung mouth has thick lips and bands of fine teeth in each jaw. Three pairs of barbels project from the chin. The first gill arch carries approximately 12 rakers.

DISTRIBUTION

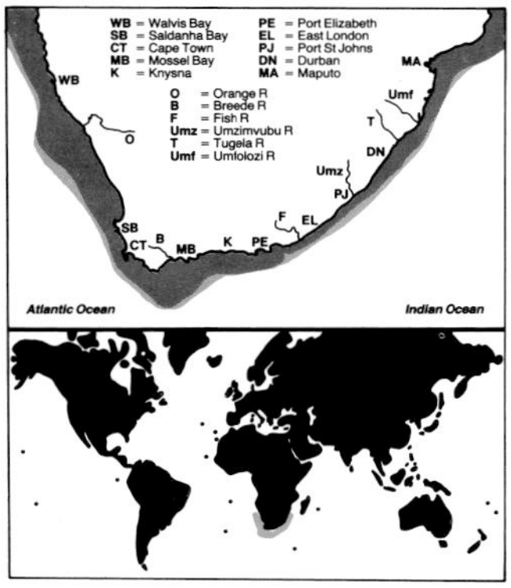

NATURAL HISTORY

This seacatfish is a shallow-water species which is tolerant of low salinities and turbid conditions. It inhabits reefs, muddy banks and estuaries, but prefers protected waters and is frequently found deep within submarine caves or below rocky ledges. Feeding occurs exclusively on the bottom where the barbels function to 'feel out' prey, especially in very muddy waters. Crayfish are most favoured, but the diet also includes small fish and crabs. Little has been documented on its breeding cycle, though it is known that the pea-sized eggs are 'nursed' by the male who carries them in his large mouth until they hatch. The young use estuaries as nursery areas, especially those along the Transkeian and eastern Cape coasts. Research in the United States has shown that relatives of this species have evolved a system of sound communication through vibrations in the body cavity which are amplified by the air bladder. It is not known, however, whether *G. feliceps* has this facility. The poisonous spines are dangerous and wounds from these should be immediately treated by immersion in very hot water for at least thirty minutes. A doctor should also be consulted.

CAPTURE

Though often solitary, the white seacatfish does occasionally gather into large shoals and at these times it can be the curse of both shore and ski-boat anglers as little else is caught. Despite its lack of popularity it makes good eating, and similar species are caught in tropical areas for local fresh-fish markets.
SA angling record - 3,8 kg.
SA spearfishing record - 2,6 kg.

SPECIFIC CATCH RESTRICTIONS

None.

NAME DERIVATION

Galeichthys, weasel-like fish; *feliceps,* cat-like head. White seacatfish, a reference to its white underside and cat-like whiskers.

SIMILAR SPECIES

This species closely resembles the black seacatfish *(G. ater).* Until recently the two were often confused. Research at the JLB Smith Institute has helped to resolve this problem, *G. ater* being confined to the Cape south coast and identifiable by its dark-brown, pigmented belly.

Atherina breviceps

Valenciennes, 1835
Common name SA - Cape silverside
[Smith 111□1]

IDENTIFYING FEATURES

COLOUR, SHAPE AND SIZE

This is a small, elongate fish with a relatively small head. Freshly caught specimens are translucent, with a brilliant, silver, lateral stripe down each flank. The body is often speckled with black pigmentations known as melanophores. The upper surface, especially the snout, is a dusky colour. After preservation, these striking colours are lost and the fish becomes white or brownish. Can attain 10 cm.

EXTERNAL ANATOMY

The fins are well developed, with two separate dorsals set well back on the body, the first comprises 5-8 spines, and the second has one spine plus 11-15 rays. The anal fin comprises one spine plus 15-18 rays, the first dorsal is positioned directly above the end of the pelvic-fin tips, and the caudal is moderately forked. The eyes are noticeably large in comparison to the overall head size. A significant feature of this genus is the smooth edge of the pre-operculum, which in many other silversides bears a distinct notch. The terminal mouth opens upwards and bears very fine, villiform teeth in each jaw. The gill rakers are well developed, numbering 17-20 on the lower limb of the first arch. The scales of the Cape silverside are rather smaller than most other atherinid fishes and usually number 44-50 along the lateral line, with 7-11 transverse rows down each side.

NATURAL HISTORY

This is a common, endemic species of estuarine and coastal waters, moving about in fair-sized shoals. The Cape silverside can withstand a reasonable reduction in salinity, and is apparently one of the few marine fish species able to complete its life cycle within the estuarine environment. The eggs produced are not only rather large by comparison with most other fish, but also equipped with well-developed, adhesive filaments, which allow them to be attached to plants or other structures. Being endowed with well-developed gill rakers, the Cape silverside is able to feed on quite large planktonic animals such as copepods, crab larvae and the fry of other fishes. On the other hand, this silverside itself represents an important link in the food web, as it is extensively preyed upon by a wide variety of gamefish and piscivorous birds.

DISTRIBUTION

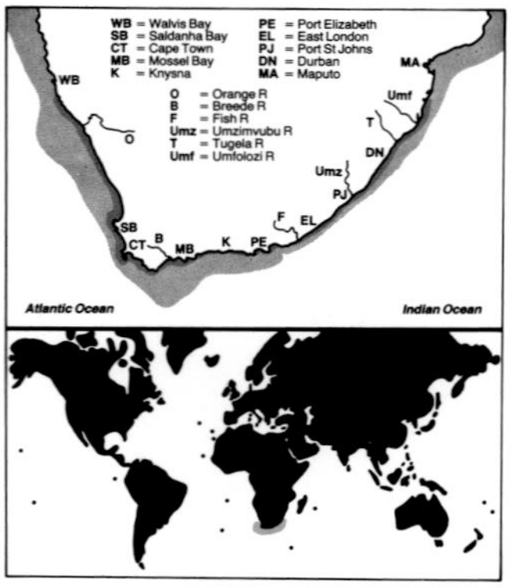

SPECIFIC CATCH RESTRICTIONS

None.

CAPTURE

While the Cape silverside is seldom caught for food, it does represent an excellent source of bait. A carefully rigged silverside bait is certain to tempt estuarine fish predators such as the kob, river snapper and kingfish.

NAME DERIVATION

Atherina, Old Greek for smelt; *breviceps,* short head. Cape silverside, from its prevalence in Cape waters and bright-silver, lateral stripe.

SIMILAR SPECIES

Silversides are generally a rather difficult group of fishes to identify. The Cape silverside is fairly distinct, however, and may be distinguished from several related species by having seven or more transverse rows of scales, no pre-opercular notch, a first dorsal before or opposite the pelvic fin tips, and an absence of numerous denticles on the side of the face.

Atherinomorus lacunosus

(Forster, 1801)
Common name Worldwide – hardyhead silverside
[Smith 111□3]

IDENTIFYING FEATURES

COLOUR, SHAPE AND SIZE

This small, yet robust, fish has a noticeably broad head which results in a superficial resemblance to mullet (family Mugilidae). The overall body colour is silvery, but the upper parts are pale green and, especially in fresh specimens, an iridescent blue stripe is evident along each flank. The fins are dusky and, when seen underwater, the hardyhead silverside appears partly translucent. Attains 15 cm.

EXTERNAL ANATOMY

The 40-50 series of large, firm scales that cover the body give the fish rigidity. The fins are well developed and include a double dorsal set well back on the body and consisting of five or six spines followed by one spine plus nine or ten rays, and an anal of one spine plus 13 or 14 rays. The pectoral fins are short and located high on the sides of the body, approximately in line with the top of the gill covers. The pelvic fins are also short and the caudal is strongly forked. The jaws of the wide mouth slant downwards to a point below the middle of the noticeably large eyes. Several rows of fine, villiform teeth are set in each jaw and extend partially onto the lips. In addition, relatively large, pharyngeal teeth occur in the gullet. There are 22-26 long rakers on the first gill arch. The body cavity is lined with a layer of black tissue which presumably minimizes the amount of light that would otherwise penetrate this translucent, shallow-water fish.

NATURAL HISTORY

This common fish is widely distributed throughout the shallow waters of the tropical Indo-Pacific region. Present throughout the year, it usually occurs close to the shore off sandy beaches, or in estuaries. During the day, hardyhead silversides gather into large shoals to shelter in the lee of reefs. At night, however, they scatter to feed on zooplankton and also on insects that may be floating at the surface. Research conducted by the University of Natal in Pietermaritzburg indicates that maturity is attained at a length of 10 cm and that spawning occurs close to estuaries from October to January. The eggs have fine filaments which secure them either to the sea-bed or to some submarine object.

DISTRIBUTION

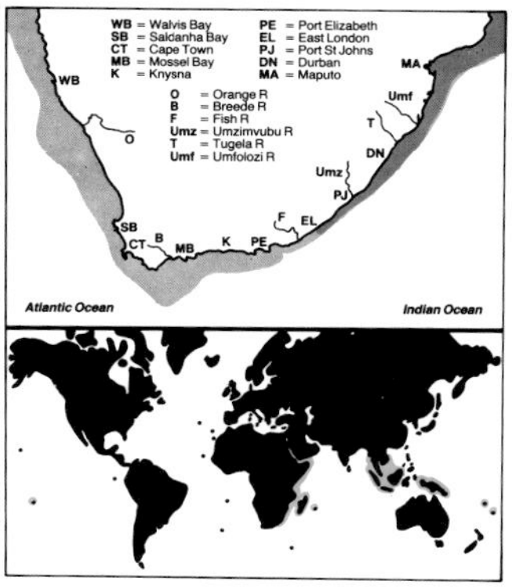

CAPTURE

Easily captured in small seine nets, the hardyhead silverside is an excellent source of bait for anglers. It is an equally good source of food and though not exploited in southern Africa, in several eastern countries this fish regularly appears in fish markets, either fresh or salted and dried.

SPECIFIC CATCH RESTRICTIONS

None.

NAME DERIVATION

Atherinomorus, resembling a smelt; *lacunosus,* full of hollows. Hardyhead silverside, a reference to its broad, hard head and to the iridescent stripe along each flank.

SIMILAR SPECIES

While minute anatomical differences exist between this and other silversides, the hardyhead is distinctly larger and more robust. It is one of several silversides common to southern Africa. In Cape estuaries and shallow inshore regions, the Cape silverside (*Atherina breviceps*) is more prevalent and can be distinguished from the hardyhead by its six or seven dorsal spines and more slender body.

Balistoides conspicillum

(Bloch & Schneider, 1801)
Common names Worldwide – clown or waistcoat triggerfish.
[Smith 263□4]

IDENTIFYING FEATURES

COLOUR, SHAPE AND SIZE
This handsomely coloured fish is unmistakable with its orange 'clown's lips' and numerous large white spots on the lower sides of the jet-black body. The body is deep and strongly compressed. Can attain 35 cm.

EXTERNAL ANATOMY
The body is encased in 43 series of large rhomboid scales which form a flexible armour. There are three spines plus 25 rays in the dorsal fin, the anal fin consists of 22 rays and the caudal is truncate. The pelvic fins are reduced to a short ventral spine. The first dorsal spine is much enlarged and can be 'locked' into an upright position by the second dorsal spine or 'trigger'. Both jaws of the small terminal mouth have stout incisors. A deep groove is noticeable across the snout, just below the eyes. The gill openings are somewhat small. The eyes are set well back from the mouth, on a head that is almost one third of the total body length.

NATURAL HISTORY

The clown triggerfish inhabits shallow rocky and coral reefs such as those of the St Lucia Marine Reserve. Here it feeds on hard-shelled crustaceans, gastropods and, especially, sea urchins which are disarmed by biting off the spines. The strong teeth are well suited to its diet. The ability of this species to lock its first dorsal spine into an upright position serves as a defence mechanism either to deter predators or to wedge itself securely into a hole or crack in the reef. The second dorsal and anal fins are used for propulsion, while the caudal merely acts as a rudder. Scuba divers often hear grunting noises made by these fish which are produced by vibrations of the air bladder. This facility may function as a means of communication between individuals. It is doubtful if many fish prey on adult triggerfish, but the juveniles are known to be eaten by tuna and dolphinfish. These juveniles are distributed over large areas and shelter beneath floating objects borne along by ocean currents.

DISTRIBUTION

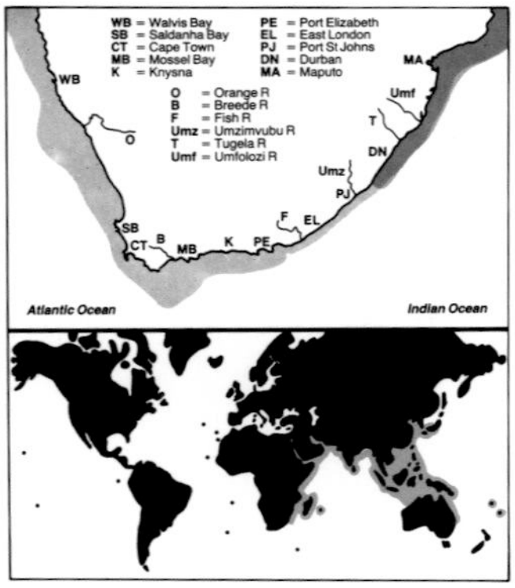

CAPTURE

For obvious reasons this fish is much sought after by marine aquarists and is sometimes sold at high prices, a practice which should be discouraged. The clown triggerfish is not regarded as edible and is occasionally held responsible for food poisoning. SA angling record – 0,8 kg.

SPECIFIC CATCH RESTRICTIONS

None.

NAME DERIVATION

Balistoides, from *ballista,* an instrument for firing arrows, a reference to the trigger-like spine; *conspicillum,* conspicuous. Clown triggerfish, a reference to its bright colours and trigger-like spine.

SIMILAR SPECIES

The distinctive markings of this species cannot possibly be confused with those of any other.

Rhinecanthus rectangulus

(Bloch & Schneider, 1801)
Common name Worldwide – rectangular triggerfish.
(Perhaps this fish is best known by its attractive Polynesian name used in Hawaii: 'humuhumu nukunuku apuaa'.)
[Smith 263□14]

IDENTIFYING FEATURES

COLOUR, SHAPE AND SIZE

The striking colours and unmistakable markings of this small triggerfish make it easy to identify. A bright-blue band surrounds the upper jaw and contrasts strongly with the orange snout. A broad, black or dark-brown band extends diagonally across the body from the eye to the anal fin and completely separates the upper flanks from the head and pale chest. The caudal peduncle is also dark-brown or black. The fins are dusky to translucent, the pectoral fins being marked with a fine orange bar. Can attain 23 cm.

EXTERNAL ANATOMY

The somewhat angular body is encased in distinct rhomboid scales, their regular arrangement in series creating a conspicuous 'criss-cross' pattern. The modified scales on either side of the caudal peduncle carry five rows of short, sharp spikes. The dorsal fin is in two parts, the first consisting of three spines and the second of 22-24 rays. As with all triggerfishes, the first dorsal spine is very stout and can be locked into an upright position by the second spine or trigger. The spineless anal fin has 20 rays. The pectoral fins are large and rounded while the pelvics are reduced to a spiny projection at the lowest part of the body. Both jaws of the small mouth bear strong incisors. Small, rounded gill openings occur just before the pectoral fins.

NATURAL HISTORY

The conspicuous, rectangular triggerfish can be seen on almost any shallow coral or rocky reef throughout the subtropical and tropical waters of its range. Here it feeds on a diet of corals and encrusing organisms, all of which are easily snapped off by the strong teeth. This triggerfish is easily approached underwater, but it is nevertheless difficult to catch as, once alarmed, it will, without any apparent haste,take refuge in a tiny hole or crevice. Here, by erecting its dorsal and pelvic spines, it wedges itself tightly and, even if the tail remains accessible, the sharp caudal spikes protect the fish from rear assault. If persistantly molested, the triggerfish will repeat a series of short grunts. Little information about its breeding cycle is available, though a late-winter spawning season is indicated, as very small rectangular triggerfish may be seen on reefs during the summer.

CAPTURE

The rectangular triggerfish is a popular aquarium species and will thrive in captivity if a large tank with adequate rocks and shelter is provided. Though difficult to dislodge underwater it is easily caught on a small hook. It is not generally eaten.

SPECIFIC CATCH RESTRICTIONS

None.

DISTRIBUTION

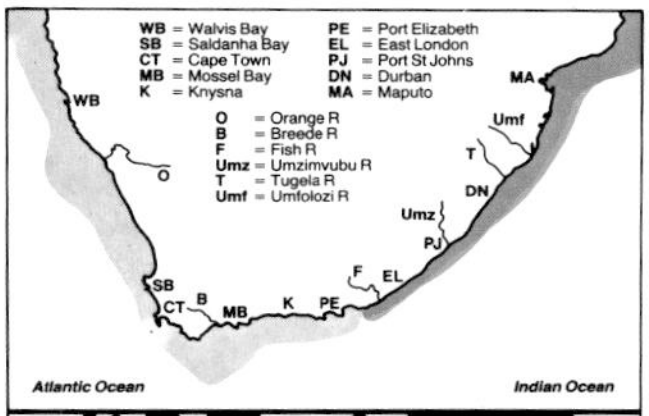

NAME DERIVATION

Rhinecanthus, a file-like spine: *rectangulus,* right angled. Rectangular triggerfish, a reference to its geometric scales and body shape.

SIMILAR SPECIES

The absence of a groove before the eye, and their characteristic markings, will distinguish this and closely related species from other triggerfishes.

Sufflamen fraenatus

(Latrielle, 1804)
Common name Worldwide - bridle triggerfish
[Smith 263□17]

IDENTIFYING FEATURES

COLOUR, SHAPE AND SIZE

In common with most triggerfish, this species has a compressed body which, in profile, is shaped rather like a rugby ball. It is far less colourful than many of its relatives being brown overall, but somewhat pale below. A pinkish-yellow ring encircles the snout and a brighter yellow line extends, on either side of the head, from the corner of the mouth almost to the pectoral fin base. These two marks combine to form the characteristic 'bridle' pattern. Juveniles and females lack this bridle pattern. The dorsal fins, as well as the anal and caudal fins, are dark brown. Can attain 50 cm.

EXTERNAL ANATOMY

Rigid, rhomboid scales cover the entire body and their regular arrangement forms a distinct 'criss-cross' or diamond pattern. The scales on the head are small, but, behind the gill openings, several are enlarged into bony plates. On the caudal peduncle, the scales have small ridges and are arranged in 12 or 13 series. As with the majority of Balistidae, the eyes are small,but just preceding them, in this species, is a well-defined groove. The first dorsal fin consists of three spines, the first two of which are long and form the typical 'trigger' mechanism. The second dorsal fin has 29-31 rays and the anal fin has 26-28 rays. The caudal fin is slightly emarginate or truncate and the pelvics are reduced to a single, short, movable spine. The white teeth of the small terminal mouth are very strong, but not fused into a beak.

NATURAL HISTORY

This is probably one of the most common triggerfish off the East Coast of southern Africa, where it inhabits coral and rocky reefs to depths of 100 m. The diet includes coral polyps, as well as coralline seaweeds and other sedentary organisms which are chiselled off the reef with the strong teeth. It is an active fish and, between feeds, propels itself about the reef with rapid undulations of the soft dorsal and anal fins, the caudal fin only being used as a rudder. While swimming in this manner the dorsal spines lie flat within a sheath. If alarmed, however, the stout, first dorsal spine is triggered and held by the second to present an uncompromising spike, and it is unlikely that many marine predators look to this and other triggerfish for their food. Spawning has been recorded during the summer in more tropical regions and the juveniles are common amongst seaweeds, vegetation and other drifting objects at sea.

CAPTURE

On some reefs this fish is always first to reach the bait, much to the annoyance of ski-boat fishermen. It adapts well to aquarium life and is always interesting to watch. The bridle triggerfish is not considered edible.

SA angling record - 2,0 kg.

SPECIFIC CATCH RESTRICTIONS

None.

DISTRIBUTION

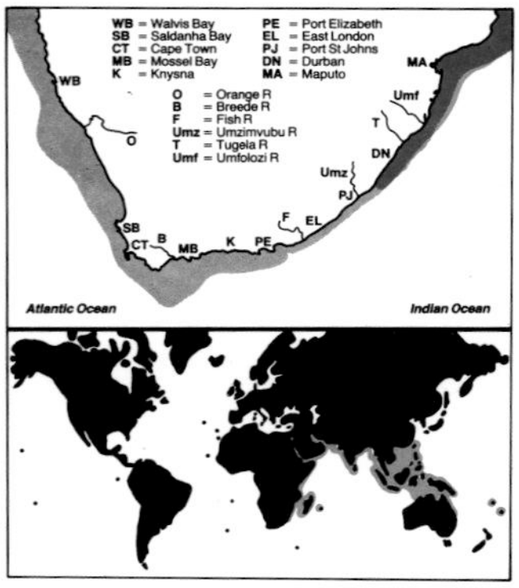

NAME DERIVATION

Sufflamen, an impediment, a reference to the second dorsal spine which prevents the depression of the first; *fraenatus,* bridled. Bridle triggerfish, a reference to the bridle-like markings and the dorsal spines.

SIMILAR SPECIES

The ridged scales on the caudal peduncle extend forward to below the dorsal fin. This feature together with the groove below each eye are distinctive of all *Sufflamen* species. The colour and patterns are distinctive of individual species.

Ablennes hians

(Valenciennes, 1846)
Common names SA – barred needlefish, garfish, longtom. Elsewhere – barred needlefish [Smith 113□1]

IDENTIFYING FEATURES

COLOUR, SHAPE AND SIZE
This elongate, strongly compressed fish is bluish-green along its dorsal surface with approximately 15 dark, transverse bands along each of the silvery sides. The interior of the mouth is orange and the belly is pale.Can attain 100 cm.

EXTERNAL ANATOMY
The body is covered with numerous, minute scales. The spineless fins are rather small and include a dorsal of 22-25 rays and an anal of 25-27 rays. Both are situated well back towards the forked caudal, the lower lobe of which is the longer. The jaws extend into a long 'beak' and carry many sharply pointed teeth. The gill arches have no rakers.

NATURAL HISTORY

This needlefish is a common and voracious offshore predator. It is intolerant of low salinities and turbid water and, therefore, rarely ventures inshore. It hunts just below the surface, feeding mainly on small fish, especially those sheltering beneath flotsam. The large, fearsomely armed jaws, however, quite often enable relatively big prey to be taken. When plentiful, squid, mantis shrimps and krill are also eaten. This species can 'skip' along the surface, driving itself forward with the anal and caudal fins which remain just below the surface.
In this manner, it is able to evade large predators. The body may contain tapeworm larvae, but these are harmless to man. Though its biology is obscure, sexually active specimens have been recorded off the Natal coast during summer and the females produce relatively few, but large eggs which presumably become attached to floating objects, and are then dispersed.

CAPTURE

The barred needlefish is only caught offshore. It takes small lures or fresh bait and fights aggressively on light tackle.
World angling record – 1,9 kg.
SA angling record – 3,1 kg.
SA spearfishing record – 2,6 kg.

SPECIFIC CATCH RESTRICTIONS

None.

NAME DERIVATION

Ablennes, lacking mucus; *hians,* gaping. Needlefish, a reference to its body shape, jaws and teeth.

SIMILAR SPECIES

The absence of gill rakers and compressed body are unique to this needlefish.

DISTRIBUTION

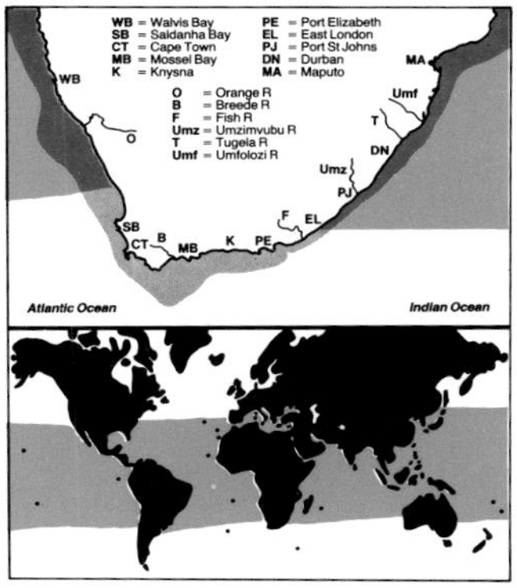

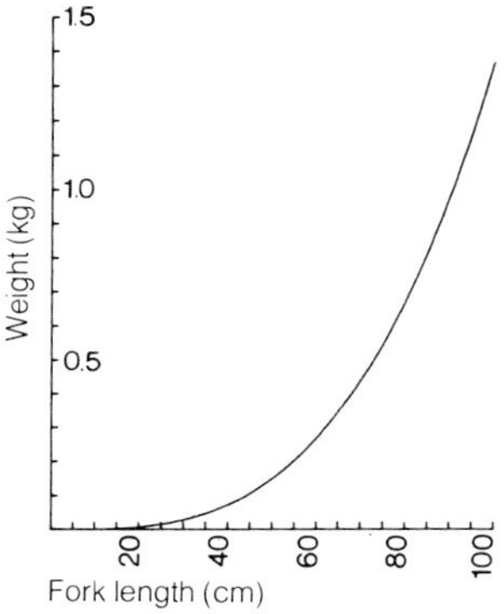

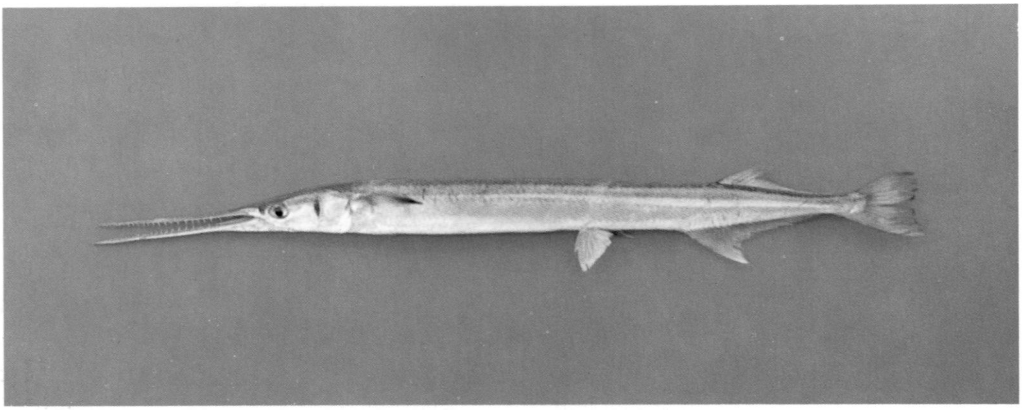

Strongylura leiura

(Bleeker, 1851)

Common names Worldwide – yellowfin needlefish or garfish [Smith 113□3]

IDENTIFYING FEATURES

COLOUR, SHAPE AND SIZE

The elongate, almost cylindrical body is generally green above, silvery green along the sides, and white below. The fins are dusky or translucent, though the tip of the dorsal is reddish, the anal tip yellowish and the pectorals may have a black blotch. Can attain 138 cm in length.

EXTERNAL ANATOMY

Numerous thin, cycloid scales cover the body. The fins are small and the single dorsal of 18-21 rays and the anal of 22-26 rays both occur well back along the body, near the square-edged caudal fin. The exceedingly large mouth has elongate jaws set with rows of numerous, pointed teeth. There are no rakers on the gill arches.

NATURAL HISTORY

The yellowfin needlefish is a powerful, aggressive predator of surface waters and, though it sometimes occurs in small groups offshore, it is more frequently found in shallow water, estuaries and harbours. It is often seen striking into shoals of small or juvenile fish such as the young of mullet or similar estuarine species, especially those that shelter below floating objects. The streamlined needlefish is capable of considerable bursts of speed and when alarmed or disturbed is often seen 'skipping' across the surface using its anal and caudal fins in conjuction to drive it through the water. Tapeworm larvae may occur in the body cavity of adult specimens, but these are harmless to man. The female produces relatively large, but few, eggs, and as the fry are not usually found in the inshore habitat, it is probable that they are distributed by ocean currents.

DISTRIBUTION

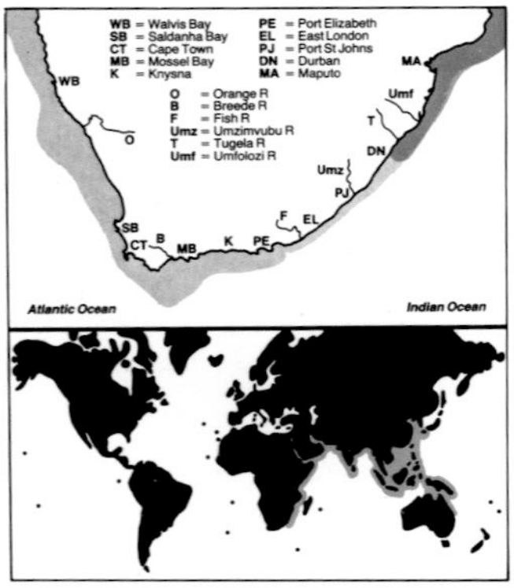

CAPTURE

Though easily caught with small, live bait or a rapidly retrieved artificial lure, the yellowfin needlefish's fighting abilities are best displayed when landed by anglers using trout rods. Despite the numerous green bones the flesh makes good eating. It is not speared by divers.

All-Africa angling record – 5,1 kg.

SA angling record – 6,5 kg.

SPECIFIC CATCH RESTRICTIONS

None.

NAME DERIVATION

Strongylura, callous tail; *leiura,* smooth tail. Yellowfin needlefish, from its yellowish anal fin and general body shape, jaws and teeth. Garfish, from the Old English *gar,* meaning spear.

SIMILAR SPECIES

Though similar to the crocodile needlefish *(Tylosurus crocodilus),* the latter has 21-24 dorsal rays and a lower caudal fin lobe that is distinctly longer.

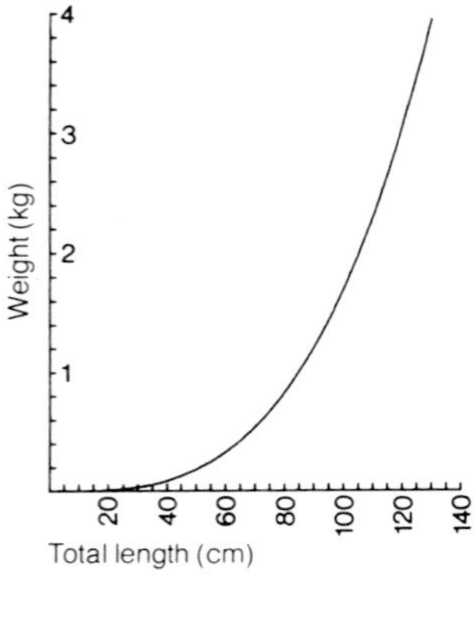

Scartella emarginata

(Günther, 1861)
Common name Worldwide - maned blenny
[Smith 235□40]

IDENTIFYING FEATURES

COLOUR, SHAPE AND SIZE
This robust little fish has a well-rounded head region with a steep profile. The body colour varies but is normally brownish, with darker crossbars and spots. Specimens darken considerably after shock or death. Can attain 10 cm.

EXTERNAL ANATOMY
The mucus-coated body of the maned blenny is smooth and scaleless. The fins are well developed. A single, long dorsal fin extends from the head region to the caudal peduncle and comprises 11-13 spines plus 12-16 rays. The anal fin is also long, about half the body length, and consists of two spines plus 14-18 rays. The fleshy, muscular pelvic fins are modified for use as 'legs' and the caudal fin is rounded. Immediately above the large eyes, and also just before the dorsal fin are paired, or single, short tentacles. Comb-like teeth are set along the outer edge of the well-defined 'lips' of the mouth. The gill openings extend right across the throat.

DISTRIBUTION

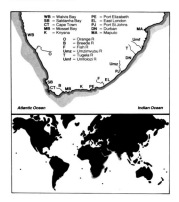

NATURAL HISTORY

This species is probably the most common and widespread member of the blenny family and lives exclusively within the tidal zone, usually on very shallow reefs and in rock pools. To illustrate its abundance, approximately six maned blennies occupy each square metre of intertidal reef along parts of the Natal coast. Their substantial numbers make them an important food source for larger predators and they are heavily preyed upon by carnivorous fishes as well as by cormorants. Like the goby, the blenny can survive for long periods out of the water as it retains oxygenated water in its gill chambers and is also able to absorb a little oxygen directly into the bloodstream through the skin. This ability, combined with the stout, limb-like pectoral fins, enables it to move from pool to pool and thereby to take advantage of food that would otherwise be inaccessible. Though hydrozoa, rock mussels and a variety of small crustaceans are regularly eaten, the most important items of diet are red and green seaweeds. The comb-like teeth are well-suited to its browsing habit and the long gut, common to many herbivorous fish, is a further indication of its vegetarian preferences. Breeding occurs throughout the year and 400-800 eggs are laid in any suitable receptacle - empty oyster and mussel shells being favoured. Males guard the eggs which hatch, after approximately six months, into 3,5-mm-long larvae. Sexual maturity is reached within a year at a length of 4-5 cm.

CAPTURE

This successful aquarium fish is easily captured on small baits or with a scoop net. It is strongly territorial and its highly aggressive behaviour towards other blennies can cause problems within the tank environment. The maned blenny is an entertaining fish to observe in rock pools and a most suitable subject for nature study.

SPECIFIC CATCH RESTRICTIONS

None.

NAME DERIVATION

Scartella, one who leaps; *emarginata,* emarginate. Maned blenny, a reference to the dorsal crest and from *blennos,* meaning slime, a reference to the mucus-covered body.

SIMILAR SPECIES

Blennies are difficult to distinguish and often require microscopic examination and more extensive references to ensure positive identification.

Pseudorhombus arsius

(Hamilton-Buchanan, 1822)
Common name Worldwide – largetooth flounder
[Smith 259□17]

IDENTIFYING FEATURES

COLOUR, SHAPE AND SIZE

This flatfish is strongly compressed and oval-shaped. Though the general body colour varies, it is predominantly sandy-brown with black-and-white mottling on the left side and pale on the right or 'blind' side. These rather drab colours and patterns are carried through onto the fins. Along the lateral line, three small, indistinct, dark blotches occur – one at the point where the curved lateral line becomes straight, one along the midpoint of the straight lateral line, and the third closer toward the tail. Can attain 35 cm.

EXTERNAL ANATOMY

One of the characteristic features of this and related species is that the eyes are situated on the left side of the body. Both the dorsal and anal fins are long. The dorsal fin extends from the head region to the caudal peduncle and comprises 72-78 rays, while the anal fin, which also terminates at the peduncle, comprises 54-60 rays. The caudal fin is rounded. Pectoral and pelvic fins are present, but the pectoral on the 'blind' side of the body is very small. The mouth is symmetrical and armed with long, canine teeth. The large, projecting lower jaw extends backwards to below the hind edge of the 'left' eye. The first gill arch has 9-13 rakers on its lower limb. The conspicuous lateral line curves above the pectoral fin, and has two branches on the head.

NATURAL HISTORY

The largetooth flounder is one of the most common and typical members of the Bothidae. It is confined to the bottom, generally in shallow or muddy regions such as estuaries, and, though present throughout the year, it is most common during spring. Often the only indication of this fish's presence are the two eyes protruding from the sand, but even when lying uncovered on the seabed, its mottled, nondescript colours provide an excellent camouflage. Much of the time, it lies dormant in this manner, ready to pounce on unsuspecting prey such as crabs, marine worms and small fish. During these 'ambushes', or when disturbed, the fish can move surprisingly quickly by undulating the dorsal and anal fins, while using the pectorals for steering and stability. When juveniles hatch, they look very much like any other fish, but within a few days they begin to swim with the left side facing upwards. At the same time, the right eye begins to migrate towards the left side, and the skull also twists. Gradually, too, the right side loses its colour. Only when these processes are complete does it take up residence on the bottom.

NAME DERIVATION

Pseudorhombus, almost diamond-shaped; *arsius,* to lift (from the bottom). Largetooth flounder, a reference to the canine-like teeth, and from *flandre,* a northern European word meaning flat.

SPECIFIC CATCH RESTRICTIONS

None.

CAPTURE

Divers often spot this fish, and it is sometimes landed by shore anglers. Most, however, are caught in seine or trawl nets, and in some eastern countries the largetooth flounder is a valuable food resource.
SA angling record – 0,5 kg.

DISTRIBUTION

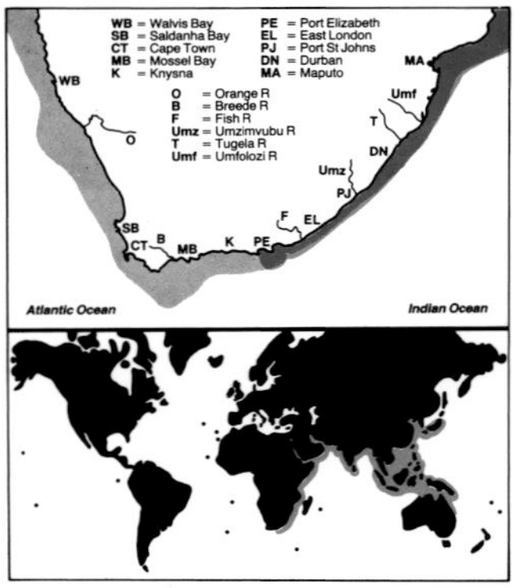

SIMILAR SPECIES

Most species in this family have eyes located on their left side, although individual species are not always easy to identify. The largetooth flounder closely resembles the smalltooth and ringed flounders (*P. natalensis* and *P. elevatus* respectively).

Caesio teres

Searle, 1906
Common name beautiful fusilier
[Smith 182□2]

IDENTIFYING FEATURES

COLOUR, SHAPE AND SIZE

This gorgeous fish has a small, fusiform body that is almost round in cross section. The colours are most striking, with a yellow upper surface that typically extends onto the tail. The uppermost surface may be blue, as is the layer of skin underlying the scales. The fins are tinged with red. Seen underwater, these colours are most striking, though they can vary considerably depending on the mood of the fish. Can attain 30 cm.

EXTERNAL ANATOMY

Like all other fusiliers, this species' body is well covered with small thin scales numbering 55-58 along the lateral line. These scales are quite easily shed, as seen in the specimen here. The fins are well developed, with a single dorsal of ten spines plus 15 rays, an anal of three spines and 12 rays, and a deeply forked caudal. The terminal mouth is rather small and bears a band of very fine teeth in each jaw. The eye is large, its diameter almost equalling the snout in length. There are 35-37 well-developed gill rakers on the first gill arch.

NATURAL HISTORY

Fusiliers are common tropical coral-reef fishes, but only two species venture into South African waters. Their striking colours make them popular with divers, especially as shoals of these fishes are easily approached underwater. Their preferred habitat is the water column directly over coral reefs, quite often near the surface. Here the fusiliers mill about, usually facing into the current so as to capture any planktonic organisms that may come drifting by. These include the larvae of other fish and the young stages of crabs, crayfish and prawns. When threatened, the entire shoal suddenly sounds and takes refuge amongst the coral. Fusiliers spawn in open water, and the fertilized eggs are dispersed by ocean currents. However, their precise breeding season and size at maturity remain unknown. Previously, this family was included in family Lutjanidae with the snappers. Some of their habits are quite similar.

DISTRIBUTION

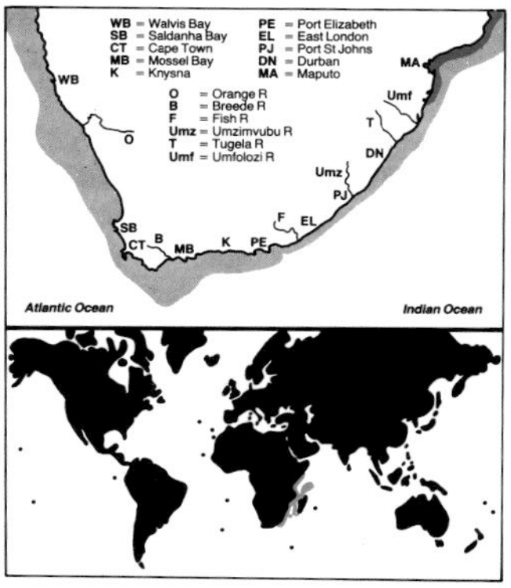

CAPTURE

The beautiful fusilier is seldom caught in South Africa, though it is a popular fish with divers, especially off Sodwana Bay where it is common. Their bright colours can be seen at a distance underwater, and the sighting of fusiliers is often the first indication that a coral reef is nearby. In the East, moderate numbers of fusiliers are caught with gill nets or driven into set-nets. In parts of Japan, this and related species are considered a delicacy.

SPECIFIC CATCH RESTRICTIONS

None.

NAME DERIVATION

Caesio, blue-grey, a reference to the colour of the type specimen; *teres,* cylindrical, a reference to the body shape. Fusilier, a reference to the bright colours of these fishes, not unlike the brightly coloured uniforms of British fusilier regiments of the past.

Alepes djedaba

(Forsskål, 1775)
Common name Worldwide – shrimp scad
[Smith 210□3]

IDENTIFYING FEATURES

COLOUR, SHAPE AND SIZE

The body is more elongate than in most kingfish, and the upper and lower profiles are smoothly curved. This silvery fish has a blue-green sheen when viewed from above, and is white below. There is a distinct, dark spot on the upper edge of the gill covers. The caudal fin in freshly caught specimens is often a strikingly bright yellow. The dorsal fin is greenish-grey, but the two longest rays may be white-tipped. Other fins are pale yellow. Can attain 40 cm, but local specimens seldom exceed 20 cm.

EXTERNAL ANATOMY

The entire body, including the breast region, is covered with small scales. The lateral line curves steeply for about half its length, but becomes straight towards the tail. This rear and horizontal portion is armed with 33-51 scutes. The fins are well developed. The double dorsal fin comprises one forward-pointing spine plus eight normal spines, which are followed by a single detached spine plus 23-25 rays. The anal fin has a slightly shorter base than the second dorsal fin, and consists of two detached spines followed by one spine plus 18-20 rays. The caudal fin is forked, and the long, sickle-shaped pectorals sweep backwards. A single row of small teeth occurs in each jaw, and patches of finer teeth may be found on the roof of the mouth. The upper jaw slopes downwards to a point below the large eyes, which have a layer of adipose tissue covering all but the front half.

NATURAL HISTORY

The shrimp scad is one of the smaller members of the kingfish family. It is, nevertheless, an aggressive predator, and may be quite common near inshore reefs, even in fairly turbid water. Large shoals often gather around rocky pinnacles, where they feed predominantly on a variety of free-swimming crustaceans such as shrimps, mantis shrimps, megalopa crab larvae and mysids. The life history of this species has not been adequately studied, but spawning is believed to occur in shallow coastal waters.

DISTRIBUTION

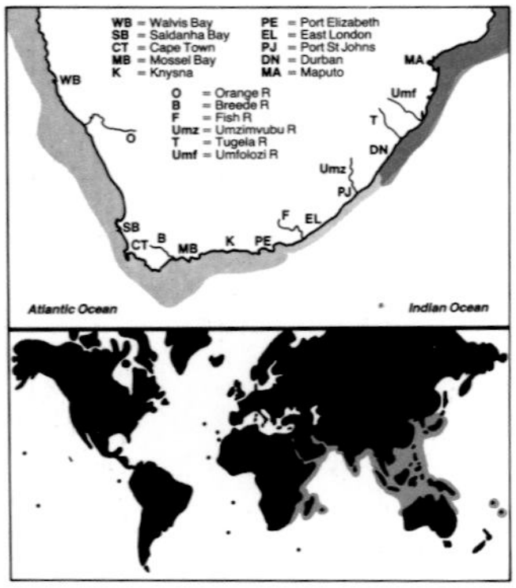

SPECIFIC CATCH RESTRICTIONS

None.

CAPTURE

Though rarely caught from the shore, ski-boat anglers often land this species. Fishermen in southern Africa usually consider the shrimp scad too small to be of great interest, but in the Far East, large numbers are caught for food. It is a good eating fish that readily takes small bait.

NAME DERIVATION

Alepes, without scales; *djedaba,* named after the original specimen that came from Djeddah in Saudi Arabia. Shrimp scad, an obvious reference to its preferred diet. *Scad* is an old word of unknown origin, apparently first used in Cornwall to describe the horse mackerel or maasbanker.

SIMILAR SPECIES

This is the only *Alepes* species in our waters. The yellowtail scad (*Atule mate*) is similar, but has both front and rear halves of the eye covered with adipose tissue.

Alectis ciliaris

(Bloch, 1787)

Common names SA – threadfin mirrorfish. Elsewhere – pennant trevally

[Smith 210□1]

IDENTIFYING FEATURES

COLOUR, SHAPE AND SIZE

This very deep-bodied and compressed fish changes its body shape considerably with growth. Young specimens are almost round in profile and though adults become more elongate they retain the deep-bodied front section. Large specimens of this species are frequently confused with the adult Indian mirrorfish. At all stages of development, the threadfin mirrorfish may be distinguished by its rounder and more smoothly curved head profile. The overall body colour is silvery, but bluish above and paler or pearly below.

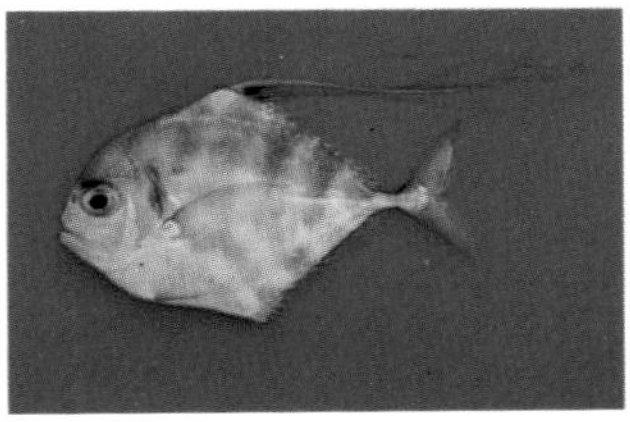

Juveniles have several darker crossbars and their fins range from pale yellow to dusky. Can attain 90 cm in length.

EXTERNAL ANATOMY

The scales of this fish are reduced and difficult to detect, and the entire chest region is completely scaleless. The arrangement of the fins is characteristic; in specimens of less than about 40 cm in length, a number of soft rays on both the dorsal and anal fins are extremely elongate and often more than twice the body length. These rays become progressively shorter with age, but in all specimens the dorsal fin comprises six spines preceding one spine plus 18-22 rays, while the anal fin has two detached spines preceding one spine plus 18-20 rays. The caudal fin is strongly forked. Though the forehead is very steep, the diameter of the eye is greater than, or equal to, the distance between the eye and the upper jaw. The teeth are rather feeble and consist of fine, villiform bands in each jaw. There are 16-23 rakers on the first gill arch.

DISTRIBUTION

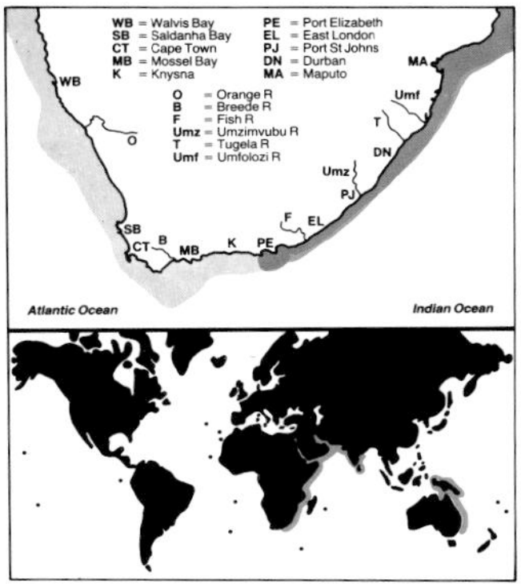

NATURAL HISTORY

This curious, invariably solitary fish frequents shallow coastal waters and though it is nowhere abundant, it is quite often found along the East Coast. The threadfin mirrorfish is rather sluggish and, not surprisingly, its diet consists of slow-swimming or sedentary prey. Small crabs, mole crabs (sea lice) and occasionally small fish have been recorded from the stomachs of landed specimens. The breeding cycle is unknown, but juveniles do become more abundant in beach seine-net catches during summer. The significance of the long dorsal and anal rays has not been determined and it is remarkable that these delicate structures do not become more damaged.

CAPTURE

Adults are fine shore and ski-boat angling fishes, especially on light tackle. Their flesh is of good eating quality. Juveniles make attractive aquarium fish, but most succumb after a few days in captivity.

World angling record – 20,1 kg.

SA angling record – 9,2 kg.

SA spearfishing record – 7,2 kg.

NAME DERIVATION

Alectis, meaning cockerel; *ciliaris,* threadlike. Threadfin mirrorfish, a reference to the elongate fins and to its silvery body.

SIMILAR SPECIES

The two South African mirrorfish species are easily confused in their adult phase. The most obvious difference lies in the head profiles illustrated here.

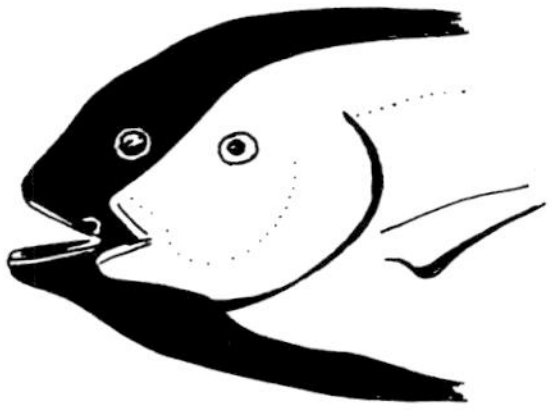

Head profiles of A. ciliaris *(left) and* A. indicus *(right).*

Alectis indicus

(Rüppel, 1830)
Common names SA – Indian mirrorfish. Elsewhere – threadfin trevally
[Smith 210□2]

IDENTIFYING FEATURES

COLOUR, SHAPE AND SIZE

Adult specimens of this strongly compressed, deep-bodied fish are very similar in shape to adult threadfin mirrorfish, and both have iridescent silver bodies with blue or black fins. The Indian mirrorfish, however, has an almost vertical head profile and while large specimens tend to have more elongate hindquarters, this diagnostic feature is most obvious when specimens of both species are seen side by side. Juveniles are

very different from those of the threadfin mirrorfish and have six, faint, vertical bars on the flanks. Can attain 100 cm.
Note: Radical change in body proportion with growth is common to many Carangidae, but is especially well shown in this genus.

EXTERNAL ANATOMY

The scales of the Indian mirrorfish are very small and, being set well into the skin, are virtually invisible. The first of two dorsal fins has six spines which become embedded with age and therefore less obvious, and the second has one spine plus 18-20 soft rays. The anal fin has two detached spines, which also become embedded with age, followed by a further spine plus 18-20 rays. The soft anal and dorsal fins, as well as the pelvics, are very long and in juveniles with a weight less than 2,5 kg and extend into fine trailing plumes. As the fish grows to 4 kg, these gradually shorten and by the time 10 kg is exceeded, all trace of these long rays has disappeared. The caudal peduncle is thin and the caudal fin is deeply forked. The lateral line has two distinct regions; it curves steeply from the head around the pectoral fin, but from a point opposite the ninth dorsal ray to the caudal peduncle, it is straight and 'armed' with 5-12 feeble scutes. The protractile jaws have minute, villiform teeth. There are approximately 30 long, slender rakers on the first gill arch.

DISTRIBUTION

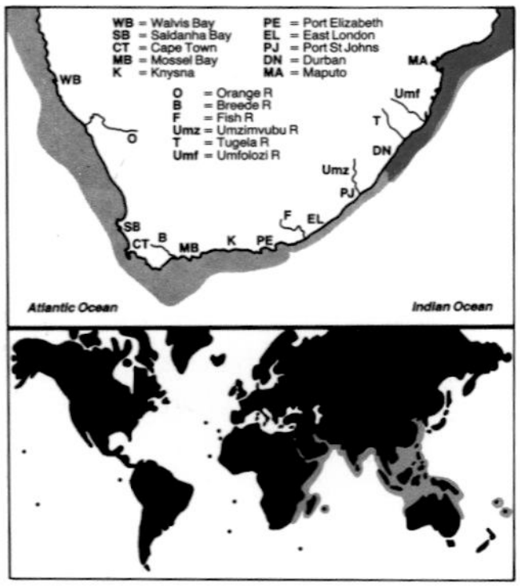

NATURAL HISTORY

The life cycle and habits of the Indian mirrorfish are not well known. Adults tend to congregate in large shoals and range widely in tropical coastal waters, while most juveniles are solitary and often enter estuaries. This species is sluggish and, excepting large specimens, is not a particularly aggressive predator. Diet comprises juvenile fish and small squid, some of which are filtered by the gill rakers. Mole crabs (sea lice) are also frequently eaten.

CAPTURE

Occasionally, large specimens of this good eating fish are hooked by sport anglers or speared by skindivers. Unfortunately, the lovely Indian mirrorfish does not thrive in aquaria. Juveniles, with their extremely long fin rays, invariably evoke much curiosity when landed or washed ashore.
SA angling record – 9,2 kg.
SA spearfishing record – 21,4 kg.

SPECIFIC CATCH RESTRICTIONS

None.

NAME DERIVATION

Alectis, a cockerel; *indicus,* a reference to India where it was first found. Indian mirrorfish, a reference to its region of greatest abundance and to its silvery body.

SIMILAR SPECIES

See note on page 133.

Carangoides armatus

(Rüppell, 1830)
Common names SA – longfin kingfish. Elsewhere – longfin cavalla
[Smith 210□5]

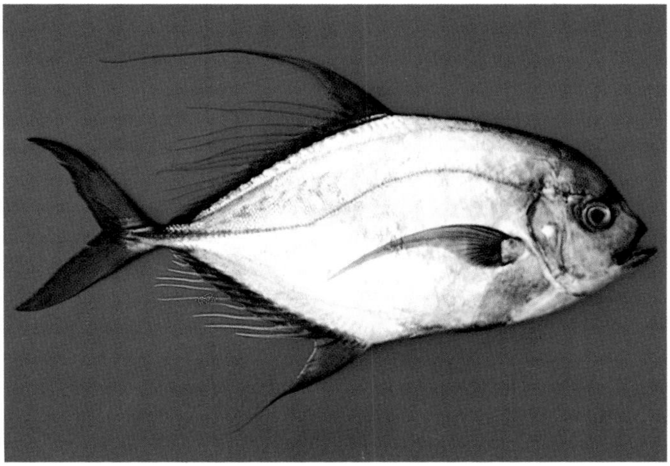

IDENTIFYING FEATURES

COLOUR, SHAPE AND SIZE
The longfin kingfish is deep-bodied and compressed with a steep, but straight, head profile. The general body colour is silver, tending towards blue-green along the dorsal surface. The anal rays may be white. Colour and body proportions, however, vary between the populations of this species throughout the world. Juveniles sometimes have six lateral crossbars. Can attain 60 cm.

EXTERNAL ANATOMY
The small scales are absent on the breast and bases of the pectoral and pelvic fins. This characteristic naked region is shown in the illustration. The first dorsal fin,

which is folded and not obvious in this specimen, consists of one forward plus eight normal spines, and is followed by a second dorsal fin of one spine plus 19-22 rays. The anal fin comprises two detached spines followed by one spine plus 16-18 rays. The pectoral fins reach beyond the origin of the anal fin and the caudal fin is forked. Juveniles up to 20 cm in length have large, black pelvic fins, but these become considerably reduced with age. In adults the central dorsal rays extend into extremely long filaments, but in

males the anal rays are also elongate, a conspicuous feature which makes the sexes easily identifiable. The lateral line has two distinct regions: a longer curved section above the pectoral fin and a shorter, straight section which extends backwards from a point opposite the 13th dorsal ray. This rear section has 11 or 12 feeble scutes. The large mouth has protractile jaws, the lower of which is slightly protruding. Both jaws bear several rows of fine, conical teeth. There are 31-37 rakers on the first gill arch.

NATURAL HISTORY

The longfin kingfish inhabits rocky and coral coastlines as well as shallow bays, while juveniles make limited use of estuaries as nursery areas. Small groups of longfin kingfish often swim along the edges of reefs hunting small fish, squid, swimming crabs and mantis shrimps. The capture of minute midwater organisms is aided by the long rakers, which strain food items from water passing through the gills. Sexual maturity is attained at a fork length of 21-22 cm.

DISTRIBUTION

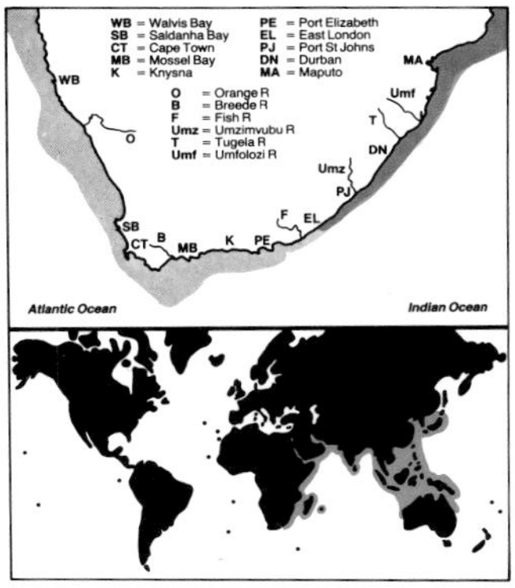

CAPTURE

From time to time this species is caught by shore and ski-boat anglers using fish bait or small lures. It is landed by spearfishermen along Zululand reefs, and is of fair eating quality. SA angling record – 3,2 kg.

SPECIFIC CATCH RESTRICTIONS

None.

NAME DERIVATION

Carangoides, resembling caranx; *armatus,* with arms – i.e. long pectorals.

Carangoides caeruleopinnatus
(Rüppel, 1830)

Common names SA – shortfin kingfish. Elsewhere – deep-body kingfish
[Smith 210□6]

IDENTIFYING FEATURES

COLOUR, SHAPE AND SIZE

This noticeably deep-bodied kingfish has an almost oval body profile and a long, particularly steep forehead. Though the fish has an overall mother-of-pearl sheen, the upper body region is somewhat bluish and the underside is white. Irregular, pale yellow blotches are scattered over the upper flanks, but these disappear some time after capture. A black spot marks each gill cover. The fins are yellow-green or dusky. Can attain 50 cm.

EXTERNAL ANATOMY

The body is covered with fine scales arranged in numerous series along the lateral line. On the breast, however, there is a naked

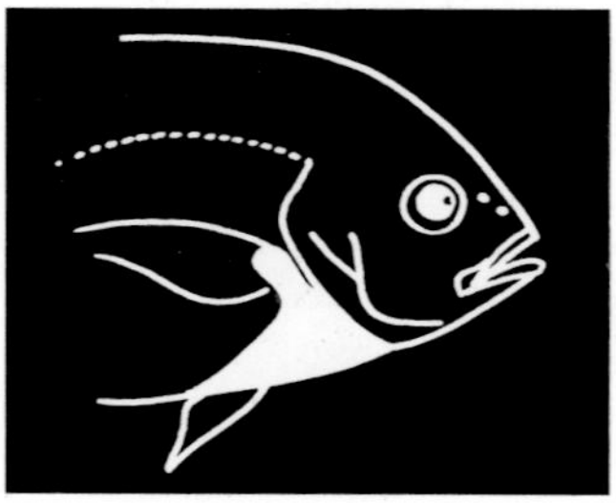

triangular-shaped patch which includes the pectoral and pelvic fin bases. The scaleless area is clearly shown in the accompanying illustration. The lateral line curves above the pectoral fins, and this rounded section is longer than the straight hind section which bears 20-38 weak scutes. The dorsal fin is in two parts: the first, comprising six or seven spines, is followed by a second of one spine plus 20-23 rays. The anal fin has two detached spines preceding one spine plus 16-20 rays. The sickle-shaped pectoral fins are very long and the caudal fin is forked. As with the other members of this genus, the jaws are set with fine villiform teeth, arranged in bands which widen towards the front of the mouth. The first gill arch has 21-27 rakers.

DISTRIBUTION

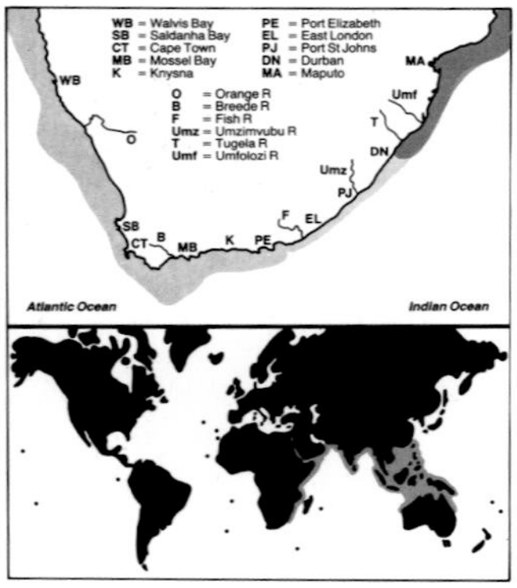

NATURAL HISTORY

There has been a great deal of confusion between this and related species and, previously, most have merely been called 'kingfish'. Consequently, information relating specifically to the life history of this species has been sparse. The shortfin kingfish is common over deeper coastal reefs and seldom found close to shore. It is rather sluggish when compared with most kingfish and it normally occurs in small shoals. The soft mouth and weak teeth preclude the capture of large prey and its diet consists mainly of small midwater organisms such as mantis shrimps, squid, krill and juvenile fish. The breeding cycle of the shortfin kingfish is unknown.

CAPTURE

Though frequently landed by ski-boat anglers, this fish is virtually unknown to shore anglers. Its flesh makes fine eating, and in the East the species has limited commercial value.
SA angling record – 3,7 kg.

NAME DERIVATION

Carangoides, a reference to *Caranx,* the genus to which these fish are closely related; *caeruleopinnatus,* blue-finned (there appears to have been some confusion in the original naming of this species as none of the fins has any blue colouration whatsoever). Shortfin kingfish, a reference to the fin length which distinguishes it from the similar *C. chrysophrys* and to its relationship to the true kingfishes of the genus Caranx.

SIMILAR SPECIES

This species is often confused with another kingfish, *Carangoides chrysophrys,* which can, however, be distinguished by its 18-20 dorsal rays, 15-17 anal rays and proportionately larger fins.

Carangoides chrysophrys

(Cuvier, 1833)
Common name longnose kingfish
[Smith 210□7]

IDENTIFYING FEATURES

COLOUR, SHAPE AND SIZE

The body is compressed and oval-shaped, with a smoothly curved dorsal profile that becomes abruptly steep just above the mouth cleft. The overall colour is silvery, with a somewhat darker green-grey upper surface and white underside. Most specimens display a yellowish tinge along the lateral line and lower flanks. Can attain 60 cm, but few exceed 40 cm.

EXTERNAL ANATOMY

The fins are reasonably developed, and typical of the kingfishes. There is a double dorsal, the first of eight spines, and the second of one spine plus 18-20 rays. The anal fin has two detached spines followed by one spine plus 14-17 rays. In younger specimens the lobe of the soft dorsal fin can be quite long and falcate. However, this shortens with age, as shown in the specimen pictured here. The caudal fin is deeply forked, while the pectorals are quite long, reaching to the straight section of the lateral line. There are 20-37 poorly developed scutes along this hind section of the lateral line. Fine scales cover the body, though the breast is distinctly scaleless over an area reaching to a point behind the origin of the pelvic fins, and upwards to include the pectoral fin base. The mouth opens wide, and the jaws are set with fine, villiform teeth. A total of 22-26 well-developed gill rakers occurs on the first gill arch.

DISTRIBUTION

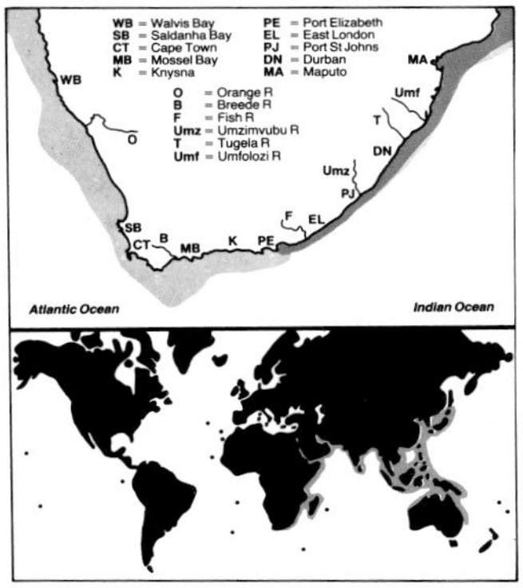

NATURAL HISTORY

This is a widely distributed species of Indo-Pacific coastal waters, often encountered within the shelter of large bays, but never in estuaries. This species appears to be slightly more tolerant of dirty water than most other kingfishes, as catches have been reported from the Tugela Banks and similarly turbid regions. Though it may be caught from the beach, this species has also been reported from depths of 60 m. Exceedingly little is known about the reproduction of the longnose kingfish, though juveniles have been reported from shallow water in Delagoa Bay and also, occasionally, off Durban's beach front. This soft-mouthed kingfish favours a prawn diet, though small fish and crabs are also selected for food.

CAPTURE

While not many longnose kingfish are reported caught, this is thought to be partly a result of misidentification. This species freely takes a small bait and makes good eating.
SA angling record - 2,3 kg.
SA spearfishing record - vacant.

SPECIFIC CATCH RESTRICTIONS

None.

NAME DERIVATION

Carangoides, like the *Caranx,* the genus to which this fish is most closely related; *chrysophrys,* golden. Longnose kingfish, from its moderately long snout, and its relationship to the true kingfishes.

SIMILAR SPECIES

The longnose kingfish is quite easily confused with related species, especially *C. malabaricus, C. caeruleopinnatus* and *C. hedlandensis.* However, it may be distinguished from these by its gently sloping snout profile with its abrupt vertical section, specific gill raker and fin ray counts, and distinctive shape of the naked breast.

Carangoides ferdau

(Forsskål, 1775)

Common names SA - blue or ferdy kingfish. Elsewhere - Ferdau's cavalla

[Smith 210□10]

IDENTIFYING FEATURES

COLOUR, SHAPE AND SIZE

This rather oblong kingfish has a smoothly rounded profile. It is distincly blue above and has silvery or whitish flanks and underside. The fins are dusky green or purple while the two lowest caudal rays and the longest anal rays are bluish-white. Numerous small, golden spots may occur on the body and in juveniles five darker vertical cross-bars are visible, though these fade rapidly after death. Can attain 70 cm.

EXTERNAL ANATOMY

The entire body is covered with small scales, except for a naked triangular patch on the breast that

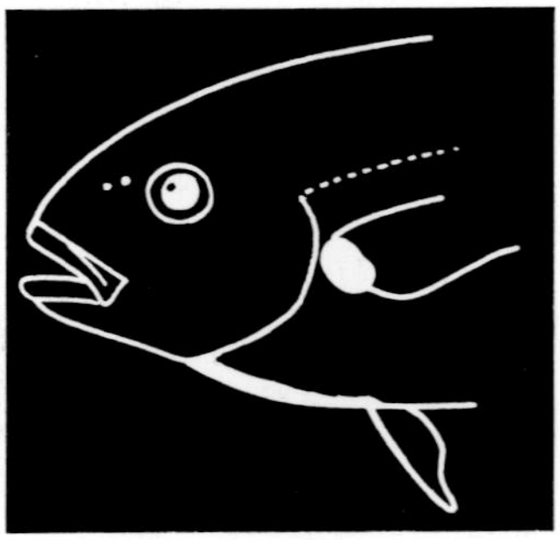

extends around the ventral surface, and only slightly up the sides as shown in the illustration. The lateral line is smoothly curved in front and the shorter, straight hind section carries 21-37 feeble scutes. The fins are well developed with the anal and dorsal rays being sickle-shaped. The dorsal fin is in two parts: the first consists of one partially embedded and forward-pointing spine plus seven normal spines; and the second has one spine plus 26-34 rays. The anal fin has two detached spines followed by one spine plus 21-26 rays. The pectorals are long and sickle-shaped and reach a point opposite the eighth anal ray. The caudal fin is forked. The jaws are weak and, owing to the rows of very small, villiform teeth, the mouth is rather soft. The eyes are set low and almost level with the tip of the snout. There are 24-29 rakers on the first gill arch.

DISTRIBUTION

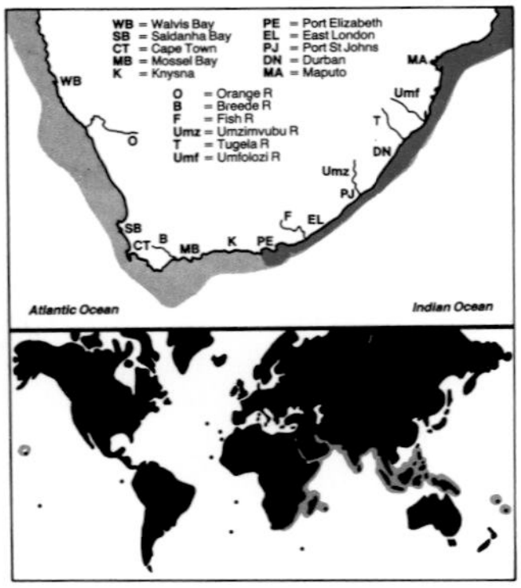

NATURAL HISTORY

Though the blue kingfish's distribution includes Algoa Bay, this species is far more plentiful along the Zululand coast, particularly north of Cape Vidal. It favours sandy beaches where it feeds mostly on prawns, mole crabs (sea lice), small fish and any other soft organisms suited to the weak teeth and jaws. It would appear that this member of the Carangidae can adapt to several environments, as it has also been found to depths of 60 m, often near coral reefs. It seems, though, that it is not tolerant of low salinities as few records exist of its occurrence in estuaries. The abundance of this species remains fairly constant throughout the year, but few reproductively 'ripe' specimens have been recorded. Small juveniles are not usually found in local waters.

CAPTURE

The blue kingfish is popular with both shore and ski-boat anglers and will take almost any small bait that is offered. Catches are best made at dawn and dusk. This good sport fish also makes excellent eating.

SA angling record – 6,0 kg.

SA spearfishing record – 8,0 kg.

SPECIFIC CATCH RESTRICTIONS

None.

NAME DERIVATION

Carangoides, a reference to *Caranx,* the genus to which these fish are closely related; *ferdau,* named after Ferdau who was probably the original collector. Blue kingfish, a reference to its blue body colour and to its relationship to the true kingfishes of the genus *Caranx.*

SIMILAR SPECIES

With its 26 or more dorsal fin rays and distinctive naked breast area, this species should not be confused with any other.

Carangoides fulvoguttatus

(Forsskål, 1775)
Common name Worldwide – yellowspotted kingfish
[Smith 210□11]

IDENTIFYING FEATURES

COLOUR, SHAPE AND SIZE

The yellowspotted kingfish has an oblong body with a rounded snout and is very similar to the following species. Body colours range from blue-green along the dorsal surface to silver along the sides. The underside is white. Though not obvious in this specimen, a number of yellow spots occur on the flanks and there is also a black blotch on the gill covers. A further three or more large, black blotches overlie the hind portion of the lateral line, while numerous black dots occur on the chest. It is important to note, however, that all these markings may be indistinct on some specimens. The outer edge of the anal fin is white and the trailing edge of the caudal fin is black. Can attain 100 cm.

EXTERNAL ANATOMY

The body is covered with fine scales except for a naked area in front of the pelvic fins. This scaleless region is clearly shown in the accompanying illustration.

There is much adipose tissue on the forehead. The lateral line is slightly arched above the pectoral fin and has 15-21 feeble scutes in the region of the caudal peduncle. The double dorsal fin has six or seven spines followed by one spine plus 25-30 rays, and the anal fin has two detached spines followed by one spine plus 21-26 rays. The caudal fin is deeply forked. Bands of fine, villiform teeth occur in both jaws. The outer teeth are slightly enlarged. The first gill arch carries 20-27 (but usually 25 or fewer) stubby rakers. Precise, comparative measurements will show differences between this species and the bludger. However, a simple but reliable method of distinguishing between them is to draw a string from the tip of the snout to the fork of the tail; the string will pass well below the eye if the specimen is a yellowspotted kingfish, but will pass through or very close to the lower edge of the eye if it is a bludger.

DISTRIBUTION

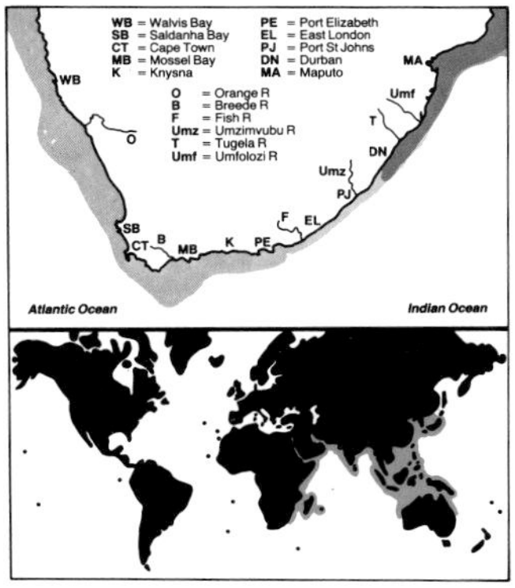

NATURAL HISTORY

The yellowspotted kingfish is a coastal gamefish which prefers rocky and coral reefs, but it is also occasionally found over offshore banks to depths of 100 m. It is intolerant of low salinities and turbid water and, therefore, does not enter estuaries. Individuals and small groups frequently 'patrol' the edges of reefs in search of food, which consists mainly of small invertebrates and juvenile fish. These include anchovies, swimming crabs, mantis shrimps, shrimps and, occasionally, small squid.

CAPTURE

Though this fish does not occur in great numbers, regular catches are made during the summer, a time when most specimens are reproductively 'ripe'. The yellowspotted kingfish is most likely to be caught some distance from shore by boat fishermen using small baits and, occasionally, lures. It is a fine angling fish and provides good sport on light tackle. It is also a favourite with spearfishermen.
SA angling record – 16,0 kg.
SA spearfishing record – 18,0 kg.

SPECIFIC CATCH RESTRICTIONS

None.

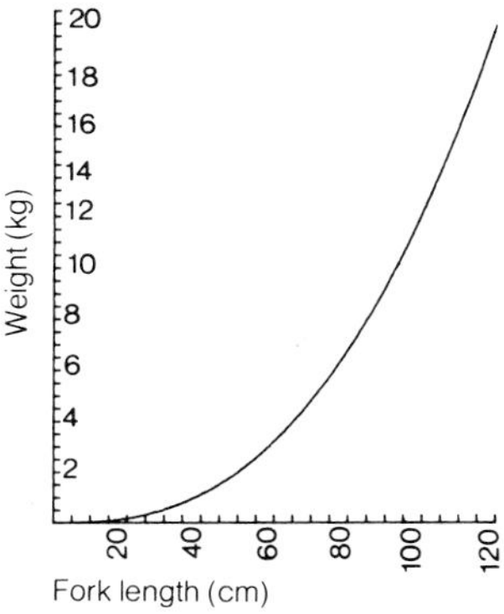

Carangoides gymnostethus

(Cuvier, 1833)
Common name Worldwide – bludger
[Smith 210□12]

IDENTIFYING FEATURES

COLOUR, SHAPE AND SIZE

This elongate kingfish is similar to the yellowspotted kingfish as it also has smoothly rounded dorsal and ventral profiles and a noticeably blunt snout. It is silvery overall, but greenish to pearly above and pale to white below. In small, freshly caught specimens there is often a yellow line along the lower side of each flank as well as a number of small, golden spots. The fins are dusky or yellowish. Can attain 100 cm.

EXTERNAL ANATOMY

Fine scales cover the body except in the region of the breast where a large naked patch, which includes the pectoral fin bases, extends backwards beyond the origin of the pelvic fins. This scaleless area is clearly shown in the accompanying illustration. The slightly arched lateral line bears 20-31 small scutes on its posterior section. The double dorsal fin consists of two

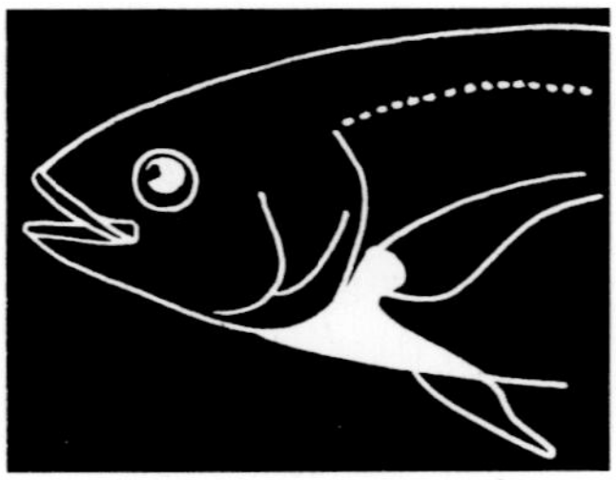

parts: the first comprises one embedded, forward-pointing spine plus seven or eight normal spines; and the second has one spine plus 28-32 rays. The anal fin has two detached spines followed by one spine plus 24-26 (but usually 25 or 26) rays. Teeth are set in fine bands in each jaw of the soft mouth and 25-31 (but usually 27 or more) rakers occur on the first arch. Precise, comparative measurements will show differences between this species and the yellowspotted kingfish. However, a simple, but reliable method of distinguishing between them, is to draw a string from the tip of the snout to the fork of the tail; the string will pass through or very close to the lower edge of the eye if the specimen is a bludger, but will pass well below the eye if it is a yellowspotted kingfish.

DISTRIBUTION

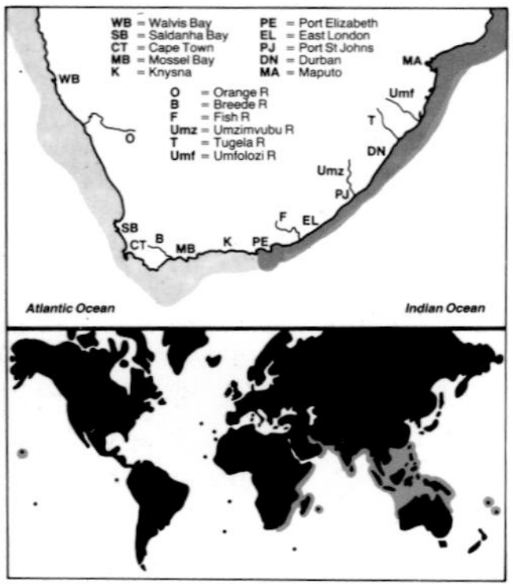

NATURAL HISTORY

The bludger is most common over moderately deep offshore reefs and though the young often move about in small shoals, larger specimens tend to be solitary. The soft mouth and weak jaws do not suggest strong predatory habits and, accordingly, the diet consists mainly of small animals such as shrimps, small crabs, mantis shrimps and tiny fish. Information about the breeding of this fish is sparse and very few juveniles have been recorded from southern Africa. Adult specimens occur throughout the year, but only a few of the specimens captured have displayed any signs of reproductive activity. It is likely, therefore, that spawning occurs in more tropical regions such as the waters off Moçambique.

CAPTURE

Though not abundant, regular catches are made by ski-boat anglers and spearfishermen. This kingfish makes excellent eating.
SA angling record – vacant.
SA spearfishing record – 9,2 kg.

SPECIFIC CATCH RESTRICTIONS

None.

NAME DERIVATION

Carangoides, a reference to *Caranx,* the genus to which these fish are closely related; *gymnostethus,* naked breast. Bludger, a reference to its blunt head.

SIMILAR SPECIES

Most easily confused with the yellow spotted kingfish – see text for differences.

Carangoides hedlandensis

(Whitley, 1933)
Common name bumpnose kingfish
[Smith 210□13]

IDENTIFYING FEATURES

COLOUR, SHAPE AND SIZE

This small kingfish has a very deep, compressed body, with an extremely steep head profile that bears a noticeable bump just in front of the eyes. The overall body colour is silvery, with a pearly, greenish upper surface and pale underside. The tailfin is yellowish. Can attain 30 cm.

EXTERNAL ANATOMY

The fins are well developed, especially the dorsal and anal filamentous lobes, which lengthen with age. A most significant feature is the fin structure, which differs between the sexes, with mature males having their third to eighth dorsal rays produced into filaments. Clearly the specimen pictured here is a female. The double dorsal consists of eight spines followed by one spine plus 20-22 rays, while the anal has two spines followed by one spine plus 16-18 rays. The caudal fin is deeply forked, and the pectorals are long and falcate. There are 17-19 feeble scutes along the rear, straight section of the lateral line. The body is covered with minute scales, except for an extensive naked area that covers the entire breast to behind the pelvic fins. Several rows of fine, villiform teeth cover the large jaws, while 20-27 gill rakers occur on the first arch. The eye is quite large, and its diameter usually equals or exceeds the snout length.

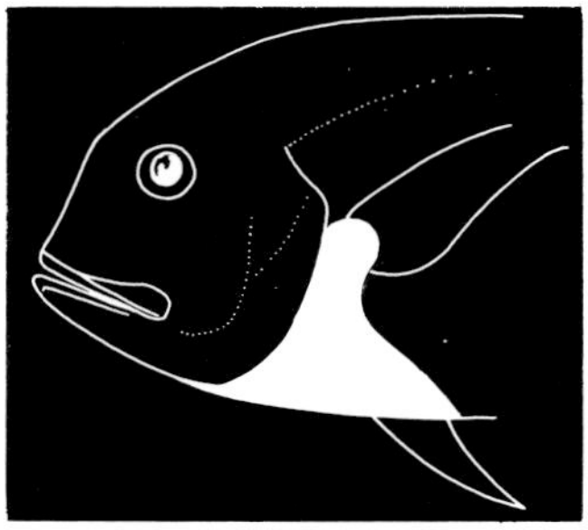

DISTRIBUTION

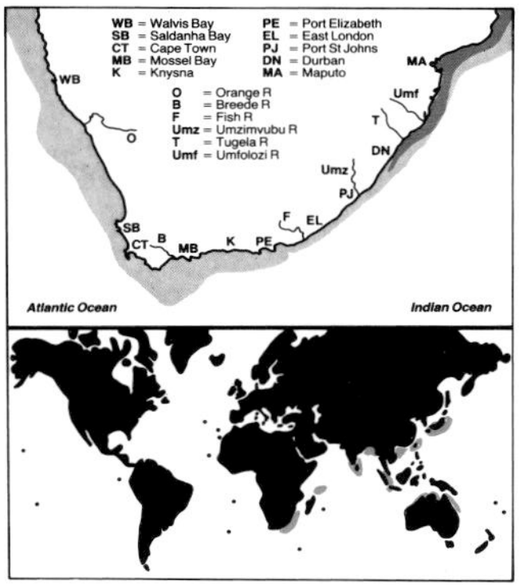

NATURAL HISTORY

This attractive kingfish has been reliably reported from a number of widely separated localities throughout the Indo-Pacific. It is fairly common close inshore along the Natal coast, especially in the coastal bays such as at Durban and St Lucia. While the bumphead kingfish seems intolerant of estuaries with their lowered salinities, this species does occur in moderately dirty water near river mouths. Most of its time is apparently spent swimming close to shore in small groups of two or more individuals. Here it will hunt its prey, known to consist mainly of shrimps, small crabs and juvenile fish. Although spawning adults have not yet been recorded off Natal, 'young of the year' juveniles are often caught in Durban's beach seine nets during summer.

CAPTURE

The bumpnose kingfish is not infrequently caught by shore and light-tackle, ski-boat anglers. Most catches are made from the piers and breakwaters around Durban. Any small bait will attract this edible species.
SA angling record - vacant.

SPECIFIC CATCH RESTRICTIONS

None.

NAME DERIVATION

Carangoides, like the *caranx,* the genus to which this fish is most closely related; *hedlandensis,* after Port Hedland in Western Australia, from where the species was first discovered. Bumpnose kingfish, an obvious reference to the bump over the eyes and its relationship to the true kingfishes.

SIMILAR SPECIES

Though a number of kingfishes superficially resemble the bumpnose kingfish, a combination of the following features will confirm its identity: scaleless breast, steep snout with bump, eye diameter equal to snout, and distinctive gill raker count.

Carangoides malabaricus

(Bloch & Schneider, 1801)
Common names SA – Malabar or nakedshield kingfish. Elsewhere – Malabar trevally
[Smith 210□14]

IDENTIFYING FEATURES

COLOUR, SHAPE AND SIZE

This deep-bodied and strongly compressed fish has a steeply curved dorsal profile. The overall body colour is silvery, but greenish above and white below. Living specimens have a mother-of-pearl sheen and there is a black blotch on the gill covers. The fins are dusky and translucent, with the tips of the dorsal, anal and lower caudal fins often edged in white. Juveniles have about five darker, broad vertical bars which fade with age. Can attain 60 cm but 35 cm is more usual.

EXTERNAL ANATOMY

Small scales cover the body, but the breast has a distinct and large scaleless area which extends from the head and pectoral bases to the vent. This naked region is clearly shown in the accompanying illustration. The first dorsal fin has

one forward and eight normal spines, and the second dorsal has one spine plus 20-23 rays. The anal fin has two detached spines followed by a single spine plus 17-19 rays. The caudal fin is forked and the long pectorals extend to a point opposite the middle of the second dorsal fin. The lateral line has two regions: a longer, curved, forward section and a shorter, straight hind section, which has 19-36 feeble scutes. The large mouth has protractile jaws, the lower being the longer. Both are set with small, villiform teeth. There are 32-38 rakers on the first gill arch.

DISTRIBUTION

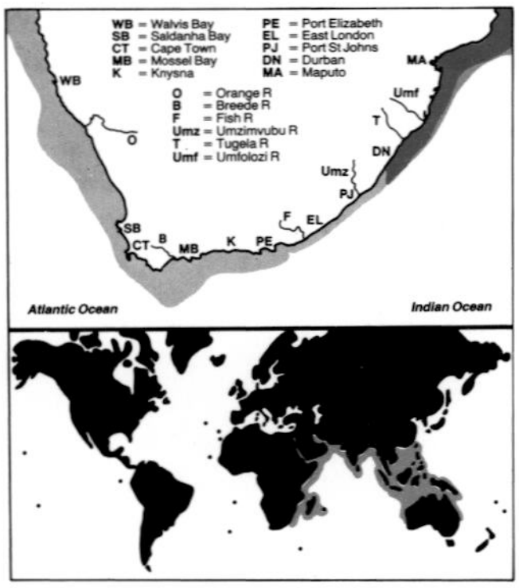

CAPTURE

The Malabar kingfish is best caught by anglers using light tackle and shrimp or similar bait. It is sometimes also speared by divers. Despite its commercial value in India, locally it is regarded as being of poor eating quality and generally too small to warrant great interest.
SA angling record – 0,6 kg.
SA spearfishing record – vacant.

NATURAL HISTORY

This fish normally frequents coral and rocky reefs, but may also be found in shallow, sandy bays. It appears to be moderately tolerant of turbid water. Though its breeding cycle is not known, small shoals of juveniles have been recorded in sheltered bays along the Natal coast. This rather small kingfish is not particularly aggressive, and feeds on midwater organisms such as krill, prawns, small fish, squid, mysids and mantis shrimps.

SPECIFIC CATCH RESTRICTIONS

None.

NAME DERIVATION

Carangoides, a reference to *Caranx,* the genus to which these fish are closely related; *malabaricus,* a reference to Malabar, a town in India. Nakedshield kingfish, a reference to the scaleless breast region and to its relationship to the true kingfishes of the genus *Caranx.*

SIMILAR SPECIES

Two closely related species occur elsewhere in the Indian Ocean, and this species is most readily confused with the shortfin kingfish. However, differences in gill raker count and naked breast areas should confirm identity.

Caranx ignobilis

(Forsskål, 1775)

Common names SA – giant kingfish. Elsewhere – jack, trevally or karambisi

[Smith 210□17]

IDENTIFYING FEATURES

COLOUR, SHAPE AND SIZE

The giant kingfish has a deep, robust body and is generally olive green with a darker dorsal surface and a white belly, which darkens considerably after capture. Irregular, small black spots occur on the back and upper sides and the translucent fins may have a yellowish tinge. Most specimens average 60 cm, but some exceed 100 cm and there have been reports of even greater fish.

EXTERNAL ANATOMY

Small scales cover the body, except for a small naked patch before the pelvic fins and at the base of the pectorals. This scaleless region is clearly shown in the accompanying illustration. The first of two dorsal fins has one

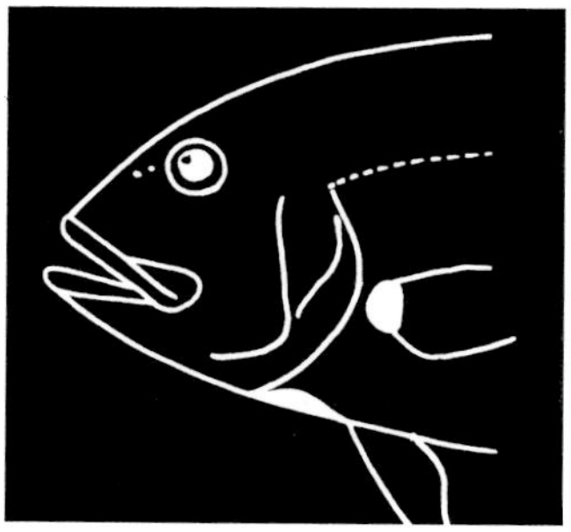

forward-pointing and eight normal spines and the second dorsal has one spine plus 18-21 rays. The anal fin has two detached spines followed by a single spine plus 15-17 rays. The caudal fin is deeply forked and the long, sickle-shaped pectorals extend beyond the vent. There are 26-28 armed scutes along the rear, straight portion of the lateral line. The first gill arch bears 17-23 stubby rakers. A thick layer of adipose tissue covers the rear half of each eye.

NATURAL HISTORY

This is the largest and most aggressive of the kingfish and is indeed one of the fiercest fish predators in the sea. It moves swiftly from reef to reef, sometimes hunting in exceedingly shallow water. Some 70 per cent of the diet comprises fish, the balance being made up of squid, mantis shrimps and other crustaceans. Prey is largely located by sight and this species tends to be more active during the day, especially at dusk and dawn. Though not generally regarded as estuarine, the giant kingfish has been recorded in almost-fresh water from Kosi Bay and St Lucia. Very large specimens are invariably solitary, but smaller fish may be found in groups, especially during winter. Sexual maturity coincides with a fork length of 60 cm and an age of approximately three years. Breeding occurs during summer in tropical areas. Males are more numerous than females and are generally slightly darker in colour.

CAPTURE

The giant kingfish is an exceptionally strong and determined gamefish that usually fights to the bitter end. It is best caught using live or fillet bait from both ski-boats and the shore. It is also much sought after by spearfishermen. The flesh makes excellent eating.

World angling record – 65,99 kg.

SA angling record – 55,3 kg.

SA spearfishing record – 45,4 kg.

DISTRIBUTION

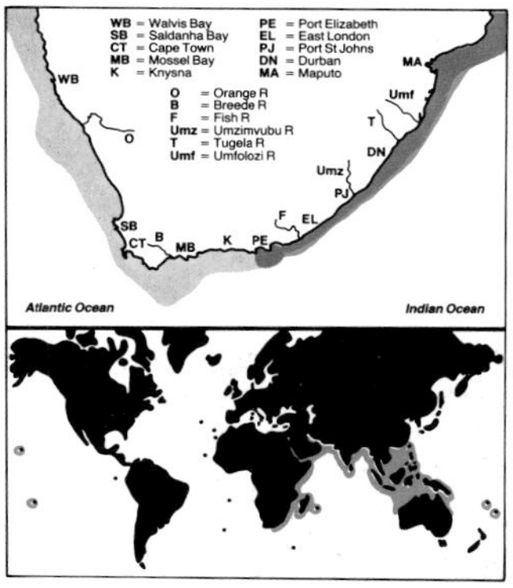

SPECIFIC CATCH RESTRICTIONS

None.

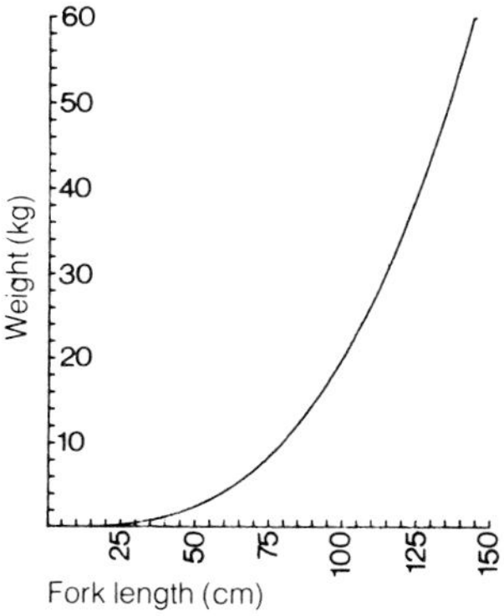

Caranx melampygus

Cuvier, 1833

Common names SA – bluefin kingfish. Elsewhere – bluefin jack, bluefin trevally

[Smith 210□19]

IDENTIFYING FEATURES

COLOUR, SHAPE AND SIZE

The bluefin kingfish has an oblong body with a moderately steep forehead. The overall body colour is a dark, dusky green with electric-blue markings, especially along the dorsal fin base and the rear, straight, region of the lateral line. The flanks and the dorsal surface are densely patterned with small, grey to black spots which are frequently iridescent blue in live specimens. The fins are translucent or dusky, but, in live individuals the dorsal and anal fins are brilliant blue, while the pectoral fins are yellow. Can attain 100 cm.

EXTERNAL ANATOMY

Small scales cover the body, including the breast which has only a minute naked patch just before the pelvic fins. The double dorsal fin has one partially embedded and forward pointing spine followed by eight normal spines, plus one spine preceding 21-24 rays. The anal fin has two detached spines followed by one spine plus 17-20 rays. The long pectoral fins are sickle-shaped and the caudal fin is forked. The lateral line curves from the head region to a point below the third dorsal fin ray and continues as a slightly longer, straight section armed with 27-42 sharp scutes. Both jaws of the large mouth bear a row of stout, conical teeth in front, while smaller teeth occur behind. Fine teeth are also found on the tongue and the palate. There are 25-29 rakers on the first gill arch.

NATURAL HISTORY

This beautiful fish has a great affinity for coral and rocky regions where it usually hunts in small groups about a metre above the reef. Thus it covers large areas in search of prey and while most active during early morning and late afternoon, it also hunts at night. Fishes comprise most of the diet though small shrimps, mantis shrimps and squid are also occasionally eaten. The bluefin kingfish also has a habit of following larger fish which may assist it by driving out hidden prey. Winter marks its period of peak abundance, but spawning occurs during the summer months. The extent of breeding and the distribution of juveniles, however, is unknown. Sexual maturity is attained at a fork length of 40 cm, and males tend to be slightly larger than females.

CAPTURE

This fish is popular with anglers and spearfishermen alike, as the flesh makes excellent eating. Small lures, especially if vertically retrieved are most successful in tempting the fish to strike. The bluefin kingfish is sometimes rather inquisitive, an advantage to spearfishermen, but if startled it will dart off and divers may not get a second chance.

World angling record – 10,12 kg.

SA angling record – 8,8 kg.

SA spearfishing record – 8,0 kg.

SPECIFIC CATCH RESTRICTIONS

None.

DISTRIBUTION

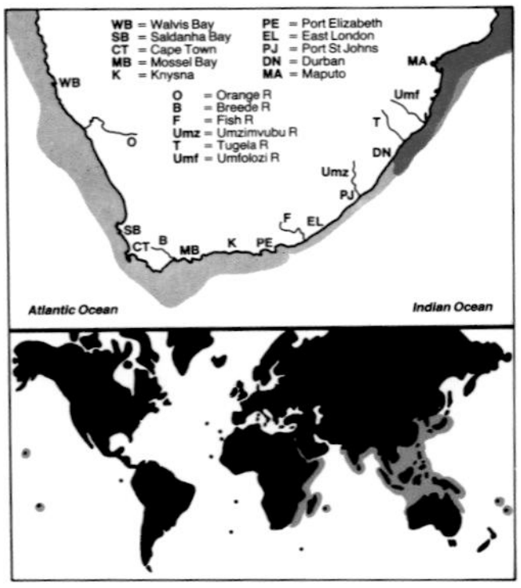

NAME DERIVATION

Caranx from the Portuguese *acarauna* and the French *carangue,* both common names for these fish; *melampygus,* black spotted.

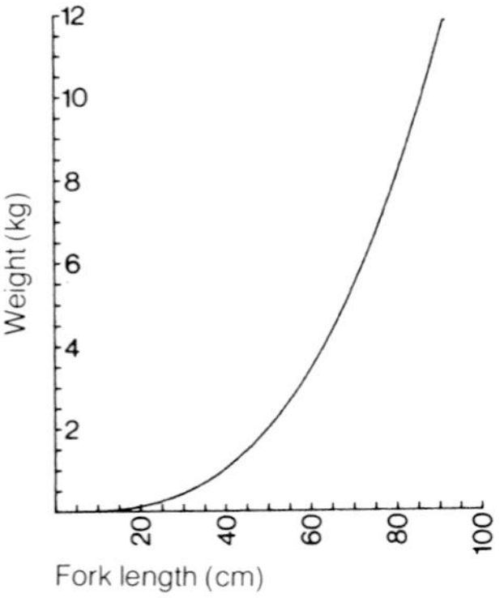

Caranx papuensis

Alleyne and MacLeay, 1877
Common name Worldwide – brassy kingfish
[Smith 210□20]

IDENTIFYING FEATURES

COLOUR, SHAPE AND SIZE

This slightly oblong fish is generally greenish-bronze along the dorsal surface and upper sides and has a silvery-white underside. With age, irregular, small, black spots appear on the upper sides. The fins are dusky-yellow, but the upper and lower lobes of the caudal fin are a striking slate-grey and bright yellow respectively. The lower edges of the caudal and anal fins have narrow, but distinct, white bands. These colours and patterns should readily distinguish this species from the similar, yellowtail kingfish. Can attain 80 cm.

EXTERNAL ANATOMY

Scales cover the entire body, except for a small naked patch on the lower breast. Both eyes are coated with a layer of adipose tissue. The double dorsal fin comprises one forward-pointing spine followed by seven normal spines, plus one detached spine preceding 21-23 rays. The anal fin has two detached spines preceding one spine plus 16-19 rays. The caudal fin is deeply forked. The anterior section of the lateral line is curved, while the straight hind section is armed with 31-39 sharp scutes. Both the upper and lower jaws carry a row of sharp teeth and there are patches of finer teeth on the tongue and palate. There are 26-30 rakers on the first gill arch.

NATURAL HISTORY

Previously, this fish had only been recorded from the central Indian Ocean, but it is now known to be relatively common in Natal waters. The first local recordings were made by anglers in Tongaland. Though the brassy kingfish is present throughout the year, catch statistics indicate a peak abundance during summer. This inshore fish moves either singly or in pairs over reefs and pinnacles, as well as along sandy beaches, between rocky outcrops. It is primarily a predator of small fish, especially reef-dwelling species, though squid, prawns and crabs are also eaten. While juveniles occur in some Zululand estuaries, adults are intolerant of turbid water and low salinity environments. Little else is known of its habits and life history.

DISTRIBUTION

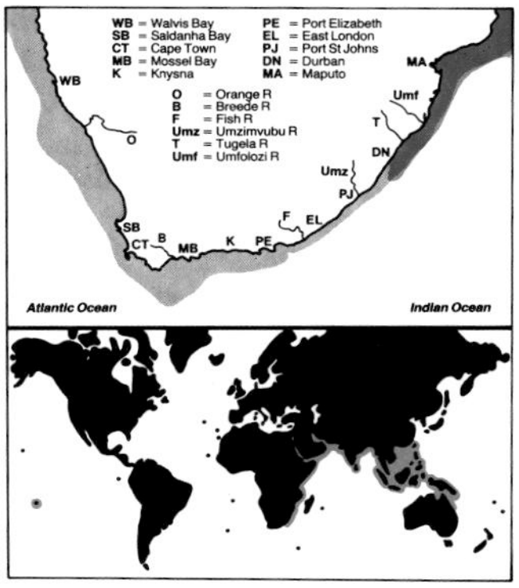

NAME DERIVATION

Caranx, a corruption of the Portuguese *acarauna* and the French *carangue,* both common names for these fish; *papuenis,* from the region of its first description, Papua. New Guinea. Brassy kingfish, a reference to its brass coloured upper body, and to its great fighting strength and 'regal' bearing.

CAPTURE

The brassy kingfish makes excellent eating and is caught by shore anglers and spearfishermen. It takes lures and bait, especially fillets or small, whole fish and squid.
SA angling record – 4,0 kg.
SA spearfishing record – 5,2 kg.

SPECIFIC CATCH RESTRICTIONS

None.

SIMILAR SPECIES

While the brassy kingfish may resemble several other kingfishes, none have the distinct white edge to the lower caudal.

Caranx sem

Cuvier, 1833

Common names Worldwide – blacktip or yellowtail kingfish [Smith 210□21]

IDENTIFYING FEATURES

COLOUR, SHAPE AND SIZE

The rather elongate and robust body of this fish is silver-green, but darker above and with a white belly. The fins are yellow or dusky. The soft dorsal and anal fins are bright yellow. The caudal fin is also bright yellow, but the upper tip is distinctly black. There are no characteristic body markings and this, together with the colours described, should prevent confusion with the similar, brassy kingfish. Attains 100 cm.

Note: The process of elongation with growth, typical of many Carangidae, is well illustrated by comparing the adult with the immature specimen also shown.

EXTERNAL ANATOMY

Small scales cover the entire body except for a small naked patch on the lower breast. This scaleless region is clearly shown in the accompanying illustration. The

scales along the rear, straight portion of the lateral line are enlarged into 30-40 strong scutes. The double dorsal fin consists of one forward-pointing spine plus seven normal spines followed by a single detached spine plus 19-21 rays. The anal fin has two detached spines preceding one spine plus 15-17 rays. The deeply forked caudal fin has a stout peduncle. Both jaws have a row of strong teeth while the tongue and palate bear rows of much finer teeth. Some 24-27 rakers occur on the first gill arch.

DISTRIBUTION

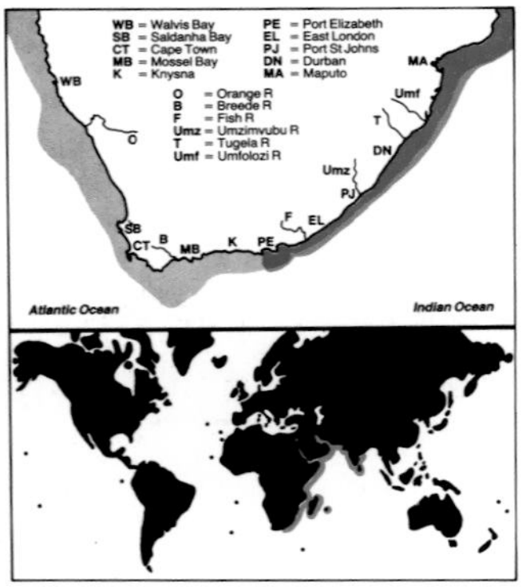

NATURAL HISTORY

The blacktip kingfish is a summer gamefish that prefers clean, open coastal water and the adults are seldom found in turbid or estuarine areas. It is particularly common over moderately deep rocky reefs and pinnacles where it often congregates into small shoals. Here it feeds on a wide variety of animals, especially squirrelfishes, blacktail and pinkies. Anchovies, squid, shrimps, mantis shrimps, swimming crabs and, occasionally, small crayfish are also eaten. It is most abundant in southern African waters during the summer and though few breeding fish have been recorded, probably because spawning occurs in more tropical regions, juveniles are quite common in coastal bays and large, unspoilt estuaries.

CAPTURE

This fish is caught by shore anglers and ski-boat fishermen and speared by skindivers. Successful baits include pilchards, squid and small feathers or lures, especially if they are retrieved vertically along a rocky ledge or pinnacle. Despite the tapeworm larvae that often infest this fish, its flesh makes excellent eating if well cooked.

SA angling record – 12,5 kg.

SA spearfishing record – 11,2 kg.

SPECIFIC CATCH RESTRICTIONS

None.

SIMILAR SPECIES

The black tip to the caudal is distinctive of this species.

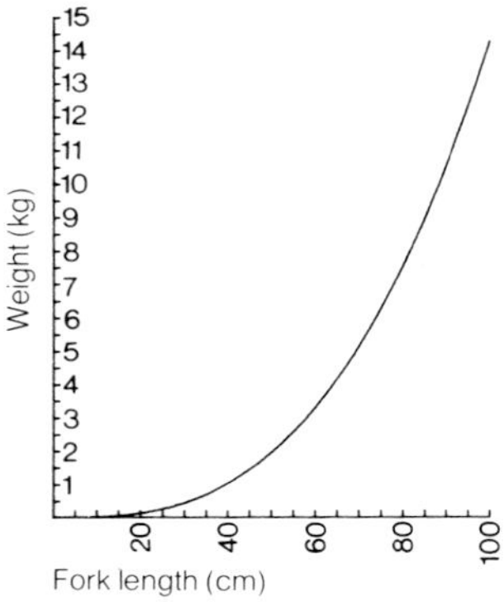

Caranx sexfasciatus

Quoy & Gaimard, 1825
Common names SA – bigeye kingfish. Elsewhere – dusky jack.
[Smith 210□22]

IDENTIFYING FEATURES

COLOUR, SHAPE AND SIZE

The upper body surface of this robust, oblong fish is dusky-grey or greenish-blue and the belly is white. There is a distinct, black spot on the gill covers, and the dusky anal and dorsal fins have conspicuous, white tips. Juveniles have six dusky crossbars, but these become less distinct with age. Can attain 80 cm.

EXTERNAL ANATOMY

With the exception of a very small, naked patch just before the pelvic fins, minute scales cover the body. The noticeably large eyes are partially covered with adipose tissue. The first dorsal fin has one forward and eight normal spines, and the second dorsal has one spine plus 19-22 rays. The anal fin has two detached spines preceding one spine plus 14-17 rays. The caudal fin is deeply forked and the pectorals are long and sickle-shaped, and sweep back to a point opposite the first anal ray. The straight hind section of the lateral line is armed with 27-36 scutes. A single row of conical teeth occurs in the lower jaw, while the upper jaw has a single, outer row of conical teeth and an inner band of villiform teeth. There are 21-25 rakers on the lower limb of the first gill arch.

NATURAL HISTORY

This fish hunts alone and moves from reef to reef in search of food which consists mainly of small reef fish. The diet is, however, supplemented with prawns, mantis shrimps, swimming crabs and other midwater organisms. Adult fish are sensitive to changes in temperature and salinity and prefer clean, clear water away from river mouths. Sexual maturity is attained at a fork length of about 50 cm and spawning occurs during summer, when juveniles have been recorded in estuaries.

DISTRIBUTION

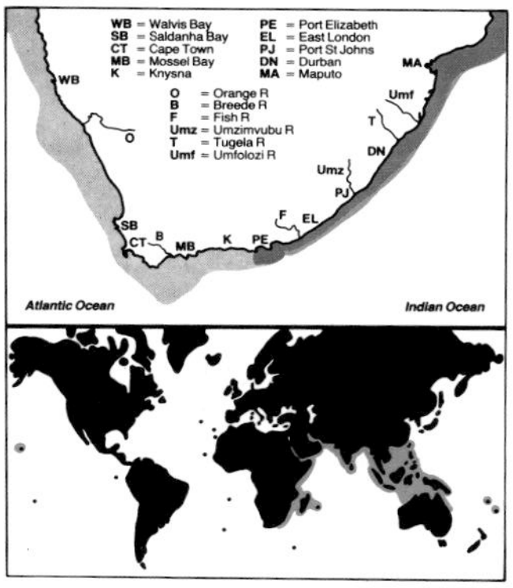

CAPTURE

The bigeye is a strong fighter that takes most fish baits and lures, especially when drifted from ski-boats. It appears to be the most nocturnal of kingfishes as good catches are invariably made at night. This fine table fish is also occasionally speared by divers.
World angling record – 8,19 kg.
SA angling record – 7,8 kg.
SA spearfishing record – 7,0 kg.

NAME DERIVATION

Caranx, a corruption of the Portuguese *acarauna* and the French *carangue,* both common names for these fish; *sexfasciatus,* six-banded. Bigeye kingfish, a reference to the noticeably large eyes and to its great fighting strength and 'regal' bearing.

SPECIFIC CATCH RESTRICTIONS

None.

SIMILAR SPECIES

This species resembles the much scarcer tille kingfish *(C. tille),* but can be distinguished by the white tipped dorsal and smaller opercular spot.

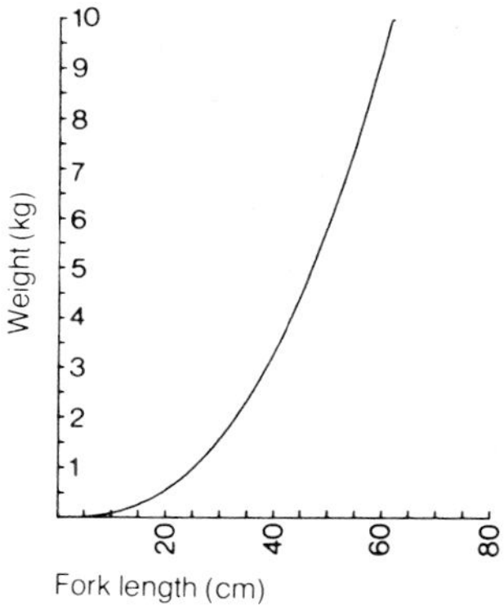

Decapterus macrosoma

Bleeker, 1851
Common names SA – slender scad. Elsewhere – shortfin scad
[Smith 210□27]

IDENTIFYING FEATURES

COLOUR, SHAPE AND SIZE

At first glance, this fish is rather sardine- or mackerel-like in appearance, with a very elongate and slender body that is almost round in cross-section. The overall body colour is metallic blue above with silvery flanks and a whitish belly. There is a distinct, black blotch on the rear edge of the operculum. Can attain 25 cm.

EXTERNAL ANATOMY

The body is completely covered in scales, but these are too fine to count individually. However, over the lateral line, the scales are more distinctive, and may be enlarged to form moderate scutes. The number of these scutes and shape of the lateral line are distinctive features: the front section is curved with 58-72 scales, followed by a straight section of 14-29 scales plus 24-40 scutes. The fins include a double dorsal, the first comprizes eight spines, and the second one spine plus 33-39 rays, the last of which forms a single, detached finlet. The anal fin comprises two spines followed by a single spine that precedes 27-30 rays, the last of which also forms a single detached finlet. The pectoral fins are noticeably short, and do not reach to below the origin of the second dorsal fin. There is a terminally set mouth, which bears a single row of fine teeth in the lower jaw and none in the upper. The rear edge of the upper jaw is concave in shape, though this may require careful examination to detect. The rather large eyes are completely covered with adipose tissue, except for a small slit centred directly over the pupil. The gill rakers are well developed, and number 43-50 on the first arch.

DISTRIBUTION

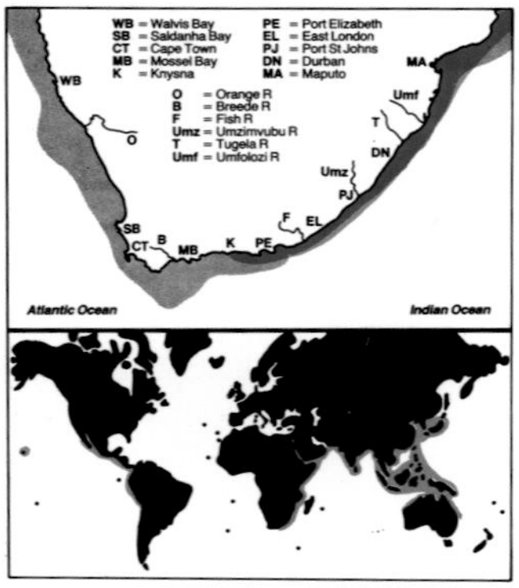

NATURAL HISTORY

The shortfin scad is widely distributed throughout Indo-Pacific coastal waters, and commonly occurs along the East Coast at least to Algoa Bay. This is a shoaling species, usually found in large concentrations of similar-sized individuals. However, it is also often found in association with other shoaling species, especially pilchards and mackerel. The shortfin scad does not usually enter the surf zone, but ranges freely between depths of 10-170 meters. Small pockets of these fish often congregate on the outer edge of Natal's shark nets. Scads, with their long gill rakers, are filter-feeding fishes, straining small zooplankton such as copepods from the water.This species appears to be most common along the East Coast from midwinter to early summer, possibly as a result of a migration from Moçambique waters. It is probable that most spawning occurs further northwards, as most specimens examined have been reproductively inactive.

CAPTURE

This fish is only caught in seine and trawl nets, usually as a by-catch or because a shoal has been mistaken for a shoal of sardines. It represents a fine source of food for human consumption, and makes an excellent bait for gamefish.

SPECIFIC CATCH RESTRICTIONS

None.

NAME DERIVATION

Decapterus, ten fins; *macrosoma,* large bodied. Shortfin scad, a reference to the short pectoral. The word *scad* is of unknown origin, but was apparently first used in Cornwall to describe the horse-mackerel or maasbanker.

SIMILAR SPECIES

There are at least another five species of scad in South African waters, and all are very similar. The most definitive features of *D. macrosoma* are the scale and scute counts, the upper jaw shape and the short pectoral fin. It can be distinguished from sardine-like fishes by its double dorsal and lateral scutes, from mackerel-like fishes by the far smaller number of finlets and lateral scutes, and from the maasbanker *(Trachurus capensis)* by its single, detached anal and dorsal finlets and the scutes that cover only the rear lateral line.

Elagatis bipinnulatus

(Quoy & Gaimard, 1825)
Common name Worldwide – rainbow runner
[Smith 210□31]

IDENTIFYING FEATURES

COLOUR, SHAPE AND SIZE

The rainbow runner is an elongate, almost spindle-shaped fish with a pointed head. The general body colour is blue-green above and silvery-white below. Double blue lines separated by a bright yellow band extend along the upper flanks.Colour changes after capture are marked, however, especially the yellow band which fades rapidly. Can attain 90 cm.

EXTERNAL ANATOMY

Some 100 series of fine, cycloid scales cover the entire body. The double dorsal fin consists of six spines followed by one spine plus 25-30 rays, while the anal fin consists of two detached spines plus 18-22 rays. A finlet comprising the last two rays is situated between the dorsal fin and the deeply forked caudal, and also on the ventral surface between the anal and caudal fins. The slightly curved lateral line bears no scutes. Fine teeth occur in both jaws, on the roof of the mouth and on the tongue. There are 34-38 rakers on the first gill arch.

NATURAL HISTORY

This swift and graceful predator favours open water, sometimes over deep coral and rocky reefs. Small pelagic fish and crustaceans such as megalopa crab larvae, mantis shrimps and krill provide the bulk of the diet. Small shoals of juveniles may congregate in the vicinity of floating objects at sea, but older fish are pelagic and solitary. It is uncommon in most regions and its life history has remained obscure, though spawning fish have been recorded from numerous localities during spring. Young fish have been observed swimming very close to large sharks accompanied by pilotfish *(Naucrates ductor).* The pilotfish is also a carangid which for some unknown reason seems unpalatable to sharks. The juvenile rainbow runner's association with this related species appears to be a form of protective mimicry. The rainbow runner constitutes part of the natural diet of marlins and is consequently an excellent billfish bait. Occasional specimens have been reported off the southern Cape when the Agulhas current penetrates further southward.

DISTRIBUTION

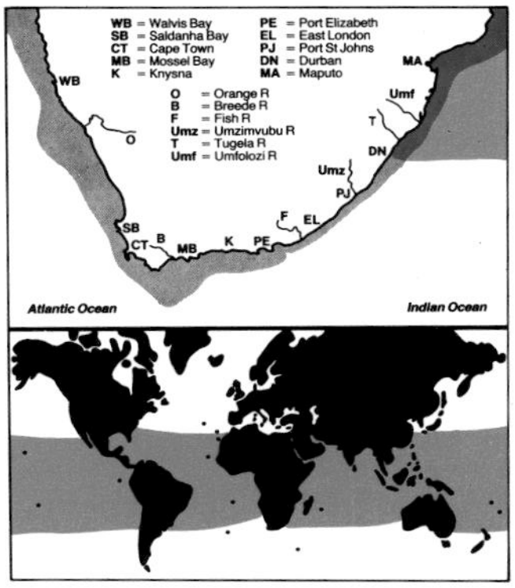

CAPTURE

This superb fighting fish is usually only caught offshore by boat anglers using trolled lures and small, dead or live, fish baits. The fisherman, however, requires great skill to prevent the hook being torn from the soft mouth.

Spearfishermen have little success. The rainbow runner is an excellent table fish, which in Japan is eaten raw or with a special sauce.

Despite being uncommon, recent research suggests that the species may be globally under-exploited.

World angling record – 15,25 kg.
SA angling record – 8,6 kg.
SA spearfishing record – 9,6 kg.

SPECIFIC CATCH RESTRICTIONS

None.

NAME DERIVATION

Elagatis, spindle-shaped; *bipinnulatus,* double winged, a reference to the forked caudal fin. Rainbow runner, a reference to its striking colours and fast surface-running habit when hooked.

SIMILAR SPECIES

Though not easily misidentified, the rainbow runner is characterized by the two-rayed, detached finlets and absence of lateral scutes. *Decapterus* spp. also have finlets but with only one ray.

Gnathanodon speciosus

(Forsskål, 1775)
Common names SA - golden kingfish. Elsewhere - golden toothless trevally
[Smith 210□32]

IDENTIFYING FEATURES

COLOUR, SHAPE AND SIZE
The overall colour of this robust, oblong fish depends on its size: those less than 25 cm are golden-yellow, but those larger are silvery-yellow. All specimens have 8-12 darker vertical bars running down the flanks, with the first passing through the eye. The fins are yellow except for the tips of the caudal which are black. Attains 120 cm.
EXTERNAL ANATOMY
Small scales cover the entire body, including the breast. The first dorsal fin has one forward and seven or eight normal spines and the second dorsal has one spine plus 18-20 rays. The anal fin comprises two detached spines followed by one spine plus 15-17 rays. The caudal fin is deeply forked and the pectoral fins are long and sickle-shaped. The lateral line curves above the pectoral fin, but straightens below the eighth dorsal ray and carries 17-26 feeble scutes. The protractile mouth is large and the upper jaw reaches a point below the front of the eyes. Teeth are absent in specimens longer than 8 cm. Some 27-30 rakers occur on the first gill arch.

NATURAL HISTORY

This coastal species is confined to coral and rocky reefs where it normally hunts in small groups. It is a daytime feeder and, unlike many Carangidae, does not seek out individual prey. Instead, the protractile, toothless jaws are extended to form a tube through which small, bottom-living organisms, hidden amongst algae and concealed in cracks in the reef, are sucked into the mouth. These include shrimps, crabs, amphipods, molluscs and small fish. Though not very common in

Close-up of head showing protractile, tube-like mouth.

Natal, the golden kingfish is caught from Zululand beaches during April and May and juveniles have been recorded as far south as Delagoa Bay. Young specimens, like those of the rainbow runner, mimic and closely resemble the true pilotfish and display 'piloting' habits with sharks and other large predators, apparently to secure protection.

DISTRIBUTION

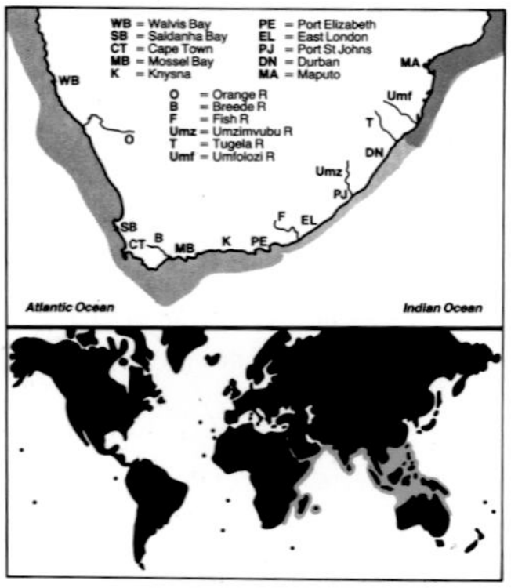

SPECIFIC CATCH RESTRICTIONS

None.

CAPTURE

This fish may be caught on small lures or prawn bait, especially along the outer edges of reefs. Divers often see shoals of golden kingfish but most specimens are too small to interest the spearfisherman. Though not commercially exploited, the golden kingfish makes excellent eating.
World angling record - 4,9 kg.
SA angling record - 14,0 kg.
SA spearfishing record - 14,8 kg.

NAME DERIVATION

Gnathanodon, toothless jaws; *speciosus,* beautiful. Golden kingfish, a reference to the colour of young specimens and to its relationship to the true kingfishes of the genus *Caranx.*

SIMILAR SPECIES

Notice that this species has no adipose eyelids, lacks teeth and has distinctly fleshy lips.

Lichia amia

(Linnaeus, 1758)
Common names Worldwide – garrick, leervis
[Smith 210□33]

IDENTIFYING FEATURES

COLOUR, SHAPE AND SIZE
The garrick is large and elongate with a slightly pointed snout. The overall body colour is silvery, but the flanks and dorsal surface are dusky to blue-grey while the belly is white. The fins are predominantly dusky. Juveniles less than 10 cm long have conspicuous, orange-yellow and black crossbands. Can attain 150 cm.

EXTERNAL ANATOMY
The leathery skin and minute scales of the species give it the appearance of being scaleless. The dorsal fin consists of two sections, the first of eight small, almost separate, spines and the second of one spine plus 19-21 rays. The anal fin has two separate spines preceding one spine plus 17-21 rays. The wavy lateral line is very distinctive. The large mouth carries bands of very fine teeth and the first gill arch has 7-9 rakers.

DISTRIBUTION

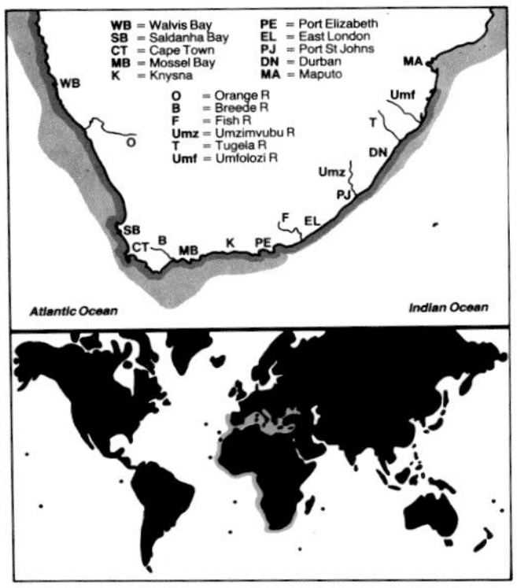

NATURAL HISTORY

This coastal species prefers the wave zone where it forms small shoals which hunt along the surf backline off beaches and rocky points. It is one of the most aggressive fish predators and shows great preference for elf, pinkies and karanteen. Garrick have been known to trap a shoal of baitfish in a gully before systematically consuming them. Seasonal migrations occur with garrick moving to Natal in winter and to the Cape in summer. Winter migrations usually coincide with the onset of the annual Natal sardine run and take place during a period of increased reproductive activity. Sexual maturity is attained at a fork length of about 60 cm and spawning occurs off the Natal coast during spring. The Agulhas Current probably distributes the young among the estuaries of the eastern Cape, and damage to estuarine ecology along this coast could well affect the future abundance of the species. Virtually every specimen has a number of harmless external copepod parasites which may be found 'skating' over the surface of the fish many hours after capture.

CAPTURE

The garrick is of no major commercial significance, but is a popular sport fish and frequently provides hours of hectic fishing for shore anglers. It readily takes lures and live bait, especially whole mullet or sardines. As the garrick is particularly vulnerable to capture on rod and line, over-zealous fishermen are urged to moderate their activities in the interests of continued good catches in the future. The species is equally sought after by spearfishermen. It is of fair eating value.
World angling record – 18,8 kg.
All-Africa angling record – 32,2 kg.
SA angling record – 32,2 kg.
SA spearfishing record – 31,2 kg.

SPECIFIC CATCH RESTRICTIONS

Protected species; minimum legal size is 70 cm total length.

NAME DERIVATION

Lichia, corpse-like, a reference to its leathery skin and overall greyish colour; *amia,* an ancient name for a bonito-like fish. Leervis, from the Dutch *leer* meaning leather. Garrick, meaning obscure, possibly a corruption of an Indian or Mauritian name.

SIMILAR SPECIES

The sinuous lateral line is distinctive.

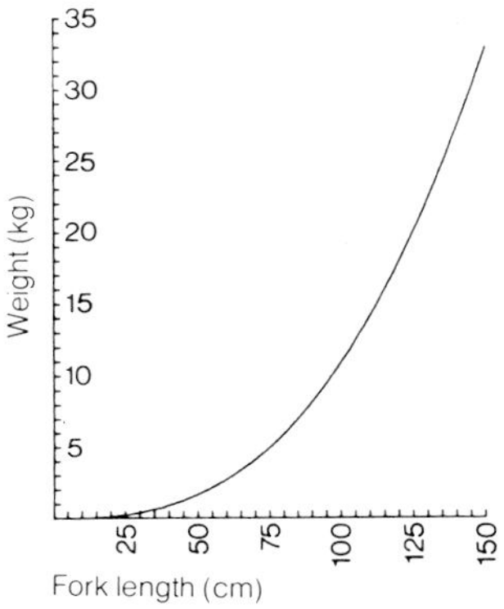

Megalaspis cordyla

(Linnaeus, 1758)
Common name Worldwide – torpedo scad
[Smith 210□34]

IDENTIFYING FEATURES

COLOUR, SHAPE AND SIZE

Though shown here with its mouth widely extended, in the typical fashion of filter-feeding Carangidae, this species is distinctly torpedo-shaped, with a pointed snout and a deep mid-body region which tapers to a thin, but strong, caudal peduncle. The dorsal surface is green, while the flanks and underside are silvery. There is a distinct, black spot on both gill covers. The fins are predominantly translucent, but the first dorsal is darker, and the caudal is dusky yellow. Can attain 50 cm, but captured specimens rarely exceed 35 cm.

EXTERNAL ANATOMY

The body is covered with small scales, but those over the hind part of the lateral line are enormously enlarged to form 51-59 strong, sharp scutes. The fins are well developed. The first dorsal fin has eight spines, and the second dorsal one spine preceding 18-20 rays, the last 7-9 in the form of finlets. The anal fin has two detached spines followed by a single spine and 16-17 rays, the last 8-10 in the form of finlets. The pectoral fins are exceptionally long. The teeth are very small and occur on the jaws, palate and tongue. Adipose tissue covers the eyes. Well-developed rakers occur on the first gill arch.

NATURAL HISTORY

The torpedo scad is a shoaling species of coastal waters, and is normally found near the surface, sometimes in association with young elf. It is not found in estuaries, and is considered intolerant of turbid water. The diet consists of planktonic organisms, which are filtered from the water passing over the gill rakers. These include crab larvae, mantis shrimps, krill and juvenile fish. The torpedo scad is tropical in habit, but its distribution extends further south during the summer months, when these waters become warmer as a result of the greater penetration of the Agulhas Current. Little is known of its life history, though spawning has been recorded during summer. It is an important food source for larger gamefish.

DISTRIBUTION

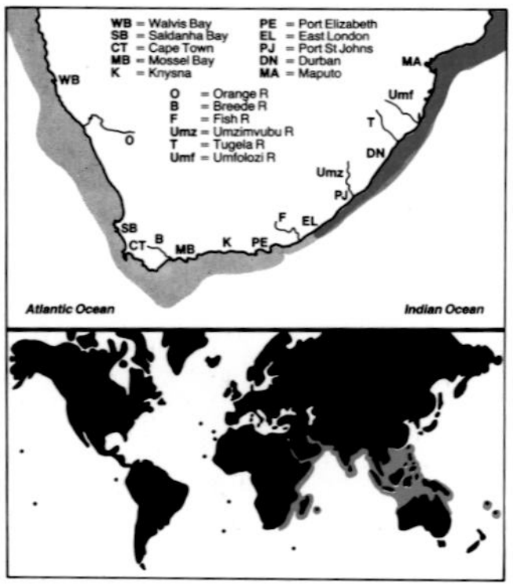

CAPTURE

The torpedo scad is extensively netted in the Far East, but is only occasionally landed in local beach seines. It fights gamely on light tackle, and freely takes small lures. Anglers on Durban's South Pier often land more of this than any other species. Its flesh makes good eating, but is not very popular.
SA angling record – 1,3 kg.

SPECIFIC CATCH RESTRICTIONS

None.

NAME DERIVATION

Megalaspis, large scutes; *cordyla,* mackerel. Torpedo scad, a reference to the body shape. *Scad* is an old word of unknown origin, apparently first used in Cornwall to describe the horse-mackerel or maasbanker.

SIMILAR SPECIES

There are no other fish that possess such large scutes as well as detached finlets.

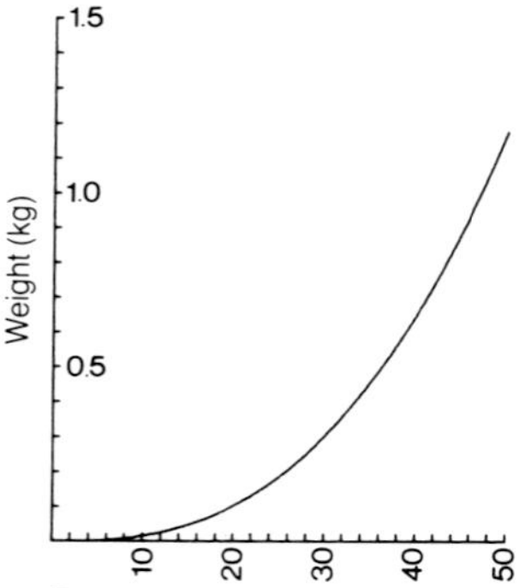

Scomberoides commersonnianus

Lacepède, 1801

Common names Worldwide – largemouth, giant or Talung queenfish

[Smith 210□38]

IDENTIFYING FEATURES

COLOUR, SHAPE AND SIZE

This elongate, mackerel-shaped fish has a blunt snout and a very large mouth. The overall body colour is silver, but dusky-green above, frequently golden-yellow along the flanks and with 5-8 distinct dark blotches just above the lateral line. The belly is white and the fins are yellowish or dusky. Can attain 120 cm.

EXTERNAL ANATOMY

The body is covered with needle-like scales that are partially embedded in the skin. The first of two dorsal fins has one forward-pointing spine that becomes embedded with age, followed by six or seven separate spines, while the second fin has one spine plus 19-21 rays. The anal fin has two detached spines followed by one spine plus 16-19 rays. In large specimens, the posterior rays of both dorsal and the anal fins may separate into finlets. The pectoral fins are short and the large caudal is deeply forked. The lateral line carries no scutes and is straight, except in the region below the first dorsal fin where it is slightly wavy. The jaws, which extend below, and well beyond, the eye, bear several rows of fine teeth, while villiform teeth occur on the palate and tongue. There are 8-15 stubby rakers on the first gill arch.

NATURAL HISTORY

The largemouth queenfish is a pelagic predator of tropical coastal regions and, though it periodically occurs in estuaries, it is generally intolerant of low salinities and turbid water. Though not a true shoaling fish, it swims in small groups which usually frequent reefs and rocky pinnacles. It is primarily a daytime feeder, and prey includes small pelagic and bottom-dwelling fish as well as mantis shrimps, swimming crabs and squid. Most specimens are host to a considerable variety of parasites, including tapeworm and roundworm larvae. Little is known of its life history. It is most abundant during summer, a time when it is not usually in a breeding condition. Juveniles have not been recorded in southern African waters.

DISTRIBUTION

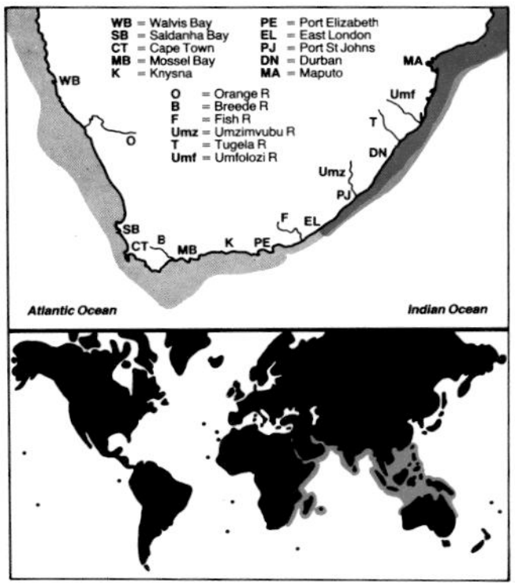

CAPTURE

This species is the favourite of many fishermen and may be caught from the shore and from ski-boats. It shows a preference for small live baits, though lures and fresh fish fillets may also be used. It is often speared by divers, but its habit of associating with enormous whale sharks can make spearfishing rather problematic. Though edible, the flesh is coarse and rather tasteless and is better smoked.

World angling record – 14,5 kg.
SA angling record – 11,7 kg.
SA spearfishing record – 14,4 kg.

SPECIFIC CATCH RESTRICTIONS

None.

NAME DERIVATION

Scomberoides, a reference to the similarity of these fish to the mackerels (family Scombridae); *commersonnianus,* after the eighteenth century naturalist, Commerson. Largemouth queenfish, a reference to its cavernous mouth and to its more graceful lines when compared with the kingfishes.

SIMILAR SPECIES

The noticeably large spots, uniformly coloured first dorsal, and posterior extention of the jaw will distinguish this from the other two queenfish species in South African waters.

Scomberoides tol

(Cuvier, 1832)
Common name SA - needlescaled queenfish
[Smith 210□40]

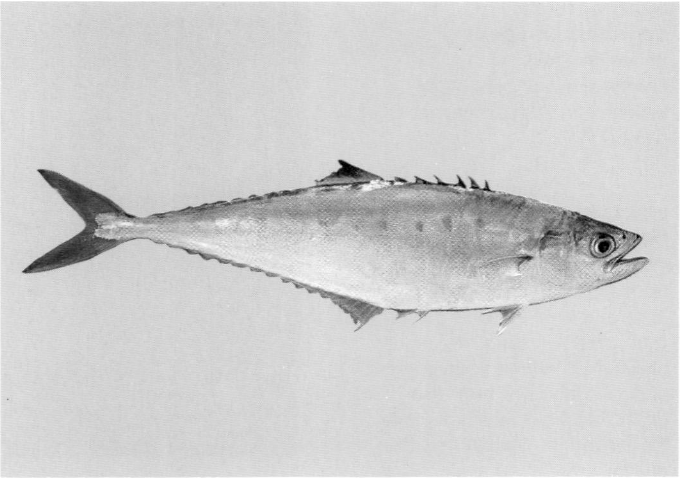

IDENTIFYING FEATURES

COLOUR, SHAPE AND SIZE
This strongly compressed, mackerel-shaped fish is silver overall, but the upper body is darker. Some 5-8 dark, oval spots occur on or above the lateral line. The fins are translucent or dusky, and the tip of the second dorsal fin is black. Can attain 50 cm.

EXTERNAL ANATOMY
Small, partially embedded, spear-shaped scales cover the body. The fins are particularly well developed. The dorsal fin is complex; the first spine points forward and precedes a further six separate spines which point alternately to the left and right; these are followed by one normal spine plus 19-20 rays, the last 8-10 of which form small semi-detached finlets. The anal fin has two spines followed by one spine and 18-20 rays, the last 8-10 of which form detached finlets. The large caudal fin is deeply forked. Two bands of fine teeth occur in each of the jaws, the hind edges of which reach a point directly below the middle of the eyes. The first gill arch carries 21-26 long rakers.

NATURAL HISTORY

The needlescaled queenfish is the smallest of the genus, and is confined to coastal waters, where it usually forms shoals, often in association with other fish such as elf, kingfish or mullet. Unlike the largemouth queenfish, this species does not enter estuaries and appears to be intolerant of low salinities. Its diet consists mostly of mid-water organisms such as small fish, krill, mantis shrimps and small squid. It is most abundant during the summer months, a period that coincides with its breeding season.

SPECIFIC CATCH RESTRICTIONS

None.

DISTRIBUTION

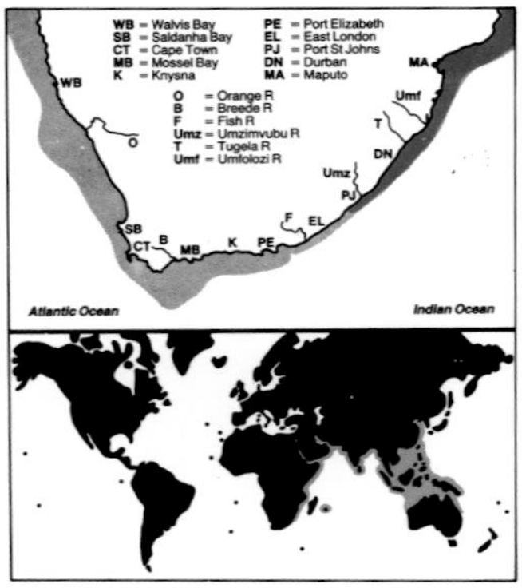

CAPTURE

This queenfish is quite frequently caught by shore and ski-boat anglers using light tackle. Though not highly esteemed for the quality of its flesh, it is edible if skinned to remove the sharp scales. Care should be taken to avoid laceration by the dorsal and anal spines as these may carry toxins.

NAME DERIVATION

Scomberoides, a reference to the similarity of these fish to the mackerels (family Scombridae); *tol,* courageous. Needlescaled queenfish, a reference to the pointed scales found on each flank, and to its more graceful lines when compared with the kingfishes.

SIMILAR SPECIES

This queenfish has needle-like scales, a short jaw, and a single row of small dots that distinguish it from other queenfish. The related doublespotted queenfish (*S. lysan*) has two rows of dots, and a jaw that extends to below the rear margin of the eye.

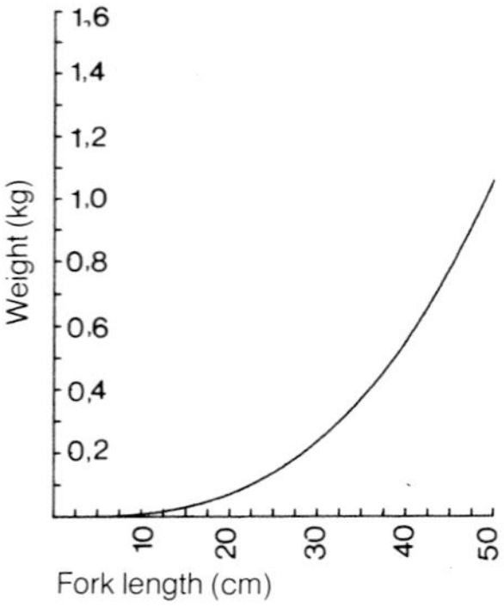

Seriola lalandi

Valenciennes, 1833

Common names SA – Cape yellowtail. Elsewhere – southern yellowtail, yellowtail amberjack [Smith 210□44]

IDENTIFYING FEATURES

COLOUR, SHAPE AND SIZE

This robust, torpedo-shaped fish has a depressed head. The upper body is blue-green, but separated from the silvery flanks by a broad yellow or bronze band which stretches from the snout through the eye and along the entire length of the body. The belly is white and the fins are dusky or yellow. The true brilliance of these colours, especially the bronze band and yellow tail, is only evident in live specimens. Can attain 150 cm, but fish of 100 cm are more common.

EXTERNAL ANATOMY

The body is covered with small scales. The double dorsal fin consists of 6-9 spines followed by one spine plus 30-35 rays, while the anal fin comprises two spines followed by one spine plus 19-22 rays. The large caudal fin is forked and there is a keel on either side of the peduncle. The lateral line is distinct. Each jaw is set with several rows of very fine teeth. Some 22-29 short rakers occur on the first gill arch.

NATURAL HISTORY

The Cape yellowtail is a common, but seasonal, gamefish of great esteem. It is mainly an inhabitant of Atlantic waters, but each winter it follows the pilchard migrations, or 'sardine run', up the East Coast to Transkei and Natal. Whereas most Cape yellowtail congregate in large offshore shoals which range to depths of 50 m, occasional specimens venture into the surf zone in pursuit of prey. This fast and powerful predator has such strong gregarious instincts that huge shoals may follow hooked and struggling fish to the surface from considerable depths. The diet consists of small fish and squid, though mantis shrimps and crabs have also been noted in the stomach contents of landed specimens. Spawning has been recorded off the Natal coast, but juveniles occur as far south as False Bay. Some experts report three sub-species of this fish from different regions.

DISTRIBUTION

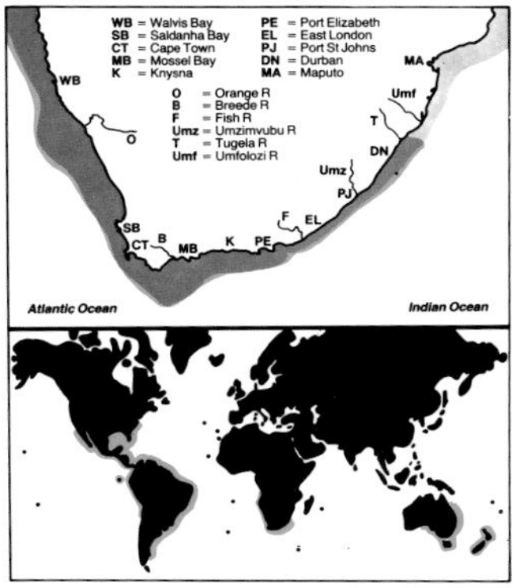

CAPTURE

The Cape yellowtail is commonly caught from ski-boats, and purse-seine trawlers often net great numbers. Shore anglers, however, may land good catches during the annual sardine run, when yellowtail freely take lures, spoons or sardine bait. This excellent table fish is also popular with spearfishermen.

World angling record – 52,0 kg.
All-Africa angling record – 33,1 kg.
SA angling record – 58,5 kg.
SA spearfishing record – 34,2 kg.

SPECIFIC CATCH RESTRICTIONS

Open species.

NAME DERIVATION

Seriola, an old Italian name for these fish; *lalandi,* named after the early naturalist Delalande. Cape yellowtail, a reference to its region of major occurrence and its bright-yellow tail.

SIMILAR SPECIES

No other *Seriola* species have a yellow tail. The greater yellowtail, or amberjack, (*S. dumerili*) has a deeper jaw and lacks keels on the peduncle.

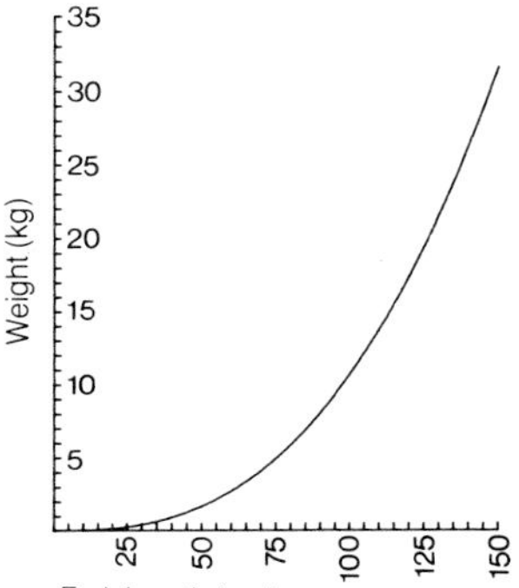

Seriola rivoliana

Valenciennes, 1833
Common names SA – longfin yellowtail, tropical yellowtail. Elsewhere – Almaco Jack
[Smith 210□45]

IDENTIFYING FEATURES

COLOUR, SHAPE AND SIZE

This is a moderately elongate fish with a smoothly curved upper profile. The overall body colour is a silvery-olive above, with paler flanks and an almost-white belly. Live specimens often have a coppery sheen to their bodies. Most have a distinct dark band that runs from the eye obliquely backwards 'across' the neck, hence it is called the nuchal bar. Freshly caught specimens may also display an amber-yellow band running backwards from the eye, along the middle of each side. The fins are mostly dusky, except for the anal which is edged in white.Juveniles have different colour-patterns and, in addition to the nuchal bar, also have dark, vertical body bars. Attains 103 cm, though most do not exceed 65 cm.

EXTERNAL ANATOMY

This yellowtail is completely covered in scales, though these are rather small and difficult to count. No enlarged scales occur along the distinct lateral line. The fins are well developed. A short first dorsal of seven spines precedes a long second dorsal that has one spine plus 27-33 rays. The anal fin has two detached spines preceding one spine plus 18-22 rays. The pectoral fins are short, considerably smaller than the pelvics, and also less than the height of the second dorsal fin. There are short, but well-developed gill rakers on the first arch, their number reducing slightly with age. Young fish have 24-29 rakers, but older fish in excess of 20 cm have 22-26 rakers. A broad band of minute teeth occurs in each jaw. A further diagnostic feature is the broad-ended maxillae which reach to below the mid-eye.

DISTRIBUTION

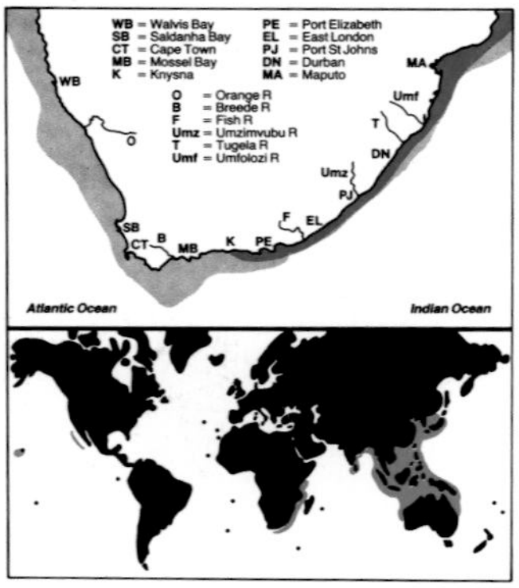

NATURAL HISTORY

This is a moderately common gamefish of tropical and warm temperate waters. It is usually found singly or in small groups, occasionally in proximity to the coast, but more often some distance from shore. The longfin yellowtail seems as much at home in open oceanic waters as it does cruising over coral and rocky reefs. In both cases, it is engaged in pursuing its prey of small fish. Spawning takes place in tropical waters during spring, and the young are widely distributed by ocean currents, sheltering below floating objects at sea. Many such young have been seen by ski-boaters in summer.

CAPTURE

This species is most often caught using trolled baits or artificial lures from craft at sea. Few, if any, are caught from the shore, though spearfishermen also succeed in catching this fish. It is of excellent eating quality.
World angling record – 59,9 kg.
SA angling record – 15,8 kg.
SA spearfishing record – 21,0 kg.

SPECIFIC CATCH RESTRICTIONS

None.

NAME DERIVATION

Seriola, an old, Italian name for these fish; *rivoliana,* a reference to its original place of capture. Longfin yellowtail, a reference to the rather long dorsal fin rays, and its relationship to the true yellowtails with their bright-yellow caudals.

SIMILAR SPECIES

While the longfin yellowtail is similar in appearance to several other species, its nuchal bar, short pectoral fin, high gill-raker count and broad maxillae serve to confirm identity.

Seriolina nigrofasciata

(Rüppell, 1829)

Common names SA – blackbanded or dusky yellowtail. Elsewhere – blackbanded amberjack

[Smith 210□46]

IDENTIFYING FEATURES

COLOUR, SHAPE AND SIZE

The dusky yellowtail is an elongate, robust fish, with a smoothly rounded dorsal profile. The upper body surface is dusky olive-brown, while the flanks are silvery and the underside is white. Young specimens have five or six darker bars running down the body, but these become less distinct with growth and finally disappear in adult fish. The body is also marked with five or six faint brownish bands that extend from the snout to the yellow caudal fin. The remaining fins are brownish or dusky. Can attain 70 cm.

EXTERNAL ANATOMY

The entire body, including the breast region, is covered with small scales, none of which is enlarged into scutes. Though a lateral line is visible, this is smoothly curved and not abruptly bent as in most kingfishes. The fins are well developed, and it is important to note that, as with other members of the genus, the soft dorsal fin is much longer than the soft anal fin. The dusky yellowtail has two dorsal fins, the first consists of one forward-pointing spine (that is not always visible) plus 5-7 normal spines, while the second has one spine plus 30-37 rays. The anal fin has one detached spine followed by one spine plus 15-18 rays. The caudal fin is forked. Characteristic are the short pectoral fins. There are bands of fine villiform teeth in the jaws, both of which extend backwards to below the hind edge of the eye. The 5-7 rakers on the first gill arch are also a distinctive feature of this fish. These are reduced to short knobs and differ from those of similar species.

DISTRIBUTION

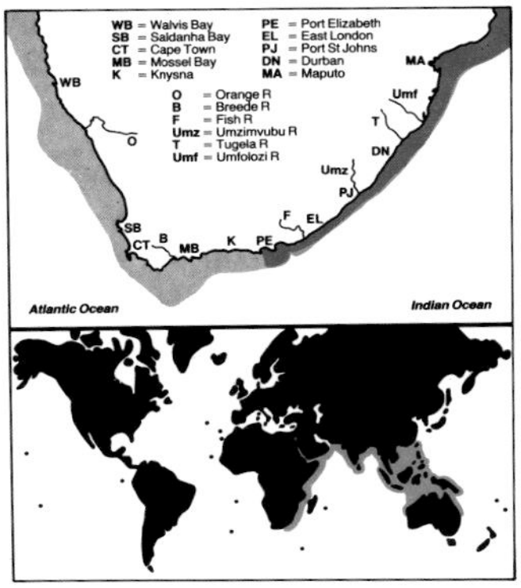

NATURAL HISTORY

The dusky yellowtail is not rare, but, because it is often confused with other yellowtails, specific information is sparse. It is widespread throughout tropical waters, is generally solitary, and is seldom seen close to the shore. Favoured habitats appear to be offshore reefs, especially those such as the Aliwal Shoals which rise close to the surface. Though not particularly aggressive, this species does prey on smaller shoaling fishes and crustaceans such as mantis shrimps, small crabs and prawns. One of its close relatives is the true pilotfish (*Naucrates ductor*),well known for its association with large sharks. In fact the juvenile dusky yellowtail rather resembles the pilotfish and this may indicate a form of protective mimicry.

CAPTURE

Occasionally this fish is caught by ski-boat anglers, but most are landed by spearfishermen. In the tropical Far East bottom trawls, traps and handlines are used and, particularly in the Philippines, this excellent eating fish is marketed commercially.

SA angling record – 5,2 kg.

SA spearfishing record – 5,2 kg.

SPECIFIC CATCH RESTRICTIONS

None.

NAME DERIVATION

Seriolina, a reference to its close relationship to the genus *Seriola; nigrofasciata,* black banded. Dusky yellowtail, a reference to the dusky body colours and yellow caudal fin. Blackbanded, refers to the 5-7 dark bars that run across the body of juveniles.

SIMILAR SPECIES

The broadly rounded maxillae and very short gill rakers distinguish this species from other yellowtails. Notice also that it lacks the lateral scutes found in the kingfishes.

Trachinotus africanus

Smith, 1967

Common names Worldwide – African or southern pompano

[Smith 210□47]

IDENTIFYING FEATURES

COLOUR, SHAPE AND SIZE

Live specimens of this robust, blunt-nosed species are silver, with a bluish back and white belly. After death, however, the body often becomes blotchy and bright yellow. The fins are dusky or yellowish. Attains 80 cm.

EXTERNAL ANATOMY

The greater part of the body is well covered with very small scales, but the head region is virtually naked. The front section of the double dorsal fin comprises a concealed forward spine followed by six detached spines, while the hind section has one spine plus 21-23 rays. The anal fin has two detached spines followed by one spine plus 19-21 rays. The large caudal fin is deeply forked and the pectoral fins are sickle-shaped. Scutes are lacking along the fairly straight lateral line. Bony projections may occur along the vertebrae in larger specimens, but this is not an abnormality. Feeble, almost invisible, teeth are located in both jaws, while a set of very strong grinding plates occurs further back in the gullet. The first gill arch carries 21 or 22 rakers.

NATURAL HISTORY

The African pompano favours shallow, warm-water regions marked with reefs or rocky outcrops. It is also tolerant of low salinities. The preference of this pelagic fish for warm water is highlighted by its peak abundance during the summer months. Black and brown rock mussels are this pompano's main source of food, with sand mussels, sand dollars, crabs and mole crabs (sea lice) also being of importance. Its unimpressive teeth are more than compensated by the powerful, pharyngeal grinding plates. This mill-like feeding mechanism can crush the hardest mussels within seconds. The African pompano has a remarkably high growth rate, and attains sexual maturity before the age of three. The young make extensive use of sheltered bays as nursery areas, and are common off Durban's beachfront. Adults are usually encountered singly or in pairs, though shoals of up to 100 individuals may occur during the spring breeding season.

DISTRIBUTION

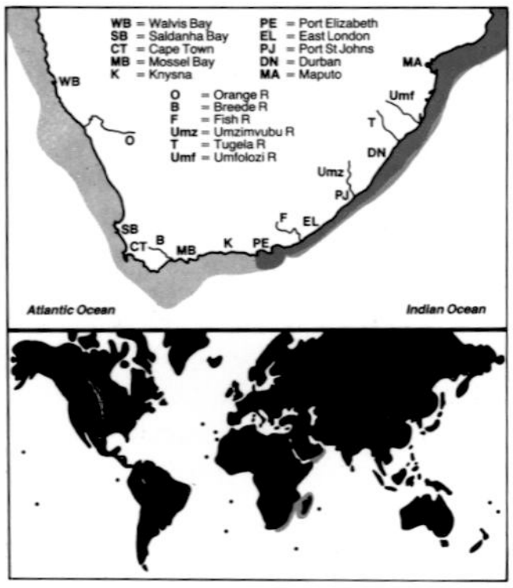

CAPTURE

The pompano is a superb table fish and a firm favourite of sport anglers and spearfishermen alike. Any of its natural food items will succeed as bait, especially in the surf zone. Though the angling record presently stands at just over 14 kg, specimens in Durban's Seaworld have exceeded 25,0 kg.

SA angling record – 14,1 kg.

SA spearfishing record – 13,6 kg.

SPECIFIC CATCH RESTRICTIONS

None.

NAME DERIVATION

Trachinotus, rough back; *africanus,* of Africa. Pompano, from the Spanish *pampano,* meaning grape leaf, presumably a reference to the body shape. The name of the African pompano is used in the USA for the threadfin mirrorfish, *Alectis ciliaris* (p 133).

SIMILAR SPECIES

The absence of spots along the body and associated fin ray counts will distinguish this pompano from the other three species found in South African waters.

Trachinotus blochii

(Lacepède, 1801)
Common names Worldwide – snubnose or longfin pompano
[Smith 210□49]

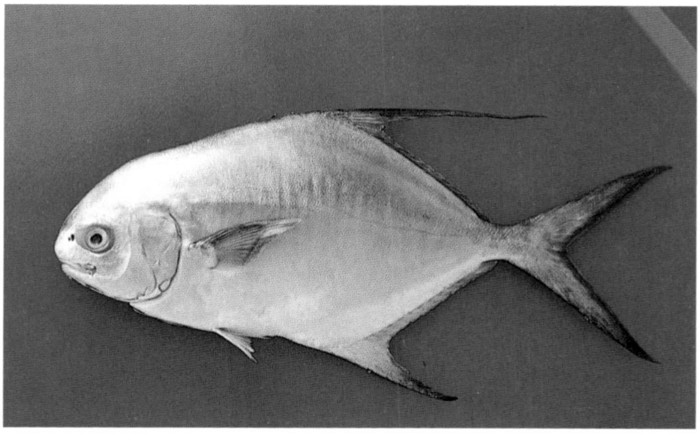

IDENTIFYING FEATURES

COLOUR, SHAPE AND SIZE
This is a robust fish, moderately compressed and ovoid in body shape, but with a somewhat 'humped' back in larger specimens such as the one pictured here. The overall colour is silvery, with a bluish upper surface and white underside. Many freshly caught specimens are a striking, golden-yellow colour, especially on the lower flanks. There are no marks or distinctive body spots. The fins are usually tinged with yellowy-orange, especially the anal fin, which is a dirty orange with a brownish tip to the lobe. Can attain 65 cm.
EXTERNAL ANATOMY
Numerous small, tightly adhering scales cover most of the body, except the head region which is naked. The fins are distinctive in shape, and both anal and dorsal fins have long, falcate lobes. The dorsal has six short spines which become increasingly embedded with age. This precedes one spine plus 18-20 rays. The anal fin has two short, detached spines preceding a single spine plus 16-18 rays. The caudal fin is large and deeply forked, and the pelvic fins are shorter than the pectorals. There are no sharp scutes on the flanks of this fish, although the lateral line is distinct and irregularly wavy. The mouth is positioned just below the bluntly rounded snout, each jaw being set with a band of minute, villiform teeth. The gill rakers are stubby and number 13-18, including the rudiments.
A significant diagnostic feature of this and related pompanos lies in the shape of the supraoccipital bone of the skull. This requires dissection of the specimen. The juveniles of the snubnose pompano are more rounded in body shape.

DISTRIBUTION

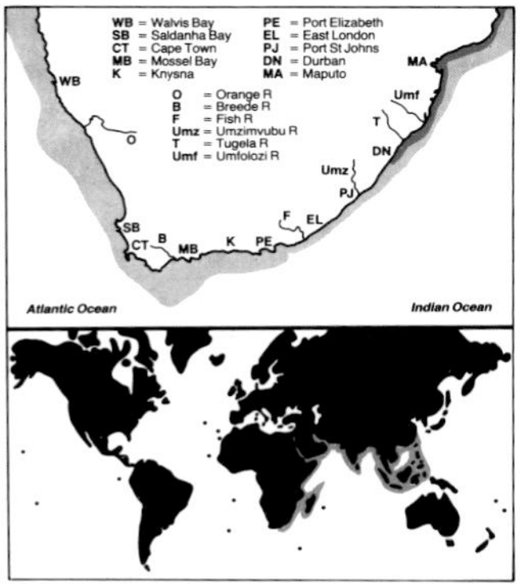

NATURAL HISTORY

There has been little research and few observations on the life history of this fine angling fish. This is partly due to its frequent confusion with the African pompano. This is a shallow-water gamefish that becomes progressively more abundant from Sodwana Bay northward, though snubnose pompano are caught at Durban. Its diet consists mainly of bivalve molluscs that live in the sandy surf zone, black rock mussels, small crabs and especially mole crabs (sea lice). All these hard-shelled organisms are easily cracked by the strong pharyngeal teeth. To what extent this species competes with the African pompano for food and space is not known, though there are certain to be differences between these two related species. While the African pompano occasionally enters estuaries, there appear to be no records of the snubnose doing so. Its spawning season is probably during spring in more tropical regions.

CAPTURE

This strong fish will readily take a prawn or mussel bait and can provide both good sport and excellent cuisine. Most are caught from the beach, and few, if any, are landed by ski-boaters.
SA angling record – 2,9 kg.

SPECIFIC CATCH RESTRICTIONS

None.

NAME DERIVATION

Trachinotus, rough back; *blochii,* named after Bloch, the famous German ichthyologist of the early 19th century. Snubnose pompano, a reference to its blunt snout and from the Spanish *pampano* meaning grape leaf, presumably a reference to its body shape.

SIMILAR SPECIES

While pompanos are quite distinctive in their shape, this species and the African pompano are often confused, especially in their juvenile stage when they closely resemble each other.
The most significant differences between these two lie in the ray counts of their anal and dorsal fins and the relative length of their fins.

Trachinotus botla

(Shaw, 1803)

Common names SA – largespot pompano, moonfish. Elsewhere – largespot pompano, wave trevally [Smith 210□50]

IDENTIFYING FEATURES

COLOUR, SHAPE AND SIZE

This robust, oval fish has a blunt snout. The overall body colour is silver, but bluish above and white below. There are three or four darker, oval spots on each flank, either on, or just above, the lateral line. The fin lobes are a metallic indigo-blue. Can attain 60 cm.

EXTERNAL ANATOMY

Except for the naked head, the body is covered with small cycloid scales. The front section of the dorsal fin comprises six spines, the first of which points forward, while the hind section has one spine plus 22-24 rays. The anal fin has two detached spines followed by a single spine plus 19-22 rays. The first rays of the dorsal and anal fins become more sickle-shaped with age. The deeply forked caudal fin has long pointed lobes. Minute, villiform teeth are found in smaller specimens, but mature adults are toothless. Some 18-20 distinct rakers occur on the first gill arch.

DISTRIBUTION

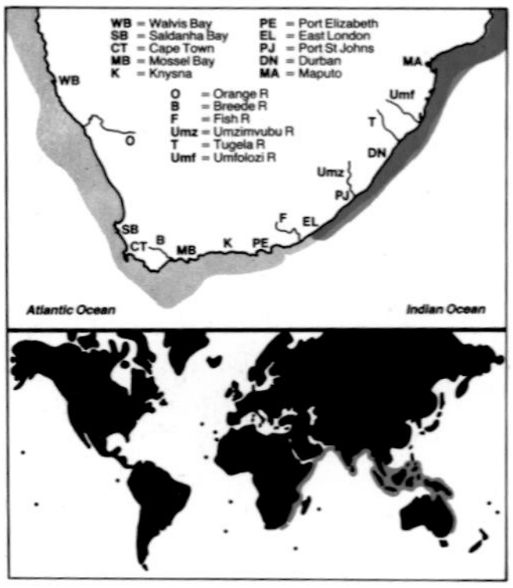

NATURAL HISTORY

This fast-swimming fish prefers the rough surf zone along sandy beaches, and will often swim on its side to enter very shallow water. It is, however, intolerant of fresh or muddy water. Mole crabs (sea lice), which are plentiful along sandy beaches, are principal items of diet, but sometimes small clams, sand mussels and marine worms are also eaten. Larger predators, such as the giant kingfish, prey on this pompano. Spawning occurs off Zululand beaches and the juveniles live in the shallowest part of the surf zone, where they are often stranded by receding waves, or trapped in mole crab nets. Nearly all largespot pompano host a pair of isopod parasites within the mouth, the larger of which is female and sometimes carries young. Though the full significance, or effects, of these parasites have yet to be studied, they are known to damage the host's tongue.

CAPTURE

This fine, light-tackle gamefish takes a variety of baits, though mole crabs are undoubtedly favoured. The flesh is very palatable, but the fish has no commercial significance. The largespot pompano is not sought after by spearfishermen.

SA angling record – 2,5 kg.

SA spearfishing record – vacant.

SPECIFIC CATCH RESTRICTIONS

None.

NAME DERIVATION

Trachinotus, rough back; *botla*, of unknown Indian origin. Largespot pompano, a spotted relative of the true pompano. Moonfish, a reference to the sickle-shaped fins and the soft silvery sheen.

SIMILAR SPECIES

Only the smallspot pompano (*T. baillonii*) resembles this species (though it has distinctly smaller spots, usually smaller in size than the eye diameter). Previously this fish was known as *T. russelli*.

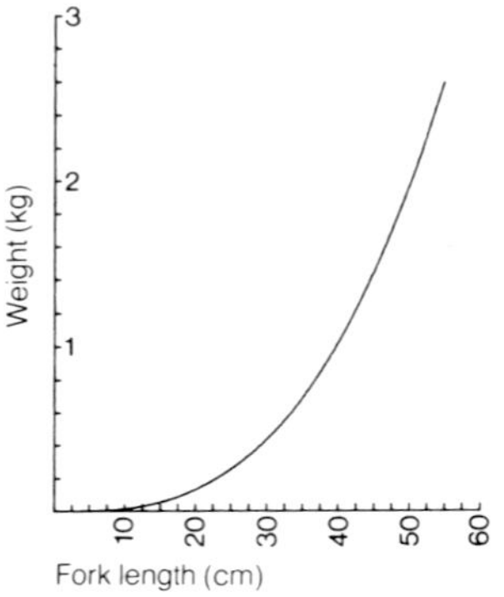

Trachurus trachurus

Linnaeus, 1758

Common names SA – maasbanker. Elsewhere – horse mackerel, scad [Smith 210□52]

IDENTIFYING FEATURES

COLOUR, SHAPE AND SIZE

The maasbanker is an elongate fish that is almost round in cross-section. The overall body colour is silver, but olive-green to grey above and white below. Darker, vertical bars may be visible on the flanks and there is always a distinct black spot on the gill covers. The fins are translucent or dusky. Can attain 70 cm.

EXTERNAL ANATOMY

The body is covered with about 75 series of scales arranged along the lateral line. The scales of 40 of these series are sharply spiked. The double dorsal fin comprises one forward plus eight normal spines, which are followed by one spine plus 30-36 rays. The anal fin consists of two detached spines plus one spine followed by 24-32 rays. The caudal fin is deeply forked. Bands of minute, villiform teeth occur in both the upper and lower jaws. Some 50 elongate rakers occur on the first gill arch. The large eyes are extensively covered with adipose tissue.

DISTRIBUTION

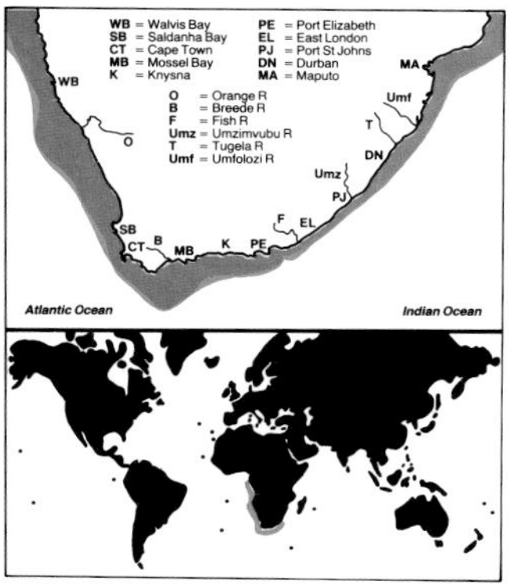

NATURAL HISTORY

The maasbanker is a pelagic shoaling species of cooler coastal waters and ranges from the surface to depths of 400 m. Considerable vertical movement has been recorded, however, with shoals rising to feed in surface waters at night and, conversely, moving downwards to spend the daylight hours near the bottom. The diet consists of krill, mysids and amphipods, most of which are filtered from the water by the elaborate gill rakers. Dolphins, tuna and sea birds prey extensively on this species. Sexual maturity is attained at the age of three years, at an equivalent total length of about 20 cm. Spawning occurs from late winter to spring and the young are widely distributed by ocean currents. It is possible that the fry of maasbanker, like the young of the closely related North Sea horse mackerel, shelter below very large jellyfish during their first months. Presumably these young fish are immune to the stinging cells of the jellyfish.

CAPTURE

The maasbanker is of considerable commercial importance in southern Africa. Most catches are made in bottom trawls during daylight and much of it as a bycatch. While catches have declined in recent years, the maasbanker may yet prove to be underexploited. Anglers catch this fish from ski-boats and consider it an excellent bait for the larger gamefish. The Maasbanker is also of value as bait in the rock lobster industry.
SA angling record – 1,4 kg.

SPECIFIC CATCH RESTRICTIONS

Open species; commercial catches are subject to quota.

NAME DERIVATION

Trachurus, rough tail. Maasbanker, an old Dutch name for a similar, but fresh-water, fish that lives on the shallow banks of the river Maas in Holland.

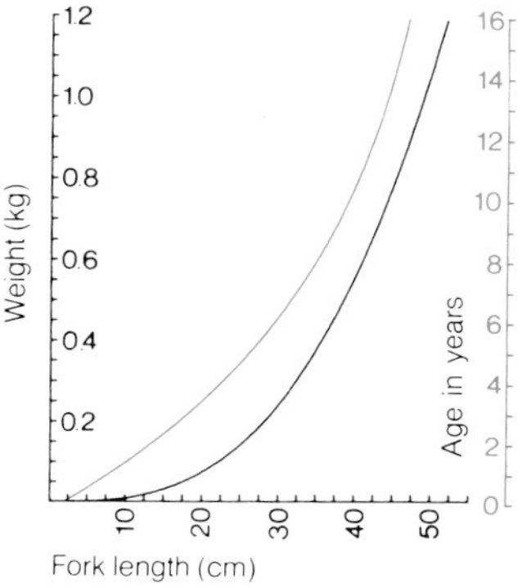

Aeoliscus punctulatus

(Bianconi, 1855)
Common names Worldwide – razorfish, shrimpfish
[Smith 148□1]

IDENTIFYING FEATURES

COLOUR, SHAPE AND SIZE

The elongate, strongly compressed body and peculiar, 'upside-down' swimming position make this fish unmistakable. The overall body colour is light brown or occasionally greenish-grey, overlaid with numerous black dots that are particularly dense and conspicuous around the snout. Seen underwater, the body appears translucent, thus making the dots even more obvious. Attains 20 cm.

EXTERNAL ANATOMY

Though scaleless, the body of the razorfish is covered with a series of bony plates which are, in fact, lateral extentions of the vertebral column. Along the dorsal or leading edge of the fish these plates are rounded, but ventrally they are fused to form a sharp edge. The fins of razorfishes have been modified to suit their curious habits and, accordingly, the spine which projects upwards from the hindmost part of the body is really the first dorsal spine. The dorsal fin, consisting of three spines plus 10-11 rays, faces backwards and is located in the conventional tail position. Further down on the ventral side is the caudal fin which is followed by the anal fin comprising 12-13 rays. The pectoral fins are quite large but the pelvics are reduced. The very small mouth of the razorfish is situated at the tip of the long, tube-like snout.

NATURAL HISTORY

The unique life style of the razorfish makes it an endlessly fascinating subject for study. Such observations will clearly show how this most unusual animal has evolved to suit its upside-down world. The most immediate and obvious features are the unpaired

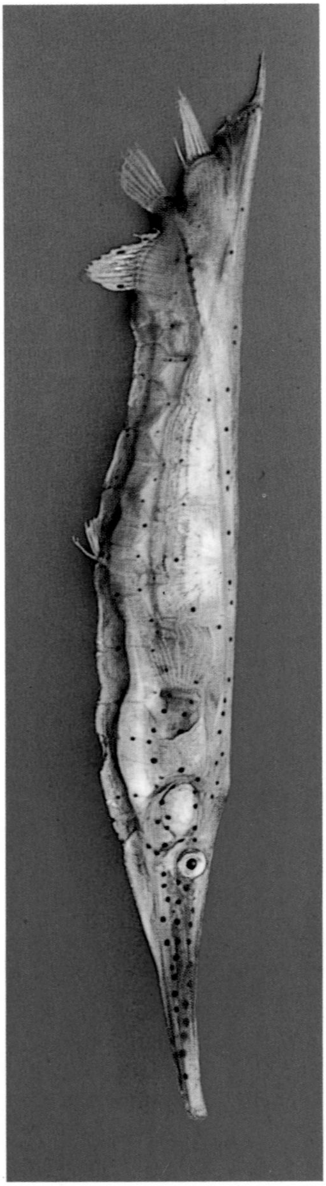

fins which, being all arranged along the ventral edge, can act in concert to propel the fish lengthways, or horizontally, through the water. The pectoral fins are equally important in locomotion as these produce 'lift', that is, the ability to move vertically upwards. Thus this fish is capable of the extremely fine manoeuvres necessary to position the tiny mouth directly over an item of food. The diet includes amphipods, copepods, shrimps, crab larvae and other small midwater crustaceans. A further instance of the razorfish's success is its ability to blend with its surroundings; the body is almost transparent and, when in the middle of a shoal of plankton, the conspicuous body spots resemble these tiny organisms so closely that the fish becomes all but invisible. This camouflage is important not only as a defence strategy, but also for feeding purposes, as plankton may remain unaware of the razorfish and therefore would not disperse. During the summer months the razorfish is quite common along the edges of shallow reefs and, in more tropical regions, it is frequently found among stands of seagrass. Information about the reproductive cycle is sparse.

DISTRIBUTION

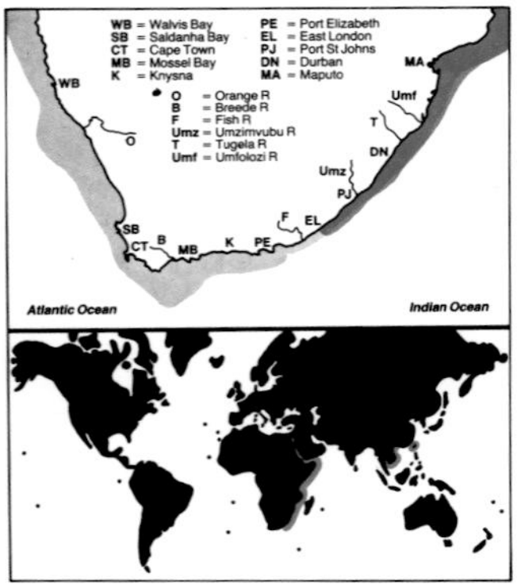

CAPTURE

The razorfish's unique anatomy and swimming style make it a popular species with many marine aquarists. Though it can be successfully maintained in captivity, it requires careful attention and a constant and varied supply of live planktonic food.

SPECIFIC CATCH RESTRICTIONS

None.

Chaetodon auriga

Forsskål, 1775
Common name Worldwide – threadfin butterflyfish
[Smith 205□1]

IDENTIFYING FEATURES

COLOUR, SHAPE AND SIZE
The body of this strongly compressed, oval fish is white, but overlaid with dark, broken lines arranged diagonally. The dorsal and anal fins, as well as the caudal region, are predominantly yellow. Most characteristic, however, is the black eye-spot on the soft dorsal fin of most specimens and the complete, or partial, black eye-band. Notice that this eye-band is broader below the eye than above. Attains 18 cm.

EXTERNAL ANATOMY
Small, distinctly ctenoid scales cover the body and are arranged in 27-32 series along the lateral line. The fins are well developed and include a dorsal of 12 or 13 spines plus 23 or 24 rays, and an anal of three spines plus 20 or 21 rays. The caudal fin is truncate. In older specimens, one or two of the dorsal rays extend into trailing filaments which often project beyond the caudal fin. The small mouth at the tip of the pointed snout has long, thin teeth in each jaw.
Note: A sub-species occurs in the Red Sea, and is distinguished by the absence of the black eye-spot and shorter dorsal filaments.

DISTRIBUTION

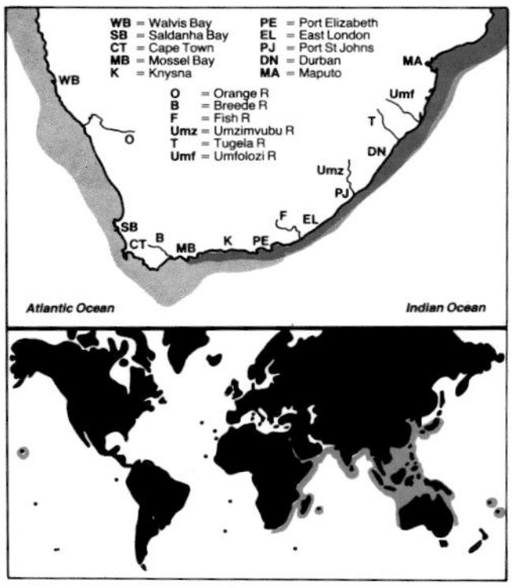

NATURAL HISTORY

This is one of the more common and widely dispersed butterflyfishes. It usually frequents shallow coral and rocky reefs, and juveniles often occur in intertidal rock pools. Threadfin butterflyfish move placidly about the reef in pairs, but will dart off if disturbed. Feeding takes place continuously during the day, but also at night, and large areas of reef are sometimes covered in the search for food. The varied diet of small reef organisms includes crabs, amphipods, marine worms, gastropod eggs, sea urchin tentacles, shrimps, sponges, anemones and other invertebrates. All are carefully pecked from crevices in the rocks or torn off sedentary animals. Little is known of the life history and though no migrations have been recorded, it is likely that seasonal changes in local abundance do occur. Though hybridization is extremely rare in marine fishes, this species is known to have crossed with the halfmoon butterflyfish and, possibly, one other member of the Chaetodontidae.

CAPTURE

This hardy little fish thrives in captivity, and is much sought after by aquarists. It is relatively easy to catch, as the juveniles appear to be dependant on intertidal rock pools as nursery areas. Because of this, however, the threadfin butterflyfish is vulnerable to over-exploitation, and it is advisable that the juveniles be protected along certain parts of the coast to ensure viable adult populations.

SPECIFIC CATCH RESTRICTIONS

None.

NAME DERIVATION

Chaetodon, hair-like teeth; *auriga,* ear shaped. Threadfin butterflyfish, a reference to the filamentous projection of the dorsal fin rays, and to the fish's bright colours and its flitting movements, reminiscent of a butterfly moving from flower to flower.

SIMILAR SPECIES

This species can be immediately recognized by the trailing filaments to its dorsal fin. The black eye spot and shape of the eye-band are also distinguishing aids.

Chaetodon blackburnii

Desjardins, 1836
Common names SA – brownburnie, Elsewhere – brown butterflyfish, Blackburn's butterflyfish
[Smith 205□3]

IDENTIFYING FEATURES

COLOUR, SHAPE AND SIZE

The brownburnie is not as intricately coloured or patterned as many of the other butterflyfishes. Nonetheless, this compressed little fish has distinctive markings: the body is predominantly yellow in front, and brown towards the tail; some 6-8 blackish stripes radiate outwards from behind the pectoral fins towards the dorsal and tail regions; and there is also a conspicuous, dark, vertical eye-band. The dorsal, anal and caudal fins are dark, while the pectoral and pelvic fins are yellow and translucent. Can attain 13 cm.

EXTERNAL ANATOMY

The body is covered with ctenoid scales arranged in 34-36 series along the lateral line. The fins are well developed and include a dorsal of 16-17 spines (the highest number found in any *Chaetodon* species) plus 22 or 23 rays, and an anal of three spines plus 16-18 rays. The caudal fin may be either slightly rounded or slightly forked. The small mouth is almost drawn to a point and both jaws bear small, bristle-like teeth. There are about 15 rakers on the first gill arch.

NATURAL HISTORY

The brownburnie may be solitary or paired, and usually frequents the edges of shallow rocky reefs, where it darts about in search of small crabs, amphipods and marine worms, all of which are pecked from crevices in the rocks. It occasionally also enters quiet bays and harbours and may even be quite common around silt-covered rubble. Though it occurs all year round, summer marks its period of peak abundance. The drab colours of this species contrast strikingly with other Chaetodontidae in this region. Whereas the elaborate patterns and colours of most butterflyfishes may serve to confuse would-be predators, the comparatively nondescript colours of the brownburnie suggest that its particular defence strategy is based on camouflage against the backdrop of a reef. While this species is common on most shallow-water, Natal reefs, it is particularly plentiful on Limestone Reef, Durban.

DISTRIBUTION

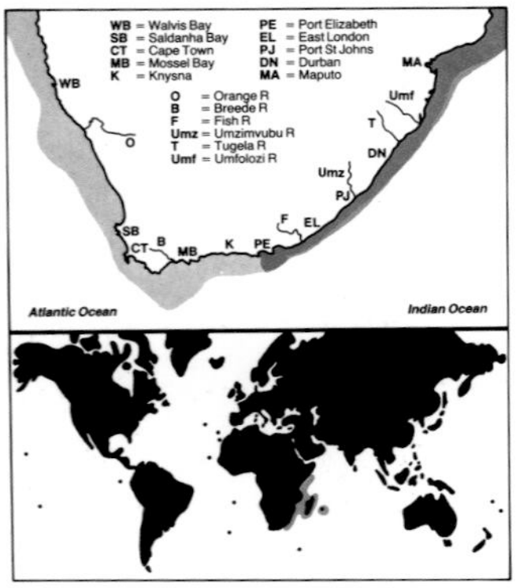

CAPTURE

The brownburnie is relatively successful as an aquarium fish, but may prove reluctant to feed in captivity unless a wide variety of food is available.

SPECIFIC CATCH RESTRICTIONS

None.

NAME DERIVATION

Chaetodon, hair-like teeth; *blackburnii,* named after the naturalist Blackburn. Brownburnie, derived from its colours and scientific name.

SIMILAR SPECIES

The high dorsal fin count of 16-17 spines is unique to this species. Underwater, it is easily distinguished by its overall brown appearance.

Chaetodon guttatissimus

Bennet, 1832

Common names Worldwide – gorgeous gussy, spotted butterflyfish

[Smith 205□6]

IDENTIFYING FEATURES

COLOUR, SHAPE AND SIZE

This compressed, disc-shaped little fish has a pale, yellowish body, delicately patterned with numerous rows of small, black spots. There is a distinct and uninterrupted, black eye-band, a feature that distinguishes this species from similar varieties in the Pacific Ocean. The entire outer edge of both the dorsal and anal fins is brighter yellow, while the caudal fin is translucent. A black bar extends down the caudal peduncle. Can attain 12 cm.

EXTERNAL ANATOMY

Small scales cover the body and are arranged in 27-39 series along the lateral line. The fins are well developed and include a dorsal of 13 spines plus 20-23 rays, an anal of three spines plus 17-19 rays, and a rounded caudal. The terminal mouth protrudes slightly to form a short beak. Both jaws are set with fine, bristle-like teeth.

DISTRIBUTION

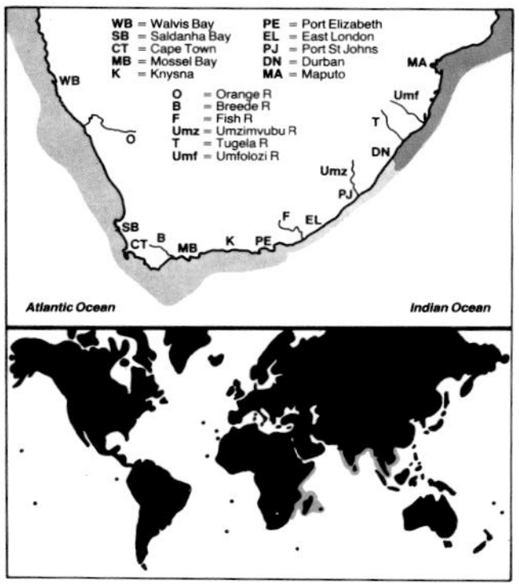

NATURAL HISTORY

This species is one of the smallest of the Chaetodontidae. It is common and widely distributed throughout the Indian Ocean, where it frequents rocky and coral reefs, ranging in depth from 4 to 25 m. The gorgeous gussy occurs singly, in pairs, or in small groups, and may be seen as it moves about reefs, carefully searching cracks and crevices for food. The diet consists mainly of small invertebrate organisms such as amphipods, copepods and marine worms. Various species of seaweed and, occasionally, soft corals are also eaten. As with most *Chaetodon* species, details of the breeding cycle are sparse. However, juveniles are known to resemble adults in shape and body markings.

CAPTURE

Aquarists often capture these beautiful little fish, but not all specimens survive in the artificial tank environment, because of their reluctance to accept food. To avoid such unnecessary deaths, therefore, it is suggested that only small gorgeous gussies are collected for aquaria, and if these prove unwilling to feed within seven days of their capture, they should be returned to their natural habitat.

SPECIFIC CATCH RESTRICTIONS

None.

NAME DERIVATION

Chaetodon, hair-like teeth; *guttatissimus* spotted body. Spotted butterflyfish, an obvious reference to its body markings and to its flitting movements, reminiscent of a butterfly moving from flower to flower. Gorgeous gussy, derived from its scientific name.

SIMILAR SPECIES

Although several less common butterflyfish have a black-spotted body, none are as distinct as in the gorgeous gussy. The much rarer *C. dolosus* (incorrectly called *C. miliaris*) has much fainter spots and lives at depths of 200 m.

Chaetodon kleinii

Bloch, 1790

Common names SA – whitespotted butterflyfish. Elsewhere – Klein's butterflyfish

[Smith 205□7]

IDENTIFYING FEATURES

COLOUR, SHAPE AND SIZE

This rather small butterflyfish is almost round in profile. The general body colour is brownish-yellow. In many specimens the distinct black eye-band is followed by a paler or off-white vertical bar, extending from the dorsal spines to the pelvic fin base. Each of the scales along the flanks has a white centre, thus giving the fish an overall speckled or mottled appearance. Can attain 14 cm in length.

EXTERNAL ANATOMY

The body is covered with ctenoid scales, arranged in 30-38 series along the lateral line. The well-developed fins include a single dorsal of 12 or 13 spines plus 20-23 rays, an anal of three spines plus 18-19 rays, and a slightly rounded caudal. The mouth is moderately extended into a snout, and each jaw bears a single row of bristle-like teeth.

NATURAL HISTORY

The whitespotted butterflyfish is common throughout the Indian and western Pacific oceans, where it inhabits coral and rocky reefs ranging in depth from 10 to 40 m. It may be encountered singly, or in small groups, as it forages about the reef during the day. The diet includes small crabs, amphipods and marine worms, as well as lesser amounts of seaweed, all of which are carefully pecked from the reef substrate. With its slightly protruding mouth, a feature of most Chaetodontidae, this little fish probes the deeper recesses and cracks in the reef for any item of food sheltering within. In this manner, it is able to exploit a food source inaccessible to many other groups of reef-dwelling fish. Details of the breeding biology of this species are unknown, but hybrid crosses with the limespot butterflyfish have been reported from the Marshall Islands in the western Pacific Ocean.

DISTRIBUTION

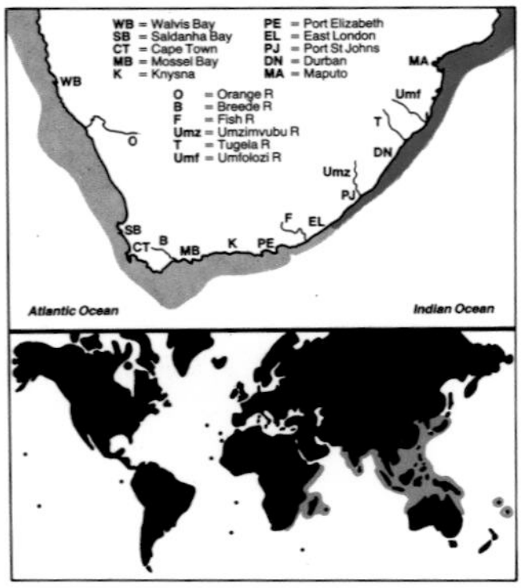

CAPTURE

As its colours and body patterns are less striking than those of most members of this family, the whitespotted butterflyfish is not in great demand with aquarists. Nevertheless, it adapts successfully to the artificial environment of an aquarium tank, provided that its natural habitat is carefully simulated and special attention is given to its diet.

SPECIFIC CATCH RESTRICTIONS

None.

NAME DERIVATION

Chaetodon, hair-like teeth; *kleinii,* a reference to Klein, the ichthyologist after whom it was named. Whitespotted butterflyfish, a reference to the fish's colours, body markings and flitting movements, reminiscent of a butterfly flying from flower to flower.

SIMILAR SPECIES

This species has been described by numerous authors and, in the process, has been given different names. Consequently, despite its wide distribution, there has been much confusion about its correct identification. Nevertheless, the overall yellow colour and mottled appearance are distinctive. The blackback butterflyfish (*C. melanotus*) is somewhat similar, but has 18-20 dorsal rays, faint, black lines and a black bar across the caudal peduncle.

Chaetodon lunula

(Lacepède, 1803)
Common names SA – halfmoon butterflyfish. Elsewhere – racoon butterflyfish
[Smith 205□9]

IDENTIFYING FEATURES

COLOUR, SHAPE AND SIZE

This compressed little fish is disc-shaped and has a slightly protruding snout. The general body colour is yellow, but is overlaid with a complex arrangement of bars and stripes. A broad, black eye-band precedes a white bar which extends across the forehead. The upper flanks are dark and include three transverse, yellow bands. The lower flanks have a number of thin, diagonal red stripes and the caudal peduncle has a broad, dark saddle. Juveniles have a black eye-spot on the soft dorsal fin, but this disappears with age. Can attain 20 cm in length.

EXTERNAL ANATOMY

The scales, especially those towards the front of the body, are larger than those of other butterflyfishes, and are arranged in 35-43 series along the lateral line. The fins are well developed and include a dorsal of 12 sharp spines plus 23-25 rays, and an anal of three spines plus 17-19 rays. The caudal fin is rounded. Fine, long teeth occur in both jaws of the terminal mouth.

DISTRIBUTION

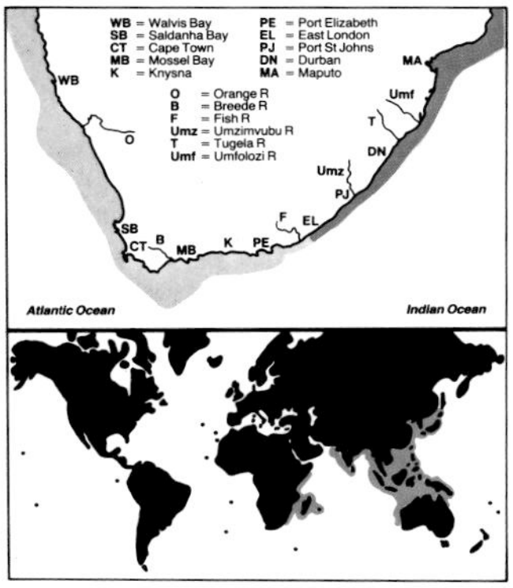

NATURAL HISTORY

The halfmoon butterflyfish is a common resident of rocky shores and reefs, ranging from the shallows to depths of 30 m. It is also often seen in intertidal rock pools and around harbour pilings. During the day it stays close to reefs, but activity increases after nightfall when it darts about, foraging for food. Many butterflyfishes are known to form pairs and while this tendency may be stronger in a few other species, halfmoon butterflyfish are invariably seen in twos. The diet includes, in order of importance, small gastropod snails, marine worms, amphipods, crustacean and fish eggs, as well as a wide variety of other small invertebrates, most of which are pecked from rock crevices. Seaweeds are also eaten in small quantities. The large eyes suggest an ability to adjust to low light levels, undoubtedly a useful adaptation to its nocturnal habits. The halfmoon butterflyfish is probably the most common and widespread of the Chaetodontidae in southern African waters, but little is known of its life history except that juveniles almost certainly use the intertidal zone as a nursery area. Research has revealed that within its natural environment in certain tropical regions, this species will breed with the threadfin butterflyfish to produce a hybrid.

CAPTURE

Though common, the halfmoon butterflyfish is popular with marine aquarists as it thrives in captivity and feeds on a variety of food.

SPECIFIC CATCH RESTRICTIONS

None.

NAME DERIVATION

Chaetodon, hair-like teeth; *lunula,* moon-shaped. Halfmoon butterflyfish, a reference to the white, crescent-shaped marking on the face, which can also be likened to those of a racoon, and to its flitting movements, reminiscent of a butterfly moving from flower to flower.

SIMILAR SPECIES

The colour patterns described are unique to this species.

Chaetodon madagaskariensis

Ahl, 1923

Common names Worldwide – pearly or Madagascar butterflyfish [Smith 205□10]

IDENTIFYING FEATURES

COLOUR, SHAPE AND SIZE

This dainty little fish is compressed and has a pointed snout. It is generally pearly-white in colour, with a broad, bright-orange bar that runs down the rear of the body, incorporating much of the soft dorsal and anal fins. There is also an orange bar on the caudal fin. Some 6-8 black chevron-like markings run vertically down the sides, and there is also a conspicuous black eye-band. Just before the first dorsal spine there is a short black bar, edged in white, which distinguishes this species from similar butterflyfishes elsewhere in the Indo-Pacific. The pearly butterflyfish was previously incorrectly known as *C. chrysurus.* Can attain 15 cm.

EXTERNAL ANATOMY

There are 33-38 series of ctenoid scales arranged along the distinct lateral line. The fins are well developed with spines being quite prominent. The single dorsal fin consists of 12 or 13 spines plus 20-21 rays and the anal fin of three spines plus 16-17 rays. The caudal fin is truncate. Long, bristle-like teeth occur in both jaws of the terminal mouth.

NATURAL HISTORY

The pearly butterflyfish inhabits rocky and coral reefs ranging in depth from 10 to 40 m and it is especially common on the steep, outer or seaward edges. This fish is also likely to be found where the sea-bed is strewn with loose boulders and rock fragments. Whether the result of natural 'break-off' from reefs, or the result of man-made marine structures like piers, breakwaters and harbour wharfs, such rubble yields a rich food supply, for the countless recesses, nooks and crannies thus formed, provide an ideal habitat for the small crustaceans which form the bulk of this fish's diet. Small amounts of seaweed are also taken. The pearly butterflyfish is most active during the day, and at dusk it will select a sheltered spot on the reef where it remains hidden throughout the night.

DISTRIBUTION

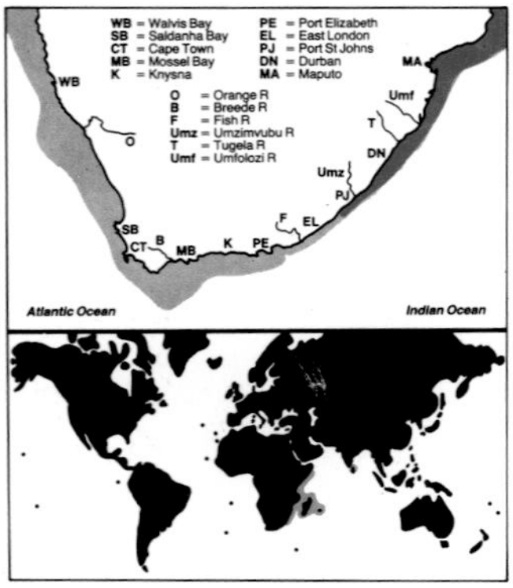

SPECIFIC CATCH RESTRICTIONS

None.

CAPTURE

Like many of the colourful fish species that frequent coral reefs, the pearly butterflyfish adapts successfully to aquaria and, assuming that careful attention is paid to its environment, it will thrive in captivity for many years.

NAME DERIVATION

Chaetodon, hair-like teeth; *madagaskariensis,* a reference to the island of Madagascar from where it was first described. Pearly butterflyfish, named in allusion to its pearly colours especially seen underwater and to its movements, reminiscent of a butterfly flitting from flower to flower.

SIMILAR SPECIES

The black pre-dorsal bar, chevron-like markings, and absence of a bar across the caudal peduncle will distinguish this species from any other butterflyfish.

Chaetodon marleyi

Regan, 1921
Common name doublesash butterflyfish
[Smith 205□11]

IDENTIFYING FEATURES

COLOUR, SHAPE AND SIZE

The round, compressed body is predominantly silvery-white, and on each scale there is a small yellow spot. A narrow, dark, vertical band passes through each eye, and two broader, golden-brown bars run down each side. There is also a distinct, white-ringed 'eye-spot' on the middle of the dorsal fin, but this fades somewhat with age. The fins are yellowish, orange or translucent. Can attain 20 cm but few exceed 10-15 cm.

EXTERNAL ANATOMY

The ctenoid scales are rough to the touch and are arranged in 36-42 series along the lateral line. The fins are well developed and include a single dorsal of 11 spines plus 22-25 rays, an anal of three spines plus 18-19 rays, and a truncate caudal. The terminal mouth protrudes slightly and has fine, elongate teeth in each jaw. There are nine or ten rakers on the first gill arch.

NATURAL HISTORY

This is the only butterflyfish to occur in both the Atlantic and the Indian oceans. Though not tolerant of salinity fluctuations, the doublesash is one of the few Chaetodontidae that enters estuaries; this is especially so of the juveniles which inhabit estuarine weedbeds. Adults favour rocky or coral reefs ranging in depth from 1 to 120 m, but are also often found around harbour wharfs. A wide range of food is eaten, including small invertebrates such as amphipods, crabs and marine worms, most being pecked from small cracks in reefs. Seaweeds are also eaten and aquarium specimens can frequently be seen 'grazing' the algae growing on the sides of their tank. As with many of its close relatives, this agile butterflyfish normally occurs in pairs, and when threatened or alarmed will dart away to hide in a small crevice.

DISTRIBUTION

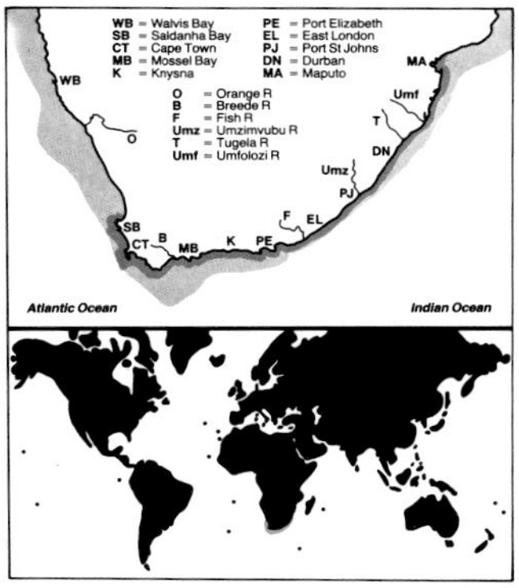

CAPTURE

This fish is valued by marine aquarists, and adapts well to an artificial tank environment. It does, however, require considerable care during captivity and its capture should not be attempted without the correct holding equipment. Of vital importance is the maintenance of the tank water at 18-20°C. This is cooler than for most butterflyfish, as this species is generally found in more temperate waters.

SPECIFIC CATCH RESTRICTIONS

None.

NAME DERIVATION

Chaetodon, hair-like teeth; *marleyi,* named after Mr. H.W. Bell-Marley, Natal Fisheries officer and keen naturalist in the 1920's. Doublesash butterflyfish, a reference to the two bars down each flank, and to its flitting movements, reminiscent of a butterfly moving from flower to flower.

SIMILAR SPECIES

This species closely resembles Hoefler's butterflyfish (*C. hoefleri*), which is common along the west coast of Africa (probably only from Angola northwards). The two species can be distinguished by different fin counts (*C. hoefleri* has 16-18 anal rays). It would also appear that the second body bar is narrower and further forward in *C. hoefleri.*

Chaetodon meyeri

Bloch & Schneider, 1801
Common names SA – maypole butterflyfish. Elsewhere – Meyer's butterflyfish.
[Smith 205□13]

IDENTIFYING FEATURES

COLOUR, SHAPE AND SIZE
The body is almost disc-shaped, and strikingly marked with nine or ten distinct black bands and stripes, which curve around the head and across the flanks and fins. The fins and outer margins of the body are yellow, while the sides are bluish. Young fish are predominantly bluish, especially when alive. Can attain 20 cm.

EXTERNAL ANATOMY
Some 41-47 series of small, ctenoid scales cover the entire body, making it rough to the touch. Though the fins are well developed, their close association with the body and its colours and patterns makes them less distinct. The single dorsal fin has 12 spines plus 23-24 rays and the anal fin has three spines plus 18-20 rays. The caudal fin is truncate. Long, bristle-like teeth occur in each jaw of the small, slightly pouting, terminal mouth.

DISTRIBUTION

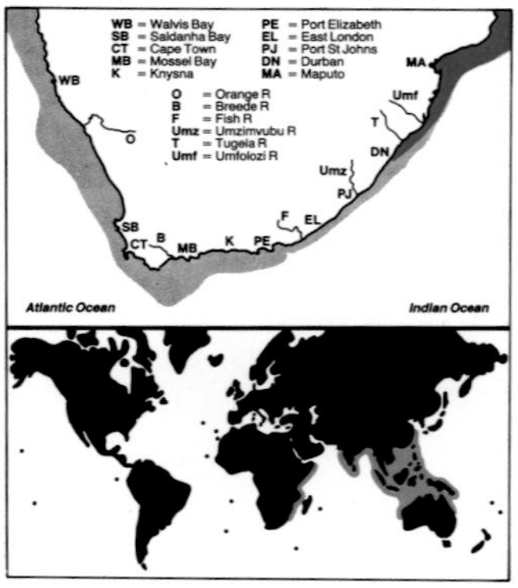

NATURAL HISTORY

This beautiful little fish is confined to coral reefs. In southern Africa, therefore, it occurs primarily in the St. Lucia Marine Reserve in Zululand. Here it is most likely to be encountered at depths ranging from 5-25 m as it darts about in pairs or small groups, constantly foraging for food. The maypole butterflyfish's almost total dependence on the coral reef environment is linked to its specialized diet, for it feeds virtually exclusively on soft coral polyps. Occasionally, however, it also preys on small crustaceans and worms. Though its breeding cycle is obscure, this species has been reported to cross with one or two other Chaetodontidae, especially in the Palan Islands of the Micronesian Pacific.

CAPTURE

Though it is a most desirable aquarium specimen, the maypole butterflyfish is difficult to capture and even more difficult to maintain in captivity. It is better left undisturbed.

SPECIFIC CATCH RESTRICTIONS

None.

NAME DERIVATION

Chaetodon, hair-like teeth; *meyeri,* a reference to Meyer, the ichthyologist after whom this species was named. Maypole butterflyfish, a reference to its markings, reminiscent of maypole streamers, and to its movements, rather like those of a butterfly flitting from flower to flower.

SIMILAR SPECIES

This is a most distinctive species, being found only on coral reefs, and the only butterflyfish with curved black lines on the body.

Chaetodon trifascialis

Quoy & Gaimard, 1825

Common names SA – rightangle butterflyfish. Elsewhere – chevroned butterflyfish [Smith 205□14]

IDENTIFYING FEATURES

COLOUR, SHAPE AND SIZE

This species is rather more elongate than most of the butterflyfish, and the anal and dorsal fin rays are extended so as to give a somewhat rectangular overall appearance. Its basic colour is pearly-white with about 20 chevron-like black markings on each side. There is also a distinct, black eye-band. The dorsal and anal fins are yellow. Can attain 18 cm in length.

EXTERNAL ANATOMY

There are 21-27 series of ctenoid scales arranged along the lateral line. The fins are well developed and include a dorsal of 14 spines plus 14-16 rays, an anal of four spines plus 14-15 rays, and a truncate caudal. The anal fin of this species is unusual in that there is one more spine than in most other butterflyfishes. Bristle-like teeth of varying lengths occur in each jaw of the slightly upturned mouth.

DISTRIBUTION

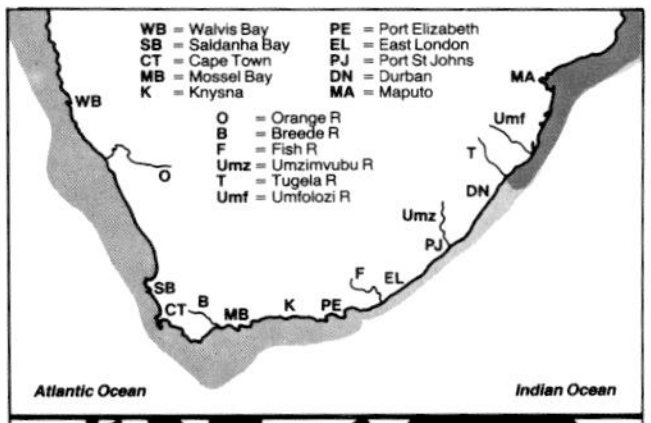

NATURAL HISTORY

This butterflyfish is closely associated with the coral reef environment, for, like the previous species, it is largely dependent on coral polyps for its food. In southern Africa, it is virtually confined to the reefs of the St Lucia Marine Reserve, where it ranges from three to 20 m. The rightangle butterflyfish is one of the most territorial of the Chaetodontidae, and males vigorously defend their domains (usually a group of three or four coral heads) against other members of their species, as well as against other fishes feeding over coral reefs. Despite the almost total specialization of the diet, small amounts of algae are also eaten. Little is known of the breeding cycle of this fish. There is considerable controversy regarding the correct taxonomic classification of this species, and though there is much justification for placing it in the genus *Megaprotodon,* further research is needed.

CAPTURE

Despite its attractive appearance, this species is not popular with aquarists; it is extremely difficult to maintain because of its coral dependence, and it does not adapt to alternative diets. It is better left undisturbed.

SPECIFIC CATCH RESTRICTIONS

None.

NAME DERIVATION

Chaetodon, hair-like teeth; *trifascialis,* triple-banded. Right-angle butterflyfish, a reference to the rectangular appearance of its dorsal and anal fins, and to its flitting movements, reminiscent of a butterfly moving from flower to flower.

SIMILAR SPECIES

The distinctive fin spine and ray counts and angular body shapes are typical of this species. No other South African butterflyfish is of similar appearance.

Chaetodon unimaculatus

Bloch, 1787

Common names SA – limespot butterflyfish. Elsewhere – teardrop butterflyfish

[Smith 205□16]

IDENTIFYING FEATURES

COLOUR, SHAPE AND SIZE

This compressed, round-bodied fish is lime-yellow and, just below the last few dorsal spines, it has a distinct black spot which overlies the lateral line. With increased age, this spot extends downwards to become tear-shaped. A vertical black bar passes through each eye, and a further thin black bar runs down the trailing edge of the dorsal and anal rays, and across the caudal peduncle. Attains 20 cm. *Note:* Specimens taken from Australian and Pacific island waters display slightly different patterns and paler colours.

EXTERNAL ANATOMY

There are 35-41 series of rough, ctenoid scales arranged along the lateral line. The fins are closely associated with the body, and include a single dorsal comprising 13 spines plus 21-23 rays, an anal of three spines plus 17-20 rays, and a truncate caudal. Both jaws of the terminal mouth have long bristle-like teeth.

DISTRIBUTION

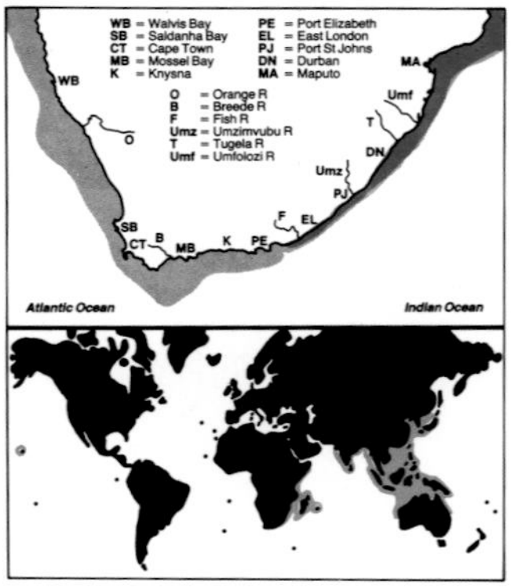

NATURAL HISTORY

This brightly coloured fish is common around most coral reefs in southern Africa, where it ranges from five to 25 m. It is also well known in many other parts of the world, and is undoubtedly one of the most widely distributed of the *Chaetodon* species. During the summer months, with the greater southwards push of the warm Agulhas Current, it occasionally takes up residence on rocky reefs as far down the East Coast as Durban. Of all the members of the family, this gregarious species has one of the strongest tendencies to form permanent pairs. Limespot 'couples' frequently gather in small groups which flit about the reefs, rather in the manner of butterflies on land, in their constant daytime search for food. The diet includes soft corals and small crustaceans. Though the coral reef habitat is undoubtedly important to the well-being of this species, its greater summer distribution away from this environment illustrates its ability to adapt. It is interesting to note that aquarium specimens will only thrive if there is adequate algal growth in the tank. The breeding cycle of the limespot butterflyfish is unknown, but on the Enewetak Atoll in the Pacific Ocean it has been known to hybridize with the whitespotted butterflyfish.

CAPTURE

The limespot butterflyfish makes an attractive aquarium specimen and will adapt successfully, provided its tank is carefully maintained. Despite its preference for coral polyps, it will adapt to a diet of tiny fish pieces.

SPECIFIC CATCH RESTRICTIONS

None.

NAME DERIVATION

Chaetodon, hair-like teeth; *unimaculatus,* single-spot. Limespot butterflyfish, a reference to the black spot on the lime-yellow body, and to the fish's flitting movements, reminiscent of a butterfly.

SIMILAR SPECIES

No other butterflyfish in the southern African region resembles this species. Specimens from Australian and Pacific island waters have slightly different patterns and paler colours, and may well prove to be distinct sub species.

Chaetodon vagabundus

Linnaeus, 1758
Common name Worldwide – vagabond butterflyfish
[Smith 205□17]

IDENTIFYING FEATURES

COLOUR, SHAPE AND SIZE
This butterflyfish is larger than most members of its family. It is whitish overall, but each flank is distinctively marked with two sets of parallel black lines. The first set comprises about eight lines running diagonally upwards from the head and gill covers to the dorsal spines. The second set of some 12 lines runs at right angles to the first, downwards across the flanks, to the base of the anal fin. A black eye-band is prominent and two further black bars occur, one following the base of the dorsal, caudal and anal fins, and the other following the curve of the outer edge of the soft dorsal and anal fins, and running through the caudal peduncle. Towards the tail, the fish becomes increasingly yellow. Fine orange bands bridge the steep forehead. Can attain 23 cm in length.

EXTERNAL ANATOMY
The body is covered with ctenoid scales arranged in 31-38 series along the lateral line. The fins are well developed and include a single dorsal of 12 or 13 spines plus 23-26 rays, an anal of three spines plus 19-21 rays, and a rounded caudal. Both jaws of the moderately protruding mouth bear fine, bristle-like teeth.

NATURAL HISTORY

This widespread species is common throughout its range, where it inhabits shallow coral and rocky reefs varying from 3-30 m. As with the limespot butterflyfish, this species has an exceptionally strong tendency to form permanent pairs, a fact readily confirmed by underwater or aquarium observations. It does not, however, appear to have the well-developed territorial instinct of many Chaetodontidae, and pairs range over large areas of reef as they forage for food. The diet consists of small invertebrate animals such as small crabs, amphipods and marine worms, all of which are carefully pecked from crevices in the reef. A certain amount of seaweed is also consumed. Little is known of its breeding biology.

DISTRIBUTION

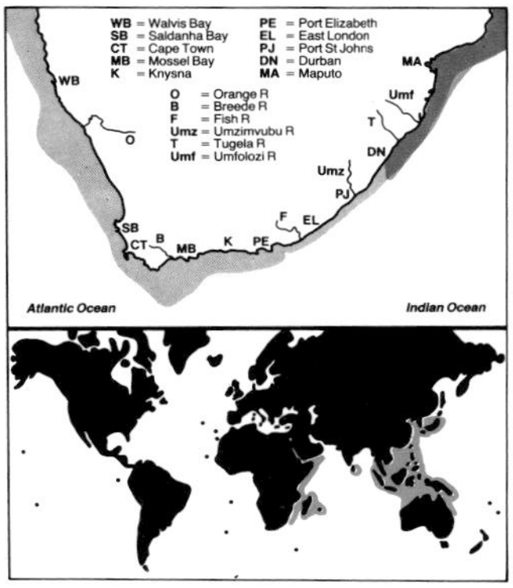

CAPTURE

A common and successful inmate of many aquaria, the vagabond butterflyfish is relatively easy to maintain. It readily accepts food and many have thrived in well-kept tanks for years.

SPECIFIC CATCH RESTRICTIONS

None.

NAME DERIVATION

Chaetodon, hair-like teeth; *vagabundus,* wandering. Vagabond butterflyfish, a reference to its wide-ranging habits and to its flitting movements, reminiscent of a butterfly moving from flower to flower.

SIMILAR SPECIES

While several butterflyfishes may resemble this species (such as *C. auriga*), the absence of an eye-spot, and the two sets of parallel lines across the body are distinctive.

Forcipiger flavissimus

Jordan & McGregor, 1898

Common name Worldwide – longnose butterflyfish

[Smith 205□20]

IDENTIFYING FEATURES

COLOUR, SHAPE AND SIZE

This compressed little fish has a long, and very distinctive, tube-like snout. Its general body colour is brilliant yellow, with a black-and-white head, and a black 'eye-spot' on the hind part of the anal fin. The fins are also bright yellow or translucent. Attains 15 cm.

EXTERNAL ANATOMY

The body is covered with 69-80 series of small, ctenoid scales. The fins are well developed, strongly spined, and include a dorsal fin of 12 spines plus 22-24 rays, and an anal fin of three spines plus 17 or 18 rays. The caudal fin is rounded. The mouth is small, but armed with tiny, sharp teeth, and is situated at the tip of the long snout. The first gill arch carries 15-20 rakers.

DISTRIBUTION

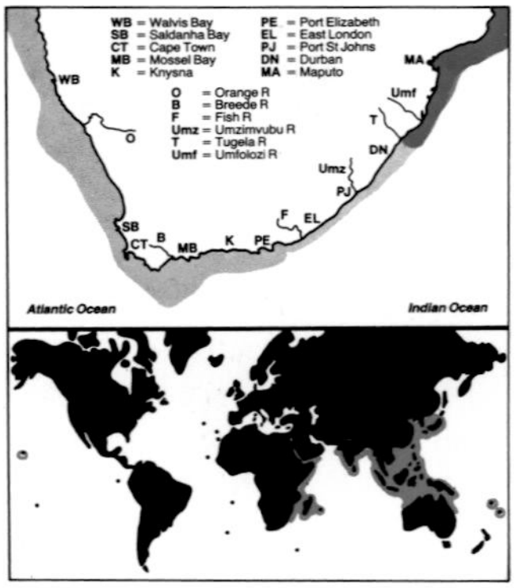

NATURAL HISTORY

Small groups or pairs of the widely distributed longnose butterflyfish frequent rocky shores and shallow coral reefs, ranging in depth from 5-25 m. They are especially abundant during summer, when individual pairs may occupy set territories for a certain period of time. Possibly this territorial instinct is linked to the species, breeding cycle, but details of its reproductive biology are unknown. The distinctive and highly specialized, tubular mouth allows this fish to probe deeply into holes and crevices, reaching food items inaccessible to most other species. The sharp teeth also assist in tearing off pieces of sessile animals. Feeding occurs during daylight, and the diet includes marine worms, sea urchin tentacles, copepods, amphipods, shrimps, gastropod and fish eggs, crab larvae and other small invertebrates. Though not proven, the black spot on the anal fin is believed to represent a false eye, which could mislead would-be predators as to the fish's direction of movement.

CAPTURE

Though a desirable specimen for marine aquarists, the longnose butterflyfish is extremely agile and difficult to catch. If its survival in captivity is to be ensured, this fish demands great care, with special attention being paid to the stability of its tank environment, as well as to its diet.

SPECIFIC CATCH RESTRICTIONS

None.

NAME DERIVATION

Forcipiger, shaped like small forceps, a reference to the snout; *flavissimus,* yellow. Longnose butterflyfish, a reference to its elongate snout and its flitting movements, reminiscent of a butterfly moving from flower to flower.

SIMILAR SPECIES

Although no similar species occurs in South Africa, the closely related *F. longirostris* has been reported from islands in the southwest Indian Ocean, and may be recognized by its longer snout, and having only 11 dorsal spines.

Heniochus acuminatus

(Linnaeus, 1758)
Common names SA – coachman. Elsewhere – common or longfin bannerfish
[Smith 205□22]

IDENTIFYING FEATURES

COLOUR, SHAPE AND SIZE
This round, compressed little fish has a rather steep forehead and a slightly protruding mouth. Though basically pearly-white in colour, this species has two broad, black bars that sweep diagonally down the flanks from the tips of the dorsal spines. The forward bar extends across the pelvic fins, and the second bar includes the hind half of the anal fin. The snout is tipped with black and there is also a short, black eye-bar. The pectoral, soft dorsal and caudal fins are yellow. Can attain 25 cm.

EXTERNAL ANATOMY
The body has 49-56 series of ctenoid scales arranged along the lateral line. The dorsal fin comprises 11 or 12 spines, the fourth of which extends in a great sickle-like sweep that almost exceeds the length of the body. The anal fin consists of three spines plus 17-19 rays. The caudal fin is small and truncate. Bony projections, or 'horns', develop above the eyes of older specimens. The small pouting mouth has tiny, sharp teeth in each jaw.

NATURAL HISTORY

This fish is one of the more widely distributed members of its family, and is normally found, singly or in pairs, close to the bottom of rocky and coral reefs. The vertical range of the coachman extends from 2-30 m and it also occurs along wharfs and jetties in many harbours. The mouth is well adapted to pecking at its small invertebrate prey, especially amphipods and tiny crabs. Juveniles are frequently observed removing the external parasites adhering to larger fish. The life history of the coachman has not been well documented, and little is known about its breeding habits and juvenile stages. Several closely related species have a similar distribution, but these fill different ecological niches, thereby avoiding direct competition. For example, some feed on plankton and therefore live more in the midwater region where these minute organisms occur, while other species are more demersal and form dense shoals which range widely in their search for food.

DISTRIBUTION

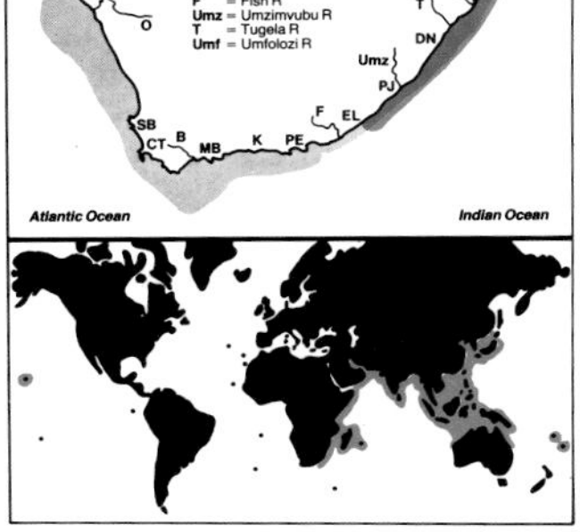

CAPTURE

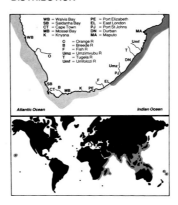

Divers with scoop nets, or anglers using ultra-light tackle, catch this fish for aquaria. It is hardy, but its tendency to peck at other inhabitants of a tank may create problems. In the Far East the coachman is caught in fair numbers, and is dried and eaten.

SPECIFIC CATCH RESTRICTIONS

None.

NAME DERIVATION

Heniochus, from *henion* meaning reins or bridle; *acuminatus,* pointed fin. Coachman, a reference to the pennant-like dorsal spine which resembles a coachman's whip.

SIMILAR SPECIES

There are three coachman species in southern African waters, all rather similar in appearance. The masked coachman (*H. monoceros*) has a black face, while the shoaling coachman (*H. diphreutes*) has a shorter snout and a black mark just below the eye (see also Moorish Idol).

Chanos chanos

(Forsskål, 1775)
Common names SA – milkfish. Elsewhere – milkfish, dandang, salmon herring
[Smith 58□1]

IDENTIFYING FEATURES

COLOUR, SHAPE AND SIZE
This elongate fish is brilliant silver overall, but blue-green above and white below. The caudal fin is edged with black, and the inside edges of the pectoral and pelvic fins are dark. Can attain 180 cm, but specimens less than 100 cm are more common.

EXTERNAL ANATOMY
The milkfish is covered with small, cycloid scales arranged in 78-90 series along the distinct lateral line. The primitive, spineless fins include a dorsal of 13-17 rays, an anal of 8-10 rays, pelvic fins which are set far back on the body, and a deeply forked caudal. The small, toothless mouth has a slightly projecting upper jaw and the gill arches have numerous, thin, long and closely set rakers. The eyes are covered with a thick layer of adipose tissue.

DISTRIBUTION

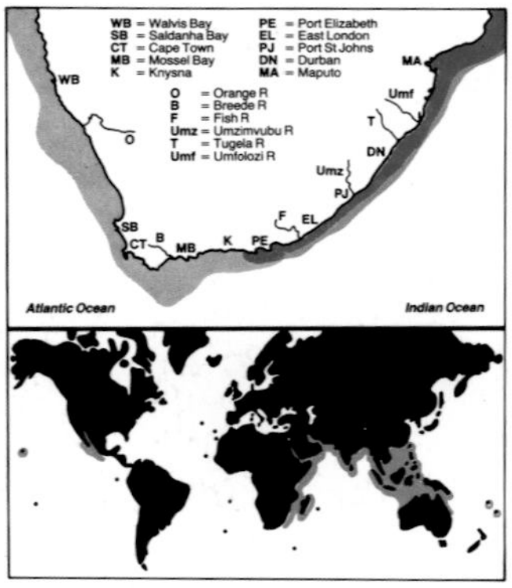

NATURAL HISTORY

This powerful fish frequents coastal waters, bays and estuaries, and is able to tolerate widely ranging salinities, including completely fresh water. The milkfish is most abundant during summer and is usually found in small shoals near the surface. Large specimens are frequently seen feeding in shallow estuaries, head down and with their tails protruding from the water. Like mullet, the diet consists mainly of dead organic matter and microscopic organisms that live in or on the muddy bottom. Occasionally small crustaceans, worms and fish are also eaten. Ovary development begins when females reach a total length of 50 cm. Though males only start to mature at about 90 cm, the process is faster and both sexes are reproductively active by the age of four, at a corresponding length of 110 cm. Spawning occurs at sea, normally during a breeding season that may last up to three months. Soon after fertilization the eggs hatch into ribbon-like larvae. These translucent juveniles are distributed by ocean currents until they reach estuaries where they change to a bright silvery colour, resembling the adult form.

CAPTURE

This fine angling fish should be 'stalked' with great patience and is best caught using fly tackle over shallow estuarine mudbanks. Chumming milkfish with small pieces of bread may often induce these excellent fighting fish to strike at small, but carefully prepared baits. Despite its fine flesh, edibility is spoiled by the numerous small bones. In India, Indonesia and other eastern countries, milkfish fingerlings are netted in great numbers and transported to lagoons and rice paddies. Here, as part of a highly successful fish-farming programme, many grow to a considerable size. Though spawning rarely occurs in enclosed waters, recent advances in the study of pituitary hormones have provided technology whereby spawning can be artificially induced in captured fish.
SA angling record – 11,8 kg.
SA spearfishing record – 18,0 kg.

SPECIFIC CATCH RESTRICTIONS

None.

NAME DERIVATION

Chanos, open-mouthed. Milkfish, a reference to its milky lower sides and belly.

SIMILAR SPECIES

The small mouth will distinguish the milkfish from the closely related ladyfish and tarpon, both of which have a large gape. The bonefish is similar but does not have a terminal mouth.

Chirodactylus brachydactylus

(Cuvier, 1830)
Common names twotone fingerfin, butterfish
[Smith 215□3]

IDENTIFYING FEATURES

COLOUR, SHAPE AND SIZE
The oblong body of this species is reddish-brown to dusky above, but paler below. A darker, lateral band passes through the eye and extends towards the tail. This distinctive streak tends to split the overall colouration of the twotone fingerfin into darker upper sides and lighter lower sides. This contrast, however, is most apparent in living specimens seen underwater, and is less noticeable in dead fish. There are five white or bluish spots on each flank, directly above the lateral line. Can attain 40 cm in length.

EXTERNAL ANATOMY
This fish has 45-55 series of distinct scales arranged along the lateral line. The fins are well developed and include a single dorsal of 17-18 spines plus 28-31 rays, an anal of three spines plus 8-10 rays, and a moderately forked caudal fin. The pectoral fins are distinctly large and the inner five or six rays are elongate and fleshy. Full lips surround the small mouth, which has a band of fine teeth in each jaw. There are 16-21 rakers on the first gill arch.

DISTRIBUTION

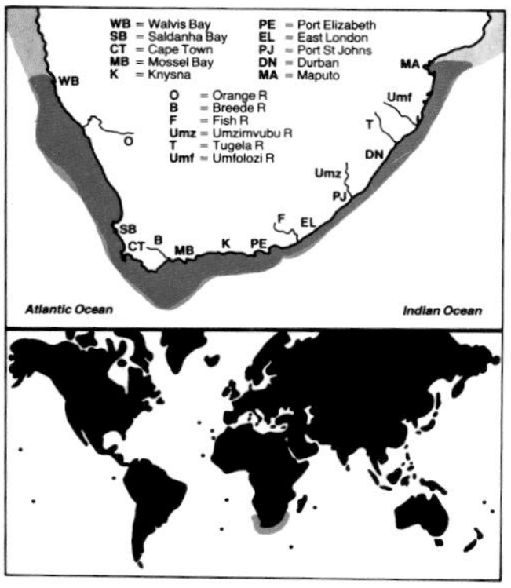

NATURAL HISTORY

This endemic species is most commonly found over shallow coastal reefs and, though it occasionally enters tidal rock pools, it never ventures into estuaries. Some have been caught offshore, however, to depths of 240 m. It is omnivorous and feeds on a variety of small reef organisms including crabs, bivalves, amphipods and other small crustaceans. Part of its feeding strategy is rather similar to that of the grunter as it randomly grabs mouthfuls of sand between the rocks and then gradually sifts out the edible organisms. Before swallowing the food, however, the inedible sand is discarded through the gill openings. Fish in excess of 25 cm are sexually mature and spawn during early summer. The young, which are common in intertidal rock pools, do not resemble adults as they lack the detached pectoral rays, are not as elongate and have a far more compressed body. Divers find the twotone fingerfin very approachable, especially when it lies perched on a rocky ledge, stabilized by its extended pectorals.

CAPTURE

The twotone fingerfin does not freely take bait, and most are landed by spearfishermen. This fish is often the most common edible species on heavily angled reefs in Natal.
SA angling record - 0,9 kg.
SA spearfishing record - 2,6 kg.

SPECIFIC CATCH RESTRICTIONS

None.

NAME DERIVATION

Chirodactylus, a hand with fingers; *brachydactylus,* short-fingered. Twotone fingerfin, a reference to its distinctive and contrasting colours when alive, and its finger-like pectoral fins. Butterfish, a reference to its rich, palatable flesh.

SIMILAR SPECIES

There are three species of fingerfin in southern African waters, all with fleshy pectoral fins. This species is instantly recognizable by its two-toned colouration - especially evident when seen underwater.

Chirodactylus jessicalenorum

(Smith, 1980)
Common name Natal fingerfin
[Smith 215□5]

IDENTIFYING FEATURES

COLOUR, SHAPE AND SIZE

The colouration of this elongate, moderately compressed fish is a distinctive feature, being dark pink with silvery sides. Juveniles tend to be more silvery overall. The trailing edge of each scale is usually darker pink. A further characteristic is the obvious, black blotch at the pectoral fin base. Can attain 75 cm.

EXTERNAL ANATOMY

The lateral line is conspicuous, and has 46-54 series of scales arranged along its length. The fins are well developed, and include a single dorsal of 17-18 spines plus 26-27 rays, an anal of three spines plus 7-8 rays, and a caudal fin that is deeply forked. Most distinctive are the large pectoral fins, both of which include six elongate, detached, fleshy rays, the longest of which extends backwards to the anus. Small teeth occur in bands in both jaws, just within the full lips, the lower of which is the thicker. There are 20-22 rakers on the first gill arch.

DISTRIBUTION

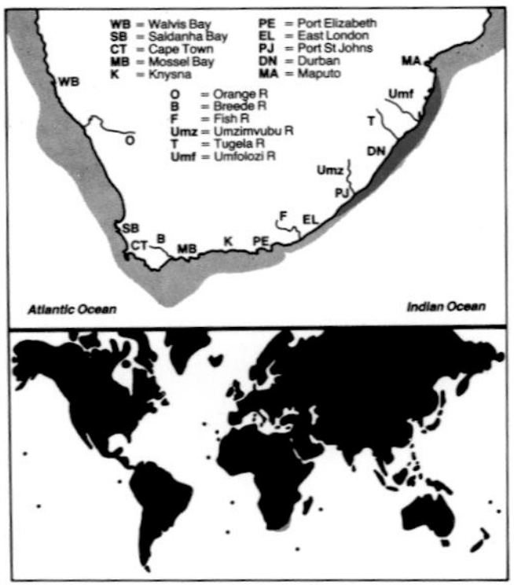

NATURAL HISTORY

This common, endemic fish inhabits shallow, coastal waters, possibly not deeper than 20 m. It prefers rocky banks where, during the day, it feeds on small, bottom-dwelling invertebrates such as marine worms, crabs and molluscs. Occasionally, squid and small fish are also eaten. The fleshy pectoral rays may have some sensory function, but they are most certainly used by the fish to steady itself when resting on the bottom. This is particularly evident at night, when the Natal fingerfin finds rest and shelter along a shelf in the reef. At certain times of the year this species congregates into loosely packed shoals, presumably as a prelude to spawning. The young of this and related species are widely distributed throughout the ocean by sheltering below floating objects at sea. During the first few months after hatching, the juvenile's pectoral rays are neither fleshy nor detached, and this can cause confusion and make identification a little tricky.

CAPTURE

This is a fine sport and food fish, which makes excellent eating. Although it is occasionally caught by ski-boat anglers, the Natal fingerfin is most popular with spearfishermen.
SA angling record – vacant.
SA spearfishing record – 10,2 kg.

SPECIFIC CATCH RESTRICTIONS

None.

NAME DERIVATION

Chirodactylus, a hand with fingers; *jessicalenorum,* named in honour of Jessica and Len Jones, well-known Durban diving personalities, who have made many valued contributions to ichthyology. Natal fingerfin, a reference to the region in which it is exclusively found, and its finger-like pectoral rays.

SIMILAR SPECIES

This new species was described by Prof. Margaret Smith, when she noticed its difference to the larger bank steenbras (*C. grandis*). The latter is also endemic, but lives in deeper water along the Cape south and west coasts. The bank steenbras is less brightly coloured, lacks the pectoral blotch and has a lower dorsal-fin ray count (22-24).

Chirocentrus dorab

(Forsskål, 1775)

Common names SA – wolfherring, silky. Elsewhere – dorab, wolfherring

[Smith 56□1]

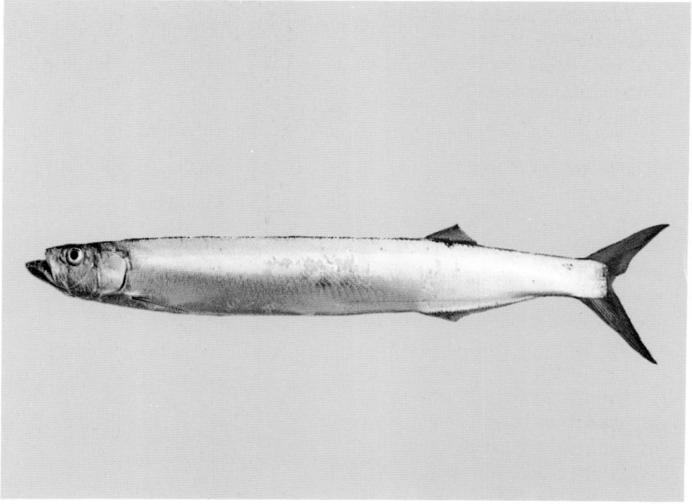

IDENTIFYING FEATURES

COLOUR, SHAPE AND SIZE

The dorsal surface of this extremely elongate and compressed fish is iridescent blue-green while the flanks are silver. The extreme tips of both dorsal and anal fins are usually black while the fins are dusky to translucent. Can attain 100 cm in length.

EXTERNAL ANATOMY

The wolfherring has no lateral line and is covered with numerous series of small, cycloid scales that are very easily shed. The fins are composed of rays only; 16-19 in the dorsal and 29-36 in the anal. Both the dorsal and anal fins are set well back, beyond the mid-point of the body. The pelvic fins are small and the caudal fin is deeply forked. The large mouth, with its protruding lower jaw, carries big, fang-like canines. There are 11-20 rakers on the first gill arch. A thin layer of adipose tissue covers the eyes.

DISTRIBUTION

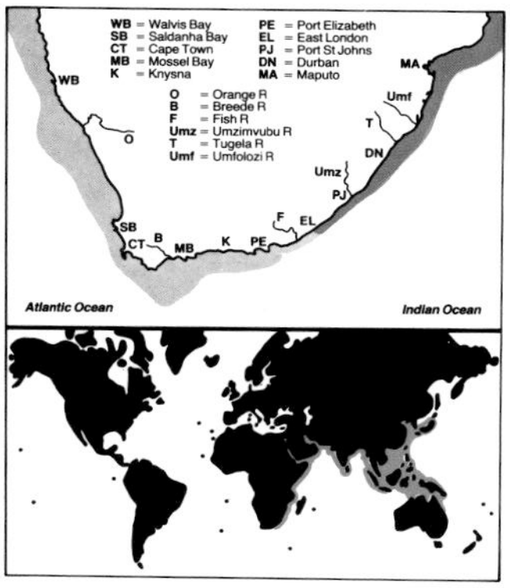

NATURAL HISTORY

This voracious, pelagic predator of coastal waters ranges from just behind the surf zone to depths of 120 m. Occasionally, it is seen leaping from the water either in pursuit of prey or in an attempt to escape from larger predators such as the king mackerel. Though not strictly a shoaling species, the wolfherring does congregate in small groups, especially when hunting small fish, such as anchovies and goatfish, and the juveniles of many other species. Details of its reproduction, migrations and growth rates in southern African waters have not been documented. Though wolfherrings are placed in a family of their own, they are closely related to the true herringfishes and indeed belong to the same order Clupeiformes. A noticeable difference, however, is the poorly developed gill rakers in Chirocentridae which, unlike other herringfishes, do not filter-feed on minute organisms, but prey instead on larger animals. There is some debate, however, as to whether this is a primitive or an advanced evolutionary characteristic.

CAPTURE

Despite its palatable flesh, the wolfherring is only of moderate interest to sport fishermen, though it is an excellent trolling and drift bait for larger fish. It is best caught from piers and jetties by anglers using small lures, feathers or small, live fish bait.

SA angling record – 1,8 kg.

SPECIFIC CATCH RESTRICTIONS

None.

NAME DERIVATION

Chirocentrus, from *chiros* meaning hand and *centrum* meaning middle; *dorab,* skin or hide. Wolfherring, the fiercest of the herring-like fishes. Silky, a reference to its soft silk-like skin.

SIMILAR SPECIES

The only other species in this family, *C. nudus,* may possibly also occur in the region. This species can be recognized by the pale tips to its dorsal and anal fins, and a somewhat longer pectoral fin.

Cirrhitichthys oxycephalus

(Bleeker, 1855)
Common name Worldwide – spotted hawkfish
[Smith 214□2]

IDENTIFYING FEATURES

COLOUR, SHAPE AND SIZE

This small, elongate fish has a moderately compressed body. Its overall colour is cream or pink, but overlaid with numerous large, darker red blotches. These marks are often arranged into bars and may also extend on to the head and fins. Can attain 10 cm.

EXTERNAL ANATOMY

Approximately 40 series of distinct scales can be counted along the lateral line. The fins are well developed and spines are prominent. The single dorsal fin comprises ten spines plus 12 rays, while the anal fin has three spines plus six rays. The caudal fin is truncate. Characteristic of this family are small, tassel-like tufts that project from the tip of each dorsal spine. However, as the specimen shown here demonstrates, not all display this feature. The pectoral fins are large, their lower 5-8 rays being thicker and larger than the rest. As with most hawkfishes the bulbous eyes project considerably. Both jaws bear sharply pointed canine teeth, while finer, villiform teeth occur on the palate. The pre-operculum is serrated.

DISTRIBUTION

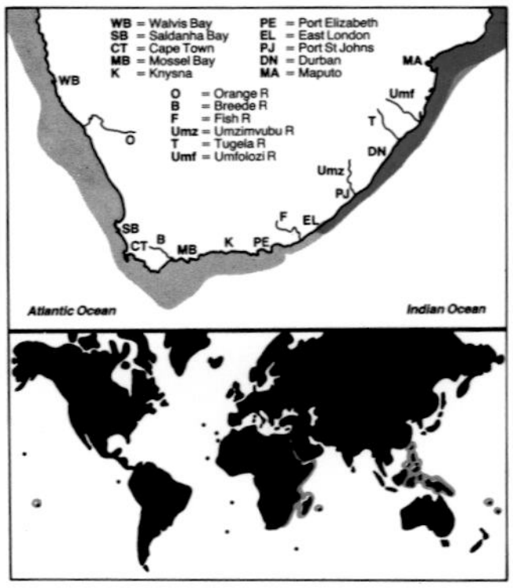

NATURAL HISTORY

No coral reef environment would be complete without its hawkfishes. The common name is apt, for these solitary and intensely territorial little fish spend a great deal of time 'perched' prominently on a branch of coral. From here they watch over their domains, waiting perfectly still for any prey that may wander within range. As soon as this happens the hawkfish darts off after it, and, whether successful or not, it invariably returns to its original resting place to repeat the procedure. The diet consists mainly of very small fishes and shrimps, which are taken in midwater and held firmly in the sharp canines. Two anatomical features are noteworthy in respect of the hawkfish's curious hunting strategy. Firstly, the eyes are highly movable, so that, without moving its head or body, the fish has a wide field of vision, an ability equally suited to watching for prey as for potential predators. Secondly, the thickened pectoral rays act as stabilizers, giving the fish a firm base as it rests on the coral. Little is known of the spotted hawkfish's reproductive biology.

CAPTURE

Undoubtedly a worthwhile aquarium specimen, this fish is both interesting to observe and easy to keep alive. The tank should, however, be large enough to provide an adequate territory.

SPECIFIC CATCH RESTRICTIONS

None.

NAME DERIVATION

Cirrhitichthys, locks of hair, a reference to the tufts on the dorsal spines; *oxycephalus*, pointed head. Spotted hawkfish, a reference to its markings, and to its habit of perching, as raptors do, on a vantage-point to wait for prey.

SIMILAR SPECIES

While there are seven hawkfish species in southern African waters, this and the freckled hawkfish are most often observed. The freckled hawkfish (*Paracirrhites fosteri*) has similar habits to those of the spotted hawkfish, but may be recognised by the blue, yellow and black body colours, extensively overlaid with black dots and lines.

Pavoclinus graminis

(Gilchrist & Thompson, 1908)
Common name grass klipfish
[Smith 237□28]

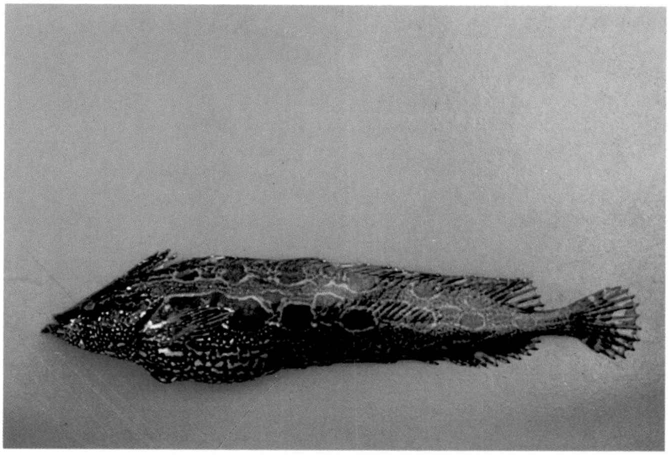

IDENTIFYING FEATURES

COLOUR, SHAPE AND SIZE
Though the colours vary widely according to environment, the body patterns of this compressed, elongate fish remain relatively constant. Brightly variegated browns, greys and reds are most usual. Occasionally shades of green may occur. Attains 20 cm.

EXTERNAL ANATOMY
Distinct, overlapping scales cover the entire body. The single, lengthy dorsal fin is typically crested in front, and consists of 30-35 spines plus 4-6 rays, which extend from the head region to the caudal peduncle. The anal fin has two spines plus 21-24 rays, while the caudal fin is slightly rounded. As with all Clinidae, each of the grass klipfish's pelvic fins is modified into three elongate and fleshy rays. Unlike most other members of the family, however, this species lacks a lateral line, and there are no tentacles over the eyes. The mouth has small, but sharp, teeth.

DISTRIBUTION

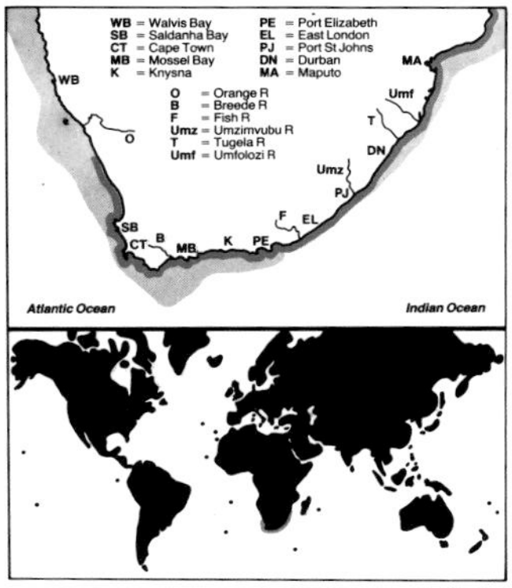

NATURAL HISTORY

This endemic species is one of the largest and most common of the Clinidae. It occurs singly or in small groups, and is normally confined to the inshore region, especially the intertidal zone. The grass klipfish is often found in stands of green or red seaweed, where it usually lies on its side, well camouflaged and ready to pounce on unsuspecting prey such as small fish, shrimps, crabs and marine worms. The eyes of the grass klipfish can move independently, rather in the manner of chameleons, and the wide range and depth of vision that this adaptation provides is undoubtedly an important factor in its particular hunting strategy. Female grass klipfish, as with other members of the family, undergo internal fertilization which is often preceded by courtship displays. A 'romantic' male will try hard to woo a female into a specially prepared nesting site. This behaviour involves numerous postures and gestures such as short, jerky movements, chasing and butting. The male grass klipfish invariably assumes a brighter colouration during such rituals.

NAME DERIVATION

Pavoclinus, from *pavo,* a peacock, and *clinus,* lying to the side; *graminis*, grass.

CAPTURE

Though not of great angling importance, the grass klipfish provides hours of 'sport' for budding young anglers along wharfs and in rock pools. It takes most flesh baits and is quite edible.

SPECIFIC CATCH RESTRICTIONS

None.

SIMILAR SPECIES

While the identification of this species is relatively easy because of its distinctive patterning and colour, the other clinid species are far from simple to identify and require more detailed study.

Etrumeus teres

(De Kay, 1842)

Common names East Coast roundherring, red-eye sardine [Smith 54□1]

IDENTIFYING FEATURES

COLOUR, SHAPE AND SIZE

This endemic sardine species has an elongate body, is almost cylindrical in shape and has a smoothly rounded belly without any obvious sharp scutes. The East Coast roundherring is generally a blue-green colour above, but noticeably metallic or silvery along the flanks when freshly caught. Can attain 25 cm.

EXTERNAL ANATOMY

Like all herring- and sardine-like fishes, this species has only a single, spineless dorsal fin comprising 15-18 rays, and a short-based anal of 7-8 rays. Significant to this genus is the position of the pelvic fins, which are located directly below the rear end of the dorsal fin. The caudal fin is quite strongly forked. The snout is relatively elongate and bears a small, terminal mouth with jaws that are set with minute, almost invisible teeth. The gill rakers are elongate, but far fewer in number than is the case with most other sardine-like fishes, numbering only 30-35 on the lower limb of the first gill arch. The rather large eye is completely covered with adipose tissue.

NATURAL HISTORY

This is an abundant, pelagic species, generally confined to coastal waters and ranging to depths of at least 150 m. It is also strongly gregarious and forms huge shoals, not infrequently in association with shoals of the true pilchard, *Sardinops ocellatus*. Both species undergo extensive seasonal migration, though confusion about the correct identification of South African red-eyes has invalidated some of the past theories. The East Coast roundherring has a definite spawning season which is known to be during late winter and spring off the East Coast. Large quantities of eggs are produced to ensure good recruitment of juveniles to future stocks. This is a filter-feeding species, showing a preference for the larger types of zooplankton, such as copepods and the larvae of crabs, shrimps and krill among others. While large concentrations, of this species undergo longshore migrations, these usually take place in deeper water and are less spectacular than the coast-hugging migrations of the pilchard. This roundherring, nevertheless, represents a prime source of food for gamefish, sharks, dolphins, seals and the larger piscivorous birds.

DISTRIBUTION

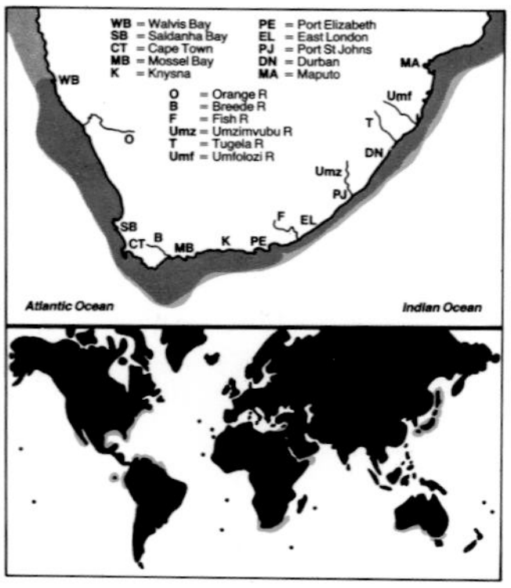

CAPTURE

Considerable quantities of this fish are purse-seined by South African fishermen - much of the catch being processed into fish meal and a variety of other products. This fish is considered inferior to the pilchard as a source of food for humans. Nevertheless, it is an excellent eating fish that could well be better utilized in these times of dwindling fish resources.

SPECIFIC CATCH RESTRICTIONS

None.

NAME DERIVATION

Etrumeus, round belly; *teres,* of the land. East Coast roundherring, a reference to its migration, which takes place in South African waters, and its spikeless, rounded belly. The most commonly used name for this fish, red-eye, is possibly derived from the ease with which its eyes are damaged and appear red after capture.

SIMILAR SPECIES

East Coast roundherrings are most commonly referred to as red-eye and very frequently simply classed as pilchard. Significant features exist, however, that should confirm identity; the positioning of the pelvics in relation to the dorsal, the absence of belly scutes, the lack of black spots on the body and a gill raker count of 30-35. The very closely related *E. whiteheadi* is best distinguished by its 35-40 lower gill rakers. These two species allegedly overlap in distribution off the south eastern Cape, though more samples are needed to confirm this.

Gilchristella aestuaria

(Gilchrist, 1914)
Common name Estuarine roundherring
[Smith 54□3]

IDENTIFYING FEATURES

COLOUR, SHAPE AND SIZE
This tiny, compressed fish has a rounded belly and is basically translucent, but with a brilliant, silver, lateral stripe. Attains 7 cm.

EXTERNAL ANATOMY
The estuarine roundherring lacks a lateral line. Cycloid scales cover the body and are arranged in 38-40 series along each flank. A hard, sharp keel extends along the front of the belly. Fin spines are lacking and the dorsal fin, originating behind the pelvic fin base consists of 14-15 rays, while the anal has 20 rays. The caudal fin is forked. The small, toothless mouth has a slightly projecting lower jaw. At least 40 slender rakers occur on the first gill arch. The eyes are noticeably large.

DISTRIBUTION

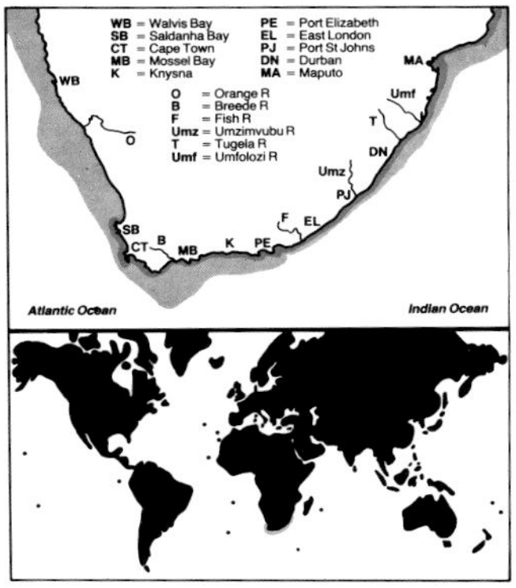

NATURAL HISTORY

This endemic, shoaling fish is very common in estuaries, bays and vleis. It can withstand completely fresh water for prolonged periods, while in Groenvlei in the Wilderness area, and in Lake Sibaya, Tongaland, this species has been isolated from the sea for many years. It has also been recorded near Worcester in Brandvlei and the Breede River. The estuarine roundherring provides a good example of a filter-feeding fish, as it uses its well-developed gill rakers to good effect in sieving copepods, mysids, crab and mollusc larvae from the water. Feeding is known to occur during daylight only and reaches a peak during the afternoon. Sexual maturity is attained within 12 months and spawning occurs in estuaries year-round. The large, sticky eggs probably adhere to submarine vegetation. This species is one of the very few euryhaline fishes that actually spawns within estuaries. As this species appears to be largely restricted to estuaries, the degradation of many of these finely balanced environments could well limit, or even reduce its abundance. This would, in turn, place stress on the overall foodweb, as the estuarine roundherring is 'fodder' for many birds and larger fish.

CAPTURE

This fish can only be caught using seine-nets and represents an excellent source of bait. It is also quite edible, either fresh, or dried and salted.

SPECIFIC CATCH RESTRICTIONS

None.

NAME DERIVATION

Gilchristella, named after the 'father of marine science' in South Africa, J.D.F. Gilchrist, who was responsible for establishing the Department of Sea Fisheries in early 1900; *aestuaria*, estuarine. Estuarine roundherring, a reference to its round belly and estuarine habitat.

SIMILAR SPECIES

While this species may superficially resemble many other 'sprat'-like fishes, it is easily recognized by its terminal mouth, smooth and rounded belly, and the fact that its pelvic fins originate in front of the dorsal fin base.

Hilsa kelee

(Cuvier, 1829)

Common names SA – kelee shad, razorbelly. Worldwide – fivespot herring

[Smith 54□5]

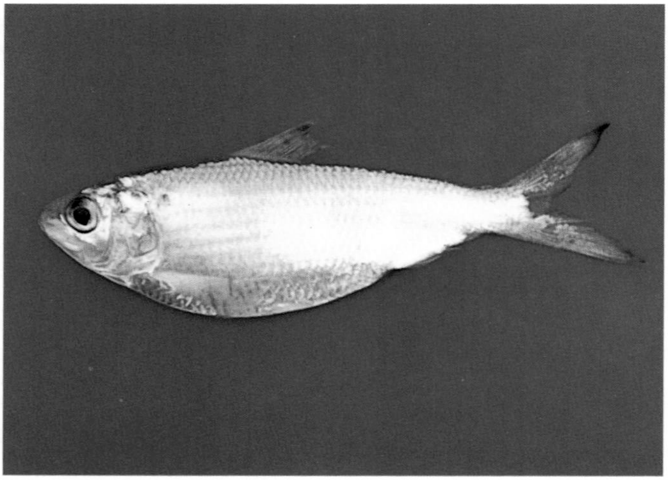

IDENTIFYING FEATURES

COLOUR, SHAPE AND SIZE

This small fish is very strongly compressed, especially in the deep belly region which narrows to a 'V' The dorsal surface is blue-green and the flanks are bright silver. There is a black spot behind each of the gill covers which may be followed by 3-7 similar spots along the sides. Can attain 40 cm.

EXTERNAL ANATOMY

There is no lateral line. Cycloid scales cover the body, and are arranged in 42-44 series along the flanks. These scales are very tough and give the body rigidity. The 'V'-shaped belly is armed along its edge with a sharp keel. Spines are completely absent in the fins and the dorsal comprises 16-19 rays, while the anal has 20-22 rays. The caudal fin is deeply forked. As with all other Clupeidae, the lower jaw folds into the upper jaw. The 100-150 well-developed gill rakers are long and slender. The eyes are covered with adipose tissue.

DISTRIBUTION

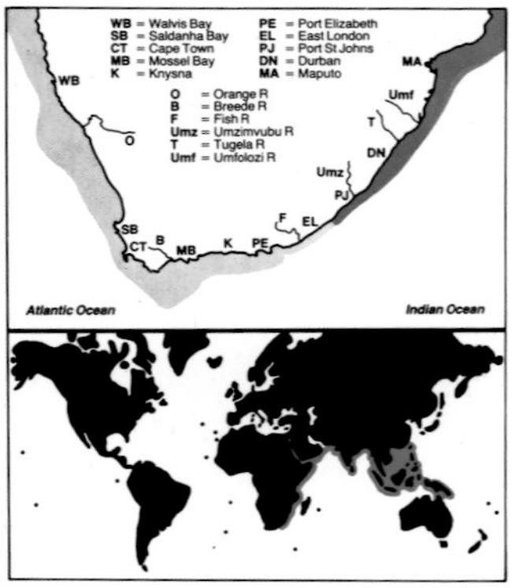

NATURAL HISTORY

The kelee shad is one of the most widely distributed of the herring-like fishes in the Indian Ocean, but is generally confined to coastal waters. It is a pelagic shoaling fish, and despite the fact that it often enters estuaries or shallow bays, it is not very tolerant of low salinities. The numerous, fine gill rakers are an effective feeding adaptation which allows small planktonic organisms to be filtered from water passing through the gills. These food items include copepods, diatoms, mysids, and crab and mollusc larvae. Kelee shad are an important food source for larger predators such as king mackerel and tuna. Breeding occurs from September to February when small shoals of adult fish enter shallow water to spawn. Juveniles of 2-4 cm in length enter the lower parts of estuaries 1-2 months later, where they remain for 2-3 months before returning to the sea. Sexual maturity is attained after one year, at a length about of 15-17 cm.

CAPTURE

This species is not generally caught by fishermen in southern Africa, but in the East, gill and seine nets are used and catches are frequently smoked, or dried and salted. The flesh is palatable but bony. Massive shoals have been known to enter Durban harbour and, occasionally, tons are stranded in the dry-dock when this is drained. It is puzzling that so few anglers use this fish for bait.

SPECIFIC CATCH RESTRICTIONS

None.

NAME DERIVATION

Hilsa, from *helza* meaning sword or dagger, a reference to the sharp keel; *kelee*, keeled. Kelee shad, a reference to the keel, and the shad-like appearance of this fish. Razorbelly, a reference to the sharp keel at the base of the belly.

SIMILAR SPECIES

The deep body and sharply keeled belly serve to distinguish this from most other clupeid fishes. Viewed from the front, the upper jaw should also have a distinct median notch to confirm identity.

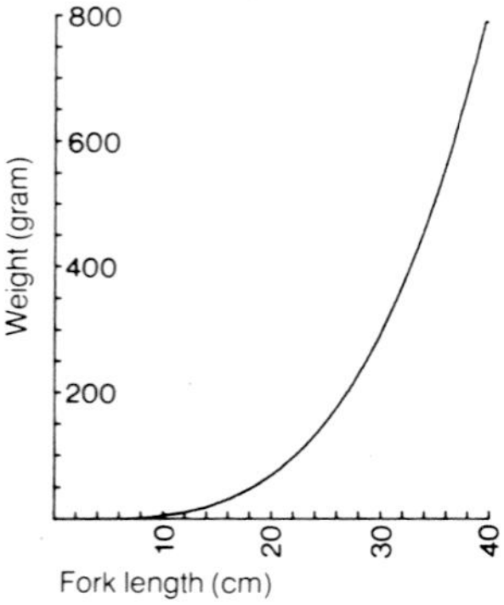

Sardinops ocellatus

(Pappe, 1853)
Common names Worldwide – pilchard, sardine
[Smith 54□12]

IDENTIFYING FEATURES

COLOUR, SHAPE AND SIZE
This spindle-shaped fish is silver overall, with a bluish dorsal surface and a white belly. There is a distinct row of 10-15 dark spots along the flanks, and the fins are yellowish or translucent. Can attain 30 cm.

EXTERNAL ANATOMY
There is no lateral line. Some 50-60 series of thin scales are arranged along the flanks, but are very easily shed. The primitive, spineless fins include a single dorsal of 17-19 rays, an anal of 18-20 rays and a forked caudal. The mouth has a short, but deep, toothless lower jaw which is typical of the Clupeidae. The first gill arch bears 100-120 exceptionally long and well-developed rakers. Transparent adipose tissue partially covers the eyes.

DISTRIBUTION

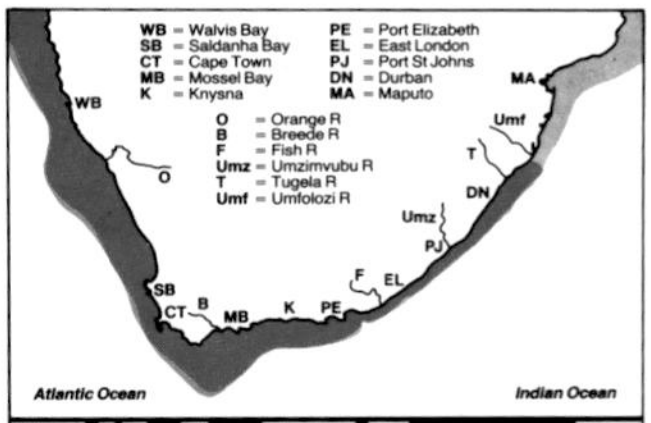

NATURAL HISTORY

This offshore species forms vast shoals and has for many years formed the backbone of the South African pelagic fishing industry. It is also the species responsible for the famous annual 'sardine run' along the East coast when ocean currents and frenzied game fish often drive the shoals, which normally occur several kilometres out to sea, right into the surf zone. The diet consists of planktonic animals such as krill, larval crabs and other small crustaceans. The pilchard is, in turn, an important 'fodder' fish for numerous larger gamefish, birds, dolphins, seals and man. Though the traditional breeding grounds are located off the western Cape and Namibian coasts, recent research has revealed that spawning also occurs off the East Coast during the winter months. Sexual maturity is attained after the third year when fish exceed 20 cm in total length. Age and growth rates have been determined from the annual rings marking the otoliths, or ear-stones. Closely related species occur in California and Australia.

CAPTURE

Most pilchards are caught by purse-seiners, but in Natal catches are also made using beach seine nets. Despite its resilience, the gregarious nature of this species makes it vulnerable to over-exploitation, especially by fishing fleets armed with sophisticated, shoal-detecting equipment. The majority of the annual catch is canned, or converted to fish meal and oil. Sport anglers look forward to the sardine run for the great numbers of gamefish that follow the shoals. The flesh of the 'Natal sardine' has a firmer texture than that of specimens caught in Cape waters and is valued as a bait. Fishermen often use cast nets to catch large numbers which they stockpile in freezers.

SPECIFIC CATCH RESTRICTIONS

Commercial capture is restricted by permit and quota.

NAME DERIVATION

Sardinops, sardine-like; *ocellatus*, spotted. Pilchard, from *pilcher*, an old name for herring-like fishes.

SIMILAR SPECIES

The pilchard is often confused with the red-eye sardine, *Etrumeus teres* (see page 182).

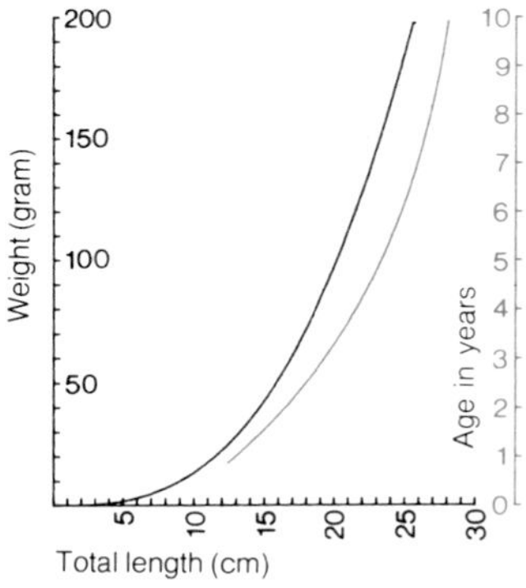

Coracinus capensis

(Cuvier, 1831)
Common names galjoen, damba and many others
[Smith 187□1]

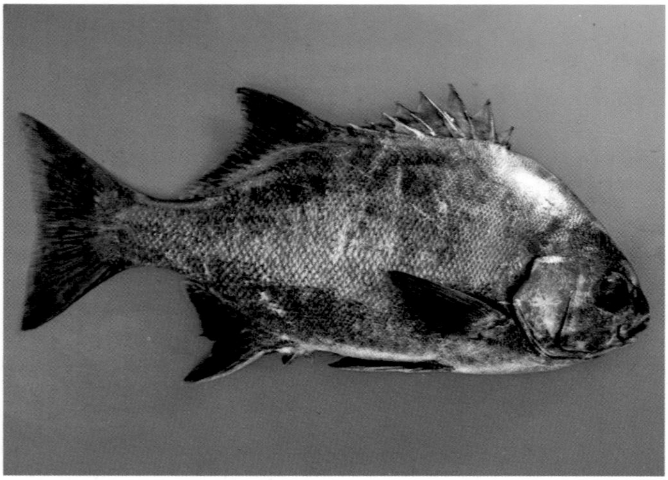

IDENTIFYING FEATURES

COLOUR, SHAPE AND SIZE
The basic colour of this robust, deep-bodied fish is variable, and can range from silver-bronze to almost completely black. Viewed underwater, specimens appear lighter and may have 7-9 vertical bars on each flank. Attains 80 cm.

EXTERNAL ANATOMY
Small, tough, ctenoid scales are arranged in 60-65 series along the distinct lateral line. The fins are well developed and have prominent spines. The forward section of the dorsal fin consists of ten spines and is almost separated from the hind section of 18 or 19 rays. The soft dorsal and anal fins both taper towards the tail. The stout caudal fin is slightly emarginate. Fleshy lips surround the small terminal mouth, and the jaws are set with a row of large, curved incisors in front and smaller teeth further back. Crushing teeth occur in the gullet. There are 17-20 rakers on the first gill arch.

DISTRIBUTION

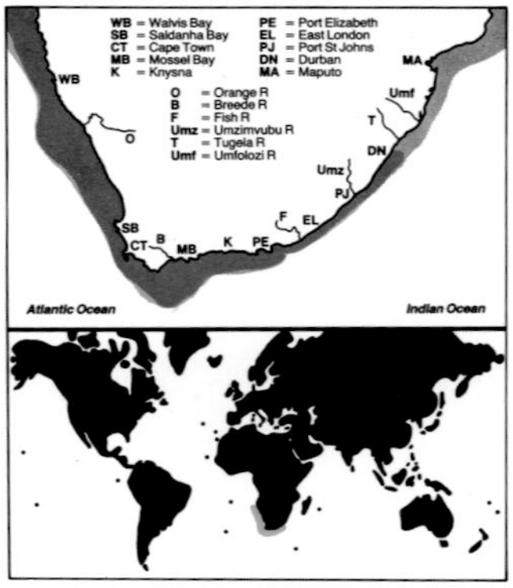

NATURAL HISTORY

The galjoen was one of the first species recognized as being endemic to southern African coastal waters. It is South Africa's national fish and ranks as one of the most popular angling species. Small groups usually congregate in turbulent water off rocky shores, gullies and kelp beds. Though it consumes a fair amount of red and coralline seaweed, about 75 per cent of its diet consists of ascidians (red bait), small mussels and barnacles. The galjoen once occurred in great numbers throughout its range, but today it is quite scarce in most regions. This regretable situation, a probable result of overfishing by net and line, has resulted in legislation to protect the species. While enormous migrations have been documented between Namibia and the Cape, galjoen appear to be semi-resident for at least part of the year. The establishment of reserves is therefore likely to ensure future stock abundance. Sexual maturity is reached at a length of about 34 cm and, in the Cape, spawning occurs during the summer. The distribution of juveniles remains obscure, although they are thought to mature in deeper kelp beds. Promising experiments in captive breeding have been undertaken.

CAPTURE

Few fish are guaranteed to provide better thrills for light-tackle enthusiasts, and along many stretches of the Cape coast this is the only species that can be regularly caught. Previously, the galjoen was netted in considerable numbers, but in view of its present scarcity, commercial exploitation should not be allowed. Though its flesh is an acquired taste it makes excellent eating.
SA angling record - 6,5 kg.
SA spearfishing record - 5,2 kg.

SPECIFIC CATCH RESTRICTIONS

Protected species; closed season: 15 October to 28 February. Not to be sold. Minimum legal size: 35 cm total length.

NAME DERIVATION

Coracinus, a crow's beak, a reference to the body shape; *capensis*, Cape, its area of greatest abundance. Galjoen, a Dutch word meaning galleon, a reference to its fighting ability when hooked.

SIMILAR SPECIES

Though easily distinguished from the banded galjoen (*C. multifasciatis*) because it lacks stripes, it does resemble chubs and stonebream. See also p. 187.

Coracinus multifasciatus

(Pellegrin, 1914)
Common name Worldwide – banded galjoen
[Smith 187□2]

IDENTIFYING FEATURES

COLOUR, SHAPE AND SIZE
This robust, deep-bodied fish has an overall silvery sheen, with a whitish belly and dusky-brown fins. On the flanks of specimens viewed underwater, there are 15-20 obvious, vertical, brown bars which alternate in thickness. These often merge after capture and become less distinct. Attains 30 cm.

EXTERNAL ANATOMY
Small, tough, ctenoid scales are arranged in 65-75 series along the lateral line. The fins are well developed and include a dorsal of ten spines plus 21-23 rays, and an anal of three spines plus 13 or 14 rays. The soft anal and dorsal fins both taper towards the tail, but are less pointed than those of the true galjoen. The stout caudal fin is slightly forked. Fleshy lips surround the mouth and the jaws are set with a row of incisors in front and finer teeth further back. Crushing teeth occur in the gullet. The first gill arch has 17-20 rakers.

DISTRIBUTION

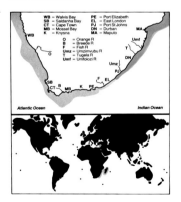

NATURAL HISTORY

The banded galjoen is a semi-resident inhabitant of the warmer regions of the East Coast, where small groups of up to 20 individuals are common in turbulent waters along rocky shores. This carnivore consumes a wide variety of invertebrate organisms which, in order of importance, include Bryozoa, ascidians (red bait), marine worms, amphipods, Cumacea and, occasionally, barnacles, mussels and periwinkles. Exceptionally large amounts of sand and shell are often found in the stomachs of landed specimens, and this material is probably taken in together with food as a mechanical aid to digestion. Sexual maturity is attained at a length of 20-22 cm and spawning occurs off the Natal coast during winter and spring. Juveniles occur during the summer months over shallow reefs and in tidal rock pools. This species is often found together with the stonebream and probably has habitat preferences similar to those of the true galjoen of Cape waters.

CAPTURE

This fish is readily caught by light-tackle anglers using prawn, crayfish or red bait. The best catches are made in gullies from rocky ledges close to the shore. It is not commercially exploited and is too small to be of interest to spearfishermen. The flesh is excellent, although it is not at all like the flesh of the Cape galjoen.
SA angling record – 1,7 kg.

SPECIFIC CATCH RESTRICTIONS

None.

NAME DERIVATION

Coracinus, a crow's beak, a reference to the body shape; *multifasciatus*, many banded. Banded galjoen, a banded relative of the true galjoen.

SIMILAR SPECIES

Galjoens can be distinguished from chubs, which have larger scales and more slender bodies. The stonebream has much smaller spines and higher fin ray counts.

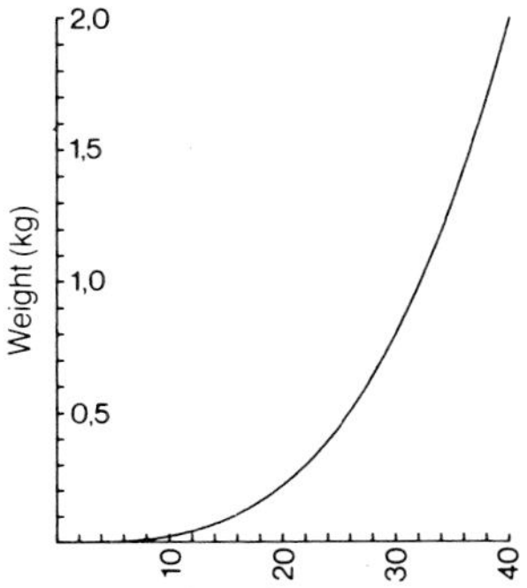

Coryphaena hippurus

Linnaeus, 1758
Common names Worldwide – dolphinfish, dorado
[Smith 211□2]

IDENTIFYING FEATURES

COLOUR, SHAPE AND SIZE

It is virtually impossible to describe, or to capture photographically, the brilliant colours of a living dolphinfish. Live specimens of this elongate, compressed fish are predominantly metallic blue-green in colour, often with orange or golden flecks and blotches. The fins are dusky, though the anal may be golden. Behaviour patterns and trauma, however, can cause marked changes in overall colouration. Silvery-blue, for instance, denotes a feeding phase, whereas yellow indicates stress or capture shock. After death, colour changes to an overall bluish-grey with small, black spots scattered on the back and sides. The forehead is steeply profiled, and becomes steeper with age, especially in males. Can attain 180 cm, but most do not exceed 100 cm.

EXTERNAL ANATOMY

The body is covered with about 260 series of minute, cycloid scales arranged along the lateral line. The long, single, spineless dorsal fin has 58-67 rays, and extends virtually the entire length of the body, from above the eye to just before the deeply forked caudal fin. The anal fin extends from the vent to the caudal peduncle, and has 1-3 small spines preceding 25-30 rays. There are 8-12 rakers on the first gill arch, but these diminish with age. There is no air bladder.

NATURAL HISTORY

The dolphinfish is a fast, wide-ranging, oceanic fish which, unlike many other pelagic species, normally occurs in pairs. The diet includes small fish, especially juvenile triggerfish sheltering beneath flotsam, squid and *Nautilus,* as well as a wide variety of planktonic organisms such as mantis shrimps and crab and crayfish larvae. Virtually all feeding takes place at the surface during daylight. Little is known about its migratory habits except that it follows warm currents. The peak spawning season is in summer, but breeding has been recorded throughout the year. Larval dolphinfish are frequently caught in plankton nets. This species has an exceptionally high growth rate, and its weight for any given length can vary greatly.

DISTRIBUTION

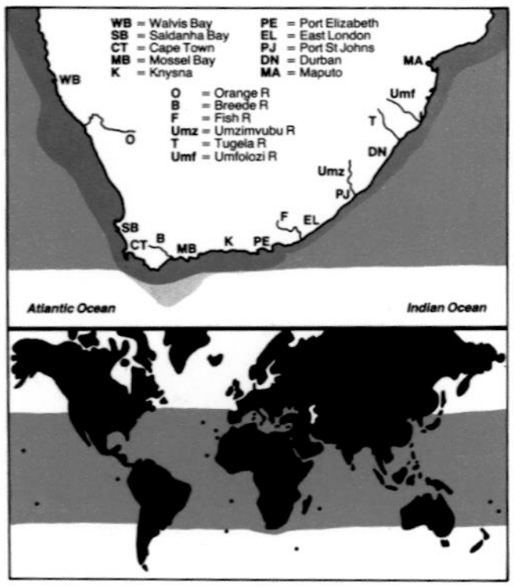

CAPTURE

Wherever the dolphinfish occurs, it is caught by trolling with bait or lures, but, in some parts of the world, traps and purse-seines are also used. This fine gamefish makes exceedingly good eating, and though a number of intestinal and gill parasites occur, these are harmless to man.

World angling record – 39,5 kg.
SA angling record – 26,3 kg.
SA spearfishing record – 10,0 kg.

SPECIFIC CATCH RESTRICTIONS

None.

NAME DERIVATION

Coryphaena, named by Aristotle after its 'helmet-shaped' head; *hippurus*, horsetail. Dolphinfish, a reference to the smooth, rounded profile which resembles that of the mammalian dolphin. Dorado, gilded or golden, a reference to the brilliance of live specimens.

SIMILAR SPECIES

It is probable that the closely related *C. equiselis*, with its deeper body and 52-59 dorsal rays, occurs in southern African waters.

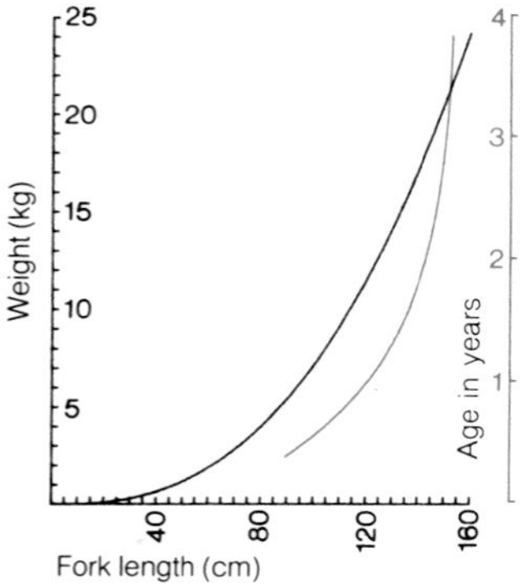

Paraplagusia bilineata

(Bloch, 1787)
Common name Worldwide – fringelip tonguesole
[Smith 261□10]

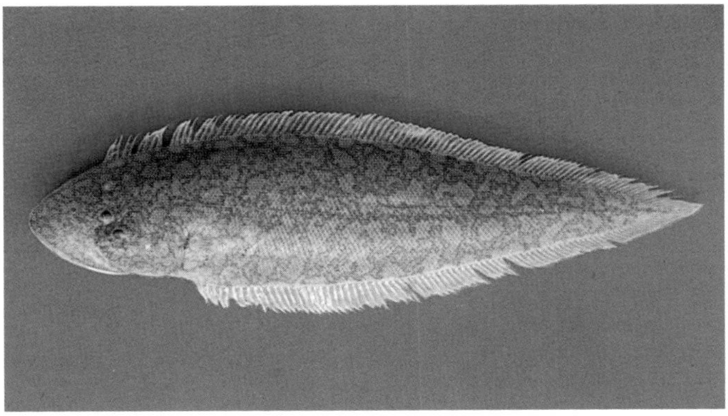

IDENTIFYING FEATURES

COLOUR, SHAPE AND SIZE

This rather elongate flatfish has a rounded head region, and a body that tapers to a pointed tail. The 'eyed' or upper surface is mottled brown, while the 'blind' side is yellowish-white. Can attain 35 cm.

EXTERNAL ANATOMY

The body is covered with 100-120 series of ctenoid scales arranged along the central lateral line. The dorsal fin originates on the convex snout just before the eyes, and continues round the body incorporating the caudal and anal into a single fin comprising 99-110 and 75-86 rays above and below respectively. Pectoral fins are absent, and only the left pelvic fin is present, continuous with the anal fin. The eyes are set close together on the left side of the body, and are positioned near the asymmetrical mouth, which has minute teeth in the right-hand jaw only. Significantly, the lips bear a fringe of tentacles. Two distinct lateral lines occur on the eye side of the body in addition to several branches on the head. There is no lateral line on the blind side.

NATURAL HISTORY

This common flatfish frequents coastal waters, and, while it is most abundant in extremely shallow regions, some have been trawled to depths of 80 m. Like most similar fish, it is sluggish and confined to the bottom, where it often buries itself below the sand. This habit, and the ability to change colour to blend with its immediate surroundings, makes it inconspicuous to both predators and prey. The diet includes small, bottom-living invertebrates such as crabs, shrimps and marine worms. The fringelip tonguesole always swims on its side with undulations of the continuous dorsal and anal fins. Nothing is known of its breeding cycle. The unusual proliferation of the lateral line system may well indicate that this species is particularly adaptable to excessively turbid waters. This supposition is supported by the great numbers of these tonguesoles that congregate over the very muddy Tugela Banks. Furthermore, the small, bony tubercles occurring on the underside of many flatfishes, may, in tonguesoles, be developed into tiny filaments which act as highly sensitive organs of touch.

DISTRIBUTION

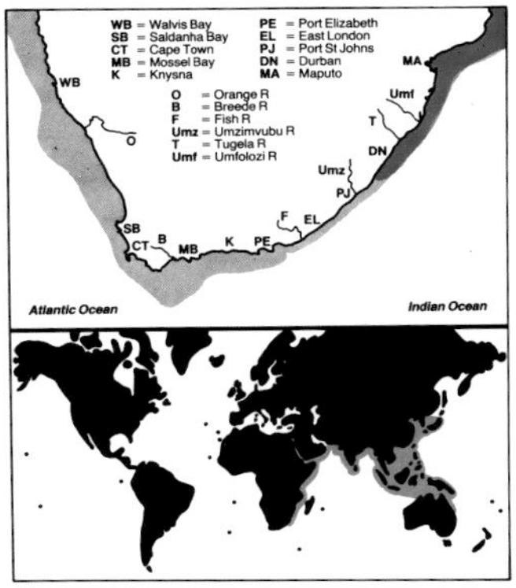

CAPTURE

Though occasionally caught by anglers, this flatfish is more regularly landed by seine and trawl net fishermen.It is an excellent table fish, despite its small size, and is of considerable commercial importance elsewhere in the world.
SA angling record – vacant.

SPECIFIC CATCH RESTRICTIONS

None.

NAME DERIVATION

Paraplagusia, beside the crabs; *bilineata,* double lined. Fringelip tonguesole, a reference to the fringe-like tentacles on the lips and the tongue-shaped body.

SIMILAR SPECIES

While the ten species of tonguesole in southern African waters are not always easy to identify, the fringelip tonguesole is most distinctive because of its marbled colouration, and especially because of the frilled lips.

Dinoperca petersi

(Day, 1875)

Common names Worldwide – cavebass, lampfish

Note: The commonly used local name 'lanternfish' is incorrect and confusing as this term refers to a large group of fishes confined to the great ocean depths.

[Smith 180□1]

IDENTIFYING FEATURES

COLOUR, SHAPE AND SIZE

This medium-sized fish has a deep, compressed body. Its overall colour is blackish-grey, with darker fins and numerous, distinct, pearly-white spots on the upper flanks. Though juveniles resemble adults in body shape, their colours differ considerably; young fish are creamy overall and marked with a number of darker, oblique crossbars. Can attain 75 cm.

EXTERNAL ANATOMY

Small ctenoid scales cover the entire body and also extend onto the fins. These scales are arranged in about 100 series along the well-defined lateral line. The darkly coloured eyes are noticeably large. Spines are prominent in the fins, which include a single dorsal of 9-11 spines plus 18-20 rays, an anal of three spines plus 12-14 rays, and a square caudal. The soft dorsal and anal fins are large and considerably higher towards the rear. The terminal mouth is very big and bears several rows of fine, villiform teeth which extend onto the palate. This species lacks canine teeth. The first gill arch carries 30-35 elongate, well-developed rakers.

NATURAL HISTORY

This common fish lives on rocky reefs, ranging from a few metres behind the surf zone to depths exceeding 50 m. During daylight it is almost entirely confined to the darkness of deep caves, but after dusk the cavebass ventures out to forage more openly round the reef. Its nocturnal habits are undoubtedly assisted by its large eyes, which are able to detect prey in dim light. Its diet includes small shrimps, mantis shrimps, crab larvae and the fry of numerous other reef fishes.

Individuals reach maturity at a length of about 30 cm, and sexually active cavebass are known to spawn over reefs along the Natal coast during winter, the time of their greatest abundance in southern African waters. The cavebass is a solitary species, and its irregular geographic distribution throughout the Indo-Pacific region remains somewhat puzzling.

DISTRIBUTION

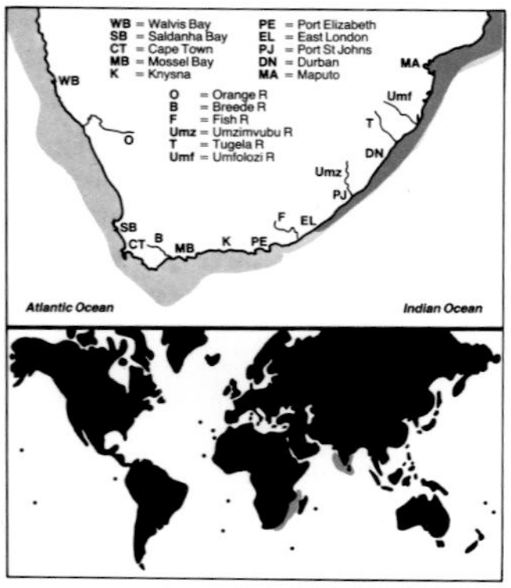

CAPTURE

Cavebass are caught all year round, but the largest hauls are made in winter. The fish is much sought after by ski-boat anglers, shore anglers and spearfishermen. Most small baits are successful.

SA angling record – 5,2 kg.

SA spearfishing record – 5,8 kg.

SPECIFIC CATCH RESTRICTIONS

None.

NAME DERIVATION

Dinoperca, a fearful perch; *petersi,* named after the ichthyologist, Peters. Cavebass, a reference to its cave dwelling habits and close relationship to seabasses.

SIMILAR SPECIES

The shape and colouration of the cavebass is quite distinctive. Notice the scales that extend onto the fins.

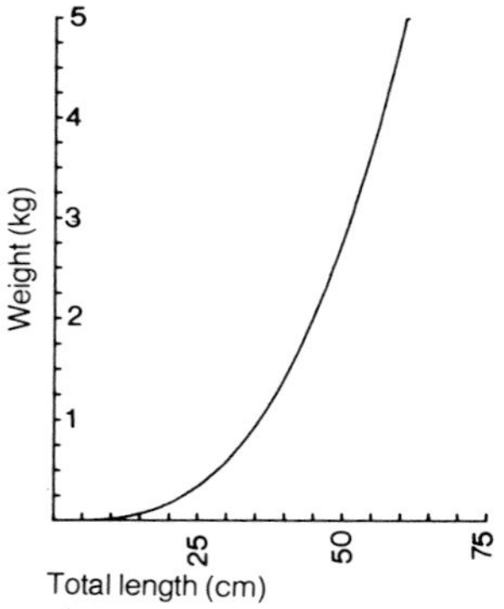

Drepane longimanus

(Linnaeus, 1758)
Common names SA – concertina fish. Elsewhere – sickle fish [Smith 1951]

IDENTIFYING FEATURES

COLOUR, SHAPE AND SIZE

The concertina fish is a wedge-shaped, deep-bodied species that is strongly compressed. It is generally silver in colour, with 4-11 broken, black bars running down the flanks. The fins are dusky, with the dorsal being faintly spotted. Occasional specimens have parts of their skull or skeleton enlarged, a phenomenon known as hyperostosis. This often gives the fish unusual external features, but these should not be regarded as abnormalities. Can attain 45 cm.

EXTERNAL ANATOMY

Except for naked patches in front of the eyes and on the pre-operculum, the body is covered with scales arranged in 46-55 series along the lateral line. The first and second dorsal fins are continuous and consist of eight or nine spines and 19-22 rays respectively. The anal fin has three stout spines followed by 17-19 rays, and the long, sickle-shaped pectoral fins usually reach the caudal peduncle. The small, protractile mouth can extend into a downward-pointing tube. Minute teeth occur in each jaw. There are 11-15 rakers on the first gill arch.

NATURAL HISTORY

This species reaches peak abundance in Natal during summer, when it is most frequently found in the leeward waters of reefs, shallow coastal bays and harbours. Being tolerant of slightly reduced salinities, it is also encountered in larger estuaries. Small crabs, shrimps and marine worms are important in the diet, and the specialized mouth is well suited to pecking these from the sea bottom. In doing so, large quantities of mud are often ingested, but this is later harmlessly passed as faeces. The breeding season is short and restricted, and spawning fish have been recorded close inshore during spring.

DISTRIBUTION

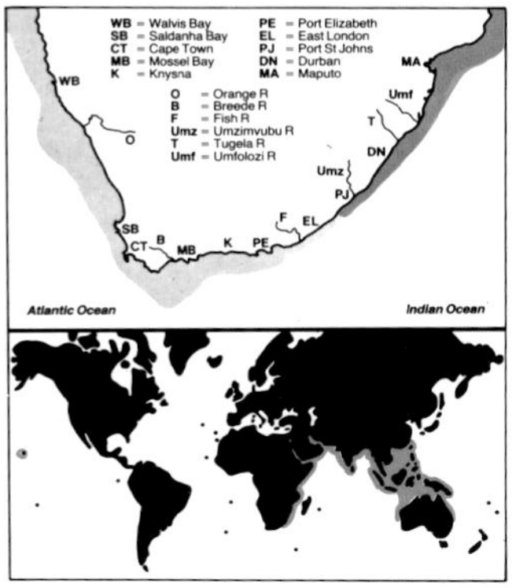

CAPTURE

Though these fish have no commercial importance in southern Africa, many are caught in fish traps and trawls in the Far East. Its flesh is palatable, but not highly esteemed. The concertina fish is seldom hunted by spearfishermen.
SA angling record – 2,3 kg.
SA spearfishing record – 2,4 kg.

SPECIFIC CATCH RESTRICTIONS

None.

NAME DERIVATION

Drepane, a corruption of a Greek word meaning bird, possibly a swallow; *longimanus*, longfinned. Concertinafish, a reference to its protruding mouth that can be expanded and contracted.

SIMILAR SPECIES

The closely related *D. punctatus* can be recognized by its having vertical rows of black spots down each flank.

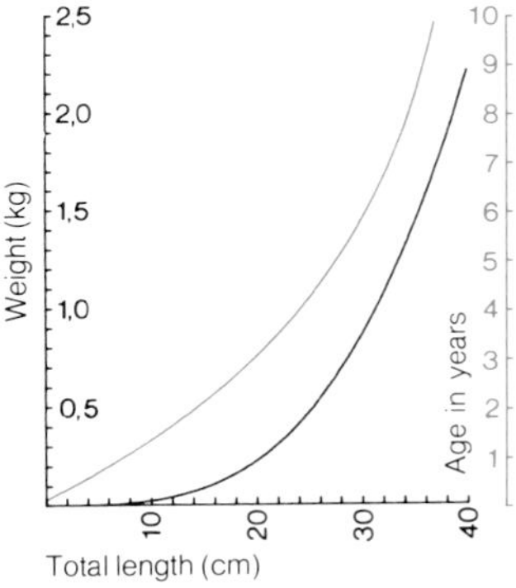

Echeneis naucrates

Linnaeus, 1758
Common names Worldwide - shark remora, shark sucker
[Smith 213□1]

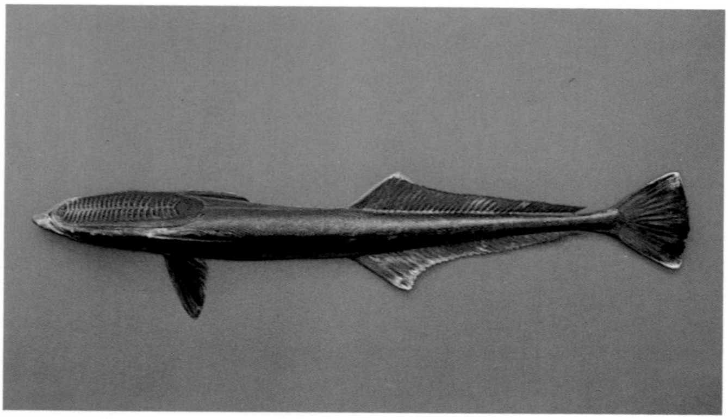

IDENTIFYING FEATURES

COLOUR, SHAPE AND SIZE

This curious, elongate fish is almost cylindrical in cross-section. The body is dark brown overall, but paler below. Two white stripes, separated by a broad, dark band, run the entire length of the body, and, while these are most distinctive when seen underwater, the contrast is soon lost in landed specimens.
Can attain 100 cm.

EXTERNAL ANATOMY

Most obvious is the remora's large sucking disc which is located on top of the head. This highly specialized structure has evolved

from the dorsal spines, and consists of 21-28 deep grooves, or laminae. These are clearly shown in the close-up photograph. Though scales are present, these are minute and indistinct. The fins are spineless and include a dorsal of 34-42 rays, an anal of 32-38 rays, and a slightly emarginate caudal. The pectoral fins are pointed, and the inner rays of the pelvic fins are attached to the body by a thin membrane. Bands of fine, villiform teeth occur in both jaws, the lower of which is longer and projects forward.

NATURAL HISTORY

The shark remora has evolved a life-style whereby it clings firmly to large sharks and, in so doing, it hitches free rides without expending its own energy. This unique behaviour ensures that it is always 'on site' when a meal is available, for it feeds mainly on the small pieces of fish that break away when the shark tears into its prey. It also has the seemingly distasteful habit of feeding on the faeces of its host. To attach itself, the remora manoeuvres its sucking disc against the body of the host fish. Then, by raising the laminae, a partial vacuum is formed. The seal thus created is extremely difficult to break except when the fish voluntarily relaxes the laminae.
A single shark may host a number of remoras, but these are not necessarily always attached. Even when free-swimming, however, the remora employs an energy-saving trick, for though a powerful swimmer, it will often glide effortlessly alongside or below its host, relying mainly on the slipstream to pull it forward. This habit is well illustrated by remoras in the shark tank of Durban's Seaworld. The life history of this fish is not well understood, largely because it is difficult to obtain adequate specimens for study.

CAPTURE

Though never a target species for anglers, the remora is occasionally hooked by shore and boat fishermen, its flesh is very palatable. In some parts of the world, this fish is allegedly put to a bizarre use; after attaching a rope to the tail of a landed specimen, the 'angler' releases his catch, only to retrieve it once it is attached to a large fish, turtle or shark.
SA angling record - 3,4 kg.

DISTRIBUTION

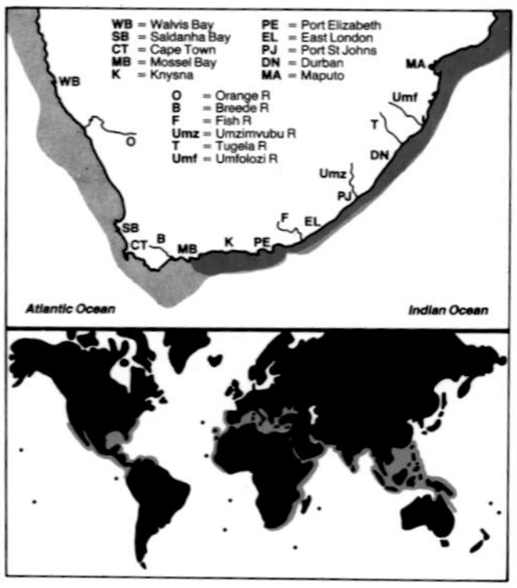

SPECIFIC CATCH RESTRICTIONS

None.

NAME DERIVATION

Echeneis, an old Greek name for this fish which means literally 'to hold a ship', a reference to its supposed power; *naucrates*, a pilot. Remora, a Latin word meaning to delay or hinder, also a reference to the belief among the ancients that this fish could stay the course of any ship to which it adhered.

SIMILAR SPECIES

The slender body and 21-28 disc laminae distinguish this from the other species found here.

Elops machnata

(Forsskål, 1775)

Common names SA – springer, ladyfish. Elsewhere – tenpounder [Smith 36□2]

IDENTIFYING FEATURES

COLOUR, SHAPE AND SIZE

This fish has an elongate body which in cross-section is almost cylindrical. It is predominantly silvery in colour, but has a blue-green back and dusky-yellow fins. Can attain 90 cm but 50 cm is more common.

EXTERNAL ANATOMY

The body is covered with small scales arranged along the lateral line in 96-103 series. The springer is a primitive fish; it has no spines, its fin rays are unbranched, and the supplementary gill structure on the inside of the operculum is poorly developed. The single dorsal fin comprises 22-27 rays, and the anal fin has 15-18 rays. The caudal fin is forked and has a broad peduncle. Bands of fine teeth occur in both jaws and on the palate. There are about 21 rakers on the first gill arch. The eyes are extensively covered with adipose tissue.

DISTRIBUTION

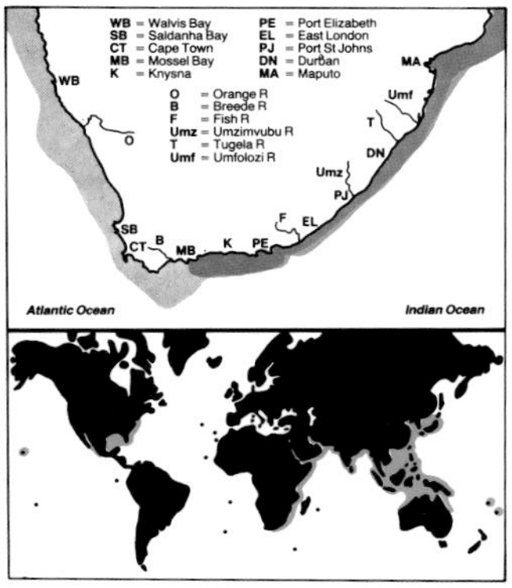

NATURAL HISTORY

This aggressive, coastal predator frequently penetrates well into estuaries, either individually or in small groups. It hunts during early evening, and the diet includes small fish and shrimps. The springer will often patrol the perimeter of a shoal of food fish, making periodic rushes into it to snatch prey. Despite its generally non-gregarious behaviour, large shoals of breeding adults are found off Mocambique during winter. Detailed information on the life history is lacking, though juveniles closely resemble transparent eel larvae, and can best be distinguished from these by their forked tails. This species forms part of the Elopiformes, one of the more primitive groups of modern-day bony fishes. A feature common to all these herring-like families, and well demonstrated in the springer, is the direct connection between the oesophagus and the air bladder.

CAPTURE

The springer is an excellent shore-angling fish, especially if light tackle is used. It fights gamely and leaps repeatedly from the water during a fight. Almost any flesh bait will tempt this fish; for example, live or dead fish, prawns and squid. Lures are also successful. Each season, a number of large specimens are also speared by divers. Though not very palatable, and full of small bones, the flesh is marketed, either fresh or salted, in several Eastern countries.

All-Africa angling record – 11,8 kg.
SA angling record – 11,8 kg.
SA spearfishing record – 9,0 kg.

SPECIFIC CATCH RESTRICTIONS

None.

NAME DERIVATION

Elops, a corruption of an old word meaning to drive or move; *machnata*, derived from *mache* meaning battle and *nata*, to swim, references to the fighting prowess and speed of the fish. Springer, a reference to its leaping ability. Tenpounder, an American name of uncertain origin.

SIMILAR SPECIES

The terminal mouth, small scales and absence of spines distinguish this from similar species.

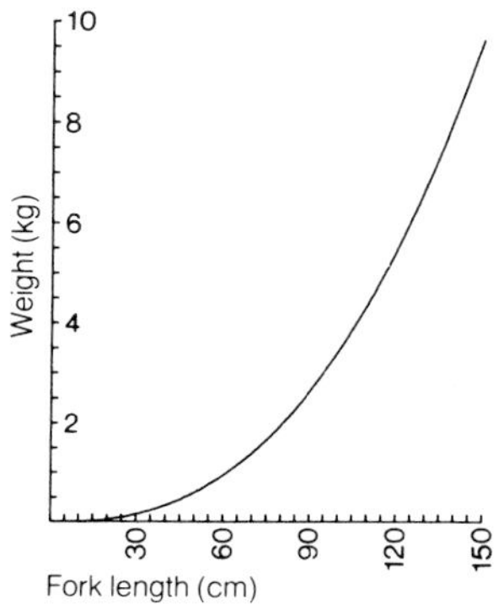

Engraulis japonicus

Schlegel, 1846
Common name Cape anchovy
[Smith 55□1]

IDENTIFYING FEATURES

COLOUR, SHAPE AND SIZE

This slender-bodied fish is slightly flattened from side to side, with a distinctly rounded belly. The overall body colour, when freshly caught, is bright silvery, with a bluish upper surface and whitish belly. There is a bright-silver stripe down each flank. Can attain 13 cm.

EXTERNAL ANATOMY

The snout of this and related species, typically consists of a blunt projection that overhangs the mouth. In the Cape anchovy, the maxillae are rather short, and do not reach beyond the edge of the pre-operculum. The body is covered with scales which are easily shed and number 40-45 along the lateral line. A diagnostic feature is the absence of sharp scales and scutes along the belly, a feature found in many other anchovy types. The fins are poorly developed, with only a single dorsal of 12-14 rays, an anal of 13-18 rays, and the origin of the anal fin positioned well behind the level of the last dorsal ray. The pelvic fins originate in front of the level of the first dorsal. Gill rakers are very well developed, and number 26-39 on the lower limb of the first arch.

DISTRIBUTION

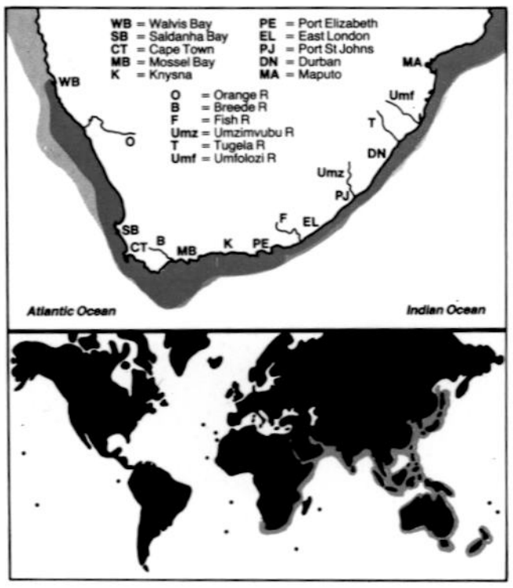

NATURAL HISTORY

This is one of the most abundant and extensively exploited fish in South African waters. It is a pelagic species that inhabits coastal waters from the surface to depths of 400 m. Enormous concentrations are found off the Cape and Transkei, often displaying diurnal migrations, with shoals closer to the bottom at night. The Cape anchovy is a filter feeder, and strains small planktonic animals, such as copepods, from the water. As plankton often proliferates in places of upwelling, it follows that anchovy also congregate in these nutrient-rich waters. The Cape anchovy is a serial spawner, which means that it has a prolonged breeding season that occurs mainly during spring and summer. The young grow rapidly, and often become catchable by the purse-seine fleet before they attain one year, a factor that may ultimately influence their stock abundance. This species represents a most important source of food for numerous other marine organisms, including bony fish, sharks, dolphins, whales, seals and birds. Shoals of anchovy are often pursued by gamefish, such as tuna. When attacked from below, the anchovy move to the surface where they attract terns and other piscivórous birds. These diving birds then provide the clue to fishermen that feeding gamefish are about.

CAPTURE

South African fleets of purse-seiners land about 270 000 tonnes of anchovy annually, though this amount varies considerably, especially since the collapse of the pilchard fishery. Evidence based primarily on catch statistics suggests that the Cape anchovy increased its abundance in response to decreased pilchard abundance. As anchovy are smaller than pilchard, the fleets reduced the mesh size of their nets in order to land anchovy. This in turn holds a threat for the recovering pilchard stocks, as juvenile fish are now caught accidentally. Most of the anchovy catch is converted to oil and fishmeal products, which are used in the animal feed industry. Anchovy are excellent eating, and it is puzzling that none are marketed fresh or salted, as practised in Mediterranean countries.

SPECIFIC CATCH RESTRICTIONS

Commercial capture is by permit and quota.

NAME DERIVATION

Engraulis, an old Greek word meaning small fish; *japonicus,* of Japan, where it was first discovered. Cape anchovy, a reference to its area of abundance, and from the Spanish *anchova,* meaning herring.

SIMILAR SPECIES

Superficially, the Cape anchovy resembles the other five anchovies of South African waters, but it may be positively distinguished by the absence of scutes on the rounded belly, and the maxillae that do not reach beyond the pre-operculum.

Thryssa vitrirostris

(Gilchrist & Thompson, 1908)
Common names SA – glassnose, glassnosed anchovy, bony. Elsewhere – orangemouth thryssa [Smith 55□6]

IDENTIFYING FEATURES

COLOUR, SHAPE AND SIZE

This elongate fish is strongly compressed and its bluntly rounded, almost translucent snout distinctly overlaps the large, underslung mouth. The overall body colour is silver, but the fish is usually bluish along its dorsal surface. The belly is white. The fins are translucent or dusky-yellow and the inside of the mouth is conspicuously orange. Attains 20 cm in length.

EXTERNAL ANATOMY

There are about 40 series of scales arranged along the lateral line, many of which are lost during capture. The scales along the underside are developed into 25-41 scutes which give the belly a sharply edged keel. None of the fins have spines. The dorsal fin comprises 13-14 rays, and the anal some 34-43 rays. The caudal fin is strongly forked. Both jaws bear very fine teeth, and the upper jaw extends far back, but not beyond the pectoral base, as in the case of the similar, but more tropically distributed *T. setirostris.* The 30 or more rakers on the first gill arch are long and serrated.

DISTRIBUTION

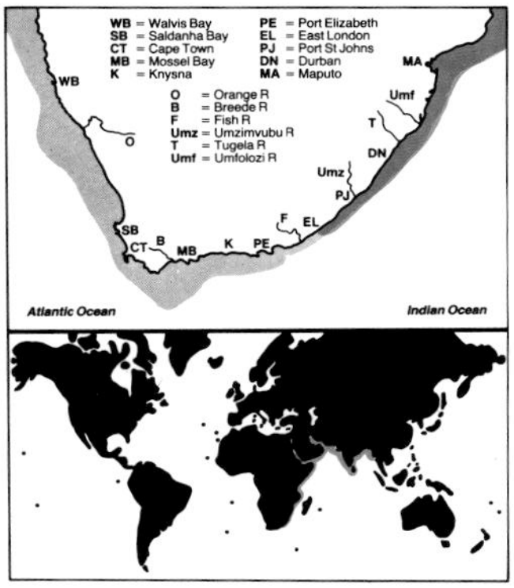

NATURAL HISTORY

This coastal fish is most common in calm bays and estuaries, often in, or near, fresh or muddy water. It is invariably found in very large, midwater shoals. These vast congregations of fish feed in synchrony – as the shoal passes through water rich in minute food items, each member opens its mouth wide. The shoal thus forms a huge 'living net' with each individual using its elaborate gill rakers to strain plankton from the water. These tiny food organisms include fish larvae and eggs as well as small crustaceans, but in some estuaries the fry of the estuarine roundherring constitutes as much as 90 per cent of the daily food intake. The glassnose is itself extensively preyed upon, and represents an important food source for gamefish during the winter and spring, when it is most abundant. Sexual maturity is attained after one year at an approximate length of 8 cm; males mature at a smaller size than females. Spawning takes place during the winter, within or just outside estuaries. Females produce fairly large, sticky eggs which, after fertilization, presumably adhere to marine vegetation or other submarine objects. Within a few days, they hatch into larvae.

CAPTURE

Large numbers are netted in discoloured water off Durban from August to November. Though not caught on rod and line, this fish is always in demand with anglers as a sure bait for a number of gamefish, particularly the king mackerel. In the Far East the glassnose is an important and heavily exploited food resource.

SPECIFIC CATCH RESTRICTIONS

None.

NAME DERIVATION

Thryssa, from the Greek *thrissa* meaning anchovy; *vitrirostris*, glassy snout. Glassnose, also a reference to the translucent snout.

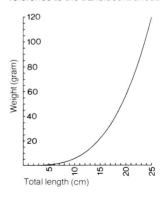

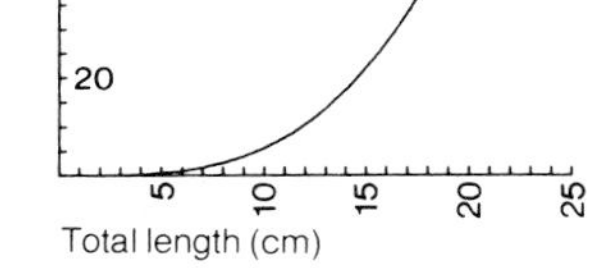

Platax teira

(Forsskål, 1775)

Common name Worldwide – longfin batfish

[Smith 192□3]

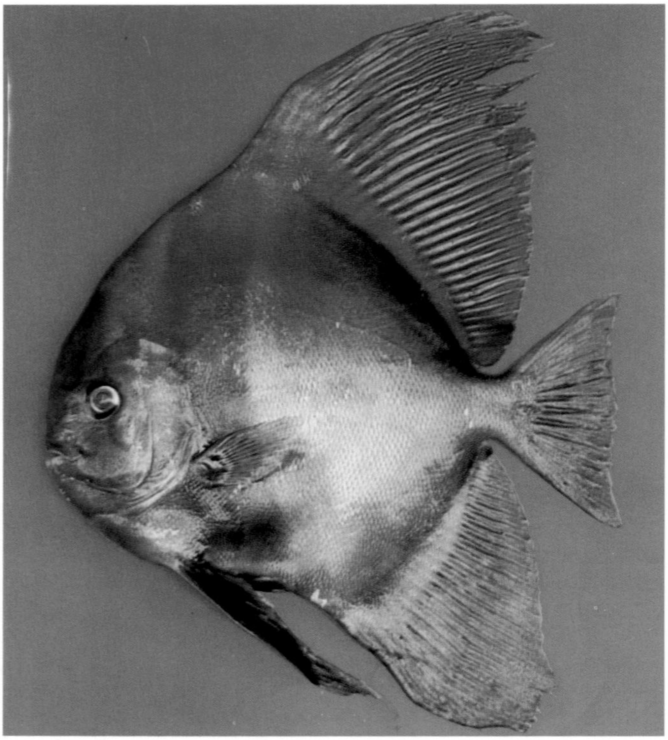

IDENTIFYING FEATURES

COLOUR, SHAPE AND SIZE

The body of this batfish is basically deep, rounded and very compressed, but, together with the large, swept-back dorsal and anal fins, the fish has an overall, delta-wing shape. The general body colour ranges from yellow-orange in juveniles to dark brown in adults, and several dark, vertical bars may occur on the sides, at least one of which passes through the eyes. Can attain 50 cm.

EXTERNAL ANATOMY

The body is covered with small, rough scales arranged in 48-53 series along the arched lateral line. The dorsal, anal and pelvic fins are long in young fish, but become progressively shorter with age. The dorsal fin consists of five concealed spines which precede 28-34 rays. The anal fin has three spines plus 22-28 rays, and the caudal fin is truncate. The small mouth bears tricuspid teeth. Though indistinct, about ten short rakers usually occur on the first gill arch.

NATURAL HISTORY

This coastal species inhabits coral reefs and seaweed beds. Small groups of batfish also frequently congregate around protective shark nets, shipwrecks and jetties, and many divers have been followed by these inquisitive fish. The diet is varied, and includes small crabs, worms and other invertebrates that adhere to underwater structures or reefs. Shrimps, swimming crabs and mantis shrimps are also eaten, and batfish are known to feed on offal. Their abundance increases during summer, and the young sometimes frequent estuaries. Here they mimic and closely resemble leaves, especially the fading yellow leaves of the red mangrove. By drifting horizontally, or feigning death, these juveniles are able to escape the attention of predators, and thus improve their chances of survival during the highly vulnerable early stages of life. Occasionally, small batfish mimic marine flatworms, and there is some evidence to suggest that this alternative strategy occurs in regions devoid of mangroves.

DISTRIBUTION

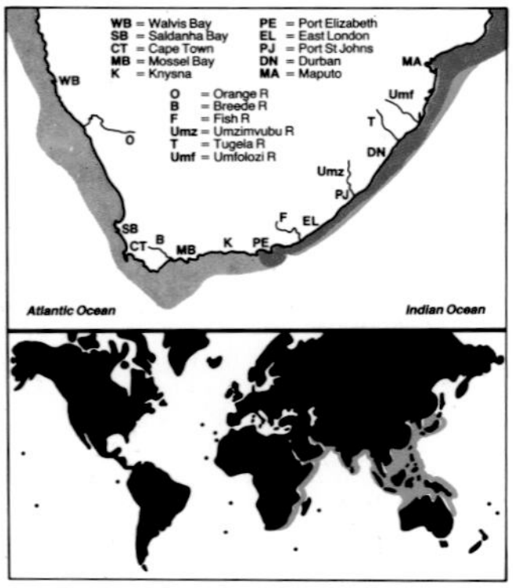

CAPTURE

The batfish is rarely of angling importance, though it is of considerable value to marine aquarists. Given adequate space and a balanced diet, this fish will survive in captivity for many years. Though edible, the greyish flesh is rather insipid and not esteemed. SA spearfishing record – 5,8 kg.

SPECIFIC CATCH RESTRICTIONS

None.

NAME DERIVATION

Platax, flat bodied; *teira,* meaning obscure. Batfish, a reference to its alleged similarity to a bat in flight.

SIMILAR SPECIES

The concealed dorsal spines will aid the distinction of batfishes from other Ephippidae. The longfin batfish can be distinguished from its two close relatives by its rounded mouth profile and 28-34 dorsal fin rays.

Tripterodon orbis

Playfair, 1866
Common name Worldwide – spadefish
[Smith 1924]

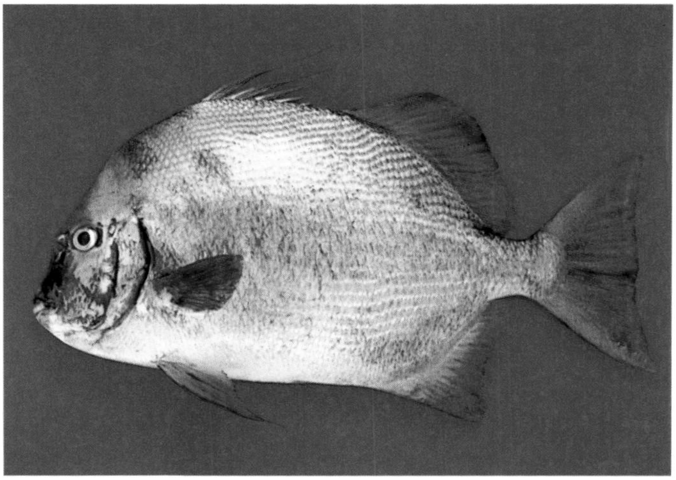

IDENTIFYING FEATURES

COLOUR, SHAPE AND SIZE

The spadefish is a rounded, compressed fish with a silvery body. The head region is somewhat darker, and there are approximately eight, dark, vertical bars running down the flanks, but these are more obvious in smaller specimens, especially when viewed from above. The dorsal spines are yellow. Can attain 75 cm in length.

EXTERNAL ANATOMY

The body is covered with small scales arranged in 45-55 series along the arched lateral line. The fins are well developed. The dorsal fin comprises nine spines (the third, fourth and fifth being the longest) plus 19-21 rays. The anal fin has three spines plus 15-17 rays, and the caudal fin is emarginate. Thick lips surround the small mouth, which is set with tricuspid teeth in each jaw. There are about 15 rakers on the first gill arch.

DISTRIBUTION

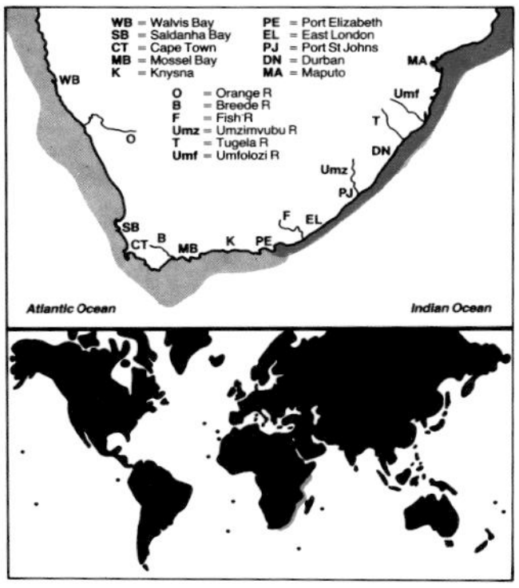

NATURAL HISTORY

Although the spadefish is common around shallow, inshore reefs, some have been recorded to depths of 30 m, often in small groups of up to 15 fish. Estuaries are seldom entered, as it is not tolerant of turbid water and low salinities. It is an inquisitive fish, and frequently approaches divers, a habit which makes it an easy target for spearfishermen. The diet includes midwater invertebrates such as scaphopods, pteropods, swimming crabs and their larvae, marine worms, shrimps and, occasionally, small fish. The spadefish also nibbles encrusting organisms from reefs, a feeding habit for which the chisel-like, tricuspid teeth are well adapted. Spawning has been recorded off the Natal coast during late summer, but the distribution of the young is unknown. A closely related and similar species occurs elsewhere in the Indo-Pacific region. As with many other similar-shaped fishes, the highly compressed spadefish is able to manoeuvre in and out of narrow crevices in the reef in search of food and protection. Its streamlined body and powerful caudal fin, however, also enable it to swim at speed in open water.

CAPTURE

This fine light-tackle angling fish is caught either from ski-boats, along rocky shores or off piers. It is also one of the more common species landed by spearfishermen. Its flesh is fairly palatable.

SA angling record – 6,3 kg.
SA spearfishing record – 8,0 kg.

SPECIFIC CATCH RESTRICTIONS

None.

NAME DERIVATION

Tripterodon, triple-winged and toothed; *orbis,* circular, a reference to its round body shape. Spadefish, a reference to its flattened body.

SIMILAR SPECIES

This is the only spadefish species in southern African waters, and can be distinguished from the batfishes by the clear visibility of its dorsal spines. Notice too that its pectoral fins are much shorter than those of the concertinafish.

Thyrsites atun

(Euphrasen, 1791)
Common names SA - snoek.
Worldwide - snoek, barracouta
[Smith 247□8]

IDENTIFYING FEATURES

COLOUR, SHAPE AND SIZE
The general body colour of this elongate, somewhat compressed fish is predominantly silver. The dorsal surface is grey-blue and the underside is white. The fins are dusky to black but the prominent dorsal spines are much lighter. The lateral line is conspicuous and wavy. Attains 150 cm.

EXTERNAL ANATOMY
The body is covered with numerous minute scales arranged in series along the well-defined lateral line. The single dorsal fin consists of 18-19 long, stout spines followed by 10-12 rays plus five or six finlets, while the anal fin has three spines followed by 8-11 rays plus five to six finlets. The large caudal fin is forked, and the small pelvic fins are situated far forward on the body, just below the pectoral fins. Sharp, triangular teeth arm the large mouth. The first gill arch has 20-25 small, paired rakers.

DISTRIBUTION

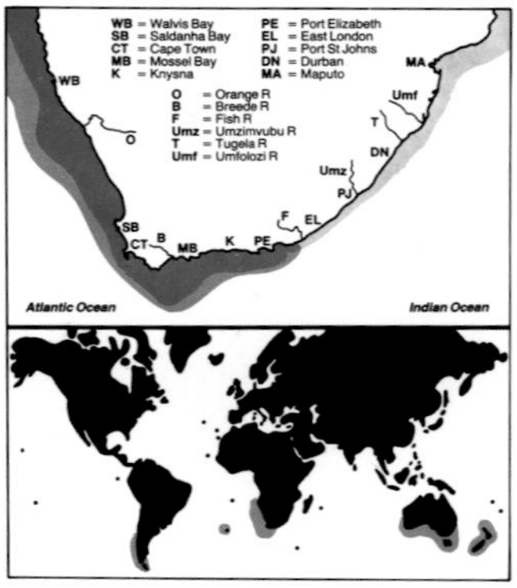

NATURAL HISTORY

This fierce, shoaling predator undertakes extensive migrations along the West Coast each year. Though generally found in coastal waters, it also occurs off-shore, where considerable catches are made by trawlers. Despite its size and formidably armed jaws, the snoek shows a preference for small food such as krill, anchovies, pilchards, other small fish and squid. There is considerable seasonal variation in the condition of snoek, and during late winter and in spring, the fish is normally in a poor state of health. This coincides with the breeding season and is associated with the low oil and protein content of its flesh. The nematode parasites which heavily infest the body do not, however, affect the quality of the fish. Sexual maturity is attained at a length of about 60 cm, and the juveniles frequently use protected areas such as False Bay.

CAPTURE

Most snoek are caught by commercial fishermen using fish-baited handlines, but the species is equally popular with sport anglers though rarely with spearfishermen. The snoek is well respected by all who catch it, as it is extremely vicious, and, once hooked, it is rapidly retrieved and immediately killed to avoid severe lacerations. The flesh makes excellent eating, freshly cooked, dried or smoked.
SA angling record - 8,6 kg.
SA spearfishing record - 5,4 kg.

SPECIFIC CATCH RESTRICTIONS

Open species; minimum legal size is 60 cm total length.
For many years a closed season was observed from August 31 to November 30. This has been lifted, but it should not be regarded as an indication that stocks are inexhaustible, and care should be taken not to over-exploit the species during this period when most specimens are reproductively 'ripe'.

NAME DERIVATION

Thyrsites, resembling a straight staff; *atun,* obscure. Snoek, a reference to its resemblance to the Dutch 'snoek', the European pike.

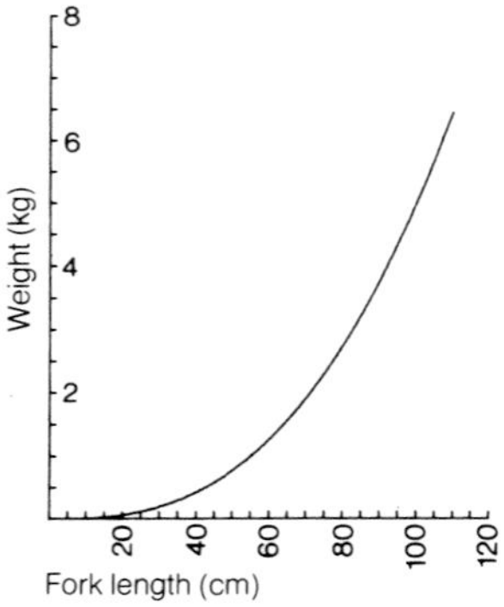

Gerres acinaces

Bleeker, 1854

Common names SA – smallscale pursemouth, pouter. Elsewhere – majorra, silver-belly, silver biddy [Smith 194□1]

IDENTIFYING FEATURES

COLOUR, SHAPE AND SIZE

This rather elongate fish has a pointed snout and a long, sloping forehead. It is predominantly silver-grey, but has about ten inconspicuous, grey-brown bands running the length of the body. The fins are dusky, and the lower edge of the caudal has a bright blue margin. Can attain 25 cm.

EXTERNAL ANATOMY

The body is covered with small, but distinct, scales arranged in 42-47 series along the conspicuous lateral line. The fins are well developed. The single dorsal fin is high in front and consists of 9-10 spines plus 9-10 rays, while the anal fin has three spines plus seven rays. The long pectoral fins reach beyond the vent, and the deeply forked caudal fin has long lobes. The small, terminal mouth is protractile, and points downward when fully extended. The lips are fleshy, and the jaws are set with fine, villiform teeth. The first gill arch bears about 11 slender, pointed rakers.

NATURAL HISTORY

This small fish is common in the brackish and shallow waters of tropical and subtropical regions, where it usually occurs in small, loosely packed shoals. It is known to be tolerant of considerable salinity fluctuations and is, therefore, frequently encountered in estuaries. It is a clear-water species, however, and though it is found all along the Natal coast, it is understandably most prolific in relatively silt-free systems such as Kosi Bay. The smallscale pursemouth is primarily a bottom feeder, and it preys to a large extent on the syphons of burrowing bivalve molluscs, when these are projected above the sea-bed. The diet also includes amphipods, small crabs and polychaete worms, the fish's highly protractile mouth being particularly well suited to selecting these food items from the mud. The fine gill rakers assist in filtering out smaller food organisms. This species is continuously abundant and appears to breed all year round. Individuals exceeding 8-9 cm in length are sexually mature. Spawning occurs at sea, and it would appear that once mature fish leave their estuarine nursery grounds they do not return.

DISTRIBUTION

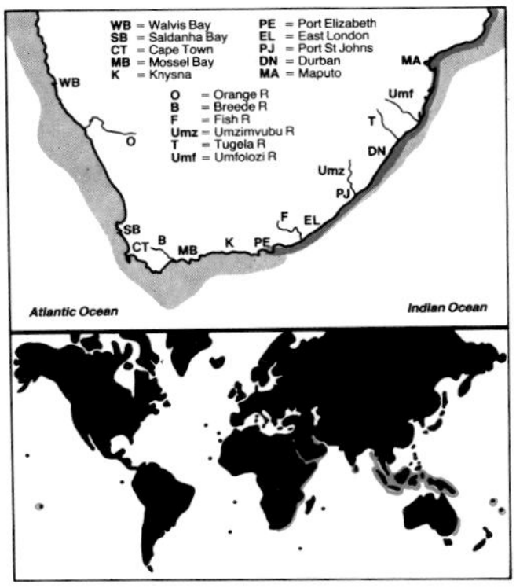

CAPTURE

Although it is not of prime sport or commercial angling importance, in Moçambique and Tongaland, this fish is valued as a protein source. In the Far East and India, large numbers are caught in nets and fish traps for human consumption. It is also a good bait fish.

SA angling record – 0,4 kg.

SPECIFIC CATCH RESTRICTIONS

None.

NAME DERIVATION

Gerres, the name given this and similar fishes by Pliny, the Roman historian; *acinaces,* a short sword or scimitar. Smallscale pursemouth, a reference to the small scales and to the purse-like folding jaws. Pouter, a reference to its protruding lips.

SIMILAR SPECIES

Another three pursemouths closely resemble this species; only detailed measurements and scale counts will distinguish these.

Gerres filamentosus

Cuvier, 1830

Common names SA – threadfin pursemouth, pouter. Elsewhere – whipfin majorra, threadfin silverbelly, silver biddy [Smith 194.2]

IDENTIFYING FEATURES

COLOUR, SHAPE AND SIZE

The threadfin pursemouth is an oblong fish with a pointed snout and a long sloping forehead. The general body colour is silver, but the dorsal surface is blue-green. Bluish blotches, arranged in 8-10 broken, vertical bars are located along the flanks. These, however, are most obvious when the fish is viewed from above. Can attain 25 cm, though specimens measuring less than 15 cm are more common.

EXTERNAL ANATOMY

The body is covered with distinct scales arranged in 40-45 series along the conspicuous lateral line. The fins are well developed, and include a single dorsal of nine spines (the second being filamentous and very long) plus ten or 11 rays; and an anal comprising three spines plus seven or eight rays. The long pectoral fins extend beyond the vent, and the caudal fin is deeply forked. The small, terminal mouth is protractile and the jaws bear fine, villiform teeth. About 11 rakers are on the first gill arch.

NATURAL HISTORY

The threadfin pursemouth prefers shallow water, especially in tropical estuaries, and is fairly tolerant of low salinities. It usually occurs in small shoals, which are common in the lagoons of Moçambique and Zululand, particularly Kosi Bay. However, many have been recorded periodically in estuaries to the south. Feeding takes place during the day only, and prey includes, in order of importance: amphipods, polychaete worms, bivalve molluscs, dead organic matter, small crabs and shrimps and, occasionally, plant material. These food organisms all occur on the sea-bed, and are scooped up from the mud or sand in the protractile mouth, which is fully extended during feeding to form a dredger-like bucket. Spawning has been recorded as far south as Delagoa Bay, and the juveniles enter estuaries soon after hatching.

DISTRIBUTION

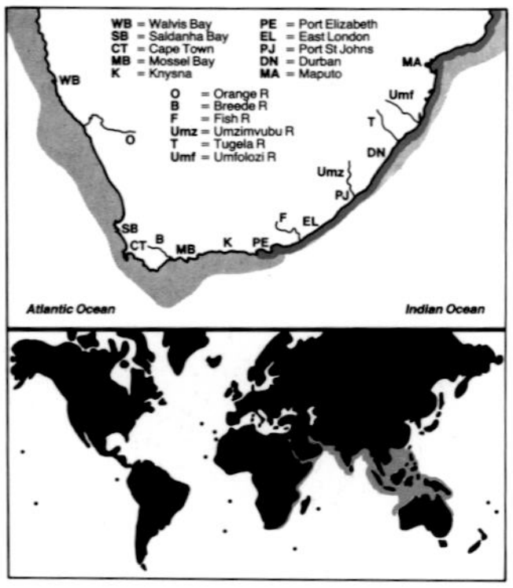

CAPTURE

Though rarely caught by anglers, this fish is not difficult to hook on ultra-light tackle and worm bait. In some countries, nets and fish traps are used to exploit this fish. The flesh is palatable and can be eaten fresh, dried or salted.

SA angling record – vacant.

SPECIFIC CATCH RESTRICTIONS

None.

NAME DERIVATION

Gerres, name given to this and similar fishes by Pliny, the Roman historian; *filamentosus*, a reference to the elongate dorsal spines. Threadfin pursemouth, a reference to the elongate fins and to the purse-like folding jaws. Pouter, a reference to the protruding lips.

SIMILAR SPECIES

This is the only pursemouth with a distinctly filamentous dorsal fin spine.

Glossogobius giurus

(Hamilton-Buchanan, 1822)
Common names SA – tank goby. Elsewhere – bar-eyed goby
[Smith 240□44]

IDENTIFYING FEATURES

COLOUR, SHAPE AND SIZE

The forward section of this elongate fish is cylindrical in cross-section, but the body becomes compressed towards the tail. The immediate head region, however, is depressed and slightly pointed. Though colour and markings are variable, the general body colour is brownish and most specimens have two rows of four to six dark blotches along the flanks. Can attain 50 cm.

EXTERNAL ANATOMY

There is no lateral line and the body is covered with well-developed scales arranged in 29-33 series along the flanks. The dorsal fin consists of two sections, the first of six spines and the second of a single spine plus 8-10 rays. The anal fin has one spine plus 7-9 rays, and the caudal fin is rounded. The pelvic fins are fused to form a weak sucking disc, a characteristic feature of this family. The mouth opens upwards and has a reptile-like, forked tongue. Both jaws bear several rows of teeth, those of the outer row being enlarged.

NATURAL HISTORY

The tank goby is the largest member of this prolific family and it is widely distributed in warm marine, estuarine and even fresh waters. In some cases specimens are known to have adjusted to completely fresh water, and several have been caught in streams at an altitude of 1 000 m above sea level. The tank goby normally occurs singly or in pairs, and is confined to shallow water, where its drab colouration and sedentary habits make it cryptic and inconspicuous. The diet is exclusively carnivorous, and consists primarily of prawns and small slow-swimming fish that are unsuspectingly snatched. During the breeding season, long eggs are laid which adhere to submerged objects. The eggs are probably guarded by the parents until they hatch. The distribution and whereabouts of the larvae are almost certainly confined to lagoons, as small juveniles may be caught there throughout the year.

DISTRIBUTION

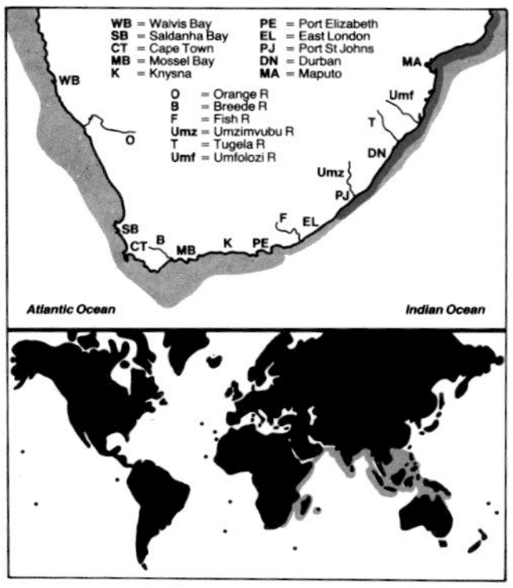

CAPTURE

Though frequently hooked by estuarine anglers, the tank goby is not regarded as a sport fish. It is also commonly caught in drag-nets, prawn-netting operations and in fish traps. In India it is valued as an important source of food.
SA angling record – 0,3 kg.

SPECIFIC CATCH RESTRICTIONS

None.

NAME DERIVATION

Glossogobius, derived from *glosso*, a tongue and *gobius* an old name for these small fish; *giurus*, narrow tailed. Tank goby, a reference to its robust tank-like body.

SIMILAR SPECIES

The identification of gobies is tricky at best of times, though the tank goby can be recognized by its large size, bi-lobed tongue and freshwater habits.

Periopthalmus koelreuteri

Eggert, 1935

Common names Worldwide – African mudhopper, mudskipper [Smith 240□78]

IDENTIFYING FEATURES

COLOUR, SHAPE AND SIZE

This drab little fish has an elongate body and a steep head profile. The general body colour is grey-brown, with occasional irregular markings. The dorsal fin is reddish. Can attain 15 cm in length.

EXTERNAL ANATOMY

The body is covered with tiny, inconspicuous scales arranged in some 90 series along the flanks. The double dorsal fin has 7-15 spines followed by a single spine plus 10-12 rays, and the anal has one spine plus 9-10 rays. The first dorsal is high in front and the caudal fin is rounded. The pelvic fins are fused to form a sucking disc, a typical feature of this family. The pectoral fins are powerfully developed. Fine teeth occur in the jaws, and the protruding, bulbous eyes, situated on top of the head, are able to rotate independently and have movable lower eye-lids. There is an anal papilla which is enlarged in males and is a useful means of external sex determination.

NATURAL HISTORY

This amphibious fish inhabits muddy water, estuarine shores and mangrove swamps. It is able to withstand prolonged periods out of water. This is made possible by virtue of its capacity to retain oxygenated water in the gill chamber, and because of its fine, superficial blood vessels which are able to absorb oxygen directly from the surrounding air. The African mudhopper is very agile on land, using its muscular pectoral fins to crawl and skip with surprising speed. The sucker formed by the fused pelvic fins helps it to cling to twigs and rocks. The chameleon-like eyes give a wide angle of vision, especially useful in spotting danger as well as prey. The diet consists of small crabs, mud-prawns and molluscs that are captured on land, and shrimps, marine worms and fish larvae that are taken in the water. Breeding occurs in estuaries, where eggs are laid in underground chambers specially constructed by the male fish for this purpose. These 'rooms' are about 5 cm in diameter and are inter-connected by several tunnels with external turrets. The African mudhopper is an intensely territorial fish and males 'flash' their red dorsal fins when proclaiming their domains. Pairs also make attentive parents and take good care of newly hatched juveniles.

CAPTURE

Its agility makes the African mudhopper difficult to catch, but once caught, this fascinating fish thrives in captivity if a muddy habitat is provided both above and below the waterline. Owing to its territorially aggressive nature, only a few specimens should be accommodated in one tank. It is possible to condition this fish to perform a few simple 'tricks' – a facility which has made it a useful participant in a number of psychological behaviour studies.

SPECIFIC CATCH RESTRICTIONS

None.

DISTRIBUTION

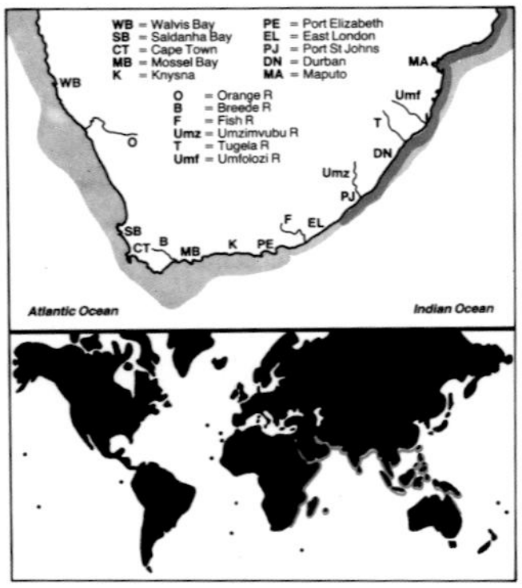

NAME DERIVATION

Periopthalmus, literally 'around-eyes'; *koelreuteri*, named after the early naturalist Koelreuter. African mudhopper, a reference to its distribution and 'amphibian' habits.

SIMILAR SPECIES

Mudhoppers are readily recognised by their habitat and behaviour. A second species (*P. sobrinus*) is virtually identical but has 14-17 dorsal fin spines.

Grammistes sexlineatus

(Thunberg, 1792)
Common name sixstripe soapfish
[Smith 167□3]

IDENTIFYING FEATURES

COLOUR, SHAPE AND SIZE

This relatively plump, robust fish is dark brown to black overall. Six or more broken white or golden-yellow stripes run lengthways along the body. The number of stripes varies with age. The fins are yellowish and translucent. Can attain 27 cm.

EXTERNAL ANATOMY

One of the most immediately noticeable features of the sixstripe soapfish is the excessive slimy mucus exuded, especially after capture. Small scales are arranged in 59-72 series from the head to the tail. The fins are well developed, and include a double dorsal of six or seven spines plus 13-14 rays, an anal of three spines plus nine rays, and a rounded caudal which has a stout peduncle. Just below the lower lip is a short barbel. There are 7-10 rakers on the first gill arch. Though the sixstripe soapfish is closely related to the rockcods (family Serranidae), it is considered distinct because of the lower dorsal fin count and the small barbel occurring on the chin.

NATURAL HISTORY

This solitary fish inhabits rocky shores, coral reefs and tidal pools. It is a nocturnal predator and remains inactive during daylight, often sheltering in caves. The diet includes small crabs, shrimps and juvenile crayfish. The sixstripe soapfish is a timid fish, and is not easily approached by skindivers. Although it is not generally abundant, it may be common in localized areas. As with other members of the family, the ability of the sixstripe soapfish to produce slime undoubtedly plays an important role in the fish's defence strategy. If under attack, or even if there is undue agitation near by, it will exude a thick mucus that, on contact with the water, turns into a soapy froth which is mildy poisonous or, at least, sufficiently irritating to halt the advance of a would-be predator. Notwithstanding its toxic nature, it has been discovered that this mucus also has antibiotic properties and inhibits the growth of some bacteria. Very little is known of this fish's life history.

DISTRIBUTION

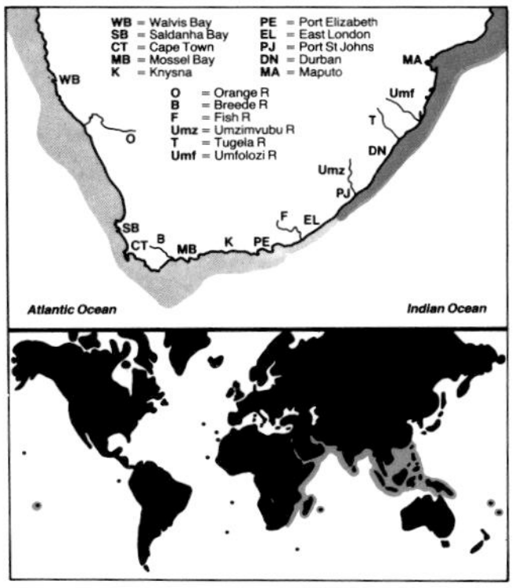

CAPTURE

Whereas this species is not of any angling or spearfishing importance, it does make a suitable aquarium specimen, and will thrive if adequate shelter is provided in its tank. The excessive slime produced after capture should not be allowed to enter the tank, however, as it may be toxic to other fish. The goldstriped rockcod is not edible owing to the bitter taste of the flesh.

SPECIFIC CATCH RESTRICTIONS

None.

NAME DERIVATION

Grammistes, marked with lines; *sexlineatus*,six-lined. Sixstripe soapfish, a reference to its six yellow stripes and to the excessive amounts of soapy mucus produced by this fish.

SIMILAR SPECIES

While the four South African soapfishes are quite similar in body proportions, this species is readily identified by its distinctive patterns and colour.

Diagramma pictum

(Thunberg, 1792)
Common names SA – sailfin rubberlip. Elsewhere – painted sweetlips
[Smith 179□1]

IDENTIFYING FEATURES

COLOUR, SHAPE AND SIZE

The robust, oblong and somewhat compressed body is typical of Haemulidae, but this species has a noticeably more slender and elongate caudal peduncle. It is a rather drab fish, dusky-grey to black overall, and usually marked with darker spots, especially on the fins. Though juveniles resemble adults in general appearance, they are more colourful, and their yellowish bodies are patterned with a number of dark, longitudinal bands. With growth, these bands gradually break up into rows of oval or roundish spots. Attains 100 cm.

EXTERNAL ANATOMY

The entire body is covered with small ctenoid scales which are arranged in 82-117 series along the lateral line. The fins are well developed and the spine and ray counts are diagnostic for this species. The single dorsal fin consists of nine or ten spines plus 22-25 rays, the hind section being considerably longer than the spiny front section. In juveniles, the dorsal spines are noticeably elevated. The anal fin comprises three spines plus seven rays, and the caudal is square or slightly emarginate. Thick, fleshy lips surround the small mouth which has four or five rows of fine teeth in each jaw. The teeth of the outer row are enlarged. There are no teeth on the roof of the mouth. Some 20-24 rakers occur on the first gill arch.

NATURAL HISTORY

The sailfin rubberlip is very widespread and common throughout its range, especially in shallow coastal areas and around coral reefs. It is generally not found deeper than 80 m. Adults are solitary and forage about reefs in search of prey. This includes a variety of invertebrates such as shrimps, polychaete worms and small crabs, as well as the juveniles of many coral-reef fishes. The attractive juveniles are most common during late summer, when they may congregate in small groups in shallow water and, occasionally, in beds of seaweed. Breeding fish have been recorded off the coast of East Africa from August to October. However, little else is known of its life history.

DISTRIBUTION

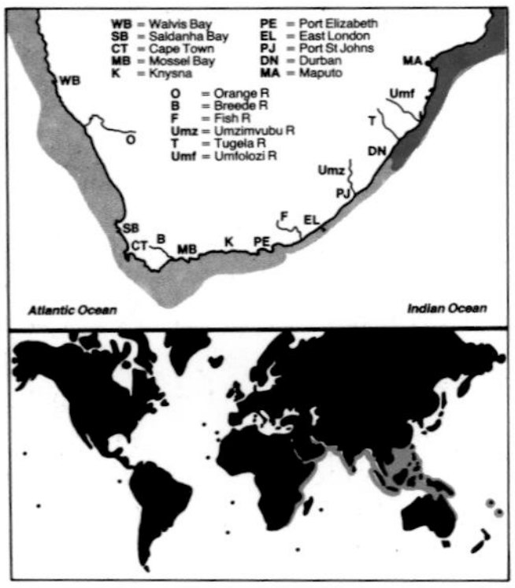

CAPTURE

The sailfin rubberlip is reluctant to feed on large, unnatural baits, and despite being common, not many are caught by anglers. Fair numbers are, however, landed by spearfishermen. It is an excellent eating fish, and in tropical countries it is fairly important as a source of food.

SA spearfishing record – 8,6 kg.

SPECIFIC CATCH RESTRICTIONS

None.

NAME DERIVATION

Diagramma, figure or plan; *pictum*, painted. Sailfin rubberlip, a reference to the elevated dorsal fin of juveniles and to the pouting lips.

SIMILAR SPECIES

This is the only member of this family that has 9-10 dorsal spines; all others have 11-14. It is also noticeably plain coloured when seen underwater.

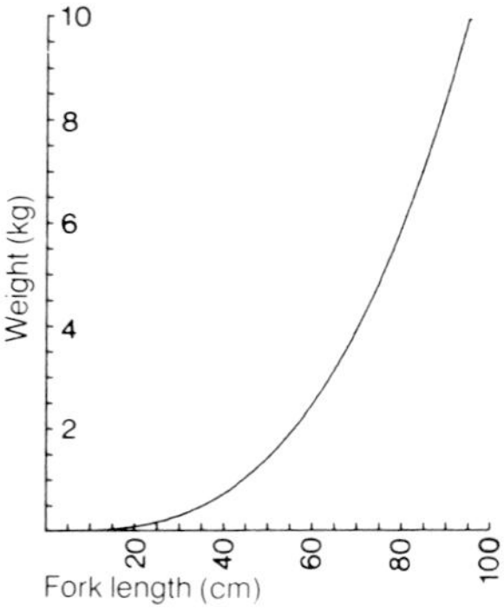

Plectorhinchus chubbi

(Regan, 1919)
Common name Worldwide - dusky rubberlip
[Smith 179□2]

IDENTIFYING FEATURES

COLOUR, SHAPE AND SIZE
This robust fish is neither conspicuously marked nor distinctively coloured. It is dark grey or bronzy-brown overall, but the underside may be paler. The fins are darker brown, Juveniles are a lighter, reddish-brown overall. Can attain 85 cm.

EXTERNAL ANATOMY
The body is covered with small, but distinct, scales arranged in 60-70 series along the well-defined lateral line. The spine and ray counts of the dorsal and anal fins are diagnostic. The single dorsal fin comprises 11 spines plus 16-17 rays, while the anal has three spines plus seven or eight rays. The stout caudal is barely emarginate, and the pectoral and pelvic fins are short. With increasing age the lips surrounding the mouth become progressively thicker and more fleshy. Both jaws bear several bands of fine villiform teeth. Some 35-40 distinct rakers occur on the first gill arch. The eyes of this species appear to be larger than in any other *Plectorhinchus* species.

NATURAL HISTORY

Though relatively common, the dusky rubberlip is infrequently seen, as it is rather secretive and does not freely take baits. It is a bottom-dwelling fish and, while it often inhabits very shallow reefs, it also ventures to depths of 80 m. Prey consists mainly of invertebrate organisms such as small crabs, juvenile fish, shrimps and polychaete worms. Spawning takes place over deeper reefs, but newly hatched juveniles make extensive use of shallow intertidal reefs as nursery areas. Research conducted by the Oceanographic Research Institute in Durban has shown that groups of 3-20 juvenile dusky rubberlips are normally associated with patches of drifting and decaying seaweed. These 'mini-environments' provide a ready food source for the tiny fish, as they feed on a certain species of shrimp (*Macropotasma* sp.), which in turn is known to feed extensively on this rotting plant material. The seaweed also provides shelter, with both the dusky rubberlips and these tiny crustaceans remaining inconspicuous and well hidden within the floating mass.

DISTRIBUTION

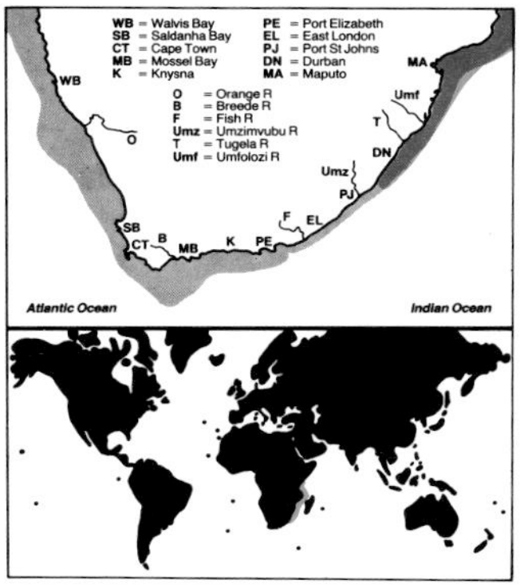

CAPTURE

Ski-boat anglers only occasionally land this fish, as it is generally reluctant to take baits or lures. Spearfishermen are more successful, however, partly because the dusky rubberlip is easily approached. Its flesh makes excellent eating.
SA angling record - 9,4 kg.
SA spearfishing record - 8,8 kg.

SPECIFIC CATCH RESTRICTIONS

None.

NAME DERIVATION

Plectorhinchus, plaited snout; *chubbi* named after Mr. Chubb, erstwhile curator of the Durban museum. Dusky rubberlip, a reference to its drab colour and to its thick, fleshy lips.

SIMILAR SPECIES

All other rubberlips in this region have 12 or more dorsal spines, the dusky rubberlip only has 11. Most other Haemulidae have more distinctive colours and patterning than this species.

Plectorhinchus flavomaculatus

(Ehrenberg, 1830)
Common name Worldwide – lemonfish
[Smith 179□3]

IDENTIFYING FEATURES

COLOUR, SHAPE AND SIZE
Unlike the previous species, this robust, moderately compressed fish is beautifully marked. Its overall body colour is grey, but lighter below and extensively patterned with orange-yellow spots. On the head, these spots are fused into wavy bands. The fins are also spotted, and the bases of the pectoral fins are red. These markings are particularly distinct in young fish and tend to fade with age. Can attain 60 cm.

EXTERNAL ANATOMY
Scales cover the body, and are arranged in about 60 series along the lateral line. Spines are prominent in the fins, and the single dorsal usually comprises 13 spines plus 20-22 rays, while the anal has three spines plus seven rays. The caudal fin is only slightly emarginate, while the rounded pectoral and pelvic fins are short. Bands of very fine teeth occur in both jaws, and the mouth is surrounded by exceptionally thick, fleshy lips. The first gill arch bears 28-34 stubby rakers.

NATURAL HISTORY

The lemonfish is fairly common in coastal waters, where it is generally confined to coral and rocky reefs as deep as 80 m. It is a sluggish species and is most active during the half-light of dawn and dusk when it preys mainly on bottom-living invertebrates including small crabs, marine worms and shrimps. Small fish are also sometimes eaten. Young lemonfish have a curious, fluttering swimming style not unlike the motion of a drifting leaf; this behaviour could be a form of protective mimicry, but it is not clearly understood and disappears with age. Whereas adults are mainly solitary, juveniles may congregate in shallow tidal pools with good stands of seaweed. Very little is known of the species' life history. Observations by divers, however, confirm the lemonfish's bottom-dwelling habits, as it is frequently encountered skulking near reefs. Though essentially rather timid, it is nevertheless inquisitive, and initially will swim right up to a diver before retreating behind some rocky outcrop or into a cave.

DISTRIBUTION

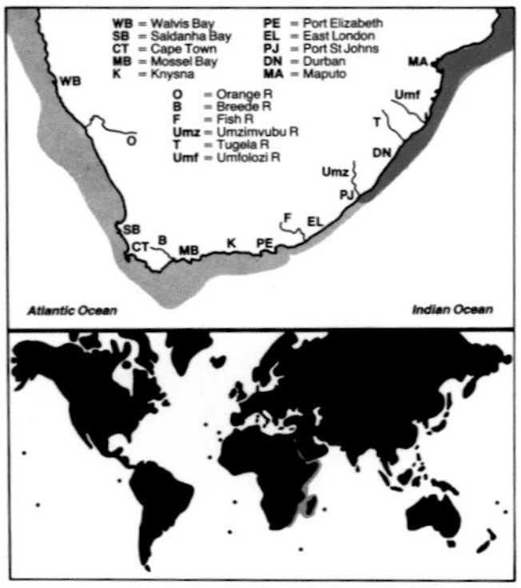

CAPTURE

The lemonfish is readily approached underwater and this makes it a relatively easy target for spearfishermen. Anglers have less success, probably because the fish appears reluctant to take large baits. Nevertheless, it is a fine sport fish and of excellent eating value. Juveniles are often maintained in aquaria, but soon outgrow the tank.
SA angling record – 2,8 kg.
SA spearfishing record – 4,4 kg.

SPECIFIC CATCH RESTRICTIONS

None.

NAME DERIVATION

Plectorhinchus, plaited snout; *flavomaculatus*, yellow spotted. Lemonfish, a reference to its yellow markings.

SIMILAR SPECIES

The golden-orange lines on the head and body are unique to this species, and should preclude misidentification, even in the case of larger fish.

Plectorhinchus playfairi

(Pellegrin, 1914)
Common name Worldwide – whitebarred rubberlip
[Smith 179□7]

IDENTIFYING FEATURES

COLOUR, SHAPE AND SIZE

This robust fish is unmistakably marked. Its overall body colour is dark bronze-brown, sometimes almost black, and three very distinct, white, vertical crossbars mark each flank. A fourth bar runs down the side of the head, in line with the hind edge of the gill openings. These markings contrast sharply when seen underwater, but in many instances become less distinct after death. The white crossbars also tend to be less obvious in very large individuals. Both the lips and the interior of the mouth are pink. The dorsal spines and the hind edge of the gill covers may be tipped with red. Can attain 90 cm in length.

EXTERNAL ANATOMY

About 60 series of small scales are arranged along the well-defined lateral line. The fins have strong spines and the dorsal consists of 12 spines plus 19-20 rays, while the anal has three spines plus seven rays. The caudal fin becomes increasingly emarginate with age, and the pectoral and pelvic fins are typically short. Both jaws are set with bands of fine, villiform teeth. Fleshy lips surround the mouth, and these thicken progressively with age. There are 30-34 stubby rakers on the first gill arch.

NATURAL HISTORY

This solitary fish occurs on rocky and coral reefs ranging in depth from the intertidal zone to 80 m. It is relatively common and its abundance remains constant throughout the year. The whitebarred rubberlip is most active during daylight when it can be seen searching for food either above, or along the edges of reefs. The diet comprises small invertebrate animals such as shrimps, marine worms, small crabs and, occasionally, the juveniles of other fish. Seen underwater, individuals are very conspicuous, but they are also wary and will seldom allow a diver to approach too closely. The life history of the species has not been studied, and consequently its breeding cycle is not known.

DISTRIBUTION

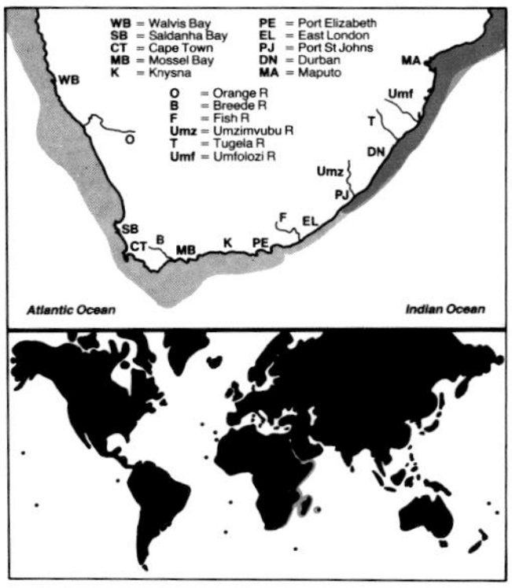

CAPTURE

Of the few whitebarred rubberlips caught by anglers, the majority have been landed along the Tongaland coast. Spearfishermen pay little attention to these fish, as most are too small to warrant interest. Nevertheless, their flesh is excellent, and they represent a valuable food resource, especially in more tropical regions.
SA angling record – 2,6 kg.
SA spearfishing record – 6,8 kg.

SPECIFIC CATCH RESTRICTIONS

None.

NAME DERIVATION

Plectorhinchus, plaited snout; *playfairi*, after the famous ichthyologist, Playfair. Whitebarred rubberlip, a reference to its distinctive markings and to its thick, fleshy lips.

SIMILAR SPECIES

The white bars across the almost black body are most distinctive, and make this species very easy to identify. This is especially evident underwater.

Plectorhinchus schotaf

(Forsskål, 1775)
Common names SA – minstrel.
Elsewhere – grey sweetlips
[Smith 179□8]

IDENTIFYING FEATURES

COLOUR, SHAPE AND SIZE

The robust and plain-coloured minstrel superficially resembles other *Plectorhinchus* species. The subtle details of its body colours and markings are, however, diagnostic. Live specimens are grey overall, but with bronze undertones, and occasionally the flanks are marked with three indistinct, pale, vertical crossbars. The underside is much paler. After death these subtle shades fade rapidly to a uniform, darker, dull grey overall. The interiors of the mouth and the gill covers are scarlet. Can attain 80 cm.

EXTERNAL ANATOMY

The lateral line is well defined, and along it are arranged about 55 series of scales. The fins have strong spines and include a single dorsal of 12 spines plus 19-21 rays, and an anal of three spines plus seven rays. Juveniles have a truncate caudal fin, but this becomes slightly emarginate with age. Both the pectoral and pelvic fins are rather short. Thick lips surround the mouth and these grow increasingly fleshy in older specimens. Bands of fine, villiform teeth occur in both jaws. Some 26-29 rakers are located on the first gill arch.

NATURAL HISTORY

This wide-ranging species is present throughout the year, and is probably the most common representative of the genus *Plectorhinchus* in southern Africa. Its range, however, does not extend as far south as that of the dusky rubberlip, and the minstrel is most common along the Zululand coast. Here it frequents coral and rocky reefs ranging from the surf zone to depths of 80 m. Its diet consists primarily of small, invertebrate organisms such as shrimps, crabs and marine worms, but small fish are also occasionally taken. Spawning occurs on offshore reefs, and the newly hatched young make their way into tidal rock pools, where they shelter until large enough to cope with deep-water conditions.

DISTRIBUTION

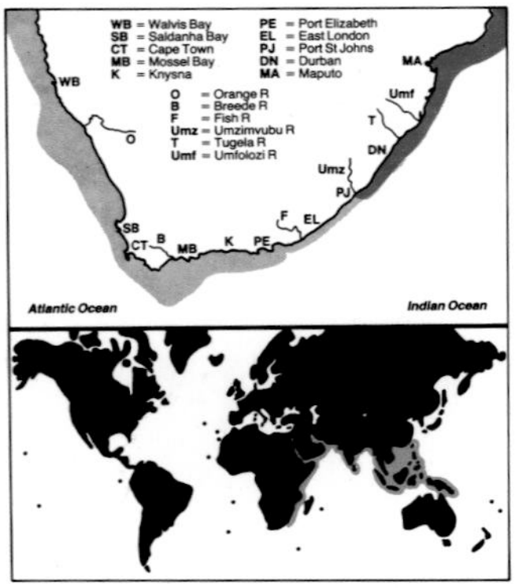

CAPTURE

Shore and ski-boat anglers occasionally land the minstrel, but most are bagged by spearfishermen. This is explained by the fact that, while the minstrel is often slow to take a bait, it is easily approached underwater. Throughout the Indo-Pacific it is valued as a source of food, and many catches are made in primitive fish traps.

SA angling record – 5,0 kg.
SA spearfishing record – 10,0 kg.

SPECIFIC CATCH RESTRICTIONS

None.

NAME DERIVATION

Plectorhinchus, plaited snout; *schotaf*, origin unknown. Minstrel, a reference to the croaking 'song' emitted by this fish.

SIMILAR SPECIES

The minstrel can be confused with several other rubberlips. It may be distinguished from the dusky rubberlip by its higher dorsal fin and gill raker counts. It also closely resembles the redlip rubberlip (*P. sordidus*) from which it may best be distinguished by the length of the soft dorsal fin base, which equals head length in *P. sordidus,* but is distinctly longer than head length in *P. schotaf.*

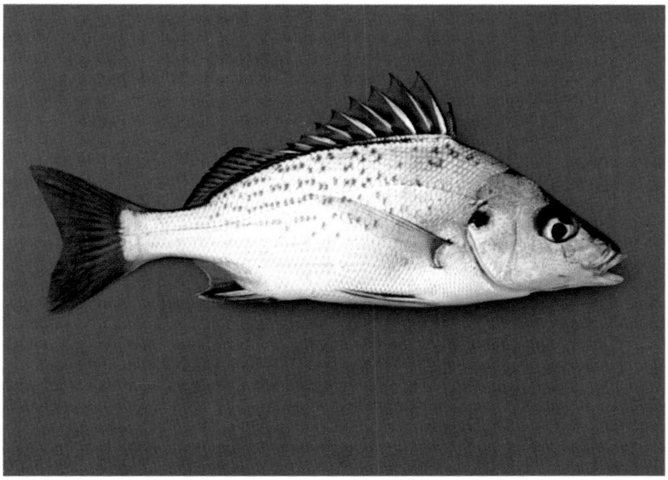

Pomadasys commersonni

(Lacepède, 1801)
Common names SA – spotted grunter. Elsewhere – small spotted grunt, javelin fish
[Smith 179□10]

IDENTIFYING FEATURES

COLOUR, SHAPE AND SIZE

This oblong, compressed fish has a long, sloping forehead and a pointed snout. The overall body colour is bright silver, with a distinct mother-of-pearl sheen on the upper flanks. The belly is pale. The flanks and the dorsal surface are covered with rows of small, dark-brown spots, which extend onto the dorsal fins, but not onto the head. A very distinct black blotch occurs on the gill covers. The fins are translucent or dusky. Though individuals can attain 80 cm, most average 40 cm.

EXTERNAL ANATOMY

Except for the snout, the entire body is covered with ctenoid scales arranged in 52-54 series along the lateral line. The fins are well developed and have prominent spines. The single dorsal fin has 11-12 spines plus 13-16 rays, while the anal has three spines plus 8-10 rays. The caudal fin is slightly forked. Thick lips surround the small mouth, which bears several rows of very fine teeth in each jaw. Tough, pharyngeal teeth occur on muscular pads in the gullet. There are about 22 long rakers on the first gill arch. The edge of the pre-operculum is exceptionally sharp.

NATURAL HISTORY

The spotted grunter inhabits shallow coastal regions, and is frequently found in the brackish water of estuaries or sheltered lagoons. It can tolerate fresh water. Using the pumping action of its large gill chambers 'in reverse', the spotted grunter forces a jet of water through the mouth to 'blow' prey such as worms, crabs, mud-prawns and cracker-shrimps from their burrows in the muddy sea-bed. Mole crabs (sea lice) and small bivalves are also eaten. This grunter is essentially a summer fish, and is most abundant in the Cape once summer water temperatures rise. Maturity is attained at a length of 40 cm, at a corresponding age of three years. Spawning occurs in the open sea during late winter. Both the newly hatched fry and the post-spawning adults make their way into estuaries to forage in the nutrient-rich waters of those regions. This partial dependence on estuaries may make the spotted grunter more vulnerable than most Haemulidae, as siltation, pollution and large-scale dredging degrades these delicate environments.

DISTRIBUTION

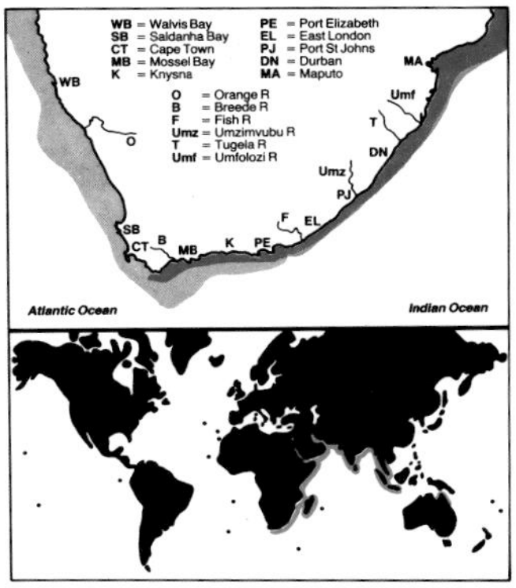

CAPTURE

Though not considered of commercial importance, irregular catches are trawled off East London and Port Elizabeth. The spotted grunter is an exceptionally fine table fish, and is much sought after by anglers. Most catches are landed either along sandy beaches or in estuaries, particularly at St Lucia which is famed for its summer grunter run. It is also frequently speared by divers.
SA angling record – 9,5 kg.
SA spearfishing record – 7,8 kg.

SPECIFIC CATCH RESTRICTIONS

Minimum legal size is 40 cm total length.

SIMILAR SPECIES

This species can be easily identified by the distinctive spots. The cock grunter has spots covering the head as well.

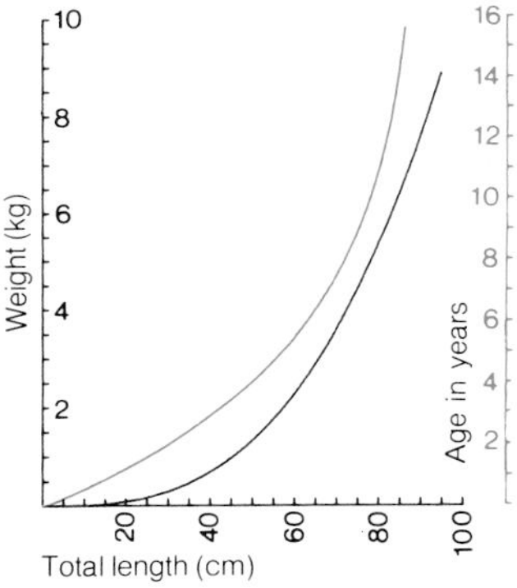

Pomadasys furcatum

(Bloch & Schneider, 1801)
Common name Worldwide – grey grunter
[Smith 179□11]

IDENTIFYING FEATURES

COLOUR, SHAPE AND SIZE

This deep-bodied grunter has a steep head profile and a noticeably short snout. The overall body colour is silvery, with six or seven darker, parallel stripes along the flanks. The fins are translucent or dusky. Though few exceed 30 cm, the grey grunter can attain 50 cm.

EXTERNAL ANATOMY

Ctenoid scales cover the body, and are arranged in 50-55 series along the distinct lateral line. The fins are well developed and spines are prominent. The dorsal fin has 12 strong spines followed by 14-16 rays, while the anal fin has three spines plus seven or eight rays. The caudal fin is almost truncate. The jaws of the small, terminal mouth bear several rows of minute teeth, while pharyngeal teeth occur in the gullet. The first gill arch has 12-15 rakers and the edge of the pre-operculum is strongly serrated.

DISTRIBUTION

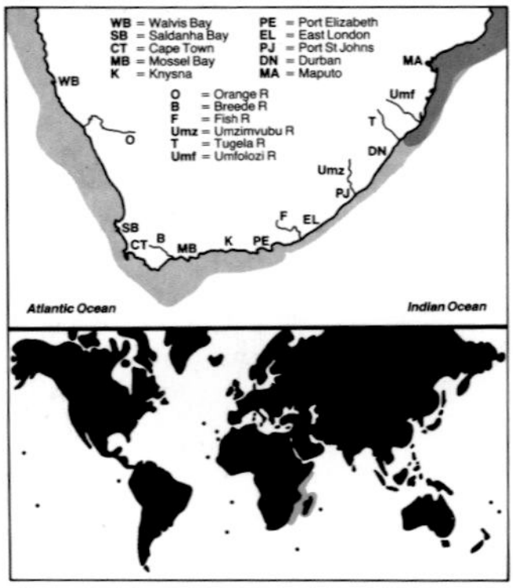

NATURAL HISTORY

This shallow-water, shoaling fish usually occurs over sandy patches lying between scattered reefs. It is especially common off the Zululand coast. Shoals are not large, however, and are often found in association with tasselfishes (*Umbrina sp.*). Small crabs, shrimps, polychaete worms and, occasionally, mole crabs (sea lice) constitute the diet. During feeding, the grey grunter 'blasts' the sandy sea-bed in the manner of other grunters. The prey thus disturbed is taken into the mouth along with quantities of sand, but before swallowing, the excess sand, as well as pieces of shell, are ejected through the gill openings. Sexual maturity is attained at about 20 cm, and 'ripe' female fish have been encountered during spring.

CAPTURE

The grey grunter makes good eating, and is best caught with light tackle using crayfish, prawn or mole crab as bait. However, it is not caught by sportfishermen as often as its relative abundance would suggest. It is easily approached by skindivers and is, therefore, potentially vulnerable to spearfishing; most are too small, however, to warrant great interest. To the indigenous coastal people of Tongaland and southern Moçambique, this species represents an important source of protein as it is prolific and can be easily caught with unsophisticated tackle.

SA angling record – 1,0 kg.

SPECIFIC CATCH RESTRICTIONS

None.

NAME DERIVATION

Pomadasys, rough operculum; *furcatum*, forked, a reference to the body stripes in juveniles being forked at the front end.

SIMILAR SPECIES

No other grunter has 6-7 longitudinal body stripes, though some may have less or more.

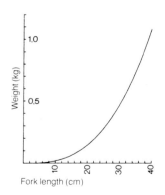

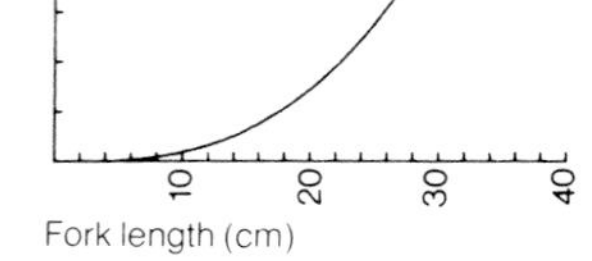

Pomadasys kaakan

(Cuvier, 1830)

Common names SA – javelin grunter, silver grunter. Elsewhere – javelin fish, banded grunt [Smith 179□13]

IDENTIFYING FEATURES

COLOUR, SHAPE AND SIZE

This oblong, compressed fish has a long, sloping forehead and a pointed snout. Individuals grow progressively more robust with age. The overall body colour is silvery, but olive green above and pale below. About five dark, broken bars run down each flank, although these disappear on larger fish. A dark blotch occurs on the gill covers. Can attain 75 cm, but smaller specimens are more common.

EXTERNAL ANATOMY

Ctenoid scales cover the body and are arranged in 43-47 series along the distinct lateral line. The fins are well developed and the spines are very strong. The dorsal fin comprises 12-18 spines plus 13-15 rays, and the anal fin has three spines plus seven or eight rays. Though small, the mouth has thickish lips and minute teeth set in each jaw. Toothed pharyngeal plates occur in the gullet. There are 15-18 moderate rakers on the first gill arch.

NATURAL HISTORY

The javelin grunter is common in shallow, coastal water, and frequently occurs in estuaries such as Richards Bay. However, it is equally at home on offshore banks, and may be found to depths of 75 m. This bottom-feeding species shows a great preference for small crabs and polychaete worms, and, in the manner of the previous species, it blasts them from their burrows with a jet of water ejected from the mouth at force. During feeding, quantities of fine mud are invariably ingested, but these are harmlessly passed as faeces. Juveniles feed extensively on small copepods. The javelin grunter is tolerant of moderate reductions in salinity. Also, its apparent ability to contend with muddy conditions undoubtedly benefits the young, as they are able to make use of turbid estuarine waters as nursery areas. Spawning takes place during winter, mostly in the vicinity of river mouths. Though adults are solitary for much of the year, shoals form during the breeding season.

DISTRIBUTION

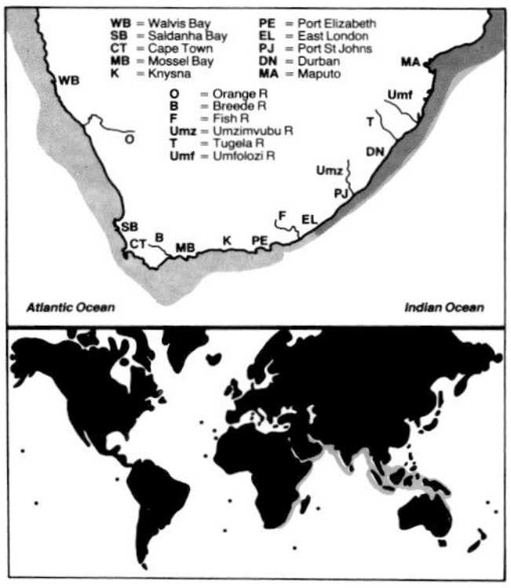

CAPTURE

The javelin grunter is not usually a target species, but anglers using light tackle and shrimp or mud-prawn as bait often land this fish, especially in the mouths of estuaries. It is a good source of bait for offshore fishermen. During the winter, when breeding shoals gather over offshore banks, this excellent table fish is landed in fair numbers by ski-boat anglers. It is not of spearfishing importance. SA angling record – 6,0 kg.

SPECIFIC CATCH RESTRICTIONS

None.

NAME DERIVATION

Pomadasys, rough operculum; *kaakan*, meaning obscure. Javelin grunter, a reference to its spear-shaped snout, and the croaking sounds emitted when landed.

SIMILAR SPECIES

This species closely resembles the saddle grunter, but lacks the obvious saddle-like mark across the nape.

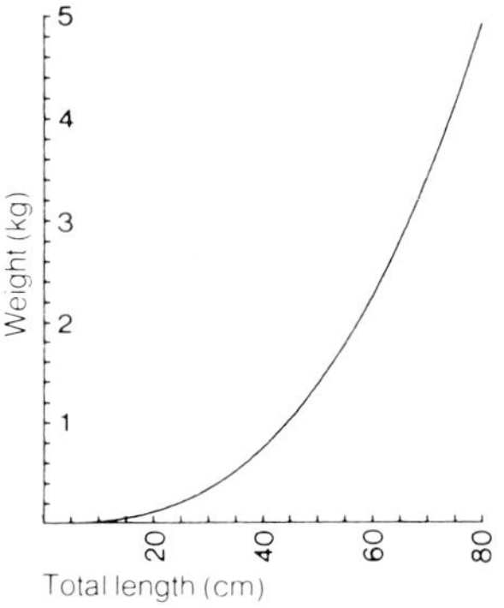

Pomadasys maculatum

Bloch 1797

Common names SA – saddle grunter. Elsewhere – blotched grunt [Smith 179□15]

IDENTIFYING FEATURES

COLOUR, SHAPE AND SIZE

This species is one of the smaller grunters, and, though it has the characteristic body shape of its close relatives, the head profile is more rounded and the snout is much shorter. The overall body colour is silvery-grey, and the belly is white. Dark, but incomplete, blotchy crossbars occur on the upper flanks and on the caudal peduncle, while the gill covers are marked with a less distinct spot. A conspicuous black patch straddles the dorsal spines. The fins are translucent and pale to dusky. Can attain 50 cm, but few specimens exceed 20 cm.

EXTERNAL ANATOMY

Ctenoid scales cover the body, and are arranged in 50-60 series along the lateral line. The fins are well developed and strongly spined. The single dorsal fin consists of 12 spines plus 14 or 15 rays, and the anal of three spines plus seven rays. The caudal fin is almost truncate. Several narrow bands of fine, pointed teeth are set in the jaws of the small, but thick-lipped mouth. Pharyngeal teeth are located in the gullet. There are some 18 stubby rakers on the first gill arch.

NATURAL HISTORY

The saddle grunter inhabits coastal waters, ranging to depths of 40 m. Though more common in tropical regions, it is fairly often also found as far south as Durban. It is gregarious, and large, loosely packed shoals gather over the sandy bottom along the edges of reefs. Bottom-living invertebrates make up the bulk of the diet which includes shrimps, small bivalve molluscs, polychaete worms and, occasionally, small fishes. Few saddle grunters have been found in estuaries and most seem rather intolerant of muddy water. The species' life history has not been well documented, but it appears that migrations to cooler waters take place in summer.

DISTRIBUTION

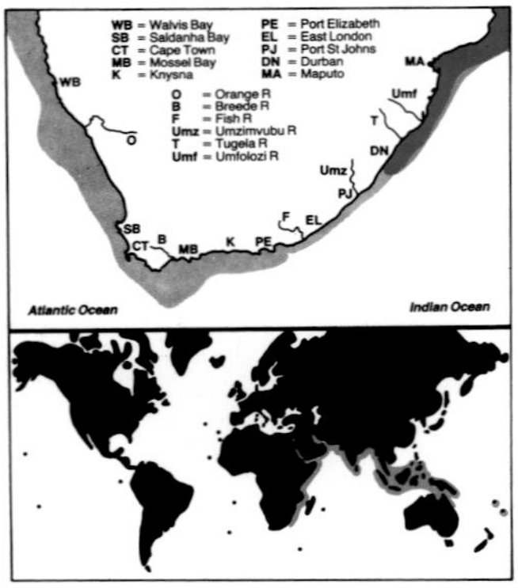

CAPTURE

Though easily hooked on light tackle, this fish is seldom the target of anglers. Its flesh is palatable, though most specimens are rather small for the table. It is not of spearfishing importance. In other parts of the world this fish represents a considerable food resource, and is either trawled or caught in traps. This grunter will thrive in a large aquarium.

SA angling record – vacant.

SPECIFIC CATCH RESTRICTIONS

None.

NAME DERIVATION

Pomadasys, rough operculum; *maculatum*, blotched. Saddle grunter, a reference to the blotch on the dorsal spines and to the fish's habit, in common with other grunters, of emitting croaking noises when landed.

SIMILAR SPECIES

The noticeably black saddle across the nape distinguishes the saddle grunter from the javelin grunter. Though its behaviour and habitat are similar to the piggy, the body patterns are quite different.

Pomadasys multimaculatum

(Playfair, 1866)
Common name Worldwide – cock grunter
[Smith 179□16]

IDENTIFYING FEATURES

COLOUR, SHAPE AND SIZE
This oblong and robust fish is not unlike the javelin grunter in profile, but because of its similar colour and markings, is more likely to be confused with the spotted grunter. It is silvery overall with a white belly, and there are numerous rows of dark-brown spots on the upper sides. Unlike the spotted grunter, however, these marks also extend onto the cheeks, forehead and snout. Can attain 75 cm.

EXTERNAL ANATOMY
Ctenoid scales cover the body, and are arranged in 49-54 series along the distinct lateral line. As with all grunters, the fins are well developed and spines are prominent. The dorsal fin has 12 stout spines plus 13 rays, while the anal fin has three spines plus seven rays. The caudal fin is slightly forked. Fleshy lips surround the small mouth, which bears minute villiform teeth in each jaw. Pharyngeal grinding teeth occur in the gullet. There are about 15 moderate rakers on the first gill arch, and the pre-operculum has a serrated edge.

NATURAL HISTORY

The distributions of this species and the very similar spotted grunter overlap to a large extent, but, in southern African waters, this species is less abundant. The two closely related species also share very similar behaviour. A bottom feeder, the cock grunter either blows or sucks its prey of small crabs, worms and bivalve molluscs from their muddy burrows in the sea-bed. The pharyngeal teeth in the throat are used to crush hard-shelled animals but, before swallowing the flesh, pieces of broken and empty shell are ejected through the gill openings. Virtually nothing is known of its life history, though sexually active specimens have been encountered in waters off Moçambique. The cock grunter appears to be equally at home in estuaries and along sandy beaches. It is, however, probably not very tolerant of temperature extremes and great variations in salinity. As with the other fish of this genus, captured individuals grind their pharyngeal teeth to produce a loud grunting noise.

DISTRIBUTION

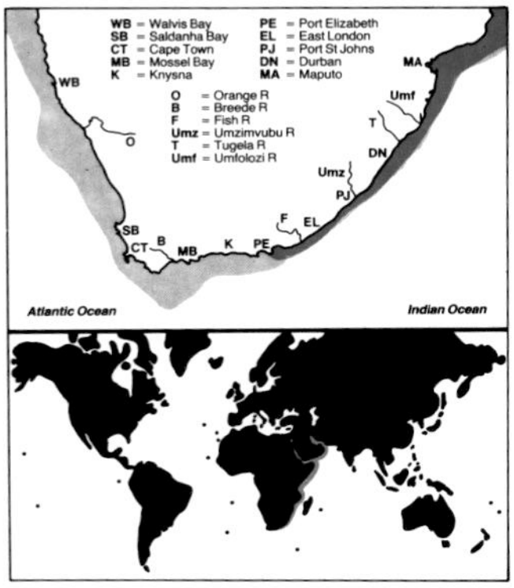

CAPTURE

The cock grunter is often caught amongst shoals of spotted grunter. It is popular with many anglers as it freely takes prawn or worm bait. In Moçambique, fishermen using trawl and seine nets land fair catches. Spearfishermen occasionally bag this exceptionally tasty fish.
SA angling record – 7,2 kg.
SA spearfishing record – 5,8 kg.

SPECIFIC CATCH RESTRICTIONS

None.

NAME DERIVATION

Pomadasys, rough operculum; *multimaculatum,* many spotted. Cock grunter, previous confusion with the spotted grunter led anglers to believe this was the male of the species, that is, the 'cock' fish.

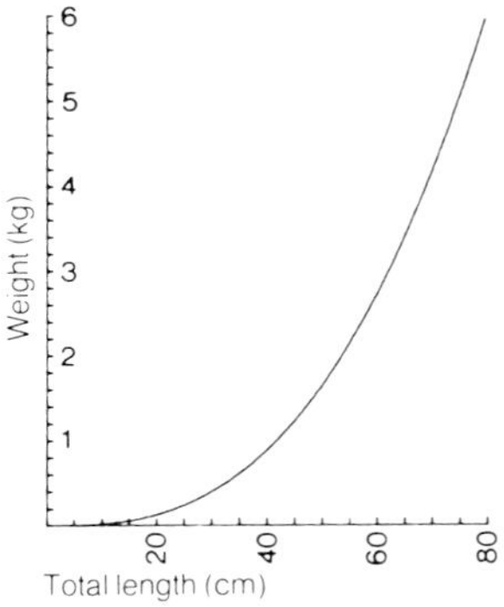

Pomadasys olivaceum

(Day, 1875)

Common names SA – piggy, pinky. Elsewhere – olive grunt

[Smith 179□17]

IDENTIFYING FEATURES

COLOUR, SHAPE AND SIZE

The piggy is one of the smallest and most elongate member of the genus *Pomadasys* and has a somewhat short snout. The overall body colour is silvery olive-grey, but pinkish above and pale below. There is a conspicuous black spot on the gill covers. The fins are translucent to dusky, but in living or freshly caught specimens are slightly yellowish. Although it can attain 25 cm, most inshore piggies do not exceed 15 cm.

EXTERNAL ANATOMY

Ctenoid scales cover the body and are arranged in some 54 series along the distinct lateral line. The fins are well developed and include a dorsal of 12 strong spines plus 15 or 16 rays, and an anal of one spine plus 11 or 12 rays. The eyes are relatively large when compared with those of other grunters. Several rows of fine, villiform teeth are set in the jaws of the small mouth, while pharyngeal grinding teeth occur in the gullet. There are about 13-15 rakers on the first gill arch and the edge of the pre-operculum is strongly serrated.

NATURAL HISTORY

This small fish occupies a most significant place in the foodweb. Young piggies occur in large shoals around shallow-water reefs, where they feed mainly on a small variety of shrimp which, in turn, feeds on the organic detritus that accumulates in these regions. During the course of the year, juvenile piggies consume vast quantities of this shrimp, together with small octopuses, polychaete worms and hydrozoa, before migrating to deeper offshore reefs where they mature. Thus, via a number of intermediate links, the detritus from shallow reefs is effectively transported to deep water. Here the piggy is heavily preyed upon by many pelagic fish and, particularly, dolphins. Hence, damage to the piggy's food-rich, reef environment could have far reaching consequences in terms of the greater foodweb. Sexual maturity occurs at a length of about 13 cm and spawning takes place in deep water virtually year-round. The juveniles then disperse to the very shallow coastal waters to perpetuate their role in the food cycle. These inshore shoals often become so densely packed that they literally form underwater 'clouds'.

DISTRIBUTION

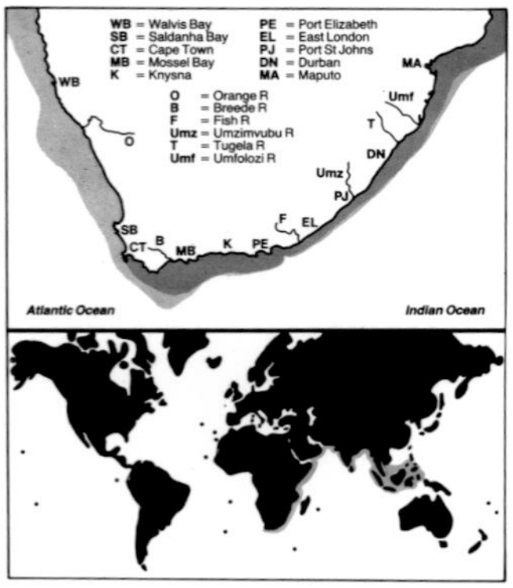

CAPTURE

Although the piggy is too small to be considered a sport fish, it is edible, and anglers' catches are large enough for it to consitute an important source of protein. It is also an ideal bait for larger fish such as elf, garrick and kob. This fish has no commercial or spearfishing value.

SA angling record – 0,3 kg.

SPECIFIC RESTRICTIONS

None.

NAME DERIVATION

Pomadasys, rough operculum; *olivaceum,* olive coloured. Piggy, literally, a small grunter; Pinky, a reference to the pinkish colour which mantles the dorsal surface of live specimens.

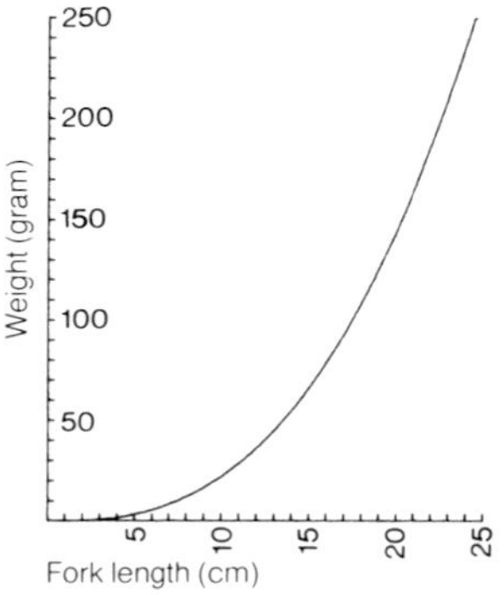

Pomadasys striatum

(Gilchrist & Thompson, 1908)
Common name Worldwide – striped grunter
[Smith 179□18]

IDENTIFYING FEATURES

COLOUR, SHAPE AND SIZE

The striped grunter is more elongate than most Haemulidae, and has an evenly rounded dorsal profile which lacks the distinctive 'pitch' of related species. The overall colour is silvery brown, and the belly is white. There are three, very distinct, dark-brown stripes along the upper flanks, the lowest passing directly through the eye. The fins are translucent, but the anal may be yellowish. Can attain 22 cm in length.

Note: Previously this and three other South African grunter species belong to genus *Rhonciscus*. Recent studies place these fish now in the genus *Pomadasys*. They can be immediately recognized by their longitudinal stripes. Their rather secretive habits have led to the popular misconception that these fishes are rare.

EXTERNAL ANATOMY

Ctenoid scales cover the body, and are arranged in some 50-55 series along the lateral line. A number of scales on the lower flanks run obliquely upwards. The fins are well developed and have prominent spines. The dorsal fin has 12 spines plus 13 or 14 rays, while the anal has three spines plus six or seven rays. The caudal fin is slightly forked. Minute teeth occur in the small, terminal mouth, and pharyngeal teeth are located in the gullet. The first gill arch has about 18 rakers and the pre-operculum is strongly serrated.

NATURAL HISTORY

A common fish of quiet bays and protected rocky shores, the striped grunter swims in small shoals over the sandy bottom between scattered reefs. Here it feeds primarily on small crustaceans, especially the shrimps and crabs that inhabit reef edges. Its feeding strategy is similar to that of other grunters and involves 'blasting' these tiny food items from their burrows by directing a powerful jet of water through the mouth at the sandy sea-bed. It is not found in estuaries and is, therefore, probably intolerant of turbid water and extremes in salinity. Details of its life history have not been investigated and, consequently, little is known of its breeding cycle and growth rate.

DISTRIBUTION

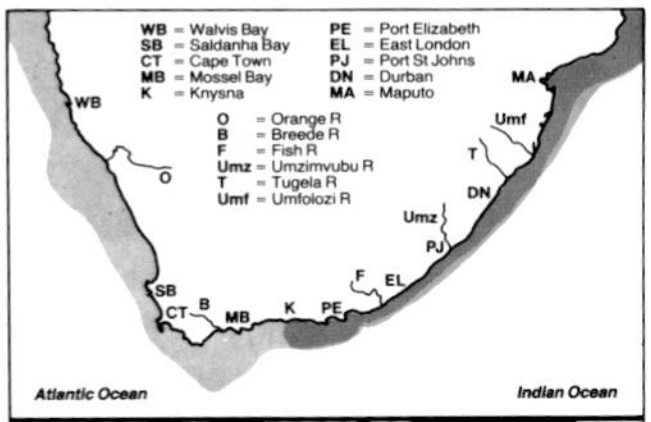

CAPTURE

Reports by divers indicate that this fish occurs in fair abundance, but it is rarely caught by anglers. Small flesh baits on light tackle are likely to be most successful. Though edible, the striped grunter is generally too small to be of great angling importance.

SA angling record – vacant.

SPECIFIC CATCH RESTRICTIONS

None.

NAME DERIVATION

Pomadasys, rough operculum; *striatum*, striped. Striped grunter, a reference to its body colours and to its habit, as with other Haemulidae, of emitting loud grunting noises when landed.

SIMILAR SPECIES

While the three stripes are an important feature, care should be taken not to confuse this species with the lined grunter *(P. stridens)* which does not have a stripe passing through the eye, but does have a distinct opercular blotch.

Hemiramphus far

(Forsskål, 1775)
Common name Worldwide - spotted halfbeak
[Smith 115□2]

IDENTIFYING FEATURES

COLOUR, SHAPE AND SIZE
This fish has an elongate, almost cylindrical body. The very long, beak-like lower jaw tapers to a fine point which accentuates the fish's needle-like appearance. The general body colour is green above and white below. Though not always obvious, four large, dark spots usually occur along the flanks. The caudal fin appears dusky and the upper lobe is tinged with yellow. When viewed underwater, however, the caudal fin has a brilliant blue appearance. The tip of the black beak is orange-red. Can attain 35 cm.
Note: Internal colouration is distinctive: the bones and vertebrae are bright blue and the lining of the gut cavity is black.

EXTERNAL ANATOMY
The body is covered with thin, but distinct scales arranged in 50-60 series along the lateral line. The spineless dorsal and anal fins, as well as the pelvics, are set far back on the body. The dorsal and anal fins have 13-15 and 11-13 rays respectively. The lower lobe of the forked caudal fin is the longer. The small mouth bears very fine teeth, and the lower jaw extends well beyond the upper, and represents 20 per cent of the total body length. There are about 27 long rakers on the first gill arch.
Note: The air bladder, revealed if the fish is gutted, is divided into many separate compartments.

NATURAL HISTORY

This common, shallow-water shoaling fish often occurs in the lee of reefs, and, though it has been recorded from estuaries, it is not tolerant of salinity changes. (The smaller halfbeaks that live in harbours and coastal lakes are members of the genus *Hyporhamphus*). The proximity of the anal and dorsal fins to the caudal, gives greater 'lift' and enables the spotted halfbeak to 'skip' along the surface, either when chased by a predator or when disturbed by a vessel. The diet consists of floating plant and animal food, which is gathered by raising the short upper beak so as to skim the water's surface. Small shrimps, mantis shrimps, crab larvae and sometimes insects and their larvae are eaten. During the spawning season, females produce large eggs which have adhesive filaments by means of which they attach to floating objects and seaweed. Details of juvenile dispersal are scant. Sexual maturity is attained at a length of 25 cm.

DISTRIBUTION

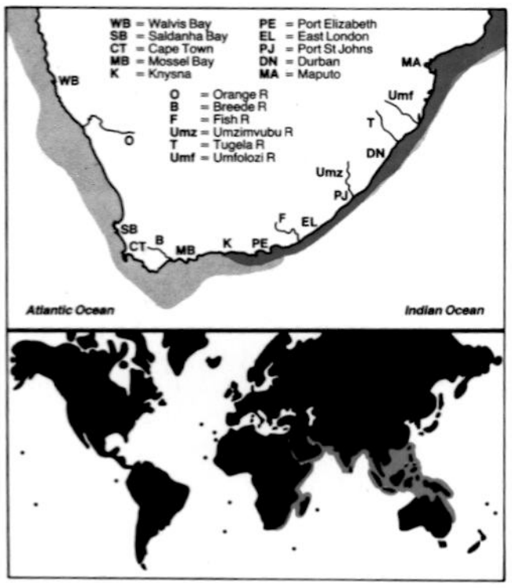

CAPTURE

Anglers using minute pieces of bait on ultra-light tackle may succeed in hooking the spotted halfbeak. Large numbers are netted in various parts of the world and many are caught at night after being attracted to lights suspended over the water. It is of good eating quality. If carefully prepared, this species also makes an ideal bait for large game fish such as marlin and, in Florida in the United States, thousands are rigged for this purpose each year.
SA angling record - 0.5 kg.

SPECIFIC CATCH RESTRICTIONS

None.

NAME DERIVATION

Hemiramphus, half beak; *far,* long. Spotted halfbeak, a reference to the black markings on the flanks and to the extended lower jaw.

SIMILAR SPECIES

The short, triangular upper, and elongate lower jaw are distinctive of all but one of the six species in this family. This species can be distinguished from the smaller *hyporhamphus* species by its scaleless upper jaw and alveolar air bladder.

Myripristis murdjan

(Forsskål, 1775)

Common names SA – blotcheye soldier. Elsewhere – bigeye squirrelfish, crimson squirrelfish [Smith 132□26]

IDENTIFYING FEATURES

COLOUR, SHAPE AND SIZE

The blotcheye soldier is a small, oblong fish with a pointed snout. The general body colour is red, with a blackish edge to the gill covers and a dark blotch just above the pupil of each large eye. The soft dorsal, anal, pelvic and caudal fins are a darker red and edged in white, while the pectoral fins are translucent pink. Attains 25 cm.

EXTERNAL ANATOMY

The body is covered with rough, ctenoid scales arranged in 27-32 series along the lateral line. The fins are well developed and include a dorsal of 11 spines plus 13-15 rays, an anal of four spines plus 11-13 rays, and a forked caudal. There is also a single, sharp spine on each gill cover. Rows of fine teeth occur in both jaw. There are a number of short, spiky rakers on the first gill arch.

DISTRIBUTION

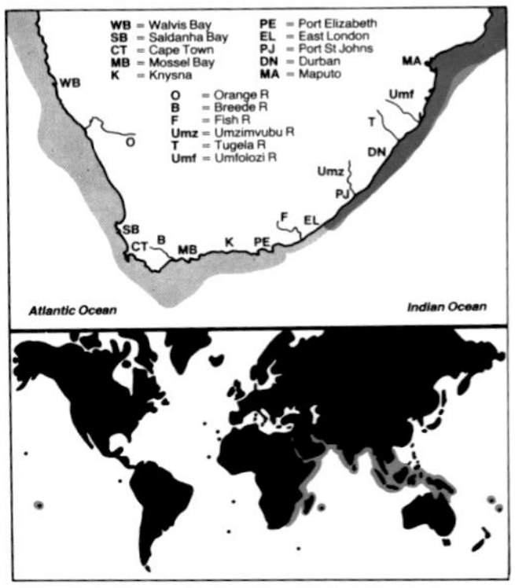

NATURAL HISTORY

This cave-dweller of tropical and subtropical regions often occurs in small groups or shoals, and, though common around shallow reefs it has also been recorded from deeper waters. Like the previous species, it is primarily nocturnal, and during daylight it can only be found at the back of deep, dark caves or below rocky ledges. Within 30 minutes after sunset, blotch eye soldiers emerge from their hiding places and congregate directly above the reef. From here they disperse towards the open sea, the darker the night, the greater the extent of the migration. In these offshore waters, feeding commences. These fish prey extensively on megalopa crab larvae, shrimps, mysids, juvenile fish, polychaete worms, mantis shrimps and krill. The large eyes suggest good vision in low light levels, undoubtedly a useful adaptation to nocturnal foraging habits. Some 40 minutes before sunrise these soldierfishes reassemble, and within ten minutes all have taken refuge within their daytime shalters. Colouration also changes with the onset of darkness, and the deep-red body described above, becomes somewhat silvery overall. This species is known to spawn on reefs, but the juveniles are widely distributed by ocean currents. Further details of the breeding cycle remain undocumented.

CAPTURE

The blotcheye soldier is seldom caught by anglers or spearfishermen, but is often captured for marine aquaria. It will thrive in a tank, provided low-intensity lighting is installed. The flesh is palatable and in Hawaii is considered a delicacy.

SA angling record – 0,2 kg.

SPECIFIC CATCH RESTRICTIONS

None.

NAME DERIVATION

Myripristis, a myriad of spines: *murdjan,* from the Gothic *maurthrjan,* meaning murderer. Blotcheye soldier, a reference to its dark eye-patch and well-armed spiny body.

SIMILAR SPECIES

The blotcheye soldier is best distinguished from the other soldierfishes in southern African waters by its white-edged fins, slightly projecting lower jaw and red dorsal fin.

Sargocentron diadema

(Lacepède, 1801)
Common name Worldwide - crown squirrelfish
[Smith 132□6]

IDENTIFYING FEATURES

COLOUR, SHAPE AND SIZE
The crown squirrelfish is a small, oblong fish with a pointed snout. The general body colour is red and there are about 8-12 horizontal white lines along the flanks and on the head. The first dorsal fin is red with white tips, while the other fins are translucent pink. Attains 20 cm.

EXTERNAL ANATOMY
The body is covered with rough, conspicuous scales arranged in 46-50 series along the lateral line. The fins are well developed, and the spines are prominent. The double dorsal fin consists of 12 spines plus 11-14 rays, and the anal fin has four spines plus 8-10 rays. The caudal fin is forked. Spines also occur on the gill covers, the longest reaching the gill opening. Rows of small teeth occur in both jaws, and the large eyes have conspicuous black pupils. There are 16-19 rakers on the first gill arch, but most are poorly developed.

NATURAL HISTORY

This species is common in shallow, tropical seas, and is generally confined to caves and reef overhangs. As its large eyes suggest, the crown squirrelfish's vision adapts well to low light-levels. Not surprisingly, therefore, its habits are mainly nocturnal, and it will only emerge from hiding under cover of darkness when it feeds on the small crabs, shrimps and other crustaceans common on coral reefs. The large pre-opercular spine can inflict deep cuts on careless handlers and these wounds are aggravated if the fish's body mucus enters the wound. This squirrelfish, and close relatives, are known to make audible sounds during displays of aggression and courtship, probably a form of territorial behaviour. Spawning occurs over reefs, but the exceptionally spiny young may be found scattered in open waters.

DISTRIBUTION

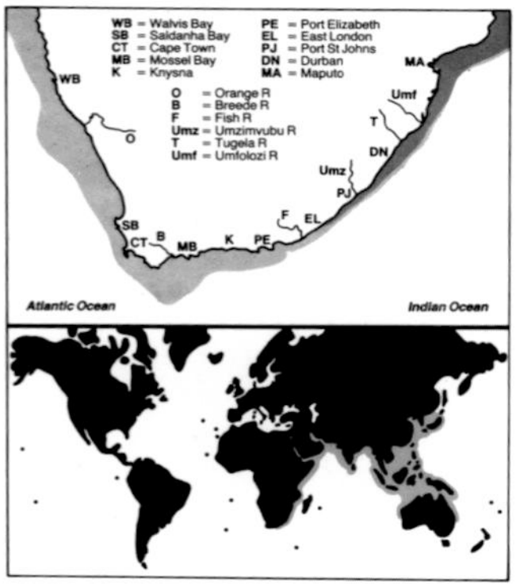

CAPTURE

Though occasionally caught by ski-boat fishermen, it is not considered to be of angling or spearfishing importance, despite its good eating quality. Many specimens have been kept successfully in aquaria where the light level has been held low to prevent damage to the eyes.

NAME DERIVATION

Sargocentron, plated scales; *diadema,* crown. Crown squirrelfish, a reference to the white band along the dorsal fin, and an allusion to its cave-dwelling habits, as in the case of true squirrels.

SPECIFIC CATCH RESTRICTIONS

None.

SIMILAR SPECIES

There are a great variety of squirrelfishes in the region but none have the distinctive markings of this species. The absence of conspicuous black marks, the characteristic fin colouration and the high scale count are important aids to identification.

Istiophorus platypterus

(Shaw & Nodder, 1791)
Common name Worldwide – sailfish
[Smith 252□1]

IDENTIFYING FEATURES

COLOUR, SHAPE AND SIZE
The sailfish is a streamlined, graceful fish, elongate and compressed with a long, spear-like snout. Its elegant lines are enhanced by its metallic-blue body and cobalt-blue sail dotted with black markings. There may also be a number of lighter or grey, vertical bars on the flanks, but these and other colours and markings will most likely disappear after death. Can attain 300 cm.

EXTERNAL ANATOMY
A tough, hide-like skin covers the body, and the pointed scales are well embedded. The sail-like dorsal fin is very distinctive, and, when raised, forms a high crest which runs the greater length of the body. Of the 40-47 dorsal rays, those in the middle are longest. There is also a small second dorsal fin of 6-8 rays, as well as two anal fins of 8-14 and 5-8 rays respectively. The large caudal fin is sickle-shaped. The pectoral fins have 17-20 rays and the thin, retractable pelvic fins exceed the length of the pectorals, and are longer than those of most other billfish species. The long bill is round in cross-section, and the mouth has very fine, rasp-like teeth. No rakers are on the gill arches.

NATURAL HISTORY

This striking, pelagic fish is generally found near land masses, but is known to migrate great distances. One tagged specimen travelled 3 000 kilometres in six months, and it is probable that such long-distance movements are related to spawning and feeding. Countless food items have been recorded from the stomachs of landed specimens. Prominent among these are small fish species which often live in association with flotsam. Small tuna, mackerel, mullet and anchovies are also important items of diet, as are various species of squid and cuttlefish. Feeding occurs during daylight, often only after 09h00, and may involve 'balling the bait', whereby prey is herded into a tight, round shoal. Though most are observed near the surface over the continental shelf, sailfish have been recorded to depths of 160 m. Many are found singly, but loose shoals of three to 30 individuals may form during the afternoon in some regions, especially if fodder fish are present. This great, leaping fish shows bursts of speed during feeding. These, however, are slower than the 'sprints' of other billfish. The main breeding season is during summer, and larval sailfish have been recorded during the period January-April. Females tend to be slightly predominant, and maturity is attained at a length of 150 cm, corresponding to an age of three years. The growth rate is high and few reach ten years.

CAPTURE

This is the billfish most commonly caught by southern African anglers. It freely takes trolled lures as well as whole, or strip bait. Many are caught close to the edges of reefs, but also occasionally from the shore. Despite tiring rapidly during capture, released or tagged specimens have a high survival rate. Sailfish are rarely speared. The flesh makes good eating.
World angling record – 100,2 kg.
SA angling record – 64,9 kg.
SA spearfishing record – 50,8 kg.

DISTRIBUTION

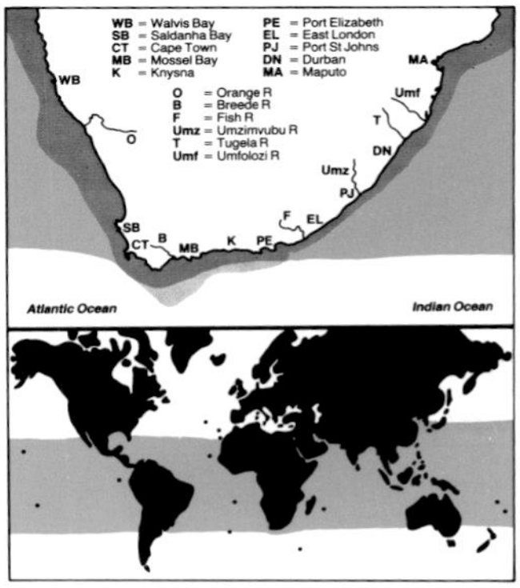

SPECIFIC CATCH RESTRICTIONS

Open species.

NAME DERIVATION

Istiophorus, to bear a sail; *platypterus,* flat wings. Sailfish, a reference to the sail-like dorsal fin.

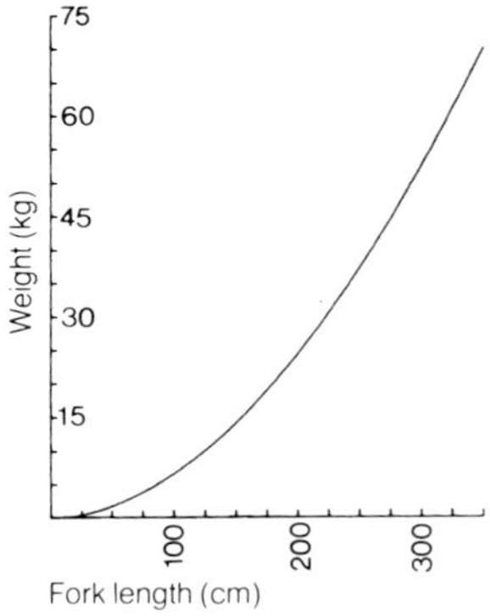

Makaira indica

(Cuvier, 1831)

Common name Worldwide - black marlin

[Smith 252□2]

IDENTIFYING FEATURES

COLOUR, SHAPE AND SIZE

Although robust, this species is long and well streamlined, with a steep forehead and a long, sharp, spear-like snout. In live specimens, the overall body colour is metallic blue-black and the belly is white, but the fish rapidly changes to an overall deep black once landed. Can attain 400 cm.

EXTERNAL ANATOMY

Thin, thorn-like scales cover the body, but are embedded in the tough skin. A single, lateral line is present, but this is only visible once the skin has been removed and dried. Though tall, the height of the dorsal fin in front measures less than the distance between the pectoral fin base and the base of the dorsal fin. The fins have no spines: the two separate dorsal fins consist of 38-42 rays and six or seven rays respectively, while the two anal fins consist of 13 or 14 rays and six or seven rays. The rigid pectoral fins have 19 or 20 rays, project at right angles to the body and cannot be folded against the flanks, as with those of other members of the family. The caudal fin is large and the characteristic sickle-shape is pronounced. The stout bill is almost circular in cross-section, and is just shorter than the head length. Small, rasp-like teeth occur in the large mouth. Rakers are absent on the gill arches.

NATURAL HISTORY

This enormous, highly migratory and pelagic species, ranges freely across vast stretches of ocean, and is probably the most common marlin in southern African waters. This fast predator will eat virtually any fish, especially tuna, bonito, kingfish, dolphinfish, rainbow runner, yellowtail and squid. Much of the prey is slashed with, or impaled by, the rough bill. Although popularly believed to be a surface fish, most commercial catches are made at depths from 400-1000 m. The black marlin is normally solitary, but at certain times loose shoals may form. Notwithstanding Japanese long-line records, which indicate an increased abundance during July and August along the East Coast, anglers catches have been most intense during November-February, especially at Sodwana Bay. There appears to be a very great predominance of females, seven to one in some regions, but the reasons for this seeming imbalance still require clarification. The length at which spawning begins varies according to sex; most females exceed 200 kg by their first breeding season. The young initially have no bill and are distributed by ocean currents.

DISTRIBUTION

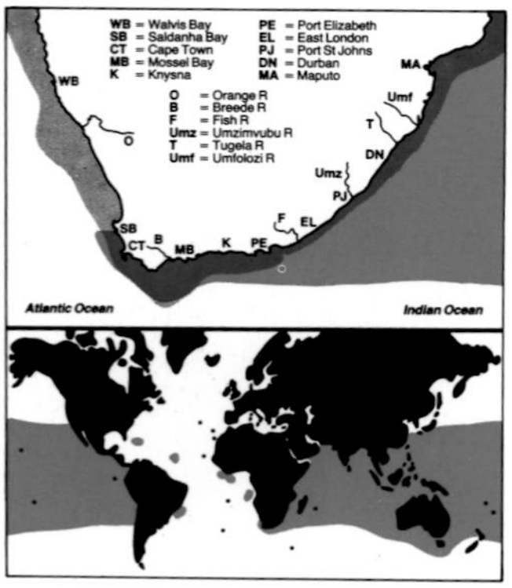

CAPTURE

Whereas this prized gamefish can be caught by deep-sea anglers using lures, the biggest catches are invariably made on well-prepared tuna baits and outriggers. Only the best spearfishermen succeed in landing black marlin. More and more game fishermen are tagging and releasing marlin. Worldwide annual commercial exploitation totals about 3000 tonnes. The flesh can be prepared smoked, fresh, or raw as in sashimi.

World angling record – 707,6 kg.
SA angling record – 354,2 kg.
SA spearfishing record – 238,0 kg.

SPECIFIC CATCH RESTRICTIONS

Open species.

NAME DERIVATION

Makaira, marlin; *indica,* black. Black marlin, a reference to its colour and to its bill which resembles a marlin-spike, an instrument used in splicing rope.

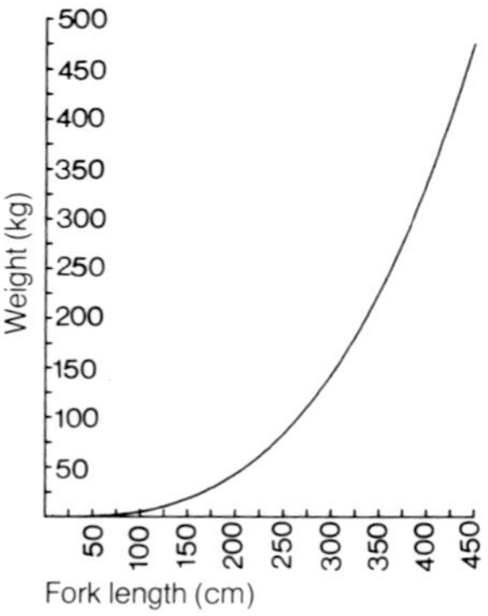

Makaira mazara

(Jordan & Snyder, 1901)
Common name Worldwide – Indo-Pacific blue marlin
[Smith 252□3]

IDENTIFYING FEATURES

COLOUR, SHAPE AND SIZE

This robust, but long and streamlined fish is oval in cross-section. The forehead is not as steep as that of the black marlin, but the bill is just as sharp and stout. The general body colour of live specimens is cobalt-blue above, with a white belly, and faint vertical bars on the flanks. After death, the body turns a slate grey. Attains 400 cm.

EXTERNAL ANATOMY

The body is covered with a tough skin, embedded in which are long, thin, thornlike scales. The lateral line is complex, and consists of a series of loops, but this is only visible if the skin is removed and dried. The dorsal fin is higher in front than that of the previous species, and equal to or exceeding the distance from the pectoral fin base to the base of the dorsal fin. Spines are absent. The double dorsal fin consists of 39-45 rays plus six or seven rays, and the double anal fin has 14-17 rays plus 6-8 rays. The large caudal fin is sickle-shaped. Both pectoral fins have 20-22 rays, and can be easily folded back against the sides. The bill is slightly oval in cross-section, and is approximately as long as the head. The mouth bears fine, rasp-like teeth. There are no gill rakers.

NATURAL HISTORY

This wide-ranging blue marlin does not form shoals, but extensive migrations take place, often between the tropics of the northern and southern hemispheres. Hopefully, tagging studies will help to explain this behaviour more fully. Japanese long-line fishermen claim this to be the largest of the billfish, especially the females, which are larger than the males, but less frequently caught. According to commercial catch statistics, July marks its period of peak abundance off the East Coast. This pelagic predator feeds extensively on shoaling gamefish such as tuna, bonito and dolphinfish, as well as on squid. The actual composition of the diet varies between regions, and depends on the feeding depth. Occasionally, reef fish are eaten, and feeding is known to occur during the day, primarily between 10h00 and 11h00. The size at which maturity is attained ranges from 35-44 kg in males and 47-61 kg in females.
There are distinct breeding populations, and spawning occurs between 30° N and 30° S, especially during the summer, when larvae of 0,3-5,2 cm are often found in ocean currents. Specific spawning grounds, however, have yet to be identified. Blue marlin have a moderate growth rate and they can live for about fifteen years.

DISTRIBUTION

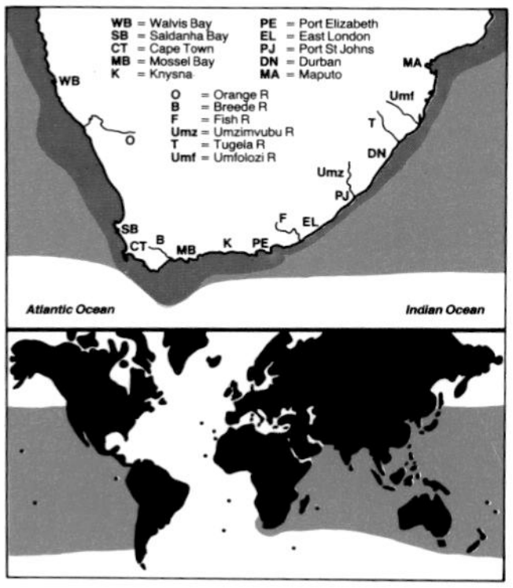

SPECIFIC CATCH RESTRICTIONS

Open Species.

CAPTURE

Many trolled baits have proved successful in attracting blue marlin, but these should be rigged professionally to ensure success. These baits include mackerel, mullet, tuna, bonito, and garfish, but artificial lures or strip bait may also be used. This superb angling fish makes excellent eating, and in Japan the flesh is often prepared raw as sashimi, a traditional dish. The total annual commercial catch is 25 000 tonnes worldwide.
World angling record – 624,1 kg.
SA angling record – 258,6 kg.
SA spearfishing record – 21,8 kg.

NAME DERIVATION

Makaira, marlin; *mazara,* meaning obscure. Blue marlin, a reference to its overall body colour and its bill, which resembles a marlin spike.

SIMILAR SPECIES

This fish was only recently recognized as being distinct from the Atlantic blue *(M. nigricans),* hence some of the notes may not apply to both species.

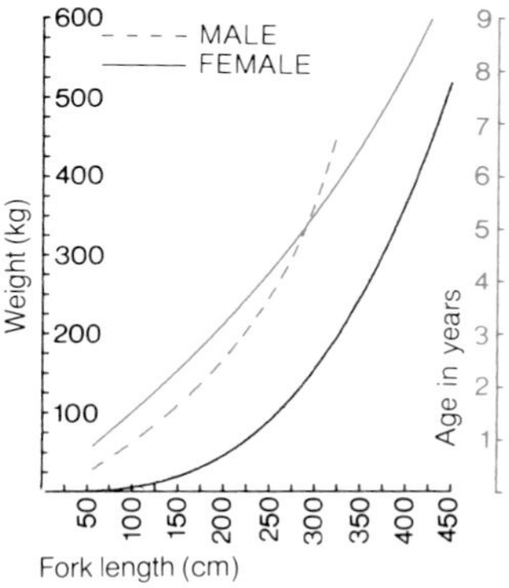

Tetrapturus audax

(Philippi, 1887)

Common name Worldwide – striped marlin

[Smith 252□6]

IDENTIFYING FEATURES

COLOUR, SHAPE AND SIZE

This long, streamlined fish is oval in cross-section, but is noticeably more sleek and compressed than either the blue or the black marlin. The general body colour is cobalt-blue and black with definite, lighter vertical stripes. After death, this bright colouration invariably fades to an overall dark grey, but the stripes remain visible. Can attain 320 cm in length.

EXTERNAL ANATOMY

The body is densely covered with pointed scales that are well embedded in the tough skin. Although a single lateral line is present, this can only be seen once the skin has been removed and dried. The first dorsal fin of 37-42 rays is pointed, and the height in front is equal to the body depth. The second dorsal fin has six rays, and the double anal fin has 13-18 plus five or six rays. The caudal fin is sickle-shaped, and stout keels occur on either side of the peduncle. The pectorals, each with 18-22 rays, can be folded flat against the body. The long bill is equal to 1,01-1,14 times the head length and is almost round in cross-section. The mouth carries fine, file-shaped teeth in each jaw. There are no rakers on the gill arches.

NATURAL HISTORY

This swift predator embarks on considerable seasonal migrations during the winter months, when there is a tendency to move towards the equator. In December and January the reverse occurs, and populations disperse north and southwards. A day-time feeder, the diet of the striped marlin is wide and varied, and includes small shoaling fish such as anchovies, sardines, mackerel and flying fish, as well as squid. Spawning takes place from October to December, and larvae have been recorded between 10 and 20°S. Maturity is attained at 180-200 cm. The overall sex ratio is 1:1, but males tend to predominate in individual spawning groups. Though many are caught in relatively shallow coastal waters, striped marlin are known to range down to the thermocline in oceanic regions.

DISTRIBUTION

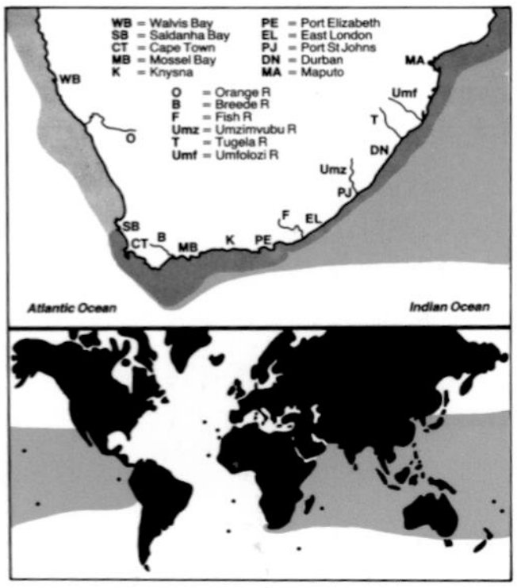

CAPTURE

The striped marlin is one of the most superb fighting fish, and its incredible leaping abilities have led some game fishermen to claim that once hooked it spends more time in the air than in the water! It is also renowned for its 'lighting up' colouration during capture. Trolling a strip or whole bait, or a lure are effective methods of attracting this fish. Its red flesh is the least palatable of billfish meat, but it is nevertheless quite edible and of great commercial importance. About 13 000 tons are taken from the world's oceans each year.

World angling record – 224,1 kg.

SA angling record – 91,2 kg.

SPECIFIC CATCH RESTRICTIONS

Open species.

NAME DERIVATION

Tetrapturus, four-winged tail, a reference to the wing-like caudal keels; *audax,* bold. Striped marlin, a reference to its unmistakable lateral stripes, and to its bill which resembles a marlin-spike, a pointed tool used in splicing rope.

SIMILAR SPECIES

Frequently confused with the blue marlin, the striped marlin's dorsal fin height is approximately equal to its body depth. In both blue and black marlins the dorsal fin height is much less than the body depth.

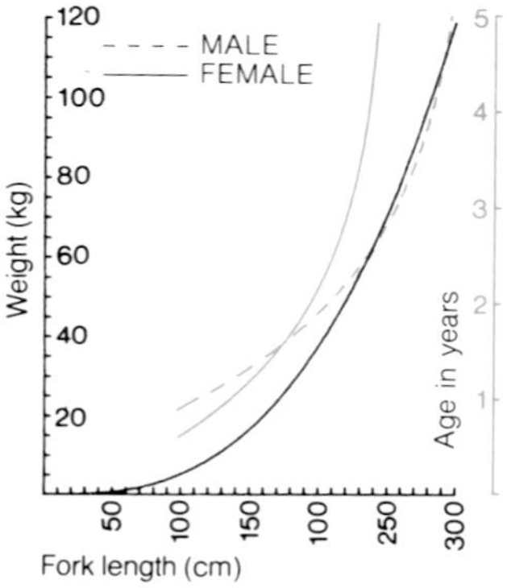

Kuhlia mugil

(Schneider, 1801)
Common name Worldwide – barred flagtail
[Smith 164□1]

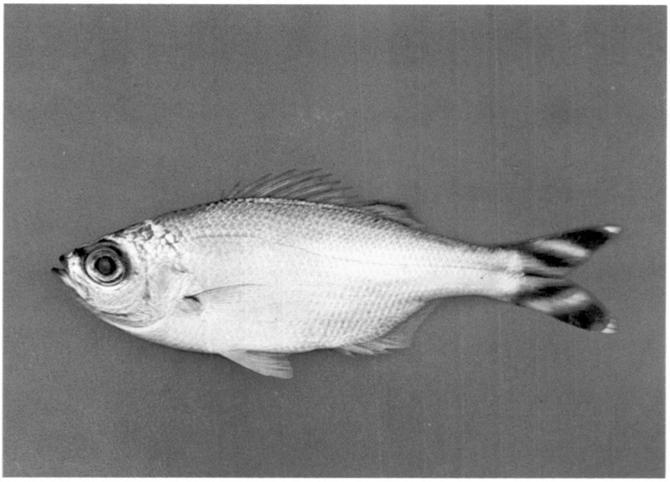

IDENTIFYING FEATURES

COLOUR, SHAPE AND SIZE

The barred flagtail is a small, but fairly robust fish. The general body colour is bright silver, but blue-grey above and white below. The caudal fin has five dark stripes, and each lobe has a distinct, white tip. Can attain 20 cm.

EXTERNAL ANATOMY

The body is covered with ctenoid scales arranged in 50-55 series along the lateral line. The bridge between the large eyes, however, is scaleless. The single dorsal fin consists of ten spines plus 9-11 rays, and the anal consists of three spines plus 9-11 rays. There is a deep indentation between the spines and rays of the dorsal fin. The caudal fin is slightly forked. The lateral line is conspicuous, and two distinct spines occur on the gill covers. Bands of very fine teeth occur in the jaws, and the first gill arch carries approximately 26 rakers.

Note: There has been considerable debate about the evolutionary position of fishes in this family, but the presence of spines on the gill covers, and other anatomical features, suggest a fairly close relationship to the rockcods (family Serranidae).

NATURAL HISTORY

The barred flagtail is most abundant in shallow tropical waters and is occasionally recorded from relatively salt-free estuaries. Juveniles are particularly common in intertidal pools, which serve as nursery areas, while larger fish live in slightly deeper water. Adults are mainly nocturnal in habit, and, after their nightly forays, shoals congregate for the day in the sheltered lee of reefs. The diet consists mainly of free-swimming crustaceans such as megalopa crab larvae, mantis shrimps and krill, but sometimes small fish are also eaten. The barred flagtail is an inquisitive fish, and will readily accept food from divers. This shoaling species is known to spawn along the Natal Coast throughout the year, a fact indicated by the permanent abundance of juvenile fish. Little else of its life history has been documented.

DISTRIBUTION

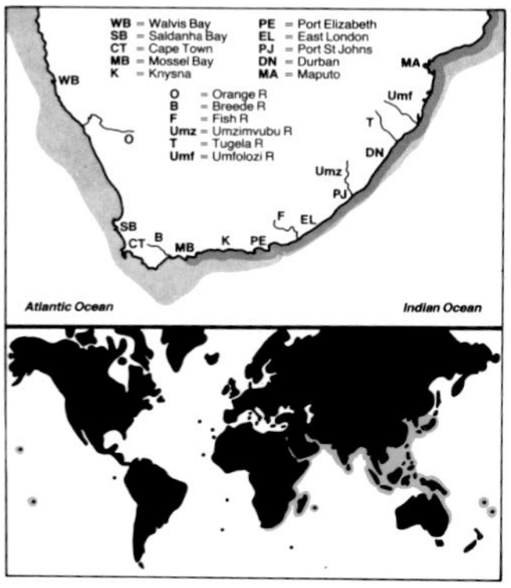

CAPTURE

Though edible and easily caught on ultra-light tackle, this fish is too small to interest most fishermen, except as a source of bait. It does make an attractive and hardy aquarium fish, and will thrive on most types of food. A closely related species occurring in Hawaii grows to 30 cm, and is regarded as a delicacy.

SPECIFIC CATCH RESTRICTIONS

None.

NAME DERIVATION

Kuhlia, named after Kuhl, the naturalist who 'discovered' this fish in the waters off the coast of Java; *mugil,* an allusion to its resemblance to the mullet (genus Mugil). Barred flagtail, a reference to the striped tail, reminiscent of a flag waving as the fish swims.

SIMILAR SPECIES

The less common rock-flagtail *(K. rupestris)* can be recognized by its unmarked caudal fin and much greater size, sometimes in excess of 2,5 kg.

Kyphosus biggibus

Lacepède, 1801

Common name Worldwide - grey chub

[Smith 189□1]

IDENTIFYING FEATURES

COLOUR, SHAPE AND SIZE

This robust, heavily built fish is dull grey overall. Distinctive body markings are lacking, although freshly caught specimens usually have a golden sheen. Occasionally, however, a pigment disorder, known as a xanthic phase, causes a striking overall change in colour to bright yellow. Individuals thus coloured are very conspicuous underwater. Can attain 70 cm.

EXTERNAL ANATOMY

The almost oval-shaped body is covered with smooth scales which also extend onto the head and fins. These small scales are arranged in approximately 65-75 series along the lateral line. The fins are well developed and include a single dorsal of 12 spines plus 12 rays, an anal of three spines plus 11 rays, short pectorals, and a slightly forked caudal. The mouth is small, and each jaw bears a row of long incisors. In addition, several bands of much finer teeth are located on the roof of the mouth and tongue. Molar teeth are lacking. The first gill arch has 20-22 short rakers.

NATURAL HISTORY

The grey chub is most common around shallow subtropical reefs well covered with algae. Here, large numbers may congregate to graze the seaweed and other marine growths such as redbait. The closely set incisors provide the jaws with sharp cutting edges well suited to cropping algae and other marine plants. The long gut, too, manifests the herbivorous diet. This alimentary adaptation is typical of vegetarian fishes, for it allows more effective and complete digestion of low-energy plant matter. Spawning occurs during spring over tropical reefs, but how the newly hatched juveniles are dispersed is not known. A curious, internal feature is the well-developed swim bladder that divides into two towards the tail. The body cavity often contains considerable fat deposits, especially before the start of the spawning season.

DISTRIBUTION

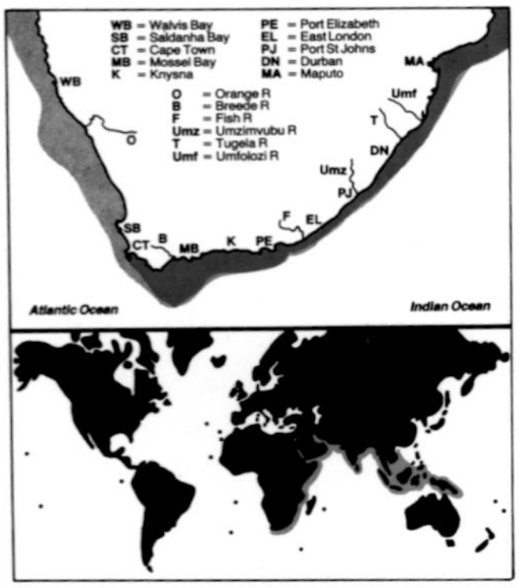

CAPTURE

Anglers using light tackle along Zululand beaches are often provided with excellent sport by the grey chub. Crayfish or redbait and even pieces of seaweed may prove a tempting bait for this fish. It is occasionally speared by divers. The flesh is edible, but not exceptional and most people are put off by the unpleasant smell of the gutted fish. The odour, characteristic of herbivores, is caused by partially digested vegetable matter in the alimentary system.

SA angling record - 6,8 kg.

SA spearfishing record - 10,0 kg.

SPECIFIC CATCH RESTRICTIONS

None.

NAME DERIVATION

Kyphosus, from *cypnus* meaning a hump, allegedly this misnomer arose because the first specimen described had a noticeable deformity; *biggibus,* largest (of the genus). Chub, a reference to its plump, 'chubby' body. In other parts of the world this and related species are known as rudderfishes, apparently because of their habit of following ships.

SIMILAR SPECIES

Three chub species occur in the region. They are best distinguished by their dorsal fin rays which are clearly elongate in the blue chub *(K. cinarescens).* In the grey chub the soft dorsal fin base is shorter than the spinous section, while the opposite is true in the brassy chub *(K. vaigiensis).*

Anchichoerops natalensis

(Gilchrist & Thompson, 1908)
Common name Natal wrasse
[Smith 220□4]

IDENTIFYING FEATURES

COLOUR, SHAPE AND SIZE
The general body colour of this robust fish is red-orange, with blue-black mottlings or bright-orange spots covering the head region. Some 7-10 dark, vertical bars are often visible on the flanks shortly after capture, but these soon fade. It has also been reported (by A.R. Thorpe) that these brighter colours fade to a darker brown at an approximate size of 5 kg. Can attain 70 cm.

EXTERNAL ANATOMY
The body is covered with scales arranged in 50-60 series along the lateral line. The fins are well developed, and include a dorsal of 13 spines plus nine rays, an anal of three spines plus ten or 11 rays, and a very broadly rounded caudal. The dorsal spines are enveloped in a fleshy membrane. The prominent mouth has exceptionally thick, fleshy lips and the jaws are armed with large canine teeth. Pharyngeal grinding teeth are present within the gullet. There are approximately 12 rakers on the lower part of the first gill arch.

NATURAL HISTORY

This sluggish, reef-dwelling fish is frequently seen underwater by Natal skindivers as it swims leisurely along the outer edges of reefs or around projecting headlands. It is very inquisitive and will often swim right up to divers. The main elements of this wrasse's diet are sponges, ascidians, corals, crabs and crayfish. Large crabs, often with sharp, strong pincers, are easily disarmed and eaten. The fleshy, protrusible lips are undoubtedly important in the feeding technique, probably by assisting to manoeuvre prey. This territorial fish appears to have a very restricted distribution, hence its rate of exploitation should be controlled to avoid the 'fishing out' of localized areas. Though common in some areas, very few specimens have been studied. Little is known of its life history, therefore, but spawning has been recorded around reefs in Natal. In Australian waters, a closely related wrasse displays considerable colour differences between males and females, a phenomenon which previously resulted in much confusion as to the species' correct identity. Perhaps the Natal wrasse's variable colouration is an indication of a similar distinction between the sexes.

DISTRIBUTION

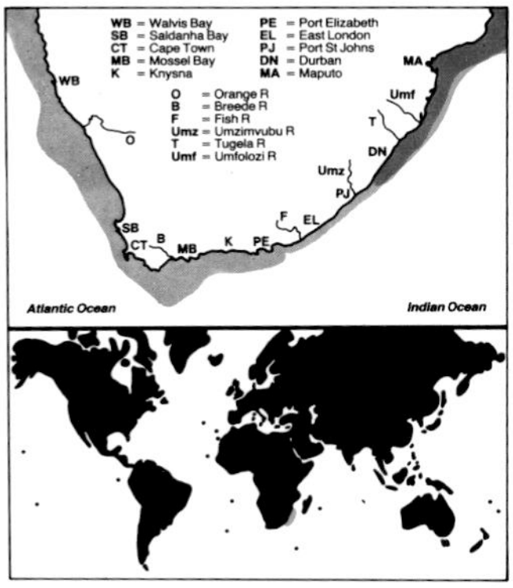

CAPTURE

The Natal wrasse finds few baits acceptable and it is rarely caught by ski-boat anglers. Its inquisitive nature and slow movements, however, make it an easy target for spearfishermen and for this reason it is protected by law. Its flesh is of fine eating quality.
SA angling record – 10,4 kg.
SA spearfishing record – 15,4 kg.

SPECIFIC CATCH RESTRICTIONS

Spearfishing of this species is illegal in Natal.

NAME DERIVATION

Anchichoerops, like a hog; *natalensis,* of Natal. Natal wrasse, a reference to its distribution and to *wrach,* a Cornish word meaning 'old wife', presumably an allusion to the fish's less-than-attractive looks.

SIMILAR SPECIES

This is the only wrasse that has 13 dorsal spines, the first three of which are almost separate from the rest, and has distinctly thick, fleshy lips.

Bodianus bilunulatus

(Lacepède, 1801)

Common names SA – saddleback hogfish, saddleback wrasse. Elsewhere – blackfin wrasse [Smith 220□7]

IDENTIFYING FEATURES

COLOUR, SHAPE AND SIZE

The general body colour of this robust, but somewhat elongate wrasse is basically reddish along the dorsal surface and sides, with a paler, yellow belly. Most noticeable is the large, black, saddle-like marking that is located just behind the soft dorsal fin, on top of the caudal peduncle. Both the anal and caudal fins are edged in black. As it increases in size, however, this species undergoes considerable changes in colouration which may lead to its misidentification. Can attain 60 cm.

EXTERNAL ANATOMY

Tough scales, arranged in 28-30 series along the straight lateral line, cover the body. The single dorsal fin consists of 12 spines plus nine or ten rays, and the anal of three spines plus 12 rays. The stout caudal fin is lunate, and the pectoral fins are crescent-shaped. Each jaw has a single row of closely set conical teeth with two pairs of forward-protruding canines. Mill-like, pharyngeal teeth occur in the gullet. There are 17-21 rakers on the first gill arch.

NATURAL HISTORY

The saddleback hogfish haunts deeper coral and rocky reefs. During the day, it forages around the reef, either singly or in pairs seeking out food, which consists primarily of gastropods, limpets, sea urchins and crabs. All prey is crushed by the powerful, pharyngeal grinding plates, and most of the hard, inedible shell pieces are rejected through the gill openings. At night this fish will often hide out in a cave or crevice where it appears to sleep. Little else is known of its habits or breeding cycle.

DISTRIBUTION

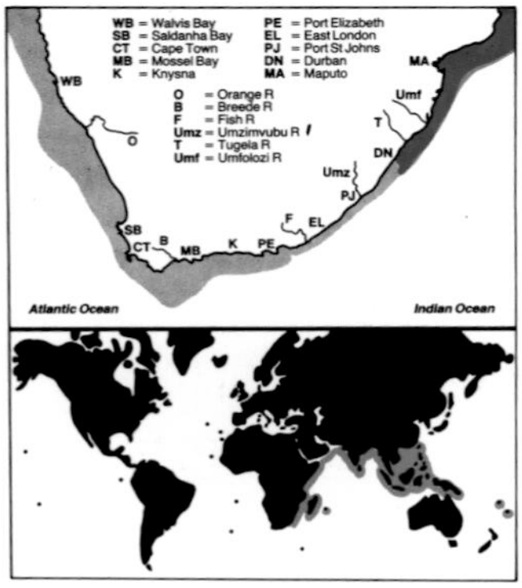

CAPTURE

Though commonly caught by ski-boat anglers, this reasonably palatable fish is usually rather small for the table. It is rarely speared by divers.

SA angling record – 1,6 kg.

SA spearfishing record – 1,4 kg.

SPECIFIC CATCH RESTRICTIONS

None.

NAME DERIVATION

Bodianus, a corruption of the Portuguese *bodiano* or *pudiano* meaning modesty; *bilunulatus,* double crescent. Saddleback hogfish, a reference to the pitch black saddle, and to a pig – in allusion to its fleshy lips. Wrasse, from the Cornish word *wrache* meaning 'old wife'.

SIMILAR SPECIES

There are five hogfish species in South African waters, most easily distinguished by their distinctive colouration. However, this species has been previously confused with *B. hirsutus,* but this close relative can be distinguished from *B. bilunulatus* by its darker overall colouration, and its much larger black blotch which extends uninterrupted from the dorsal fin to the lower surface of the caudal peduncle.

Bodianus diana

(Lacepède, 1801)
Common name Diana's hogfish
[Smith 220□8]

IDENTIFYING FEATURES

COLOUR, SHAPE AND SIZE
This elongate wrasse has a long, sloping forehead, a pointed snout and an almost-straight ventral profile. The general body colour is red. A distinct, black spot marks the tail, the scales of the upper body are edged in black, and there are three or four golden, or bluish, spots on the upper flanks between the dorsal fin and the lateral line. In most Labridae, juveniles resemble adults, but in the majority of *Bodianus* species,individuals undergo a complete metamorphosis in colour and pattern when changing from juveniles to adults. This phenomenon is particularly noticeable in *B. diana*. Juveniles are black overall, and distinctly marked with a dozen or more large, white blotches. Can attain 25 cm.

EXTERNAL ANATOMY
The scales are arranged in 30-32 series along the distinct lateral line. The fins are well developed, and include a single dorsal of 12 spines plus ten rays, an anal of three spines plus 12 rays, and a square caudal. The terminal mouth bears sharp, canine teeth at the front of each jaw, followed by lateral teeth which are fused to form bony ridges. Pharyngeal grinding teeth occur in the gullet and there are 15-18 rakers on the first gill arch.

NATURAL HISTORY

This species frequents rocky and coral reefs, ranging from the surf zone to depths of 80 m. It is mostly solitary, and spends a great deal of the daylight hours actively foraging around the reef in search of food. This consists mainly of hard-shelled organisms such as shelled molluscs, corals, crabs and sea urchins which are broken open by its strong teeth. Many wrasses rely predominantly on the rhythmic beating of their pectoral fins for propulsion. This and other *Bodianus* species, however, use both pectorals and their caudal fin to move foward. The life history of Diana's hogfish is not well documented, and its breeding habits and the dispersal of juveniles are unknown.

DISTRIBUTION

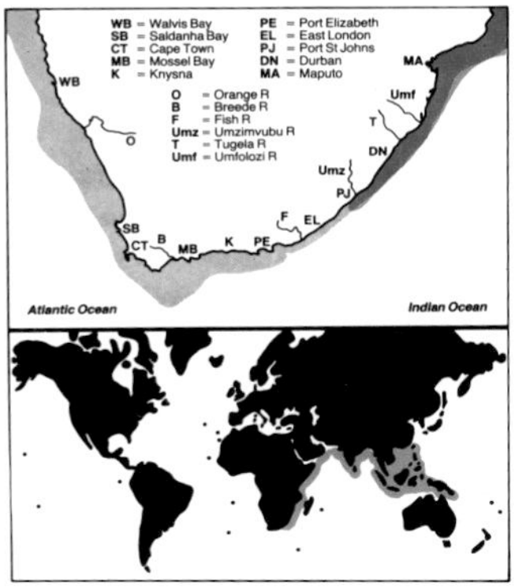

NAME DERIVATION

Bodianus, a corruption of the Portuguese *bodiano* or *pudiano,* meaning modesty; *diana,* a reference to Diana, the huntress in Roman mythology. Diana's hogfish, derived from the specific name and the fish's hoglike snout.

CAPTURE

Though not a sportfish, many specimens are hooked by anglers fishing offshore. Its flesh is not very palatable. It does, however, make an attractive and successful aquarium fish, and is especially interesting if captured in its juvenile phase and observed as it changes to its adult colours and patterns.

SPECIFIC CATCH RESTRICTIONS

None.

SIMILAR SPECIES

In its adult phase Diana's hogfish is readily identified by its colours and patterning and the combination of 12 spines plus ten rays in the dorsal fin. During the early life phase, however, this species closely resembles the turncoat hogfish *(B. axillaris).* This slightly smaller and bi-coloured species can be distinguished by its white-tipped snout.

Bodianus leucostictus

(Bennet, 1831)
Common name Worldwide – lined hogfish
[Smith 220□9]

IDENTIFYING FEATURES

COLOUR, SHAPE AND SIZE
The lined hogfish is somewhat elongate and robust and, as with most *Bodianus* species, strikingly coloured and marked. The upper flanks and the dorsal surface are red, but this fades to a creamy yellow underside. Five stripes run along each flank, the upper three being red and black, while the lower pair are plain red. Fin colours correspond roughly to those on the adjacent body. Can attain 25 cm.

EXTERNAL ANATOMY
The body is covered with cycloid scales which adhere strongly to the skin. These scales are arranged in 30-35 series along the slightly curved lateral line. The fins are well developed and include a single dorsal of 12 spines plus ten rays, an anal of three spines plus 12 rays, and a slightly rounded caudal. The small, terminal mouth is partly protractile, and is surrounded by thick lips. Each jaw bears prominent canines, and,in addition, a set of grinding plates is located in the gullet. Some 17-19 short rakers occur on the first gill arch.

NATURAL HISTORY

Though not particularly common, this species does provide a fine example of the 'typical' wrasse. It usually frequents slightly deeper coral and rocky reefs where, during the day, it forages for food. The diet consists of gastropod and bivalve molluscs as well as coral polyps, all of which are easily crushed by the strong teeth. The lined hogfish occurs singly or in pairs. It is strictly diurnal, and rests up at night. For its nocturnal 'sleep' a hole or crevice in the reef is carefully selected, though competition often arises between the members of this and other similar species for the 'ownership' of a specific hole. These squabbles frequently become protracted, resulting in both the victor and the vanquished retiring unusually late! During these contests, they are particularly vulnerable to predation by crepuscular carnivores. Very little is known about this species' breeding biology.

DISTRIBUTION

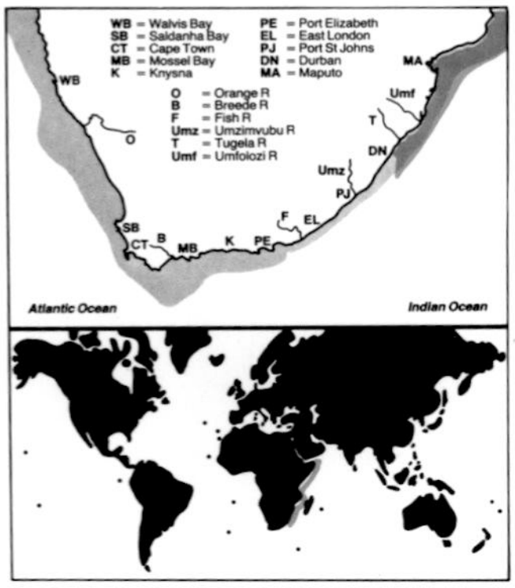

SPECIFIC CATCH RESTRICTIONS

None.

CAPTURE

Ski-boat anglers catch this fish from time to time, but, though it is edible, most are too small to constitute a source of food. The lined hogfish makes a beautiful and successful aquarium fish.
SA angling record – vacant.

NAME DERIVATION

Bodianus, a corruption of the Portuguese *bodiano* or *pudiano* meaning modesty; *leucostictus,* white-spotted. Lined hogfish, also a reference to its markings, as well as to its alleged pig-like features.

SIMILAR SPECIES

The distinctive patterns and colouration should ensure correct identification. This species has also been described as *B. trilineatus* and more specimens are needed to confirm its identity.

Bodianus perditio

(Quoy & Gaimard, 1834)
Common names SA – goldsaddle hogfish. Elsewhere – goldenspot pigfish
[Smith 220□10]

IDENTIFYING FEATURES

COLOUR, SHAPE AND SIZE

This is one of the most robust members of the wrasse family. The overall body colour is red to orange and is particularly bright towards the head. The head and foreparts of the fish are characteristically marked with yellow-orange 'freckles'. A broad pale or yellow patch marks each flank and extends from beneath the eighth to tenth dorsal spines to just below the lateral line. There appears to be some variability among specimens of this species, as a few goldsaddle hogfish also display a black saddle-like patch on the caudal peduncle. The first 3-6 dorsal spines are normally black, but those of some individuals may be golden-red or yellow. Juveniles differ from adults and their overall brownish bodies have a white crossbar followed by a large black blotch. Can attain 80 cm.

EXTERNAL ANATOMY

The body is covered with distinct scales arranged in 33 series along the lateral line. The single dorsal fin consists of 12 strong spines plus ten rays: while the anal comprises three spines plus 12 rays. The pectoral fins are short, but the pelvics and the tips of the caudal become progressively elongate with age. Both jaws are armed with numerous, strong, conical teeth, at least two pairs of which are enlarged and protrude outwards. A set of powerful pharyngeal grinding plates is located further back in the gullet. Some 19-23 short, stocky rakers are located on the first gill arch.

NATURAL HISTORY

A common fish of deeper rock and coral reefs, the goldsaddle hogfish is often confused with other similar species, most of which are only known as 'wrasses'. The habits of this species are also very similar to those of the other hogfish described in this book, as is its diet which consists mainly of invertebrate organisms such as sea urchins, crabs, gastropod molluscs and other hard-shelled animals. All are grasped firmly by the stout teeth before being taken into the gullet where they are crushed by the powerful pharyngeal plates. The goldsaddle hogfish is most active during daylight and, like many other Labridae, it shelters by night in a suitable hole or crevice in the reef. Details relating to the breeding biology of this wide-ranging species are sparse, but the few adults examined from South African waters have been reproductively inactive.

CAPTURE

Ski-boat anglers fishing over deep reefs are most likely to catch this fish, and some are also landed by spearfishermen. It is, however, seldom hooked by shore anglers. Its flesh makes fair eating.
SA angling record – 3,5 kg.
SA spearfishing record – 7,2 kg.

NAME DERIVATION

Bodianus, a corruption of the Portuguese *bodiano* or *pudiano* meaning modesty; *perditio,* to destroy. Allegedly this fish was thus named because the vessel from which the first recorded specimens were taken almost perished in a storm. Goldsaddle hogfish, a reference to the yellow blotch on the upper flanks, and to the fish's pig-like snout.

DISTRIBUTION

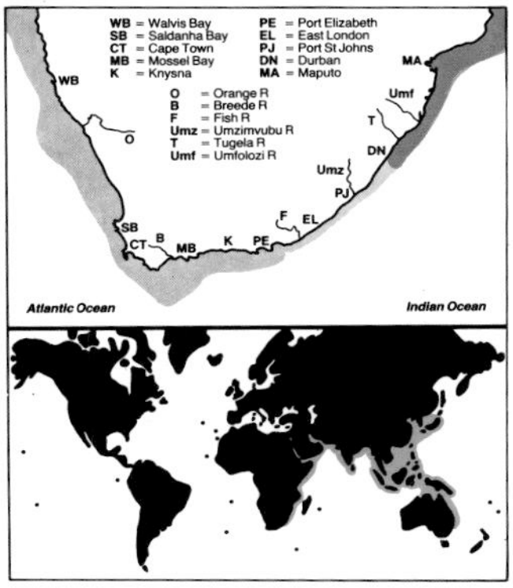

SPECIFIC CATCH RESTRICTIONS

None.

SIMILAR SPECIES

This fish is occasionally confused with the saddleback hogfish, but it can be easily distinguished as its black saddle is much less prominent.

Labroides dimidiatus

(Valenciennes, 1839)
Common name Worldwide – bluestreak cleaner wrasse
[Smith 220□41]

IDENTIFYING FEATURES

COLOUR, SHAPE AND SIZE

This small and very elongate fish is strikingly coloured. In adults the front half of the body is grey or brownish-white, while the rear is bright blue. The entire body is marked on each flank by a long, broad, black band which begins at the snout, passes through the eye and, towards the tail, becomes progressively wider. Though not obvious in the 'side-on' view presented here, a black band also marks the dorsal surface from head to tail. Juvenile bluestreak cleaner wrasse are similarly marked, but lack the whitish grey that mantles the fore-parts, the entire body being a bright blue or black.

EXTERNAL ANATOMY

The single lateral line curves abruptly downwards towards the tail, and along its length fine, adherent scales are arranged in 50-52 series, however, a magnifying glass may be necessary to count them. The fins are well developed, and include a single dorsal of nine spines plus 11 rays, an anal of three spines plus ten rays, and a square caudal that is barely distinguishable from the body. The small mouth is located at the tip of the pointed snout, and is surrounded by thick lips, the lower of which is split in two. Each jaw bears a patch of small canines as well as a band of finer teeth. The first gill arch has 7-10 short rakers.

NATURAL HISTORY

A common and extremely active little reef fish, the bluestreak cleaner wrasse has a most remarkable life-style. It depends for its food on the ectoparasites and mucus covering other, larger fish. Any such fish wishing to rid its body of ectoparasites which it itself is unable to remove will passively submit to a complete and thorough scouring by the cleaner wrasse. The 'client' fish often also opens its mouth and gill covers to allow the wrasse to continue its work. Yet even more remarkable than this habit, is the species' territorial behaviour. It actually sets up cleaning stations which are voluntarily visited by parasite-infested fish which occasionally even 'queue' for their turn. Each cleaning station is 'manned' by a single male and his attendant harem. Should the male die, or be removed, within half an hour the dominant female will begin to display aggressive behaviour, and within 2-4 days the process of sex reversal is complete. Sometimes the male from a neighbouring station may invade the harem, and, if sufficiently aggressive, may succeed in 'overthrowing' the resident male, thereby incorporating that harem into his own. This inherent ability to control the production of males within a species also occurs in the sea goldie. Mimicry is well known in the animal kingdom, and there is a small blenny *(Aspidontes taeniatus)* which closely resembles the cleaner wrasse. Its intentions, however, are very different, for instead of removing ectoparasites, it uses its relatively large fangs to tear chunks of flesh from the unsuspecting host! Obviously, aquarists must identify these fish correctly.

DISTRIBUTION

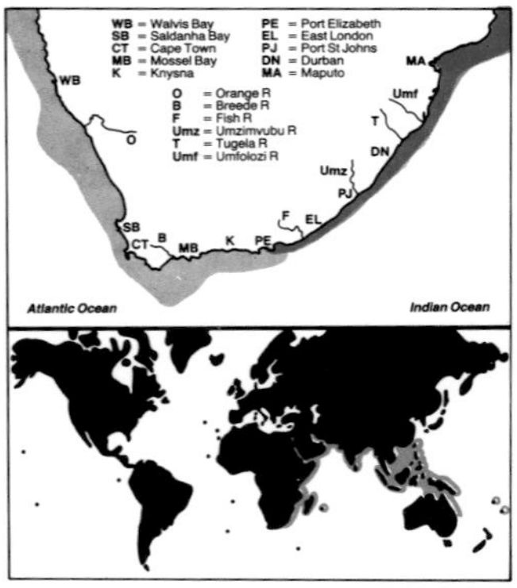

CAPTURE

This successful and desirable occupant of any marine aquarium, is easily caught in rock pools.

SPECIFIC CATCH RESTRICTIONS

None.

NAME DERIVATION

Labroides, from *labrum* meaning lip; *dimidiatus,* halved. Bluestreak cleaner wrasse, an obvious reference to its colours and habits, and from the Cornish word *wrach* meaning 'old wife'.

Thalassoma hebraicum

(Lacepède, 1801)
Common name Worldwide – goldbar wrasse
[Smith 220□61]

IDENTIFYING FEATURES

COLOUR, SHAPE AND SIZE

The elongate, slightly compressed body of this wrasse is variably, but strikingly coloured, especially in live specimens. The terminal male body colour is green or blue, with a number of obvious, darker-blue or violet stripes along the sides of the head. A most conspicuous yellow bar runs from the origin of the dorsal fin to just behind the base of the pectoral fins. The colour of the fins usually matches that of the adjacent body. Can attain 25 cm.

EXTERNAL ANATOMY

The body is covered with cycloid scales arranged in about 25 series along the lateral line. Near the tail, the lateral line dips abruptly downwards. The single dorsal fin consists of eight spines plus 13 rays, while the anal fin has three spines plus 11 rays. The upper and lower rays of the caudal fin are long, and trail behind the fish as it swims. The small, terminal mouth is set with a row of strong, canine teeth. A set of powerful grinding plates is located in the gullet. There are 20-23 short rakers on the first gill arch.

NATURAL HISTORY

Of all the Labridae this species is probably the most common in southern African waters. It frequents rocky and coral reefs and particularly, shallow tidal pools. As with all wrasses, the goldbar wrasse has evolved a system of propulsion ideally suited to its habitat. It drives itself forward with rhythmic 'wing-beats' of the pectoral fins, thus leaving the caudal fin free to act as a rudder as the fish weaves effortlessly amongst the rocks in search of food. The diet consists primarily of hard-shelled organisms such as corals, sea urchins and their spines, and gastropod molluscs. Food items are first broken off by the strong canines, and then crushed in the pharyngeal mill. Most of the indigestible shell matter is ejected through the gill openings before the flesh is swallowed. Juvenile goldbar wrasse are often found in rock pools and presumably these sheltered habitats are used as nursery areas. This solitary species is strongly territorial and adult males are very aggressive towards each other. During much of the year this species may be found in pairs. However, during breeding season, small groups, consisting of one male and several females, may be seen. Sex reversal takes place.

DISTRIBUTION

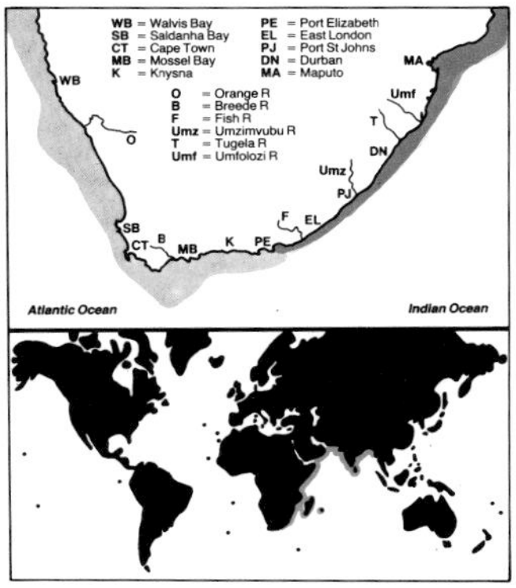

CAPTURE

The goldbar wrasse can be kept successfully in a large aquarium. Though edible, few are caught for this purpose. On some offshore reefs, this fish is extremely common and is often the bane of ski-boat anglers, for it avidly snatches bait intended for more desirable species.
SA angling record – vacant.

SPECIFIC CATCH RESTRICTIONS

Spearfishing of this species is illegal in Natal.

NAME DERIVATION

Thalassoma, animal from the sea; *hebraicum.* Hebrew, an obscure reference. Goldbar wrasse, a reference to the conspicuous yellow bar down each side, and from the Cornish word *wrach* meaning 'old wife'.

SIMILAR SPECIES

The patterns and colours pictured and described are unique to the terminal male phase of this species. Primary phase fish have two longitudinal lines of large yellow spots on their blackish bodies (see also family note on page 97).

Thalassoma purpureum

(Forsskål, 1775)
Common names Worldwide – rainbow or surge wrasse
[Smith 220□63]

IDENTIFYING FEATURES

COLOUR, SHAPE AND SIZE
The colours and markings of this elongate species are variable and change with maturity and sex. The terminal males are, however, distinctive, and consist mainly of reddish-pink stripes and blotches on a generally green background. Most conspicuous in older specimens are the pink markings that radiate from behind the eyes. Occasionally parts of the body, especially the bases of the pectoral fins, may be shaded yellow. The caudal fin may be orange. Males tend to grow larger and to be more brightly coloured than females. Can attain 35 cm.

EXTERNAL ANATOMY
The body is covered with 25-30 series of cycloid scales arranged along the lateral line. The fins are well developed and include a single dorsal fin of eight spines plus 13 rays, an anal fin of three spines plus 11 rays, and a well-rounded caudal fin with a thick peduncle. Both jaws have sharp canine teeth towards the front, followed by molars further back. Grinding teeth occur in the gullet. The first gill arch carries 20-25 short rakers.

NATURAL HISTORY

This small species frequents coastal waters around coral and rocky reefs, as well as intertidal rock pools. The rainbow wrasse is able to enter exceedingly shallow water and, as with most members of the family, the pectoral fins are used for propulsion, the caudal fin being used only in the case of an emergency. Its cryptic colours make it very inconspicuous among weed or in crevices. This effect is heightened by its habit, as with many wrasse, of remaining quite still for long periods. In this state of apparent sleep the fish is easily handled, but if disturbed will slowly move off, only to return later to its original spot. Aggression is shown by adult males towards other members of the species. Rainbow wrasse do, however, congregate in loose groups when searching for food. This is especially evident when rocks or coral are disturbed by larger fish or divers, and the organisms sheltering beneath are exposed. The diet comprises mostly hard-shelled animals such as crabs, sea urchins, bivalve and gastropod molluscs and brittlestars. Small fish and worms are also eaten. Like its relatives, this species undergoes sex reversal from female to male – probably at a size of about 15 cm. Adult males are territorial, and usually have a harem.

DISTRIBUTION

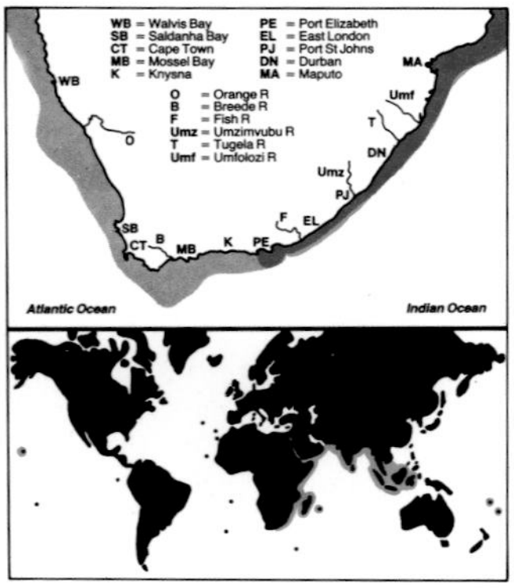

CAPTURE

Many rainbow wrasse are caught by shore anglers casting into gullies, and by ski-boaters over deeper reefs. Though palatable, few are eaten, and this wrasse is more valued as a colourful and successful aquarium species. A drawback, however, is its aggressive nature towards other species sharing the tank. It holds little interest for the spearfisherman. SA angling record – 1,4 kg.

SPECIFIC CATCH RESTRICTIONS

None.

NAME DERIVATION

Thalassoma, animal from the sea; *purpureum,* purple. Rainbow wrasse, a reference to its bright colours and from the Cornish *wrache* meaning 'old wife'.

SIMILAR SPECIES

The illustration here is of a terminal male. In primary phase fish the two red body lines are broken into smaller spots and lines, some of them maroon coloured (see also family note on page 97).

Thalassoma trilobatum

(Lacepède, 1801)
Common name Worldwide – ladder wrasse
[Smith 220□65]

IDENTIFYING FEATURES

COLOUR, SHAPE AND SIZE
The ladder wrasse is elongate, but slightly more robust than other *Thalassoma* species. Body colours and patterns of terminal males are distinctive; orange overall with two 'ladder-like' rows of bright, powder-blue stripes along each flank. There is also a blue line along each of the dorsal, anal and caudal fins, while the pectoral fins are yellow with blue tips. Can attain 30 cm.

EXTERNAL ANATOMY
The body is covered with cycloid scales which adhere tightly to the skin. These are arranged in some 25 series along the lateral line. Nearer the tail, the lateral line dips abruptly downwards. The fins include a single dorsal of seven or eight spines plus 13 rays, an anal of three spines plus 11 rays and a truncate caudal. Both jaws of the small mouth bear strong canine teeth, while powerful grinding plates are located in the gullet. The first gill arch carries about 18-24 short rakers.

DISTRIBUTION

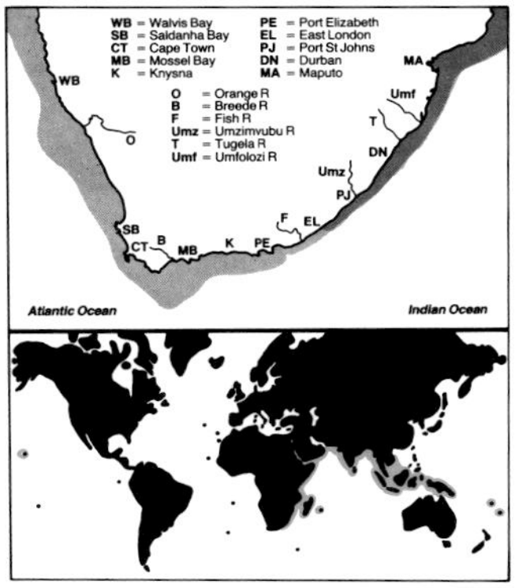

NATURAL HISTORY

The members of this species often occur in pairs, and are relatively common around coral and rocky reefs throughout their range. The ladder wrasse seldom ventures deeper than 5 m and preys on hard-shelled animals such as sea urchins, corals and gastropod molluscs. Its feeding technique is similar to that of other Labridae; prey is grasped or broken off by the strong canines, and then taken into the gullet where it is crushed in the pharyngeal mill. Locomotion, too, is typical; using only its pectoral fins, the ladder wrasse glides deftly amongst the rocks and coral heads. It is active during daylight only, and with the approach of darkness, a sheltered ledge or nook is sought, where the fish 'sleeps' throughout the night, well protected from nocturnal predators. The precise breeding season is not known, but ladder wrasses are often seen to congregate into small groups known as 'spawning aggregations'. These consist of one terminal male with several mature females in attendance. Sex reversal from female to male is known to occur. The juveniles are frequently found in shallow rock pools, but little else is known of the life cycle.

CAPTURE

This attractive and successful aquarium fish is easily caught on light fishing tackle. At low spring-tide on dark nights, ladder wrasses may even be caught by hand as they lie dormant in the rocky shallows. It is edible, but is not generally regarded as a source of food.
SA angling record – 0,8 kg.

SPECIFIC CATCH RESTRICTIONS

None.

NAME DERIVATION

Thalassoma, an animal from the sea, *trilobatum,* like a trilobite, a prehistoric animal with a segmented body. Ladder wrasse, a reference to the barred flanks, and from the Cornish word *wrach* meaning 'old wife'.

SIMILAR SPECIES

The terminal male pictured here is readily identified by its colourful patterns. Primary phase fish resemble the rainbow wrasse except that the red stripe down the snout runs diagonally and not vertically as it does in *T. purpureum* (see also family note on page 97).

Gazza minuta

(Bloch, 1797)

Common names SA - toothed soapy. Elsewhere - toothed ponyfish

[Smith 201□1]

IDENTIFYING FEATURES

COLOUR, SHAPE AND SIZE

Though compressed, the toothed soapy is more elongate than most Leiognathidae. The overall body colour is silvery, but bluish along the dorsal surface with numerous, irregular, brownish markings above the distinct lateral line. The chest and belly are white, while the pectoral axils are black. The fins are translucent to dusky. Can attain 15 cm in length.

EXTERNAL ANATOMY

The head and chest regions are naked, and, though scales cover the rest of the body, these are generally too thin to be visible. The dorsal fin consists of seven or eight slender spines plus 16 rays: the anal fin of three spines plus 14 rays: and the caudal fin is moderately forked. As with other members of this family, the mouth is protractile but, as illustrated here, when extended, it is directed forwards, and not downwards like that of other soapies. Each jaw bears distinct canine teeth. The eyes are large. Some 18-20 well-developed rakers occur on the first gill arch.

NATURAL HISTORY

This very widely distributed shoaling fish inhabits shallow coastal waters and often enters brackish bays and estuaries. However, shoals also frequently move to depths of 40 m where they are found predominantly near the sea-bed. This is presumably where most feeding occurs, as the diet consists of bottom-living animals including small crustaceans such as shrimps, as well as polychaete worms and tiny fish. Estuaries are used by juveniles as nursery areas, but further details of the toothed soapy's life history in southern African waters are scant. Studies conducted in India, however, indicate a short breeding season restricted primarily to tropical waters during June. Furthermore, it appears that mature fish move into deeper offshore waters immediately prior to spawning. This facilitates the oceanic dispersal of fertilized eggs and newly hatched larvae.

DISTRIBUTION

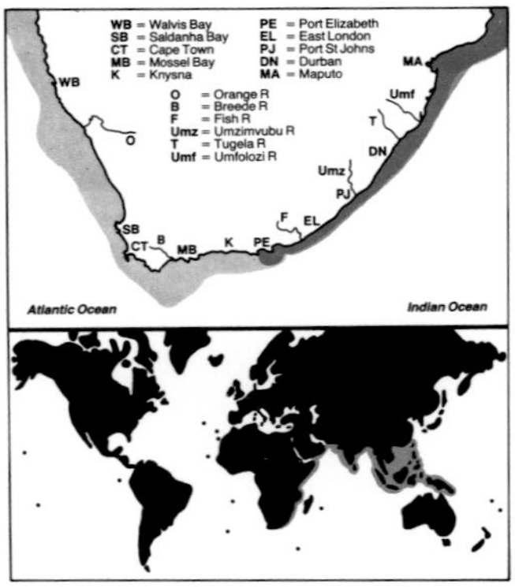

CAPTURE

Whereas toothed soapies are of commercial value in some countries, few are caught in southern African waters besides those landed in beach seine nets in Durban. In the Far East they may be marketed fresh, or processed into fish-meal and used as a poultry food. Though rather small and bony, their flesh makes good eating.

SA angling record - vacant.

SPECIFIC CATCH RESTRICTIONS

None.

NAME DERIVATION

Gazza, possibly derived from *gaza,* an old Persian word meaning 'the royal treasury', presumably an allusion to the rich silvery colours of this fish; *minuta,* small. Toothed soapy, a reference to the distinct canines and smooth, almost soap-like body.

SIMILAR SPECIES

The toothed soapy is easily distinguished from all other members in this family because it is the only species that has distinct teeth. The pursemouths are occasionally confused with this species, but can be identified by the presence of scales on their head, which is noticeably scaleless in soapies.

Leiognathus equula

(Forsskål, 1775)
Common names SA – slimy, soapy. Elsewhere – common or greater ponyfish
[Smith 201□3]

IDENTIFYING FEATURES

COLOUR, SHAPE AND SIZE

This deep-bodied, strongly compressed fish has a prominent horse-like 'muzzle'. The body has an overall iridescent, silvery sheen, with a number of dark, vertical bars running down the flanks. These are especially evident in living specimens. A small, brown saddle occurs on the caudal peduncle. The fins are translucent to dusky and may occasionally be tinged with yellow. Can attain 25 cm.

EXTERNAL ANATOMY

Except for the naked head and chest, the body is covered with numerous scales, but these are difficult to detect as they are so minute. A thick layer of mucus also coats the body. The single dorsal fin has eight spines plus 15 or 16 rays, while the anal fin has three spines plus 14 rays. The spines of both fins can be locked into an upright position. There are also small spines on the forehead, and a sharp, partially concealed spine precedes the dorsal fin. The caudal fin is forked, and the pectoral fins extend backwards to a point in line with the origin of the anal fin. Bands of minute teeth occur in the mouth which is protractile and points downwards when fully extended. There are 19-23 short rakers on the first gill arch. The eyes are slightly enlarged, and there is a distinctly curved lateral line.

NATURAL HISTORY

This common shoaling fish of coastal waters and estuaries is tolerant of very turbid environments, as well as almost fresh water. It is generally not very active, and large shoals can often be observed 'suspended' in midwater. Feeding occurs at two different levels, depending on size. Young fish feed on midwater, planktonic crustaceans such as copepods, crab larvae and shrimps, while larger specimens eat small crabs, prawns and marine worms that live on the bottom. Sexual maturity is attained at a length of 15 cm and spawning has been recorded from October to March along the Natal coast, in the vicinity of river mouths. Juveniles make extensive use of estuaries and mangrove-lined waters as nursery areas, and large shoals of 3-8-cm-long fish can be netted in these regions during late summer. In addition to exuding great amounts of mucus, the slimy often produces a croaking sound when captured, this is very evident when large numbers are caught.

DISTRIBUTION

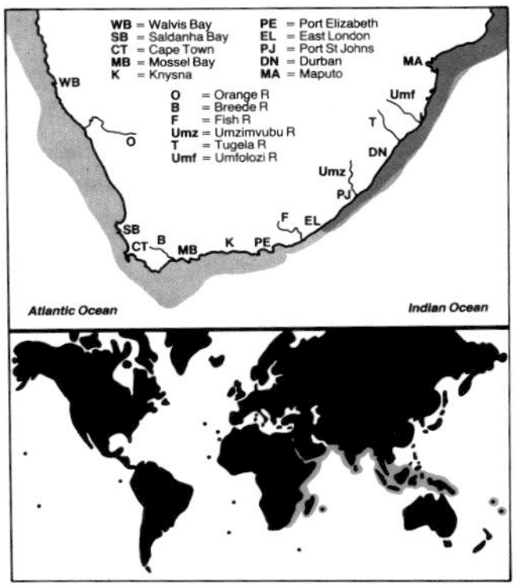

CAPTURE

Although not specifically sought by anglers, this fish is often hooked on light tackle. In the Far East, slimies are caught in trawl nets and fish traps and, dried or fresh, represent an important food resource.
SA angling record – 0,2 kg.

SPECIFIC CATCH RESTRICTIONS

None.

NAME DERIVATION

Leiognathus, smooth mouth; *equula,* like a horse, a reference to the equine head. Slimy or soapy, a reference to its excessive mucus secretions.

SIMILAR SPECIES

This genus is characterised by its downward protruding mouth. The related *L. elongatus* is twice as elongate as this species.

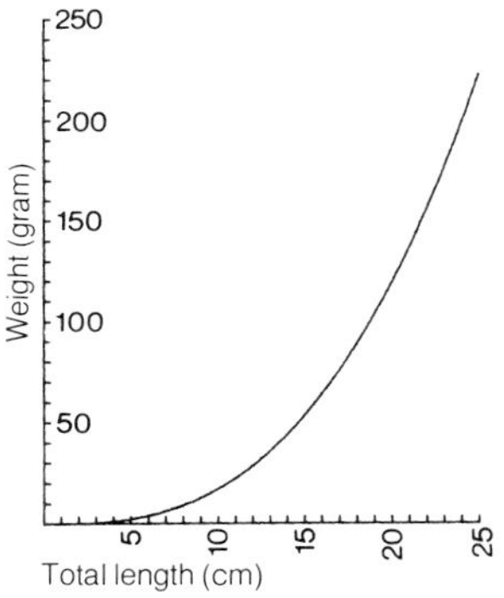

Secutor insidiator

(Bloch, 1787)
Common names SA – slender or deep-sea soapy. Elsewhere – pugnose ponyfish.
[Smith 201□4]

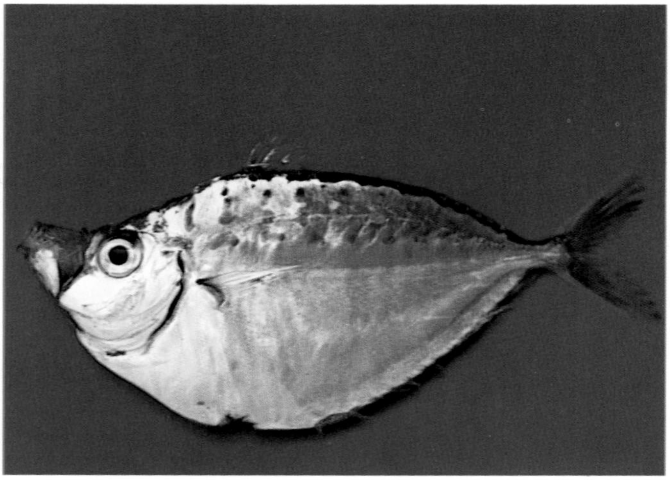

IDENTIFYING FEATURES

COLOUR, SHAPE AND SIZE

The slender soapy is compressed and oval-shaped. Though shown here with its mouth fully protracted, this fish has a characteristic, squashed and pug-like snout. The body has an overall silvery sheen, with blue-green spots arranged in vertical bars along the upper sides. The fins are translucent to dusky. Can attain 15 cm.

EXTERNAL ANATOMY

Minute, indistinct scales cover the body. The lateral line, though clearly visible, does not extend as far as the caudal peduncle. The fins are well developed and include a dorsal of eight or nine spines plus 15-17 rays, an anal of three spines plus 14 rays, a forked caudal, and little pelvics. Two short spines also occur on the forehead. The small, highly protractile terminal mouth can be extended into an upward-directed tube, and the jaws are set with small, inconspicuous teeth. There are 24-28 rakers on the first gill arch.

DISTRIBUTION

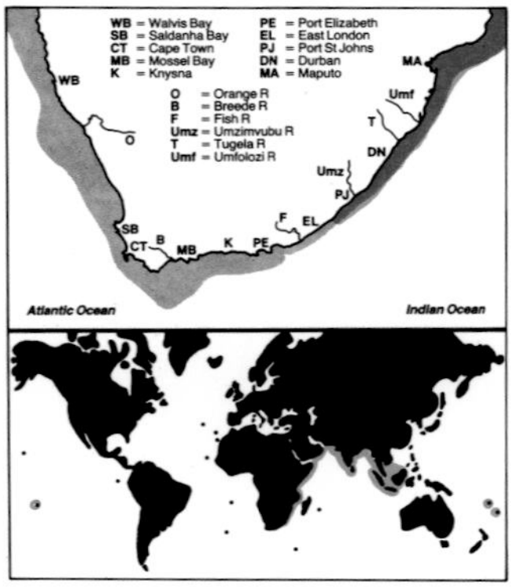

NATURAL HISTORY

The slender soapy is primarily found in coastal waters, ranging from the inshore region to depths of 150 m. It is also common in brackish lagoons and estuaries. It is a poor swimmer, and the sometimes dense shoals that congregate, tend to move slowly over the sea-bed in search of food. This consists primarily of planktonic organisms such as copepods, mysids, and the larvae of larger crustaceans and fish. These morsels are sucked into the mouth which, during feeding, extends into a vacuum-cleaner-like tube. Shoals of juveniles have been recorded along the Natal coast during the summer months, and spawning occurs near estuaries. This fish is extensively preyed upon by gamefish, and is probably an important link in the food chain. Through the microscopic study of the progressive development of eggs within the ovaries, scientists in India have established that spawning periods extend over at least three months. During these protracted breeding seasons, individuals spawn on a number of successive occasions, a fact confirmed by the all-year abundance of juvenile slender soapies in seine-net catches.

CAPTURE

Though not caught by anglers, it is frequently netted in beach seines, or caught in trawls over offshore prawn-fishing grounds. In the Far East, however, large numbers are caught commercially, processed into fish-meal, and used as poultry or cattle feed.

SPECIFIC CATCH RESTRICTIONS

None.

NAME DERIVATION

Secutor, armed gladiator; *insidiator,* insidious. Slender soapy, a reference to the excessive mucus secretion and to the fact that it is not as deep-bodied as the common soapy.

SIMILAR SPECIES

Members of this genus can be recognized by their upwardly directed mouths when protruded. The only other *Secutor* species found here *(S. ruconius)* has only one small spine above the eye, while the sleeker-bodied *S. insidiator* has two.

Gymnocranius griseus

(Schlegel, 1844)
Common names SA – grey barenose. Elsewhere – grey large-eye bream
[Smith 185□2]

IDENTIFYING FEATURES

COLOUR, SHAPE AND SIZE
The grey barenose is a compressed and slightly elongate fish. Its overall body colour is silvery grey to blue, and some 5-8 darker, vertical crossbars mark the flanks. These bars are most conspicuous in younger fish, or in individuals under stress. In older specimens however, these markings become less distinct. The fins may have a reddish tinge. Can attain 80 cm.

EXTERNAL ANATOMY
Scales are arranged in 46-51 series along the distinct lateral line, but the flat bridge between the eyes is characteristically devoid of scales. The fins are well developed and include a single dorsal fin of ten spines plus 9-10 rays, an anal fin of three spines plus 9-10 rays, and a deeply forked caudal. The outer teeth of the terminal mouth are conical, and several are enlarged into canines. Finer teeth occur further back in both jaws. The first gill arch bears about eight stubby rakers. Most distinctive are the large eyes above each of which is a black blotch.

NATURAL HISTORY

Not unlike the true sea-breams of the family Sparidae, this species and its many kin are more common in warmer to tropical waters. Here, it inhabits coastal reefs and offshore banks to depths of 80 m. The grey barenose is primarily nocturnal, and spends much of the day resting under sheltered overhangs and other dark recesses in the reef. The enlarged eyes indicate the sensitive vision necessary to hunt by sight in low light levels. Prey includes bottom-living crustaceans such as crabs, shrimps, crayfish and mantis shrimps as well as smaller reef fish. Its life history has been little researched in southern Africa, but some spawning fish have been recorded off the Zululand Coast during summer. In the tropical waters off Kenya the adult members of this species are known to be reproductively 'ripe' from September to December.

DISTRIBUTION

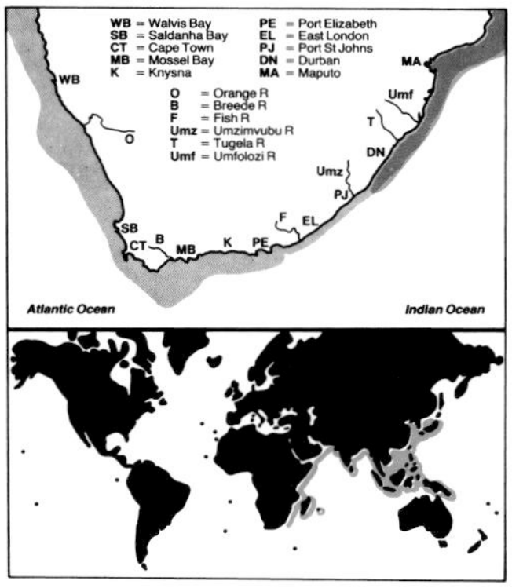

CAPTURE

This fish is caught irregularly by ski-boat anglers and sometimes by spearfishermen. It will take a wide variety of bait and makes an excellent table fish. At several localities throughout the Indian Ocean, this fish is sufficiently abundant to sustain commercial trawling operations. Most are marketed fresh, particularly in the Seychelles.

Note: The fact that many fishermen in southern Africa have not recognized this fish as a distinct species, probably accounts for the unclaimed angling records.

SA angling record – vacant.
SA spearfishing record – vacant.

SPECIFIC CATCH RESTRICTIONS

None.

NAME DERIVATION

Gymnocranius, naked head; *griseus,* blue-grey. Grey barenose, a reference to the body colours and to the naked forehead.

SIMILAR SPECIES

The grey barenose can be distinguished from the closely related emperors by the presence of scales on its cheek. Notice also that it does not have the molar teeth commonly found in seabreams. The related rippled barenose (*G. robinsoni)* can be identified by the presence of wavy blue lines on the head.

Lethrinus crocineus

Smith, 1959

Common name Worldwide - yellowfin emperor
[Smith 185□5]

IDENTIFYING FEATURES

COLOUR, SHAPE AND SIZE

This species is one of the most distinct in a family of fishes that are often difficult to identify. The yellow fin emperor, with its steep forehead, is usually distinctively coloured, though slight variations can occur. The overall body colour is generally yellowish, but darker above, paler below, and with a dark spot on most scales. Darker brown mantles the forehead, while the red interior of the mouth is clearly visible. Noticeable are the characteristically yellow fins, especially the dorsal, caudal and anal. Some specimens display faint crossbars, especially those preserved in formalin for scientific collections. Attains 60 cm.

EXTERNAL ANATOMY

The lateral line is clearly visible, and approximately 50 series of scales are arranged along its length. Between the lateral line and the dorsal fin lie six rows of scales, and, though careful inspection may be required to detect this, it is an important diagnostic feature. The fins are well developed, and include a single dorsal of ten spines plus nine rays, an anal of three spines plus eight rays, and a caudal that is moderately forked. The pectoral fins are fairly long, and reach well beyond the origin of the anal fin. The eyes are located high on the head, close to the dorsal profile, and well behind the level of the hind edge of the jaws. Molars and strong, canine teeth are set in both jaws. The first gill arch bears about six or seven very short rakers.

NATURAL HISTORY

This rather deep-bodied emperor was discovered only recently by the late Professor J.L.B. Smith. It is primarily an inhabitant of the more tropical East Coast waters to the north of southern Africa, but it is nevertheless plentiful in the St Lucia Marine Reserve throughout the year. The yellowfin emperor is most commonly found over rocky and coral reefs, usually in mid-water where it feeds. Though the diet has not been studied in detail, it is likely to include a variety of organisms such as squid, pteropods, mantis shrimps and juvenile fish. Little is known about the life history of this species in local waters, but off the Kenyan coast most are known to be in breeding condition during October and January. No doubt, however, spawning also occurs in other regions within its range.

DISTRIBUTION

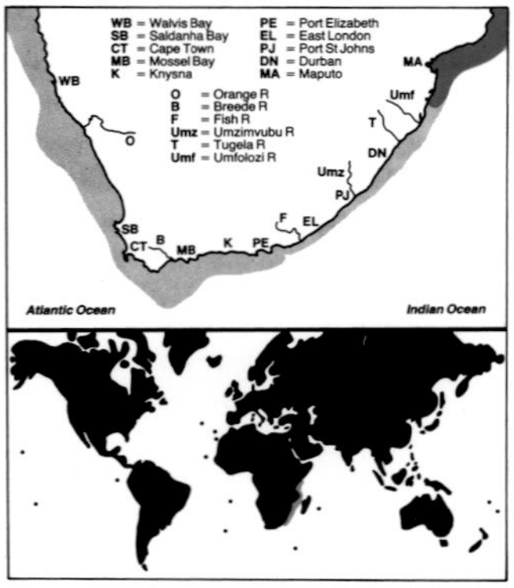

CAPTURE

Like many other members of the family, the yellowfin emperor eagerly takes bait. It is an excellent food fish with delicate flesh.
SA angling record - vacant.
SA spearfishing record - 8,8 kg.

SPECIFIC CATCH RESTRICTIONS

None.

NAME DERIVATION

Lethrinus, from the underworld; *crocineus,* a reference to the crocus, a flower from which saffron, a yellow flavouring substance, is obtained. Yellowfin emperor, an obvious reference to its conspicuous and distinctive fins, and its bright body colours.

SIMILAR SPECIES

This species can best be identified by its yellow fins, absence of a red blotch on the operculum, and the presence of five rows of scales between the lateral line and the dorsal fin.

Lethrinus elongatus

Valenciennes, 1830

Common names SA – longnose emperor, scavenger, mata-hari. Elsewhere – longface emperor, capitaine

[Smith 185□6]

IDENTIFYING FEATURES

COLOUR, SHAPE AND SIZE

This elongate fish has a pronounced and long snout. The general body colour is brownish, and each scale has a pale centre. The head, however, is much darker and the fins are translucent or orange-yellow. Other body markings are variable. The interior of the mouth is conspicuously red. Attains 90 cm.

EXTERNAL ANATOMY

There are 44-47 series of distinct scales arranged along the lateral line, but the head region is almost entirely scaleless. The fins are well developed and include a single dorsal of ten spines plus nine rays, an anal of three spines plus eight rays, and a strongly lunate caudal. The pectoral fins do not, as with other species of the genus, extend to a point opposite the vent. Fleshy lips surround the terminal mouth, and each jaw bears conical teeth, several of which are enlarged into canines. The palate and tongue are toothless. The first gill arch carries 8-10 short rakers.

NATURAL HISTORY

The longnose emperor is a common fish of warmer waters, but it is generally confined to sandy coastal environments in the vicinity of coral and rocky reefs. Here, loosely packed shoals often 'hang' above the reefs, their only movements being the occasional flick of the pectoral fins to maintain stability and direction. This ability enables the species to take advantage of the rich midwater food nutrients, which include small crabs, mantis shrimps, shrimps, small fish and marine worms. Shoaling is especially prevalent during summer in tropical waters, at a time when breeding occurs. This is closely related to the lunar cycle as spawning is known to take place at full moon. Juveniles are distributed by ocean currents and seldom occur in great numbers close inshore.

DISTRIBUTION

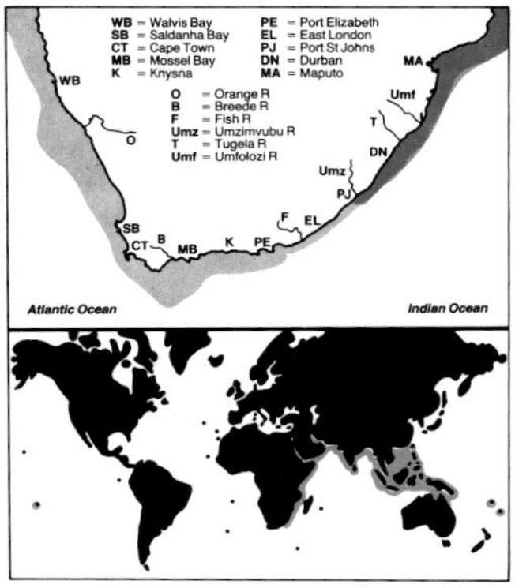

CAPTURE

Although it freely takes a bait and is easily hooked, the longnose emperor is not a target species for anglers, despite its excellent tasting flesh. The habit of remaining motionless in shoals makes the fish especially vulnerable to netting and, in Moçambique and other countries where this fish constitutes a fresh food source, catches are made using seine and gill nets.

SA angling record – vacant.
SA spearfishing record – vacant.

SPECIFIC CATCH RESTRICTIONS

None.

NAME DERIVATION

Lethrinus, from the underworld; *elongatus,* a reference to its elongate body. Longnose emperor, a reference to its extended snout and to the rich body colours.

SIMILAR SPECIES

The longnose emperor is one of the easiest lethrinid fishes to identify as it is distinctly elongate, has a pointed snout and also six rows of scales between the lateral line and the dorsal fin.

Lethrinus nebulosus

(Forsskål, 1775)

Common names Worldwide – blue emperor, scavenger, mata-hari [Smith 185□13]

IDENTIFYING FEATURES

COLOUR, SHAPE AND SIZE

This moderately elongate fish has a large head, a long, sloping forehead, and an almost pointed snout. The olive-green or fawn upper body colour fades to a white underside. Each scale has a bluish centre, and there are blue bands radiating from the eyes, one of which extends across the forehead. The fins are translucent or pinkish. The interior of the mouth is reddish. Can attain 75 cm.

EXTERNAL ANATOMY

The lateral line is distinct, and has 45-51 series of scales arranged along its length. The head region is, however, scaleless. The fins are well developed, and include a single dorsal of ten spines plus nine rays, an anal of three spines plus eight rays, a forked caudal, and pectoral fins that reach beyond the level of the vent. The terminal mouth can be extended slightly, and is surrounded by fleshy lips. Each jaw bears conical teeth, with a few of those towards the front of the mouth being enlarged into canines. There are 5-9 stubby rakers on the first gill arch.

NATURAL HISTORY

This common, tropical fish inhabits coral and rocky reefs. Though it often frequents shallow water, it is also found to depths of 50 m. Small, loosely packed shoals often remain suspended several metres above the reef's surface, and sometimes the only sign of life from individual members is the occasional movement of the pectoral fins to maintain stability and direction. This behaviour is typical of members of this genus, and enables the fish to take maximum advantage of rich midwater nutrients. The diet consists mainly of small crabs, marine worms and molluscs, but suspended or planktonic organisms such as mantis shrimps, small shrimps, crab larvae and juvenile fish are also taken. Sexual maturity is attained during the fourth year at a length of 50-60 cm. Spawning occurs in warmer water, primarily during March to July and the fry are widely distributed by ocean currents. Some have been recorded off the Natal coast, presumably borne down from regions further to the north by the powerful Agulhas Current.

DISTRIBUTION

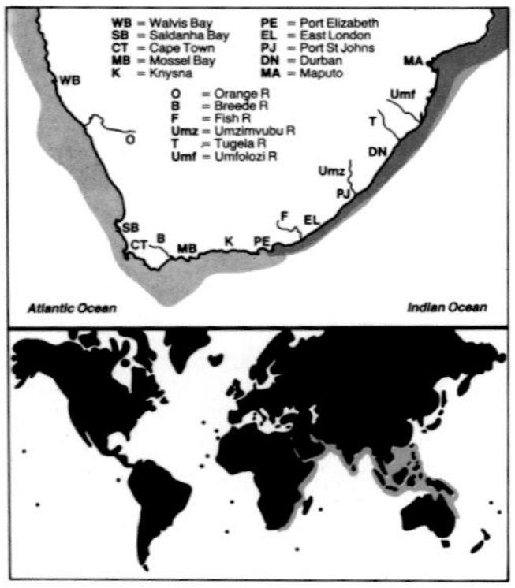

CAPTURE

The blue emperor is popular with ski-boat anglers and with spearfishermen operating around coral reefs. In some parts it is caught in beach seine, trawl and gill nets. The slightly pinkish flesh makes fine eating, and in Japan this delicacy is consumed either raw or boiled.

SA angling record – 6,8 kg.

SA spearfishing record – 7,4 kg.

SPECIFIC CATCH RESTRICTIONS

None.

NAME DERIVATION

Lethrinus, from the underworld; *nebulosus,* clouded. Blue emperor, a reference to its colourful markings.

SIMILAR SPECIES

There are no other emperors that have the radiating blue eye bands and absence of red colour on the operculum.

Lobotes surinamensis

(Bloch, 1790)
Common names SA – tripletail, flasher. Elsewhere – tripletail, jumping cod
[Smith 202□1]

IDENTIFYING FEATURES

COLOUR, SHAPE AND SIZE
This robust, deep-bodied fish has a long, sloping forehead and an undershot lower jaw. The body is blackish, especially the head region, but changes to silvery-grey below. The fins are also dark, though the pectorals and outer margins of the caudal fin may be pale yellow. Fish of less than 10 cm are black in front, while the hind part of the body is translucent white. Attains 100 cm.

EXTERNAL ANATOMY
The body is covered with fairly large, strong scales arranged in 42-45 series along the lateral line. The fins are also large and well developed, especially the soft dorsal, caudal and anal, which together give the tail region its characteristic tri-lobed appearance. The dorsal fin has 11 or 12 spines plus 15 or 16 rays, while the anal fin has three spines plus 11 rays. The spines of juveniles are very long, and the transparent tail is most inconspicuous. The small mouth, with its protruding lower jaw, has narrow bands of villiform teeth. The pre-operculum has a serrated edge and there are 13-15 rakers on the first gill arch.

NATURAL HISTORY

This sluggish relative of the rockcods (family Serranidae,) inhabits shallow coastal waters, particularly muddy estuaries and large river mouths. The solitary tripletail forages around the sea-bed for food, which comprises bottom-dwelling crustaceans including crabs, prawns, mud-prawns and, sometimes, small fish. Spawning occurs in summer and the young are occasionally found in Natal estuaries. Here they mimic mangrove leaves by drifting slowly on their sides with the current. In this way many manage to avoid the attentions of would-be predators.

DISTRIBUTION

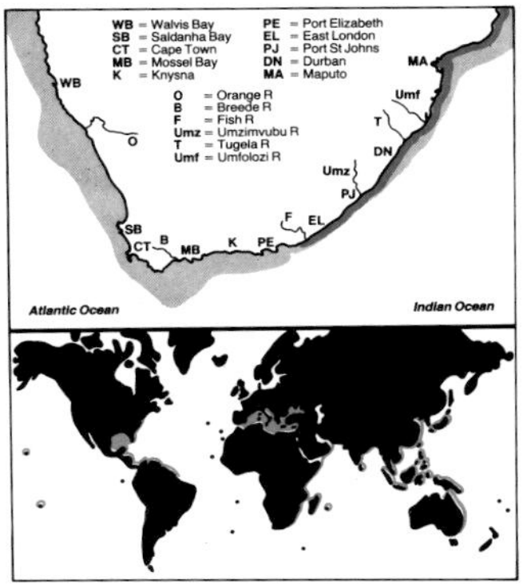

Leaf-like juvenile.

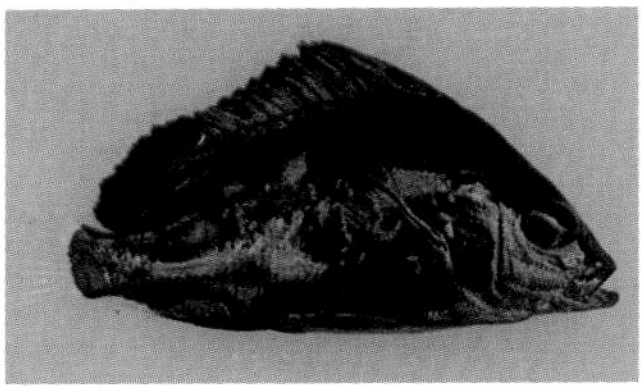

CAPTURE

Although they are nowhere abundant, many tripletails are caught unintentionally in fish traps and seine nets in the East. They are a strong-fighting, excellent sport fish of good eating quality. A variety of baits is successful in tempting tripletails. Poultry intestines are allegedly favoured by those inhabiting the Tugela Estuary. It is rarely speared by divers.
SA angling record – 16,8 kg.
SA spearfishing record – 2,2 kg.

SPECIFIC CATCH RESTRICTIONS
None.

NAME DERIVATION

Lobotes, a reference to its lobed fins; *surinamensis,* of Suriname, the region in which it was first found. Tripletail, a reference to the tri-lobed appearance of the hindquarters. Flasher, a reference to its sideways fighting stance when hooked.

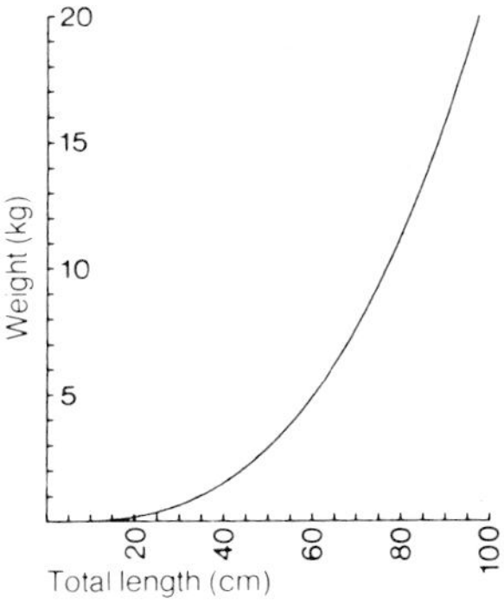

Aprion virescens

Valenciennes, 1830

Common names SA – kaakap. Elsewhere – green jobfish, streaker [Smith 181□3]

IDENTIFYING FEATURES

COLOUR, SHAPE AND SIZE

This large, sleek, but robust fish has a blunt snout. The bridge between the eyes is flat. The body colour is predominantly olive to dark green above, while the underside is pale. There appear to be two distinct populations of this species in the Indian Ocean, with the members of one growing much larger than those of the other. Can attain 110 cm.

EXTERNAL ANATOMY

Scales are strong and arranged in 48-50 series along the obvious lateral line. The upper snout and the region between the eyes are naked. The fins are well developed and include a single dorsal of ten spines plus 11 rays, an anal of three spines plus eight rays, and a deeply forked caudal with pointed lobes. The pectoral fins are short and almost equal to the length of the snout. The mouth is large, with fine bands of teeth in each jaw and several large canines in front. The moderately large eyes are preceded by a distinct horizontal groove. The first gill arch carries 19-24 rakers.

NATURAL HISTORY

The kaakap is a common and powerful predator of tropical and subtropical regions. It ranges from shallow coastal waters to depths of 100 m, but is most commonly found between midwater and the surface, directly above coral and rocky reefs. Though usually solitary, the kaakap does occasionally form loosely packed shoals which hunt swiftly over extensive areas of reef, especially at night. It may occur close to the sea-bed during daylight. Small reef fishes comprise about 50 per cent of the diet, but much of the balance is made up of plankton, including such organisms as fish eggs, larval mantis shrimps, megalopa crab larvae and swimming crabs. Spawning occurs in tropical East African waters from January to May, and the juveniles have been recorded far from land, borne along by ocean currents. Sexual maturity is reached at a length of 70-75 cm, at an equivalent age of 3-4 years.

DISTRIBUTION

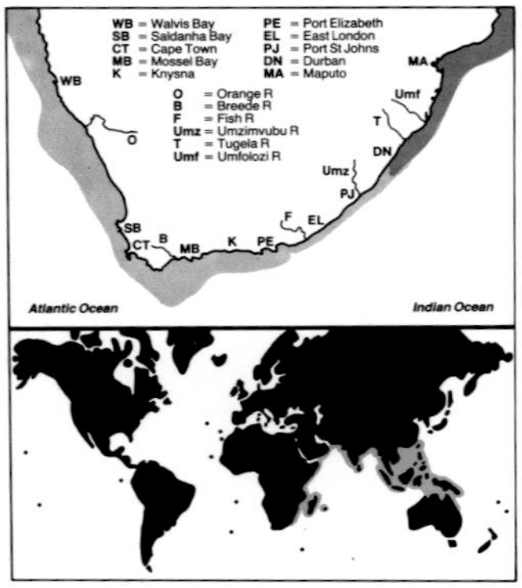

CAPTURE

When kaakap are present over a reef, they are certain to be first to strike, especially if a trolled bait or artificial lure is used. It is an excellent and sought-after game fish, and, though seldom caught by shore fishermen, it is commonly landed by ski-boat anglers, especially at Sodwana Bay in Zululand.

World angling record – 10 kg.
SA angling record – 12,8 kg.
SA spearfishing record – 12,0 kg.

SPECIFIC CATCH RESTRICTIONS

None.

NAME DERIVATION

Aprion, 'without a saw', an oblique reference to the skull structure; *virescens,* growing green. Kaakap, probably this name is of East Indian origin, and is believed to be a corruption of the Dutch *kaalkop,* meaning naked head.

SIMILAR SPECIES

The sleek body, relatively short pectoral, groove below the eye and absence of filamentous dorsal and anal rays should confirm the identity of this species.

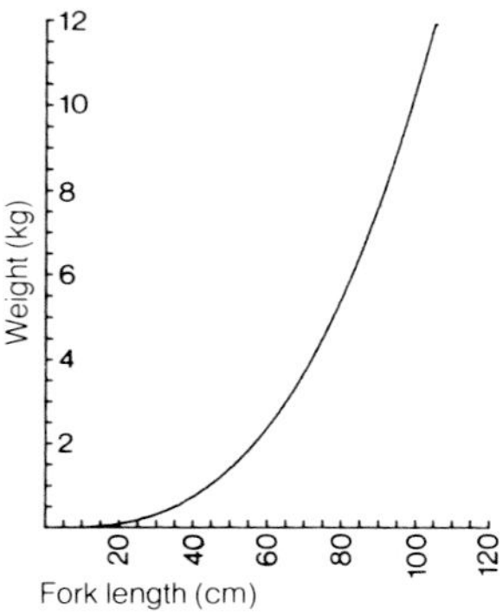

Lutjanus argentimaculatus

(Forsskål, 1775)
Common names SA – river snapper, river Roman. Elsewhere – mangrove red snapper
[Smith 181□5]

IDENTIFYING FEATURES

COLOUR, SHAPE AND SIZE
This large, robust fish has an elongate, coppery-red body with a paler underside. After death it becomes a deeper red overall. Whereas adults have no distinctive marks or patterns, juveniles of less than 15 cm are usually paler overall. In addition, these young fish have a number of darker longitudinal lines on the body and, occasionally, a few blue-green iridescent streaks on the head. Can attain 100 cm.

EXTERNAL ANATOMY
The body is well covered with strong scales arranged in 44-56 series along the lateral line. The scales above the lateral line run parallel to it in front, but slant obliquely upwards below the soft dorsals. The fins are well developed and include a single dorsal of ten spines plus 13-15 rays, an anal of three spines plus 7-9 rays, and a truncate caudal. The large mouth bears bands of teeth, those of the outer band in each jaw being enlarged. Both jaws are also armed with a pair of conspicuous canine teeth. Rakers are reduced and number 14-16 on the first gill arch.

NATURAL HISTORY

This relatively common and widespread snapper is a powerful predator, and, though younger individuals frequent small estuaries, older fish only occur over offshore reefs down to 80 m. It is a patient hunter, and will remain motionless until the very last moment before making a great rush towards unsuspecting prey. In estuaries this includes mullet and stumpnose in particular, while offshore, a variety of reef fish, crabs and crayfish are eaten. The 'ambushing' tactics, employed when hunting, are most effective when the river snapper is hidden in a cave, below some rocky ledge or amongst prop roots of mangrove trees. The young are more common in estuaries, where they can tolerate very reduced salinity levels. Larger fish move offshore, where spawning occurs during summer among specimens longer than 45-60 cm. The fry are widely distributed by ocean currents, but, when about 5 cm long, they migrate into estuarine nursery areas.

DISTRIBUTION

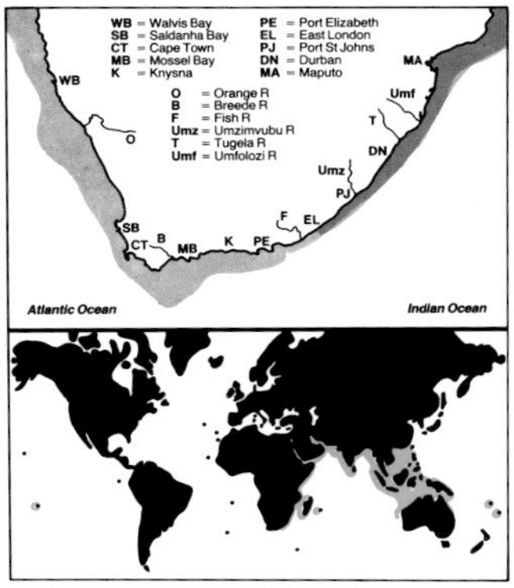

CAPTURE

The river snapper is one of the finest and most exciting estuarine angling fish, as it eagerly swoops on any live fish bait. Some specimens are caught using fish fillets and prawns, while ski-boat anglers succeed with a variety of baits. It is equally popular with spearfishermen. The flesh of this snapper makes excellent eating.
SA angling record – 12,2 kg.
SA spearfishing record – 16,6 kg.

SPECIFIC CATCH RESTRICTIONS

None.

NAME DERIVATION

Lutjanus, from the Malayan *Ikan lutjang,* a common name for this family; *argentimaculatus,* silver spotted. River snapper, a reference to its estuarine habitat and fierce jaws.

SIMILAR SPECIES

The direction of scale rows is a critical distinguishing feature.

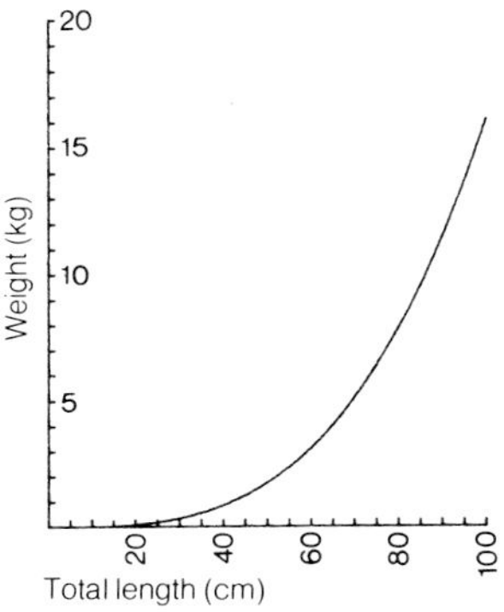

Lutjanus bohar

(Forsskål, 1775)
Common names SA - twinspot snapper. Elsewhere - twospot snapper
[Smith 181□6]

IDENTIFYING FEATURES

COLOUR, SHAPE AND SIZE
This elongate, robust fish is purple-red in colour, but much darker above, and it often has yellowish cheeks. The scales along the flanks have pale centres. The fins are dark, with some partially edged in white, while the tips of the dorsal spines are distinctly white. Juveniles have two, obvious, white blotches just below the dorsal fin. Can attain 75 cm.

EXTERNAL ANATOMY
There are 48-53 series of distinct scales arranged along the lateral line, those on the upper body running obliquely upwards and those below usually running horizontally. The fins are well developed, and include a single dorsal of ten spines plus 13-14 rays, an anal of three spines plus eight rays, and an emarginate caudal. The pectorals are long, and reach a point opposite the origin of the anal fin. The large mouth bears a single row of conical teeth in each jaw, with several of the forward pairs enlarged into canines. Villiform teeth occur deeper within the mouth. The first gill arch carries 13-18 rakers. A distinct groove runs across the snout from the eyes to the nostrils.

NATURAL HISTORY

The twinspot snapper is fairly common over tropical and subtropical reefs ranging from shallow waters to depths of 70 m. It is a solitary, unobtrusive species and inhabits caves, or hides below coral overhangs. Here it feeds aggressively on other species of fish, especially smaller reef dwellers which make up 50 per cent of the diet. The balance comprises crabs, prawns, mantis shrimps, pteropods, mysids and marine worms. Larger fish show a marked preference for squid. Breeding takes place in tropical East African waters throughout the year, but is particularly intense during March and again in October-November. Spawning occurs mainly over the continental slope. Sexual maturity is attained after about five years, at a corresponding length of 45-50 cm. Males grow considerably larger than females. Juveniles mimic harmless damselfishes and, so doing, can unobtrusively approach their prey, which would otherwise have swum away.

DISTRIBUTION

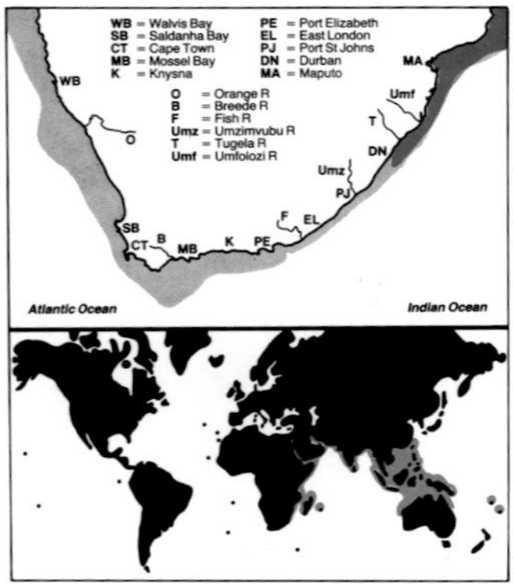

SPECIFIC CATCH RESTRICTIONS

None.

CAPTURE

Although not a target species in southern African waters, the twinspot snapper is nevertheless a fine ski-boat angling fish that takes a variety of baits and fights strongly. It is also popular with more experienced spearfishermen. Many are caught on handlines in the South China Sea, where they represent a valuable food source. Though it makes fine eating, it has been implicated in ciguatera poisoning, on some tropical islands but never in South Africa. As with several members of this family, it repeatedly snaps its mouth open and shut after capture, a hazard to careless handlers.
SA angling record - vacant.
SA spearfishing record - 11,0 kg.

NAME DERIVATION

Lutjanus, from the Malayan *Ikan lutjang,* a common name for this family; *bohar,* obscure, possibly of Arabic origin. Twinspot snapper, a reference to the two white blotches on the bodies of juveniles and to its snapping jaws.

SIMILAR SPECIES

This species, often confused with the river snapper, is best distinguished by the differences in scale directions on the upper flanks.

Lutjanus fulviflamma
(Forsskål, 1775)
Comon names SA – spotsnapper, greedy guts. Elsewhere – blackspot snapper
[Smith 181□8]

IDENTIFYING FEATURES

COLOUR, SHAPE AND SIZE

This small, elongate fish is greenish above, silvery-pink below and usually marked with longitudinal golden stripes (especially in younger fish). A conspicuous black blotch occurs on the lateral line below the junction of the dorsal spines and rays. Can attain 35 cm.

EXTERNAL ANATOMY

The body is covered with scales arranged in 40-50 series along the distinct lateral line. The fins are well developed and include a single dorsal of 10-11 spines plus 12 or 13 rays, an anal of three spines plus eight rays, a caudal fin that is almost truncate, and long pectoral fins that reach a point opposite the origin of the anal fin. Several rows of fine teeth occur in each jaw, the outer row comprising conical teeth in addition to several canines. There is also an arrowhead-shaped patch of fine teeth on the palate. The first gill arch carries about ten short rakers on the lower limb.

DISTRIBUTION

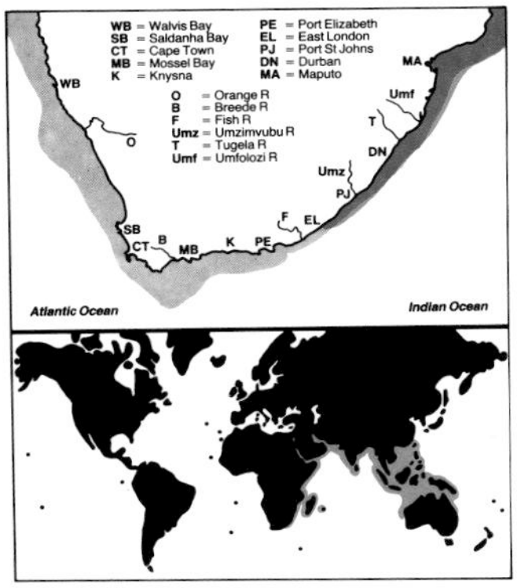

NATURAL HISTORY

The spotsnapper is certainly one of the most widespread of the Lutjanidae. It is especially common off rocky shores, but is equally at home in estuaries, over muddy bottoms or in stands of eelgrass. Most of those frequenting estuaries, however, are juveniles ranging from 2-12 cm in length. The diet includes a variety of small crustaceans, particularly crabs, isopods, prawns, mantis shrimps, mysids and marine worms. Small fish, especially anchovies and gobies, are also eagerly consumed when available. Although not a shoaling species, the spotsnapper does congregate in groups, and the young often associate with juvenile stumpnose in estuaries. The spoiling of many estuarine nursery areas, and the removal of eelgrass beds have resulted in a lowered abundance of this species in some regions. Sexual maturity is attained at a length of 16-17 cm and spawning takes place over deeper reefs from August to December.

CAPTURE

Though small, this fine eating fish is popular with younger anglers and freely takes small shrimp bait. Some are caught from ski-boats over deeper reefs. It is a valued aquarium specimen, but is frequently rather aggressive towards its fellow 'inmates'.
SA angling record – vacant.

SPECIFIC CATCH RESTRICTIONS

None.

NAME DERIVATION

Lutjanus, from the Malayan *Ikan lutjang,* a common name for this family; *fulviflamma,* tawny fire, a reference to its golden stripes. Spotsnapper, a reference to the distinct black blotch on each side, and to its snapping jaws.

SIMILAR SPECIES

In its adult phase, this species is easily confused with Russell's snapper. Note, however, that the spot snapper usually has 13 dorsal rays while Russell's snapper has fourteen. While there are other differences in detail, the distinction between these two species in the field remains a problem.

Lutjanus gibbus

(Forsskål, 1775)
Common name Worldwide – humpback snapper
[Smith 181□10]

IDENTIFYING FEATURES

COLOUR, SHAPE AND SIZE
This deep-bodied fish is red overall, but dusky above and somewhat lighter below. The caudal, second dorsal and anal fins are all edged in white and the pectoral axils are bright orange. Can attain 50 cm.

EXTERNAL ANATOMY
The body is covered with distinct scales arranged in 45-55 series along the well-defined lateral line. The scales all run obliquely upwards. The strong fins include a single dorsal of ten spines plus 13-15 rays and an anal of three spines plus eight or nine rays. Two diagnostic features of the humpback snapper are the rounded lobes of the forked caudal fin and the deep, narrow notch in the pre-operculum into which an articulating knob fits snugly. The small, sharp canine teeth are set in rows in each jaw. The eyes are relatively large and the first gill arch carries about 25 small, but well-developed rakers.

DISTRIBUTION

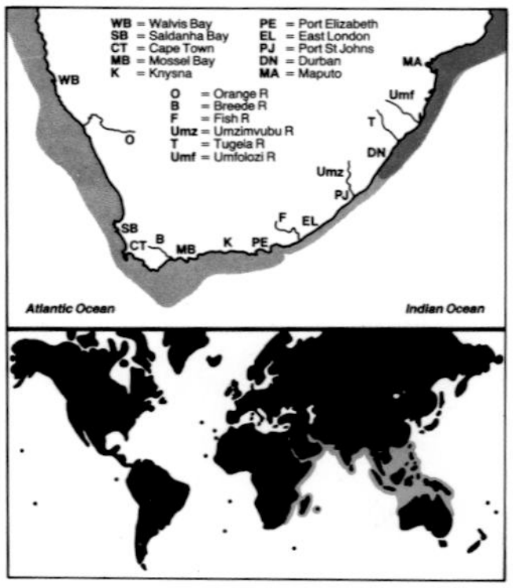

NATURAL HISTORY

The humpback snapper is a tropical species which inhabits rocky and coral reef areas as deep as 60 m. It is not typically a shoaling fish, but small groups may congregate, often with one or two individual fish hurrying from pinnacle to pinnacle, presumably scouting for food. The diet consists primarily of invertebrates such as small crabs, coral shrimps, barnacles and small squid. As this species is most active at night, however, it also feeds extensively on nocturnal organisms, especially zooplankton, which is taken near the surface. The humpback snapper is most common in southern African waters during the summer, but no spawning fish have been recorded here. Juveniles are known to shelter in tropical estuaries, especially those with extensive mangrove stands. Details of its life history are sparse, though sexual maturity is known to occur at a length of 25-30 cm.

SPECIFIC CATCH RESTRICTIONS

None.

CAPTURE

Ski-boat anglers and spearfishermen often land this fish, but it is rarely caught from the shore. Though its flesh is edible, specimens caught in tropical waters have been held responsible for cases of ciguatera poisoning. It is, nevertheless, an important source of food, and, in the East, most are caught by handlines and in traps.
SA angling record – vacant.
SA spearfishing record – vacant.

NAME DERIVATION

Lutjanus, from the Malayan *Ikan lutjang,* a common name for this family; *gibbus,* convex. Humpback snapper, a reference to its particularly deep body, and to the snapping jaws.

SIMILAR SPECIES

There is little chance of misidentification here, as the humpback with its deep body, opercular notch and rounded caudal fins is most distinctive.

Lutjanus kasmira

(Forsskål, 1775)
Common name Worldwide – bluebanded snapper
[Smith 181□11]

IDENTIFYING FEATURES

COLOUR, SHAPE AND SIZE

This rather elongate snapper has a vivid yellow body with a reddish underside. Four broad, bright-blue stripes run along the upper flanks, with 7-10 narrower stripes occurring along the lower sides. These conspicuous markings are all finely edged in black or dark brown. This pattern is characteristic and distinguishes the bluebanded snapper from two or three closely related species. The fins are yellow, and in many, but not all, specimens there is a black blotch on each flank just below the dorsal fin rays. Can attain 30 cm.

EXTERNAL ANATOMY

Distinct scales cover the body and are arranged in 49-51 series, with those above the lateral line running obliquely upwards. The fins are well developed, and include a single dorsal of ten spines plus 14-15 rays; an anal of three spines plus eight rays, and long pectoral fins that reach a point opposite the vent. The caudal fin is slightly forked. Both jaws are lined with small, sharp teeth. A notch occurs in the pre-operculum. The first gill arch carries 19-21 rakers, at least five of which are very short.

NATURAL HISTORY

The bluebanded snapper is gregarious, and stationary shoals are usually found around the pinnacles or ledges of coral and rocky reefs at depths of 50-60 m. At night these fish become more active when they feed on small shrimps, crabs, fish and zooplankton. Sexual maturity is attained at a length of 17-20 cm, and spawning appears to occur only once a year, during late winter and spring. Males tend to outnumber females in some localized areas, but this seeming imbalance, largely based on catch statistics, could well be attributed to the inherently 'greedier' nature of male fish. The young are distributed over large areas and though their nursery areas are unknown, it is probable that most juveniles grow to sexual maturity within the reef environment.

DISTRIBUTION

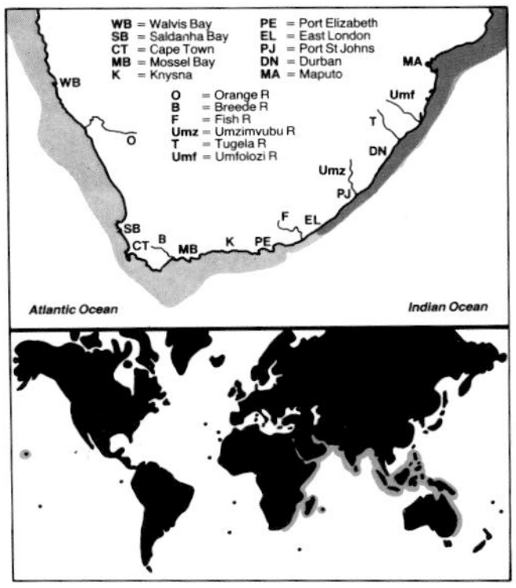

CAPTURE

Catches in southern African waters are not excessive, but in parts of India this fish may constitute 20-30 per cent of the annual commercial linefish catch. The flesh of the bluebanded snapper is excellent, but, as most specimens are rather small, the species is not a target for anglers. Aquarists with large tanks keep these fish with some success.

SPECIFIC CATCH RESTRICTIONS

None.

NAME DERIVATION

Lutjanus, from the Malayan *Ikan lutjang,* a common name for this family; *kasmira,* rather obscure, but possibly an Arabic reference to its striking colours. Bluebanded snapper, a reference to its obvious markings and to its snapping jaws.

SIMILAR SPECIES

A number of other snappers are yellow with blue lines, but only one other occurs in this region – the rarer *L. notatus,* which has 6-7 blue lines on its upper flanks.

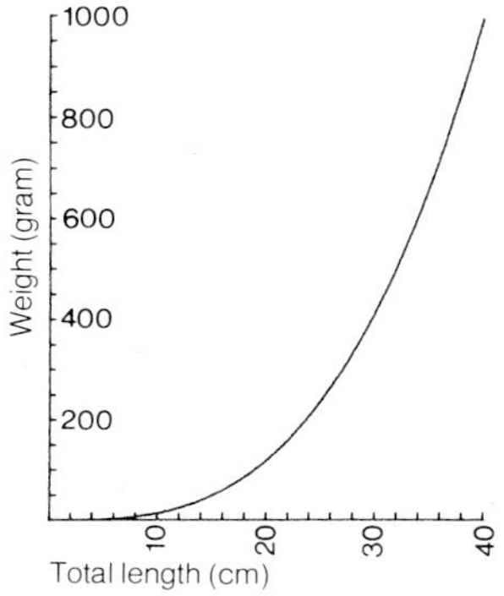

Lutjanus rivulatus

(Cuvier, 1828)
Common name Worldwide – speckled snapper
[Smith 181□16]

IDENTIFYING FEATURES

COLOUR, SHAPE AND SIZE

This deep-bodied, almost oval-shaped fish has variable colours. Most specimens are yellowish-brown overall, but somewhat lighter below. Numerous blue lines mark the head, and these become dotted in older fish. The scales have silvery-grey spots edged in black. Juveniles often have a white spot on each flank. The fins are yellow, but sometimes the caudal, pectoral and anal fins may be blue. The pectoral axils are occasionally black. Can attain 75 cm.

EXTERNAL ANATOMY

The lateral line is clearly visible and arranged along its length are 46-49 series of well-developed scales. While the scales above the lateral line run obliquely upwards, those below run horizontally. The fins include a single dorsal of ten spines plus 15 or 16 rays and an anal of three spines plus eight or nine rays, the third and fourth of which are the longest. The pectoral fins are long and reach a point above the anal spines. The caudal is slightly emarginate. A pre-opercular notch is present, though it is rather small. Both jaws carry an outer band of conical teeth, the front three pairs of which are considerably enlarged. Several inner rows of villiform teeth also occur. The first rakers on the gill arch are stubby, and vary in number from 13-17.

NATURAL HISTORY

This fish inhabits tropical reefs, and, though it may occur to considerable depths, some are quite at home in remarkably shallow water. The speckled snapper usually lives in caves or underneath ledges where it presumably lies in wait for prey. The diet consists mainly of various slow-swimming reef fishes, as well as crabs, polychaete worms, squid, octopuses, sea urchins and ascidians (redbait). If holed up in its cave or crevice, this fish will allow an intruder to approach quite closely before hurrying to some new shelter. Just before dashing off, however, it will beat its tail noisily against the sides of its cave, possibly in an attempt to intimidate the trespasser. The speckled snapper has an extended breeding season, but most spawning occurs during the summer months. Sexual maturity is attained at a length of about 45 cm. The dispersal of juveniles, however, remains obscure.

DISTRIBUTION

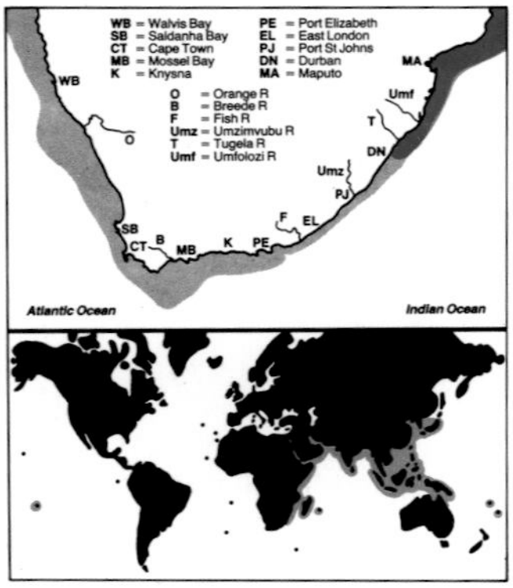

SPECIFIC CATCH RESTRICTIONS

None.

CAPTURE

Though relatively few individuals are landed, the speckled snapper is popular with rock and surf anglers as well as with spearfishermen, as it is both a fine eating fish and a strong fighter. In the East it represents a valued food source. In tropical climates care must be taken in cleaning the fish, as the liver and intestines have, at times, been responsible for cases of ciguatera poisoning.

SA angling record – 9,1 kg.
SA spearfishing record – 11,0 kg.

NAME DERIVATION

Lutjanus, from *Ikan lutjang,* a common Malayan name for this family; *rivulatus,* marked with rill-like streaks. Speckled snapper, a reference to its markings and to its snapping jaws.

SIMILAR SPECIES

No other snapper has the same colours and body patterns. Furthermore, the deep body, great size and ten dorsal spines are also distinctive.

Lutjanus russelli

(Bleeker, 1849)

Common names Worldwide – Russell's snapper, one-spot snapper

[Smith 181□17]

IDENTIFYING FEATURES

COLOUR, SHAPE AND SIZE

This fairly elongate, yet robust snapper is strikingly, but variably coloured. In most specimens the basic body colour is yellow-brown above with a deep-red head. Most conspicuous on each flank is a black blotch which overlies the lateral line directly below the point where the dorsal spines and rays meet. Many specimens also have about eight, brownish bands extending along the flanks. The pelvic, anal and caudal fins are yellow. Can attain 40 cm, but rarely exceeds 28 cm.

EXTERNAL ANATOMY

There are about 50 series of scales arranged along the distinct lateral line, those above it running obliquely upwards. Spines are prominent in the fins and the single dorsal consists of ten spines plus 14 or 15 rays, while the anal has three spines plus eight or nine rays. The pectorals are considerably elongate, and the caudal fin is barely forked. Strong, canine teeth occur in both jaws, in addition to several rows of smaller teeth. On the roof of the mouth there is a triangular patch of backward-pointing villiform teeth. The first gill arch carries about nine short rakers. This fish is often confused with the spotsnapper, but the number of rays in the dorsal fin is diagnostic for each, and, once known, the two species can be easily distinguished.

NATURAL HISTORY

Russell's snapper is common over shallow coral and rocky reefs throughout the Indo-Pacific, and is also found in tidal pools. It is an aggressive and rather territorial fish, fiercely pouncing on any prey that may stray within range. Its food consists almost entirely of crustaceans, and analysis of the stomach contents of landed specimens indicates a predominance of small crabs in the diet. This snapper normally occurs in small groups and shows a preference for living in shallow caves or below rocky overhangs. Spawning occurs from October to February and the juveniles use intertidal pools, as well as mangrove areas, as nurseries.

DISTRIBUTION

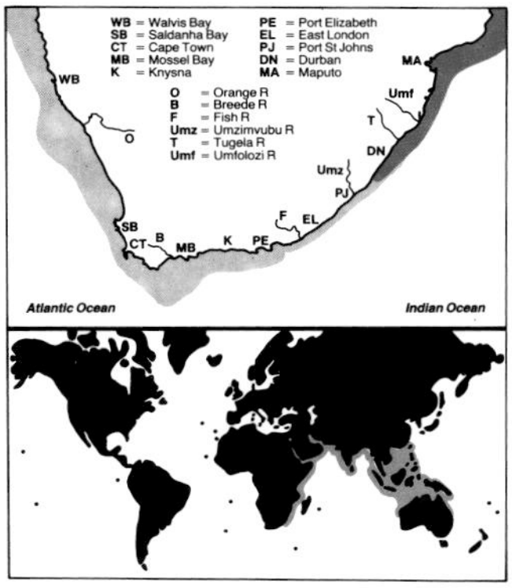

CAPTURE

Though not regarded as an important angling fish, Russell's snapper is easily caught on light tackle, and will occasionally take an artificial lure. Its flesh makes good eating.

SA angling record – 1,0 kg.

SPECIFIC CATCH RESTRICTIONS

None.

NAME DERIVATION

Lutjanus, from *Ikan lutjang,* a common Malayan name for this family; *russelli,* named after the ichthyologist, Russell. Russell's snapper, derived from the scientific name, and a reference to the snapping jaws.

SIMILAR SPECIES

Most specimens have 14 dorsal fin rays, which aids distinction with the 13 rayed spot snapper.

Lutjanus sanguineus

(Cuvier, 1828)
Common name Worldwide - bloodsnapper
[Smith 181□18]

IDENTIFYING FEATURES

COLOUR, SHAPE AND SIZE
The shape of this robust fish varies considerably with growth and adults develop a distinctive and protruding forehead. The general body colour is bright red with a silvery underside. Juveniles, however, have longitudinal stripes along the body and a dark band running from each eye to the dorsal fin. A saddle-like blotch, indistinct in most large specimens, occurs on the caudal peduncle. The fins are reddish and occasionally edged in black.
Can attain 90 cm.
EXTERNAL ANATOMY
There are 55-60 series of scales arranged along the obvious lateral line. Scales below the lateral line run horizontally, but those above slope upwards towards the tail region. The fins are well developed and include a single dorsal of 11 spines plus 13-15 rays, an anal of three spines plus nine or ten rays and an emarginate caudal. The bridge between the eyes is relatively narrow. The pre-operculum has a shallow, inconspicuous notch and the first gill arch carries 17-19 short rakers. Each jaw bears a row of conical teeth, two pairs of which are enlarged, as well as several rows of villiform teeth within. There is also a 'V'-shaped patch of fine teeth on the roof of the mouth.

NATURAL HISTORY

The bloodsnapper is a reef fish ranging to depths of 100 m. It does, however, display a distinct preference for slightly silty, turbid regions in the vicinity of sometimes quite shallow, offshore banks. Here it may replace *L. sebae* as the dominant snapper. It is mainly a nocturnal feeder and preys largely on a variety of reef-dwelling fish as well as invertebrates such as prawns, crabs, mantis shrimps, squid and zooplankton. Sexual maturity is attained after about six years at a corresponding length of 50-55 cm. Spawning occurs in the tropical waters off East Africa during June and July. Neither spawning adults nor very young fish have been recorded from southern African waters.

DISTRIBUTION

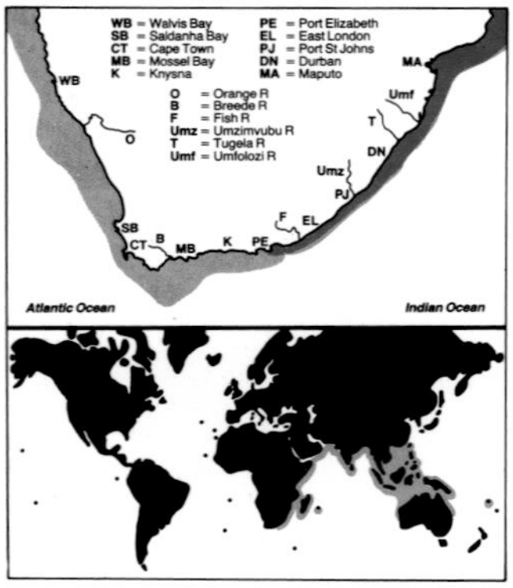

CAPTURE

Most catches of ths species are made from ski-boats or commercial line-boats operating off the coasts of Zululand and Mocambique. Spearfishermen occasionally shoot this fine eating fish. As with most other members of the family, bloodsnappers caught in tropical regions should be carefully gutted and washed to prevent ciguatera poisoning.
SA angling record - 8,6 kg.
SA spearfishing record - 9,4 kg.

SPECIFIC CATCH RESTRICTIONS

None.

NAME DERIVATION

Lutjanus, from the Malayan *Ikan lutjang,* a common name for this family; *sanguineus,* bloody. Bloodsnapper, a reference to its bright red overall colouration and to its snapping jaws.

SIMILAR SPECIES

This snapper is quite unmistakable as it is the only species with an overall red colour and bulbous forehead. Apparently the name *L. coccineus* has also been applied to this species.

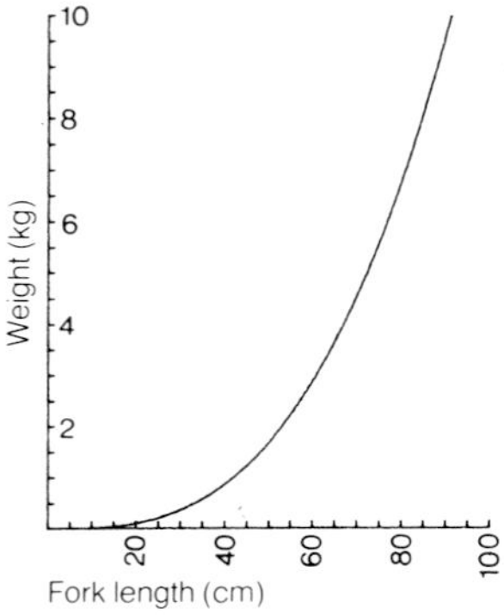

Lutjanus sebae

(Cuvier, 1828)
Common name Worldwide – emperor snapper
[Smith 181□19]

IDENTIFYING FEATURES

COLOUR, SHAPE AND SIZE
This snapper is robust, very deep bodied, and has a steep head profile. The overall colouration of adults is deep red, but each scale along the flanks has a pale centre. Young fish are marked with three distinct, darker, broad bars on the body; the first incorporates the snout; the second runs across the mid-body region, directly below the dorsal spines; and the third includes the soft dorsal fin and the tail region. The fins are reddish, and the soft anal and dorsal fins, as well as the caudal fin, may have pale margins. Can attain 100 cm.
EXTERNAL ANATOMY
The body is well covered with scales arranged in 45-60 series along the distinct lateral line. The scales on the upper flanks, and in the region of the tail, run obliquely upwards, while those below are horizontal. The fins are well developed, and include a single dorsal of 11 spines plus 15 or 16 rays, and an anal of three spines plus 10-11 rays. The pectoral fins reach the soft anal fin, and the caudal is moderately forked. The pre-operculum notch and knob are quite distinct, as are the 12-14 stubby rakers on the first gill arch. Both jaws bear rows of fine teeth, those of the outer row being enlarged and conical.

NATURAL HISTORY

Though it is not abundant this fish is found over most tropical, rocky and coral reefs. Some specimens will range to depths of 100 m. Feeding occurs both during the day and at night, and the diet consists primarily of crustaceans such as crabs, shrimps and crayfish. Occasionally, fish and squid are also eaten. Spawning occurs in more tropical regions; this is borne out by the fact that juveniles are known to make use of tropical estuarine mangrove swamps as nursery areas. The breeding season is fairly protracted, extending from November to April. Sexual maturity is attained at an age of four years and at a length of 60-70 cm. Males grow larger than females. On maturity, the emperor snapper loses its distinctive banded colouration. At this stage it also generally becomes the dominant predator on the reef and can often be seen chasing intruders from its territory.

DISTRIBUTION

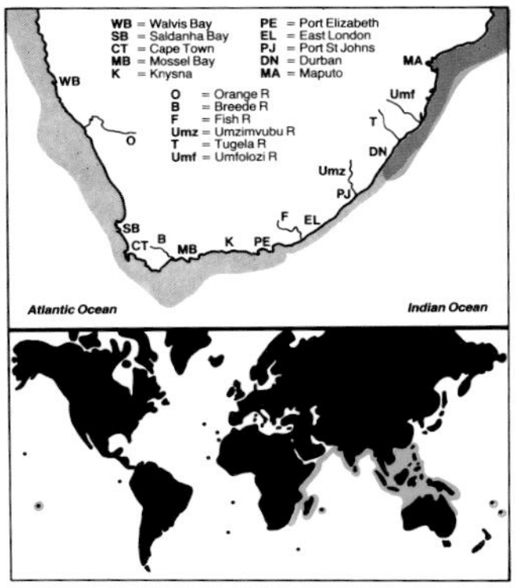

CAPTURE

Most emperor snappers are caught by ski-boat anglers, while some are speared by divers. The flesh is very palatable, but can cause ciguatera poisoning. However, if each fish is carefully gutted, the species can represent a valuable source of food.

SPECIFIC CATCH RESTRICTIONS

None.

NAME DERIVATION

Lutjanus, from the Malayan *Ikan lutjang,* a common name for the members of this family; *sebae,* tallow or fatty. Emperor snapper, a probable reference to its rich colours and dominating presence on a reef, and to its snapping jaws.

SIMILAR SPECIES

The combination of dorsal fin counts, reddish, deep body, and three broad crossbars should confirm identity.

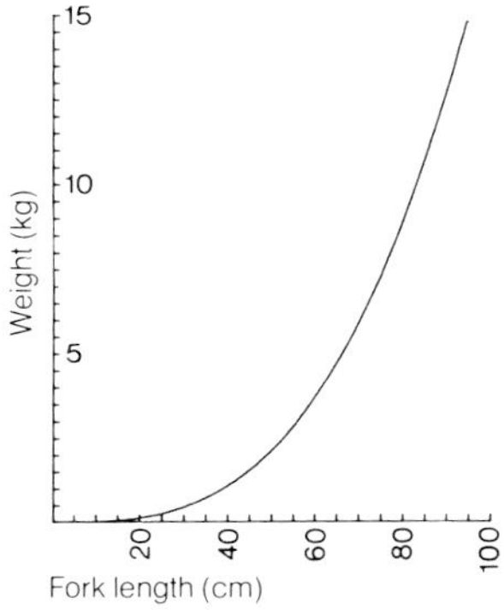

Pristipomoides filamentosus

(Valenciennes, 1830)
Common name Worldwide - rosy jobfish
[Smith 181□22]

IDENTIFYING FEATURES

COLOUR, SHAPE AND SIZE
The rosy jobfish is elongate and almost spindle-shaped. The body is silvery overall, but light reddish to brown above and paler below. Yellow dots often occur on top of the head. The fins are translucent to dusky and the soft dorsal and caudal fins may be edged in darker red. Two longitudinal yellowish lines can also sometimes be seen on the dorsal fin. Can attain 100 cm.in length.

EXTERNAL ANATOMY
The very distinct scales are arranged in 57-65 series along the lateral line. The fins are well developed and include a single dorsal of ten spines plus 11 rays, an anal of three spines plus eight rays, and a forked caudal. Characteristic are the elongate hind rays of both the dorsal and anal fins. There is no pre-opercular notch, and the first gill arch carries 23-25 short rakers. Each jaw bears a single row of conical teeth, with the front three or four pairs considerably enlarged into canines. There are also finer bands of villiform teeth in the upper jaw, in the front of the lower jaw, and also on the roof of the mouth.

NATURAL HISTORY

The rosy jobfish is more pelagic than most other Lutjanidae, and in many respects its behaviour resembles that of the kaakap. Whereas it is usually associated with the reef environment, it is most frequently seen or caught in midwater, often to depths of 150 m. Some have even been found over muddy bottoms at 180 m. Although this is a tropically dispersed species it generally prefers slightly cooler water and consequently ranges to greater depths to find lower temperatures below the thermocline. Seasonally, or when hydrological conditions permit, these fish will move on to shallower reefs. The diet comprises a variety of organisms including free-swimming crustaceans such as mantis shrimps and mysids, as well as squid and fish. Not all the diet is midwater, however, and the occasional presence of ascidians and algae suggest that some bottom feeding does occur. Reproductive biology in southern African waters is not known.

DISTRIBUTION

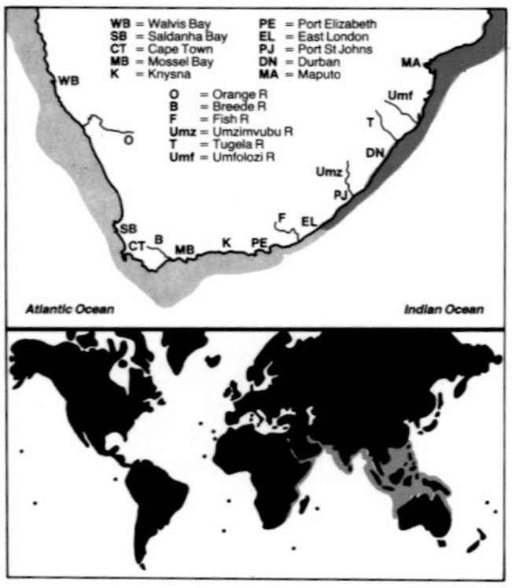

CAPTURE

During summer, ski-boat anglers land fair catches of this species along the Zululand coast. Recently, good catches were reported on Protea Banks at 100 m. Some large specimens have been landed by divers, but as most rosy jobfish are considerably smaller than their maximum size would indicate, few are of interest to spearfishermen. It is an excellent eating fish, and a valued food resource in tropical regions.
SA angling record – 3,07 kg.

SPECIFIC CATCH RESTRICTIONS

None.

NAME DERIVATION

Pristipomoides, without a serrated operculum; *filamentosus.* Rosy jobfish, a reference to its colour and an obscure allusion to the biblical Job.

SIMILAR SPECIES

The very long pectorals, filamentous last dorsal and anal rays, and presence of canine teeth are distinctive of this genus. Notice that the rosy jobfish has no clip in its dorsal fin profile - as in the case of the ruby snapper. *(Etelis coruscans).* The rather similar smalltooth jobfish *(Aphareus rutilans)* has a strikingly silver colour to its gills and mouth cavity. The rosy jobfish can further be distinguished from its close relatives by having more than 50 scales along the lateral line and 23-25 gill rakers.

Megalops cyprinoides

(Broussonet, 1782)
Common names SA – oxeye tarpon. Elsewhere – Indo-Pacific tarpon
[Smith 37□1]

IDENTIFYING FEATURES

COLOUR, SHAPE AND SIZE
This species is fairly elongate and compressed, with a distinctively 'pitched' dorsal profile, and a gently rounded belly. The body has an overall silvery sheen, with a blue-green back and white belly. Can attain 60 cm.

EXTERNAL ANATOMY
The oxeye tarpon has 30-40 series of firm, cycloid scales arranged along the conspicuous lateral line. All the fins are spineless and the single dorsal comprises 17-20 rays (the last of which is noticeably long), while the anal fin comprises 24-31 rays. The caudal fin is large and deeply forked. The upper jaw of the large, toothless, upward-opening mouth almost reaches a point below the hind edge of the eyes. The lower jaw protrudes slightly, giving the fish an undershot appearance. There are long rakers on the gill arches. The large eyes are covered with a layer of transparent, fatty tissue.

DISTRIBUTION

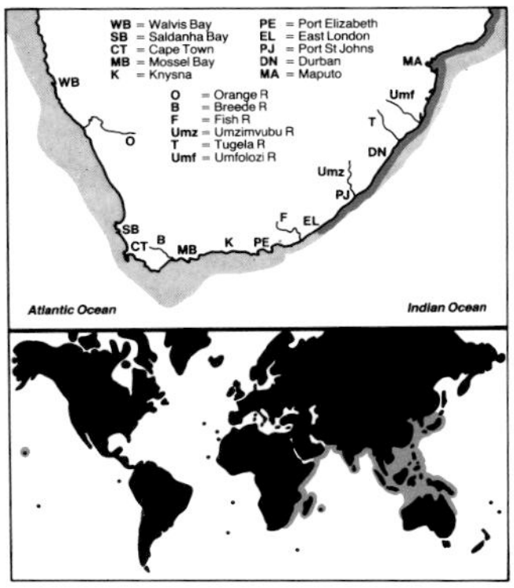

NATURAL HISTORY

The oxeye tarpon is a solitary species of coastal and, particularly, estuarine waters, but nowhere does it occur in great numbers. It is completely tolerant of fresh water, and, in parts of Moçambique and Zululand, tarpon live in freshwater pans isolated from the sea. As the strong caudal fin with its stout peduncle would suggest, this fish is a powerful swimmer. It hunts at speed, voraciously consuming small pelagic fish, the fry of larger species, and shrimps. Tarpon are prolific breeders and millions of eggs are produced each season which hatch into larvae. These fry closely resemble the ribbon-like, transparent young of eels, and it is probably during this developmental stage that these small fish wriggle their way up streams and ditches to enter freshwater lakes. These leptocephalus larvae have forked tails and shrink to half their size when changing into the recognizable tarpon shape.

CAPTURE

Though infrequently caught, once hooked, the oxeye tarpon fights superbly, providing the angler with a formidable adversary. While small in South African waters, the tarpon is an excellent target for artificial-lure fishermen. This species has no commercial value, and the flesh is insipid and very bony. Its close, but much larger, Atlantic relative is one of the world's finest gamefish, and off Angola and the United States it attains 128 kg.

All-Africa angling record – 1,8 kg.
SA angling record – 3,0 kg.
SA spearfishing record – vacant.

SPECIFIC CATCH RESTRICTIONS

None.

NAME DERIVATION

Megalops, large eye; *cyprinoides,* resembling a carp. Oxeye tarpon, from its large eyes and a corruption of *tarpum*, a Red Indian name for this fish.

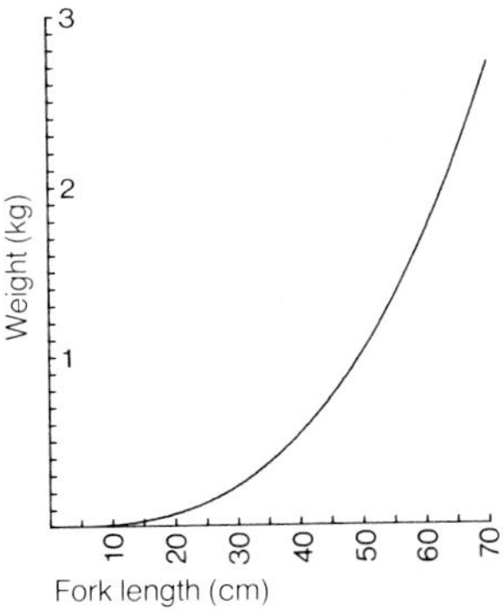

Mene maculata

(Bloch & Schneider, 1801)
Common names Worldwide – moonfish or ponyfish
[Smith 200□1]

IDENTIFYING FEATURES

COLOUR, SHAPE AND SIZE

The moonfish is disc-shaped and extremely compressed, and the very deep belly and breast regions narrow to a sharp edge. The body is silvery overall, but the dorsal surface and upper flanks are deep blue. There are two or three rows of large, dark spots arranged immediately above and below the lateral line. The fins are translucent to dusky, and the caudal fin is sometimes yellowish. Can attain 20 cm in length.

EXTERNAL ANATOMY

Scales are present, but are too small to be obvious, and the lateral line ends short of the tail. The fins are small, and include a dorsal of three or four inconspicuous spines plus 40-43 rays, an anal of 30-33 rays, and a forked caudal. With increased age, the pelvic fins become longer and the dorsal spines fewer. The terminal mouth has protractile jaws which extend upwards when opened. Even when closed, the jaws slant almost vertically upwards and both are set with minute teeth.

NATURAL HISTORY

Although this coastal shoaling fish is not rare, it is seldom seen because few are caught by anglers. It is most common in the tropics, but during summer the moonfish ventures southwards into southern African waters. However, none of the specimens caught locally has been reproductively active. Tolerance to changes in salinity and turbidity allows the moonfish to enter estuaries and, during stormy conditions, it may seek shelter behind reefs. The diet and feeding habits are not well known but, taking into account its protractile jaws and tiny teeth, it probably sucks up minute planktonic organisms such as crab and crayfish larvae, mysids and larval fish.

DISTRIBUTION

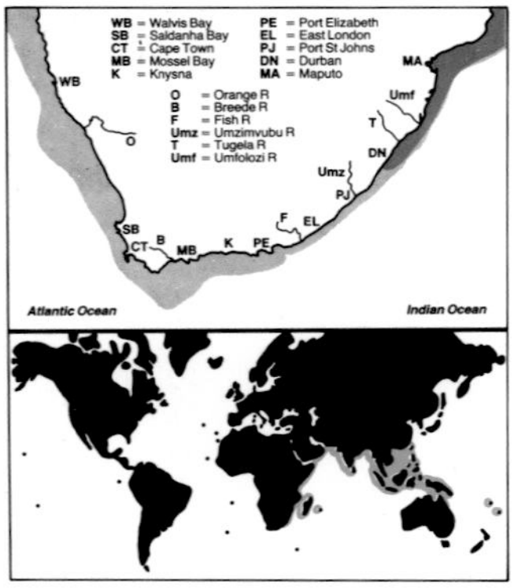

SPECIFIC CATCH RESTRICTIONS

None.

NAME DERIVATION

Mene, moon-like; *maculata,* spotted. Moonfish, a reference to its disc- or moon-shaped body.

CAPTURE

It is not caught on rod and line by anglers, but is often netted in Natal beach-seines. In India and other eastern countries, many are caught in fish traps and eaten dried.

SIMILAR SPECIES

The moonfish is not easily confused with other species, though it vaguely resembles the soapies and moonies. It may be positively identified by the complete absence of scales, and very poorly developed spines.

Merluccius capensis

Castelnau, 1861
Common name Worldwide - hake
[Smith 89□4]

IDENTIFYING FEATURES

COLOUR, SHAPE AND SIZE
This elongate and fairly robust fish has a somewhat depressed head. It is rather drab in appearance. The overall colouration of living specimens is silvery-grey, but this fades rapidly to dull grey after death. The underside is whitish and the fins are grey. Attains 140 cm.
EXTERNAL ANATOMY
The lateral line is quite distinct and along it are arranged 125-140 series of small scales. The fins are large but primitive, as spines are lacking and the rays are unbranched. The membranous tissue between the rays is extremely fragile and invariably tears during capture. The double dorsal fin consists of 10-12 rays, followed by a second fin of 38-42 rays. The anal fin has 37-41 rays, and is at least half the length of the entire body. The caudal fin is truncate. The hake has rather big eyes which are set well forward on the head. Both jaws of the large mouth bear rows of sharply pointed teeth. The first gill arch carries about 19 rakers.

NATURAL HISTORY

The hake is essentially a bottom-living species, very common off much of southern Africa's coast. It inhabits water from 50-400 m and it is probable that extensive vertical migrations occur on a daily basis. This is confirmed by fishery statistics which indicate that this species rises closer to the surface at night, presumably in synchrony with its food supply. The diet consists primarily of other fish species such as lanternfishes, rattails, maasbankers and also juvenile hake. Other important components of the diet include mysids, krill, megalopa crab larvae and squid. There are certain areas where breeding appears to be most intense, and, while spawning fish have been caught throughout the year, August and September mark the period of greatest reproductive activity.

DISTRIBUTION

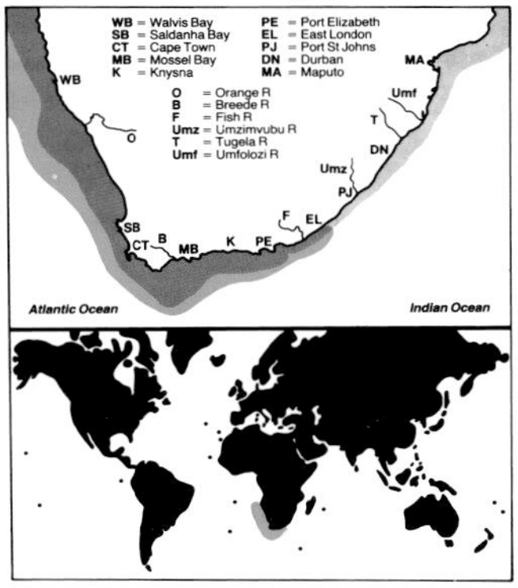

SPECIFIC CATCH RESTRICTIONS

In the Cape, the minimum legal size is 50 cm.

CAPTURE

South African commercial fishermen land 150 000 tonnes annually, which is about one third of the total catch taken by the other 11 nations fishing off the west coast. Hake can be caught by line, but most are trawled to depths of 600 m. Because of the species' nocturnal migrations towards the surface water, trawlers are most successful during daylight. The hake is of reasonable eating quality and is one of southern Africa's foremost food fishes.
SA angling record - vacant.

NAME DERIVATION

Merluccius, an ancient name meaning sea pike; *capensis,* of the Cape. Hake, derived from the Old English *haca,* to hook, a reference to the sharp teeth.

SIMILAR SPECIES

This species should be referred to as the 'shallow water hake', while the recently described and closely related species, *Merluccius paradoxus,* is best described as the 'deep water hake'. Most of the natural history is applicable to both species.

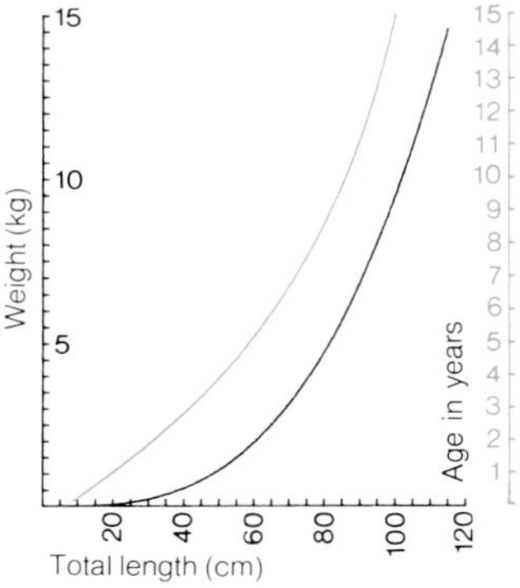

Monodactylus falciformis

(Lacepède, 1802)
Common names SA – Cape moony, kitefish. Elsewhere – kitefish, moonfish
[Smith 193□20]

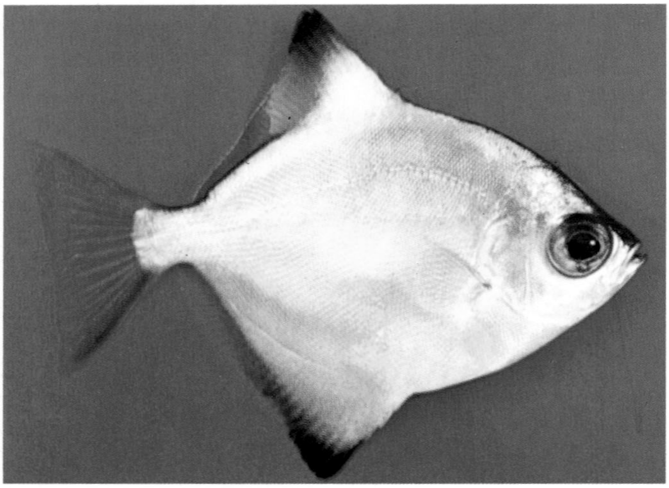

IDENTIFYING FEATURES

COLOUR, SHAPE AND SIZE
The diamond-shaped body is strongly compressed, and is generally bright silver in colour with a mother-of-pearl sheen on the anal and dorsal fins. The other fins are grey or translucent. Smaller specimens have 11 or 12 dark, vertical bars. Can attain 20 cm.

EXTERNAL ANATOMY
The body is covered with 50-65 series of small scales arranged along the distinct lateral line. Scales also extend partly onto the fins. The dorsal fin comprises eight short spines plus 25-30 rays, and the anal fin has three spines plus 25-29 rays. In both the anal and the dorsal fins, the first rays are longest, those towards the tail becoming progressively shorter. The large caudal fin is truncate, and the pelvic fins are short. The small, terminal mouth has very fine, villiform teeth in each jaw, and there are 20-24 well-developed rakers on the first gill arch.

NATURAL HISTORY

This gregarious species is commonly found in small, but closely packed shoals around jetties, wharfs and shallow reefs, and is so tolerant of varying salinities that it can acclimatize to both fresh and hypersaline water. This is made possible by special 'salt cells' situated in the gill membranes which, in a high salinity environment, aid the maintenance of the body's water-salt balance by excreting excess body salts. Feeding occurs mainly in the midwater region during the day and at night. The diet consists of planktonic organisms and small organic particles. Sometimes, shoals of moonies can also be seen feeding on floating debris. Spawning occurs in the vicinity of river mouths amongst fish exceeding 15 cm. The eggs are large and few in number. Juveniles use estuaries as nursery areas.

DISTRIBUTION

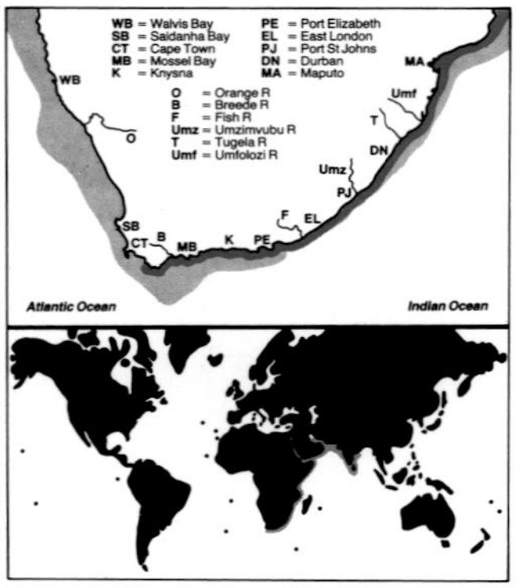

CAPTURE

Although edible and easily caught on ultra-light tackle, it is too small to be of interest to most anglers. It is, however, a successful aquarium species, and by virtue of its special adaptability, the Cape moony can even be kept in freshwater tanks. Some aquarists have managed to breed this species in captivity.
SA angling record – 0,3 kg.

SPECIFIC CATCH RESTRICTIONS

None.

NAME DERIVATION

Monodactylus, one digit; *falciformis,* sickle-shaped. Cape moony, of the Cape, and an apparent reference to the silvery, moon-like sheen of the body. Kitefish, a reference to the kite-shaped body.

SIMILAR SPECIES

There are two species of moony in southern African waters. The other is known as the Natal moony *(M. argenteus)* and can be distinguished by its deeper body. Body depth in *M. falciformis* is 1,5-2,0 and in *M. argenteus* is 1,2-1,6. *M. argenteus* juveniles have only two vertical stripes.

Liza richardsonii

(Smith, 1846)
Common names southern mullet, harder
[Smith 222□7]

IDENTIFYING FEATURES

COLOUR, SHAPE AND SIZE
The harder is an elongate fish with a pointed snout. The body has an overall silvery sheen, but is darker above and white below. There is a yellow blotch on the gill covers. Can attain 40 cm.

EXTERNAL ANATOMY
The body is covered with 44-50 series of large, distinct scales arranged along the flanks. The fins are well developed. The first dorsal fin consists of four spines, and is well separated from the second dorsal of one spine plus eight or nine rays. The anal fin consists of three spines plus nine rays, and the caudal fin is slightly forked. The terminal mouth is surrounded by thin lips, and, while the jaws of adults are toothless, juveniles of less than 10 cm have distinctly pointed teeth. There are 90-100 rakers on the first gill arch. The eyes are not covered with adipose tissue.

DISTRIBUTION

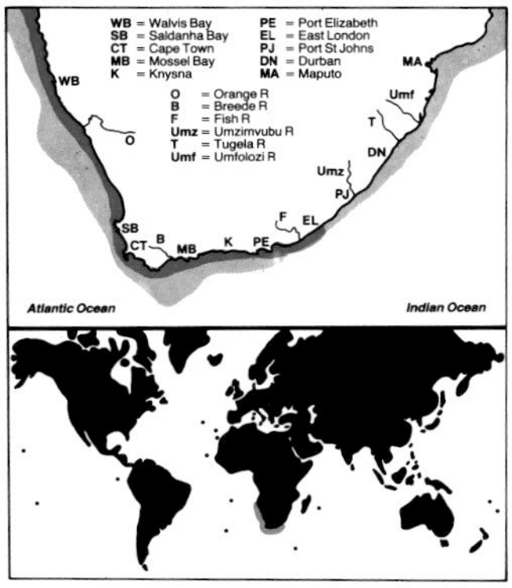

NATURAL HISTORY

Dense shoals of this abundant, cool-water species may often be seen off the rocky points and sandy beaches of the southern and western Cape coast. Many also frequent estuaries where tolerance to low salinities enables the young to use these regions as nursery areas. In place of a stomach, the harder has a long, muscular crop, rather like the gizzard of a bird. The diet consists primarily of easily-digestable, microscopic plant organisms known as diatoms. Fine sand particles are also taken in through the mouth, possibly as a mechanical aid to digestion. The totally non-aggressive harder is freely preyed upon by many large gamefish. Sexual maturity is attained at a length of about 20 cm. and spawning takes place during spring in shallow areas such as False Bay.

CAPTURE

Though it rarely takes a bait, the harder is traditionally of great importance to commercial seine and gill net operators along the Cape coast. Some 5-6 million can be caught in any one year, especially off beaches at Cape Agulhas, Strandfontein and St Helena Bay. This species continues to yield good catches, an indication of the efficient management of the fishery. Its firm white flesh makes excellent eating. Salt dried harder is known as bokkom, which, when smoked, is a veritable delicacy and traditional Cape fare. It is also a good bait.
SA angling record – 0,5 kg.

SPECIFIC CATCH RESTRICTIONS

Open species; commercial netting is controlled by permit from the Marine Development Branch.

NAME DERIVATION

Liza, a Spanish common name for these fishes; *richardsonii,* named after Richardson, a famous naturalist. Southern mullet, a reference to its distribution, and from the Latin *mullus* meaning lips. Harder, an old Dutch name for a similar European fish with a (hard) firm body.

SIMILAR SPECIES

This is by far the most common mullet in the area of its distribution. The absence of adipose eyelids, high scale count, and pectoral fins that just reach the eye when bent forward, are distinctive features.

Liza tricuspidens

(Smith, 1935)

Common name striped mullet

[Smith 222□8]

IDENTIFYING FEATURES

COLOUR, SHAPE AND SIZE

In common with a number of mullet, this particularly elongate fish has a long, tapering head and snout. The general body colour is silver, but darker above with dusky streaks along the flanks. There is a yellow blotch on each of the gill covers and the fins are pale or dusky. Can attain 75 cm.

EXTERNAL ANATOMY

The lateral line is inconspicuous, and the body has 42-53 series of scales arranged along the flanks. The fins are well developed and include a double dorsal, (the first fin of four spines being well separated from the second of one spine plus eight rays); an anal fin of three spines plus nine rays; and a slightly forked caudal fin with a noticeably broad peduncle. The terminal mouth has fleshy lips which bear tricuspid teeth, but these are so small that a magnifying glass is needed to see them. The rakers on the first gill arch are too numerous and fine to be of practical diagnostic value.

DISTRIBUTION

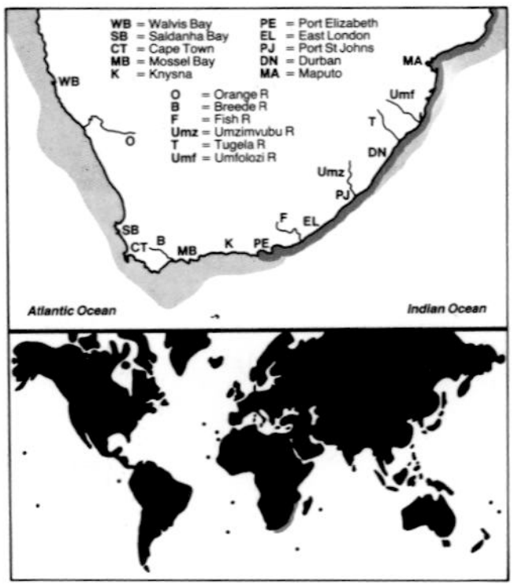

NATURAL HISTORY

This coastal, shallow-water species is normally found singly or in small shoals along rocky shores and, because of its tolerance of low salinities, also in estuaries. The striped mullet has spectacular leaping powers - sometimes reaching a height of two metres, and covering ten in a single jump - a facility which it puts to good use when escaping from drag-nets and, presumably, from would-be predators.It is also the fastest swimmer in the family. Unlike other Mugilidae, the striped mullet has a food preference for microscopic algae, including the smaller varieties of red and green seaweeds. Diatoms, foraminifera, isopods and marine worms are occasionally ingested. In common with others of the family, the striped mullet has a muscular crop instead of a stomach. Sexual maturity is attained at a length of about 47 cm, and spawning occurs along the Natal coast during winter and spring. Juveniles of the striped mullet make extensive use of estuaries as nursery areas.

CAPTURE

This is the only mullet that is regularly landed on rod and line and may be caught on any small bait that is allowed to drift freely.
It gives the angler a magnificent struggle, but it is not of spearfishing or commercial value. The flesh makes good eating despite the numerous bones.
SA angling record - 2,7 kg.

SPECIFIC CATCH RESTRICTIONS

Open species.

NAME DERIVATION

Liza, a Spanish common name for these fishes; *tricuspidens,* triple-pointed teeth. Striped mullet, a reference to the dusky lines along the body, and from the Latin *mullus* meaning lips.

SIMILAR SPECIES

Most distinctive are the tricuspid teeth. Furthermore, the high scale count, body stripes, and pectorals that reach beyond the eyes when bent forward are important features.

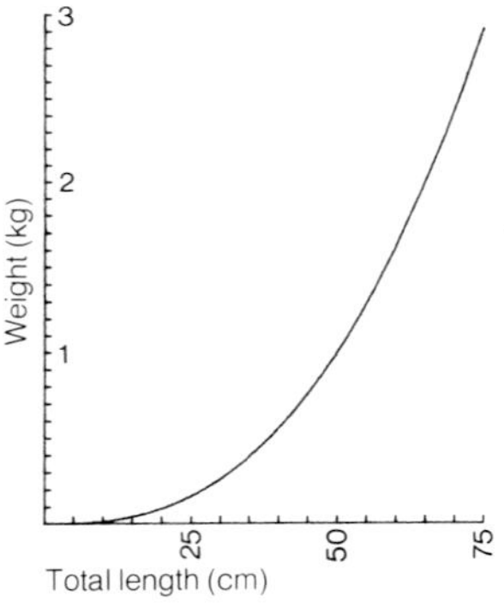

Mugil cephalus

Linnaeus, 1758

Common names SA – flathead mullet. Elsewhere – grey mullet, bull-nosed mullet

[Smith 222□10]

IDENTIFYING FEATURES

COLOUR, SHAPE AND SIZE

The flathead mullet is an elongate fish, but is somewhat more robust than most Mugilidae, and has a distinctly blunt snout. The overall body colour is silver, but darker above and white below. Dusky, longitudinal stripes run the length of the body. Can attain 80 cm.

EXTERNAL ANATOMY

The lateral line is inconspicuous, and the body is covered with scales arranged in 39-42,series along the flanks. The fins are well developed, and include a double dorsal (the first fin of four spines being well separated from the second of one spine plus 6-8 rays): an anal of two or three spines plus eight or nine rays, and a moderately forked caudal fin. The mouth, with its fleshy lips, is toothless, but juvenile specimens of less than 10 cm have small teeth which curve inwards. The rakers on the first gill arch are too numerous and fine to be of practical diagnostic value. The eyes are extensively covered by a thick, but transparent layer of adipose tissue.

NATURAL HISTORY

This coastal and predominantly estuarine species is found in large shoals of like-sized individuals. The flathead mullet has great leaping abilities, its prowess being especially evident during its annual winter spawning run along the Zululand coast. It is tolerant of turbid water and can adapt to rapid salinity changes, including instant reductions to fresh water. Sexual maturity is reached after 3-4 years at a length of about 45 cm, and spawning occurs near estuaries along the Natal coast during winter and spring. In common with others in the family, the striped mullet has a long, muscular crop as its prime digestive organ. Whereas juveniles consume planktonic crustaceans, adults feed on microscopic organisms such as foraminifera and diatoms that grow on the soft sea-bed or on submerged objects. Dead organic matter and terrestrial plant debris are also eaten. The curious, worm-like objects often found in the gizzard are, in fact, old and clogged gill rakers that have been shed, swallowed and replaced. At a length of 2,5 cm, juveniles migrate into estuaries, where they may remain for up to three years.

DISTRIBUTION

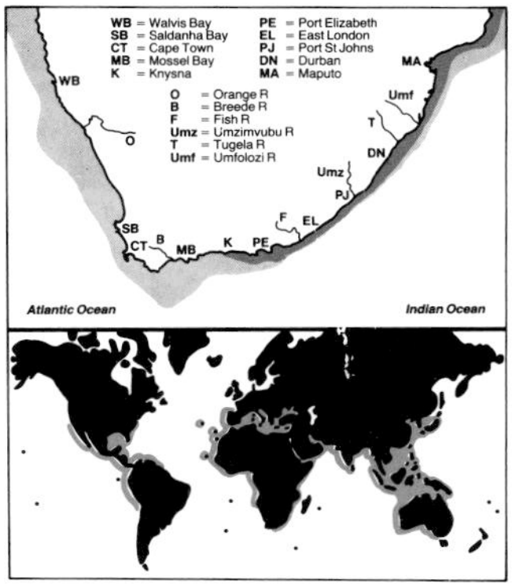

CAPTURE

Though extremely difficult to hook on rod and line, ultra-light-tackle experts using bread, flying ants or small pieces of sardine, claim fair success, and have a high regard for this fine angling fish. It makes excellent eating. It is sold live in supermarkets. It is not of spearfishing importance.The flathead mullet's ability to adapt to a salt-free environment has brought about the 'farming' of the species in freshwater tanks. Successful projects of this nature have been undertaken in Taiwan, Israel and other countries.

SA angling record – 4,5 kg.

SA spearfishing record – 1,4 kg.

SPECIFIC CATCH RESTRICTIONS

Open species.

NAME DERIVATION

Mugil, from *mulgeo,* to suck; *cephalus,* head. Flathead mullet, a reference to its large, depressed head, and from the Latin *mullus* meaning lips.

SIMILAR SPECIES

The heavy adipose eyelids and 39-42 series of scales are the most distinctive features.

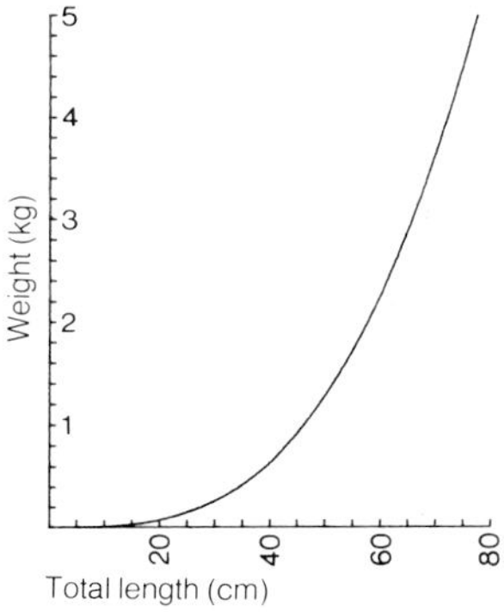

Valamugil cunnesius

(Valenciennes, 1836)
Common names SA – longarm mullet. Elsewhere – longfin grey mullet
[Smith 222□13]

IDENTIFYING FEATURES

COLOUR, SHAPE AND SIZE

This rather slender mullet has a short, wedge-shaped snout. The body is silvery overall, but the back is bluish and a dark spot marks the pectoral axils. There is also a noticeable yellow mark on the gill covers and on the upper parts of the eyes. Can attain 35 cm.

EXTERNAL ANATOMY

The scales are distinct, and cover the body in 33-36 series arranged along each flank. Typical of Mugilidae, the fins of this species include a double dorsal (the first fin of four spines and the second of one spine plus eight rays); an anal of three spines plus nine rays; and a slightly forked caudal. The pectoral fins are characteristically long, and reach to below the base of the dorsal fin. The small mouth has a fleshy upper and a thin lower lip, and no teeth are visible within. A thick layer of transparent adipose tissue covers a large part of each eye, leaving only a central area exposed. The rakers on the first gill arch are long and well developed, but too numerous to be of practical diagnostic value.

NATURAL HISTORY

This small species is rather common in Natal's coastal lagoons, particularly those that are only infrequently open to the sea. Here, in these low salinity environments, the longarm mullet feeds on a diet comprising large amounts of organic detritus. Spawning occurs at sea, but close to estuaries so that the juveniles can make use of these regions as nursery areas. The breeding season is extensive, but spawning reaches a peak during summer. Sexual maturity is attained at a length of approximately 20 cm, and the juveniles first move into estuaries at about 4-5 cm. In view of this species' apparent dependence on the semi-closed lagoon environment, it is likely to be one of the fish adversely affected by artificial and ill-timed breaching of lagoon sandbars. Wherever this occurs, juvenile fish are released prematurely into the sea and, being not yet ready for that environment, many die. Ultimately, this practice could lead to a decrease in the species' abundance.

DISTRIBUTION

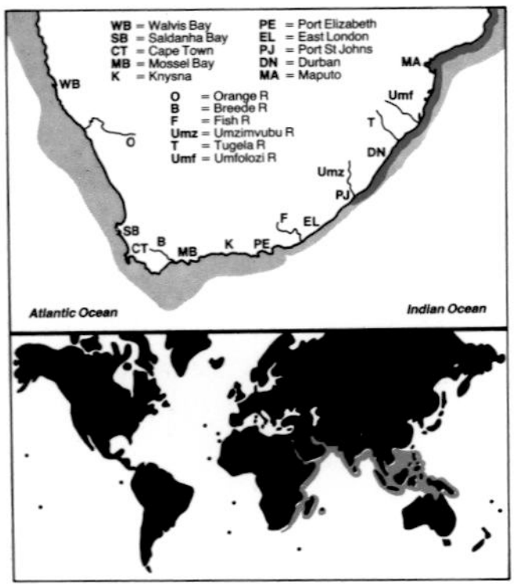

CAPTURE

The longarm mullet does not take bait, but is frequently caught in throw nets. It makes an excellent bait for larger fish, especially kob and garrick. The flesh is edible.

SPECIFIC CATCH RESTRICTIONS

Open species.

NAME DERIVATION

Valamugil, a close relative of the members of the genus *Mugil; cunnesius,* wedge-shaped. Longarm mullet, a reference to the long pectoral fins and from the Latin *mullus* meaning lips.

SIMILAR SPECIES

Mullet are never easy to identify and this species is readily confused with several others. However, the combination of a heavy adipose eyelid and yellow opercular blotch should confirm the identity of this species. The related bluetail mullet *(V. buchanani)* has a blue tail, no adipose eyelid, and grows much larger.

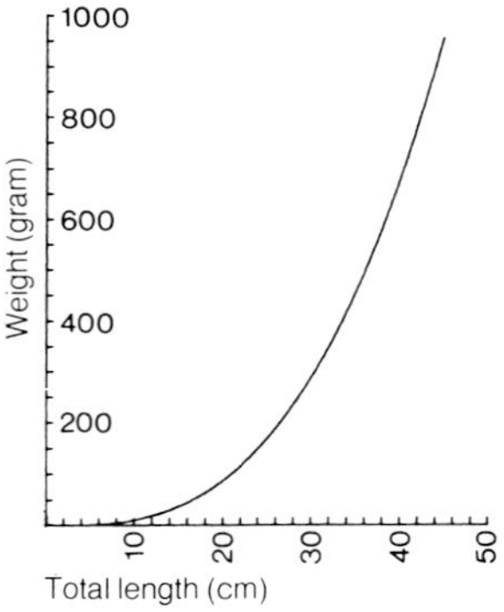

Parupeneus indicus

(Shaw, 1803)
Common name Worldwide – Indian goatfish
[Smith 196□7]

IDENTIFYING FEATURES

COLOUR, SHAPE AND SIZE

This large, robust goatfish is strikingly coloured, and its reddish-purple body is characteristically marked. A number of bluish lines occur on the head, and a most conspicuous yellow blotch is located on each flank above the lateral line, directly below the space between the dorsal fins. There is also a large black blotch on either side of the caudal peduncle. Individual scales may have blue or yellow markings, and this often gives rise to an overall striped appearance. The fins are pinkish, translucent and, occasionally, the second dorsal and anal fins may be striped. Can attain 35 cm.

EXTERNAL ANATOMY

Large scales cover the entire body, and are arranged in 29 or 30 series along the well-defined lateral line. Three or four rows lie between the dorsal fins, and eight rows occur between the second dorsal and caudal fins. The double dorsal fin consists of eight spines which precede one spine plus eight or nine rays. The anal fin comprises one or two spines plus six rays. In larger fish, such as the specimen shown here, the last ray in the anal and soft dorsal fins becomes elongate. The caudal fin is forked. The eyes of this species are rather small in relation to the size of the head. Surrounding the terminal mouth are thick lips, the lower of which has a large pair of sensory barbels projecting downwards and backwards. The fish shown here is unusual as one of its barbels is branched towards its tip. A single row of about 26 teeth occurs in the upper jaw, while the lower jaw bears a row of 18. There are no teeth on the roof of the mouth. Some 24-27 long, thin rakers occur on the first gill arch.

DISTRIBUTION

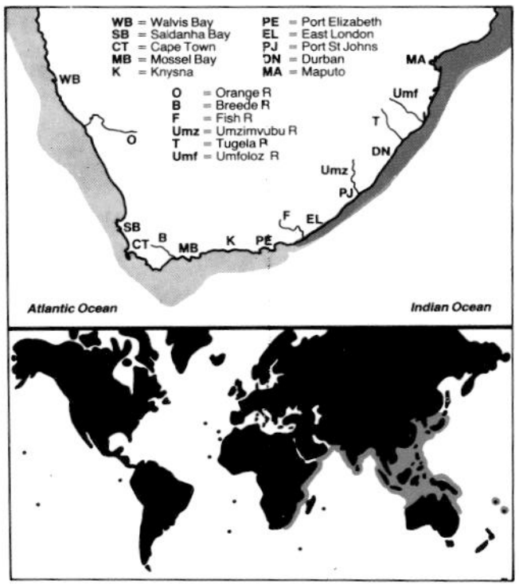

NATURAL HISTORY

One of the larger goatfish, this species is relatively common, and is very widely distributed throughout the Indo-Pacific. It occurs near rocky or coral reefs, and is also often quite plentiful in shallow sandy areas where there are scattered outcrops of reef. The Indian goatfish feeds mainly on bottom-living invertebrates and, similar to most other goatfish, it uses its barbels to probe for prey in the mud or sand of the sea-bed. Once disturbed, small crabs, amphipods, shrimps and other food items are quickly picked up in the mouth. Other important components of the diet include small octopuses, polychaete worms and small fish. Though adult fish can be caught throughout the year in southern African waters, of the few landed specimens examined, none has revealed any sign of reproductive activity. Spawning has been recorded from tropical East Africa, however, and 'ripe' fish appear to be present in these warmer waters throughout the year.

CAPTURE

This fine angling fish may be caught from the shore or from ski-boats. It makes superb eating, and is valued as a food resource in many eastern countries.
SA angling record – 1,5 kg.

SPECIFIC CATCH RESTRICTIONS

None.

NAME DERIVATION

Parupeneus, related to the genus *Upeneus; indicus,* from India. Indian goatfish, a reference to the area from where it was first described, and to its barbels, reminiscent of a goat's beard.

SIMILAR SPECIES

The presence of distinct teeth, yellow lateral blotch and black caudal spot confirm identity of this species.

Parupeneus macronema

(Lacepède, 1801)

Common names SA – banddot goatfish. Elsewhere – longbarbel goatfish

[Smith 196□8]

IDENTIFYING FEATURES

COLOUR, SHAPE AND SIZE

The small, elongate banddot goatfish is predominantly dusky red, and has a broad, dark-brown band which follows the curve of the lateral line from behind the eyes to the second dorsal fin. Both sides of the caudal peduncle are marked with a dark 'eye-spot', above which is a pale, but not always obvious, saddle. The fins are reddish or dusky, and the lower part of the second dorsal is dark, as are the outer rays of the caudal fin. Can attain 32 cm.

EXTERNAL ANATOMY

This species is very similar to a few other, less common, goatfish. There are, however, a number of distinctive characteristics displayed by the banddot goatfish which prevent confusion. The body has 27-28 series of scales arranged along the lateral line. Three rows lie between the first and second dorsal fins, while eight or nine rows follow the second dorsal fin. The fins include two dorsals, the first comprising eight spines and the second, one spine plus eight rays; an anal of one spine plus six rays; and a forked caudal. The last rays of the second dorsal and anal fins are elongate and most distinctive. The mouth bears a single row of teeth in each jaw, and a pair of sensory barbels projects from the chin. When folded back these barbels reach the base of the pelvic fins. There are 33-39 long, thin rakers on the first gill arch.

NATURAL HISTORY

This widely distributed goatfish occurs solitarily or in pairs over shallow coastal reefs. It rarely ventures deeper than 40 m. It is a bottom-living animal, and spends a great deal of time foraging for food on the sea-bed. As with all Mullidae, the hunting strategy involves 'stirring' the muddy or sandy bottom with its prehensile barbels to disturb small crustaceans which are instantly snatched up. These include amphipods, copepods and small crabs. The breeding cycle of this fish is still obscure, but juveniles have been found in surface waters off Kosi Bay during summer.

DISTRIBUTION

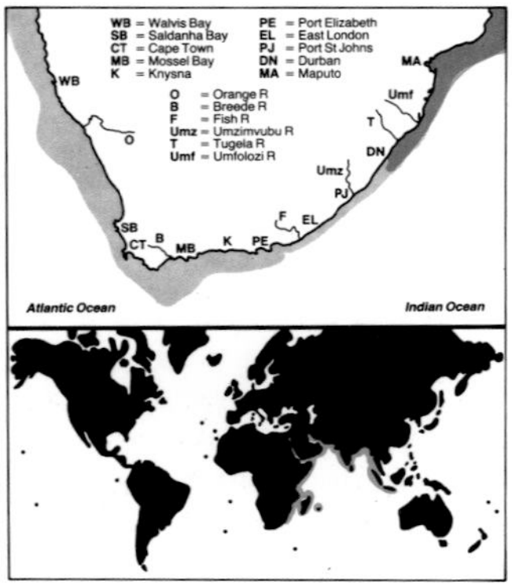

CAPTURE

Few anglers specifically pursue this fish, despite its excellent eating value and the relative ease with which it is captured. Many banddot goatfish, however, are caught in fish traps in other parts of the Indo-Pacific, and are sold on fresh-fish markets. It thrives in aquaria.

SPECIFIC CATCH RESTRICTIONS

None.

NAME DERIVATION

Parupeneus, related to the genus *Upeneus; macronema,* broad filament, a reference to the filamentous dorsal and anal rays. Banddot goatfish, a reference to its distinct markings and to the barbels on the chin, reminiscent of a goat's beard.

SIMILAR SPECIES

The row of teeth in each jaw, elongate dorsal and anal rays, and the band-dot markings serve to distinguish this species from other goatfishes. Notice too that it has no yellow colour on the body or fins.

Parupeneus rubescens

(Lacepède, 1801)

Common names Worldwide – blacksaddle goatfish, rosy goatfish [Smith 196□10]

IDENTIFYING FEATURES

COLOUR, SHAPE AND SIZE

When live, this robust, but moderately compressed goatfish has a greenish to bronze body tinged with pink. Several lighter and darker bands occur on the head, especially around the eyes. Usually the most conspicuous of these is a purplish band extending from the eyes to the snout. A pale to pinkish saddle precedes a black saddle on the upper surface of the caudal peduncle. After death, however, the fish reddens overall. The fins are translucent pink. Can attain 45 cm.

EXTERNAL ANATOMY

Some 27-28 series of distinct scales are arranged along the lateral line. The fins are well developed and include a double dorsal of seven or eight spines followed by one spine plus eight rays, an anal of one spine plus six rays, and a deeply forked caudal. The terminal mouth has fleshy lips, and each jaw has a single row of fine teeth. Two fairly long barbels extend downwards from the chin. There are 29-31 rakers on the first gill arch. The eyes are relatively large.

NATURAL HISTORY

This large and common species inhabits coastal waters, ranging from the surf zone to depths of 80 m. It is usually found near reefs, either singly or in small shoals. As with other goatfish, the movable tentacles scour and probe the sea-bed in search of food. Gullies, crevices and even stands of seaweed are favoured foraging grounds. The diet consists of small, bottom-dwelling animals disturbed by the tentacles. These include amphipods, copepods, small crabs, shrimps and occasionally larval fish, all of which are snatched up by the underslung mouth. When not in use, the barbels are tucked away beneath the chin. Tank observations of this species have revealed that these projections are also used in courtship displays, when two fish meet face to face and excitedly intertwine their barbels. Presumably this behaviour is a prelude to spawning. Little is known of the life history, although the silvery, unmarked juveniles are known to shelter beneath floating objects at sea, and to be widely distributed by ocean currents.

DISTRIBUTION

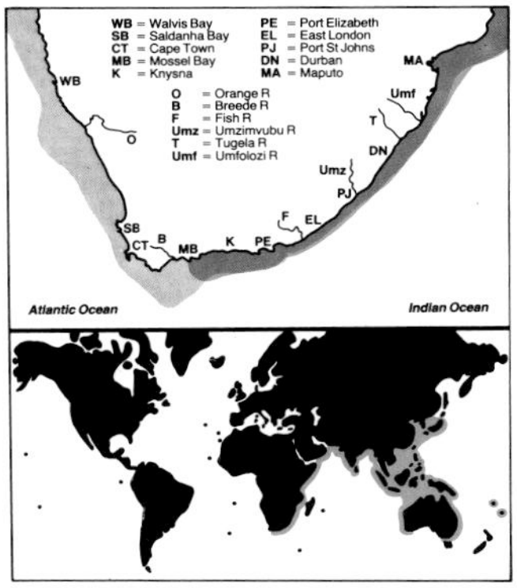

CAPTURE

The blacksaddle goatfish takes most small baits, and is often caught on light tackle. It is not a true sport fish, but it is of excellent eating quality. In the Far East it is commercially caught in bottom trawls and fish traps.

SA angling record – 2,9 kg.

SA spearfishing record – 1,4 kg.

SPECIFIC CATCH RESTRICTIONS

None.

NAME DERIVATION

Parupeneus, related to the genus *Upeneus; rubescens,* growing reddish. Blacksaddle goatfish, a reference to its markings and to its barbels, reminiscent of a goat's beard.

SIMILAR SPECIES

The combined presence of teeth, black saddle preceded by a paler patch, and darker band across the snout serve to identify this species. As some specimens have apparently not shown the black saddle, care must be taken with identification.

Upeneus vittatus

(Forsskål, 1775)

Common names SA – yellowbanded goatfish. Elsewhere – yellowstriped goatfish
[Smith 196□13]

IDENTIFYING FEATURES

COLOUR, SHAPE AND SIZE

This small, but robust fish is only slightly compressed. The overall body colour is silver,but darker above and paler below. Four yellowish-bronze stripes run the length of the upper body and flanks. Both dorsal fins are dusky, with paler stripes. The caudal fin has a characteristic pattern of alternating light and dark bands, which is most diagnostic and aids correct identification. The anal, pelvic and pectoral fins are almost transparent. Can attain 25 cm.

EXTERNAL ANATOMY

Distinct scales are arranged in 33-36 series along the lateral line There are six or seven rows of these scales between the first and second dorsal fins, while 12 rows lie between the second dorsal and caudal fins. The fins are well developed, and include a double dorsal of seven or eight spines, followed by one spine plus eight rays, an anal of one spine plus six or seven rays, and a deeply forked caudal fin. There are very fine, villiform teeth in each jaw, and patches of smaller teeth on the palate. A pair of thin barbels projects downwards from the chin. The first gill arch carries 26-31 short rakers.

NATURAL HISTORY

One of the most common representatives of this large family, the yellowbanded goatfish occurs in small shoals on, or at the edges of reefs to depths of 100 m. As with other Mullidae, this bottom-dweller employs its sensory and highly mobile 'feelers' to continuously scour the sea-bed in search of food. The small crustaceans, such as amphiphods and copepods, which are stirred up by the barbels in this manner, are instantly snatched up into the underslung mouth. Mysids, crab larvae, marine worms and fish fry also form part of the diet. Spawning fish have been recorded during summer. The plain, silvery young shelter beneath floating objects at sea, and in this manner are widely distributed by ocean currents. As with some goatfish, this species is nocturnal and, like most, it has the facility to change colour to blend with its environment.

DISTRIBUTION

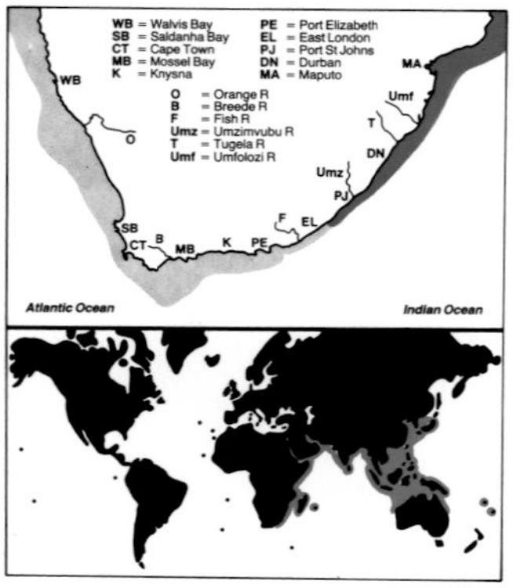

CAPTURE

The yellowbanded goatfish is easily caught on light tackle, but is not pursued as a sport fish. Considered a delicacy in the Far East, however, it is extensively exploited by commercial fishermen using seine nets and fish traps.
SA angling record – vacant.

SPECIFIC CATCH RESTRICTIONS

None.

NAME DERIVATION

Upeneus, an old Greek name for this fish that refers, obscurely, to the upper lip; *vittatus,* striped lengthwise. Yellowbanded goatfish, a reference to its lateral stripes and to its barbels, reminiscent of a goat's beard.

SIMILAR SPECIES

There are several goatfish that resemble this species, but none have the four yellow stripes and distinctive tail patterning. Notice especially the wider black bar across the lower caudal lobe, and the absence of distinct rows of teeth in the jaws.

Muraenesox bagio

(Hamilton - Buchanan, 1822)
Common names Worldwide - pike conger, silver eel
[Smith 45□1]

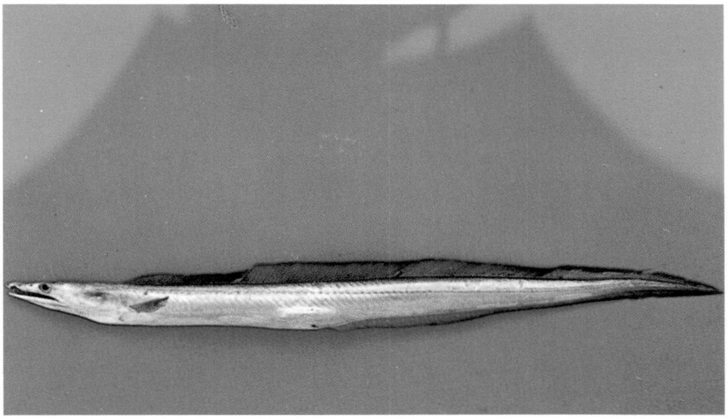

IDENTIFYING FEATURES

COLOUR, SHAPE AND SIZE

The typically elongate body of this eel tapers from the head region to the long, thin tail. The overall colour is brown or grey-brown, with a coppery sheen extending along the flanks and dorsal surface. The underside is pale and the fins are dark. Can attain 180 cm.

EXTERNAL ANATOMY

Scales are lacking, and the skin of the pike conger is smooth to the touch. The spineless dorsal and anal fins join at the point of the tail to form a single, continuous fin comprising numerous soft rays. The pectoral fins are distinct, and are located directly behind the small gill openings. The vent is situated in front of the small pelvic fins. Both jaws of the large, extended mouth are armed with several rows of sharp teeth, some of which are enlarged into canines. When the mouth is closed, these larger teeth slot into cavities in the opposite jaw. A single row of teeth also occurs on the roof of the mouth. The lower jaw extends backwards, beyond the level of the eyes. Careful examination of the distinct lateral line reveals small pores, of which there are some 35-38 between the head and the vent.

NATURAL HISTORY

The pike conger is a coastal species, often found over the muddy bottoms of offshore banks, ranging in depth from 50-75 m. It can tolerate salinity reductions and extremely turbid water. It freely enters estuaries, especially those of Richards Bay and St Lucia. This powerful predator feeds mainly on bottom-living or slow-swimming fishes such as nondi, mullet and javelin grunter. Occasionally, prawns are also eaten. The pike conger is not averse to scavenging, and any dead or decaying fish will soon attract its attention. Despite its abundance in estuaries, spawning appears to occur at sea during spring and early summer. Sexual maturity is attained at a body length of approximately 100 cm. It is predominantly solitary in habit and may shelter in burrows or depressions in the sea-bed.

DISTRIBUTION

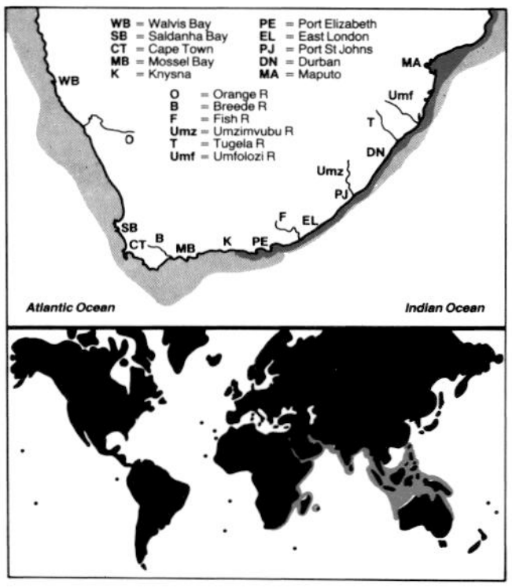

SPECIFIC CATCH RESTRICTIONS

None.

CAPTURE

The pike conger is frequently caught by estuarine anglers or in offshore prawn-trawling nets. Though this exceedingly aggressive fish makes exceptionally good eating, few are used for food.
SA angling record - 11,6 kg.

NAME DERIVATION

Muraenesox, from *muraene* meaning eel and *esox,* a pike; *bagio,* possibly an obscure reference to *boguio,* meaning hurricane. Pike conger, a reference to its fierce 'pike-like' teeth and to conger, an old name for an eel.

SIMILAR SPECIES

The features described, especially the large teeth on the roof of the mouth, should distinguish this from other eels, especially those caught in estuaries.

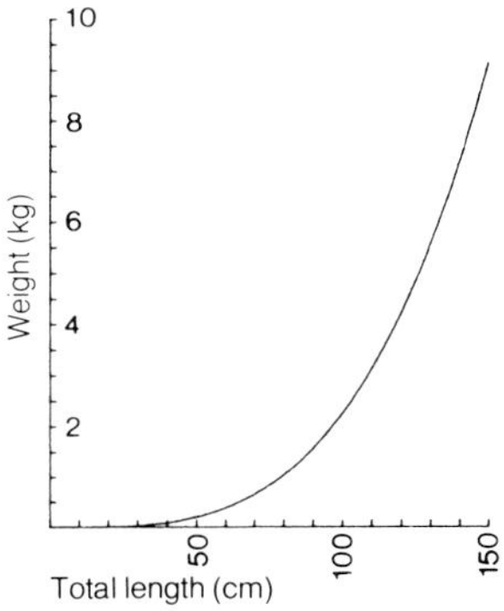

Gymnothorax favagineus

(Bloch & Schneider, 1801)
Common names SA – honeycomb moray eel. Elsewhere – honeycomb or reticulated moray
[Smith 41□11]

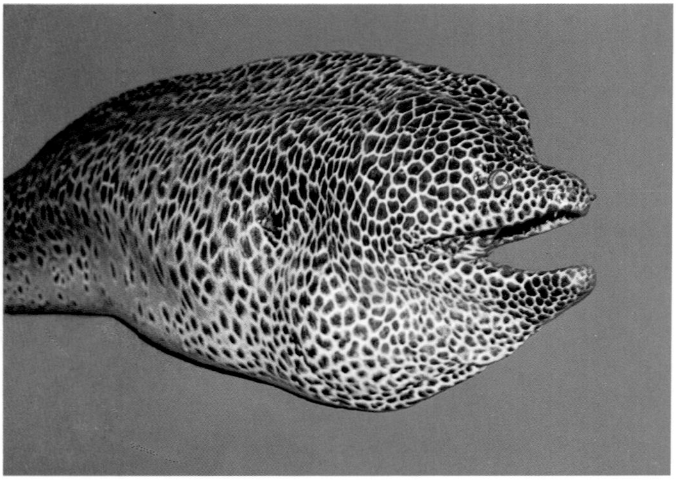

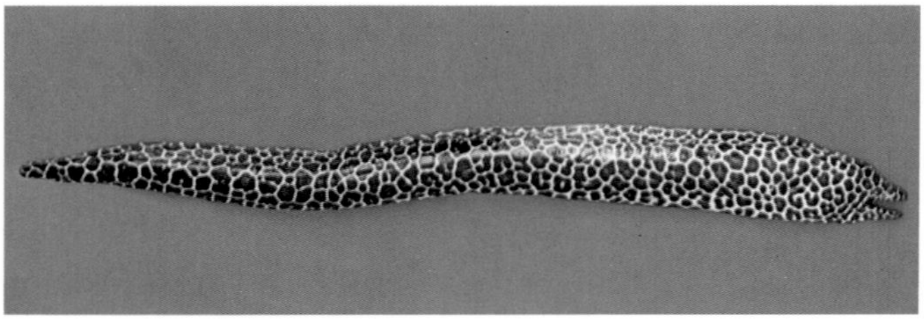

IDENTIFYING FEATURES

COLOUR, SHAPE AND SIZE

The shape and colours of this eel are unmistakable. It is robust, with a shortened head, blunt snout and long, tapering tail. Dark-brown blotches surrounded by yellow reticulations cover the entire body in a honeycomb pattern. Can attain 150 cm in length.

EXTERNAL ANATOMY

The honeycomb moray has no scales, and the smooth body is covered with mucus. The dorsal and anal fins are connected by a flap of skin around the tail, and together they form a continuous, spineless fin extending from the head region to the tail, and from the tail to the vent, which is located towards the front of the body. The large jaws have powerful teeth as well as a row of fangs along the middle of the palate. A small, round gill opening occurs in the middle of both sides of the head.

DISTRIBUTION

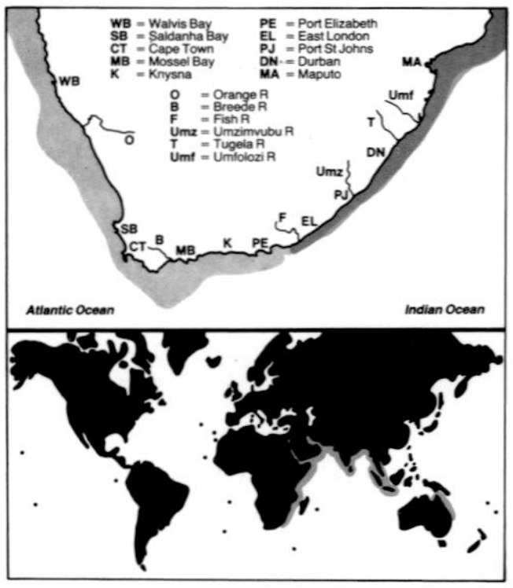

NATURAL HISTORY

This powerful, aggressive predator normally lurks in the dark holes and deep caves of coral and rocky reefs, where its cryptic colours and patterns make it difficult to spot. It often shares this gloomy habitat with crayfish. These crustaceans are heavily preyed upon by octopuses which are, in turn, a favourite food of the moray. The association is, therefore, one of mutual benefit, as octopuses entering the lair in search of prey, provide the moray with a ready food source, while the crayfish receive protection from their major predator. Aside from octopus, the diet includes a number of fish which are unsuspectingly snatched, often at night. As with most eels,the moray passes through a transparent larval, or *leptocephalus* stage before developing into its adult form.In many cases this larval phase may last for an entire year before adult colouration is assumed. Though its bite is not poisonous, many divers will attest to this eel's savage jaws. It is especially aggressive when cornered or when its territory is threatened. Nevertheless, it is possible to hand-feed this fish, and it will readily take food from a diver.

CAPTURE

The moray eel is not of specific angling value, though many large specimens have been landed. It is quite edible, but in some tropical regions it is a carrier of ciguatera poison. Hence its liver and intestines should not be eaten.
SA angling record – 18,1 kg.

SPECIFIC CATCH RESTRICTIONS

None.

NAME DERIVATION

Gymnothorax, naked or scaleless breast; *favagineus,* yellow markings. Honeycomb moray, a reference to its markings and from the Latin *muraena* meaning eel.

SIMILAR SPECIES

Moray eels are best distinguished by their distinctive patterns and colours – as is the case here.

Gymnothorax flavimarginatus

(Rüppell, 1830)
Common names SA – yellowedged moray. Elsewhere – leopard moray
[Smith 41□12]

IDENTIFYING FEATURES

COLOUR, SHAPE AND SIZE
This fairly slim-bodied eel may superficially resemble several other Muraenidae. However, its colours and patterns, though considerably variable, are quite distinctive. The body is yellowish overall, but densely mottled with irregular, brown markings. Larger specimens are generally much darker. Can attain 100 cm.

EXTERNAL ANATOMY
As with all Muraenidae, this moray is scaleless and the skin is usually smooth, albeit somewhat slimy to the touch. Also typical are the dorsal, caudal and anal fins, all of which are spineless. Pectoral and pelvic fins are lacking. A small, round gill opening is located on either side of the head, a little behind the angle of the jaw. The head is small, and the tiny eyes are situated far forward on the snout. The large mouth bears a single row of enlarged and sharp canines in each jaw, while patches of sharp teeth also occur on the roof of the mouth. The vent occurs approximately at the midpoint of the long, tapering body.

NATURAL HISTORY

This cave-dwelling fish is common on most reefs within its range. Owing to its cryptic colours and secretive habits, however, it is seldom seen. The yellowedged moray often shares its abode with crayfish, an apparently rewarding association, for the eel quickly despatches octopuses entering its cave in search of these crustaceans. Fish are more important components of the diet, however, and numerous reef-dwelling species have been recorded from the stomach contents of landed specimens.

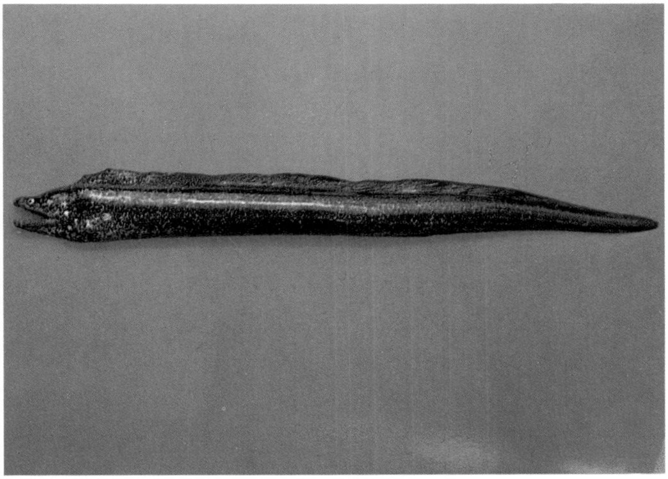

Hunting occurs mainly at night. The reproductive biology of this moray has not been studied, and, though spawning is certain to occur in southern African waters, the typical transparent larvae or *leptocephali* have yet to be identified.

DISTRIBUTION

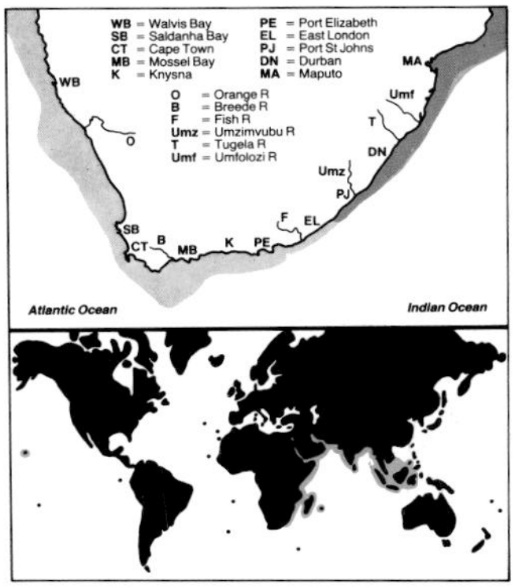

SPECIFIC CATCH RESTRICTIONS

None.

CAPTURE

Most anglers curse this eel as it freely takes a bait, and, because of its fierce jaws, removing it from a hook is a difficult and hazardous operation. Though edible, in some parts of the Indo-Pacific it is known to be a carrier of ciguatera poison. SA angling record – 2,0 kg.

NAME DERIVATION

Gymnothorax, naked or scaleless breast; *flavimarginatus,* yellow-edged. Yellowedged moray, a reference to the occasional yellow margins to the fins, and from *muraena,* Latin for eel.

SIMILAR SPECIES

Morays are best identified by their distinctive colours and patterning, as is the case in this species.

Thyrsoidea macrura

(Bleeker, 1854)

Common names SA – slender giant moray. Elsewhere – pompa [Smith 41□28]

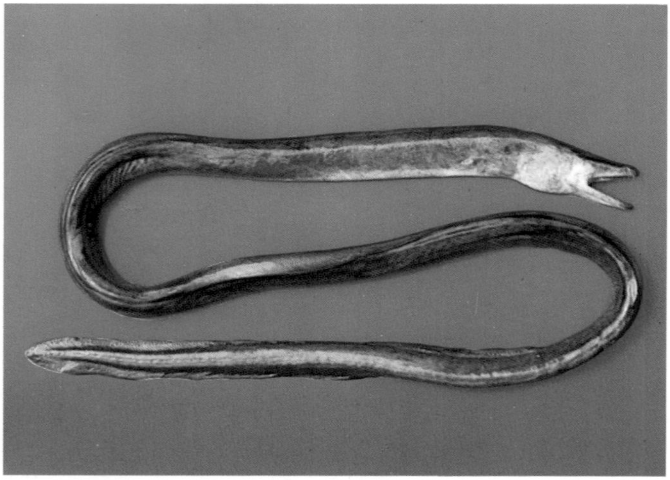

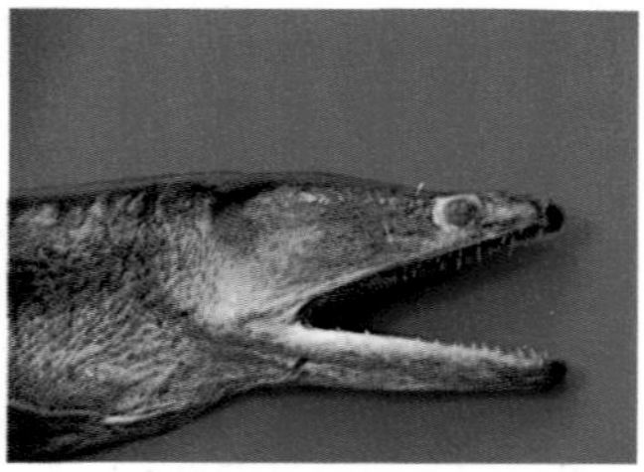

IDENTIFYING FEATURES

COLOUR, SHAPE AND SIZE

This exceptionally long and thin-bodied eel is oval in cross-section. Its overall colouration is uniform brown or olive-brown, with black-edged fins. Can attain 375 cm.

EXTERNAL ANATOMY

Despite its extreme length, the head of this moray is very short and the eyes are situated close to the tip of the snout. The gill openings occur immediately behind the jaws. The tail (the section of the body following the vent) is approximately two thirds of the total body length. The scaleless and very smooth skin envelops the dorsal and anal fins. Two conspicuous rows of pointed teeth occur in both jaws. The large canines which characterize other morays are not present in this species.

DISTRIBUTION

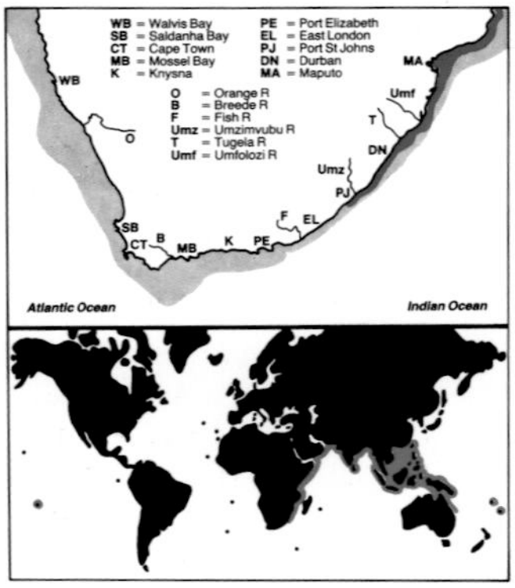

NATURAL HISTORY

This common species probably attains a length greater than that of any other marine eel. It is usually solitary and is generally confined to coastal waters and offshore banks. In contrast to many moray eels that dwell in caves, this species usually moves in more open waters and closer to the sea-bed. Many freely enter estuaries, especially those with a soft, muddy bottom. Here it feeds on bottom-living fish, prawns and small crabs. It is noteworthy that this species lacks the bright, often complex patterns of reef-dwelling eels, and its nondescript body colouration is undoubtedly more effectively camouflaged in muddy conditions or over a sandy sea-bed. The slender giant moray is not particularly aggressive. Details of its breeding cycle in southern Africa are not known.

CAPTURE

Estuarine anglers often catch enormous individuals belonging to this species, but invariably they are discarded, despite their excellent eating quality. Some are caught in offshore trawl nets.

SA angling record – 6,3 kg.

SPECIFIC CATCH RESTRICTIONS

None.

NAME DERIVATION

Thyrsoidea, without a large opening; *macrura,* long tailed. Slender giant moray, a reference to its shape and size and from *muraena,* Latin for eel.

SIMILAR SPECIES

There are very few, if any, other eels with a tail that exceeds the length of the rest of the body. The plain, brown colour and estuarine habits further confirm identification.

Scolopsis vosmeri

(Bloch, 1792)

Common names Local - silverflash spinecheek. Elsewhere - whitecheek monocle bream [Smith 186□6]

IDENTIFYING FEATURES

COLOUR, SHAPE AND SIZE

This attractive fish has a compressed body and a smoothly curved dorsal profile. Though colours and markings are variable, most individuals are dark brown overall and tinged with red or bronze. The underside is pale. A broad white bar extends from behind the eyes across the gill covers, but this feature is far more silvery and obvious when seen underwater. Each of the scales along the flanks has darker spots, and the fins are usually yellow or orange. The insides of the gill covers and the mouth are bright red. Can attain 30 cm.

EXTERNAL ANATOMY

Large scales cover the body, and are arranged in 38-41 series along the distinct lateral line. The fins are well developed and include a single dorsal of ten spines plus nine rays, an anal of three stout spines plus seven rays, and a slightly forked caudal. The first rays of the pelvic fins of some individuals extend into short, thread-like filaments. Directly below each of the large eyes there is a strong, backward-pointing spine. A similar spine occurs on the edge of both gill covers. Broad, fleshy lips surround the mouth and both jaws are set with bands of fine villiform teeth. About ten, short stubby rakers occur on the first gill arch.

NATURAL HISTORY

This striking fish inhabits shallow coral and rocky reefs throughout its extensive world range. It is particularly common around islands. In southern Africa its distribution is often irregular, with few individuals venturing south of Zululand. Curiously, however, a permanent shoal lives in the entrance channel to Durban Harbour, presumably attracted by the particularly sheltered conditions. Though the diet of the silverflash spinecheek is certain to include soft, bottom-living invertebrates, its specific food preferences are unknown. Its breeding cycle and the distribution of young have not been studied.

DISTRIBUTION

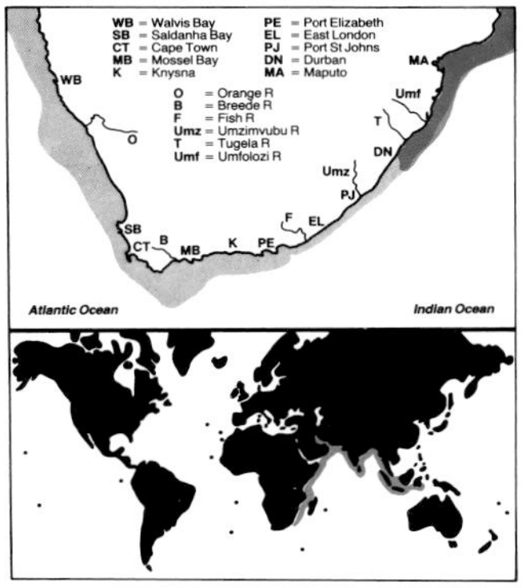

CAPTURE

Anglers using light tackle and small hooks may land this fish. It is never abundant in local waters, but in some parts of the tropical Indian Ocean, larger hauls are made in trawls and traps. These commercial catches are marketed fresh, salted, smoked or processed into fish balls. Attempts to keep the spinecheek in captivity are not always successful, largely because of the lack of knowledge about its dietary requirements.

SA angling record - vacant.

SPECIFIC CATCH RESTRICTIONS

None.

NAME DERIVATION

Scolopsis, derived from *scolopax,* a snipe; *vosmeri,* named after the ichthyologist, Vosmer. Silverflash spinecheek, a reference to the white bar which is most vivid and distinct when seen underwater, and to the pronounced spines on the sides of the head.

SIMILAR SPECIES

The fine villiform teeth, sub-orbital spine and white bar across the gill covers should distinguish this fish from other spinecheeks and most other similar fishes in the area.

Genypterus capensis

(Smith, 1847)
Common names SA – kingklip.
Elsewhere – cuskeel
[Smith 96□9]

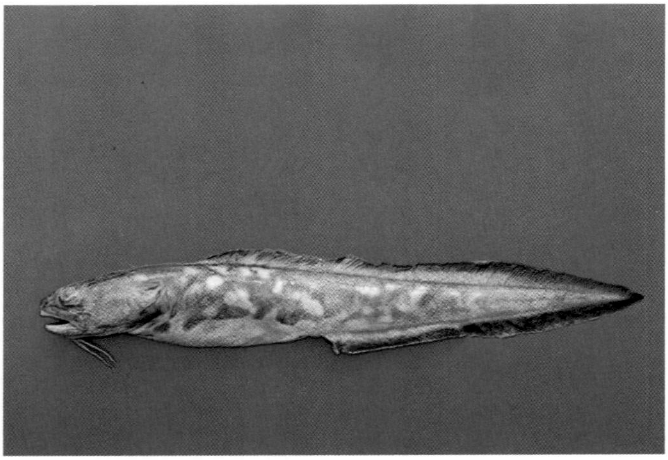

IDENTIFYING FEATURES

COLOUR, SHAPE AND SIZE
With its very elongate body tapering to a point at the tail, the kingklip bears a close resemblance to a number of eels. However, unlike most eels, which are round in cross-section, the kinglklip is moderately compressed. The body is pinkish overall, but somewhat paler below and irregularly marked with brown blotches on the upper flanks. The fins are also darker brown. Can attain 150 cm.

EXTERNAL ANATOMY
But for the head, the entire body is covered with minute scales that do not overlap one another and are arranged in oblique series along the distinct lateral line. The scales are not firm, and this soft-bodied fish is rather slimy to the touch. The fins are primitive and spineless, with the long dorsal and anal fins joining at the caudal to form a single, continuous fin. The pectoral fins are small and rounded, while the pelvics are reduced to a pair of barbel-like structures projecting from the chin. The snout is blunt, and the mouth is rather large and underslung. Both jaws bear rows of fine, sharply pointed teeth, a few of which are enlarged. Teeth also occur on the palate. There are 4-6 knobbly rakers on the first gill arch.

NATURAL HISTORY

This bottom-dwelling fish inhabits offshore banks ranging in depth from 50-500 m. The kingklip is carnivorous, and its varied diet includes, in order of importance, small bottom-living fishes known collectively as dragonets, mantis shrimps, juvenile jacopever, hake, and also small quantities of megalopa crab larvae and squid. It would appear that while most prey is taken on the bottom, midwater feeding also occurs. The kingklip attains sexual maturity at an age of four or five years, corresponding to a body length of 50-60 cm. Spawning occurs primarily from August to October, and the juveniles congregate in certain areas, often in shallower water than the adult fish. Preliminary research has revealed that there is a higher percentage of males amongst smaller fish; this possibly indicates dissimilar growth rates for the sexes.

DISTRIBUTION

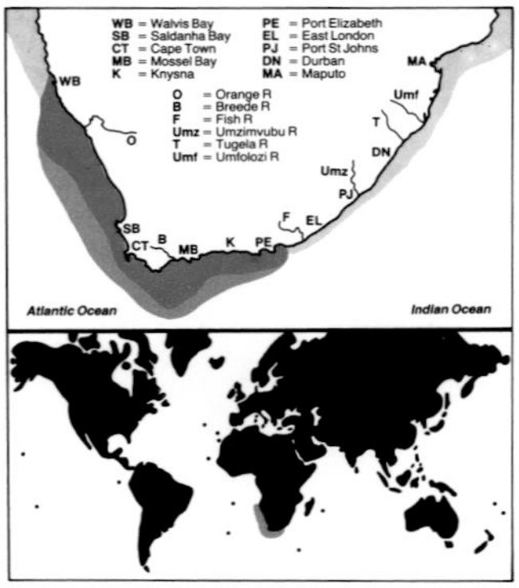

CAPTURE

This is one of southern Africa's finest eating fishes and, justifiably, its flesh commands a high market price. Considerable numbers are trawled off the West Coast and Namibia and it is also becoming a more common catch on bottom-set longlines. The new 200-km economic zone should ensure that this species is not over-exploited by foreign fishing fleets.
SA angling record – 6,5 kg.

SPECIFIC CATCH RESTRICTIONS

Netting by permit and quota only.

NAME DERIVATION

Genypterus, family with fins; *capensis,* of the Cape. Kingklip, derived from the old Dutch *koningklipvisch,* literally, the king of rock fish.

SIMILAR SPECIES

While the identification of cuskeels is not always easy, the kingklip, by virtue of its abundance and features described, should be readily identified.

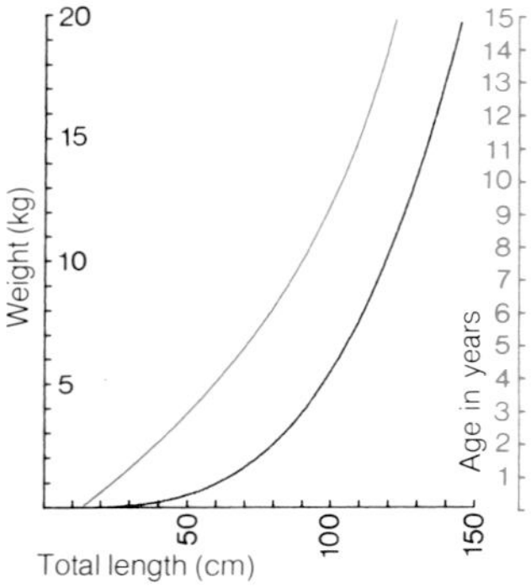

Oplegnathus conwayi

Richardson, 1840

Common names Cape knifejaw, black parrotfish, beaked galjoen, cuckoo bass

[Smith 206□1]

IDENTIFYING FEATURES

COLOUR, SHAPE AND SIZE

This robust fish has a pointed snout, armed with a parrot-like beak. Once this fish is removed from the water, the overall colour is essentially black, but living specimens can vary greatly in colour, and are often an iridescent white. Juveniles under 10 cm are strikingly coloured with a yellow-orange body and two black crossbars, one through the eye and one through the last dorsal and anal rays. Can attain 90 cm.

EXTERNAL ANATOMY

The body is covered with numerous, small scales, which adhere tightly to the skin. The dorsal fin consists of 12 spines plus 11-14 rays, and the anal of three spines plus 11-13 rays. The large caudal fin is slightly forked. The mouth is small. Young specimens have separated, incisor-like teeth, but with age, these unite to form a conspicuous, strong beak.

DISTRIBUTION

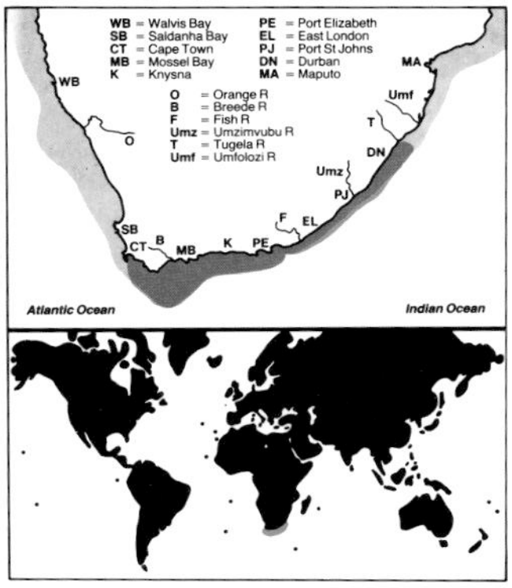

NATURAL HISTORY

This species frequents inshore reefs, favouring those exceeding 10 m in depth. Cape knifejaws usually form pairs, and these often display strong territorial behaviour. The diet is omnivorous and consists primarily of red and green seaweeds, sponges, and tunicates such as redbait. The strong beak is an effective adaptation for nibbling and tearing at food attached to the reef. Little is known of the life history, although it has been established that the juveniles occur in tidal pools, or beneath floating objects at sea. Despite the beak and similar habits, the members of this family are not at all closely related to the more tropical parrotfishes (family Scaridae).

CAPTURE

Though rarely caught by anglers, skindivers will confirm the abundance of this fish. Its inquisitiveness makes it an easy target for spearfishermen and potentially vulnerable to localized over-exploitation. The flesh of the Cape knifejaw is highly esteemed.

SA angling record – 5,7 kg.

SA spearfishing record – 5,8 kg.

SPECIFIC CATCH RESTRICTIONS

None.

NAME DERIVATION

Oplegnathus, knife-like jaws; *conwayi,* named after the ichthyologist Conway. All its common names refer to the beak-like fused teeth.

SIMILAR SPECIES

Easily identified by its fused teeth, plain, dark colouration, and much lower fin ray count than other knifejaws. It also has a distinctly sleeker body, and is the only knifejaw found south of Natal.

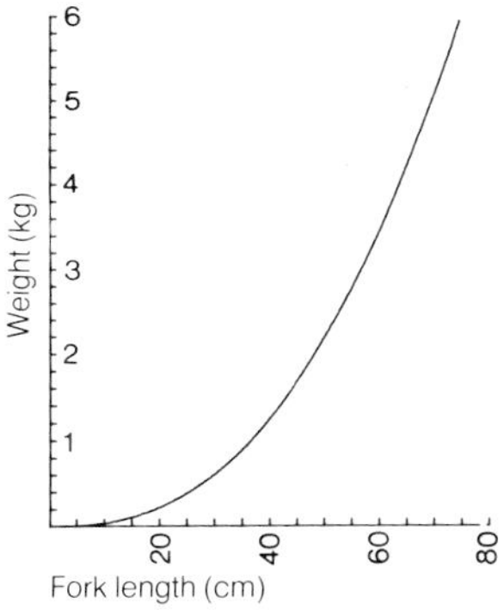

Oplegnathus robinsoni

Regan, 1916

Common names Natal knifejaw, cuckoo bass, humphead

[Smith 206□3]

IDENTIFYING FEATURES

COLOUR, SHAPE AND SIZE

This robust and deep-bodied fish is moderately compressed. The overall colour is brown or grey-brown, with the beak usually greyish. The juveniles are most distinctive and coloured differently, having a bright-yellow body with four broad, vertical, black bands, as pictured here. Can attain 60 cm.

EXTERNAL ANATOMY

The Natal knifejaw is covered in small, tightly adhering, rough scales that are too numerous to count and be of diagnostic value. Scales are absent from the snout, however, and only start over the front of the eye. The fins are well developed, with both anal and dorsal lobes, noticeably elongate. The continuous dorsal fin consists of 11 spines and 20-24 rays, and the anal has three spines and 14-17 rays, while the large caudal is moderately forked. An important diagnostic feature is the body depth which is 1,8-2,1 times the standard length, considerably deeper than the other knifejaws in the region. The mouth is terminal, and the teeth are fused into a very strong beak, not unlike that of parrotfishes. There are 16-19 gill rakers on the lower limb of the first arch.

NATURAL HISTORY

This endemic species is confined to shallow coastal waters, often close to shore, but also, reportedly, to 100 m. The Natal knifejaw appears particularly at home over coral reefs, and in South Africa it is most abundant in the St Lucia Marine Reserve. Its diet has not been studied, but is known to include ascidians (redbait), soft corals and other encrusting organisms. Divers often observe Natal knifejaws scraping at the reef with their powerful beaks. The reproduction of this species is virtually unknown, though the brightly coloured juveniles are often seen during the summer months, sheltering beneath floating objects at sea. This is known to be an effective dispersal mechanism, as the floating objects are pushed around by ocean currents. Curiously, the juveniles closely resemble the juveniles of the zebra *(Diplodus cervinus),* and it is probable that some form of mimicry takes place.

DISTRIBUTION

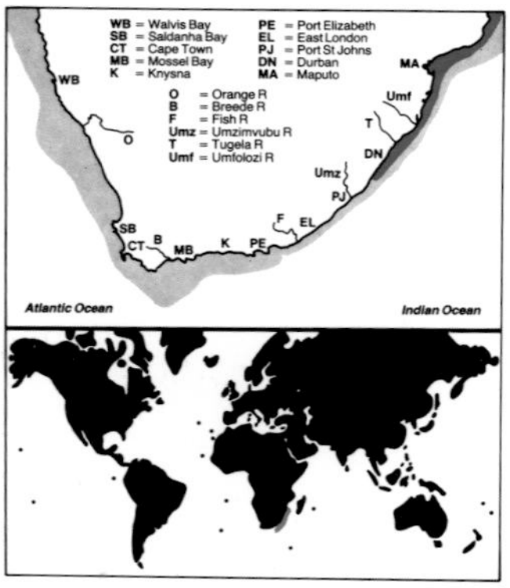

CAPTURE

The inquisitive nature of this fish makes it vulnerable to spearfishing. The Natal knifejaw is also quite

commonly reported amongst fishermen's catches. It makes excellent eating.

SA angling record – 2,2 kg.

SA spearfishing record – 3,0 kg.

SPECIFIC CATCH RESTRICTIONS

None.

NAME DERIVATION

Oplegnathus, knife-like jaws; *robinsoni,* named after Mr Romer Robinson, well-known Natal angler, correspondent and ichthyologist of the early 20th century. Natal knifejaw, a reference to its prevalence in Natal waters, and its fused, beak-like teeth.

SIMILAR SPECIES

Of the three knifejaw species that occur in South African waters, the Natal knifejaw is most distinctive because of its much deeper body. The closely related Mozambique knifejaw *(O. peaolopesi)* can be distinguished by having its body-scales begin well behind the level of the eye.

Lactoria cornuta

(Linnaeus, 1758)
Common name Worldwide – longhorn cowfish
[Smith 266□3]

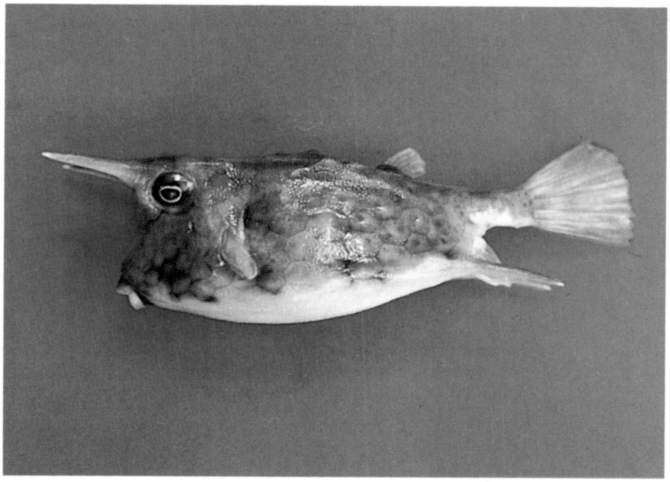

IDENTIFYING FEATURES

COLOUR, SHAPE AND SIZE

This curious fish has a rigid body, almost square in cross-section and with a distinct ridge on the dorsal surface. A long, forward-pointing spine is located above each eye, while two similar, pelvic spines project from the bottom rear 'corners' of the box-like body. The overall body colour is light green, but the underside and lips are pale yellow. Each individual scale is marked with one or two blue spots, and the fins are translucent. Though it is alleged that this fish can grow to 50 cm, few specimens exceed 20 cm.

EXTERNAL ANATOMY

The scales of the cowfish are modified into hexagonal plates which encase the body in an inflexible armour. Only the fin bases lack these rigid scales, thereby enabling the fins to move freely. The small dorsal fin has nine rays, and the anal fin consists of eight or nine rays. The large caudal fin is truncate. Immediately before each of the pelvic fins is a small gill opening. The mouth is rather small and has slightly protruding lips. Each jaw is set with small teeth, which, unlike those of some Ostraciidae, are not fused.

NATURAL HISTORY

The longhorn cowfish is a common inhabitant of almost all coral and rocky reefs throughout the Indo-Pacific. It often occurs as deep as 50 m, but it is also frequently found in tidal pools, sheltered bays and those estuaries that do not experience great salinity fluctuations. This fish is often seen searching for food just below the surface or along the edges of reefs. The diet includes a variety of floating matter, epiphytic organisms growing on seaweeds, and a variety of smaller crustaceans such as amphipods and small shrimps. Not surprisingly, because of its rather unwieldy shape, the cowfish is a slow swimmer. Forward propulsion is provided by the whirling, propellor-like movements of the pectoral fins, but, when threatened, a few beats of the large, expanding caudal fin can produce a short burst of speed. Though its horny, rigid body would appear to be unpalatable to predators, cowfish are frequently found in the stomachs of large kingfish. Details of the reproductive cycle are not known, but the quaint juveniles are seasonally common in Natal, frequently in very shallow water.

DISTRIBUTION

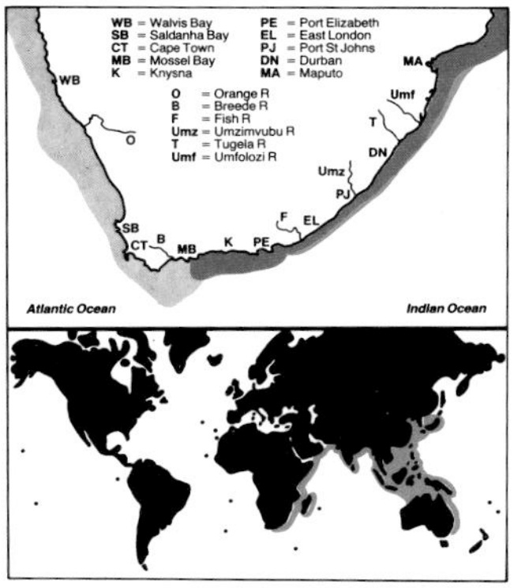

SPECIFIC CATCH RESTRICTIONS

None.

CAPTURE

Very few anglers hook the cowfish, but marine aquarists often net it for their display tanks. It is a hardy species and thrives in captivity. Because of their rigid exoskeleton, this and other boxfishes can be readily dried and used to make attractive ornaments. However, excessive exploitation for this purpose should be discouraged.

NAME DERIVATION

Lactoria, cow; *cornuta,* horned. Longhorn cowfish, a reference to the double horns which give the fish its bovine appearance.

SIMILAR SPECIES

The very long, forward-pointing spines over the eyes will distinguish this boxfish from the other nine species found in the southern African region.

Pempheris adusta

Bleeker, 1877
Common name Worldwide – dusky sweeper
[Smith 216□2]

IDENTIFYING FEATURES

COLOUR, SHAPE AND SIZE
The dusky sweeper has an oval, strongly compressed body, with an elongate tail. The overall colouration is coppery to brick red, but seen underwater the body is noticeably silver. The bases of the pectoral fins are distinctly marked with black, and, whereas the dorsal and anal fins are dark red, the paired pectoral and pelvic fins are pinkish and translucent. Can attain 17 cm in length.

EXTERNAL ANATOMY
The lateral line is distinct, and, along its length, thin, cycloid scales are arranged in 53-58 series. The fins include a short-based dorsal of six spines plus nine or ten rays, a long anal of three spines plus 37-43 rays, a slightly forked caudal, and pectorals that reach beyond the origin of the anal fin. The mouth is large, and the lower jaw projects slightly to give the fish an undershot appearance. Both jaws are set with rows of fine, pointed teeth. Some 25-31 well-developed, long rakers are located on the first gill arch. The eyes are noticeably big, and have black pupils. A large, transparent lens covers each eye; this feature is most obvious when the fish is viewed from above.

NATURAL HISTORY

The dusky sweeper is probably the most common and widely dispersed member of this family. This small fish inhabits coral and rocky reefs, and, during the day, dense shoals can be found wherever dark caves or overhanging ledges provide shelter. After nightfall, however, activity increases when the shoals venture more extensively over the reef in search of food. This consists mainly of planktonic invertebrates, as well as the larvae of other fish species. The large eyes are indicative of the dusky sweepers' nocturnal habits, and suggest that sight plays an important role in its hunting strategy. The spawning season is very extensive, and shoals of sweeper fry are almost always visible in the gullies of shallow reefs. With age, these juveniles progressively migrate to deeper reefs. Sweepers swim slowly, and propel themselves mainly by intermittent and characteristic 'sweeps' of the pectoral fins.

DISTRIBUTION

CAPTURE

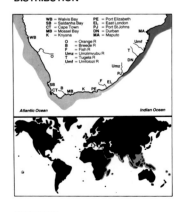

Though not of angling importance, the dusky sweeper makes an excellent aquarium fish, and will thrive in a tank environment if adequate shelter and low intensity illumination are provided. This and the other Pempheridae are edible, and make fine bait for larger fish.

SPECIFIC CATCH RESTRICTIONS

None.

NAME DERIVATION

Pempheris, a bubble, probably a reference to the bulbous eyes. (The name was given by early ichthyologists to a now-unknown species); *adusta,* dusky. Dusky sweeper, a reference to the dusky body-colours, and distinctive swimming style.

SIMILAR SPECIES

The high scale count and distinctly large eyes (the head length is less than 2,4 times the eye diameter) should distinguish this sweeper from the other three species found in this region.

Platycephalus indicus

(Linnaeus, 1758)
Common names Worldwide - bartail flathead, sand or river gurnard
[Smith 155□6]

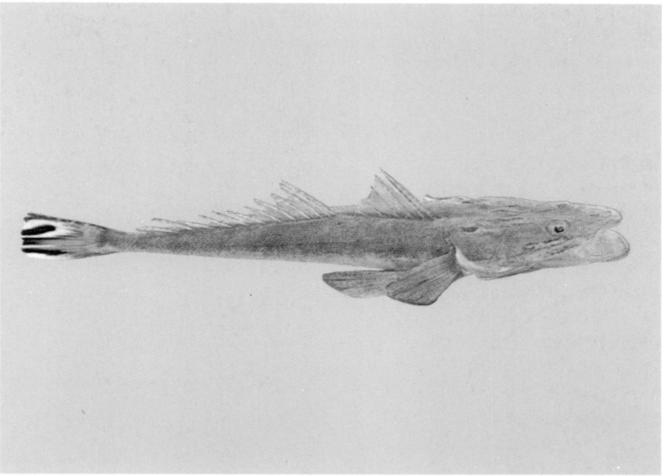

IDENTIFYING FEATURES

COLOUR, SHAPE AND SIZE

This fish has a flattened head and an elongate,depressed body which tapers towards the tail. It is generally brown above, with a white underside. Some specimens have faint crossbars, and all have a yellow tail with white-edged, dark bars. Can attain 100 cm.

EXTERNAL ANATOMY

There are some 120 series of small, rough scales arranged along the lateral line. The fins are well developed and include a dorsal of one detached spine followed by eight spines plus 13 or 14 rays, and a spineless anal fin of 13 rays. The caudal fin is truncate and the pectoral and pelvic fins are large. Sharp spines also project from the top of the head. The broad mouth, with its protruding lower jaw, bears fine villiform teeth. The small eyes are situated almost on top of the head, and just below two bony ridges. Gill rakers are absent.

DISTRIBUTION

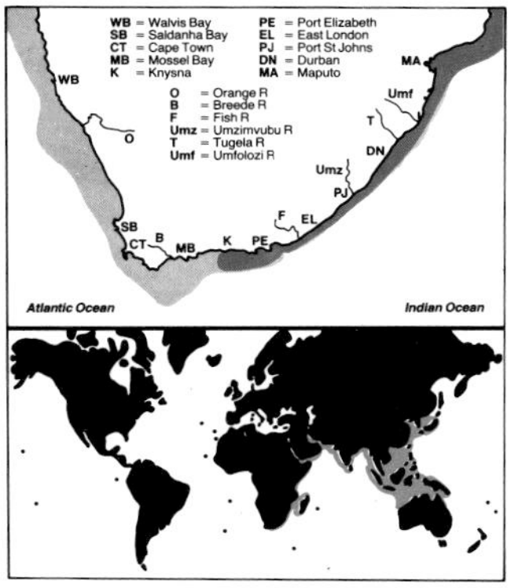

NATURAL HISTORY

The non-shoaling bartail flathead is common in estuaries and in open water where silt has been deposited. Its own muddy colouration blends well with these surroundings, and the fish is often very inconspicuous, especially when it buries itself below mud with only its eyes exposed. Here it lies, ready to snatch prey. Shrimps and gobies are particularly favoured, but polychaete worms, small crabs, mysids and other bottom-living invertebrates are also included in the diet. The sharp spines on the head are to be avoided, and, while undoubtedly a successful defence against many predators, they tend to snag trawl nets, thereby making the fish vulnerable to capture. Sexual maturity is attained at a length of 50 cm, and spawning occurs in the vicinity of Natal's estuaries from July to November. The juveniles make extensive use of estuarine mangrove areas for shelter and feeding, showing remarkable tolerance to turbid water and fluctuating salinities.

SPECIFIC CATCH RESTRICTIONS

None.

CAPTURE

This fine angling fish readily takes fish or prawn bait. Though nowhere exploited on a commercial scale, the bartail flathead is an excellent table fish. Its muddy habitat, however, makes it largely inaccessible to spearfishermen.

SA angling record - 3,7 kg.

NAME DERIVATION

Platycephalus, flat-headed; *indicus,* from India, where it was first discovered. Bartail flathead, a reference to its tail markings and depressed head. Sand or river gurnard, a reference to its habitat, and a corruption of *gornart* an old French word meaning a grumbler, a reference to the grunting noises supposedly made by this and similar fishes when removed from the water.

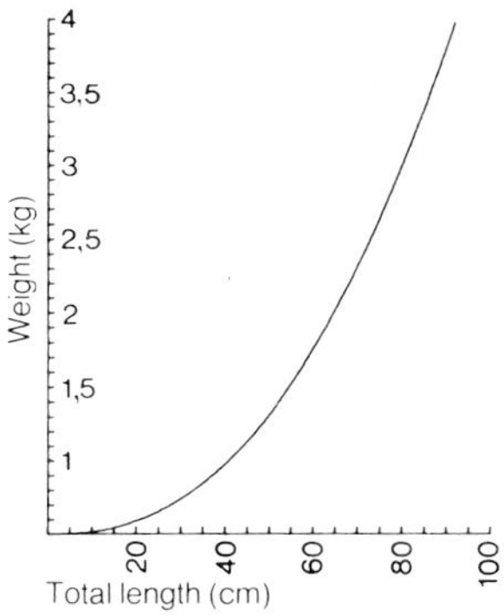

SIMILAR SPECIES

Identification of flatheads is not easy. This species is most common in estuaries and is the only one to have a single patch of villiform teeth on the roof of the mouth. All others have two patches.

Plotosus lineatus

(Thunberg, 1787)

Common names Worldwide – striped eel-catfish or striped barbel [Smith 60□1]

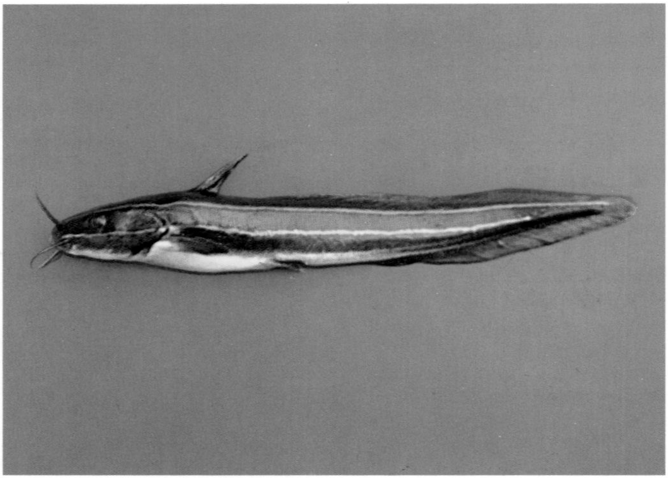

IDENTIFYING FEATURES

COLOUR, SHAPE AND SIZE

This elongate,eel-shaped fish is smaller, but very similar to *P. nkunga*. Its colours differ markedly, however; the body is brownish overall with two parallel, creamy-yellow stripes extending the length of the fish and onto the tail. Can attain 25 cm.

EXTERNAL ANATOMY

Scales are lacking and the body is smooth to the touch. The first dorsal fin comprises a single spine plus four or five rays. The second dorsal fin of 69-115 rays and the anal of 58-82 rays incorporate the pointed caudal of 9-11 rays to form a single continuous fin. The dorsal spine and the spine that occurs in each pectoral fin are sharply serrated, enveloped in toxic mucous tissue, and can be erected into an upright position. The mouth is wide and surrounded by fleshy lips and four pairs of sensory barbels. Small conical teeth occur in each jaw and on the palate. The first gill arch bears 22-32 distinct rakers.

DISTRIBUTION

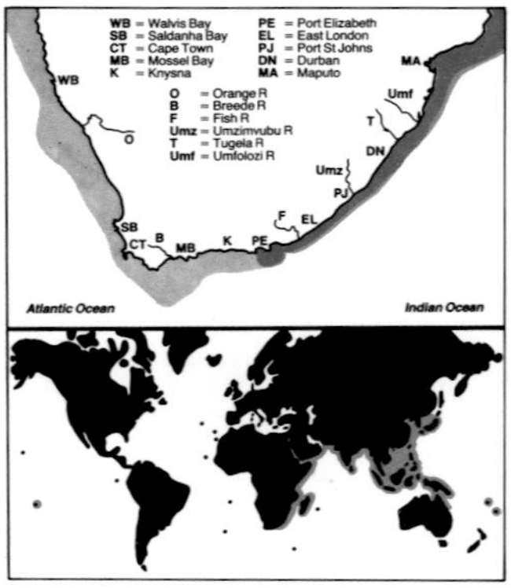

NATURAL HISTORY

Unlike *P. nkunga,* striped barbel are strongly gregarious and shoals of these little fish frequently congregate in shallow estuarine or coastal waters. Individuals mill around each other in a tightly packed seething mass, and occasionally these 'swarms' are so dense that, despite only being a metre or two in diameter, they can be discerned at some distance from the water. Their prey consists mainly of invertebrates, such as small crabs and shrimps, the detection of which is probably aided by the sensory barbels. Previously this species has been confused with *P. limbatus* and *P. nkunga,* and separate details of their life histories are not well known. The spines of the striped barbel are as toxic as those of other Plotosidae. Accidental jabs should be treated by immediately immersing the affected area in very hot water for 30 minutes to neutralize the protein toxin.

CAPTURE

Though not landed by anglers, it is easily caught in small hand-nets by aquarium enthusiasts. It thrives in captivity and often spends much time excavating holes in the sand below rocks. The purpose of such behaviour is not understood, but presumably it is a habit that also manifests itself in the fish's natural environment.

SPECIFIC CATCH RESTRICTIONS

None.

NAME DERIVATION

Plotosus a floater; *lineatus,* lined. Striped catfish or striped-barbel, a reference to the body patterns, the cat-like whiskers, and from the Latin *barba,* a beard.

SIMILAR SPECIES

The body stripes are most distinctive and serve to distinguish this species from other eel-catfish. However, it is possible that older fish may lose some of their markings, consequently fin ray counts may be needed to confirm identity.

Plotosus nkunga

Gomon & Taylor, 1982
Common names Worldwide – eel-catfish or eel-barbel
[Smith 60□2]

IDENTIFYING FEATURES

COLOUR, SHAPE AND SIZE

The robust and eel-shaped body of this catfish tapers to a pointed tail. Its overall colouration is dark brown above and pale below. Can attain 50 cm in length.

EXTERNAL ANATOMY

Scales are absent, and the soft skin is coated with mucus. Lateral line pores are distinctly visible. The first dorsal consists of a single spine plus four or five rays. The second dorsal and the anal fins incorporate the pointed caudal into a single continuous fin comprising 104-120 dorsal and 88-109 anal rays. The dorsal spine, as well as the single spine occurring in each of the pectoral fins, can lock into an erect position. All three spines are strongly serrated and covered with toxic mucous tissue. The wide, underslung mouth is surrounded by fleshy lips and four pairs of sensory barbels. Conical teeth are set in both jaws and on the palate. There are 16-21 rakers on the first gill arch.

DISTRIBUTION

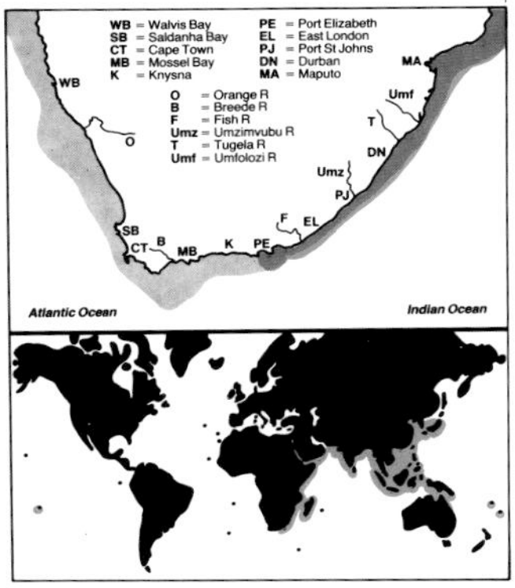

NATURAL HISTORY

The eel-catfish is usually solitary, and, while some individuals inhabit deep reefs, it is generally confined to inshore regions and estuaries. It is tolerant of low salinities and muddy water. In such turbid environments it uses its sensory barbels to locate prey, which includes crabs and several fish species. Feeding takes place exclusively near the bottom. Breeding has been recorded off the Natal coast. The eggs are exceptionally large and few in number. If the social behaviour of the members of this genus is anything like that of the much-studied freshwater barbels, it is likely that the developing embryos are protected by the parents. The function of the small, curious, bony structure just behind the vent remains obscure, though it may play a role in reproduction. The stout spines can inflict serious wounds on careless handlers, and severe poisoning can result. Immediate immersion of the affected part in very hot water for 30 minutes is essential, as this breaks down the protein poison.

CAPTURE

The eel-catfish is frequently landed by anglers using a variety of baits. Despite its unappealing appearance it is an excellent table fish. In the Far East, its close relative, *P. limbatus,* is caught in nets and fish traps. It is easily approached and speared.
SA angling record – 2,8 kg.
SA spearfishing record – 1,8 kg.

SPECIFIC CATCH RESTRICTIONS

None.

NAME DERIVATION

Plotosus, a floater; *nkunga,* the Zulu name for this fish. Eel-catfish or eel-barbel, a reference to its elongated body, its cat-like whiskers, and from the Latin *barba,* a beard.

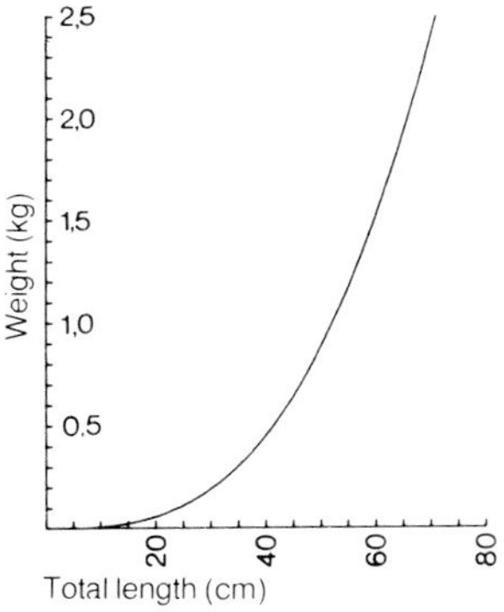

SIMILAR SPECIES

Differences between various eel-catfish species are not always easy to detect. Nevertheless, the absence of body stripes and distinctive gill raker counts should preclude misidentification.

Polydactylus plebeius

(Broussonet, 1782)
Common names SA – striped threadfin, bastard mullet. Elsewhere – common threadfin
[Smith 223□2]

IDENTIFYING FEATURES

COLOUR, SHAPE AND SIZE

This oblong, slightly compressed fish has a projecting, fleshy snout. Its overall body colour is silvery, but green-gold above and white below, and there are numerous dusky stripes down each flank. Can attain 45 cm in length.

EXTERNAL ANATOMY

Scales are conspicuous and are arranged in 58-64 series along the distinct lateral line. The fins are well developed and include a double dorsal, the first of eight spines and the second of one spine plus 13 rays, an anal of two or three spines plus 11-12 rays, and a forked caudal. The pectoral fins are characteristic, with five rays in each fin extending into long unbranched filaments. Small teeth occur in both jaws of the underslung mouth. Some 30 rakers occur on the first gill arch. The eyes are covered with transparent, adipose tissue.

NATURAL HISTORY

A rather curious, shallow-water fish, the striped threadfin occurs either singly or in small shoals. Sandy or muddy areas, including estuaries, are generally preferred habitats. With the bulbous snout and the antennae-like pectoral rays acting as sensory organs, this fish detects obstacles in poor visibility conditions, and is therefore able to navigate successfully in turbid waters. No doubt these anatomical adaptations also play a role in the hunting strategy of this species by helping it to locate prey. The diet consists of mantis shrimps, mysids, small crabs, amphipods, prawns and small fish, most of which are captured close to the bottom. Recent research in Hawaii has shown this species to be one of the few fishes in the world to have a lunar breeding cycle, with spawning always occurring during the last quarter. Egg laying takes place in sheltered shallows at high water, with the ensuing ebb dispersing the fertilized ova widely. Sex reversal has been recorded in this species and individuals of 20-25 cm are males, while those of 30-40 cm are females. In Natal, specimens exceeding 20 cm have been found in a breeding condition.

DISTRIBUTION

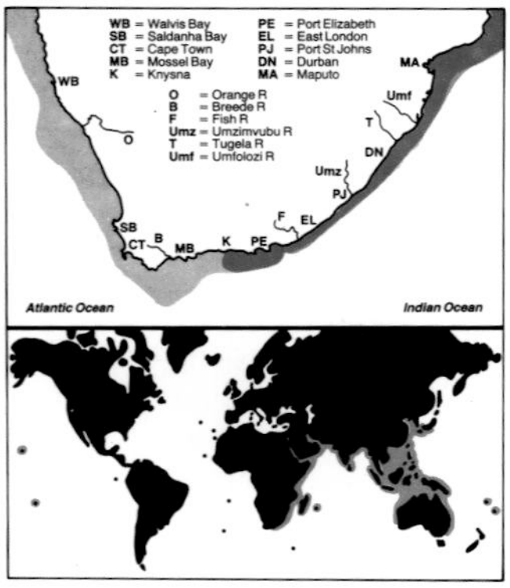

CAPTURE

Striped threadfins are frequently hooked by light-tackle shore anglers using shrimp or fish baits. More often than not, however, they are wrongly identified as mullet. Though of no commercial or spearfishing importance in southern Africa, these fish are valuable as a protein resource in other countries. The flesh makes good eating.
SA angling record – 2,4 kg.
SA spearfishing record – vacant.

SPECIFIC CATCH RESTRICTIONS

None.

NAME DERIVATION

Polydactylus, many threads; *plebeius,* vulgar or common. Striped threadfin, a reference to the elongate and separate pectoral rays; bastard mullet, a reference to the fish's superficial resemblance to a mullet.

SIMILAR SPECIES

Threadfins are readily identified and the other two species that occur locally may be distinguished by having either six unbranched pectoral rays, as in *P. sextarius* or five branched pectoral rays as in *P. indicus.*

Pomacanthus imperator

(Bloch, 1787)
Common name Worldwide – emperor angelfish
[Smith 204□9]

IDENTIFYING FEATURES

COLOUR, SHAPE AND SIZE

This round to oval-bodied fish is strongly compressed. Colours and patterns vary considerably with age. Juveniles are navy blue, or almost black, with concentric, blue-white lines on their sides. With adolescence, mature colouration is gradually adopted, and adults, are brown overall and have 20-30 almost-horizontal yellow lines marking the flanks. The caudal and pectoral fins are distinctly orange, and the dorsal spines are white. A blue-edged, black band extends across the forehead and tends to camouflage the black eyes. Though these patterns may vary between individuals this appears unrelated to sex.
Can attain 40 cm.

EXTERNAL ANATOMY

Small, rough, ctenoid scales are arranged in 77-79 series along the well-defined lateral line. The fins are well developed and include a single dorsal of 13 or 14 spines plus 19-21 rays, an anal of three spines plus 19-20 rays, and a slightly rounded caudal. The terminal mouth is small and bears slender, bristle-like teeth in each jaw. A conspicuous spine occurs at the angle of the pre-operculum.

NATURAL HISTORY

The emperor angelfish is a solitary species which inhabits coral and rocky reefs varying in depth from 3-70 m. It is most abundant in southern African waters during summer and it is not unusual to find the juveniles in intertidal pools. This spectacular fish is especially common around tropical reefs such as those in the St Lucia Marine Reserve. The emperor angelfish is agile, and, by virtue of its very compressed body, it can hide in extremely narrow cracks

Juvenile P. imperator.

and caves. For most individuals, red and brown encrusting sponges make up about 95 per cent of the diet. The remainder comprises colonial ascidians, algae and coral polyps. Small invertebrates are also carefully pecked from the reef. Reproduction is not well understood, though it is known that eggs are free-floating, and are distributed by ocean currents.

CAPTURE

The emperor angelfish is not an angling species. Neither is it of interest to spearfishermen. It is, however, a most inquisitive fish and will often swim right up to a diver. Adults can be maintained in large aquaria, but only with extreme care and correct feeding. Juveniles, though, are far more adaptable and adjust well to tank environments.

SPECIFIC CATCH RESTRICTIONS

None.

DISTRIBUTION

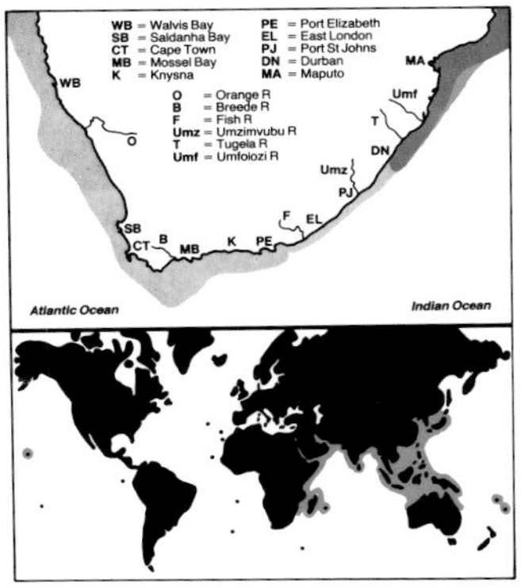

NAME DERIVATION

Pomacanthus, projecting thorn; *imperator,* emperor. Emperor angelfish, a reference to its beautiful colours and patterns.

SIMILAR SPECIES

While the patterns and colour of both adult and juvenile are most diagnostic, the juvenile may need closer inspection when seen underwater, in order to distinguish it from other angelfishes.

Pomacanthus semicirculatus

(Cuvier, 1831)

Common names SA - semicircle angelfish. Elsewhere - blue angelfish

[Smith 204□11]

IDENTIFYING FEATURES

COLOUR, SHAPE AND SIZE

In both small and large individuals, the oval and strongly compressed body is distinctly marked and coloured. Young semicircle angelfish are navy blue to black overall, with lighter-blue edges to the dorsal and anal fins. Passing down the sides are 8-10 pairs of alternating, narrow, white and blue bars arranged in a crescent or semicircle. With increased growth, however, these bright colours fade progressively to the less spectacular adult colouration. This consists of a greenish body flecked with dark blue. The fins are also green, but darker than the body. Bright-blue streaks lie across each cheek, marking the pre-opercular and opercular flanges. Can attain 40 cm in length.

EXTERNAL ANATOMY

The lateral line is well defined, and about 75 series of distinctly ctenoid scales are arranged along its length. The fins are spiny and well developed, especially the enlarged anal and dorsal fins which may have very elongate trailing filaments. The dorsal fin consists of 13 spines plus 21-23 rays, the anal fin of three spines plus 20-22 rays, and the caudal is rounded. The large spine on the hind edge of the pre-operculum is conspicuous. A single row of very elongate and pointed, bristle-like teeth occurs in both jaws of the small, terminal mouth. The first gill arch bears 17-18 very short rakers.

NATURAL HISTORY

The semicircle angelfish is a common inhabitant of warmer coral and rocky reefs, and is most abundant in southern African waters during summer. Though juveniles make extensive use of the intertidal zone and shallow-water rocky areas as nurseries, adults prefer depths ranging from 5-30 m. Here, individuals may be seen continuously browsing over the rocky bottom for sponges, ascidians and small seaweeds. The closely spaced teeth are well suited to cropping small pieces of sessile plants and animals from the rocky substrate. Juveniles have a different diet which includes free-swimming animals such as small crustaceans (mainly amphipods and shrimps). The breeding cycle has not yet been fully investigated, but the eggs and larvae are free-floating and widely distributed by ocean currents.

Juvenile P. semicirculatus.

CAPTURE

Adult semicircle angelfish are easily caught on small baits, but their flesh is inedible and therefore of little value. However, the juveniles are much sought after by marine aquarists.

DISTRIBUTION

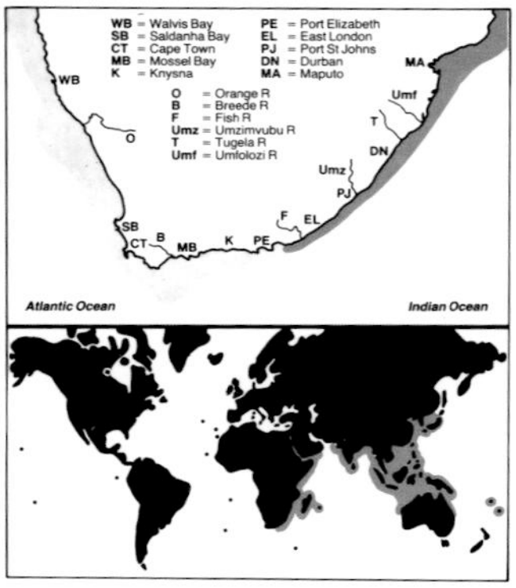

SPECIFIC CATCH RESTRICTIONS

None.

NAME DERIVATION

Pomacanthus, projecting thorn; *semicirculatus,* half circles. Semicircle angelfish, both references to the body colours and markings.

SIMILAR SPECIES

While the patterns and colours of both adult and juvenile are most diagnostic, the juvenile may need closer inspection when seen underwater in order to distinguish it from other angelfishes.

Pomacanthus striatus

(Rüppell, 1836)
Common names SA - old woman. Elsewhere - striatus angelfish
[Smith 204□12]

Juvenile P. striatus.

IDENTIFYING FEATURES

COLOUR, SHAPE AND SIZE

This strongly compressed fish is almost oval-shaped. Body colours vary with age: the young are brown to black with 15-20 narrow, blue-white, vertical bars, but these colours begin to fade at a length of 10 cm. Adults are grey-brown overall with a much paler hind third. Can attain 46 cm.

EXTERNAL ANATOMY

The body is covered with small, but rough, ctenoid scales arranged along the well-defined lateral line in 75-85 series. The fins are spiny and well developed, and include a single dorsal of 11 or 12 spines plus 22-25 rays, an anal of three spines plus 21-23 rays, and a truncate caudal. The soft dorsal and anal fins are both rather large and make the fish's body appear somewhat bigger than it is. Older specimens tend to develop a distinct hump above the head. Slender, bristle-like teeth occur in both jaws of the small terminal mouth. The pre-operculum is serrated and bears a strong spine. The first gill arch is set with 17-19 short rakers.

NATURAL HISTORY

This shallow-water species is confined to rocky shores and coral reefs. The old woman is the most common of the three *Pomacanthus* species occurring in South African waters. It is tolerant of temperate conditions, hence its distribution extends further southwards, as far as Knysna. The young frequent intertidal rock pools and are solitary, while the dull-coloured adults often congregate above reefs, in midwater or even at the surface. The small mouth, with its closely spaced teeth, is well adapted for browsing on encrusting organisms such as sponges, coral polyps and tunicates. Small invertebrates such as crabs and marine worms are also consumed. The breeding biology of this species has not been well documented, though eggs and larvae are known to be free-floating and pelagic. The young tend to be timid, and, at the slightest hint of danger, will disappear into the smallest of cracks in the reef, only to re-appear several metres away through another opening.

CAPTURE

The old woman is one of the more popular marine aquarium fish in southern Africa. It is fairly hardy and will thrive in a tank if properly cared for. Juveniles are easily caught in a hand-net, while adult old women are occasionally caught by anglers fishing with light tackle over shallow reefs or from piers or jetties, and using small pieces of shrimp as bait.

SA angling record - 3,0 kg.
SA spearfishing record - 1,8 kg.

DISTRIBUTION

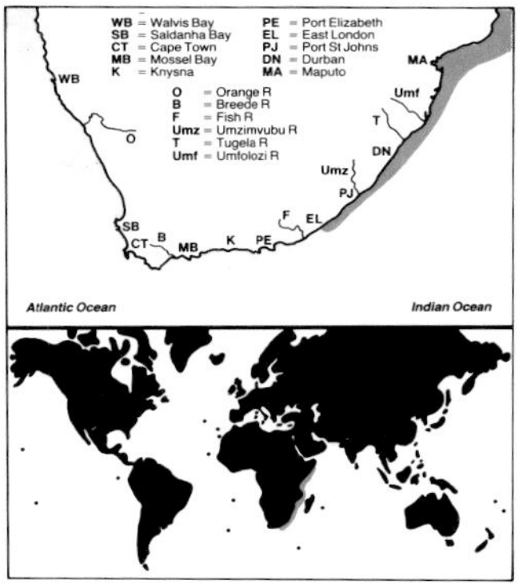

SPECIFIC CATCH RESTRICTIONS

None.

NAME DERIVATION

Pomacanthus, projecting thorn; *striatus,* striped. Old woman, a reference to the drab colours of older specimens.

SIMILAR SPECIES

While the patterns and colours of both adult and juvenile are most diagnostic, the juvenile may need closer inspection when seen underwater in order to distinguish it from other angelfishes.

Abudefduf natalensis

Hensley & Randall, 1983
Common name Worldwide – fourbar damsel
[Smith 219□1]

IDENTIFYING FEATURES

COLOUR, SHAPE AND SIZE

This deep-bodied fish has conspicuous markings that change rapidly after capture. Underwater, it is distinctly white, with four black, vertical crossbars and a black band down each of the caudal lobes. With age, however, and also after death, these crossbars become less obvious and the upper flanks gain an iridescent, blue sheen, often accompanied by irregular shades of yellowish-brown.This pretty fish is rather similar to the sergeant major, especially after death, but is readily distinguished by the two bands on the caudal fin, and the greater contrast of colours when seen underwater. Can attain 17 cm.

EXTERNAL ANATOMY

There are about 20-22 series of rough, ctenoid scales arranged along the distinct lateral line. The fins are well developed and include a single dorsal of 12-13 spines plus 12 or 13 rays, an anal of two spines plus 12 or 13 rays, and a caudal fin that is noticeably more forked than those of other Pomacentridae. The small mouth bears a row of incisors in each jaw, and the 22-26 rakers on the first gill arch are well developed and conspicuous.

NATURAL HISTORY

The fourbar damsel is fairly abundant around rocky reefs along the Natal coast, with juveniles being more common in tidal pools, and adults living in slightly deeper water. It is mainly carnivorous, and the diet comprises small crabs, amphipods, mysids and other crustaceans. Lesser amounts of red and green seaweeds are also consumed. As with most damselfishes, the fourbar damsel probably occupies a clearly demarcated home territory which is actively defended against intruders. Within the territory there is usually a specific resting site where the fish sleeps at night, where it may rest up during the day, escape from predators, or hide when alarmed. These, and other aspects of their complex social habits, make Pomacentridae, in general, ideal subjects for the study and testing of theories on the behaviour of fishes. Despite this recent and intensive research on the numerous species of damselfishes, specific facts about the biology of *Abudefduf* are not always available.

DISTRIBUTION

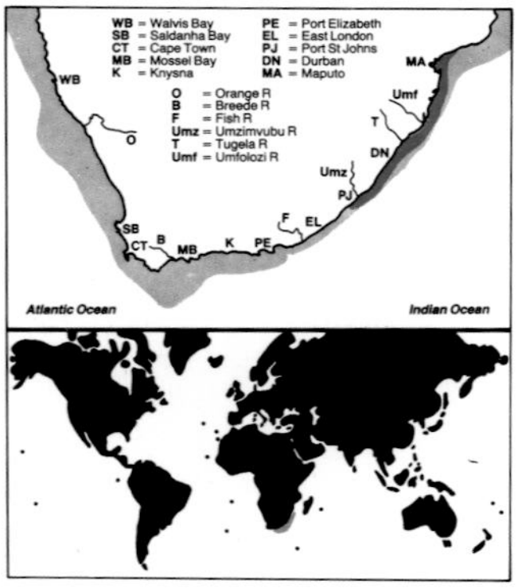

CAPTURE

The fourbar damsel is a successful, but sometimes rather aggressive, aquarium species. Though edible it is generally too small for consumption.

SPECIFIC CATCH RESTRICTIONS

None.

NAME DERIVATION

Abudefduf, the Arabic name for this group of fishes; *natalensis,* of Natal. Fourbar damsel, a reference to its banded body and dainty appearance.

SIMILAR SPECIES

Previously this species was confused with the more tropical stripetail damsel *(A. sexfasciatus).* The two can easily be distinguished, as *A. natalensis* has four body bars and *A. sexfasciatus* has five.

Abudefduf sordidus

(Forsskål, 1775)
Common names SA – spot damsel. Elsewhere – coral fish, grey-banded sergeant-major
[Smith 219□5]

IDENTIFYING FEATURES

COLOUR, SHAPE AND SIZE

This deep-bodied little fish has an overall drab, dull-grey colouration, which darkens considerably after death. Its markings, however, are distinctive and include five lighter vertical crossbars as well as a black blotch at the origin of the pectoral fins and on the saddle of the caudal peduncle. The fins are usually dusky-yellow with the hind portion of the anal and caudal fins being noticeably darker. Can attain 23 cm in length.

EXTERNAL ANATOMY

The body has 21-23 series of small, but well-developed, ctenoid scales arranged along the distinct lateral line. The dorsal fin consists of 13 spines plus 14-15 rays, the anal of two spines plus 14-16 rays, and the caudal fin is slightly forked. Distinct lips surround the small terminal mouth, and each jaw bears a single row of incisors. There are 26-28 rakers on the first gill arch.

DISTRIBUTION

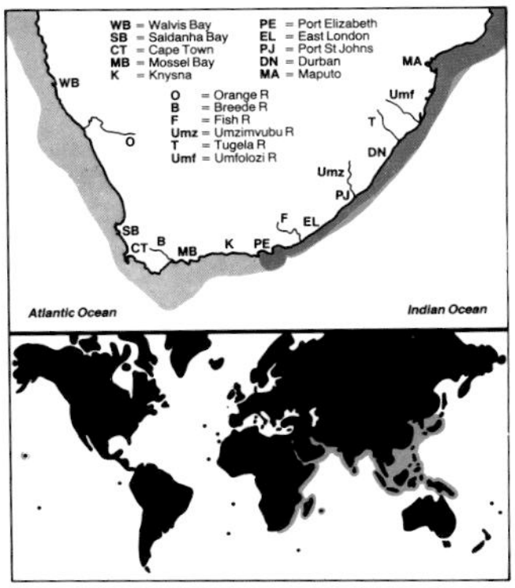

NATURAL HISTORY

The spot damsel occurs either singly or in small groups over shallow rocky or coral reefs, often close to the shore where there is moderate wave action. It also frequents the upper, seaward edges of offshore reefs. This species usually occupies a set home territory, though it is generally not too fussy about the choice of site. The domain is usually defended aggressively against intruders, and within it there may be a specific nesting and sleeping site which also provides refuge from predators. Part of the daylight hours are spent in midwater, but, because of its herbivorous diet, much time is spent grazing on the rocky bottom. Research on other, but similar, species of herbivorous damselfishes suggests remarkable 'farming' behaviour. Fish systematically remove certain undesirable species of algae from their territories, and this 'weeding' activity causes other, more desirable species to proliferate. As a result, the yield of food within such areas is greatly improved. The sharp incisors are well-adapted for nibbling at the red and green seaweeds plentiful in its habitat. The diet, however, also includes lesser amounts of tiny crustaceans such as mysids, copepods, amphipods, crabs and shrimps as well as smaller amounts of hydrozoa. Though its life cycle in southern African waters is not well known, it is apparent that the juveniles use intertidal rock pools as nursery areas. The distribution of fry at sea is assisted by their habit of sheltering below floating objects borne along by ocean currents.

CAPTURE

The spot damsel is easily hooked on ultra-light tackle, but, though quite edible, it is too small to be considered a table fish. It thrives in aquaria, however, but tends to dominate and harass smaller and newly introduced fish.

SPECIFIC CATCH RESTRICTIONS

None.

NAME DERIVATION

Abudefduf, an Arabic name for this group of fishes; *sordidus,* a reference to its drab colour. Spot damsel, a reference to the blotch on its tail and to its dainty appearance.

SIMILAR SPECIES

This species can be easily recognized by the black blotch located on the upper caudal peduncle.

Abudefduf vaigiensis

(Quoy & Gaimard, 1825)
Common names SA – sergeant major. Elsewhere – sergeant major, coral fish, five-banded damselfish [Smith 219□7]

IDENTIFYING FEATURES

COLOUR, SHAPE AND SIZE
As is common with this deep-bodied family, the colours of the sergeant major are variable. Most specimens, however, tend to be bluish-grey, but often with vivid-yellow upper flanks. There are also, normally, five dark, vertical bars running down the sides. The fins are translucent, dusky or dark. Can attain 20 cm.

EXTERNAL ANATOMY
The body has about 28 series of rough, ctenoid scales arranged along the lateral line. The dorsal fin consists of 13 spines plus 12-13 rays, while the anal fin has two spines plus 11-13 rays. The caudal fin is forked. Distinct lips surround the small terminal mouth which is full-lipped and carries a row of incisors in each jaw. There are 25-28 rakers on the first gill arch.

DISTRIBUTION

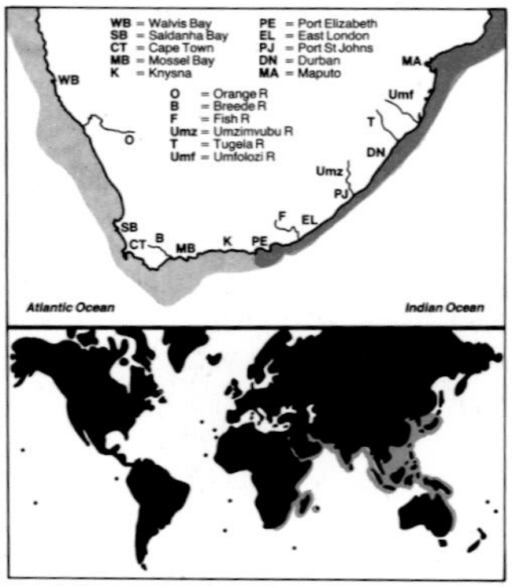

NATURAL HISTORY

The sergeant major frequents virtually all inshore reefs within its area of distribution, and is particularly common around the piers and wharfs of harbours. Whereas adults prefer deeper water, juveniles frequent shallow tidal pools, which are used as nursery areas. Studies have shown that the sergeant major is most abundant along the outer, more turbulent, upper edges of reefs, where it often forms small shoals. This omnivorous species feeds during daylight only, and the diet includes shrimps and other small crustaceans, and several species of red and green seaweed.
Juvenile fish are distributed over great areas by sheltering beneath floating objects borne along by ocean currents – the algal growths and small crustaceans that attach themselves to such flotsam presumably provide the young fish with an abundant food supply while in transit. Once in the vicinity of a suitable reef or harbour these juveniles will desert their temporary home and swim off to colonize their new-found habitat. As with other damselfishes, the sergeant major displays complex social behaviour and occupies a home-range with a specific nesting site.

CAPTURE

This small fish is edible, and, though not highly regarded in southern Africa, it does constitute a food source in parts of Japan.
It thrives in captivity though it is aggressive towards other species in its tank.

SPECIFIC CATCH RESTRICTIONS

None.

NAME DERIVATION

Abudefduf, an Arabic name for this group of fishes; *vaigiensis,* a reference to its vague similarity to other members of the family. Sergeant major, a reference to the 'military stripes' on the flanks.

SIMILAR SPECIES

The presence of five body bars and yellow dorsal-body colour should serve to distinguish the sergeant major from other damselfishes found in the region.

Amphiprion allardi

Klausewitz, 1970

Common names Worldwide – twobar anemonefish, clownfish [Smith 219□9]

IDENTIFYING FEATURES

COLOUR, SHAPE AND SIZE

This deep-bodied little fish has a well-rounded head profile. The general body colour and markings vary with age. Adult specimens have blackish-brown flanks, yellow or orange undersides and lower fins, a considerable amount of white on the caudal fin, and two, broad, bluish-white, vertical bars running down the sides of the body. Juveniles are lighter in colour, and may have a third white bar running down the caudal fin and peduncle. Can attain 15 cm.

EXTERNAL ANATOMY

The body has 35-41 series of small, ctenoid scales arranged along the lateral line. The single dorsal consists of 10-11 spines plus 15-17 rays, and the anal of two spines plus 13-15 rays. The caudal fin is slightly emarginate. Thick lips surround the small, terminal mouth, and each jaw bears a row of 40-50 small, conical teeth. The first gill arch carries 18-20 rakers and the gill covers are serrated.

DISTRIBUTION

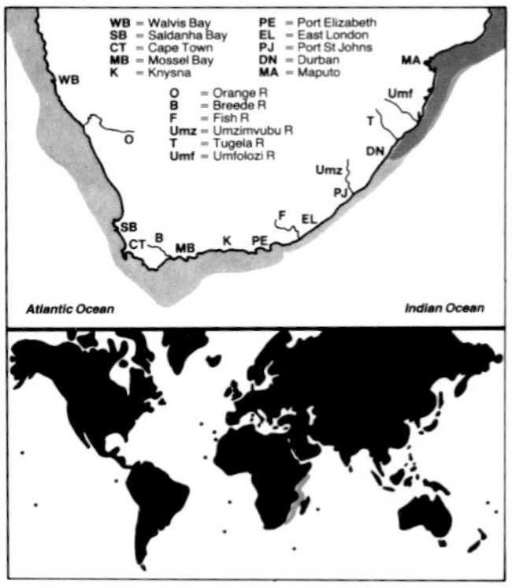

NATURAL HISTORY

This attractive and interesting fish lives in symbiosis with large sea anemones that have stinging cells harmful to most fish. The anemonefish is immune to these, however, and when danger threatens it retreats within the poisonous tentacles, where it shelters until the cause for alarm has passed. Some clownfish have even been observed entering the mouth of an anemone, which may host two or more individuals. It is not certain how the anemone is repaid for its protective services, but presumably it benefits to an extent from scraps of food that the clownfish may drop, or even from would-be predators of these fish that are lured within grasp of the anemone's tentacles. The clownfish is omnivorous, and the diet includes various algal species and invertebrates such as copepods, marine worms, amphipods, isopods and other small crustaceans. The swimming technique of the clownfish is also peculiar as it moves with a rather comical, up-and-down flopping and wriggling motion that almost matches the undulating motion of the anemone's tentacles. Breeding occurs intermittently throughout the summer. The rather large eggs are attached to the reef, usually just at the base of the anemone which protects and circulates fresh water over them, thus reducing the need for constant parental care. After hatching, the young are sufficiently well developed to be immediately self-sufficient. There is evidence that this species can change sex.

CAPTURE

This popular aquarium species is one of the very few marine fish that can be bred and reared in captivity. As it is dependent on a limited number of anemones, and therefore easy to catch with a hand net, capture should be controlled to avoid over-exploitation.

SPECIFIC CATCH RESTRICTIONS

None.

NAME DERIVATION

Amphiprion, serrated on both sides, a reference to the gill covers; *allardi*, this species was named in honour of Jacques Allard, an aquarist in Kenya. Twobar anemonefish, a reference to its markings and symbiotic relationship with the sea anemone.

SIMILAR SPECIES

There are two clownfish species in southern Africa. The other is known as the skunkclown or nosestripe anemonefish (*A. akallopisos*), which is easily recognized by its pinkish colour and white stripe down the forehead.

Pomatomus saltatrix

(Linnaeus, 1766)

Common names SA – elf, shad. Elsewhere – bluefish, tailor [Smith 178□1]

IDENTIFYING FEATURES

COLOUR, SHAPE AND SIZE

This streamlined fish is elongate and slightly compressed. Live specimens have an overall silvery sheen, with light green on the dorsal surface and upper flanks. After death, however, this colour gradually changes to blue. The underside is white. Can attain 100 cm in length.

EXTERNAL ANATOMY

Approximately 95 series of ctenoid scales are arranged along the lateral line. The fins are well developed, and two separate dorsal fins occur; the first of eight short spines, and the second of 23-28 rays. The anal fin has three spines plus 23-27 rays. The large caudal fin is forked. About 5-20 rakers occur on the first gill arch, but this number decreases with age. The large, downward-slanting mouth has an undershot lower jaw and bears exceptionally sharp teeth.

DISTRIBUTION

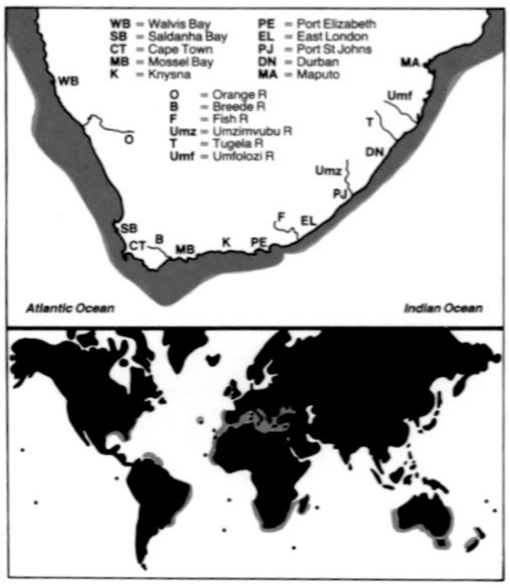

NATURAL HISTORY

Amongst the fiercest of marine predators, the elf feeds in shoals over sandy sea-beds along the edges of reefs. It hunts by sight and invariably feeds in clear water during the day. It will, however, also feed under artificial light at night. Some 87 per cent of the diet comprises fish such as anchovies, pilchards and pinkies. Much of the balance is made up of shrimps and squid. Its razor-sharp teeth are able, within seconds, to tear even its largest prey to shreds. The life cycle of this fish involves lengthy migrations each winter from the Cape to Natal where, following maturation during spring, spawning takes place. The pelagic larvae drift passively and are transported back to Cape waters by the strong Agulhas Current. Along the shallow beaches of the eastern and, particularly, the southern Cape, the juveniles spend their first year. Sexual maturity is attained at a length of 25 cm, but the number of eggs produced each season increases sharply with age. This species has been heavily exploited, but strict conservation legislation appears to be taking effect with stocks showing signs of increased abundance.

CAPTURE

Previously, this esteemed sport fish was netted in beach seines, but this practice is now restricted to False Bay. When fresh, the flesh makes excellent eating.

World angling record – 14,4 kg.

SA angling record – 10,3 kg.

SA spearfishing record – 7,8 kg.

SPECIFIC CATCH RESTRICTIONS

Protected species; closed season 1 Sept. to 30 Nov. *Not to be sold.* Minimum legal size is 30 cm total length.

NAME DERIVATION

Pomatomus, serrated operculum; *saltatrix,* one who dances. Elf, from the old Dutch *elft,* a common name for a similar, freshwater fish found in Europe; shad, a rather inappropriate reference to the northern hemisphere 'shad', a small fish of the herring family.

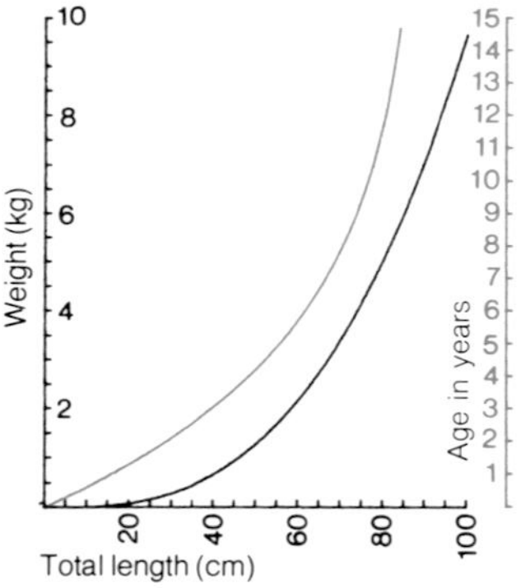

Rachycentron canadum

(Linnaeus, 1766)
Common names SA - prodigal son. Elsewhere - cobia
[Smith 212□1]

IDENTIFYING FEATURES

COLOUR, SHAPE AND SIZE

This almost cigar-shaped fish is elongate, virtually cylindrical in cross-section, and has a broad, depressed head. The overall body colour is dark brown above and creamy below. Two distinct, broad, silvery-white bands run the length of the body. These bands rapidly lose their brilliance when the fish is removed from the water, but the specimen shown here still displays this characteristic sheen on the hind part of the lower band. The prodigal son seldom exceeds 130 cm, but a 200 cm specimen estimated to weigh 68 kg was caught in Senegal in 1950.

EXTERNAL ANATOMY

Scales are present, but these are virtually invisible as they are well embedded in the thick skin. There are two dorsal fins, the first consisting of 7-9 separate, and very small, spines and the second of 1-3 spines plus 33-36 rays. The anal fin consists of 1-3 spines plus 22-28 rays, and the large caudal fin is broad and triangular. The large mouth bears fine, villiform teeth in both jaws, and there are tough rakers on the first gill arch. Narrow, adipose eyelids encircle the small eyes.

NATURAL HISTORY

This predator frequents coral and rocky reefs, and has a preference for clear, warm water. It is a migrating species, and, though its visits are somewhat erratic, peak abundance in southern African waters is during the summer months. Almost without exception, this fish feeds on crabs, especially the swimming variety. Occasionally, crayfish are also taken. It is an expert mimic of the remora, and it is not uncommon to find a number of prodigal sons in close association with whale sharks and other large fish. Almost every specimen is host to parasitic nematode worms, which infest the stomach. Despite their distasteful appearance, however, these worms do not appear to affect the health of the fish or the quality of its flesh. Sexual maturity is attained during the second or third year, when shoals of mature specimens move into shallow water in order to spawn. Females produce unusually large quantities of eggs each season, and these are dispersed by ocean currents.

DISTRIBUTION

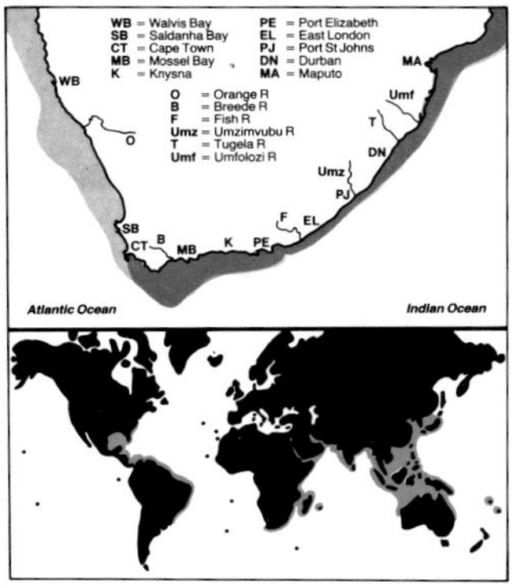

CAPTURE

This fine angling fish takes a variety of bait, including crab, mole crab (sea lice) and crayfish. Spearfishermen also frequently land large specimens. The flesh is delicious.

World angling record - 61,5 kg.
SA angling record - 39,9 kg.
SA spearfishing record - 29,0 kg.

SPECIFIC CATCH RESTRICTIONS

None.

NAME DERIVATION

Rachycentron, spinous lower back, a reference to the separate dorsal spines; *canadum*, from Canada, where, ironically, it does not occur. Prodigal son, a reference to its wide distribution and erratic appearance.

SIMILAR SPECIES

This fish is not easily misidentified. The absence of finlets and detached spines distinguishes it from the kingfishes, and the absence of a sucking disc distinguishes it from the closely related remora.

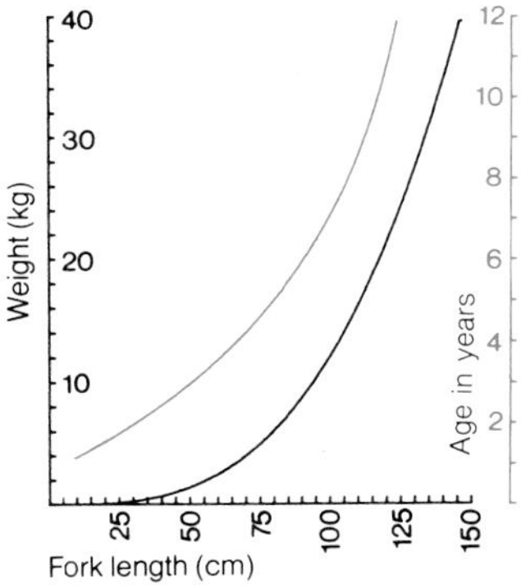

Argyrosomus hololepidotus

(Lacepède, 1801)

Common names SA – kob, kabeljou, daga. Elsewhere – drum [Smith 199□1]

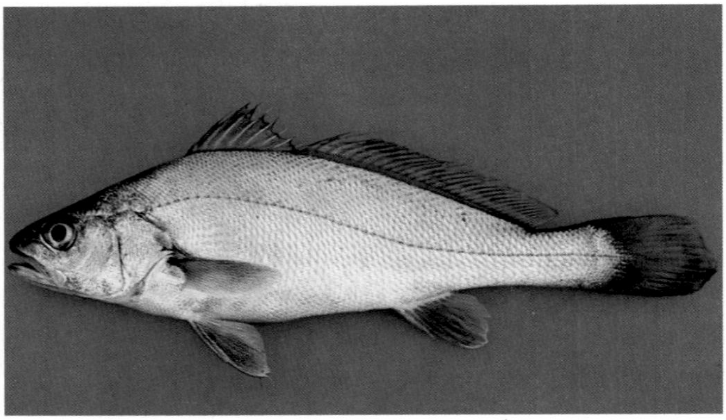

IDENTIFYING FEATURES

COLOUR, SHAPE AND SIZE

This robust fish is one of the largest, yet most delicately coloured members of the kob family. The overall body colour is silvery, and live specimens have a striking, pearly-pink sheen on the head, flanks and dorsal surface. When viewed obliquely, especially underwater, a row of brilliantly silver 'portholes' can be seen along the lateral line. The fins are dusky or translucent. Attains 200 cm.

EXTERNAL ANATOMY

The body is covered with thick scales arranged in 48-55 series along the lateral line. A small, fleshy structure projects from the pectoral axil, which, in this species, is characteristically naked. This feature is clearly shown here as a small brown patch above the pectoral fin. The double dorsal fin has ten spines followed by one spine plus 26-29 rays, and the anal fin has two spines plus seven rays. The caudal fin is truncate. There are 12-17 well developed rakers on the first gill arch. Strong canine teeth are set in each jaw.

Note: Dissection reveals a distinct and tough swim bladder with 25-35 paired branches.

NATURAL HISTORY

This shoaling predator occurs to depths of 400 m. But it is also common in shallower, coastal areas, particularly along the sandy edges of reefs and estuaries where the water is often turbid. The kob hunts mainly by combining smell and lateral line senses instead of by sight, and is, therefore, well equipped to feed at night and in dirty water. The diet comprises small fish and crustaceans such as prawns, crabs and, occasionally, squid and cuttlefish. The kob is a migratory fish which prefers the cooler waters of the Atlantic and the southern Cape coast, and only penetrates Natal waters to any great extent during winter. Sexual maturity is attained at a length of 75 cm, which corresponds to an age of four years. Spawning probably occurs off the eastern and western Cape. As with adults, juveniles are tolerant of wide-ranging salinities, and are, therefore, able to make some use of estuaries as nursery areas. Kob move in shoals, and divers frequently report sightings of migrating fish. The otoliths are exceptionally large, and are often used as ornaments, or in jewellery.

DISTRIBUTION

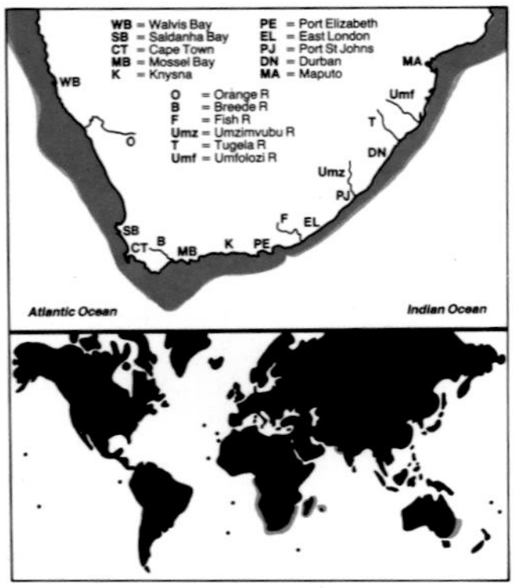

CAPTURE

The kob is commercially exploited by line-boat fishermen and by trawlers. It is also one of the best known and most widely spread of southern African sport fishes and will take most baits and slowly retrieved lures. The flesh makes excellent eating, and the worms that are sometimes reported to infest it are harmless to man, if the fish is properly cooked.

World angling record – 54,4 kg.
SA angling record – 73,5 kg.
SA spearfishing record – 48,6 kg.

SPECIFIC CATCH RESTRICTIONS

Open species; minimum legal size is 40 cm total length.

NAME DERIVATION

Argyrosomus, silver bodied; *hololepidotus*, smooth scaled. Kob, derived from the old Dutch *kabeljauw*, a stockfish.

SIMILAR SPECIES

The smooth pectoral axil best distinguishes this species from the squaretail kob.

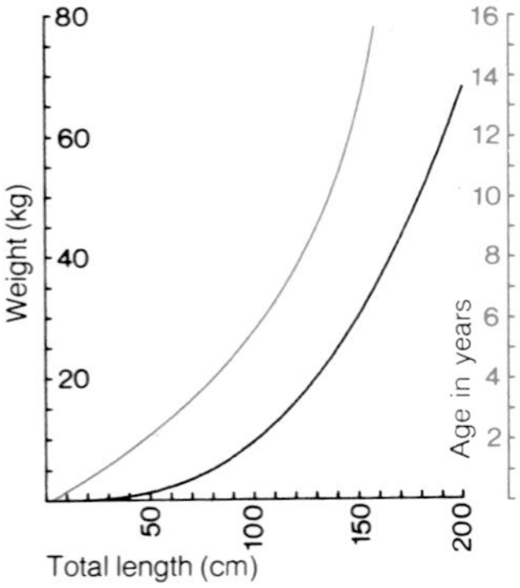

Argyrosomus thorpei

Smith, 1977
Common names Squaretail kob, king kob
[Smith 199□2]

IDENTIFYING FEATURES

COLOUR, SHAPE AND SIZE
The elongate body of this kob is silvery overall, with a slightly bluish sheen on the upper flanks and dorsal surface. The fins are translucent, yellowish-grey or dusky. Attains 120 cm.

EXTERNAL ANATOMY
There are 50-52 series of scales arranged along the lateral line. The fins are well developed, and include a double dorsal of ten spines followed by one spine plus 26-28 rays, and an anal fin of two spines plus 6-8 rays. The large mouth has several rows of teeth in each jaw, the outer of which are conical. A total of 18-20 rakers occurs on the first gill arch.
Notes: Dissection reveals a tough swim bladder with 29-31 paired appendages.
Based on the fine structure of the otoliths; there is evidence to suggest that this species could be classified in the newly proposed genus, *Afroscion*. However. when all other anatomical similarities with the true kob are taken into consideration, there is good cause to retain its grouping with *A. hololepidotus.*

NATURAL HISTORY

A fairly large and common fish, the squaretail kob appears to be a resident species, not given to extensive migrations. It congregates in large shoals around deep reefs and pinnacles, and rarely ventures near the shore or into estuaries. It is primarily a predator of small, bottom-dwelling fish, but also, occasionally, of squid and prawns. Maturity is reached at a length of 45 cm, and, though spawning occurs during winter, coinciding with its peak abundance, nothing is known of the fry and their distribution.

Despite its considerable abundance, it has only recently become recognized as a distinct species through the observations of Mr A.R. Thorpe, records officer of the SA Anglers' Union.

DISTRIBUTION

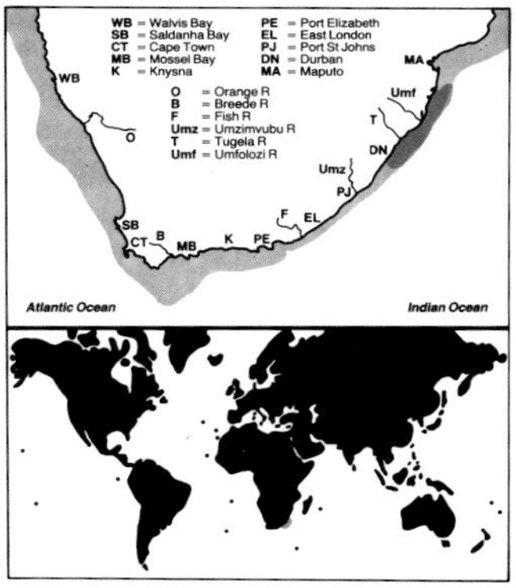

CAPTURE

The squaretail kob is extensively exploited by those ski-boat anglers who have identified the pinnacles and reef edges where shoals congregate. Most fish baits are successful in luring this fine table fish.
SA angling record – 10,5 kg.
SA spearfishing record – vacant.

NAME DERIVATION

Argyrosomus, silver bodied; *thorpei*, after A. Thorpe the collector who first brought this fish to the attention of Professor Margaret Smith at Rhodes University. Squaretail kob, a square-tailed relative of the true kob.

SPECIFIC CATCH RESTRICTIONS

Minimum legal size is 40 cm total length.

SIMILAR SPECIES

The squaretail kob is very similar to the kob, but may be distinguished by its square tail, scales on the inside of the pectoral lobes, and its smaller teeth.

Atractoscion aequidens

(Cuvier, 1830)

Common names SA - geelbek, Cape salmon. Elsewhere - teraglin [Smith 199□3]

IDENTIFYING FEATURES

COLOUR, SHAPE AND SIZE

This elongate and robust fish is bluish to coppery above and white below, with translucent-grey fins. Most conspicuous are the mouth and inner surface of the gill covers, all of which are yellow. Can attain 120 cm in length.

EXTERNAL ANATOMY

About 75 series of small, mostly ctenoid scales are arranged along the lateral line. The dorsal fin has two parts, the first of ten spines, and the second of one spine plus 26-31 rays. Two spines plus 8-9 rays comprise the anal fin, and the caudal fin is emarginate. The large, terminal mouth has several rows of needle-like teeth. There are 12-16 short, spiky rakers on the first gill arch.

Note: Dissection reveals a swim bladder with only one pair of appendages.

DISTRIBUTION

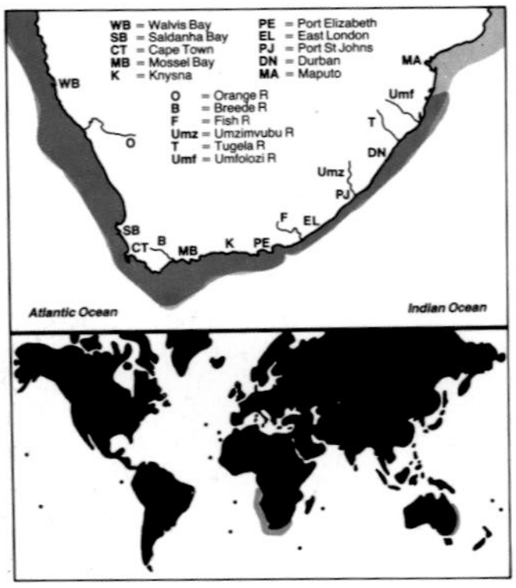

NATURAL HISTORY

The geelbek is a common shoaling fish, inhabiting waters as deep as 100 m. It is frequently found close to the bottom, near pinnacles, steep ledges or old shipwrecks. Despite its often demersal habits, this carnivorous fish voraciously pursues surface baitfish, particularly maasbanker, mackerel and pilchard, but occasionally also squid. Seasonal variations in abundance occur, and, during winter, shoals of reproductively 'ripe' geelbek migrate up the Natal coast, quite probably to spawn in the warmer waters of the Agulhas Current. From time to time, large catches are made off the Zululand coast and most of these fish are in spawning condition. Very little is known about the life history of this species, though juveniles have at times been netted in Cape estuaries and False Bay. All other close relatives of the geelbek are confined to the Pacific and Atlantic oceans off the Americas, and this is the only teraglin found in the Indian Ocean.

CAPTURE

Whereas it is a rare catch for rock and surf anglers, the geelbek is frequently landed by ski- and line-boat fishermen, and, occasionally, by trawlers. Spearfishermen often hunt geelbek, especially during, or just after, the Natal sardine run. Though undoubtedly a common species, the seasonal abundance of this fish is not always predictable, and there is considerable annual variation in the total tonnage landed by fishermen. It is an excellent eating fish and fetches a high market price.

SA angling record – 11,2 kg.
SA spearfishing record – 11,4 kg.

SPECIFIC CATCH RESTRICTIONS

Open species; minimum legal size is 40 cm total length.

NAME DERIVATION

Atractoscion, spindle-shaped; *aequidens*, uniform-sized teeth. Geelbek, Afrikaans/Dutch for yellow mouth.

SIMILAR SPECIES

This is the only member of this family with a distinctly emarginate tail fin. Another useful feature is the presence of only two appendages on the swim bladder.

Atrobucca nibe

(Jordan & Thompson, 1911)
Common names longfin kob, blackmouth croaker
[Smith 199□4]

IDENTIFYING FEATURES

COLOUR, SHAPE AND SIZE

This is an elongate fish with a blunt snout. The overall body colouration is silvery, darker above and white on the belly. In fresh specimens there may be a slight mother-of-pearl sheen across the head and flanks. Significantly, the insides of the mouth and gill chambers are black, as is the gut lining.

EXTERNAL ANATOMY

The body of this rather small, kob-like fish is covered with small, ctenoid scales, arranged in 50-51 series along the lateral line. The scales on the head, however, are of a cycloid structure. The fins are moderately developed, with a double dorsal comprising ten spines followed by one spine plus 27-31 rays, while the anal has two spines followed by seven rays. An important feature concerns the pectoral fin which is only just shorter than head length, and is 27-30 per cent of the fish's standard length. The caudal fin is rounded. The mouth is located below the snout, which is a diagnostic feature, distinguishing this fish from the *Johnius* species with their terminal mouths. The jaws are set with several rows of small teeth, including 7-8 enlarged and curved, conical teeth - three on each side. Those in the upper jaw may remain exposed when the mouth is closed. There are 14-18 short gill rakers on the first arch, and three pairs of small pores are visible on the underside of the lower jaw. After dissection, the swim bladder is seen to have distinct branches that run forward and backward in the body cavity.

NATURAL HISTORY

This is a common shoaling species of deeper waters, especially over offshore banks such as Tugela and Muoti. Most occur away from reefs, and the majority are caught by trawlers operating over a relatively smooth bottom. This endemic species is known to spawn off the Natal coast, though further study at the Oceanographic Research Institute is in progress to verify this. The diet of this species consists mostly of small, bottom-living invertebrates, including prawns and crabs. Small fishes are also consumed.

DISTRIBUTION

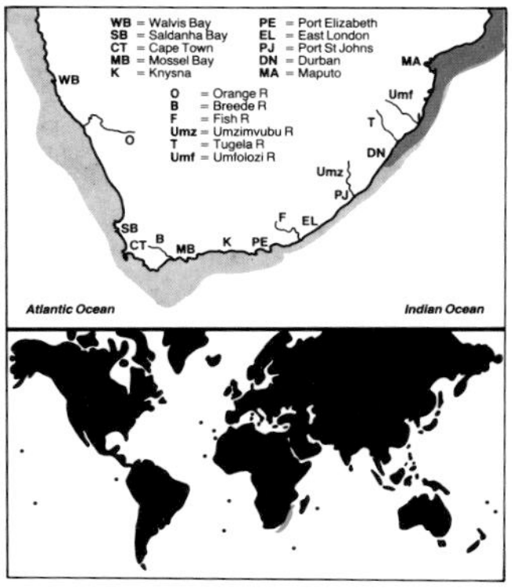

CAPTURE

Previously, this species was frequently confused with the true kob *(Argyrosomus hololepidotus)* or the silver kob, causing considerable problems at the market place. The blackmouth croaker is a fine eating fish which is probably still underexploited. Most present catches are made as a by-catch in the prawn-fishing industry, and only moderate numbers are marketed. Future research may well prove this species to be a considerable protein resource. Very few are caught by line fishermen, the odd ski-boater reporting occasional specimens from depths exceeding 25 m.
SA angling record - vacant.

SPECIFIC CATCH RESTRICTIONS

None.

NAME DERIVATION

Atrobucca, black mouthed; *nibe,* of obscure Japanese origin.

SIMILAR SPECIES

Fishes belonging to the kob family can be quite tricky to identify, and there is still considerable confusion amongst the scientific community. Three species of *Atrobucca* are known, but only this one is found in southern Africa. Its short pectoral fin, underslung mouth, black mouth interior, and posterior and anterior branches to the swim bladder serve to distinguish it from others. Previously this species was considered to be *A. marleyi,* but apparently very small differences in anatomy have now caused these two species to be considered distinct.

Johnius dussumieri

(Cuvier, 1830)
Common names SA - mini-kob, nondi. Elsewhere - Boulenger's croaker
[Smith 199□6]

IDENTIFYING FEATURES

COLOUR, SHAPE AND SIZE

This rather small, elongate species has a distinctly rounded, blunt snout. Its general body colour is silvery, with a white belly. Live specimens have an iridescent, purple sheen along the dorsal surface, but after death most turn silvery-grey with dusky yellow or grey fins. Can attain 30 cm.

EXTERNAL ANATOMY

There are 47-52 series of small, but rough, ctenoid scales arranged along the lateral line. The double dorsal fin has nine or ten spines followed by one spine plus 27-31 rays. The anal fin has two spines plus seven or eight rays and the caudal fin is almost pointed. The relatively large mouth is underslung, and, while both jaws carry small, conical, villiform teeth, canines are absent. The first gill arch bears 18-24 short, spiky or club-shaped rakers.

Note: Dissection reveals a conspicuous, hammer-shaped swim bladder with 11-13 paired appendages.

DISTRIBUTION

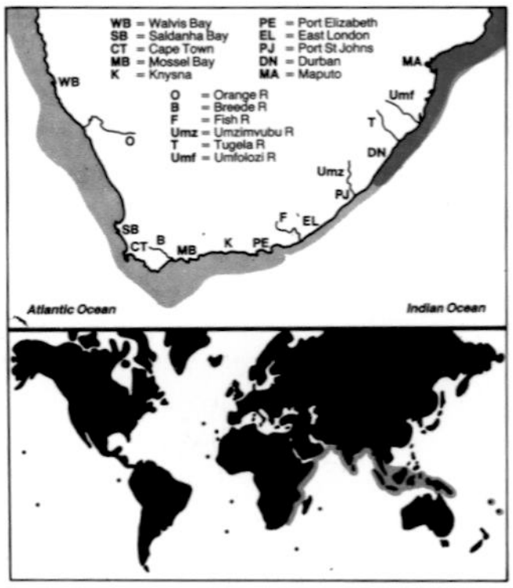

SPECIFIC CATCH RESTRICTIONS

None.

NATURAL HISTORY

This shoaling fish of shallow coastal and estuarine waters is considerably tolerant of variations in salinity and turbidity. It is rather sluggish, and feeds almost solely on bottom-living invertebrates such as small crabs. Occasionally, however, marine worms, small fish and squid are also eaten. The mini-kob is itself preyed on by larger fish such as the true kob. Small specimens are common in northern Natal estuaries, which are probably used as nursery areas. Larger, sexually mature specimens exceeding 18 cm, are trawled on the St Lucia and Tugela banks, and it is here that spawning occurs from September to February.

CAPTURE

Most anglers regard the mini-kob as a curse, as it is often responsible for persistent bait nibbling. It is frequently netted during offshore prawn-trawling operations, but is more often than not discarded as 'trash'. This is regrettable as its flesh is palatable.
SA angling record - vacant.

NAME DERIVATION

Johnius, named after John, an early missionary in Tranquebar, India; *dussumieri,* named after Dussumier, an early French zoologist. Mini-kob, a smaller relative of the true kob.

SIMILAR SPECIES

There has been much confusion about the correct identification of this and related species. These problems remain, and future research may well cause further name changes. The mini-kob is best distinguished from other kobs by its slightly underslung mouth and hammer-shaped swimbladder.

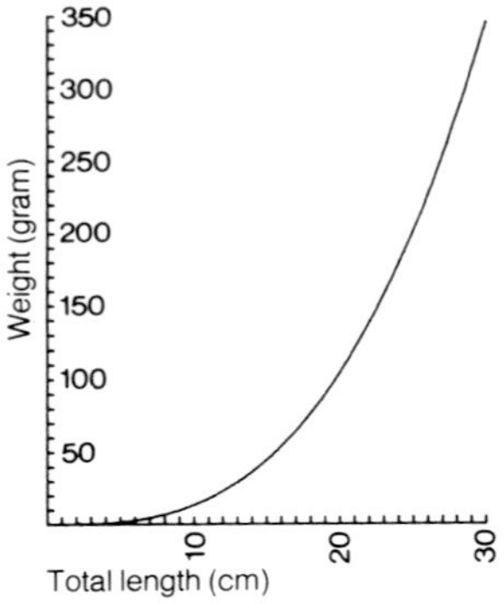

Otolithes ruber

(Schneider, 1801)

Common names SA – snapper or longtooth kob. Elsewhere – tiger-toothed croaker [Smith 199□7]

IDENTIFYING FEATURES

COLOUR, SHAPE AND SIZE

This distinctively elongate kob is bronze-red above and silvery to white below. The fins are yellowish or grey. Live fish also have a striking 'mother-of-pearl' sheen along the dorsal surface and upper flanks. Can attain 80 cm.

EXTERNAL ANATOMY

There are some 50 series of distinct scales arranged along the lateral line. The fins are well developed and include a double dorsal of ten spines followed by one spine plus 27-30 rays, and an anal of two spines plus 7-8 rays. The caudal fin is slightly pointed. The large mouth has characteristically prominent, fang-like canines, as well as several rows of smaller teeth. Two pairs of canines in the upper jaw lie outside the lower lip when the mouth is closed. There are about 15 distinct rakers on the first gill arch.

Note: Dissection reveals a conspicuous swim bladder with 30-37 paired appendages.

NATURAL HISTORY

The snapper is a shoaling fish of coastal waters, sheltered bays and large estuarine systems. It is quite tolerant of turbid water, and is able to withstand widely ranging salinities. This rather sluggish carnivore is an opportunist feeder, and preys on whatever happens to be plentiful at the time. The stomach contents of landed specimens may, therefore, contain quantities of squid, shrimp, mantis shrimp or small fish. It occurs predominantly during the summer and can be very common off Durban's beachfront. Sexual maturity is attained at about 25 cm, and spawning occurs during spring and summer in the marine environment rather than in estuaries. The distribution of juveniles is not known and, despite the estuarine habitat of many adults, the young have not been recorded from southern African estuaries. The snapper has large earstones which have the curious property of turning red when heated in a flame.

DISTRIBUTION

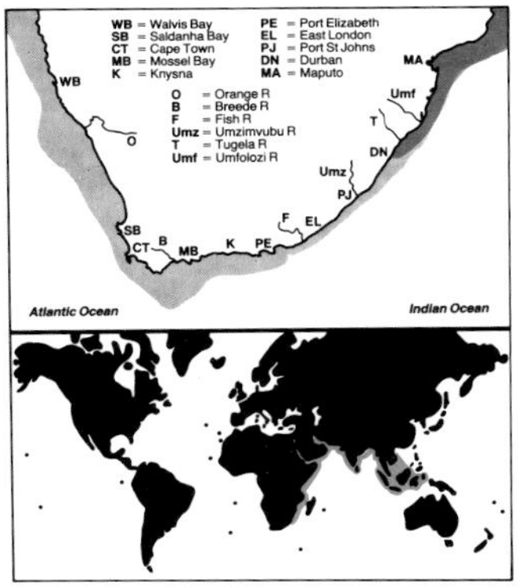

CAPTURE

This fish is frequently caught by anglers, especially paddle-ski or ski-boat enthusiasts. Fish, squid or prawn are successful baits. It is also caught by bank fishermen in Natal's estuaries. The snapper is extensively trawled in the East where it is an important source of food. It makes excellent eating.

SA angling record – 1,6 kg.

SA spearfishing record – vacant.

SPECIFIC CATCH RESTRICTIONS

None.

NAME DERIVATION

Otolithes, earstones; *ruber*, red. Longtooth kob, a reference to its fang-like teeth and to its relationship to the true kob.

SIMILAR SPECIES

The presence of large, fang-like canines will positively identify this species and distinguish it from all other kob-like fishes.

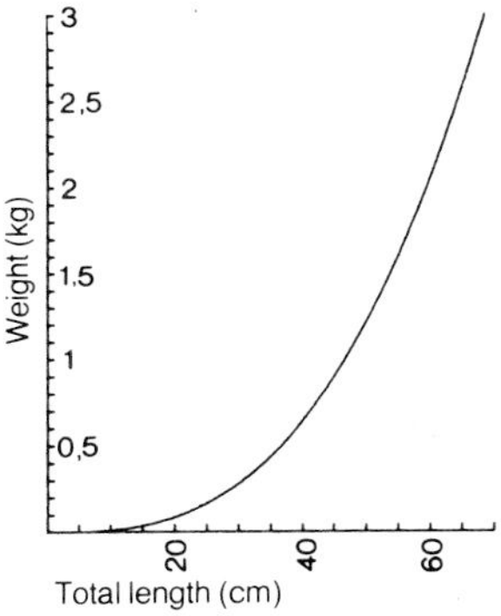

Umbrina canariensis

Valenciennes, 1843

Common names SA - baardman, tasselfish. Elsewhere - croaker [Smith 199□8]

IDENTIFYING FEATURES

COLOUR, SHAPE AND SIZE

The tasselfish is fairly robust and noticeably deeper bodied than most members of this family, and it has a steep, but evenly curved head profile. The colour of live specimens is silver to golden yellow, but this soon darkens to an overall dusky grey-brown after death. The belly is light and the fins are translucent or dusky. Can attain 75 cm in length.

EXTERNAL ANATOMY

There are 49-51 series of scales arranged along the lateral line. The fins are well developed and include a double dorsal of ten spines, followed by one spine plus 25-29 rays, an anal fin of two spines plus seven rays; and a broad, square caudal. The snout is very prominent and projects above the small, underslung mouth which bears minute teeth. A single, thick barbel and several distinct pores occur beneath the chin. There are 14-17 short rakers on the first gill arch.

Note: Dissection reveals a thick swim bladder which lacks appendages.

NATURAL HISTORY

A sluggish species, the tasselfish tends to congregate in small shoals, but is also often encountered alone. Although small, immature specimens are often trawled in deeper water, adults are usually found in shallow water along rocky shores or bays. This, and similar species, frequently form shoals with other fishes, especially the striped grunters of Natal waters. On such occasions these combined gatherings often mill about in a confined area, for example, below a rocky overhang or amongst large boulders. Its small mouth and feeble teeth restrict its predatory abilities, and it feeds primarily on small, bottom-dwelling invertebrates such as crabs, worms and prawns. Despite having been recorded from estuaries, this species is not generally considered to be tolerant of low salinities. Its breeding cycle has not yet been studied.

DISTRIBUTION

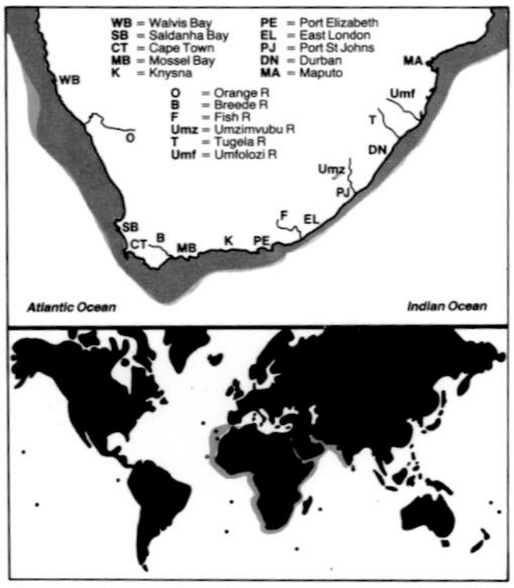

CAPTURE

Though caught by anglers using shrimp bait, the tasselfish is more frequently landed in beach seine and trawl nets. It is often speared by divers as it is slow-moving and easily approached in shallow water. Its flesh makes excellent eating.

SA angling record – 7,2 kg.

SA spearfishing record – 12,6 kg.

SPECIFIC CATCH RESTRICTIONS

None.

NAME DERIVATION

Umbrina, shade loving; *canariensis*, of the Canary Islands; the locality from which it was first described. Tasselfish, a reference to the barbel on the chin.

SIMILAR SPECIES

The various Umbrina species are rather difficult to separate and there remains some uncertainty about their correct identification. The closely related *U. ronchus* has 23-26 dorsal rays and is most common in Natal. The specimen pictured here was caught at Cape Agulhas.

Scomberesox saurus

(Richardson, 1842)
Common name saury
[Smith 114□2]

IDENTIFYING FEATURES

COLOUR, SHAPE AND SIZE
This is a highly elongate, compressed fish, with the jaws elongated to form a beak. The body colours consist of a metallic-blue upper surface, silvery flanks and a whitish belly. The greyish or translucent fins may also be slightly tinged with yellow. Can attain 50 cm.

EXTERNAL ANATOMY
Sauries are covered with small and very thin scales that are nevertheless not easily shed, and number 107-128 along the lateral line in the case of this species. Arrangement of the fins is primitive and quite distinctive. There are no fin spines, and both dorsal and anal fins are set far back on the body. The dorsal comprises 9-12 rays followed by 5-6 detached finlets, while the anal has 11-14 rays followed by 17-21 detached finlets. The caudal is moderately forked and the lower lobe is not significantly longer than the upper, as in the case of the halfbeaks and flyingfishes. The jaws are elongate, with the lower jaw always just longer than the upper. There are two rows of fine teeth towards the end of each jaw, but only a single row behind this. Gill rakers are well developed and number 39-51.

NATURAL HISTORY

This is a common species of open ocean waters, often congregating in small groups or medium-sized shoals. While most are seen at the surface, often skipping along the top, many others have been taken at considerable depths by net. The saury feeds on small, planktonic animals, including larval and juvenile fishes. The reproduction of this fish in South African waters has not yet been studied, but is likely to involve seasonal offshore spawning, with the females producing sizeable eggs. Sauries are heavily preyed on by gamefish, and many fishermen have seen their frantic attempts at escaping tuna and billfish.

DISTRIBUTION

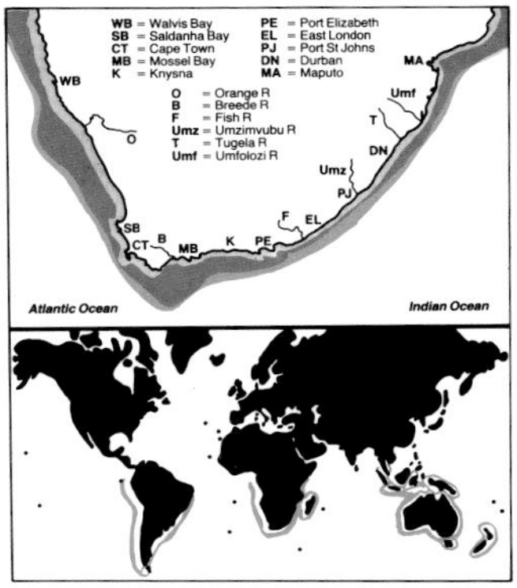

CAPTURE

Sauries do not take a bait, but numbers are caught by trawlers and purse-seines. This fish makes excellent eating, though few, if any, are marketed. It is also one of the finest baits for gamefish.
SA angling record – 0,1 kg.

NAME DERIVATION

Scomberesox, resembling a mackerel and a pike (a reference to the detached finlets as found in scombrid fishes); *saurus,* lizzard-like. Saury, a derivative of the scientific name.

SPECIFIC CATCH RESTRICTIONS

None.

SIMILAR SPECIES

The saury superficially resembles a halfbeak or garfish, though it can be instantly distinguished by the presence of detached finlets. The South African species of saury is technically a sub-species, *S. saurus scomberoides,* and differs from the northern hemisphere variety by its gill raker count.

Acanthocybium solandri

(Cuvier, 1831)
Common name Worldwide - wahoo
[Smith 249□1]

IDENTIFYING FEATURES

COLOUR, SHAPE AND SIZE
The very elongate, almost cigar-shaped wahoo has a conspicuous, long snout. Its body colours after death are dark blue above, with silvery sides and a white belly. When alive, however, some 20-30 bright, metallic, grey-green, vertical bars run down the flanks. This striking colouration disappears immediately after death. Can attain 210 cm, though 120 cm is usually considered large.

EXTERNAL ANATOMY
Scales are present, but as these are very small and narrow, the body appears almost naked. The lateral line is distinct and noticeably wavy. The fins are well developed. The first dorsal comprises 23-27 spines, and the second 11-16 rays, followed by 7-10 detached finlets. The spineless anal fin has 12-14 rays plus eight or nine finlets. The caudal fin is large and emarginate. Both jaws of the wide mouth bear a row of very sharp teeth. There are no rakers on the gill arches.

DISTRIBUTION

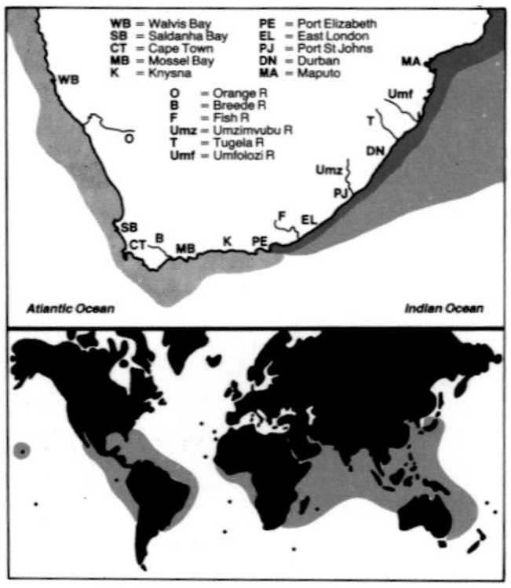

NATURAL HISTORY

The wahoo is a powerful, pelagic gamefish, which often inhabits offshore coral or rocky reefs, and, though this fish is usually solitary, small groups are occasionally reported by divers, It is one of the fastest fish in the ocean, and is capable of short bursts of 75 km/h. The bulk of this voracious predator's diet consists of fish, and includes anchovies, small tuna, kingfish, flyingfish and even boxfish. Squid are also often eaten, while prawns and mantis shrimps are taken if very abundant. Specimens of 90 cm are sexually mature, and spawning has been recorded off the coast of East Africa during most months of the year. The distribution of juveniles, however, is unknown. Many wahoo are caught off Sodwana Bay and on the Aliwal Shoals off Natal. Virtually all have one or more, leech-like, trematode parasites in their stomachs, which undoubtedly deprive the fish of some nutrition.

CAPTURE

Fast-trolled feathers or well-rigged small tuna are most likely to entice wahoo. Some ski-boat anglers specialize in catching this fine gamefish, and, in certain parts of the world, it is commercially exploited. Only the best of spearfishermen succeed in landing this delicious table fish.
World angling record – 70,53 kg.
All-Africa angling record – 55,6 kg.
SA angling record – 36,0 kg.
SA spearfishing record – 43,0 kg.

SPECIFIC CATCH RESTRICTIONS

None.

NAME DERIVATION

Acanthocybium, from *acanthus* meaning thorn or spine or *cybium*, an ancient form of cured fish; *solandri*, after its discoverer, the explorer Solander. Wahoo, derived from *wanhu*, a Red Indian word meaning 'burning bush', a probable reference to the bright metallic colours of this fish when first removed from the water.

SIMILAR SPECIES

Once the stripes have disappeared, the wahoo can resemble a king mackerel, though the wahoo has a longer, pointed snout that is half the total head length, and also lacks any gill rakers.

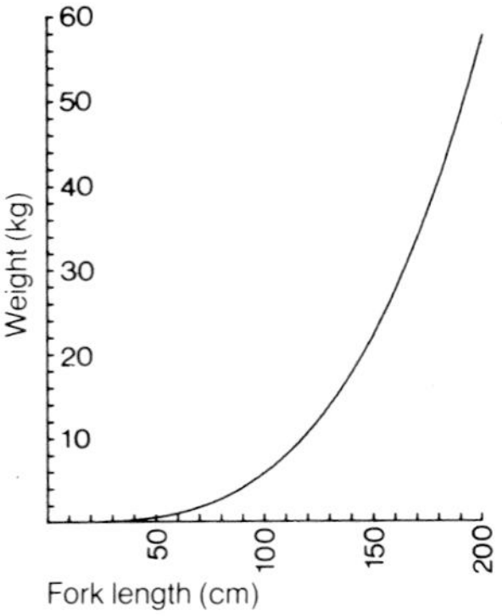

Auxis thazard

(Lacepède, 1802)
Common name Worldwide – frigate tuna
No Smith reference

IDENTIFYING FEATURES

COLOUR, SHAPE AND SIZE
This robust, elongate fish is almost round in cross-section. The body has an overall silvery-sheen, but is blue above and white below. A conspicuous pattern of 15 or more bars marks the scaleless area of the back. Can attain 50 cm.

EXTERNAL ANATOMY
Scales are confined to a corselet around the front of the body, and to those along the lateral line. The fins are well developed. The first of two dorsal fins consists of 10-12 spines, and is characteristically well separated from the second of 11 or 12 rays plus eight detached finlets. The spineless anal fin has 13 rays plus seven detached finlets. There is a distinct flap between the pelvic fins. A large keel flanked by two smaller keels occurs on either side of the caudal peduncle. The large mouth bears a single row of fine, conical teeth in each jaw, and the upper surface of the tongue has two ridges. There are 39-41 elongate rakers on the first gill arch.

NATURAL HISTORY

The frigate tuna is strongly gregarious and is invariably found shoaling with other Scombridae. It favours the surface waters of the open ocean where it is often seen racing in pursuit of prey, mainly smaller shoaling fish such as anchovies. The most significant components of the diet are squid, crab larvae and mantis shrimps, the majority of which are taken in midwater and filtered by the well-developed gill rakers. This tuna is, in its turn, an important link in the foodweb, as large predators, especially billfish, prey extensively on it. Though fairly abundant in southern African waters, most anglers confuse this species with the eastern little tuna (*Euthynnus affinis*), which is similar. Five to ten per cent of the small tuna-like species that shoal along the Natal coast are frigate tuna. Specimens exceeding 30 cm are sexually mature and reproductively 'ripe' fish are occasionally caught off the East Coast.

DISTRIBUTION

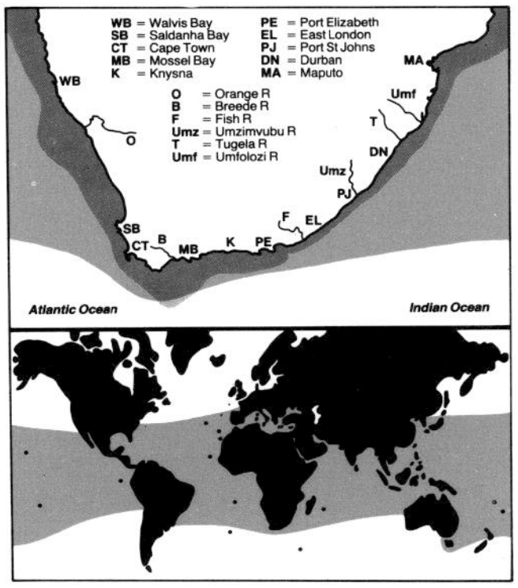

CAPTURE

Frigate tuna readily take small feathers or lures, and in some parts are caught in purse seines and fish traps, and on longlines. Though an excellent eating fish, it is not highly esteemed in southern Africa.
World angling record – 1,1 kg.
SA angling record – 1,9 kg.

SPECIFIC CATCH RESTRICTIONS

Open species.

NAME DERIVATION

Auxis, 'to spring'; *thazard*, a corruption of the French *Tassard*, a common name for mackerel-like fishes. Frigate tuna, a reference to its association with feeding frigate birds.

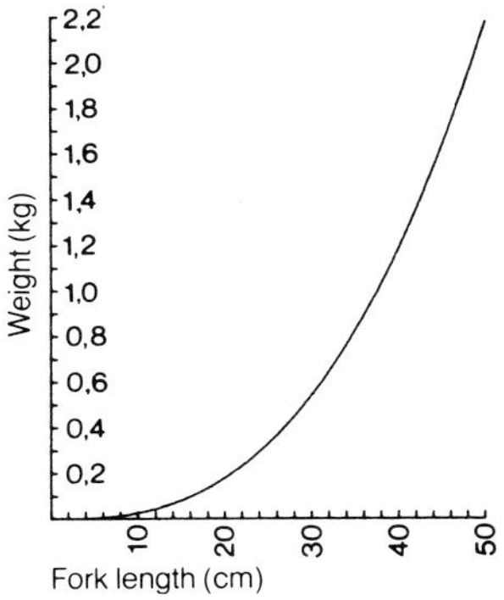

SIMILAR SPECIES

The genus Auxis can be distinguished from other tuna-like fish by the wider space between dorsal fins. Furthermore, a narrow corselet of scales along each flank and the marbled colour-pattern that does not extend forward of the first dorsal are also of diagnostic importance. In the closely related *A. rochei,* the pectoral fin does not reach the scaleless area above the corselet.

Euthynnus affinis

(Cantor, 1849)

Common names SA – eastern little tuna. Elsewhere – kawakawa, mackerel tuna

[Smith 249□4]

IDENTIFYING FEATURES

COLOUR, SHAPE AND SIZE

This robust, medium-sized tuna has an overall silvery sheen with a pattern of wavy stripes on the upper sides that does not extend forward of the pectoral fins. The back is dark blue while the lower sides and the belly are white. As many as 11 distinct, black spots may occur on the chest between the pectoral and pelvic fins. Can attain 100 cm, though fish of 50 cm are more common.

EXTERNAL ANATOMY

The body is scaleless except for a patch in the pectoral region and along the lateral line. Two well-developed dorsal fins occur. The first of 15-17 spines is barely separated from the second of 10-13 rays, which is followed by seven or eight small, detached finlets. The spineless anal fin has 12-14 rays followed by seven or eight finlets. The caudal fin is stout, with rigid lateral keels either side of its narrow peduncle. Between the pelvic fins there is a pair of small scale-like flaps. A single row of minute conical teeth occurs in each jaw – an important identifying characteristic as anglers in southern Africa often call this fish 'bonito', a name more appropriate to the genus *Sarda,* members of which have much larger teeth. There are 29-35 well-developed rakers on the first gill arch.

NATURAL HISTORY

The eastern little tuna is a wide-ranging, oceanic gamefish that usually favours surface waters near continents. It feeds voraciously on anchovies, squid and large planktonic organisms, with shoals on the hunt churning the surface in their pursuit of prey. During these feeding frenzies, the black pectoral spots become increasingly distinct. In its turn, the little tuna is extensively preyed on by larger gamefish, including marlin and sharks. Sexual maturity is attained at 45-50 cm, and spawning occurs mostly during summer at numerous localities throughout the world. The eggs and hatched larvae drift passively, and are distributed by ocean currents. The large numbers of parasites that occur in the body cavity are tape-worm larvae which, in their next life stage, will be hosted by sharks.

DISTRIBUTION

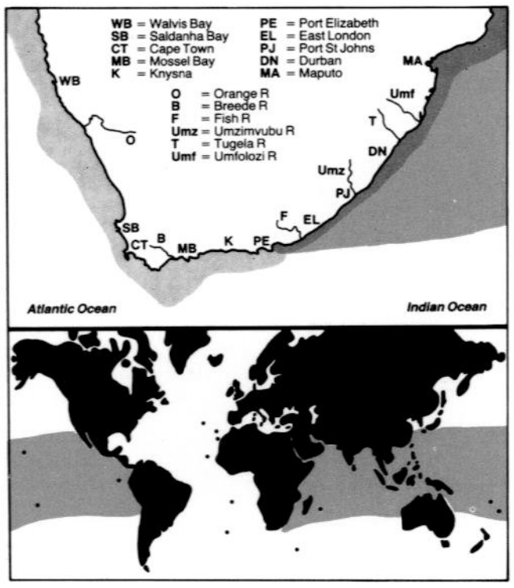

CAPTURE

In South Africa the little tuna is not commercially exploited, but in the East it constitutes an important protein source, and is either dried, smoked or canned. There is no danger of human infestation by the tape-worm larvae, especially if the meat is well-cooked before being eaten. In time, this fine gamefish could well become a favourite with South African ski-boat fishermen, as it fights vigorously if hooked on light tackle and will take a variety of lures, feathers and whole-fish bait.

World angling record – 13,15 kg.
SA angling record – 11,0 kg.
SA spearfishing record – 9,0 kg.

SPECIFIC CATCH RESTRICTIONS

Open species.

NAME DERIVATION

Euthynnus, like a tuna; *affinis*, related. Eastern little tuna, a reference to its range, and to its size in relation to *Thunnus* species.

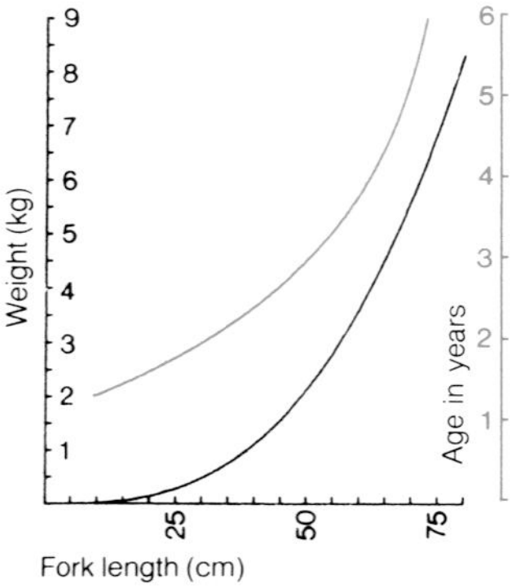

Katsuwonus pelamis

(Linnaeus, 1758)
Common names SA – skipjack, oceanic bonito. Elsewhere – skipjack, tuna
[Smith 249□7]

IDENTIFYING FEATURES

COLOUR, SHAPE AND SIZE

The torpedo-shaped body of the skipjack is almost round in cross-section, and the snout is pointed. Colouration is characteristic as, in addition to the dark-blue back and silvery-white belly, there are 4-10 distinct, black, longitudinal bands along the lower flanks of the body. These lateral stripes are not usually evident when viewed underwater, but may become visible if the fish is feeding. It is one of the smaller members of the tuna family and rarely exceeds 75 cm in southern African waters.

EXTERNAL ANATOMY

The only scales are those arranged along the lateral line and those which form a pectoral corselet. The lateral line has a distinctive dip below the second dorsal fin. The fins are well developed and include two closely spaced dorsals, the first of 14-16 spines, and the second of 14-15 rays plus 7-9 finlets; a spineless anal fin of 14-15 rays plus seven or eight finlets; and a stout caudal with a keeled peduncle. Minute teeth occur in both jaws of the large, terminal mouth. The first gill arch bears 53-63 long, well-developed rakers.

NATURAL HISTORY

This species is usually found in large shoals, in association with its prey. This includes a wide range of items such as megalopa crab larvae, krill, pteropods, anchovies, pilchards, juvenile fish, squid, mantis shrimps and other planktonic organisms. Most food is strained, by means of the elaborate gill rakers, from water entering the mouth. Though feeding takes place at moderate depths, few skipjack appear to penetrate below the thermocline. Spawning occurs during summer in coastal waters and sexual maturity is attained at 40-50 cm. The vascular system of this specialized 'warm-blooded' fish keeps the muscles well supplied with oxygen, and this enables the animal to maintain swimming speeds of about 40 km/h, thereby facilitating its extensive distribution and arduous, non-stop migrations across the oceans. It is tolerant of widely varying temperatures and may occur in waters ranging from 19-30°C. It is, however, very intolerant of low salinities.

DISTRIBUTION

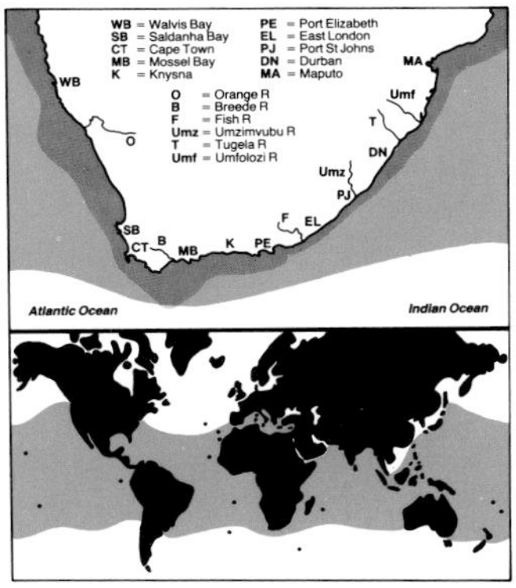

CAPTURE

Despite being a strong and plentiful gamefish with a reasonably palatable flesh, this species is little exploited in southern Africa. However, in other parts of the world, particularly Japan and India, it is an important food resource, and, fresh or dried, it is a basic ingredient of many indigenous dishes. Numerous parasites occur in the body cavity, but these are harmless to man if the meat is cleaned and cooked. The silvery, wax-like pigment which can be scraped from the chest region of these fish is used in high-quality paints for taxidermists. Recent catch statistics show that world exploitation of this species has increased markedly. Most skipjack are caught on handlines, though longlines and purse-seines are also used. The fish holds little interest for spearfishermen.
World angling record – 18,9 kg.
SA angling record – 9,1 kg.

SPECIFIC CATCH RESTRICTIONS

Open species

NAME DERIVATION

Katsuwonus, from *Katsuwo*, the Japanese name for this fish; *pelamis*, white wax. Skipjack tuna, a reference to its habit of 'skipping' along the surface.

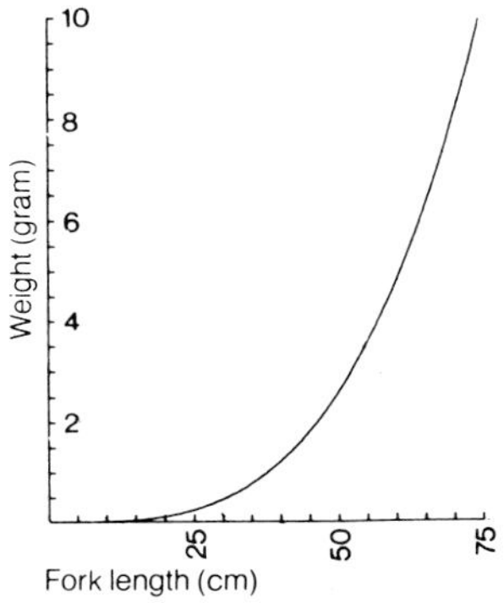

Rastrelliger kanagurta

(Cuvier, 1817)

Common names Worldwide - Indian mackerel, sugar mackerel

[Smith 249□8]

IDENTIFYING FEATURES

COLOUR, SHAPE AND SIZE

This small, but rather deep-bodied and robust fish is less round in cross-section than most tunas. It is blue-green above and white below. A row of 12-16 greyish spots occurs just below the dorsal fin as well as several, faint, lateral golden stripes. A dark spot is located in each pectoral axil. Attains 35 cm.

EXTERNAL ANATOMY

Tiny, but distinct scales completely cover the body, and are arranged in series along the conspicuous lateral line. The fins are well developed and include a double dorsal; the first of nine or ten spines being followed by a second of 11 or 12 rays plus five detached finlets. The anal fin has one or two spines plus 11 or 12 rays, and is also followed by five detached finlets. The strong caudal fin is deeply forked, and small keels occur on each side of the peduncle. Minute teeth are located in both jaws of the large, terminal mouth. The gill arch bears 45-50 long, slender rakers. A heavy layer of adipose tissue covers the moderately large eyes.

NATURAL HISTORY

This highly migratory shoaling fish has a preference for open, but protected, coastal, surface waters. Its already wide distribution was recently extended even further when it migrated through the Suez Canal into the Mediterranean Sea. Large shoals of the fast-swimming Indian mackerel are often spotted on the surface from craft at sea. The elongate gill rakers serve to filter planktonic animals from the water taken in through the widely opened mouth. It is, in turn, an important food source for king mackerel, wahoo and billfish. The Indian mackerel is abundant off the Natal coast during spring and summer. Spawning occurs in more tropical waters.

DISTRIBUTION

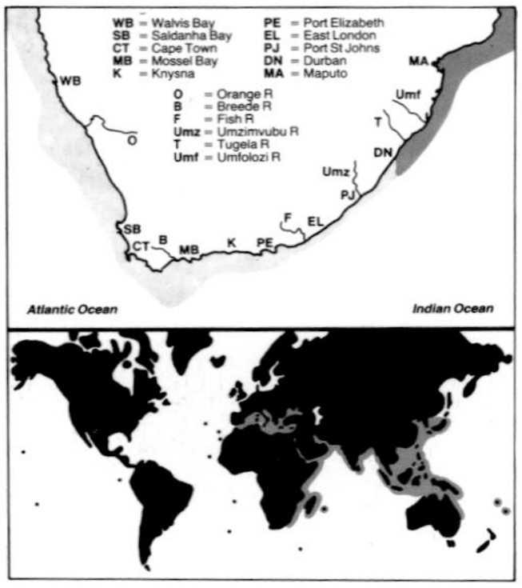

CAPTURE

Although occasionally caught on ultra-light tackle, this fish is better known in southern Africa for its superior quality as a bait, and, either whole or filleted, the Indian mackerel is certain to tempt larger gamefish. Catches are landed in beach seines along the Natal coast during spring and summer. This tasty fish is netted commercially in several parts of the world and it is prepared either dried and salted, fresh, canned or fermented.

SA angling record - 0,5 kg.

SPECIFIC CATCH RESTRICTIONS

Open species.

NAME DERIVATION

Rastrelliger, rake-like gills; *kanagurta*, a reference to Kanara, an area in western India. Indian mackerel, a reference to the area it was first found in, and to the fish's relationship to the true mackerels, genus *Scomber.*

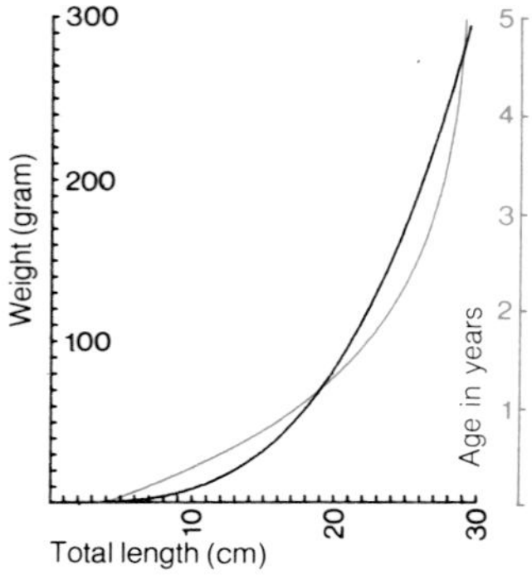

SIMILAR SPECIES

One other species of this genus may be found in southern African waters. Known as *R. brachysoma,* this slightly deeper-bodied fish can be distinguished by its much shorter gut. The entire intestinal length of *R. kanagurta* equals 3,0-3,4 times the body length, while in *R. brachysoma* the ratio is only 1,3:1-1,7:1. Notice that the Indian mackerel does not have the conspicuous zig-zag lines of other tuna-like fishes, has very long gill rakers, is completely scaled and lacks any scales as found in the kingfishes.

Sarda orientalis

(Temminck & Schlegel, 1844)
Common names SA – striped bonito. Elsewhere – oriental bonito [Smith 249□9]

IDENTIFYING FEATURES

COLOUR, SHAPE AND SIZE

Slender, and of moderate size, this bonito has a wide mouth and pointed snout. The body is steel blue above, changing to silver along the sides, and the belly is white. There are 5-11 dark, oblique stripes along the upper sides. Development of body markings is curious, however, as immature fish have vertical bars, but with age these gradually change to the longitudinal stripes which distinguish adults. Can attain 100 cm, but specimens of 30-50 cm are more common.

EXTERNAL ANATOMY

The entire body is covered with minute scales, except for a pectoral corselet which is composed of somewhat larger scales. The fins are well developed. The dorsal fins are closely spaced, the first comprising 17-19 spines, and the second 15-16 rays plus 7-9 detached finlets. The spineless anal fin has 14-15 rays plus six or seven finlets. The strong caudal fin has a keeled peduncle. There are 12-20 pointed teeth on each side of the long upper jaw which extends backwards to, or beyond a point below, the hind margin of the eyes. The first gill arch has 8-13 well-developed gill rakers.

NATURAL HISTORY

Though widespread, the striped bonito is rarely found in great concentrations. Despite being an oceanic game fish, it is most frequently encountered near land masses in waters ranging from 14-27°C. Its diet consists mainly of small crustaceans such as mantis shrimps, megalopa crab larvae and amphipods, but small fish and squid are also taken when abundant. Sexual maturity is attained at approximately 40 cm and spawning occurs in tropical coastal waters. Details of its natural history are rather scant and the distribution of the fry is unknown.

DISTRIBUTION

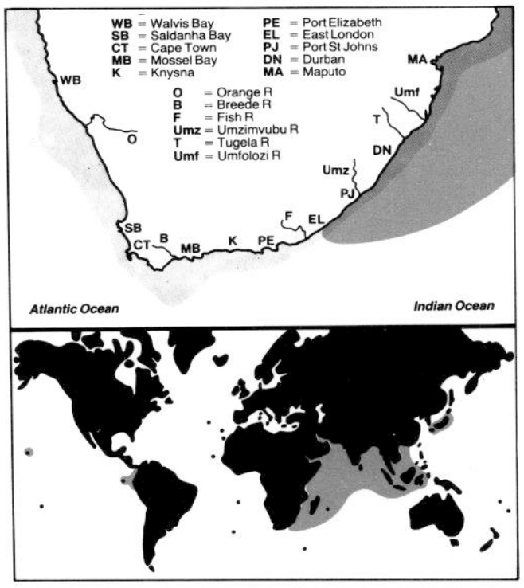

SPECIFIC CATCH RESTRICTIONS

Open species.

NAME DERIVATION

Sarda, a name given to this fish in ancient times when it was common around the isle of Sardinia; *orientalis*, a reference to its abundance in the East. Striped bonito, a reference to its body patterns and to the Spanish common name for fish of the genus *Sarda.*

CAPTURE

While this strong, game fish readily takes trolled or live baits as well as lures, a high proportion are hooked close to the bottom over deep reefs. Catches are also made on live bait or in purse-seine nets. The striped bonito is commercially exploited in some countries, but owing to its rather soft flesh it does not rate highly and is usually of secondary importance.
World angling record – 10,65 kg.
SA angling record – 5,9 kg.
SA spearfishing record – vacant.

SIMILAR SPECIES

A close Atlantic relative ranges as far as Port Elizabeth. Known as *S. sarda*, this slightly smaller fish is best distinguished by its 20-23 dorsal spines and 16-24 gill rakers. Besides this species, the true bonitos are distinctly different from other tunas because of their conspicuous conical teeth. The dogtooth (*Gymnosarda unicolor*) can be distinguished by the absence of body stripes. This fine tropical gamefish occasionally enters waters off Zululand.

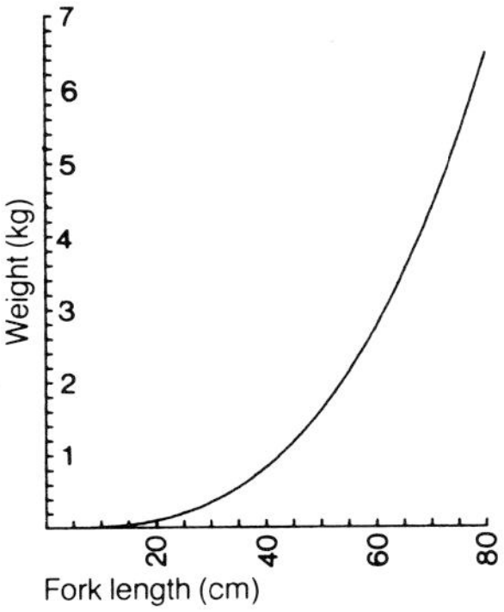

Scomber japonicus

Houttuyn, 1782
Common names SA - mackerel. Elsewhere - common, slimy or chub mackerel
[Smith 249□11]

IDENTIFYING FEATURES

COLOUR, SHAPE AND SIZE
This elongate mackerel is rounded in cross-section. It has a pointed snout and a narrow caudal peduncle. The upper body colour is a brilliant, metallic blue-green, overlaid with numerous oblique, black zig-zag lines. The lower sides and belly are silvery-white and may be marked with many faint spots. The fins are yellowish and translucent. Can attain 70 cm, but 30-40 cm is more common.

EXTERNAL ANATOMY
The entire body is covered with scales, those behind the head and around the pectoral fins being larger. The mackerel is torpedo-shaped, and has well-developed fins. There are two dorsal fins, the first has 9-10 spines, and is followed by the second of 11 or 12 rays plus five detached finlets. The distance between these two fins is roughly equal to the base length of the first. The anal fin consists of one detached spine followed by 11 or 12 rays plus five or six detached finlets. The stout, forked caudal has two small keels on either side of the peduncle. Thick, adipose tissue partially covers each eye. The wide mouth has fine teeth in each jaw, as well as on the roof of the mouth. There are 27-33 long, slender gill rakers on the first arch.

NATURAL HISTORY

The mackerel is a pelagic, shoaling fish of temperate surface waters, usually occurring close to land. Large shoals also often venture to the bottom in deep waters, possibly to 200 m. Plankton is filtered from the water, and these tiny food items include krill, mantis shrimps, megalopa crab larvae and small fish. Seasonal migrations have been noted, and these may be related to the breeding cycle. Spawning occurs during the winter, mainly from June to August, among mackerel that have reached a total length of approximately 48 cm. This length corresponds to an age of four years. 'Ripe' fish and fertilized eggs have been recorded along the entire South African coast.

DISTRIBUTION

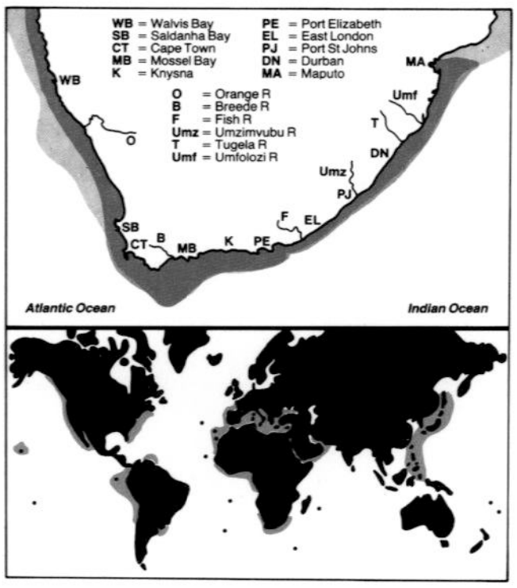

CAPTURE

In terms of South Africa's commercial fishing industry, the mackerel is one of the three most important pelagic species. Landings often exceed 10 000 tonnes per year, much of it destined for the canning industry. Most are caught in purse and beach seine nets and on handlines, but these fine eating fish are also often landed by sport anglers using a variety of baits. The mackerel is not of importance to spearfishermen. SA angling record - 2,4 kg.

SPECIFIC CATCH RESTRICTIONS

In the Cape, the minimum legal size is 15 cm total length. Closed season for commercial fishing: September 1 to December 30.

NAME DERIVATION

Scomber, an ancient Greek name for mackerel-type fish; *japonicus,* of Japan - the species was first described from a specimen collected in Japanese waters. Mackerel, a corruption of *maquerel,* an old French word for these fish.

SIMILAR SPECIES

The widely spaced dorsal fins, absence of a strong central keel on the tail, and completely scaled body serve to distinguish this from other Scombridae, especially the Indian mackerel with its longer gill rakers.

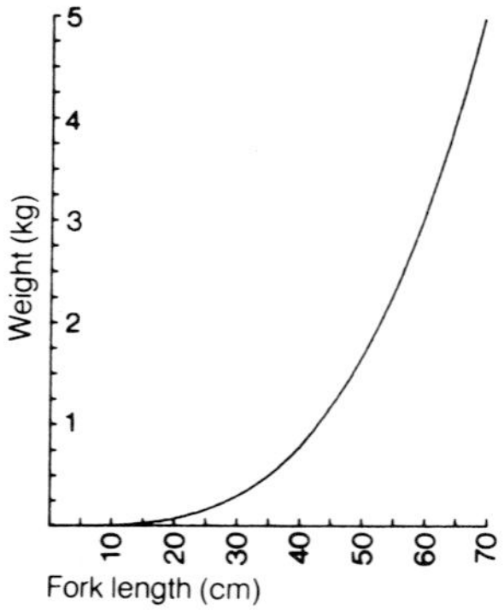

Scomberomorus commerson

(Lacepède, 1800)

Common names SA – king mackerel, couta, katonkel. Elsewhere – narrow-banded king or Spanish mackerel, tanguigue [Smith 249□12]

IDENTIFYING FEATURES

COLOUR, SHAPE AND SIZE

This large, elongate fish has a moderately compressed body with a pointed snout. Its colours are blue-grey above with silvery sides. The belly is white. Many irregular, dark, vertical bars mark the flanks, and these increase with age. Can attain 200 cm.

EXTERNAL ANATOMY

The scales are minute and almost invisible, giving the fish its characteristically smooth body surface. There is a distinct and wavy lateral line which has an abrupt dip below the level of the second dorsal fin. The fins are well developed, with the dorsal comprising two parts: the first of 15-18 spines, and the second of 15-20 rays followed by 8-10 detached finlets. The spineless anal fin has 16-20 rays, plus 7-12 detached finlets. Three lateral keels occur on the peduncle of the caudal fin, which is strong and forked. The mouth is large, and armed with razor-sharp, triangular teeth. The first gill arch carries 3-6 short rakers.

NATURAL HISTORY

This fierce predator and prime gamefish is the largest and swiftest of the mackerels, and, though very large specimens hunt alone, most king mackerel move in shoals, especially during the winter off the Zululand coast, and during the summer off Natal and Transkei. Despite being more common in slightly deeper offshore waters, angling statistics show that great numbers of king mackerel also move close in along rocky shores. The diet consists mainly of fish, especially anchovies, mackerel and lizardfish, but mantis shrimps and prawns are also eaten when these are plentiful. Sexual maturity is attained at a length of 90-100 cm, corresponding to an age of three to four years. Spawning occurs in tropical regions throughout the year. The body cavity usually contains numerous parasites, including tape- and round-worm larvae. These are harmless to the host fish and to humans, but will infest the sharks and dolphins that prey on the king mackerel.

DISTRIBUTION

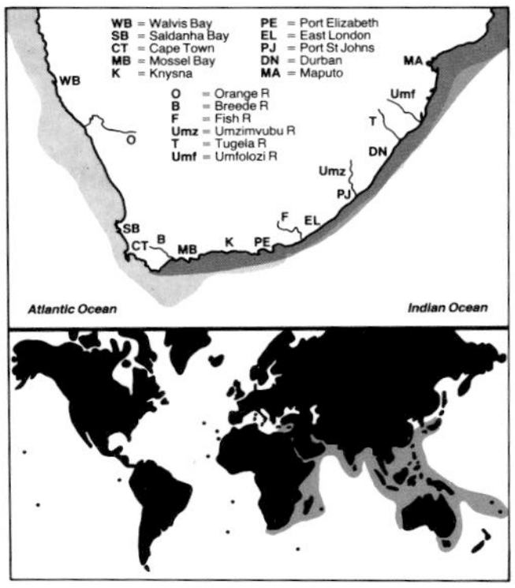

CAPTURE

One of the most sought-after gamefish in southern Africa, the king mackerel is a prime target of East Coast ski-boat fishermen, and is pursued by sport and commercial anglers alike, using lures, feathers, pilchards and anchovies as bait. Spearfishermen, too, consider this to be one of their best gamefish. In the Far East, gill nets, midwater trawls and fish traps are used, and the catch is often dried or processed into fish balls.

World angling record – 44,9 kg.
All-Africa angling record – 35,4 kg.
SA angling record – 46,4 kg.
SA spearfishing record – 34,0 kg.

SPECIFIC CATCH RESTRICTIONS

Open species.

NAME DERIVATION

Scomberomorus, an ancient name for mackerel fish; *commerson,* the name of an early naturalist. King mackerel, the largest of the mackerel-like fishes.

SIMILAR SPECIES

This fish is occasionally confused with other mackerels and wahoo, but the vertical bars and gill rakers serve to confirm identity.

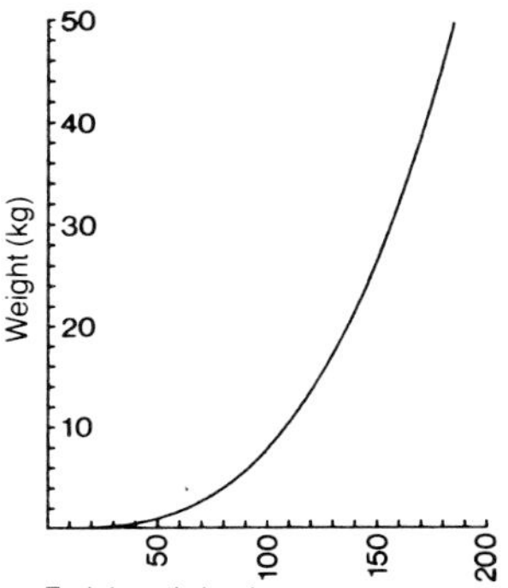

Scomberomorus plurilineatus

Fourmanoir, 1966

Common names SA – queen or spotted mackerel, Natal snoek. Elsewhere – streaked Spanish mackerel, kanadi kingfish. (The name snoek causes great confusion and should only be used to describe the Cape snoek.) [Smith 249□13]

IDENTIFYING FEATURES

COLOUR, SHAPE AND SIZE

This species is typically elongate and torpedo-shaped, but is slightly more compressed than most mackerels. It is blue-grey above, with silver sides and a white belly. A series of horizontal, broken lines and spots pattern the flanks. Can attain 120 cm.

EXTERNAL ANATOMY

The lateral line is conspicuous, and, though the body is covered with scales, these are minute and almost invisible. The fins are well developed: the dorsal consists of 15-17 spines and 19-21 rays plus 8-10 detached finlets, and the spineless anal of 19-21 rays plus 8-10 detached finlets. The large caudal fin is strongly forked, with three lateral keels on either side of the peduncle. A single row of razor-sharp, triangular teeth arms each jaw, and there are 12-15 poorly developed rakers on the first gill arch.

NATURAL HISTORY

The queen mackerel is a shoaling gamefish that is common in coastal waters, especially near rocky and coral reefs. It is a powerful predator which hunts anchovies and other small fish, as well as squid, mantis shrimps and, occasionally, krill or small pelagic shrimps. A feeding shoal of queen mackerel can be a spectacular sight, especially when it succeeds in chasing baitfish to the surface. Angling statistics point to a peak abundance of this species in autumn and winter, but especially during May, when dense shoals of food fish migrate along the Natal coast close to the surface. Later in the season, however, there is a tendency to form smaller groups of 5-20 individuals which move about close to the bottom. Sexual maturity is attained at about 80 cm, but almost 80 per cent of the specimens landed in southern African waters have not yet reached this length. Spawning occurs off the Moçambique coast in summer, and the fry probably mature in more tropical waters.

DISTRIBUTION

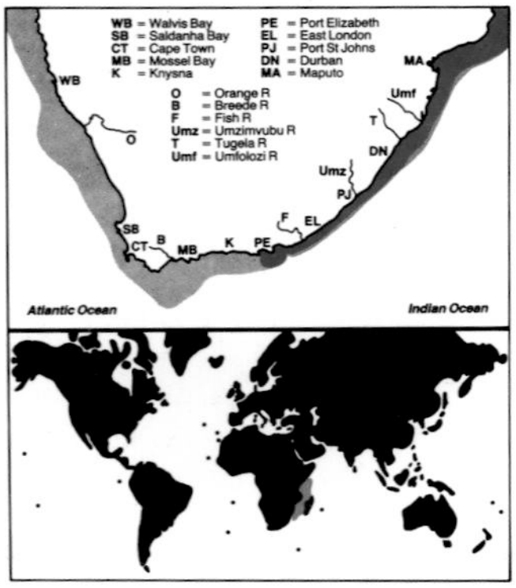

CAPTURE

The queen mackerel freely takes lures, spoons or feathers, and, during a feeding frenzy, almost any bait will guarantee a catch. Sometimes, however, queen mackerel are inexplicably 'off the bite' and will ignore all baits. It is a great favourite of the ski-boat fraternity in Natal, and also popular with spearfishermen.

World angling record – 9,8 kg.
SA angling record – 10,0 kg.
SA spearfishing record – 11,4 kg.

SPECIFIC CATCH RESTRICTIONS

Open species.

NAME DERIVATION

Scomberomorus, an ancient name for mackerel-type fish; *plurilineatus,* many lines, a reference to the striped flanks. Spotted mackerel, also a reference to the broken stripes along the flanks, and to its relationship to the true mackerel of the genus *Scomber.*

SIMILAR SPECIES

While there are similar mackerel elsewhere in the world, none occur in this region.

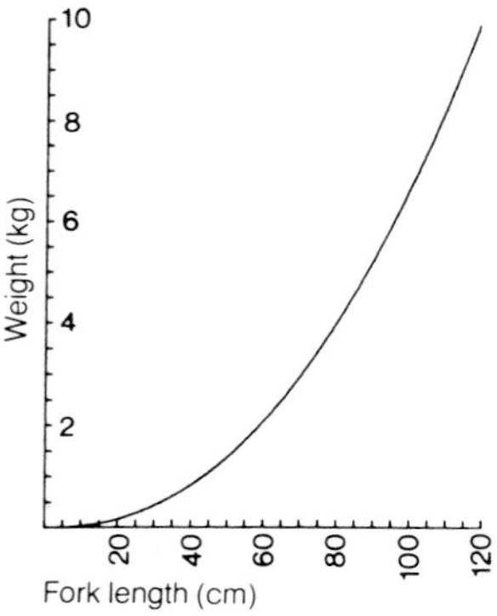

Thunnus alalunga

(Bonnaterre, 1788)
Common names SA – longfin tuna. Elsewhere – albacore, germon
[Smith 249□14]

IDENTIFYING FEATURES

COLOUR, SHAPE AND SIZE

This large fish has a robust, spindle-shaped body that is dark metallic blue above and silvery-white along the lower sides and belly. An iridescent, blue band runs along each flank, a feature particularly evident in freshly caught specimens. The fins are predominantly yellowish, except for the first dorsal which is a brighter yellow, the anal finlets which are dark grey and the caudal which has a white outer edge. Can attain 140 cm in length.

EXTERNAL ANATOMY

Small scales cover most of the body, but in the region of the pectoral fins there is a most distinct corselet of larger scales. The fins are well developed and include two, closely spaced dorsals of 12-14 spines and 13-16 rays, plus seven to nine detached finlets; a spineless anal of 13-15 rays plus 7-9 finlets; and a strong caudal with a keeled peduncle. Characteristic are the remarkably long pectoral fins which, in specimens exceeding 30 cm, reach beyond the origin of the first of the dorsal finlets. A row of strong, conical teeth occurs in each jaw and the first gill arch bears 25-31 slender rakers. The eyes are rather large.

Notes: Dissection reveals that the lower surface of the liver is striated and not smooth as is the case with other tuna genera. Though there are anatomical differences between Atlantic and Indo-Pacific longfin tuna, these are not enough to consider them separate species.

NATURAL HISTORY

The longfin is one of the most widespread tuna species, and although it occurs roughly between the equator and 40°S in all oceans, it seems to favour cooler and slightly deeper water. It feeds on numerous small marine organisms, but the greater part of the diet comprises fish such as anchovies, pilchards and lanternfish. Squid, megalopa crab larvae, amphipods and salps, however, are also important components of the diet. Feeding may occur on the surface or at considerable depths, even below the thermocline. The longfin tuna reaches peak abundance off the Cape coast from November to April, but it occurs throughout the year, sometimes in water temperatures as low as 14°C, though it prefers temperatures from 19-21°C. Sexual maturity is attained at about 90 cm, and extensive spawning grounds are known to exist at several mid-oceanic localities around the world. Remarkable migrations are undertaken by this fish, with some individuals having been tagged and recaptured at least 8 500 km apart in less than 12 months. Shoals are normally composed of equally aged individuals, and there is a tendency for shoals of older fish to prefer more tropical regions.

CAPTURE

This is an important species for tuna fishing fleets, and comprises about 10 per cent of the world's total tuna catch. Though once discarded as trash, this fish is of increasing commercial importance. Its delicate, white flesh has caused Japanese fishermen to refer to it as 'chicken of the sea'. There are, however, already signs of reduced catches, and careful management is needed to protect this valuable resource. It is a very popular gamefish, and fine catches are made from ski and tuna boats around Cape Point each season.
World angling record – 40,0 kg.
SA angling record – 35,8 kg.

SPECIFIC CATCH RESTRICTIONS

Open Species.

DISTRIBUTION

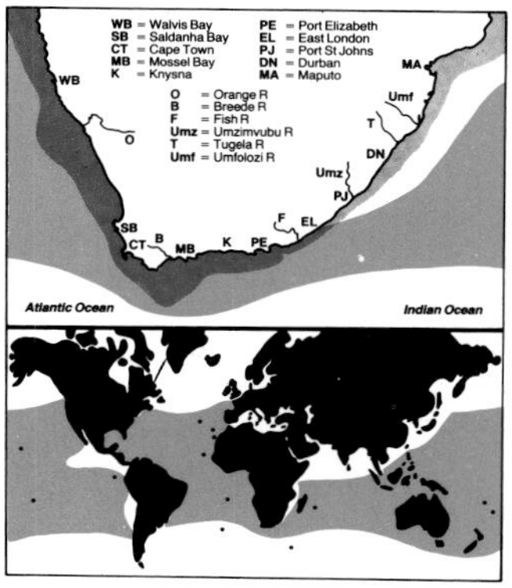

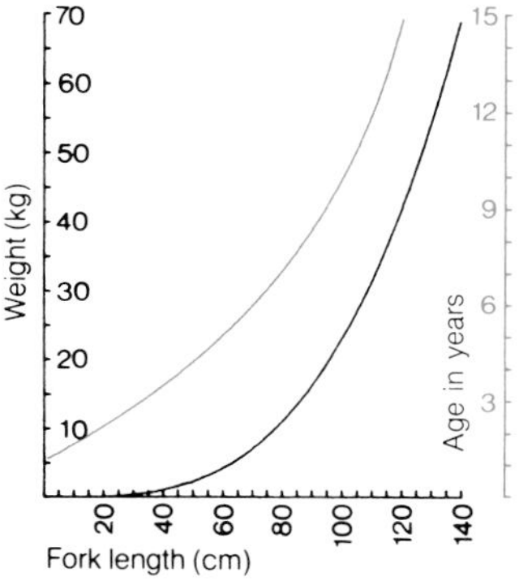

Thunnus albacares

(Bonnaterre, 1788)
Common name Worldwide – yellowfin tuna
[Smith 249□15]

IDENTIFYING FEATURES

COLOUR, SHAPE AND SIZE
This large fish has a robust, spindle-shaped body. Its back is metallic blue, changing to yellow along the sides, and the belly is silvery-white, often with about 20 pale and narrow bars. The dorsal and anal fins are yellow, while all yellow finlets are edged with a black border. Although it can attain 210 cm, few specimens in southern African waters exceed 100 cm.

EXTERNAL ANATOMY
The body is mostly covered with very small scales, but a corselet of larger scales occurs in the pectoral region. The fins are well developed and include a double dorsal of 12-14 spines followed by 13-16 rays plus 8-10 detached finlets; an anal of 12-15 rays plus 7-10 finlets, and a strong caudal with a narrow, keeled peduncle. The soft dorsal and anal fins become very elongate in large specimens. A single row of small, but strong, conical teeth occurs in each jaw. The first gill arch has 26-35 well-developed, slender rakers. The large eyes are slightly oval.
Note: Dissection reveals that the lower surface of the liver is smooth and not striated as is the case with other tuna genera.

NATURAL HISTORY

This superb gamefish of oceanic waters is normally found near the surface, but also at considerable depths, sometimes even below the thermocline. The yellowfin tuna, like other members of its family, has fins that can be folded close to the body or tucked into grooves. This hydrodynamic refinement, coupled with the fish's powerful 'red' muscles, not only makes for remarkably swift sprints, but also for persistently high speeds over long distances. The yellowfin tuna is an opportunist feeder, and preys on any small, pelagic organisms that happen to be plentiful at the time. These include small fish, mantis shrimps, crab and crayfish larvae, and squid. Small fish that hide below floating objects at sea are particularly favoured and, like many other tuna, shoals of this species may literally churn up hectares of sea in their pursuit of surface food-fish. Extensive oceanic migrations occur and these are often associated with warm-water currents. This may well be the reason for their erratic appearance. Spawning takes place in specific regions, although the actual oceanographic features of these breeding grounds remain obscure.

DISTRIBUTION

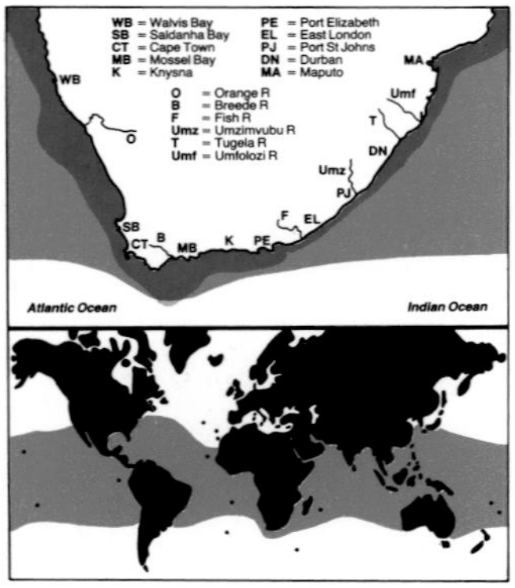

CAPTURE

A number of countries exploit this species extensively and it accounts for 22 per cent of the world's total tuna catch. Most catches are made using purse-seine nets or longlines. Tuna fishermen often remain at sea for an entire year, and keep their catches frozen at -40 to -60°C. Though the yellowfin tuna is commonly caught by ski-boaters, regrettably, too few are used for human consumption along the East Coast. The flesh is excellent, and is used for canned tuna. It is also often used in sashimi, a Japanese delicacy.
World angling record – 176,4 kg.
SA angling record – 107,5 kg.
SA spearfishing record – 43,0 kg.

SPECIFIC CATCH RESTRICTIONS

Open species; yellowfin tuna weighing less than 3,2 kg must be returned to the water alive.

NAME DERIVATION

Thunnus, an ancient name for the tuna; *albacares,* growing white. Yellowfin tuna, a reference to its bright yellow fins, and to its scientific name.

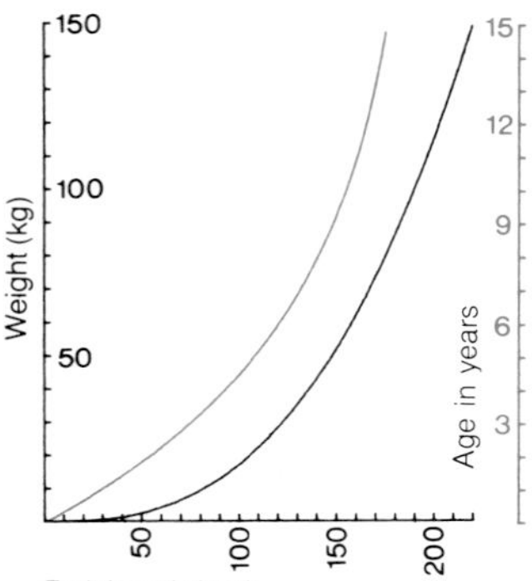

Thunnus obesus

(Lowe, 1839)

Common name Worldwide - bigeye tuna

[Smith 249□17]

IDENTIFYING FEATURES

COLOUR, SHAPE AND SIZE

This is a large tuna with a robust, fusiform body, slightly compressed from side to side. The body is metallic blue above, with a belly and lower sides which are whitish in colour. Freshly caught specimens may have an iridescent, blue stripe along each flank. The anal and second dorsal fins are yellowish, while the detached finlets are a bright yellow, edged with black. Attains 200 cm.

EXTERNAL ANATOMY

The body is covered by small, tightly adhering scales, with some of the scales enlarged to form a pectoral corselet. The strong fins comprize a double dorsal of 8-9 spines followed by 14-16 rays and 8-10 detached finlets. The anal fin has two spines preceding 11-15 rays and 7-10 detached finlets. The pectoral fins are quite long, 22-31 per cent of fork length, while the stout caudal has a strong but slender peduncle with a lateral keel set between two smaller keels. A row of conical teeth occurs in each jaw. There are 23-31 gill rakers on the first arch, and the eye is noticeably large. An important diagnostic feature concerns the liver, which is striated on its ventral surface. A swimbladder is also present.

NATURAL HISTORY

This tuna enjoys a worldwide distribution, and may be found in all oceans between 40°N and 40°S, usually in the temperature range of 13-20°C. However, bigeye favour water of 17-22°C, which corresponds to the thermocline in many regions. It follows that changes in the thermocline, due to the weather, also influence the distribution of bigeye. This is an oceanic species, seldom approaching the coast and forming sizeable shoals, quite often in association with yellowfin or skipjack tuna, that range from surface waters to a depth of 250 m. The diet of this large tuna is typical of most tunas, and includes a wide variety of small fish, squid and pelagic crustaceans such as krill. Feeding is known to occur during both day and night. This is a very fast growing species, attaining a length of 150-180 cm in three years. Enormous quantities of eggs are produced by the females, often during a double spawning season, triggered by optimal temperatures. Several spawning grounds have been identified, though breeding habits remain poorly understood. The young are widely distributed by ocean currents.

DISTRIBUTION

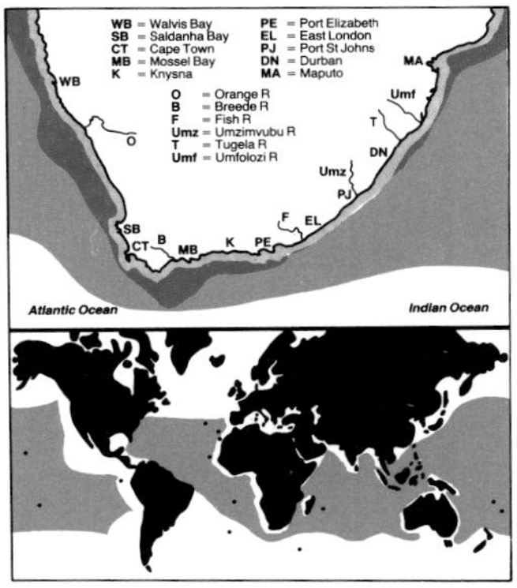

CAPTURE

There are at least 17 countries that exploit the bigeye commercially, making for a total world catch in excess of 100 000 tonnes, Japan and Korea taking most of this. South African fishermen do not actively pursue this species because of its alleged inferior quality. Canning factories are known to pay a lower price for bigeye. Most of the catch is taken on longlines set at considerable depth, each trace with up to 15 branches. Sport anglers also pit their skills against this fine fish, which is known to take a variety of trolled lures and feathers.

World angling record - 197,3 kg.

SA angling record - 89,0 kg.

SA spearfishing record - vacant.

SPECIFIC CATCH RESTRICTIONS

Open species.

NAME DERIVATION

Thunnus, from thynnos, an ancient Greek name for tuna; *obesus,* fat. Bigeye tuna, a reference to its large eye and scientific name.

SIMILAR SPECIES

The bigeye tuna is most often confused with the yellowfin tuna *(T. albacares)*, though it may be distinguished by its striated liver, non-elongate dorsal and anal fins in adults, and absence of whitish, vertical lines on the belly. The bigeye is also a little more robust and has a bigger eye. Longfin tuna *(T. alalunga)* are easily distinguished by the absence of yellow finlets, and a much larger pectoral.

Helicolenus dactylopterus

(Delaroche, 1809)
Common names SA – jacopever.
Elsewhere – blackbelly rosefish
[Smith 149□42]

IDENTIFYING FEATURES

COLOUR, SHAPE AND SIZE

This moderately compressed fish is red-orange overall,but with a white belly and a distinct, white chest. Along the base of the dorsal fin are a number of brown blotches, some of which extend onto the fin. Can attain 40 cm.

EXTERNAL ANATOMY

Between 55 and 60 series of small scales are arranged along the clearly defined lateral line. The jacopever is a very spiny fish, and, aside from those in the fins, there are also numerous sharp projections from the head and gill covers. The single dorsal fin consists of 12 spines plus 12 or 13 rays, and the anal fin of three spines plus five rays. The pectoral fins are large, and the lower few rays of both are free. The undershot mouth opens wide, and the jaws extend to a point below the very large eyes. Bands of villiform teeth occur in both jaws and also on the roof of the mouth. The first gill arch bears 27-29 rakers.

DISTRIBUTION

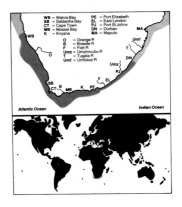

NATURAL HISTORY

The jacopever lives mainly on offshore banks and reefs between depths of 50 and 600 m. Here this rather sluggish fish frequently occurs in great abundance. It is an opportunist feeder, and very little is excluded from the diet. At least 26 different organisms have been recorded from the stomach contents of captured specimens, including krill, mysids, mantis shrimps, crabs, megalopa crab larvae, amphipods, squid, brittlestars and polychaete worms. Other fish species are also preyed upon, even the juveniles of its own species. The jacopever breeds during the summer, particularly in January, and evidence suggests that internal fertilization occurs. The eggs are soon released into the water, where, after a short, pelagic life, they hatch. It appears that False Bay is an important nursery area for eggs and larvae.

CAPTURE

This is the only member of the Scorpaenidae that is of economic value, and considerable numbers are trawled off the southern and western Cape coasts. Though edible, most are processed into animal feeds. Jacopever are very seldom caught by boat anglers, and their habitat is well beyond the range of shore fishermen.

SPECIFIC CATCH RESTRICTIONS

None.

NAME DERIVATION

Helicolenus, strong elbow or arm; *dactylopterus,* literally finger-fin, a reference to the free pectoral rays. Jacopever, derived from Jacob Evertsen, an early Dutch sailor, notorious for his drinking habits, whose ruddy complexion and prominent eyes led his shipmates to name this fish after him.

SIMILAR SPECIES

Scorpaenid fishes are best identified by the presence of spines on the head. The jacopever generally has smaller head spines and also has 12 dorsal fin spines, whereas the false jacopever has 13 spines and all other Scorpaenidae have ten or fewer.

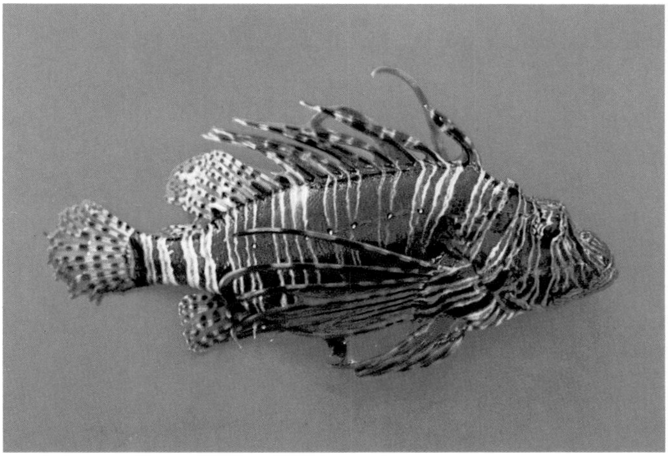

Pterois miles

(Bennett, 1828)
Common names SA – devil firefish. Elsewhere – red firefish
[Smith 149□8]

IDENTIFYING FEATURES

COLOUR, SHAPE AND SIZE
This unmistakable fish is moderately elongate and slightly compressed. Its overall red or brownish body is lined with numerous double or triple, white crossbars. In addition, white spots may occur along the lateral line and on the fins. Can attain 30 cm.

EXTERNAL ANATOMY
Small scales cover the body, and are arranged along the lateral line in 80-105 series. The fins are most distinctive, as the dorsal spines and pectoral rays are greatly extended. These, together with the numerous spines and small tentacles projecting from the head, give the fish its characteristic, maned appearance. The dorsal fin comprises 13 spines plus 9-11 rays, while the anal fin has three spines plus six rays. The caudal fin is truncate. Rows of fine teeth occur in both jaws of the terminal mouth.

DISTRIBUTION

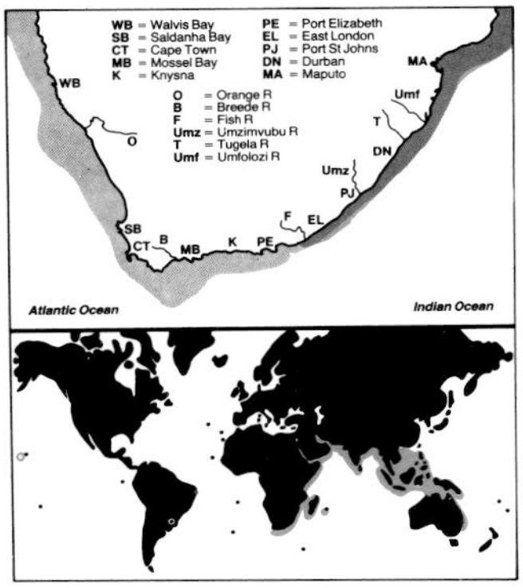

NATURAL HISTORY

There are several species in this genus, but the devil firefish is probably the most common and widespread. This solitary fish prefers quiet, sheltered regions, and is frequently encountered on shallow reefs, in tidal pools or among the pilings of harbour wharfs. Here it glides effortlessly through the water in search of prey, which consists primarily of small crabs. These crustaceans are very cautiously 'stalked' to within a few centimetres before being snatched in a final flurry. Small fish, shrimps and squid are also occasionally eaten. The dorsal spines are central to the devil firefish's defence strategy, for they are extremely sharp, and carry a powerful toxin which, though rarely fatal to humans, can cause serious wounds. Victims should be treated immediately by immersing the afflicted part in very hot water for 30 minutes, as this tends to break down the protein poison. Very young devil firefish are almost transparent, and may be found under ledges in tidal pools or estuaries. Little else has been recorded of this species' life history.

CAPTURE

Though not of angling importance, the devil firefish is very popular with marine aquarists. It thrives in captivity, and is easily caught with a hand net. Because of its extremely poisonous spines, it should always be handled with the greatest of care. As this fish has a preference for sheltered regions, the aquarist should provide suitable rocky overhangs and 'retreats' within the tank. Live fish or crabs should be provided as a source of food.
SA angling record – 1,4 kg.

SPECIFIC CATCH RESTRICTIONS

None.

NAME DERIVATION

Pterois, winged; *miles,* soldier. Devil firefish, a reference to its poisonous, flame-like fins.

SIMILAR SPECIES

There are five firefish species in South Africa, all with different body markings. This common species is best recognized by having 14 pectoral rays, and distinctly spotted caudal, anal and second dorsal fins.

Scorpaena scrofa

Linnaeus, 1758
Common name Worldwide – bigscale scorpionfish
[Smith 149□21]

IDENTIFYING FEATURES

COLOUR, SHAPE AND SIZE

This moderately elongate fish has a robust body with a rather blunt snout. Its colours and patterns are striking and variable. It is reddish overall, but with a pale to white underside, and scattered over the entire body and fins are black dots and dark mottlings. The fins are pinkish or translucent, and there is a black blotch overlying the seventh to ninth dorsal spines. Can attain 40 cm in length.

EXTERNAL ANATOMY

The lateral line is quite distinct, and along it are arranged 42-45 series of characteristically large scales. There is, however, a small scaleless area around the pectoral base and on the chest. The well-developed fins include a single dorsal of 12 spines plus nine rays, an anal of three spines plus five rays, and large pectoral fins with 8-10 rays which become progressively thicker with age. The caudal fin is broadly rounded. As with most Scorpaenidae, the head and gill covers are extensively covered with sharp spines, which become longer with age. The mouth is large and the jaws extend to a point below the eyes. Both jaws bear bands of fine teeth, those of one row being enlarged. Several patches of villiform teeth also occur on the roof of the mouth. Between 13 and 17 short, and mostly knob-like, rakers occur on the first gill arch.

NATURAL HISTORY

The bigscale scorpionfish is the largest of the southern African Scorpaenidae. It is quite common, but, owing to its solitary habits and apparent reluctance to take bait, it is not often seen. It lives in rather deep waters, preferring to range from 60-100 m, and is generally found around reefs. The diet includes a variety of organisms, especially smaller crustaceans such as crabs and mantis shrimps. Small fish and squid are also preyed upon. Despite its widespread occurrence, very little of this fish's biology has been documented.

DISTRIBUTION

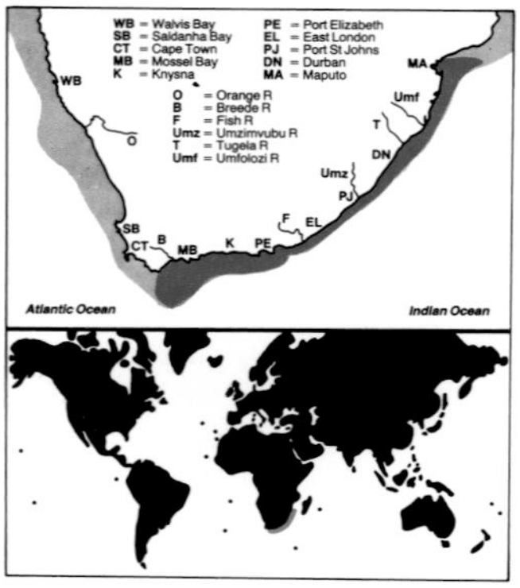

CAPTURE

Though it hardly appears appetizing, this scorpionfish is edible. Some are caught by ski-boat anglers, but these are invariably released. Occasionally, specimens are landed in trawl nets. As the body is coated with toxic mucus, this fish should be handled carefully to avoid being pricked by the many spines.

NAME DERIVATION

Scorpaena, scorpion; *scrota,* a breeding sow. Bigscale scorpionfish, a reference to its conspicuous scales and the painful wounds its spines can cause.

SPECIFIC CATCH RESTRICTIONS

None.

SIMILAR SPECIES

While the spines on the head will characterize this fish as a scorpionfish, it is the scaleless patch around each pectoral fin base and the fewer than ten dorsal fin rays that distinguish this species from the others.

Sebastes capensis

(Gmelin, 1789)
Common names SA – false jacopever. Elsewhere – cowcod
[Smith 149□43]

IDENTIFYING FEATURES

COLOUR, SHAPE AND SIZE
The body of the false jacopever is moderately elongate and slightly compressed. Its overall colour is reddish above and orange below. About four irregular, pink blotches occur on the upper flanks. Can attain 40 cm.

EXTERNAL ANATOMY
The lateral line is well defined and arranged along its length are about 110 series of small, tough scales. The fins are well developed, and include a dorsal of 13 or 14 spines preceding 13 or 14 rays, and an anal of three spines plus six rays. Each pectoral fin comprises partially free rays which are thick and filamentous. The caudal fin is truncate. Broad bands of villiform teeth occur in the large mouth. Four spines occur on top of the head and one pair projects from the forehead. A further five spines are found on the pre-operculum. The eyes are large. Between 20-24 long, serrated rakers occur on the first gill arch.

DISTRIBUTION

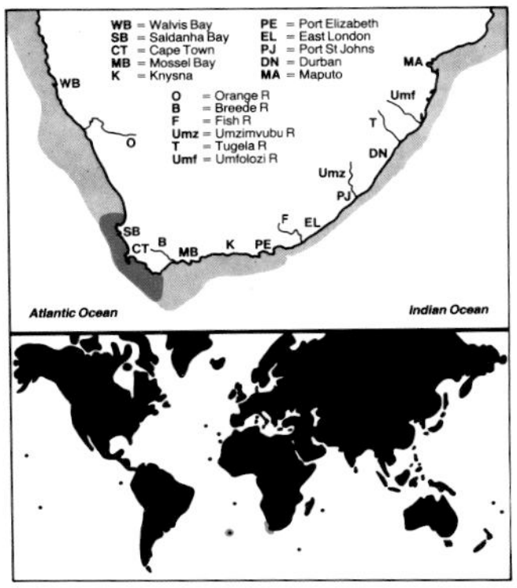

NATURAL HISTORY

The false jacopever is a reasonably common fish, generally confined to deeper reefs down to 300 m. It is a sluggish, bottom-living species that feeds mainly on small crabs, shrimps, squid and even octopuses, larger specimens are believed to prey on small, slow-swimming fish. This rather curious species belongs to one of the few groups of marine fishes in which females undergo internal fertilization and bear live young. Closely related species have been known to produce as many as two million fertilized embryos each season. Most of these fishes belong to the genus *Sebastes,* and live predominantly in the northern Pacific Ocean. Some occur in great abundance, particularly off California, and are of value to local fish markets. Many of these fishes have exceedingly beautiful colours and patterns. It is probable that a number of additional species await discovery as their deep-water habits make them largely inaccessible to marine biologists. Fossil remains of similar species have been recorded from 15-million-year-old rock deposits. Little additional information is available on the life history of this fish.

CAPTURE

Most catches are made from line-boats in the south-western Cape, and, despite the fish's preference for deeper waters, numbers are taken in False Bay. Occasionally catches are made from the beach, while some are landed by trawlers. Though the flesh makes excellent eating, the false jacopever is not normally landed in sufficient numbers to be of great significance. It is not of spearfishing importance.
SA angling record – vacant.

SPECIFIC CATCH RESTRICTIONS

None.

NAME DERIVATION

Sebastes, magnificent fish; *capensis,* of the Cape, False jacopever, a reference to its close resemblance to the true jacopever.

SIMILAR SPECIES

The presence of 13 or more dorsal spines is distinctive and separates this species from the jacopever and other scorpaenid fishes.

Synanceia verrucosa

Bloch & Schneider, 1801
Common name Worldwide – stonefish
[Smith 149□46]

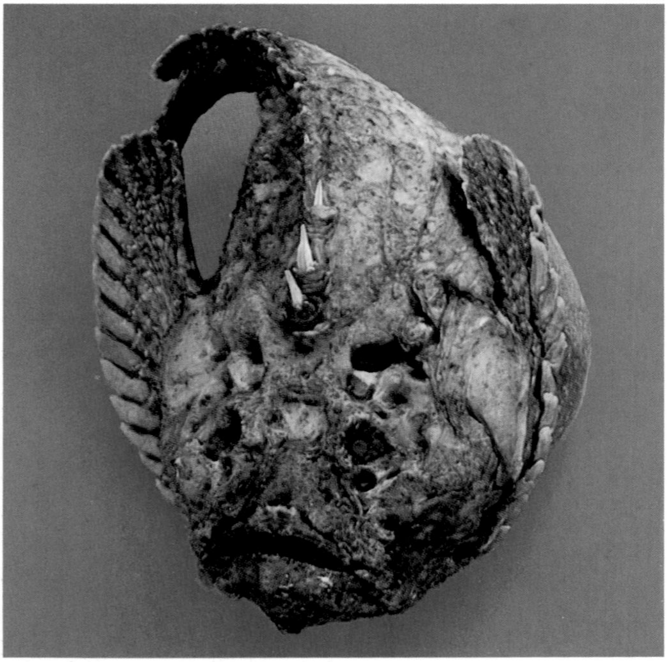

IDENTIFYING FEATURES

COLOUR, SHAPE AND SIZE
This rather grotesque fish has a squat body with a large head. It is drab brown overall, but often has mottled patches which match its surroundings. Attains 40 cm.
EXTERNAL ANATOMY
The stonefish's rough, warty skin does little to enhance its appearance. The dorsal fin has 13 strong, hollow spines, followed by six or seven rays. The anal fin has three spines plus five or six rays, while the pectorals are very large and fleshy. The caudal fin is reduced. Poison sacs are located at the bases of the dorsal spines. The mouth is large, faces upwards and bears small teeth in both jaws. The gill openings are very small, and 8-10 short rakers occur on the first gill arch. The small eyes are deeply set within depressions, and there is a conspicuous 'pit' between the eyes.

DISTRIBUTION

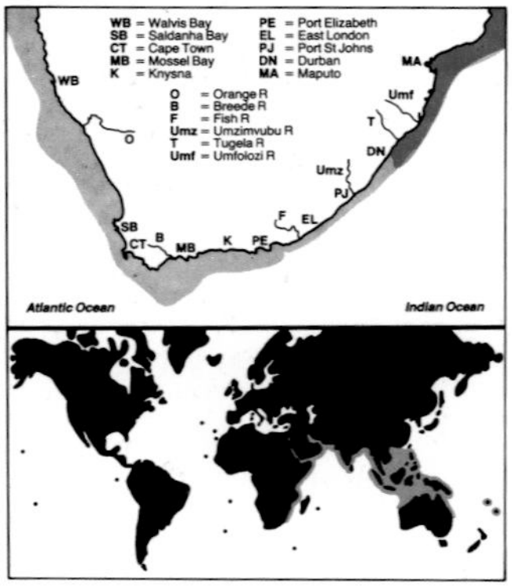

NATURAL HISTORY

This fish is not only lethally toxic, but so well camouflaged that, even at close proximity, it remains unnoticed unless physically disturbed. Not much is known of its life history. It is a solitary fish, occurring on shallow coral and rocky reefs, and, occasionally, also over sandy bottoms. The dorsal spines are exceptionally tough, and will easily penetrate the bare foot of a careless wader. When depressed in this fashion the sacs release their toxic contents, which are injected through the hollow 'hypodermic' spines into the flesh of the victim. Such wounds are excrutiatingly painful and potentially fatal. Treatment involves the immediate immersion of the affected part in very hot water for at least 30 minutes to destroy the powerful protein poison. This species should not be confused with the other scorpionfishes which are similar in appearance. Stonefish expend very little energy and lead very sedentary lives. Their feeding strategy centres on their extremely effective camouflage, and an unsuspecting prey wandering within range is gulped down whole. In Durban's Seaworld, stonefish on display have eaten fish half their own size, resulting in a startling overnight increase in body size. Fish constitute the bulk of the diet. Not surprisingly, the members of this species have few, if any, natural enemies.

CAPTURE

This is hardly a fish worth capturing, though no doubt it can be caught on small live bait. It thrives in captivity but should be handled with great care.

SPECIFIC CATCH RESTRICTIONS

None.

NAME DERIVATION

Synanceia, meaning obscure; *verrucosa,* warty. Stonefish, a reference to its uncanny camouflage – it is literally indistinguishable from the surrounding rocks of its environment.

SIMILAR SPECIES

While scorpionfishes are often incorrectly called stonefish, the true stonefish is easily recognized by its fleshy pectoral fins.

Neoscorpis lithophilus

(Gilchrist & Thompson, 1908)
Common names SA – stonebream, stinker
[Smith 190□1]

IDENTIFYING FEATURES

COLOUR, SHAPE AND SIZE

The stonebream is moderately compressed, and has a smoothly rounded dorsal profile. It is silvery-grey overall, and occasionally has slightly darker, broad vertical bars on the flanks, as shown in the smaller photograph. The fins are dusky-grey. Can attain 50 cm.

EXTERNAL ANATOMY

Covering the body are very fine scales arranged in nearly 100 series. The fins are moderately developed; the spines are somewhat reduced, and the first dorsal and anal rays are fairly long. The single dorsal fin comprises 6-8 short spines plus 20-25 rays, while the anal fin has three spines plus 23-26 rays. The caudal fin is moderately forked. Bands of fine teeth occur on both jaws of the small, terminal mouth. There are 15-20 rakers on the first gill arch.
Note: The stonebream, a relative of the chub family, is the only fish of its kind in southern Africa.

DISTRIBUTION

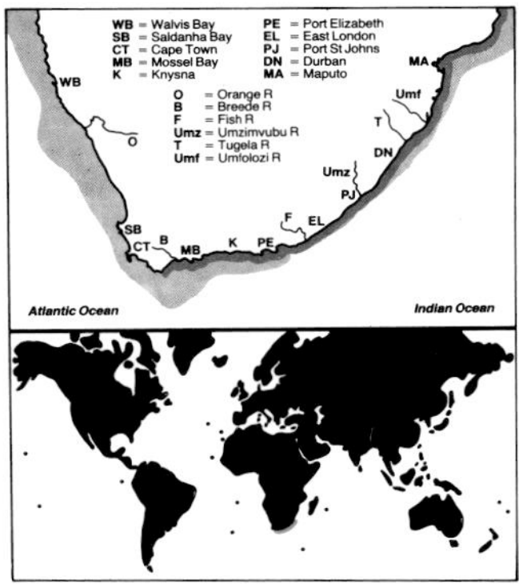

NATURAL HISTORY

The stonebream is restricted to turbulent regions and rocky shores, and is invariably found in very shallow water. It is one of the largest of the vegetarian fishes in southern Africa, and it feeds almost exclusively on red seaweeds. Occasionally, green seaweeds are also consumed. Minute animals that live in association with these algal plants, are also accidentally ingested. To derive adequate energy from its low-protein diet, the stonebream feeds continuously throughout the day. The black lining to the gut cavity probably prevents light from penetrating the digestive tract. If this were not the case, the chlorophyll of the vegetable matter in the stomach would remain active, and the oxygen formed as a by-product would literally cause the fish to blow up. Spawning has been recorded from the Natal coast during spring and summer. The onset of sexual maturity coincides with a fork length of about 30 cm. Nursery areas for this species include the entire intertidal zone and, during summer, many small stonebream are encountered in rock pools.

CAPTURE

Despite its vegetarian habits, this fish will take flesh baits, especially shrimp and redbait. The best catches are made in white-water around rocky outcrops. The noticeably bad odour emanating from the gut when the fish is

cleaned does not contaminate the flesh, which makes good eating.
SA angling record – 2,5 kg.
SA spearfishing record – 2,6 kg.

SPECIFIC CATCH RESTRICTIONS

None.

SIMILAR SPECIES

The stonebream resembles the chubs, both in appearance and habits, but may easily be distinguished by its much fewer and smaller dorsal spines, and elevated second dorsal fin.

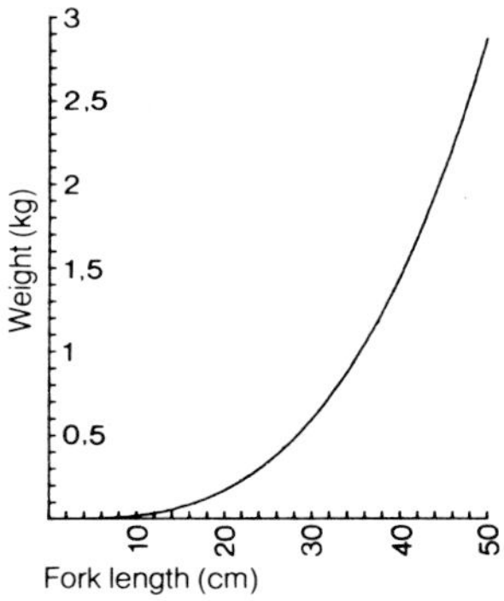

Anthias squamipinnis

Peters, 1855

Common names Worldwide - sea goldie or goldfish

[Smith 166□9]

IDENTIFYING FEATURES

COLOUR, SHAPE AND SIZE

The small, slightly compressed sea goldie is one of the few marine fishes to display distinct colour differences between the sexes. Females are orange overall, with an iridescent, blue stripe below the eyes, while the less common males have deeper-red bodies and are often marked with many darker spots. Can attain 11 cm.

EXTERNAL ANATOMY

The distinct lateral line has 40-44 series of very rough ctenoid scales arranged along its length. The dorsal fin has ten spines plus 15-17 rays, and, in males the third spine is elongate. The anal fin has three spines plus 6-7 rays, and the caudal is noticeably emarginate. Strong canines are set in both jaws of the small mouth.

DISTRIBUTION

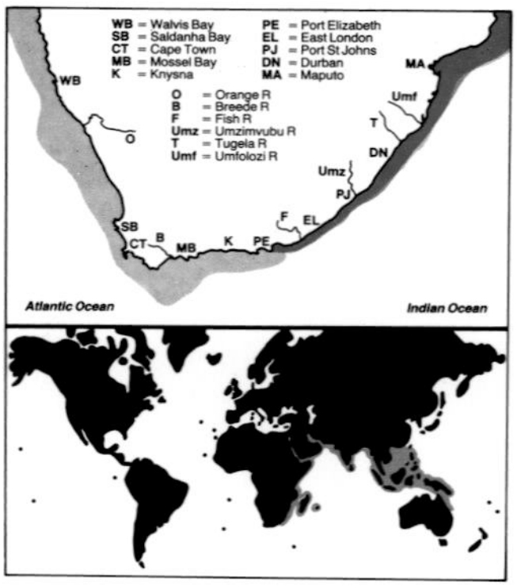

NATURAL HISTORY

As a member of the rockcod family, the sea goldie is exclusively a reef-dwelling species. It is especially fond of coral reefs, where it frequently moves in shoals, close to the roofs of caves. Curiously, this fish often swims upside down, apparently because the light reflected off the floor of the cave is mistaken for sunlight on the surface. This causes the sea goldie's orientation to be inversed. Little is known of its diet, but planktonic organisms and larval fish are probably included. A high degree of social organization is displayed within the shoal. There is a distinct parallel between the life history of this species and the cleaner wrasse. At least 85 per cent of the members of a shoal of sea goldies are female, a seeming imbalance that is logical, as only one male is required to fertilize a number of females in any one season. The method of controlling the male population is, however, remarkable, for males are literally produced on demand. All members of the species mature as females, but each has the inherent ability to change sex. Each male has a number of 'wives', but should he die or be removed, the dominant female in his 'harem' will soon begin to display greater aggression and her colours will begin to change. These are the first outward signs of sex reversal, and within a short space of time the process is complete. Individuals undergoing such changes can often be distinguished by their transitional colouration. Spawning, as well as the distribution of eggs and larvae, takes place in open water.

Female A. sqamipinnis.

SPECIFIC CATCH RESTRICTIONS

None.

CAPTURE

This beautiful fish is much prized by marine aquarists, but it is not always easily caught. Those captured, however, thrive in a tank environment, and sex changes can be induced simply by the removal of male fish.

NAME DERIVATION

Anthias, like a flower; *squamipinnis,* feather-like scales. Goldfish or sea goldie, a reference to its superficial similarity to the freshwater goldfish.

SIMILAR SPECIES

Sea goldies may be distinguished from the true rockcods by their fewer scales (less than 60), and presence of scales on the maxilla, which is naked in rockcods. This species is easily distinguished by its plain orange or reddish colour, and the blue stripe below the eye in females.

Cephalopholis argus

(Schneider, 1801)
Common name Worldwide – peacock rockcod
[Smith 166□21]

IDENTIFYING FEATURES

COLOUR, SHAPE AND SIZE
This small, but nevertheless typically robust rockcod is dark brown overall, and the entire body, including the fins, is spotted with powder-blue dots, each of which is edged in black. About seven, alternating light- and darker-brown, vertical bands occur on the sides. Though juveniles display similar patterns, they are usually more brightly coloured than adults. Can attain 50 cm.

EXTERNAL ANATOMY
Arranged in 95-110 series, small, tough scales cover the body. A distinct lateral line is lacking. Spines are prominent in the fins, and the single dorsal comprises nine spines plus 15-17 rays, while the anal has three spines plus eight or nine rays. The caudal fin is rounded. The large mouth is armed with numerous rows of sharp, pointed teeth, most of which can fold inwards. The first gill arch has 9-11 rakers. Three spines project backwards from each of the gill covers.

DISTRIBUTION

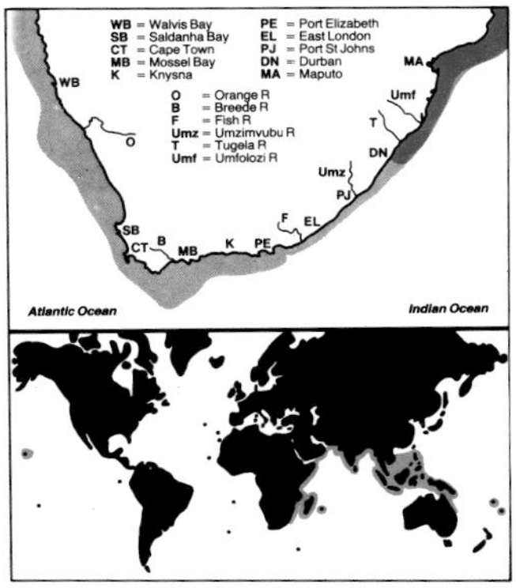

NATURAL HISTORY

This beautiful, tropical rockcod is generally found near coral reefs, but in summer it strays southwards into Natal, where the juveniles inhabit inshore, rocky reefs. It is a solitary species and will often remain motionless for long periods, waiting for prey to come within range. This consists mainly of fish, especially cave-dwelling, reef species such as soldierfishes and squirrelfishes. Small crabs living amongst coral polyps, as well as shrimps and juvenile crayfish, are also eaten. It is most active during daylight. Its life history is not well known. Catch statistics indicate that this fish is not particularly common in local waters, but divers often see the peacock rockcod, especially during the summer months. This species was artificially introduced to Hawaiian waters in 1956.

CAPTURE

Ski-boat anglers and spearfishermen occasionally land this rockcod, but though the flesh is edible, most are too small to be of great importance. Marine aquarists, however, value this fish, as it makes a successful and attractive display specimen, especially in its juvenile phase.
SA angling record – vacant.
SA spearfishing record – 2,2 kg.

NAME DERIVATION

Cephalopholis, scaly or spotted head; *argus,* a reference to the Greek myth in which Argus' 100 eyes were transformed into the peacock's tail. Peacock rockcod, a reference to its colours as well as its habitat and supposed similarity to the codfishes of the northern hemisphere.

SPECIFIC CATCH RESTRICTIONS

None.

SIMILAR SPECIES

The nine dorsal spines confirm that this belongs to the genus *Cephalopholus.* The only other similar species is the coral rockcod, *C. miniata* – which may be distinguished by its redder colour, and absence of spots underneath the lower jaw.

Cephalopholis miniata

(Forsskål, 1775)

Common names SA - coral rockcod, bluespotted rockcod. Elsewhere - vermillion seabass, coral trout

[Smith 166□26]

IDENTIFYING FEATURES

COLOUR, SHAPE AND SIZE

This small, robust fish has spectacular body colours. It is bright orange or red overall, and patterned with numerous, intensely blue spots, each of which is ringed with a thin, brown band. The fins are similarly coloured and may be edged in brown. Can attain 50 cm though few exceed 30-40 cm.

EXTERNAL ANATOMY

The body is covered with small, but distinct scales arranged in 95-110 series. Scales also extend partially onto the fin bases. Spines are prominent in the fins which include a single dorsal of nine spines plus 14-16 rays, and an anal of three spines plus nine rays. The caudal fin is rounded. Several rows of small, pointed teeth are set in both jaws of the large mouth, but lateral canines are lacking. The teeth can fold backwards. The first gill arch bears 14-20 short, spiky rakers.

DISTRIBUTION

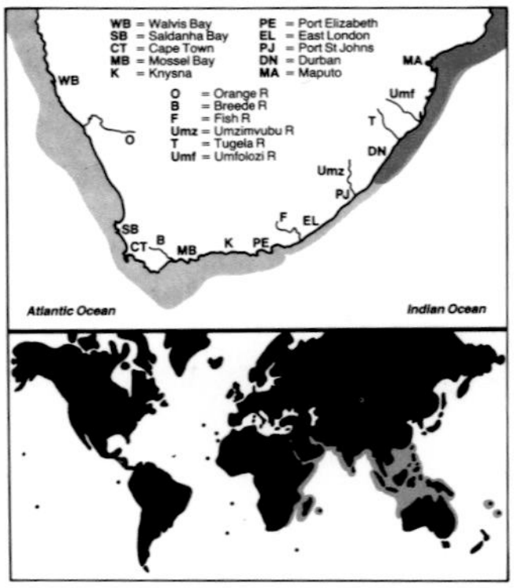

NATURAL HISTORY

This relatively common inhabitant of coral reefs occurs singly or in small groups, normally in caves or underneath ledges. Prey consists primarily of small crabs, shrimps and the juveniles of other reef fish. Occasionally, midwater crustaceans such as mantis shrimps are also eaten. The coral rockcod's very bright colours can often provide an effective camouflage among the equally striking sponges and corals of its natural habitat. Little of its life history has been documented, though reproductively 'ripe' fish have been recorded around tropical reefs during October. Sex reversal is common amongst the Serranidae, and it is likely that female coral rockcods change into males once a certain length has been reached.

CAPTURE

The coral rockcod is often caught in considerable numbers by shore and ski-boat anglers in tropical regions. It freely takes fish baits. Along the East African coast and in the Far East, this fish represents a valuable source of protein, and it is frequently sold on fresh-fish markets. Generally, it is too small to be of interest to spearfishermen.
SA angling record - 0,6 kg.
SA spearfishing record - vacant.

NAME DERIVATION

Cephalopholis, scaly or spotted head; *miniata,* bright red. Coral rockcod, a reference to its preferred habitats, and to its alleged resemblance to the codfishes of European waters.

SPECIFIC CATCH RESTRICTIONS

None.

SIMILAR SPECIES

This is a most distinctive species, which can be distinguished from the peacock rockcod by its bright red colour. This genus of rockcods has only nine dorsal spines, instead of ten or more in other groups.

Cephalopholis sonnerati

(Valenciennes, 1828)
Common names SA – tomato rockcod. Elsewhere – tomato seabass
[Smith 166□29]

IDENTIFYING FEATURES

COLOUR, SHAPE AND SIZE

This medium-sized member of the Serranidae has a deep, compressed body with a distinct dip in the head profile just above the eyes. It is a strikingly brilliant red overall, with older specimens having darker edges to the fins. Some individuals may display a fine network of blue lines on the head, while others may have numerous white spots. Occasionally, tomato rockcod are darker red with black fins. Can attain 60 cm.

EXTERNAL ANATOMY

The body is well covered with small, tough scales arranged in 110-140 series. The lateral line is only faintly visible. The fins are spiny and include a single dorsal of nine spines plus 14 or 15 rays, an anal of three spines plus nine rays, and a rounded caudal. In addition to three bands of folding teeth in each jaw, a number of canines are located towards the front of the large mouth. The first gill arch bears 9-18 short rakers as well as additional rudimentary ones.

NATURAL HISTORY

A solitary fish of coral and rocky reefs, the tomato rockcod is plentiful in specific localities such as the St Lucia Marine Reserve, and reaches peak abundance during summer. This coastal species may venture to depths of 100 m. It feeds on a variety of reef organisms, including small fish such as cardinals, and crustaceans such as crabs, shrimps and small crayfish. Fish laden with milt and roe have been recorded, primarily from October to November, off the East African coast. It is likely, however, that spawning occurs throughout summer.

DISTRIBUTION

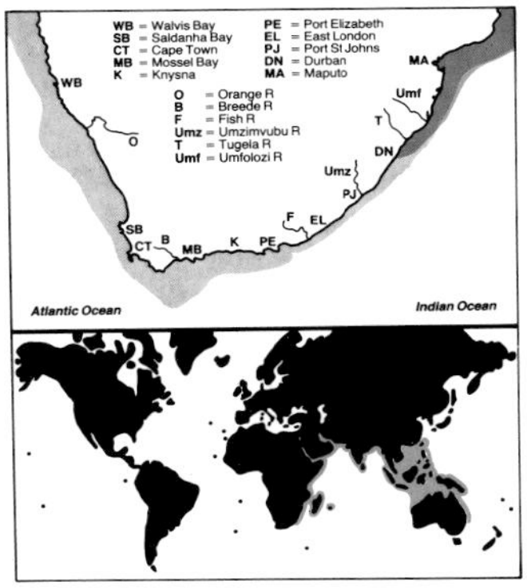

CAPTURE

The tomato rockcod is caught by ski- and line-boat anglers, and is occasionally speared by divers. It is of excellent eating quality. In the East, hand-lines and traps are used to capture this fish for local fresh-fish markets.
SA angling record – 3,0 kg.
SA spearfishing record – 4,8 kg.

SIMILAR SPECIES

While the colouration is quite distinctive, the tomato rockcod can be further distinguished by its high scale count, and a standard length 2,3 - 2,7 times its body depth.

SPECIFIC CATCH RESTRICTIONS

None.

NAME DERIVATION

Cephalopholis, scaly or spotted head; *sonnerati,* named in honour of the naturalist Sonnerat. Tomato rockcod, a reference to its vivid colours, habitat and alleged resemblance to the codfishes of European waters.

Epinephelus albomarginatus

Boulenger, 1903

Common names Worldwide – white-edged rockcod, captain fine [Smith 166□33]

IDENTIFYING FEATURES

COLOUR, SHAPE AND SIZE

This robust and moderately elongate rockcod is light brown overall, and covered with numerous, darker-brown spots. The pelvic and pectoral fins are bright yellow, while the first dorsal fin is grey with a yellow outer edge. The second dorsal, anal and caudal fins are also grey, but have conspicuous white outer edges. Can attain 100 cm.

EXTERNAL ANATOMY

There are about 102-116 series of well-developed scales arranged along the lateral line. Spines are prominent in the fins, which include a single dorsal of 11 spines plus 14 rays, an anal of three spines plus eight rays, and a caudal which is rounded. Two rows of teeth occur in both jaws of the large mouth. The teeth of the outer row are enlarged. Some 16 short, but sharply spiked rakers occur on the first gill arch. Several spines are located on the pre-operculum. *Note:* Dissection reveals a swim bladder which is large and tough.

DISTRIBUTION

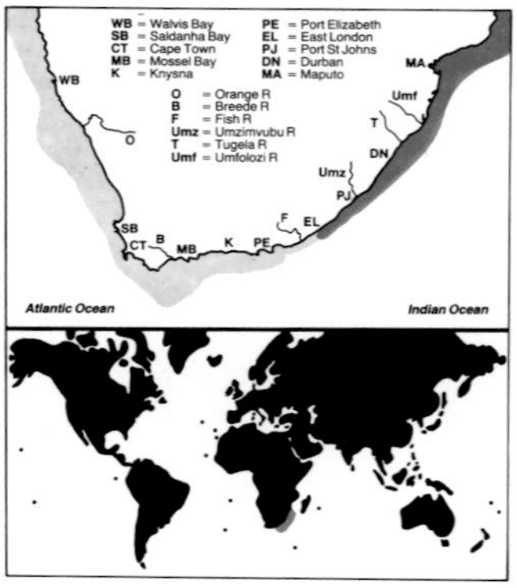

NATURAL HISTORY

This relatively common rockcod is not found inshore, as it prefers deeper waters, often to 100 m. It is a powerful predator, and its diet consists mainly of bottom-living invertebrates, especially crayfish, crab and octopuses. A number of slow-swimming fish, as well as squid, are also occasionally eaten. Reproductive activity is known to increase during spring, but as this species has yet to be studied, further details of its life history are scant. It is probably of solitary habit, and quite possibly also territorial, as newly discovered reefs initially provide good catches of this fish. The Serranidae in general, and the white-edged rockcod in particular, are receiving increased scientific attention in order to establish their fishery and sport potential. Only with a sound biological understanding can the exploitation of these fish be correctly managed and future good catches assured.Note also that this is one of the few rockcod species that is endemic, being confined to Natal and Moçambique waters. Hence its protected status.

CAPTURE

The white-edged rockcod is only caught by ski-boat fishermen, especially by those operating along the Natal north coast. A variety of baits will tempt this fish which is regarded as a most desirable catch because of its excellent flesh. Its occurrence in deeper offshore water generally places it beyond the range of spearfishermen.
SA angling record – 12,3 kg.
SA spearfishing record – vacant.

SPECIFIC CATCH RESTRICTIONS

Protected species; minimum legal size is 30 cm total length.

NAME DERIVATION

Epinephelus, 'clouded over', an allusion to the colour pattern of the type species; *albomarginatus,* white-edged. White-edged rockcod, a reference to its fin colours, and to its habitat and alleged resemblance to the codfishes of European waters.

SIMILAR SPECIES

While the spots are an important diagnostic feature, the yellow-edged dorsal spines, and white-edged dorsal and anal fin rays serve to positively identify this species. Notice, too, the truncate caudal fin.

Epinephelus andersoni

Boulenger, 1903

Common names Worldwide – catface or spotted rockcod [Smith 166□34]

IDENTIFYING FEATURES

COLOUR, SHAPE AND SIZE

This elongate and robust fish is brown overall, and the entire body is covered with darker brown spots. Two or three oblique stripes usually mark the face, running from the eye backwards. Can attain 80 cm.

EXTERNAL ANATOMY

Small scales cover the body and are arranged in some 100-105 series. The fins are well developed and spiny: the single dorsal comprises 11 spines plus 13-15 rays, the anal three spines plus eight rays, and the caudal is large and rounded. Strong canines occur in both jaws of the large mouth, as well as bands of finer teeth which can fold backwards. The first gill arch bears 22-27, short and very spiky rakers.

Note: Dissection reveals a large, tough swim bladder.

DISTRIBUTION

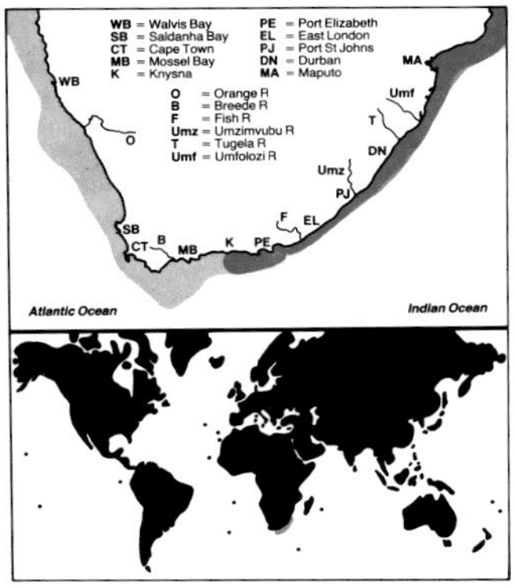

NATURAL HISTORY

The catface rockcod is one of the most common and widely distributed members of the Serranidae in southern African waters. It frequents the shallow surf zone, but also ranges to depths of at least 50 m. Occasionally, it ventures into estuaries, but it is not tolerant of low salinity conditions. It is always associated with rocky reefs, often lying motionless on the floor of a gully. Here, well camouflaged against the rocky backdrop, the catface rockcod lies in wait, ready to pounce on blennies, crayfish and crabs that venture too closely. A number of other fish species also supplement the diet. Despite its rather sluggish habits, it is one of the most important inshore reef predators along the East Coast. This resident species is present throughout the year and breeding has been recorded off the Natal coast during the late winter and spring. Sexual maturity is attained at 50-60 cm, and spawning takes place after courtship displays which involve two or more fish. Juveniles migrate to the shallow, intertidal zone after their egg and larval phases.

CAPTURE

This fine table fish is frequently caught by both ski-boat and shore anglers using a variety of baits. It is an aggressive striker, and has been known to take a lure at the surface. It is popular with spearfishermen. This endemic and vulnerable species has limited distribution, hence its protected status.

SA angling record – 7,0 kg.

SA spearfishing record – 8,0 kg.

SPECIFIC CATCH RESTRICTIONS

Protected species; minimum legal size is 30 cm total length.

NAME DERIVATION

Epinephelus, 'clouded over', an allusion to the colour pattern of the type species; *andersoni,* named after the ichthyologist, Anderson. Catface rockcod, a reference to the Abyssinian-cat-like stripes on the face, its habitat and its supposed resemblance to the codfishes of European waters.

SIMILAR SPECIES

Many rockcod species have spots on their body but none have the distinct stripes on the cheek. Notice, too, the rounded caudal fin.

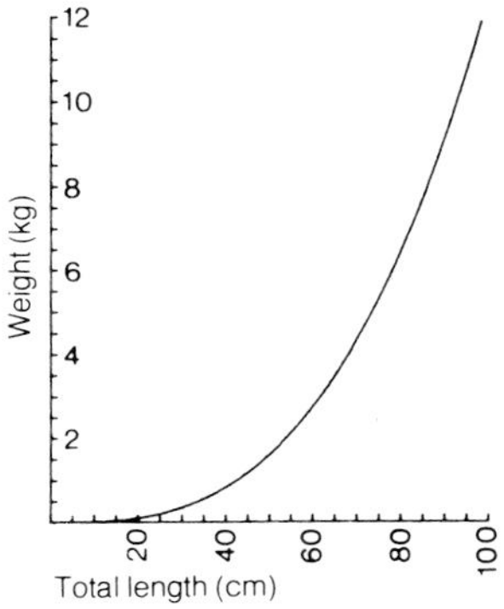

Epinephelus chlorostigma

(Valenciennes, 1828)
Common name Worldwide – brownspotted rockcod
[Smith 166□38]

IDENTIFYING FEATURES

COLOUR, SHAPE AND SIZE
This moderately elongate rockcod is easily recognized by its distinctive markings. The pale-brown body is densely patterned with darker-brown, hexagonal blotches which also extend onto the fins. It is important to note that these spots are larger than the spaces between them. The trailing edges of the caudal and soft dorsal fins are white. The belly is much paler, or white. Can attain 70 cm.
EXTERNAL ANATOMY
The lateral line is not always obvious, but arranged along its length are about 99-119 series of small ctenoid scales. The spiny fins include a single dorsal of 11 spines plus 16-18 rays, an anal of three spines plus eight rays, and a square, or slightly emarginate, caudal fin. Several bands of fine, backward-folding teeth occur in each jaw. The teeth of the outer row are slightly enlarged.
Approximately 31 short rakers occur on the first gill arch.

DISTRIBUTION

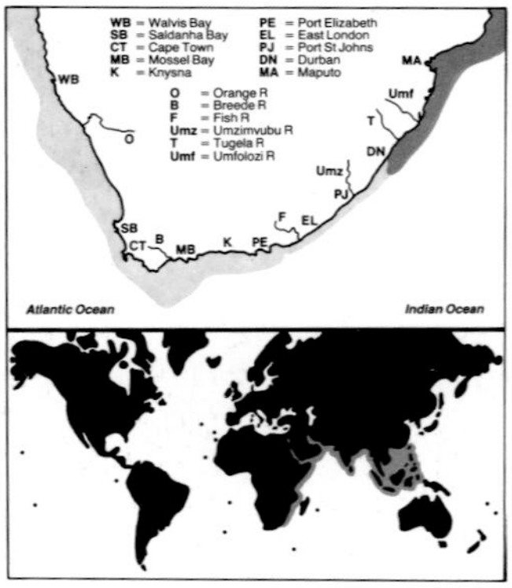

NATURAL HISTORY

The brownspotted rockcod is a relatively common inhabitant of coral and rocky reefs, especially those of more tropical regions. It generally frequents deeper reefs, and may range down to at least 150 m. In southern African waters, it is most abundant during summer. The stomach contents of the several specimens examined, have revealed a diet that includes small reef fish and crabs. Other reef organisms and squid are also likely to be eaten when available. Reproductively 'ripe' specimens have been recorded from Kenyan waters during July to September, but the breeding season is known to be extended, with spawning taking place throughout the year. The overall ratio of males to females has been established as 1:11. Sex reversal accounts for this phenomenon, as all individuals less than 37 cm long are female.

CAPTURE

From time to time, ski-boat anglers operating over slightly deeper reefs catch this rockcod. Its fine flesh is as excellent as that of any other member of the family.
SA angling record – 1,5 kg.

SPECIFIC CATCH RESTRICTIONS

None.

NAME DERIVATION

Epinephelus, 'clouded over', an allusion to the colour pattern of the type species; *chlorostigma,* green-spotted. Brownspotted rockcod, an obvious reference to its body patterns, which must have appeared greenish in the original specimen described, and an allusion to its habitat and similarity to the codfishes of European waters.

SIMILAR SPECIES

Two other species could be confused with the brownspotted rockcod. *E. areolatus* is also spotted, but the spots are larger and the caudal fin is more emarginate, while *E. gaimardi* has fewer and larger spots, and proportionally larger dorsal and anal rays. Notice too that the white trailing edge to the truncate tail fin is most distinctive.

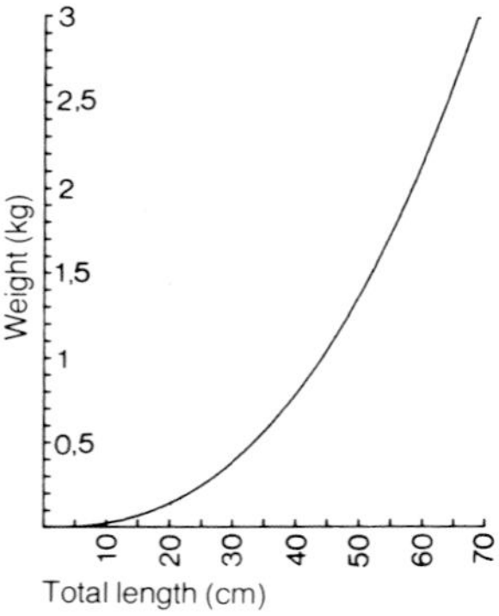

Epinephelus fasciatus

(Forsskål, 1775)

Common names SA – redbarred rockcod. Elsewhere – red-banded grouper, black tipped rockcod [Smith 166□39]

IDENTIFYING FEATURES

COLOUR, SHAPE AND SIZE

This small rockcod has an oblong, moderately compressed body with a rather pointed snout. It is reddish-orange overall and is marked with a darker red band extending from each eye to the front of the dorsal fin. A further six vertical, red bands occur on the flanks, these are especially obvious when seen underwater. The edges of the dorsal spines are dark red, and the fins are yellowish. Can attain 30 cm in length.

EXTERNAL ANATOMY

Tough scales are arranged along the body in 102-123 series.The spiny fins include a single dorsal of 11 spines plus 15-17 rays, an anal of three spines plus eight rays and a rounded caudal. Both jaws bear about four bands of fine, backward-folding teeth, while a number of canine teeth are located at the front of the large, terminal mouth. The first gill arch bears 21-25 rakers, all of which are short and spiky.

DISTRIBUTION

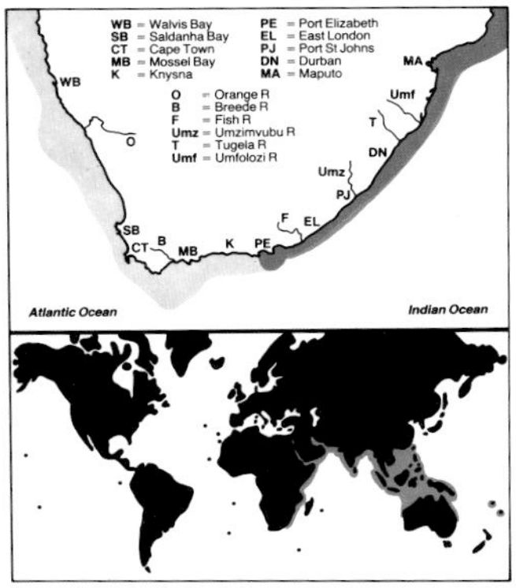

NATURAL HISTORY

A fairly abundant inhabitant of coral and rocky reefs, the redbarred rockcod generally ranges from shallow water to depths of 100 m. Individuals are often found lurking in caves or under ledges, but much time is also spent lying motionless between coral heads, often on the flat upper surface of reefs. As with other rockcods, this behaviour is probably central to a feeding strategy which involves waiting patiently and well camouflaged, for unsuspecting prey to venture within reach of the widely opening mouth. Recent research has revealed an additional aspect to this feeding strategy which may well be applicable to all rockcods. By lying on the sea-bed, the rockcod with its upward-facing eyes, is able to observe fish overhead, especially those that are silhouetted against the surface. In this way it detects food even in rather poor light, hence improving the element of surprise. Small coral-dwelling crabs provide the major food source, but this is supplemented with marine worms, shrimps and the juveniles of numerous fish species. Little of the life history has been documented, but the main spawning season is known to be during summer.

CAPTURE

The redbarred rockcod is caught by ski- and line-boat anglers, sometimes in considerable numbers. In fact, it can sometimes be a nuisance, as its eager bait-snatching habits may prevent larger fish from reaching the tempting morsel. It is generally too small to interest spearfishermen. It makes good eating and is an important food resource in some parts of the world.

SA angling record – 0,8 kg.

SA spearfishing record – vacant.

SPECIFIC CATCH RESTRICTIONS

None.

NAME DERIVATION

Epinephelus, 'clouded over', an allusion to the colour pattern of the type species; *fasciatus,* banded. Redbarred rockcod, a reference to its body markings, habitat and to its supposed resemblance to the codfishes of European waters.

SIMILAR SPECIES

The brightly coloured body with the black dorsal fin edges is most distinctive. The browback grouper *(E. retouti)* has a greyish dorsal fin border and is deeper bodied.

Epinephelus flavocaeruleus

(Lacepède, 1802)

Common names SA - yellowtail rockcod. Elsewhere - purple rockcod, blue and yellow cod [Smith 166□41]

IDENTIFYING FEATURES

COLOUR, SHAPE AND SIZE

This is one of the more squat and deep-bodied members of the family. The overall colour of young individuals is gun-metal black, providing a striking contrast to the buttercup yellow fins. The lips and forehead are also yellow and the pelvic fins are tipped with black. Living specimens may have numerous white spots or mottlings along the flukes. With increased size, however, the bright yellow fades and individuals exceeding 50 cm in length are either totally black or with greyish mottlings. The last patch of yellow to disappear is usually that on the upper lobe of the caudal fin. Can attain 90 cm.

EXTERNAL ANATOMY

The lateral line is visible in this species, and fine scales are arranged in 130-150 series along its length. The well-developed fins are spiny, and include a single dorsal of 11 spines plus 15-17 rays, an anal of three spines plus eight rays, and a square caudal. Several bands of fine, backward-folding teeth occur in each jaw. There are 20-25 stubby rakers on the first gill arch.

Note: Dissection reveals a large, tough swim bladder.

NATURAL HISTORY

This widespread species is common on most coral and rocky reefs throughout the Indo-Pacific region. Adults are solitary, and most frequently found around deeper reefs, often to 150 m. Juveniles, however, occur around shallower reefs. The yellowtail rockcod's prey consists mainly of reef fish, which, in the typical hunting strategy of Serranidae, are ambushed and taken by surprise. Crabs, crayfish and squid are also eaten. Most prey is swallowed whole. Preliminary research suggests that this fish is most active at night. The ratio of males to females is 1:6, probably as a result of the sex reversal that occurs in most, if not all, Serranidae. First indications of sexual maturity occur at a length of 35 cm, and spawning has been recorded off East Africa during summer. It is probable that breeding occurs in many other areas throughout its range.

DISTRIBUTION

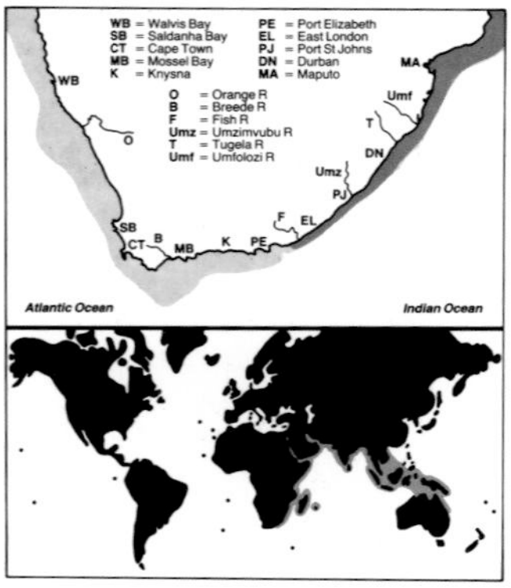

CAPTURE

Because of its solitary habits, large hauls of this fish are seldom made. It is, however, regularly caught by ski-boat anglers. A variety of baits is usually successful. The yellowtail rockcod generally lives too deep for spearfishermen. It is an excellent table fish.

SA angling record – 16,3 kg.

SA spearfishing record – 19,6 kg.

SPECIFIC CATCH RESTRICTIONS

None.

NAME DERIVATION

Epinephelus, 'clouded over', an allusion to the colour pattern of the type species; *flavocaeruleus,* yellow and blue. Yellowtail rockcod, an obvious reference to the brightly coloured caudal fin, as well as to its habitat and supposed similarity to the codfishes of European waters.

SIMILAR SPECIES

While the combination of bright yellow and blue in young fish is highly distinctive, the older fish that have lost these patterns are more difficult to identify. Confusion may arise with the white-spotted rockcod *(E. multinotatus),* which has a less deeply incised membrane between the dorsal spines.

Epinephelus guaza

(Linnaeus, 1758)

Common names SA – yellowbelly rockcod. Elsewhere – dusky perch [Smith 166□43]

IDENTIFYING FEATURES

COLOUR, SHAPE AND SIZE

One of the larger members of the rockcod family, this fish has a robust, elongate and moderately compressed body. It is deep brown overall, but with irregular, lighter blotches on the back and sides. The belly and chin are yellow, and the fins may be edged in yellow or orange. Can attain 150 cm.

EXTERNAL ANATOMY

Some 106-123 series of small scales are arranged along the lateral line. Spines are prominent in the fins, which include a single dorsal of 11 spines plus 14-16 rays, an anal of three spines plus eight rays, and a rounded caudal. The large mouth bears several rows of fine, backward-folding teeth in addition to a number of enlarged canines. The first gill arch carries 20-25 short, spiky rakers.

DISTRIBUTION

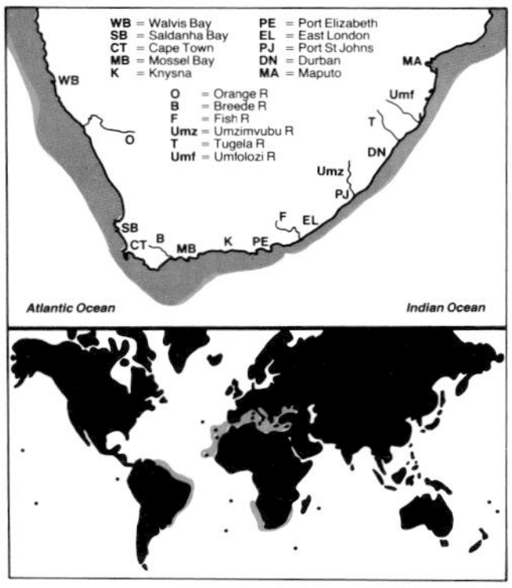

NATURAL HISTORY

This common inhabitant of rocky shores and reefs also ranges to depths of 200 m. It rarely ventures into estuaries. The yellowbelly rockcod is one of the few Atlantic members of this family to have 'rounded' the Cape and extended its distribution into the Indian Ocean. Some have even been recorded in the Red Sea, after negotiating the Suez Canal from the Mediterranean Sea. This rather sluggish fish uses the ambush tactics typical of Serranidae to capture its prey, which includes bottom-living fish and crustaceans. Crayfish are particularly favoured and are swallowed whole; the strong acid secretions of the gut serve to soften the hard exoskeletons of these crustaceans and to make digestion possible. Sexual maturity is attained at a length of 50-60 cm, and spawning has been recorded during winter, a time that coincides with its period of greatest abundance. Courtship displays precede spawning, and may involve a group of as many as ten fish. Juveniles make extensive use of intertidal rock pools as nursery areas, and, though adults are usually solitary, large caves may be inhabited by more than one fish. Tapeworm parasites occur in the body cavity, but these are harmless to man.

CAPTURE

The yellowbelly rockcod is a popular angling fish for ski-boat and shore anglers alike, as it freely takes fish bait. It is also much sought after by spearfishermen. It is a tough, aggressive fish and will survive for many hours out of water. The flesh of this rockcod is superb. Over-exploitation by spearfishermen and anglers has resulted in seriously depleted stocks of this fish in the Mediterranean Sea. Consequently, its protected status is necessary.

World angling record – 5,3 kg.
SA angling record – 26,7 kg.
SA spearfishing record – 9,6 kg.

SPECIFIC CATCH RESTRICTIONS

Protected species; minimum legal size is 30 cm total length.

NAME DERIVATION

Epinephelus, 'clouded over' an allusion to the colour pattern of the type species; *guaza,* from the Spanish *guasa,* a common Mediterranean name for this fish. Yellowbelly rockcod, a reference to its striking underside, as well as to its habitat and supposed resemblance to the codfishes of European waters.

SIMILAR SPECIES

The deeply incised dorsal fin membrane, amber-yellow belly, and slightly rounded tail fin are important diagnostic features which will distinguish this from all other rockcod in the region.

Epinephelus lanceolatus

(Bloch, 1790)

Common names SA – brindle bass, garrupa. Elsewhere – mottled-brown seabass, jewfish [Smith 166□45]

IDENTIFYING FEATURES

COLOUR, SHAPE AND SIZE

The overall colour of this very large, robust member of the rockcod family varies according to size. Brindle bass less than 90 cm in length are mottled grey, black and yellow as shown here. Juveniles less than 10 cm long are a more contrasting yellow and black. Larger fish tend to be uniformly dark brown, especially after death. In all specimens, however, the pectoral and pelvic fins tend to be lemon yellow, with darker spots and band-like markings. Attains 270 cm in length.

EXTERNAL ANATOMY

The body is covered with thick scales arranged in 89-110 series. The single dorsal fin has 11 spines plus 14-16 rays, while the anal has three spines plus eight rays. The caudal fin is large and rounded. The huge mouth bears numerous bands of fine, pointed teeth, two pairs of which are enlarged into canines. There are 18-25 short, spiky rakers on the first gill arch.

DISTRIBUTION

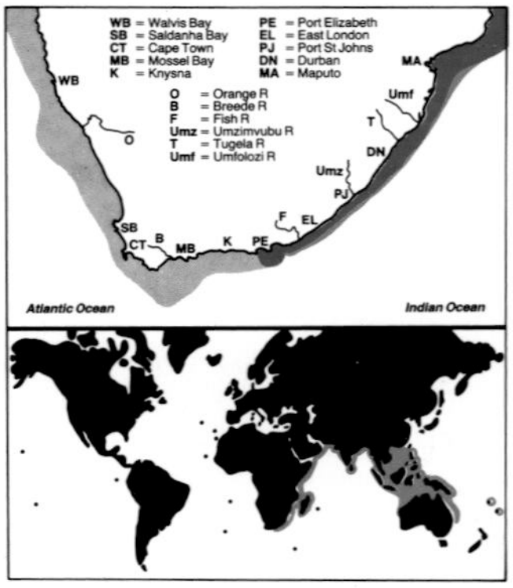

NATURAL HISTORY

The brindle bass is the largest member of the Serranidae, and it is certainly one of the biggest bony fish in the sea. It is usually solitary, but at times it may be more gregarious, when it congregates into small groups. The brindle bass shows a distinct preference for large caves in rocky and coral reefs, and, while some individuals occur in shallow water, others range to depths of 100 m. This species is also encountered in harbours and deep estuaries. It is a dominant predator on subtropical reefs, where it feeds on numerous species of fish, as well as on small sharks. Skates are also favoured, while brindle bass living in estuaries feed extensively on the large mangrove crab, *Scylla serrata.* Unfortunately, these great fish have become less common in shallow water, probably as a result of over-fishing. Susceptibility to pressure of this nature may well be a result of its slow growth rate and strong territorial instincts, which tend to reduce the number of individual bass that can be accommodated on any particular reef. There are encouraging signs, however, that conservation legislation and the newly established marine reserves have already improved this situation. The length at which sexual maturity is attained has not yet been determined, but it is known that spawning occurs during summer following courtship displays. Juveniles have been recorded from estuaries and the shallow, intertidal zone. Brindle bass are very approachable, but this strongly territorial fish is potentially dangerous to man, and has been known to attack divers and shipwreck survivors. The giant specimens in Durban's Seaworld dominate the larger shark inmates of their tank. Brindle bass are frequently accompanied by suckerfish.

CAPTURE

This fish can be caught from wharfs or ski-boats, using either live fish or crab bait. However, in view of its inshore depletion, it is recommended that this species should not be actively pursued. It was once a prime target species for divers, but at the instigation of these spearfishermen it is now on the restricted list and enjoys justified protection. The flesh is of a reasonable quality.

SA angling record – 212,7 kg.

Former SA spearfishing record – 245,2 kg.

SPECIFIC CATCH RESTRICTIONS

In Natal, spearfishing is illegal and for anglers, the minimum legal size is 30 cm total length.

NAME DERIVATION

Epinephelus, 'clouded over' an allusion to the colour pattern of the type species; *lanceolatus,* lance-shaped. Brindle bass, from its streaked markings and similar shape to the freshwater bass.

Epinephelus malabaricus

(Schneider, 1801)
Common name Worldwide – Malabar rockcod
[Smith 166□48]

IDENTIFYING FEATURES

COLOUR, SHAPE AND SIZE
This large rockcod is elongate, robust and moderately compressed. Its overall brown or olive body is irregularly marked with darker bands and blotches, as well as numerous rust-coloured spots. These markings are rather variable, however, a phenomenon which may be related to the Malabar rockcod's geographic distribution. Can attain 100 cm.

EXTERNAL ANATOMY
The body is well covered with scales arranged in 98-114 series along the lateral line. Spines are prominent in the fins which include a single dorsal of 11 spines plus 14-16 rays, an anal of three spines plus eight rays, and a rounded caudal. The mouth is large and bears numerous rows of fine, backward-folding teeth, as well as several canines. Many spiky 'teeth' also occur on the inner gill arches. There are 24-27 short rakers on the first gill arch.

NATURAL HISTORY

This strongly territorial and solitary rockcod is a common inhabitant of rocky shores and deeper reefs, ranging down to 60 m. Its mottled colours provide an effective camouflage in the shadows beneath rocky ledges or inside caves. Smaller specimens venture into estuaries, but are not tolerant of excessive salinity changes.
The diet of the Malabar rockcod consists mainly of fish, most of which are ambushed in the characteristic style of the members of this family. Crayfish and crabs are also an important source of food. Most feeding takes place during the day. Sexual maturity is attained at a length of 70-80 cm, and spawning has been recorded from August to October.

DISTRIBUTION

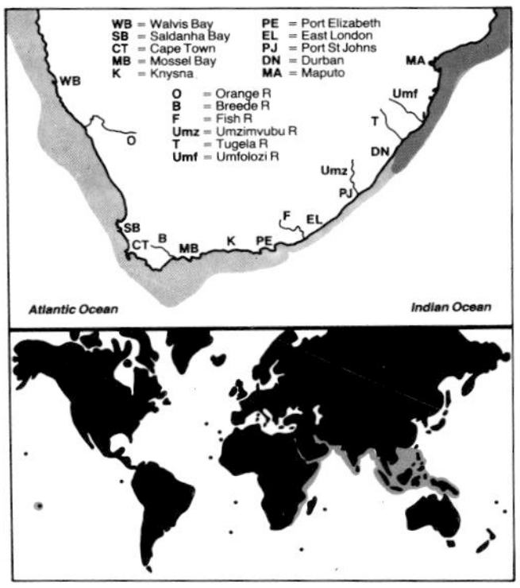

CAPTURE

The Malabar rockcod is caught by both ski-boat and shore anglers, and is also frequently bagged by spearfishermen. It will take a variety of fish baits, and whole crab and crayfish are also effective. This fish is guaranteed to provide the fisherman with a good struggle. If not too large, it is also of excellent eating quality.
SA angling record – 5,9 kg.
SA spearfishing record – 10,4 kg.

SPECIFIC CATCH RESTRICTIONS

None.

NAME DERIVATION

Epinephelus, 'clouded over', an allusion to the colour pattern of the type species; *malabaricus,* a reference to Malabar, a town in India. Malabar rockcod, a reference to the scientific name as well as to its habitat and supposed resemblance to the codfishes of European waters.

SIMILAR SPECIES

This species is often mistaken for the catface rockcod (*E. andersoni*), though it lacks the cat-like stripes across the face. Many have also been confused with the greasy rockcod *(E. tauvina),* a less common species. As a result, many of the records, and some published scientific information, while applicable to *E. tauvina,* may not be appropriate for *E. malabaricus.* The Malabar rockcod usually has three noticeably larger spots located on the interopercle that will distinguish it from other rockcods.

Epinephelus rivulatus

(Valenciennes, 1830)
Common name Worldwide – halfmoon rockcod
[Smith 166□60]

IDENTIFYING FEATURES

COLOUR, SHAPE AND SIZE

The general body colours of this rather small, elongate and moderately compressed rockcod include reds, browns and orange. The patterns formed by these colours vary considerably. Standard for all specimens, however, are about six broad bars on the flanks, and the semi-circular red mark on each of the pectoral fins. Because of the widely differing colours and markings displayed by the members of this species, there has been confusion about the correct classification and distribution of the halfmoon rockcod. As a result of this, this species has been described as *E. grammatophorus* and *E. rhyncolepis.* All three names are synonyms. Can attain 40 cm.

EXTERNAL ANATOMY

Some 86-102 series of scales can be counted along the lateral line. The fins are spiny and include a single dorsal of 11 spines plus 16-18 rays, an anal of three spines plus seven or eight rays and a slightly rounded caudal. The mouth is large and bears several rows of short, but sharp teeth. There are 16-18 short, spiky rakers on the first gill arch.

Note: Dissection reveals a large, tough swim bladder.

NATURAL HISTORY

The halfmoon rockcod is surely one of the most abundant of the Serranidae occurring off the East Coast of southern Africa. Either singly or in small groups, it frequents flat-topped, rocky reefs as deep as 80 m. It is rarely found near the shore. Crabs, shrimps and small fish are the main items of its diet. This fish will also occasionally tackle prey much larger than it is able to swallow whole. Such victims are gripped tightly in the powerful jaws before the meal is progressively swallowed and digested. Little of its reproductive biology has been documented though spawning fish have been recorded along Natal.

DISTRIBUTION

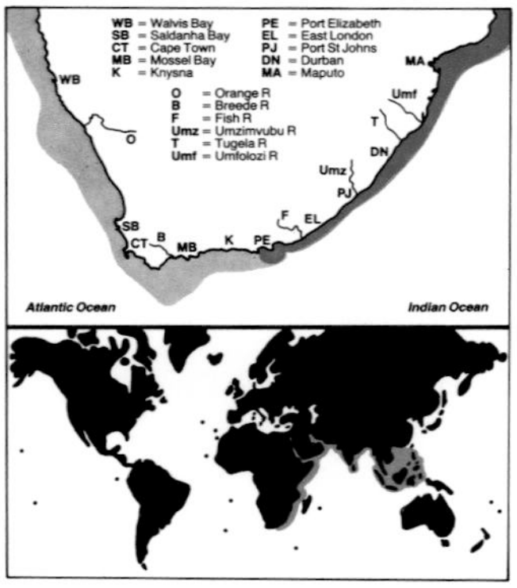

CAPTURE

The halfmoon rockcod is cursed by ski-boat anglers, as it invariably reaches the bait first, thus spoiling the fisherman's chance of hooking a more worthy opponent. Despite being small, it is of good eating quality.

SA angling record – 1,6 kg.

SA spearfishing record – vacant.

NAME DERIVATION

Epinephelus, 'clouded over', an allusion to the colour pattern of the type species; *rivulatus,* marked with rill-like streaks. Halfmoon rockcod, a reference to the distinctively marked pectoral fins as well as to its habitat and supposed resemblance to the codfishes of European waters.

SPECIFIC CATCH RESTRICTIONS

None.

SIMILAR SPECIES

No other rockcod has the reddish blotch at the pectoral fin base. Of further diagnostic value are the wavy bluish lines on the head, and triangular black blotches on the membrane behind each dorsal spine.

Epinephelus tukula

Morgans, 1959

Common name Worldwide – potato bass

[Smith 166□66]

IDENTIFYING FEATURES

COLOUR, SHAPE AND SIZE

The large potato bass is elongate and very robust. Its light-brown body is marked with a number of large, dark-brown spots. Smaller spots also occur on the head and fins. Large specimens are dark brown overall, especially after death. Attains 200 cm.

EXTERNAL ANATOMY

The body is well covered with scales arranged in 117-135 series. Spines are prominent in the fins, which include a single dorsal of 11 spines plus 15 rays, an anal of three spines plus 7-9 rays, and a large, rounded caudal. The jaws of the huge mouth bear several rows of backward-folding teeth, as well as a number of canines. The lower jaw projects increasingly with age. The first gill arch carries 19-23 short, spiky rakers.

DISTRIBUTION

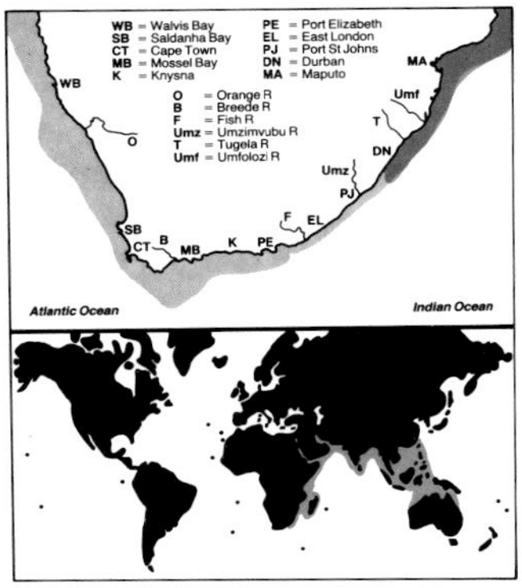

NATURAL HISTORY

The potato bass is exceedingly territorial, and is very aggressive towards unwelcome intruders. Coupled with this behaviour, the great power of this fish makes it one of the most dominant predators inhabiting rocky and coral reefs. Its diet comprises a wide variety of reef fish, most of which are surprised in 'ambush', and snatched after a short chase. Skates, crabs and crayfish are also eaten. It is an inquisitive fish, and can be a nuisance to divers, as it 'cheekily' tampers with their gear or catches. Little is known of its life history, though spawning has been recorded during spring and summer. Sexual maturity is attained at 90 cm, and catch statistics show a predominance of females. Most adults are solitary, though pairing occurs during the breeding season and involves courtship displays, during which the colours of the participating fish usually lighten.

CAPTURE

This fish may be found in very shallow water, which, together with its inquisitive nature, has made it vulnerable to over-exploitation, especially by spearfishermen. For this reason the potato bass, once a trophy for divers, is now protected by law. It is still caught by anglers, and many large specimens have been hooked to depths of 150 m. It will take a variety of large fish and crayfish baits, and puts up a good fight. If able to retreat into a cave, it is extremely difficult to land. The species has responded well to the proclamation of marine reserves; tagging studies conducted by the Oceanographic Research Institute provide confirmation of this.Compared with the excellent flesh of other Serranidae, this species is only of moderate eating value.

SA angling record – 58,0 kg.

SPECIFIC CATCH RESTRICTIONS

In Natal, spearfishing is illegal.

NAME DERIVATION

Epinephelus, 'clouded over' – an allusion to the colour of the type species; *tukula,* Malgash for 'maneater', a reference to the alleged ferocity of this fish. Potato bass, a reference to its potato-like spots and typical, bass-shaped body.

SIMILAR SPECIES

Small and medium-sized potato bass are easily recognized by their large, brown blotches. Larger fish may resemble the brindle bass, but can be recognized by differences in their scale count.

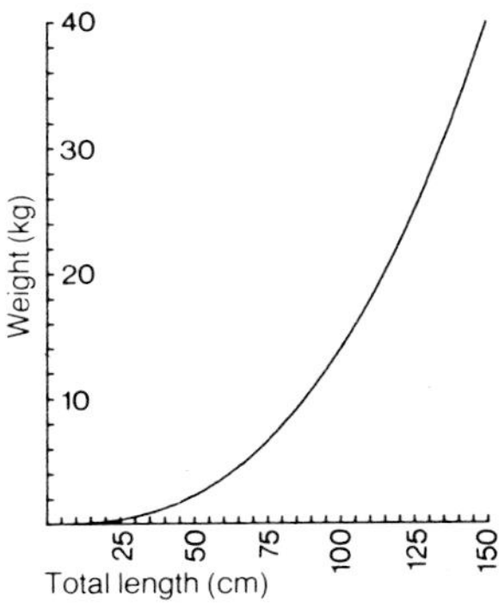

Variola louti

(Forsskål, 1775)
Common names SA – swallowtail rockcod, lyretail. Elsewhere – moontail seabass
[Smith 166□75]

IDENTIFYING FEATURES

COLOUR, SHAPE AND SIZE
This large, oblong rockcod cannot be mistaken for any other species. Its overall body colour is bright red, and it is usually marked with numerous small, iridescent, blue or purple blotches. The fins are also blue-spotted, but those of smaller specimens may have yellow hind margins. There is, however, some variability in the markings and colour, a phenomenon possibly associated with sex. Attains 80 cm.
EXTERNAL ANATOMY
The body is well covered with small, tough scales arranged in 113-135 series along the lateral line. Spines are prominent in the fins, which include a dorsal of nine spines plus 13-15 rays, and an anal of three spines plus eight rays. The deeply lunate caudal fin is most distinctive. The soft dorsal, anal and pectoral fins are elongate and pointed. The large mouth bears many rows of villiform teeth in the jaws and on the palate. Several large canines also occur. There are 20-30 short rakers on the first arch, including a number of rudimentary knobs.
Note: Dissection will reveal a large, tough swim bladder.

NATURAL HISTORY

The swallowtail rockcod is a widely distributed inhabitant of coral and, sometimes, rocky reefs. It shows a great preference for caves and gullies. Though generally confined to shallow reefs, this fish has also been recorded at depths of 100 m. It is common in the St Lucia Marine Reserve, and is most abundant in southern African waters during the summer months. This powerful predator of reef fish hunts during the day along rocky ledges. It is particularly fond of prey such as soldier-, squirrel- and cardinalfishes, while crabs are also occasionally eaten. The life history of this species still requires research, but specimens in a 'ripe' breeding condition have been recorded from November to January, especially off the Kenyan coast. No doubt, however, spawning occurs throughout its range.

DISTRIBUTION

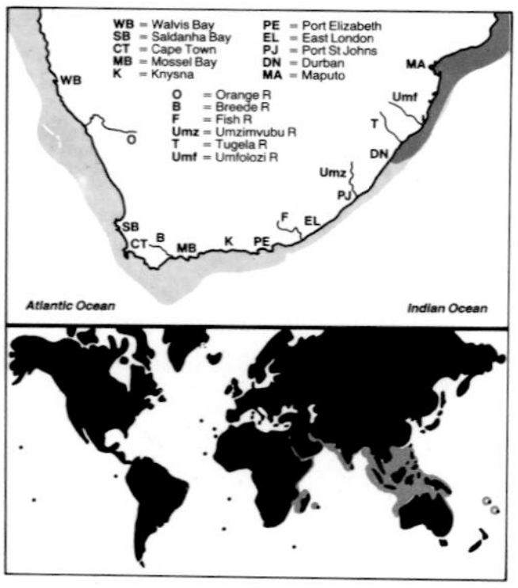

SPECIFIC CATCH RESTRICTIONS

None.

CAPTURE

The swallowtail rockcod is frequently caught by ski-boat anglers, line-boat operators and spearfishermen. It is a fine sport fish of excellent eating value. In the East, it is caught in fish traps and on hand lines for local, fresh-fish markets.
SA angling record – vacant.
SA spearfishing record – 5,0 kg.

NAME DERIVATION

Variola, smallpox, a reference to the spotted body; *louti,* arch or bow-shaped. Swallowtail rockcod, a reference to the deep 'V' of the tail, its habitat and its alleged resemblance to the codfishes of European waters.

SIMILAR SPECIES

The very deeply forked tail fin is the most characteristic feature of swallowtail rockcods. Technically, this species is known as the yellow-edged swallowtail because of the noticeable yellow border to the rear fins. The closely related white-edged swallowtail has yet to be found in the South African region, but can be distinguished by the white rear margin of the tail fin.

Siganus sutor

(Valenciennes, 1835)
Common names SA – whitespotted rabbitfish. Elsewhere – whitespotted spinefoot, shoemaker spinefoot
[Smith 245□2]

IDENTIFYING FEATURES

COLOUR, SHAPE AND SIZE
This oval-bodied, strongly compressed fish varies considerably in colour and pattern. Most specimens reveal some 30 distinct white spots on each side, though these may disappear when the fish is stressed. When viewed underwater, this fish may lack any markings and be uniformly olive-brown overall. After capture, however, black, brown and even purple patterns may appear. Can attain 40 cm.

EXTERNAL ANATOMY
Minute scales cover the body, but these are deeply embedded and scarcely visible. The mucus-covered skin is smooth to the touch. The lateral line is clearly visible and smoothly curved . The single dorsal fin has one foward-pointing spine which precedes 13 further spines plus ten rays. The anal fin comprises seven spines plus nine rays, and the caudal is slightly emarginate. A row of tiny incisors occurs in both jaws of the small, terminal mouth. The gill openings are rather small, and the lower part of the first gill arch bears 18 rakers.

NATURAL HISTORY

A shoaling fish of shallow, tropical waters, the whitespotted rabbitfish is equally at home in estuaries, and is fairly common off the Natal coast during summer. As with all rabbitfishes, the members of this species are browsers, and their vegetarian diet consists primarily of filamentous seaweeds and eelgrasses. During feeding, however, numerous small invertebrates clinging to these plants are also accidentally ingested. Juvenile whitespotted rabbitfish feed mainly on diatoms. Although plant matter is digested completely, the low calorie content of seaweed necessitates continual feeding.
Spawning occurs in tropical regions, but shoals of juveniles are known to migrate into southern African waters during summer. As the spines of rabbitfishes are very sharp, and coated with toxic mucus, these fishes should be handled with extreme care. Accidental jabs are painful, but respond rapidly to immersion in very hot water which breaks down the protein poison.

DISTRIBUTION

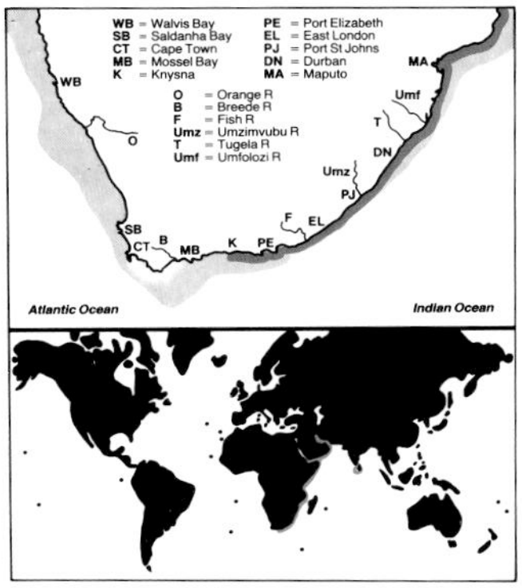

SPECIFIC CATCH RESTRICTIONS

None.

CAPTURE

The whitespotted rabbitfish has great potential in terms of aquaculture, and in the East, especially the Phillipines, it is 'farmed', often together with the milkfish, in brackish and saltwater ponds. In tropical regions, this fish is an important protein resource, and is caught in considerable numbers by commercial fishermen using trawl and seine nets, as well as fish traps. It is seldom caught by anglers in southern Africa, but, with light tackle and small bait, it may be landed. The flaky, white flesh is excellent. This fish is seldom speared by divers.
SA spearfishing record – 2,8 kg.

NAME DERIVATION

Siganus, mute or silent; *sutor,* sewer or cobbler. Whitespotted rabbitfish, an obvious reference to its body markings and to its supposed similarity, possibly in terms of its vegetarian feeding habits, to rabbits.

SIMILAR SPECIES

The only other rabbitfish species found in the region is *S. stellatus,* which has a deeply forked tail, and numerous dark spots on the body. The whitespotted rabbitfish lacks these, and is the only *Siganus* with white spots.

Sillago sihama

(Forsskål, 1775)
Common names SA – silver sillago, smelt. Elsewhere – silver sillago, whiting (Australia)
[Smith 198□3]

IDENTIFYING FEATURES

COLOUR, SHAPE AND SIZE

This elongate, almost cylindrical fish tapers from the mid-body region towards both the head and the tail, and has a long, conical snout. It is sandy brown overall, but with silvery sides, a white underside, and spotted, dusky dorsal and caudal fins. The silver sillago is capable of considerable colour changes, usually to blend with the colour of the sea-bed over which it is moving. Can attain 30 cm in length.

EXTERNAL ANATOMY

Scales cover the firm body and are arranged in 62-73 series along the length of the lateral line. The fins are well developed, and include a double dorsal; the first of 11 weak spines, and the second of one spine plus 20-23 rays; an anal of two spines plus 21-24 rays; and a caudal fin that is almost truncate or square-edged. Rows of fine, villiform teeth occur in both jaws and on the palate of the small mouth. Some 11 rakers, plus several rudimentary rakers, are located on the first gill arch. A short, sharp spine projects from each of the gill covers.

DISTRIBUTION

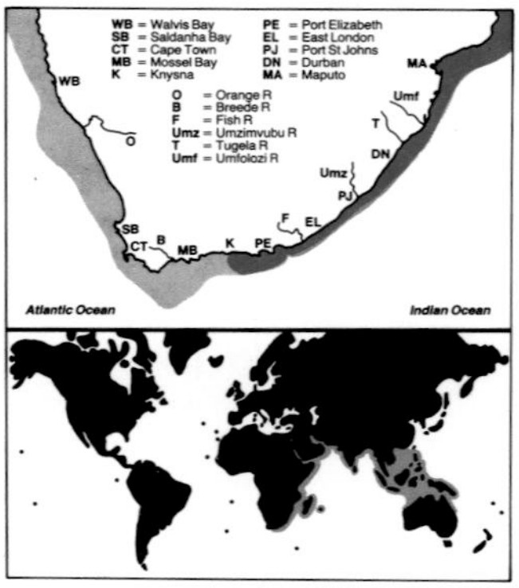

NATURAL HISTORY

The silver sillago is a shallow-water fish which frequents sandy bays and estuaries. It is known to be tolerant of moderate reductions in salinity. Juveniles feed on planktonic copepods, but, with growth, the diet alters to include increasing amounts of bottom-living invertebrates. The adult diet consists mostly of marine worms, shrimps, mud-prawns and small crabs, all of which are rooted from the muddy sea-bed by the long snout. This wide-ranging, shoaling species is common in southern African waters during summer, but spawning probably occurs further to the north, in the tropical waters of East Africa. Members of this family are timid, and, when threatened, are known to bury themselves in the sand until danger has passed. Such evasive tactics are apparently even employed when the passage of a dark cloud over the sun casts a shadow over the water. The Sillaginidae are not related to the true smelt and whitings of the northern hemisphere.

CAPTURE

Sillagos are occasionally caught by anglers using ultra-light tackle, but most are landed in seine nets. In Australia and the Far East, where the species' white flesh is highly regarded for its fine flavour and easy digestibility, it is an important food resource. It is an excellent bait for larger game fish.
SA angling record – 0,7 kg.

SPECIFIC CATCH RESTRICTIONS

None.

NAME DERIVATION

Sillago, silver; *sihama,* of unknown Arabic origin. Silver sillago, a reference to the body colour and scientific name.

SIMILAR SPECIES

Two other *Sillago* species found here are easily recognized. The clubfoot sillago *(S. chrondropus)* has a noticeably thick and club-like first pelvic spine, while the blotchy sillago *(S. maculata)* has distinct black blotches on each flank.

Austroglossus pectoralis

(Kaup, 1858)
Common name east coast sole
[Smith 262□3]

IDENTIFYING FEATURES

COLOUR, SHAPE AND SIZE
The right side of this moderately elongate flatfish is uniformly dark brown, with no distinctive markings. The blind, or left side, however, lacks pigmentation, and is almost white. The fins are noticeably darker than the body. Can attain 60 cm in length.

EXTERNAL ANATOMY
Small, ctenoid scales cover the body, making it rough to the touch. These are arranged in 140-180 series. Both eyes occur on the right side of the body. As with all Soleidae, pelvic fins are lacking, but the pectorals are well developed, with the right fin being the longer. The dorsal and anal fins join with the caudal to form a single, continuous fin, which comprises about 100 dorsal and 90 anal rays. The asymmetric mouth is quite large, and a single row of fine teeth is set in each jaw. A single lateral line is conspicuous along the 'eyed' side of the body.

DISTRIBUTION

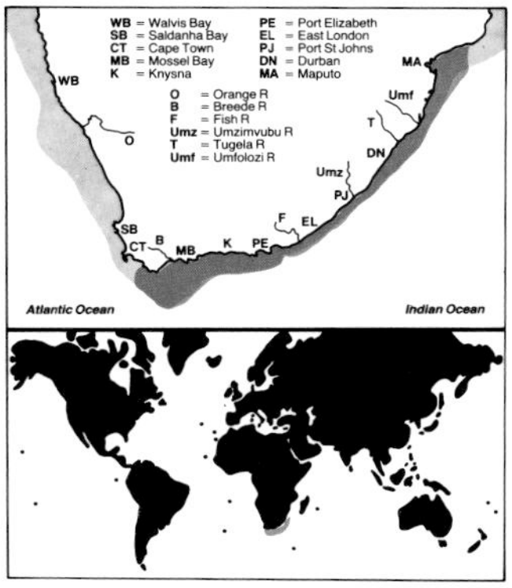

NATURAL HISTORY

This sole is restricted to areas where the sea-bed is muddy, usually between depths of ten and 100 m. It is particularly common on the Agulhas Banks. Here it feeds, often in turbid water, on small bottom-living organisms such as polychaete worms, small crabs, and many other small invertebrates. Spawning occurs on the Agulhas Banks. Males attain sexual maturity at a considerably smaller size than females; 18 cm for males as opposed to 33 cm for females - a growth difference of two years. Females also grow considerably larger, and whereas a 400 g male is considered big, some female specimens exceed 1 kg. The earstones of the east coast sole show distinctive patterns of annual growth, and have been successfully used to determine age rather in the manner of reading tree rings.

SPECIFIC CATCH RESTRICTIONS

Commercial trawling is by permit and quota only.

CAPTURE

This is surely southern Africa's most popular sole, and forms the basis of a small but viable trawling fishery centred at Mossel Bay. Catches are highly variable, sometimes 1000 tonnes per annum. Regrettably, as with so many other species, catches of the related west coast sole have dwindled alarmingly in recent years, almost certainly as a result of over-fishing.

NAME DERIVATION

Austroglossus, southern tongue; *pectoralis,* a reference to the large, right pectoral fin. East coast sole, a reference to its range and from the Latin *solea* meaning sandal or sole of the foot.

SIMILAR SPECIES

The closely related and considerably larger west coast sole *(A. microlepis)* has a pectoral ray that is shorter than its head length. In the east coast sole the pectoral ray exceeds head length.

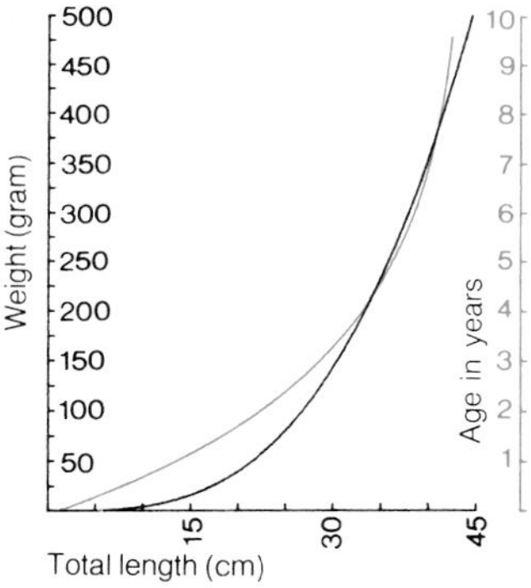

Solea bleekeri

Boulenger, 1898
Common name Worldwide – blackhand sole
[Smith 262□12]

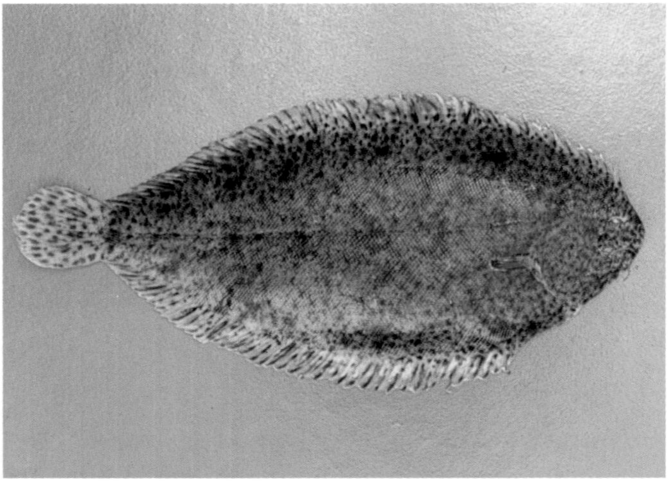

IDENTIFYING FEATURES

COLOUR, SHAPE AND SIZE
The general body colour of this oval, strongly compressed flatfish is brown, with numerous black spots and blotches which extend onto the fins. The 'blind' side is white. The pectoral fins are black.
Can attain 15 cm.

EXTERNAL ANATOMY
In common with many sole-like fish, this species has both eyes on the right side of the body. There are about 100 series of small, but distinct scales arranged along the lateral line. The dorsal fin of 60-75 rays originates on the head and extends to the tail region, but does not join with the rounded caudal to form a continuous fin. The anal fin is also separate and comprises 45-59 rays. The small, asymmetrical, inconspicuous mouth almost reaches the lower eye. The pectoral and pelvic fins are developed equally on both sides of the body. The straight lateral line has two branches on the head.

DISTRIBUTION

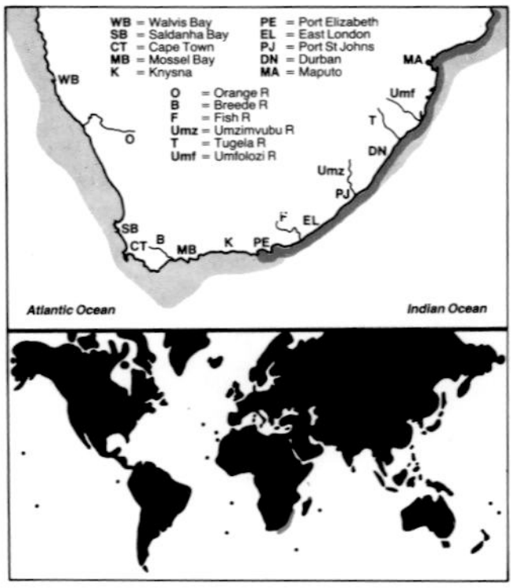

NATURAL HISTORY

This small, very common flatfish favours estuaries, and can tolerate low salinity conditions as well as muddy waters. Considerable numbers are also known to live on muddy offshore banks at St. Lucia, Richards Bay and Tugela. The blackhand sole is a bottom-dwelling fish, and, though its feeding preferences are not well known, all bottom-living invertebrates, such as minute crabs, gastropods, shrimps and marine worms, are consumed. The blackhand sole is a sluggish, resident species, and only moves from its position of muddy concealment if disturbed or to snatch at prey. Future viability of stocks, therefore, is probably greatly dependent on the state of estuarine environments. The status of the blackhand sole is important; it presently occurs in considerable numbers and is therefore, undoubtedly a significant food source for many of the larger predators which share the same habitat. Sexual maturity is attained at a length of 9-10 cm and, following a four month period of gonad maturation, spawning occurs within estuaries from June to August. Newly hatched juveniles are dispersed by ocean currents, but soon make their way back to estuaries.

CAPTURE

Although too small to be caught by anglers, this sole is very commonly landed in estuarine netting operations. Its flesh is palatable, but, owing to its small size, it is rarely of value as food. Nevertheless, some of the tribal people living along the East Coast of Africa catch this little fish for food using primitive netting gear, usually made out of hessian sacks. Some are also caught in offshore prawn trawling, but not marketed.

SPECIFIC CATCH RESTRICTIONS

None.

NAME DERIVATION

Solea, sandal or sole of the foot; *bleekeri,* named after the famous ichthyologist, Bleeker, who first noted this species. Blackhand sole, a reference to its black pectoral fins and scientific name.

SIMILAR SPECIES

The presence of two pectoral fins and a separate caudal fin serve to identify this genus. The related lemon sole *(S. fulvomarginata)* is also endemic to the region, and may be identified by its yellow-coloured median fins.

Acanthopagrus berda

(Forsskål, 1775)
Common names SA – river bream, perch. Elsewhere – black porgy
[Smith 183□1]

IDENTIFYING FEATURES

COLOUR, SHAPE AND SIZE
This deep-bodied fish has a fairly steep head profile and a pointed snout. It is normally silver-grey in colour, with a white underside, though this may be much darker in some specimens. Depending on its immediate environment, these colours may alter significantly, and, in some excessively muddy regions, the river bream is known to be completely black. This, understandably, often leads to confusion and misidentification. Attains 75 cm, but few exceed 30 cm in southern African waters.
EXTERNAL ANATOMY
Exceptionally well-developed spines dominate the dorsal and anal fins which consist of 11 spines plus 11 or 12 rays, and three spines plus eight or nine rays respectively. The pectoral and pelvic fins are also well developed, and the caudal fin is forked. There are 43-47 series of strong scales arranged along the distinct lateral line, but the bridge between the eyes is naked. The first gill arch has 5-8 feeble rakers.

NATURAL HISTORY

Because of its great tolerance to fluctuating salinities, the habitat of the river bream is virtually confined to estuaries and shallow brackish waters near river mouths. Some specimens have, in fact, been recorded in fresh water, often virtually isolated from the sea.
Its diet is wide, and includes polychaete worms, bivalve molluscs, sand dollars, crabs, shrimps and small fish.
Occasionally, this species also scavenges for dead or decaying organic matter. Sexual maturity is attained at a length of about 25 cm, and spawning takes place during winter. Eggs are shed at sea, but near estuaries, and, shortly after hatching, the juveniles return to these regions to develop. The spoiling of estuaries through siltation, pollution and infilling has reduced the extent of suitable habitat, thus seriously affecting the abundance of this species.

DISTRIBUTION

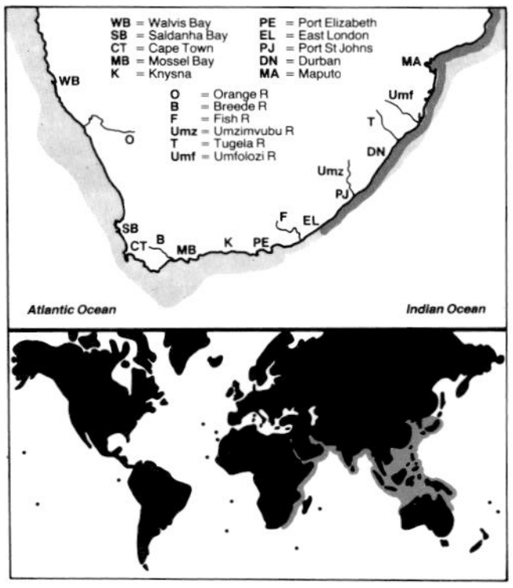

CAPTURE

Although not heavily exploited in southern Africa, the river bream is nevertheless a popular angling fish, and is also a fair source of protein in more tropical regions. Amongst the variety of baits that can be used, shrimps and marine worms are most successful, especially at St Lucia, which is regarded by many to be the best angling spot for this species.
SA angling record – 3,2 kg.

SPECIFIC CATCH RESTRICTIONS

In Natal, the minimum legal size is 15 cm fork length.

NAME DERIVATION

Acanthopagrus, literally, a thorned bream; *berda,* origin obscure. River bream, a reference to its predominant habitat, and from *breme,* an old French word for similar freshwater fishes.

SIMILAR SPECIES

The dusky colours, absence of yellow body marks, and exceptionally strong second anal spine are important diagnostic features.

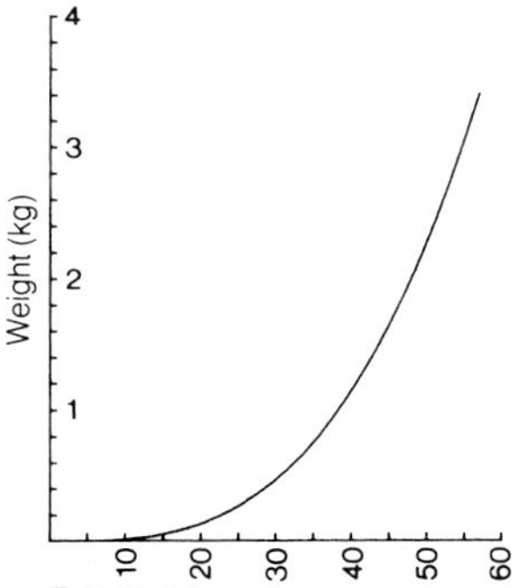

Argyrops filamentosus

(Valenciennes, 1830)
Common name soldierbream
[Smith 183□3]

IDENTIFYING FEATURES

COLOUR, SHAPE AND SIZE
This deep-bodied fish has a steep head profile which curves gently from the eyes to the dorsal fin, while the snout is usually straight, and a bulge may be present in front of the eyes - especially with age. The pinkish-red body often has an iridescent, bluish, silvery sheen. The upper surfaces are darker, the belly and chin are white, and most of the fins are pale pink in colour. Juveniles may have faint crossbars. Can attain 60 cm.

EXTERNAL ANATOMY
The well-developed fins with elongate dorsal spines are an important diagnostic feature of this and related species. In the soldierbream, the dorsal consists of 11 or 12 spines plus 8-10 rays. While the first two spines are very short, the third is abruptly elongate, distinctly longer than head length. This spine is shortened in adults, but remains longer than the head length. The fourth and fifth dorsal spines are also slightly elongate. The anal fin consists of three spines plus eight rays, the second spine usually being longer and stouter than the third. The caudal is forked. There are 50-54 series of large scales along the lateral line, and the area between the eyes is completely scaled, with a distinctly rounded ending. There are 16-17 rakers on the first gill arch. Two rows of molars and four enlarged canines are in each jaw.

NATURAL HISTORY

This is a common reef fish of the western Indian Ocean, usually occurring in small shoals at depths of 20-40 m. The soldierbream may occur directly over pinnacles, but is more frequently found at the flatter outer edges of reefs, where it feeds on small crabs, molluscs and a range of other hard-shelled invertebrates, which are crushed with the strong jaws. The breeding biology and possibility of sex reversal remain to be studied, though some spawning fish have been found off southern Moçambique. While immature soldierbream have been recorded, the whereabouts of the juveniles remains unknown.

DISTRIBUTION

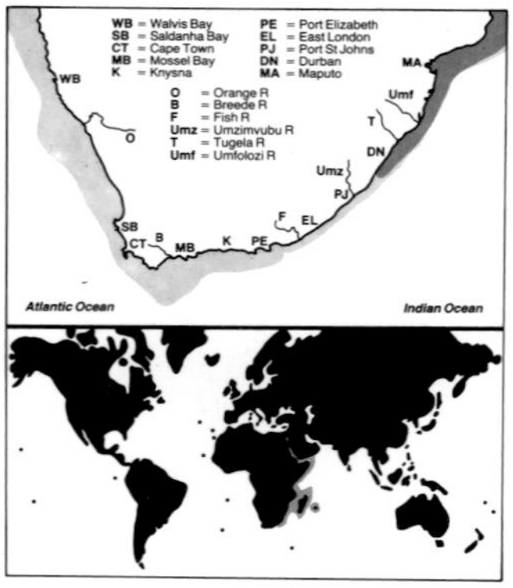

CAPTURE

Soldierbream make up a small but consistent proportion of the ski-boat linefish catch in Natal. Considerable numbers are also caught off Indian Ocean islands, often in the fish traps used there. It is an excellent food-fish, and represents a considerable protein resource in more tropical regions.
SA angling record - 7,5 kg.
SA spearfishing record - 4,8 kg.

SPECIFIC CATCH RESTRICTIONS

None.

NAME DERIVATION

Argyrops, silver eyed; *filamentosus,* filamentous. Soldierbream, a reference to spinous or 'armed' fins, and its relationship to the seabream family.

SIMILAR SPECIES

The abruptly elongate third dorsal spine should distinguish this species from other seabreams with elongate dorsal spines. Notice that this species lacks the forehead grooves of *Chrysoblephus lophus* and has a steeper head profile than *Cheimerius nufar.*

Chrysoblephus anglicus

Gilchrist & Thompson, 1908
Common name Worldwide – Englishman
[Smith 183□8]

IDENTIFYING FEATURES

COLOUR, SHAPE AND SIZE

This deep-bodied, fairly robust fish has an almost vertical head profile, with a slightly concave snout. It is rosy-pink overall, with six to eight darker-red crossbars on the sides of the body. Each scale on the upper flanks is marked with a single blue spot, and this lends an overall bluish sheen to freshly caught specimens. All the fins are distinctly pink. Attains 80 cm.

EXTERNAL ANATOMY

There are 65-68 series of scales arranged along the lateral line, but the area on the forehead between the eyes and in the region of the mouth is naked. The fins are well developed, and include a single dorsal of 12 spines plus ten rays, an anal of three spines plus eight rays, and a moderately forked caudal. The third to fifth dorsal spines are noticeably elongate. The relatively small mouth has outer canines and several rows of molars within. There are 17 or 18 rakers on the first gill arch.

DISTRIBUTION

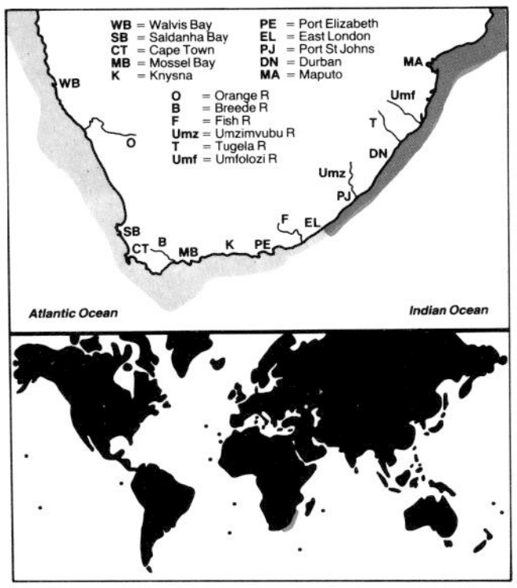

NATURAL HISTORY

The Englishman frequents offshore waters ranging between depths of 20 and 100 m. Within this environment it may occur singly or in small groups, often in association with slinger (*C. puniceus*). It feeds on crabs, hermit crabs, shrimps, bivalve molluscs, squid and sometimes other small fish. Sexual maturity is attained at a length of approximately 40 cm. Information on breeding is sparse. Studies at the Oceanographic Research Institute suggest hermaphroditism but not sex reversal. It is known that spawning occurs during spring, however further study is needed.

CAPTURE

This highly palatable line fish freely takes flesh baits, and, though never caught from the shore, the Englishman is a firm favourite with commercial and ski-boat anglers. Good, steady catches are made throughout the year, despite seasonal fluctuations in adundance. The deep-water habitat of this species puts it beyond the range of shore anglers, and, with few exceptions, also of spearfishermen.

SA angling record – 6,6 kg.
SA spearfishing record – 6,0 kg.

NAME DERIVATION

Chrysoblephus, golden eyed; *anglicus,* English. Englishman, a reference to its solemn looks and ruddy complexion, allegedly reminiscent of the archetype Englishman, John Bull.

SPECIFIC CATCH RESTRICTIONS

Protected species; minimum legal size is 25 cm.

SIMILAR SPECIES

The Englishman can easily be distinguished from similar-looking, reddish fish by its vertical forehead, absence of blue or black body marks, and moderately long third to fifth dorsal spines. These spines are, however, not as long as those of the false Englishman (*C. lophus*), and the soldierbream (*A. spinifer*).

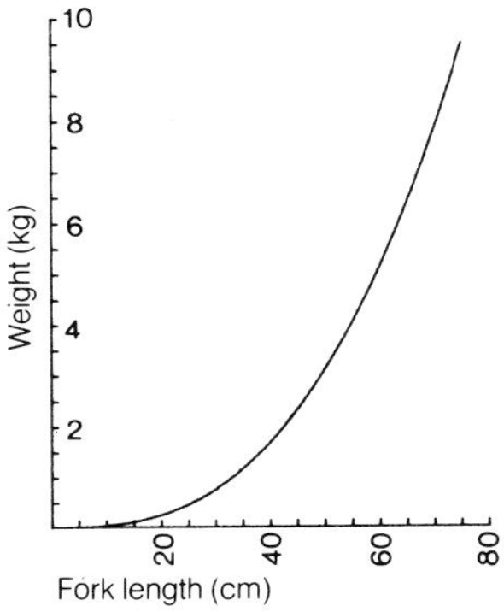

Chrysoblephus cristiceps

(Valenciennes, 1830)
Common name – dageraad
[Smith 183□9]

IDENTIFYING FEATURES

COLOUR, SHAPE AND SIZE

The dageraad's body is noticeably deep, the snout pointed, and the steep forehead slightly concave above the eyes. It is pinkish-red overall, but live fish are a much brighter red, with iridescent shades of gold, orange and blue. While both this species and the slinger have a short blue line below each eye, the dageraad also has a characteristic black spot where the soft dorsal fin joins the caudal peduncle. The fins are translucent to dusky pink. Juveniles of less than 10 cm do not resemble adults in their colouration, being more pink and having more extensive black body markings. Can attain 70 cm, but fish ranging between 30 and 40 cm are more common.

EXTERNAL ANATOMY

The body is well covered with scales arranged in 59-61 series along the lateral line. The forehead below the eyes is naked. The fins are well developed and include a single dorsal of 12 spines plus ten rays; an anal of three spines plus eight rays; pectorals that reach a point just beyond the origin of the anal fin; and a broad, slightly forked caudal. Enlarged canines and at least three rows of molars occur in both jaws of the moderately large, terminal mouth. There are about 12 short rakers on the lower section of the first gill arch.

NATURAL HISTORY

This shoaling reef species occupies a habitat in Cape waters similar to that of the slinger in Natal – it shows a preference for flat reefs and generally ranges between depths of 20 and 100 m. It appears to be most abundant during summer. The dageraad's diet is known to include small crabs, tube worms, squid and small fish, most of which are eaten in the early morning. Later in the day, once shoals have ceased feeding, they remain above the reef, but move more towards the surface. The spawning cycle of this species is unknown. Research at the Port Elizabeth museum has indicated sex reversal at about 43 cm, while maturity is first attained at 32 cm (fork length). Spawning is most intense during summer.

DISTRIBUTION

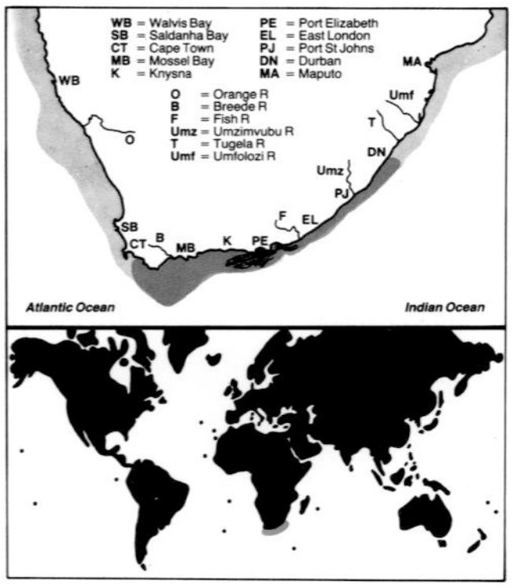

CAPTURE

Ski- and line-boat fishermen pursue this excellent table fish for the fine sport that it offers, as well as for its commercial value. It is easily hooked, especially in the morning and takes a variety of baits. It is also speared by more experienced divers.
SA angling record – 8,7 kg.
SA spearfishing record – 6,4 kg.

SPECIFIC CATCH RESTRICTIONS

Protected species; minimum legal size is 25 cm.

NAME DERIVATION

Chrysoblephus, golden eyed; *cristiceps,* crested head. Dageraad, a corruption of *dagrood,* a Dutch word meaning 'red rising sun', a reference to this fish's body colouration.

SIMILAR SPECIES

Despite its resemblance to several other seabreams, the dageraad can be immediately identified by the black spot at the base of the last dorsal rays.

Chrysoblephus gibbiceps

(Valenciennes, 1830)

Common names red stumpnose
Though it is recommended that only one common name should apply to a species to avoid unnecessary confusion, it is appropriate in this instance to record the numerous other names by which the red stumpnose is known to local fishermen along the South African coast: Miss Lucy (Port Elizabeth), Mighel (Knysna), bonte dageraad or magistraat (Struisbaai), and rooi-witkop (Hermanus).
[Smith 183□10]

IDENTIFYING FEATURES

COLOUR, SHAPE AND SIZE

The red stumpnose is noticeably deep-bodied, and has a very steep forehead that is slightly concave below the eyes. The snout is somewhat pointed. In large male fish, the upper forehead develops a bulbous projection which becomes increasingly spongy and pitted with age. The body is silvery-pink overall, but darker above. Some 5-7 darker-red, vertical bars occur on the sides. There are also numerous dark blotches on the body, especially the upper flanks. Can attain 60 cm.

EXTERNAL ANATOMY

The lateral line is clearly defined, and along it lie 51-55 series of fairly large scales. Small scales also extend forward onto the cheeks. The fins are well developed, and include a single dorsal of 11-12 spines plus 10-11 rays, an anal of three spines plus eight rays, and a strongly forked caudal. The pectoral fins are long and reach well past the vent. The mouth is not large, but the jaws extend to a point below the eyes. Each jaw bears four or five rows of molars, as well as an outer row of canines. The first gill arch carries 14-16 rakers.

NATURAL HISTORY

This beautiful fish occurs throughout the year, but is especially abundant from February to October. It is a solitary species, and individuals frequent offshore reefs to depths of 150 m. It is particularly well known in the Agulhas Bank region. The strong molars are well suited to crushing the hard-shelled organisms in its diet. These include gastropod molluscs, polychaete worms, redbait, sea urchins, octopuses, small fish and crabs, which are systematically dismembered leg by leg if too large to be taken whole. Despite its abundance, surprisingly little information has been published about the red stumpnose's biology. Specimens larger than 35 cm are usually sexually mature and there is evidence of hermaphroditism, but probably not complete sex reversal. During late spring and early summer, many are in spawning condition.

CAPTURE

Owing to its excellent flesh and attractive appearance, this species commands a high market value, and is of considerable commercial importance. Most are caught on hand lines, but occasionally catches are made by trawlers. It is encouraging to note that this species is once again being caught in False Bay, and is popular with ski-boat anglers.

SA angling record – 8,2 kg.
SA spearfishing record – 8,0 kg.

DISTRIBUTION

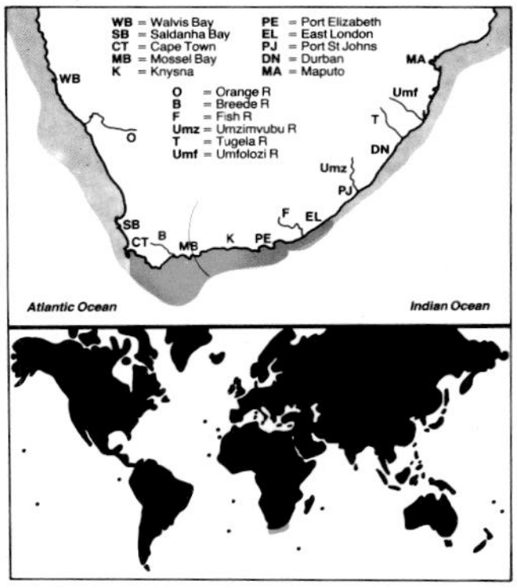

SPECIFIC CATCH RESTRICTIONS

Protected species; minimum legal size is 25 cm.

NAME DERIVATION

Chrysoblephus, golden eyed; *gibbiceps,* gibbous head. Red stumpnose, a reference to the striking body colours and short, blunt snout.

SIMILAR SPECIES

The colour and patterning (especially the irregular black blotches), as well as the concave head profile, should separate this species from any other.

Chrysoblephus laticeps
(Valenciennes, 1830)
Common name Roman
[Smith 183□11]

IDENTIFYING FEATURES

COLOUR, SHAPE AND SIZE

Though also robust, this fish is not as deep-bodied as other *Chrysoblephus* species, and its forehead is less steep. The general body colour is orange, with a characteristic white saddle over the middle of the back, which reaches below the lateral line. There is also a white bar on the gill covers. The fins are red, except for the pectorals which, immediately after capture, are deep orange. A blue line joins the eyes, and, occasionally, a border of iridescent, blue spots extends around the top of the head, joining the gill covers. Attains 50 cm, but more often only 30 cm.

EXTERNAL ANATOMY

There are 53-61 series of strong scales arranged along the lateral line, and only the snout below the nostrils is naked. The fins are well developed, and include a single dorsal of 11-12 spines plus ten rays; an anal of three spines plus seven or eight rays; relatively long pectoral fins which reach a point opposite the origin of the anal fin; and a slightly forked caudal. There are four conspicuous canine teeth in the upper jaw and two in the lower, as well as several rows of molars deeper within. The first gill arch bears 11 or 12 stubby rakers on its lower arch.

NATURAL HISTORY

This offshore reef species occurs to depths of 100 m, although juveniles are more plentiful on shallow inshore reefs. The Roman is a benthic carnivore, and feeds on crinoids, a variety of crustaceans, polychaete worms, sea urchins and many other invertebrates. Most of the food is taken whole, although larger fish do crush their prey. During December and January, Roman have been landed when reproductively 'ripe'. Individuals are known to undergo a sex change which is related to age and size. Specimens first mature at about 20 cm, but at 27-33 cm most change sex from female to male. This is accompanied by a change from a gregarious open-reef existence to a solitary, cave-dwelling one. All large Roman are males, and become strongly territorial, sometimes inhabiting a specific cave permanently.

DISTRIBUTION

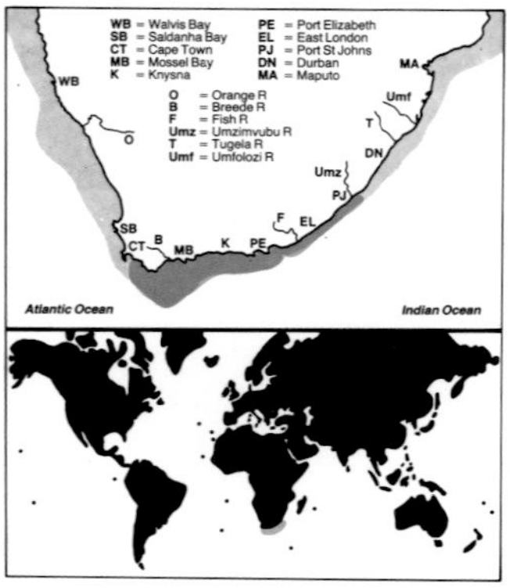

CAPTURE

The Roman freely takes most flesh baits, and is most frequently caught during winter from drifting ski-boats. Commercial line-boat fishermen also occasionally land catches of this excellent table fish. It is also frequently speared by divers.

SA angling record - 4,2 kg.
SA spearfishing record - 4,2 kg.

SPECIFIC CATCH RESTRICTIONS

Protected species; minimum legal size is 25 cm.

NAME DERIVATION

Chrysoblephus, golden eyed; *laticeps,* broad head. Roman, a corruption of *rooi-man,* a Dutch/Afrikaans word meaning 'red man', a reference to its colouration.

SIMILAR SPECIES

No other seabream or similar fish has the conspicuous white saddle below the seventh, eighth and ninth dorsal spines.

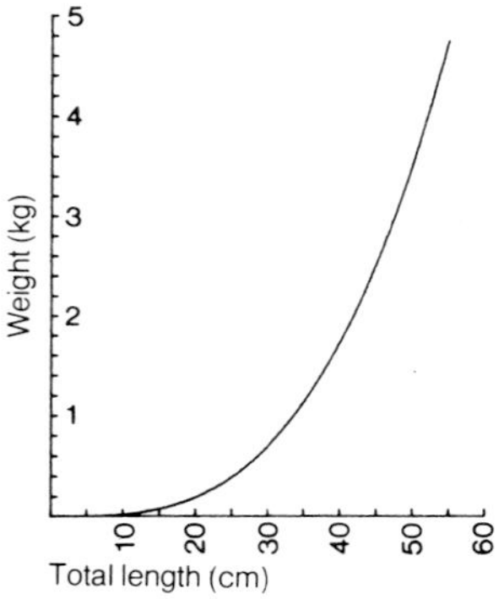

Chrysoblephus lophus

(Fowler, 1925)
Common name false Englishman
[Smith 183□12]

IDENTIFYING FEATURES

COLOUR, SHAPE AND SIZE

This striking, deep-bodied fish is, in many respects, similar to the Englishman, but is distinguished by a number of diagnostic features. Most obvious of these characteristics is the curious groove on the very steep forehead, between the eyes. The overall colouration is silvery-pink with six or seven darker bars on the flanks. Can attain 50 cm.

EXTERNAL ANATOMY

As with most Sparidae, the lateral line of the false Englishman is well defined, and 55-59 series of conspicious scales are arranged along its length. The fins are well developed, with the single dorsal comprising 11 spines plus ten rays. The third to sixth dorsal spines are elongate and particularly prominent. The anal fin consists of three spines plus nine rays, the caudal fin is forked, and the pectorals are long and extend beyond the vent. The mouth is rather small, and reaches a point just below the front of the eyes. Both jaws bear five rows of molars, as well as an outer row of canines. The first gill arch has 12 or 13 rakers.

NATURAL HISTORY

Though quite frequently caught by ski-boat anglers, the false Englishman is nowhere abundant. Its favoured habitat appears to be deeper offshore reefs, ranging to 150 m. Few individuals have been recorded from shallow water. The diet consists mainly of shellfish such as gastropod molluscs, sea urchins, crabs and crayfish. Small fish are also occasionally eaten. Spawning occurs during spring, but the length at sexual maturity and details of the dispersal of juveniles is unknown. The false Englishman is alleged to range more widely in the Indian Ocean, so it is puzzling that so little information has been published on this species. While there is evidence of hermaphroditism, sex reversal probably does not occur. This fish is being studied by the Oceanographic Research Institute in Durban.

DISTRIBUTION

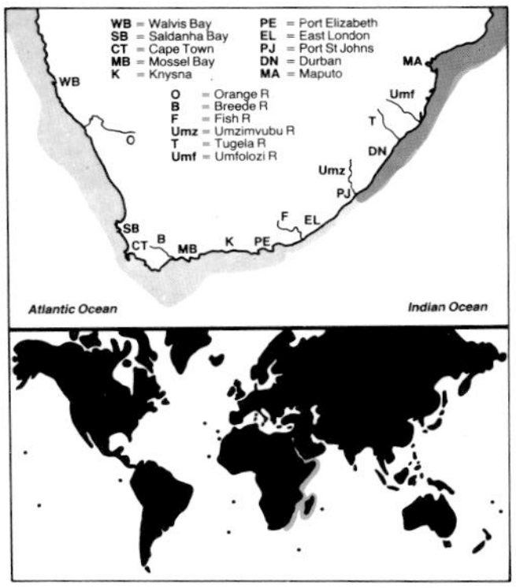

SPECIFIC CATCH RESTRICTIONS

None.

CAPTURE

Experienced ski-boat anglers in Natal regard this species as one of the tastiest food-fishes, so it is, consequently, much sought after. Although it freely takes most baits, its presence over a reef is difficult to predict, and catches are, therefore, somewhat irregular. It is also occasionally speared by divers.

SA angling record – 3,1 kg.
SA spearfishing record – vacant.

NAME DERIVATION

Chrysoblephus, golden eyed; *lophus,* crested. False Englishman, a reference to its close resemblance to the true Englishman.

SIMILAR SPECIES

While this species is closely related to *C. gibbiceps* and *C. anglicus,* it is unmistakeable, as no other fish of similar appearance or colour has such noticeable grooves across the forehead.

Chrysoblephus puniceus

(Gilchrist & Thompson, 1908)
Common name Worldwide – slinger
[Smith 183□13]

IDENTIFYING FEATURES

COLOUR, SHAPE AND SIZE
This deep-bodied species has a very steep forehead. Older specimens have a noticeable hump above the eyes. The overall body colour is rosy red, and iridescent, blue spots are visible in live specimens. A distinct, blue bar occurs just below each eye. The fins are translucent pink, and the tail has an orange tinge.Attains 60 cm, but fish of 30 cm and less are more common.

EXTERNAL ANATOMY
The body is well covered with scales arranged in 49-52 series along the lateral line, but the snout immediately above the mouth is naked. The fins are well developed and include a single dorsal of 12 spines plus ten rays, an anal of three spines plus eight rays, and a moderately forked caudal fin. Medium-sized canines and smaller molars occur in the relatively small mouth. There are 21 rakers on the first gill arch.

DISTRIBUTION

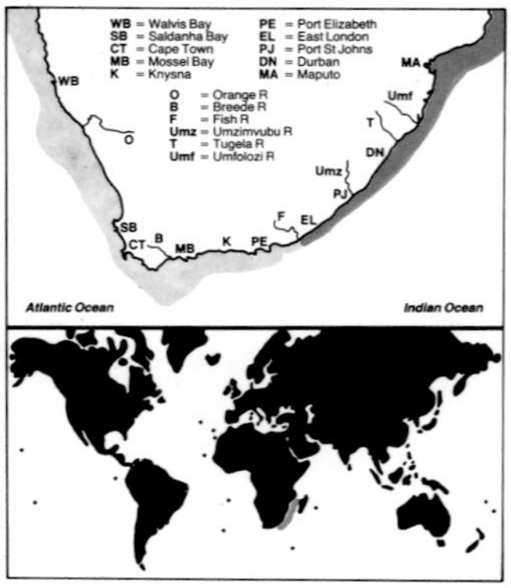

NATURAL HISTORY

This deep-water reef species occurs in great numbers, and, from the commercial fisherman's point of view, is the most important line fish off the Natal coast. It inhabits rocky sea-beds ranging between 20 and 100 m, and often forms large, but loosely packed shoals. The diet varies widely, and includes crustaceans such as crabs, hermit crabs and shrimps, as well as small bivalves, squid and, occasionally, sponges. Slinger may also feed above the reef on midwater planktonic organisms such as pteropods. Tagging studies indicate that this is a semi-resident species. Spawning occurs off Natal during summer, amongst fish that exceed 25 cm. Slinger are hermaphrodite and known to change sex from female to male at approximately 37 cm. This in turn leads to uneven sex ratios, aggravated by heavy fishing pressure. This phenomenon and its effects on the management of stocks is being studied at Durban's Oceanographic Research Institute.

CAPTURE

The slinger is a tasty, much sought after table fish. It partly supports a small, but important commercial fishing industry in Natal. It is caught in large numbers by ski- and line-boat fishermen, especially those using echo-sounders to detect shoals. This increasingly intense angling pressure is already manifesting itself in terms of diminished size and numbers. However, the introduction of marine reserves, and new management measures, are likely to benefit their long-term stability. Only spearfishermen experienced enough to make deep dives manage to spear this species.
SA angling record – 4,0 kg.
SA spearfishing record – 2,8 kg.

SPECIFIC CATCH RESTRICTIONS

Protected species; minimum legal size is 25 cm.

NAME DERIVATION

Chrysoblephus, golden eyed; *puniceus,* purple or red colouration. Slinger, a reference to the slinging aboard of these fish when they are caught in great numbers.

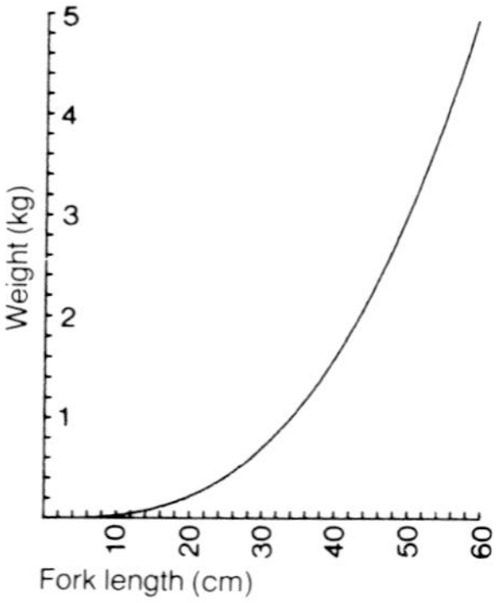

Crenidens crenidens

(Forsskål, 1775)
Common name Worldwide – white karanteen
[Smith 183□14]

IDENTIFYING FEATURES

COLOUR, SHAPE AND SIZE
But for a noticeable bulge over the eyes, this rather elongate seabream has a smooth, evenly rounded dorsal profile. The upper body surface is dusky, and the sides are silvery and marked with 13-15 faint, longitudinal stripes. The fins are translucent, and grey or yellowish, especially the anal fin, which may be bright yellow. Can attain 30 cm.

EXTERNAL ANATOMY
There are 45-55 series of scales arranged along the lateral line, but the forehead between the eyes is naked. The fins are well developed, and include a single dorsal of 11 spines plus 11 rays, an anal of three spines plus ten rays, and a moderately forked caudal. The mouth is small and bears a conspicuous row of incisors in each jaw. In young fish these teeth are often five-pointed. There are 12-16 short, but strong rakers on the first gill arch. Care should be taken not to confuse this species with the juveniles of the Natal stumpnose (*Rhabdosargus sarba*), which are superficially very similar.

NATURAL HISTORY

The white karanteen is a small, shoaling fish, generally confined to shallows and intertidal waters such as estuaries and bays. Despite these habitat preferences, however, it is not particularly tolerant of very low salinities or excessive turbidity. It grazes continuously on seaweeds, though it probably derives most of its nutrition from the epiphytic organisms that grow on these algal stems, rather than from the seaweed itself. Larger fish may also forage on the muddy bottom in search of small crabs, worms and shrimps. Although sexually mature specimens have been recorded along the Natal coast during all

seasons, none of those examined has been reproductively 'ripe'. It seems likely, therefore, that spawning occurs in Moçambique waters.

DISTRIBUTION

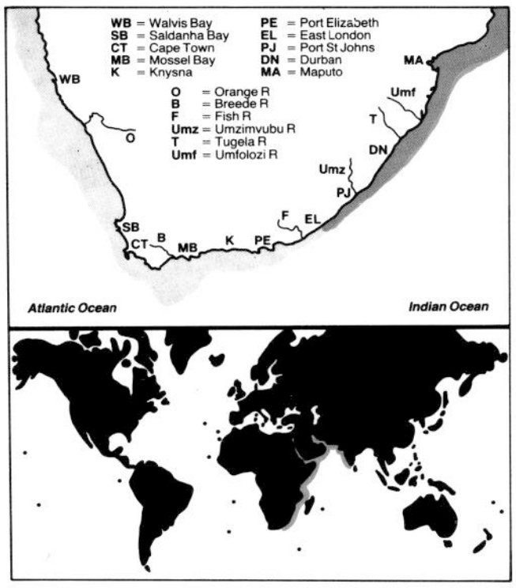

CAPTURE

Few anglers pursue this species specifically, but with ultra-light tackle, and by using small pieces of shrimp or fish bait, white karanteen can be easily caught. The flesh is of fair quality, and, though not exploited commercially in southern Africa, the species represents a considerable food resource along the shores of the Red Sea and in India, where many are netted or caught in fish traps. It is not of spearfishing importance.

SPECIFIC CATCH RESTRICTIONS

None.

NAME DERIVATION

Crenidens, a reference to the notched teeth. White karanteen, a reference to the pale body; the meaning of the name 'karanteen' is obscure, but is probably of Mauritian origin.

SIMILAR SPECIES

This species is easily distinguished from the strepie because it lacks the bright-golden stripes. Its separation from the stumpnoses is not always immediately apparent. It is, however, more elongate than *Rhabdosargus* species and the five-pointed teeth are distinctive.

Cymatoceps nasutus

(Castelnau, 1861)
Common names SA - black musselcracker, poenskop
[Smith 183□15]

IDENTIFYING FEATURES

COLOUR, SHAPE AND SIZE
This species is one of the largest members of the Sparidae. It has a deep, robust body, but the overall shape varies with size and age, with older specimens developing extended, fleshy snouts. The body colours also vary with size, although most specimens are basically sooty grey to black. Adolescents are lighter overall and two or more dark, broad crossbars may occur on the flanks. Juveniles are noticeably different; greenish-brown overall, with numerous white blotches. Attains 120 cm.

EXTERNAL ANATOMY
There are 61-65 series of tough, thick scales arranged along the lateral line, with those on the lower sides being distinctly larger. Scales also extend onto the forehead, below the level of the eyes. The fins are well developed, and include a single dorsal of 12 spines plus ten rays, an anal of three spines plus eight rays, a slightly forked caudal fin, and pectoral fins that reach a point opposite the origin of the anal fin. The moderate mouth has thick fleshy lips, and bears four conical teeth in the upper jaw and six in the lower, as well as two rows of rounded, powerful molars in each. There are ten short rakers on the lower limb of the first gill arch.

NATURAL HISTORY

The black musselcracker is a large, solitary species, and individuals are found on both shallow and deep rocky reefs. Here they feed on crabs, crayfish, sea urchins and other large, hard-shelled animals. Prey is first grabbed and held firmly by the conical teeth, before being crushed by the powerful grinding action of the stout jaws and molars. Along the East Coast, abundance increases during winter, and, though the reproductive cycle is poorly understood, these seasonal increases are thought to coincide with its breeding season.

DISTRIBUTION

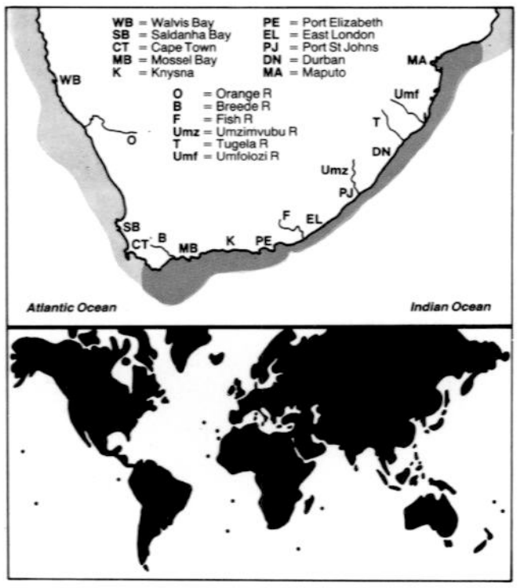

SPECIFIC CATCH RESTRICTIONS

Protected species; minimum legal size is 25 cm.

CAPTURE

The black musselcracker is often hooked by shore anglers fishing from rocky promontories, and ski-boat anglers operating over deeper reefs. Whole crayfish and redbait are most successful in tempting this fish. It is seldom landed, for its strength and dogged fighting ability make it a formidable adversary. Its sluggish habits, however, often make it a target for spearfishermen.
SA angling record - 37,8 kg.
SA spearfishing record - 36,0 kg.

Juvenile C. nasutus.

NAME DERIVATION

Cymatoceps, swollen head, a reference to the bulbous snout of older specimens; *nasutus,* prominent nose. Black musselcracker, a reference to its black body and powerful jaws.

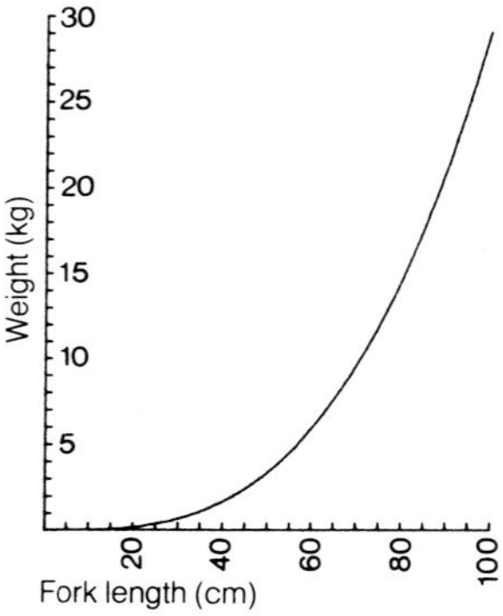

Diplodus cervinus

(Smith, 1844)
Common names SA – zebra, wildeperd
[Smith 183□16]

IDENTIFYING FEATURES

COLOUR, SHAPE AND SIZE
This species is almost oval in shape, but the snout is pointed. Five unmistakable, broad, black bars run down the sides of its golden-silvery body. A black bar also passes through each eye. The fins are translucent to dusky. Attains 50 cm.

EXTERNAL ANATOMY
There are 55-60 series of strong scales arranged along the lateral line, but the forehead between the eyes is naked. The fins are well developed, and include a dorsal of 11 spines plus 12-13 rays, an anal of three spines plus 11 rays, and a forked caudal. The moderate mouth is surrounded by soft, fleshy lips. A single row of 12 long incisors, and several rows of smaller molars occur in each jaw. A total of 17 club-shaped rakers are located on the first gill arch.

DISTRIBUTION

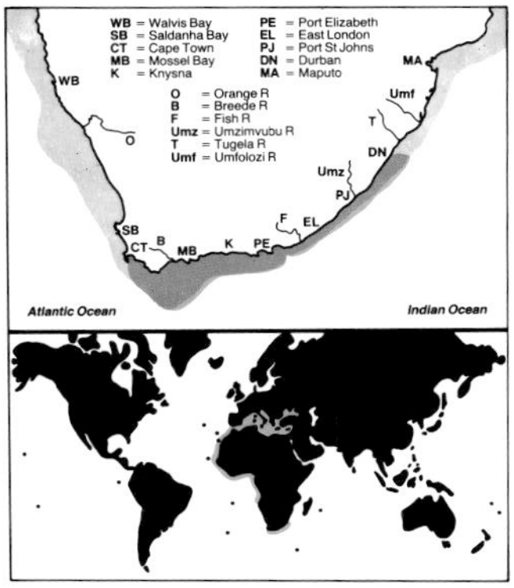

NATURAL HISTORY

The zebra ranges from inshore shallows to depths of 60 m. Feeding habits of this omnivore vary according to its whereabouts, but the diet of adults includes seaweeds, small crabs, and tube worms. The fleshy lips are almost certainly a specialized feeding aid, serving to grasp food, and then to manipulate it into a suitable position for the cutting incisors. Juvenile zebras are exclusively carnivorous, and eat copepods and shrimps as well as insect larvae.
Corresponding with the change to a predominantly vegetarian, adult diet, is a considerable lengthening of the digestive tract, providing a more efficient system for processing high-bulk, low-calorie plant matter. Though not a shoaling species, small groups of zebra do congregate, especially during the spring breeding season. Sexual maturity is attained at an age of three years, when fish are about 25 cm long, and spawning takes place in waters slightly deeper than the normal habitat. Fertilized eggs and larvae have been collected in False Bay from October to January, and juveniles have also been recorded from the eastern Cape.

CAPTURE

This species is quite commonly caught by surf anglers, particularly in gullies along the rocky shores of the Cape coast, and by ski-boat fishermen operating offshore. Its flesh is very palatable. It is also easily speared.
SA angling record – 6,3 kg.
SA spearfishing record – 3,2 kg.

SPECIFIC CATCH RESTRICTIONS

None.

NAME DERIVATION

Diplodus, double-toothed, a reference to the characteristic dentition; *cervinus,* deer-like, a reference to the thick lips and doe-like eyes. Zebra, a reference to its striped flanks.

SIMILAR SPECIES

The zebra is not easily misidentified. The South African variety is the subspecies *hottentotus*, and differs marginally from the *cervinus* subspecies of the north Atlantic.

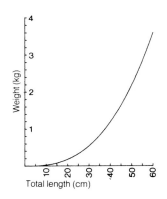

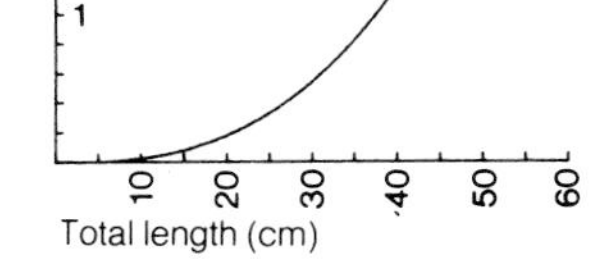

Diplodus sargus

(Smith, 1844)

Common names SA - blacktail, dassie. Elsewhere - whitebream [Smith 183□17]

IDENTIFYING FEATURES

COLOUR, SHAPE AND SIZE

The oval-shaped body with its pointed snout is predominantly silver. An unmistakable, black saddle occurs on the caudal peduncle. Juveniles of less than 5 cm are marked with 8-10 vertical crossbars. Can attain 40 cm.

EXTERNAL ANATOMY

There are about 65 series of scales arranged along the lateral line, but the bridge between the eyes is naked. The fins are well developed, and include a single dorsal of 12 spines plus 14 or 15 rays, an anal of three spines plus 13 or 14 rays, and a moderately forked caudal. Both jaws of the small, terminal mouth bear as many as eight, large incisors as well as several rows of molars. There are 14 or 15 stubby rakers on the first gill arch.

Note: Several sub-species of this fish exist throughout its range. This is *capensis.*

DISTRIBUTION

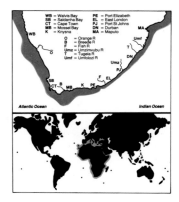

NATURAL HISTORY

The blacktail is primarily an inshore species, favouring turbulent seas and rocky shores. It moves in and out of this zone with the tides, and also often occurs in small shoals over the outer edges of deeper reefs, and around offshore pinnacles. It is tolerant of widely varying temperatures, but is rarely found in estuaries or other low-salinity regions. Like the previous species, the feeding habits and alimentary system of the blacktail change with age. From a short-gutted carnivore, the juvenile grows into an omnivorous adult with a longer intestine better able to digest the considerable amounts of plant material taken in. The diet of mature specimens ranges from red and green seaweeds to mussels, sponges and redbait, while young fish less than 3,5 cm in length feed on copepods, tube worms and barnacle larvae. The blacktail occurs throughout the year, but is most common along the East Coast from April to September. As with many Sparidae, this species undergoes periodic sex changes, and scientific evidence suggests that many blacktail are bisexual at specific times of the year. Sexual maturity is attained at a length of about 16 cm, and spawning occurs all year round, but especially during mid-winter and early spring. Juveniles of 1-3 cm inhabit shallow, tidal rock pools which serve as nursery areas. Blacktail have been recorded from the stomachs of larger gamefish, sharks and dolphins.

SPECIFIC CATCH RESTRICTIONS

Minimum legal size is 20 cm.

CAPTURE

Although it may not grow to any great size, the 'dapper' blacktail is a fine sport fish, and is actively pursued by many light-tackle enthusiasts. Small drift baits of crayfish, redbait or sardine, cast into white-water gullies, are most likely to tempt blacktail. Most do not grow to a size large enough to satisfy spearfishermen.

SA angling record - 3,0 kg.

SA spearfishing record - 1,8 kg.

NAME DERIVATION

Diplodus, double-toothed, a reference to the characteristic dentition; *sargus,* an ancient Mediterranean name for this fish. Blacktail, a reference to the distinctive saddle on the caudal peduncle.

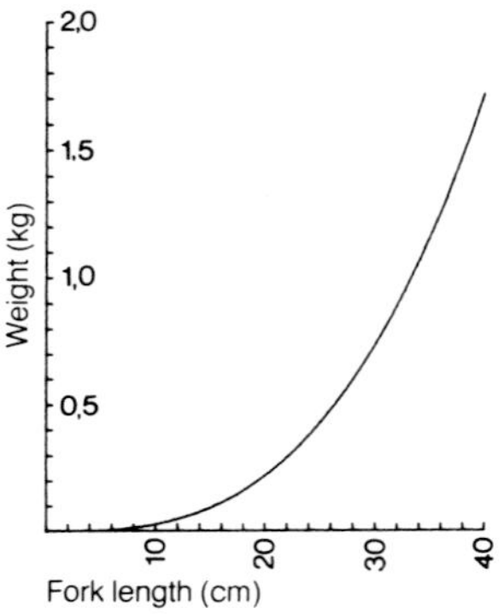

Gymnocrotaphus curvidens

(Günther, 1859)
Common names janbruin, John Brown
[Smith 183□18]

IDENTIFYING FEATURES

COLOUR, SHAPE AND SIZE
This is a plump-bodied fish with a rather blunt snout, and a steep forehead that develops a slight 'bump' over the eyes with age. The overall body colour is orange-brown, though this fades considerably after death. A striking feature of this species is the bright-blue colour of the eyes in freshly caught specimens. Attains 50 cm.

EXTERNAL ANATOMY
The body is covered with some 64-68 series of scales, though significantly there are no scales on the head, in front of the operculum. The fins are well developed, and comprise a single continuous dorsal of ten spines plus 11-12 rays, an anal of three spines and 9-10 rays, and a slightly forked, rather small caudal. The mouth is set terminally, and bears dentition that consists of an outer row of enlarged and outwardly flaring canines followed by a band of smaller conical teeth, some of which have developed into molars. There are moderately developed gill rakers present, numbering 12-15 on the first arch.

NATURAL HISTORY

This is an endemic species that apparently has a very limited distribution, ranging only from Transkei to False Bay. Most occur in close proximity to land, though some have been taken at depths of 50 m. The janbruin appears to have diminished in abundance: where it was once known to be a common catch at Port Alfred, local anglers now seldom report this fish. Reasons for this apparent decrease are uncertain. This beautifully coloured, non-shoaling fish feeds mostly on encrusting organisms, especially redbait. The strong teeth are well designed to tear off such food, which may also include small quantities of seaweed, bryozoans, polychaete worms and small crustaceans. Some of this food may be taken in very shallow, turbulent water. Virtually nothing is known of this species' spawning, but it is possible that some form of sex reversal occurs. The juveniles are known to resemble the adults at a very small size - about 4 cm - some having been taken in offshore plankton nets.

DISTRIBUTION

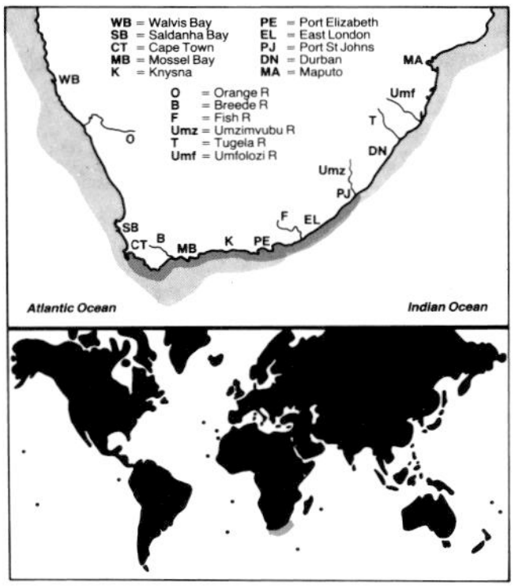

CAPTURE

The janbruin is most frequently caught by rock and surf anglers in the eastern Cape. However, numbers are also landed from craft at sea, such as this specimen shown here, which was caught off Gordons Bay. It would be advisable for anglers to report the capture of this fish to local marine scientists, so that further study can be undertaken. No doubt this is a rather shy species, difficult to capture, which may be tempted with redbait or worms. It makes excellent eating.
SA angling record - 2,8 kg.
SA spearfishing record - 3,0 kg.

SPECIFIC CATCH RESTRICTIONS

None.

NAME DERIVATION

Gymnocrotaphus, naked side of head; *curvidens,* curved teeth. Janbruin, meaning obscure.

SIMILAR SPECIES

The janbruin is a typical bream-like fish, and may be confused with the large bream, blue hottentot or German. While all these species also have large, outer, incisor-like teeth, the janbruin is further distinguished by the absence of scales on the cheek, and bright-blue eyes. In many cases, the janbruin has one less dorsal spine than other bream-like fishes.

Lithognathus aureti

Smith, 1962
Common name SA - westcoast steenbras
[Smith 183□19]

IDENTIFYING FEATURES

COLOUR, SHAPE AND SIZE
This somewhat elongate fish is deeper-bodied than other steenbras species, and has a shorter, blunt snout. The general body colour is greyish-silver, with 7-9 dusky crossbars on the flanks, but these usually fade after death. The belly is pale. Can attain 100 cm in length.

EXTERNAL ANATOMY
There are 45-49 series of distinct scales arranged along the lateral line, but the bridge between the eyes is naked. The fins are well developed, and include a single dorsal of 11 spines plus nine or ten rays, an anal of three spines plus eight or nine rays, and a moderately forked caudal which has a noticeably stout peduncle. The length of the pectoral fins equals or exceeds the length of the head. The teeth of both jaws are strong, and comprise an outer row of conical teeth and inner rows of molars. There are 21 or 22 rakers on the first gill arch.

DISTRIBUTION

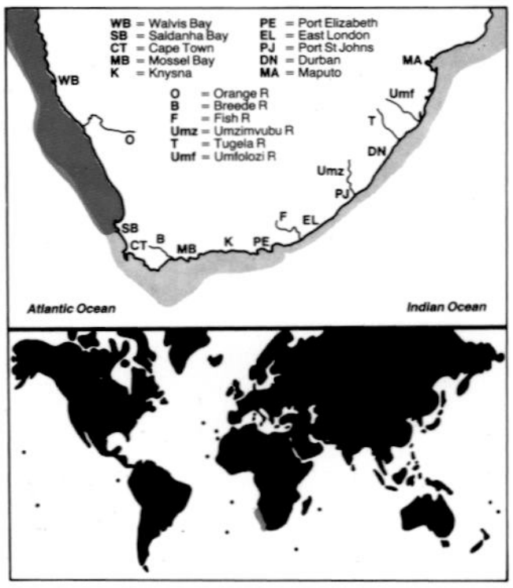

NATURAL HISTORY

This gregarious, coastal species is normally found over sandy sea-beds, either in the shallow surf zone or in deeper water, but apparently not in estuaries. Its diet consists mainly of burrowing invertebrates such as sand mussels, marine worms and crabs, most of which are 'blown' from their burrows by water pumped through the mouth by the powerful 'bellows' action of the steenbras' gill covers. This species is particularly common from Walvis Bay northwards, especially after August. During the ensuing spring and summer, massive shoals of reproductively 'ripe' fish will congregate in shallow water. At such times this species is most vulnerable to exploitation, especially by seine netting operations. Further details of its life history are not fully known, but juveniles have been recorded near Swakopmund.

CAPTURE

The westcoast steenbras is a fine sport- and good food-fish, but excessive greed on the part of some fishermen has resulted in noticeably dwindling catches. Little more than a decade ago, fish of nearly 30 kg were regularly landed, and reports of fishing competitions in which 'mountains' of steenbras were caught were common. This situation seems to indicate that the species would benefit from some form of controlled exploitation. Despite this trend, however, good catches are still made by surf anglers. This fish is often caught in remarkably shallow water by fishermen using white sand mussels, rock mussels and prawns as bait.
SA angling record – 19,3 kg.
SA spearfishing record – vacant.

SPECIFIC CATCH RESTRICTIONS

None.

NAME DERIVATION

Lithognathus, stone-jawed, a reference to the molar teeth; *aureti,* after Mr. Auret, the well known lighthouse keeper who first noticed this fish as different from the white steenbras. Westcoast steenbras, a reference to its range, and a corruption of the Dutch *steenbrasem,* the name given to a similar freshwater fish occurring in Europe.

SIMILAR SPECIES

The silvery body, with its 7-9 broad crossbars, and head that is equal in length to the pectoral are features that should distinguish this from the other two *Lithognathus* species.

Lithognathus lithognathus

(Cuvier, 1830)
Common names SA – white steenbras, pignose grunter
[Smith 183□20]

IDENTIFYING FEATURES

COLOUR, SHAPE AND SIZE

This rather large, elongate steenbras has a long, sloping forehead and a long, pig-like snout. It is silvery-grey above and white below. Living specimens often have an overall mother-of-pearl sheen, but after death this disappears, and some seven crossbars become evident on the flanks. Attains 100 cm.

EXTERNAL ANATOMY

There are 44-51 series of large, tough scales arranged along the lateral line, but the bridge between the eyes is naked. The narrow, protractile mouth is surrounded by thick lips, and the jaws bear exceedingly small teeth. Larger molars are visible deeper within the mouth. The fins are well developed and include a single dorsal of 11 spines plus eight rays, and a large, slightly forked caudal. There are 22-24 rakers on the first gill arch.

DISTRIBUTION

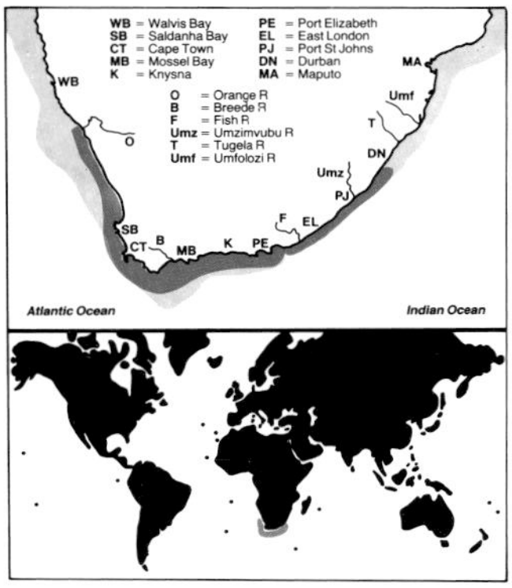

NATURAL HISTORY

The white steenbras is common in shallow water, and freely enters estuaries where it is able to tolerate almost-fresh water for extended periods. Its varied diet includes cracker-shrimps, blood worms, small crabs, periwinkles and bivalve molluscs. As with the previous species, these food items are mostly 'blown' from their burrows by a strong jet of water, which is forced through the narrow mouth by the pumping action of the powerful gill covers. In extremely shallow water, the white steenbras is often seen, tail out of the water and snout well into the sandy sea-bed, 'blasting' away at prey. Although often solitary, there are annual 'runs' of this species along the Transkeian coast, when large shoals enter shallow water. A high percentage of white steenbras are infested with harmless leech and copepod parasites throughout the year. Those that live in estuaries are not generally sexually active, but marine specimens are known to spawn from June to August. Maturity is attained after approximately five years, corresponding to a length of 40 cm. Though bisexuality is common, it does not appear to lead to complete sex reversal, as with some other Sparidae. The juveniles make extensive use of estuaries as nursery areas.

CAPTURE

This superb table fish is also one of southern Africa's favourite angling species, and is caught mainly along sandy beaches or in estuaries in the early morning by anglers using shrimp or worm bait. Once hooked, the white steenbras takes off like a steam train, and the angler is left in little doubt as to the worthiness of his opponent. There is little exploitation, and it is not sought after by spearfishermen.
SA angling record – 29,9 kg.
SA spearfishing record – 21,0 kg.

SPECIFIC CATCH RESTRICTIONS

Protected species; minimum legal size is 40 cm.

NAME DERIVATION

Lithognathus, stone-jawed, a reference to the powerful molar teeth. White steenbras, a reference to the pale colouration, and a corruption of the Dutch *steenbrasem,* the name given to a similar, freshwater fish occurring in Europe.

SIMILAR SPECIES

This steenbras is easily confused with the west coast variety, though it has a longer head that usually exceeds the pectoral fin length. The ratios of body length to depth are noticeably different; greater than 2,7:1 in *L. lithognathus*, and less than 2,6:1 in *L. aureti*.

Lithognathus mormyrus

(Linnaeus, 1758)

Common names SA - sand steenbras. Elsewhere - marmora [Smith 183□21]

IDENTIFYING FEATURES

COLOUR, SHAPE AND SIZE

The sand steenbras has an elongate body, with a rather long and pointed snout. Its overall colour is silvery, with about 14 darker, narrow crossbars. The fins are translucent to dusky. Can attain 50 cm in some regions, but few exceed 30 cm in southern African waters.

EXTERNAL ANATOMY

There are 60-64 series of small scales arranged along the lateral line, but the bridge between the eyes is naked. The protractile mouth has thin lips. The jaws are set with exceptionally small outer teeth, and rows of larger molars within. The fins are well developed, and include a single dorsal of 11 spines plus 12-13 rays, an anal of three spines plus 10-11 rays, and a moderately forked caudal. There are 25 or 26 rakers on the first gill arch.

DISTRIBUTION

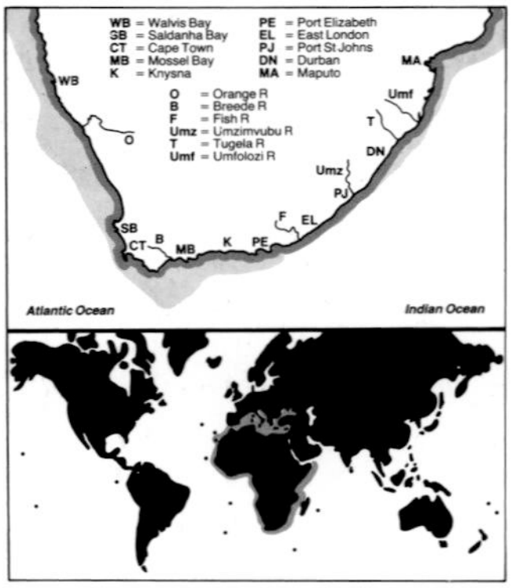

NATURAL HISTORY

As its common name suggests, this species prefers sandy habitats. It is adept at camouflage, for the darker crossbars marking its flanks blend with the ripple marks that, as result of tide and current action, pattern the plain, sandy sea-bed. Being a shallow-water fish, this effect is often accentuated by the dappled light filtering through from the surface. Thus the sand steenbras remains inconspicuous even when present in fair numbers. It feeds primarily on a diet of bottom-living invertebrates such as cracker shrimps, mole crabs (sea lice) and bivalve molluscs. Although it makes limited use of estuaries, the sand steenbras is not generally found in low salinity areas. There is no evidence to suggest that seasonal migrations take place, but this requires further study. Spawning occurs in summer over deeper water. Though breeding probably takes place throughout the fish's range, to date, the greatest concentrations of fertile eggs have been recorded from False Bay in the Cape. Juveniles use shallow marine bays as nursery areas, and are often seen in small shoals foraging over the sandy bottom in search of food.

CAPTURE

Though not specifically pursued by anglers, the sand steenbras is easily caught on a variety of small baits such as marine worms, small crabs and pieces of pilchard. It is not of commercial importance in southern Africa, but elsewhere it is a valued food resource.

SA angling record - 0,8 kg.

SPECIFIC CATCH RESTRICTIONS

None.

NAME DERIVATION

Lithognathus, stone-jawed, a reference to the molar teeth; *mormyrus,* a Greek name for a marine fish. Sand steenbras, a reference to its habitat preference, and a corruption of the Dutch *steenbrasem,* the name given to a similar, freshwater fish occurring in Europe.

SIMILAR SPECIES

The 14 or so narrow crossbars on the elongate body will serve to distinguish this from similar species.

Pachymetopon aeneum

(Gilchrist & Thompson, 1908)
Common names SA – blue hottentot, copper bream
[Smith 183□22]

IDENTIFYING FEATURES

COLOUR, SHAPE AND SIZE
This robust fish is rather similar to the following two species, but is decidedly more elongate, especially towards the hindquarters. Live specimens have a bronze sheen and a blue head. After death or capture, however, this striking colouration is soon lost, and the fish fades to an overall brownish-grey. The underside is much paler and the fins are dusky. Can attain 60 cm.

EXTERNAL ANATOMY
Small, tough scales are arranged in 75-85 series along the distinct lateral line. Most of these scales are cycloid, but some are rougher and rather more ctenoid. Scales also occur on the pre-opercular flange. As with other *Pachymetopon* species, the fins are well developed and include a single dorsal of 10-11 spines plus 11-13 rays, an anal of three spines plus ten rays, and a moderately forked caudal. The small, terminal mouth bears 30-36 outer incisors in the upper jaw and 36-40 in the lower. There are 16-22 rakers on the first gill arch.

NATURAL HISTORY

This bream is common, and, indeed, fairly abundant off Natal and the eastern Cape. It ranges to depths of 75 m, and generally favours flat, rocky reefs. Here it feeds primarily on encrusting organisms such as sponges and ascidians. The strong incisors provide a useful tool for chiselling these food items from the rocky substrate. Seaweed is also eaten, but in lesser quantities, while analysis of the stomach contents of some landed specimens has evidenced that small gastropod molluscs are also a favoured food source. Blue hottentot appear to be semi-resident, and are present throughout the year. Most mature fish are reproductively inactive, except during March. Little factual material is available on the life history of this species.

DISTRIBUTION

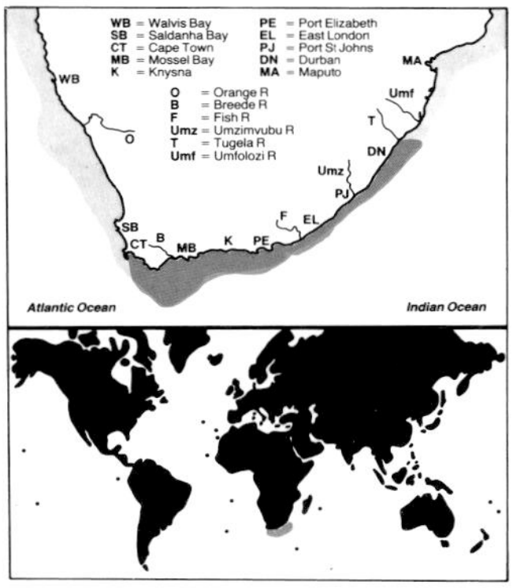

CAPTURE

Because of its offshore and deeper water habits, shore anglers seldom catch this fish. Ski-boat fishermen, however, regularly land the blue hottentot, but most are unable to distinguish it from and *P. grande,* merely classing it as a 'bronze bream'. A wide variety of baits is generally successful in tempting this fish, but, because of the relatively small mouth, care must be taken to ensure that the bait is not too large. The flesh makes excellent eating. The blue hottentot is also sought after by those divers sufficiently experienced to dive in deep water.
SA angling record – 4,7 kg.
SA spearfishing record – 2,4 kg.

SPECIFIC CATCH RESTRICTIONS

None.

NAME DERIVATION

Pachymetopon, thick forehead; *aeneum,* brassy. Blue hottentot, a reference to its colouration and similarity to the true hottentot *(P. blochii).*

SIMILAR SPECIES

The numerous incisor teeth are most characteristic, and a useful means of distinguishing between these species and the very similar, but deeper-bodied, bronze bream *(P. grande),* and the German *(Polyamblyodon germanum).*

Pachymetopon blochii

(Valenciennes, 1830)
Common name hottentot
[Smith 183□23]

IDENTIFYING FEATURES

COLOUR, SHAPE AND SIZE
The plump body of the hottentot is bluish-grey overall, but with a golden-green sheen above, and a white belly. The fins are dusky, and the pectoral axils are black. This is the smallest member of the genus, and it only rarely exceeds 40 cm.

EXTERNAL ANATOMY
There are 60-65 series of distinct scales arranged along the lateral line, but the bridge between the eyes is naked. The fins are well developed, and include a single dorsal of 10-11 spines plus 11 or 12 rays, and an anal of three spines plus ten rays. Both pectoral fins are approximately equal in length to the head. The caudal fin is slightly forked. The mouth bears 30-36 distinct incisors in the upper jaw, and 40-44 in the lower jaw. There are about 14 rakers on the first gill arch.

DISTRIBUTION

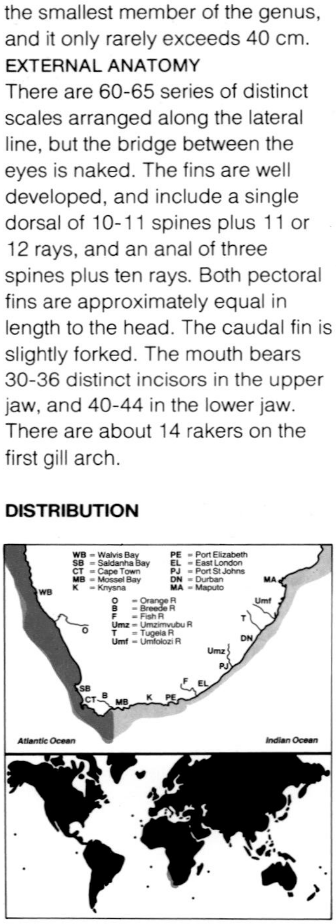

NATURAL HISTORY

This omnivorous species frequents both shallow and deep-water reefs, and though red, brown and green seaweeds predominate in the diet, amphipods, crabs and their larvae, shrimps, polychaete worms, anchovies and redbait are also consumed. With age, however, individuals turn more to algae, which they graze continuously and are able to digest completely. Sexual maturity is attained at an age of three years, corresponding to a length of about 20 cm. Breeding takes place throughout the year, with increased spawning activity during summer. Research has shown that the hottentot is a resident species, and not subject to migrations or great seasonal fluctuations in its abundance. The establishment of marine reserves, therefore, could be particularly beneficial in the preservation of its somewhat limited habitat.

CAPTURE

Redbait and shrimp baits stand the best chance of luring this mainly vegetarian species. The hottentot is caught on line by commercial and sport anglers, both from the shore, and from dinghies at sea. It is also popular with spearfishermen. It is a good eating fish, and is often sold on fresh-fish markets in the Cape. This fish is a vital source of animal protein to certain rural communities.
SA angling record - 3,0 kg.
SA spearfishing record - 2,4 kg.

SPECIFIC CATCH RESTRICTIONS

The minimum legal size is 22 cm total length.

NAME DERIVATION

Pachymetopon, thick forehead; *blochii,* named after the renowned ichthyologist, Bloch. Hottentot, a reference to the fact that this fish was one of the few species sold to early settlers by indigenous beachcombers.

SIMILAR SPECIES

The hottentot is easily distinguished from other *Pachymetopon* species by the length of its pectoral fin, which is equal to its head length. In the other species the pectoral fin length considerably exceeds the head length.

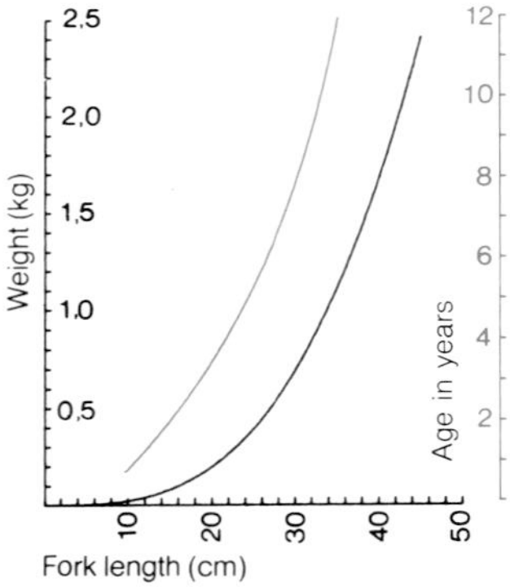

Pachymetopon grande

Günther, 1859

Common name bronze bream

[Smith 183□24]

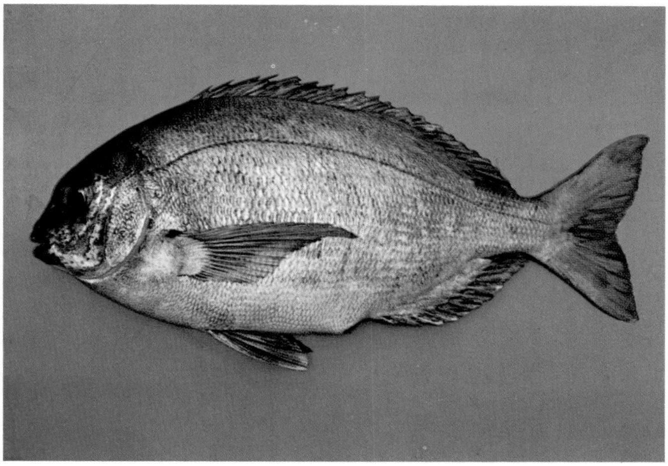

IDENTIFYING FEATURES

COLOUR, SHAPE AND SIZE

The noticeably plump, oval-shaped body of the bronze bream has an overall iridescent, bluish-bronze sheen. After death, however, this is soon lost, and the fish becomes a duller brown overall. This is the largest member of the genus, and can attain 70 cm.

EXTERNAL ANATOMY

The body is covered with 80-85 series of ctenoid scales arranged along the lateral line, but the bridge between the eyes is naked. The fins are well developed, and include a dorsal of 11 spines plus 11 rays, an anal of three spines plus ten or 11 rays, and a slightly forked caudal. The moderate terminal mouth has a row of conspicuous incisors in each jaw, 18-20 in the upper and 20-22 in the lower. A total of 14-20 rakers occurs on the first gill arch.

DISTRIBUTION

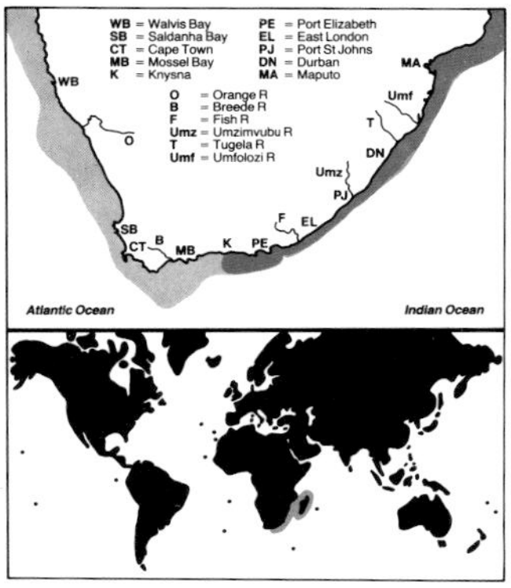

NATURAL HISTORY

A useful distinction between this species and the German and copper bream, with which it is often confused, is their differing habitats. The bronze bream is an inhabitant of shallow, sometimes turbulent, rocky shorelines, a direct contrast to the copper bream and the German which prefer deeper water. It is confined to shallows, as only in these regions can sufficient light penetrate the water to stimulate the growth of algal plants, which constitute, almost exclusively, this species' diet. The bronze bream's anatomy is well suited to its vegetarian habits; it has numerous sharp, cutting teeth and an exceptionally long gut capable of extracting maximum nutrition from the high-bulk, low-energy red and green seaweeds that are continuously grazed. As this is one of the largest herbivorous fish, it probably occupies an important link in the lower levels of the foodweb. Although present throughout the year, the bronze bream is most common during late winter and spring, a period that coincides with the breeding season. Sexual maturity is attained at 40-45 cm, and spawning adults have been recorded from the Natal south coast.

SPECIFIC CATCH RESTRICTIONS

Protected species.

CAPTURE

The bronze bream is often exceedingly timid, and, because of its herbivorous nature, is difficult to tempt with flesh baits. Once hooked, however, it fights with great determination, and is highly regarded by both anglers and spearfishermen. Despite its fatty flesh, it is a fine table fish.

SA angling record – 5,5 kg.

SA spearfishing record – 5,4 kg.

NAME DERIVATION

Pachymetopon, thick forehead; *grande,* large. Bronze bream, a reference to its metallic colouration, and to *breme,* an old French name for a similar freshwater fish.

SIMILAR SPECIES

This species is most commonly confused with both the blue hottentot and the German, but can be best distinguished from these by the fact that it has fewer teeth. While it also resembles the chub, it has a noticeably higher scale count.

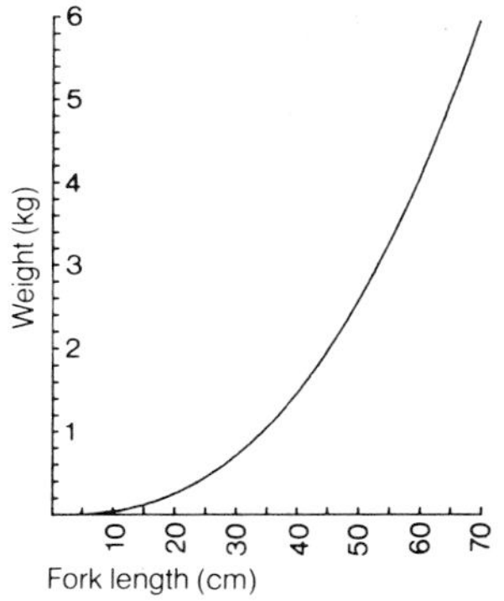

Pagellus natalensis

Steindachner, 1902

Common names SA – red tjor-tjor, sand-soldier. Elsewhere – Natal seabream

[Smith 183□25]

IDENTIFYING FEATURES

COLOUR, SHAPE AND SIZE

This elongate fish is basically pink, with a white belly. Living specimens have numerous iridescent, blue spots arranged in horizontal rows along the upper flanks. These spots combine with the basic body colour to create an overall purple sheen. A deep-red blotch is often present on the gill covers. The translucent fins have a definite pinkish tinge. This fish does not normally exceed 35 cm.

EXTERNAL ANATOMY

The body is covered with 60-67 series of scales arranged along the lateral line, but the forehead and pre-opercular flange are naked. The fins are well developed, and include a single dorsal of 12 spines plus ten rays, an anal of three spines plus ten rays, and a forked caudal. The smallish, terminal mouth has minute, sharp teeth towards the front of each jaw, as well as several rows of molars further back. There are 13-17 stubby rakers on the lower first gill arch. The eyes are relatively large.

NATURAL HISTORY

This little carnivore is abundant in fairly deep water, especially off Natal, and it lives predominantly over sandy sea-beds. It is often very inconspicuous, as its body colours blend well with its surroundings at these depths. The diet consists of crabs, polychaete worms, brittlestars, numerous small crustaceans and small, bottom-living fishes. Although the life history of this fish in South African waters is unknown, Russian biologists have studied a closely related sub species in the Gulf of Aden, where it is particularly common. Here, at an age of about three years, equivalent to a length of 20 cm, these fish spawn from June to September. Almost every skindiver who descends below 30 m over a seemingly sterile, sandy sea-bed, reports large populations of this species. It is likely that the red tjor-tjor is an important link in the foodweb, as it provides a readily available source of food for many larger predators.

DISTRIBUTION

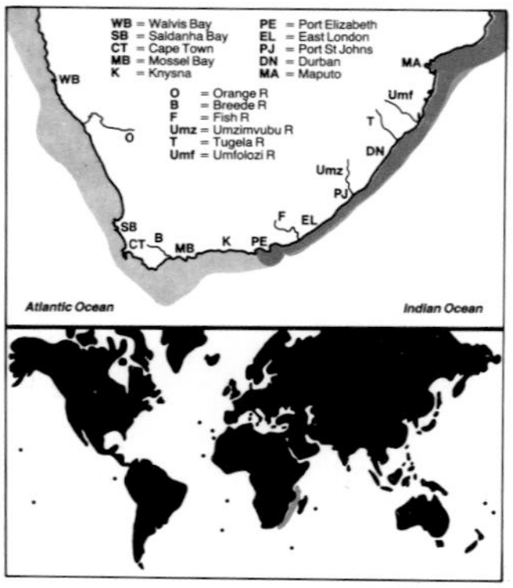

SPECIFIC CATCH RESTRICTIONS

Open species.

CAPTURE

Though the red tjor-tjor is quite palatable, it does not rate seriously with anglers or commercial fishermen in South Africa. Because of its great abundance in localized areas, it can sometimes spoil angling through incessant bait nibbling. However, in some parts of its range this is exploited to provide an important food resource.

NAME DERIVATION

Pagellus, literally, small pages, possibly an allusion to the regimented shoals formed by this fish; *natalensis,* of Natal, the region where it was first found. Red tjor-tjor, a reference to its body colours, and to the grunting noise it makes.

SIMILAR SPECIES

This may well be one of several sub-species of *P. bellotti.* Others exist in the Atlantic and northern Indian Ocean. The tjor-tjor lacks the four canine teeth of the silverfish. It is, however, easily confused with the slightly deeper bodied panga.

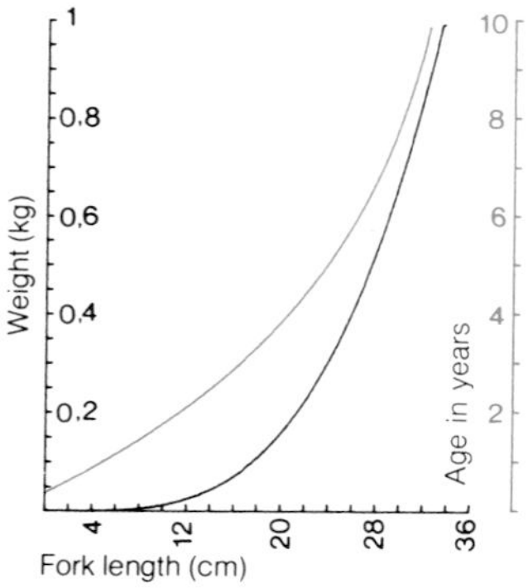

Petrus rupestris

(Valenciennes, 1830)
Common name – red steenbras
[Smith 183□26]

IDENTIFYING FEATURES

COLOUR, SHAPE AND SIZE
This is the largest of the Sparidae occurring in southern African waters. It has an elongate, robust body, with a slightly extended snout, and a bony ridge between the eyes, which is particularly evident in older specimens. The general body colour is light red to bronze, and some specimens have beautiful, yellow undersides. The fins are a darker red, especially the pectorals. Attains 200 cm.

EXTERNAL ANATOMY
There are 57-63 series of moderately ctenoid scales arranged along the lateral line, those below being slightly larger than those on the upper body. The forehead between the eyes is naked. The fins are well developed, and include a single dorsal of 11 spines plus ten or 11 rays, an anal of three spines plus eight rays, and a slightly forked caudal. The mouth is big and has an outer row of large, formidable canines, as well as several rows of finer teeth within. There are 15-17 short rakers on the first gill arch.

Note: Red steenbras differ from many other Sparidae in that they lack well-defined molars, and have noticeably short gill rakers.

DISTRIBUTION

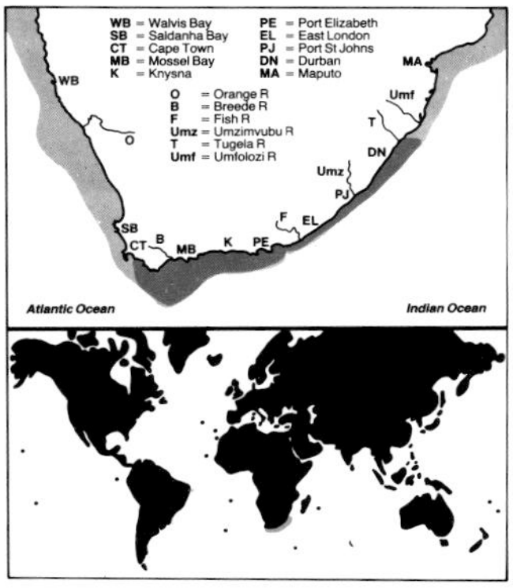

NATURAL HISTORY

The red steenbras is a powerful predator, common in deeper waters around rocky reefs. It is an active, aggressive species, and feeds voraciously on smaller fish especially fingerfins, Fransmadam, klipfish and koester. Squid and octopus are also important food. This species undergoes sex reversal, and the smaller, more numerous shoaling females eventually become large solitary males. These older, less common males are semi-resident, and may display considerable aggression in defending their territory. The breeding season is mainly from September to November, and follows a spawning migration, when large numbers of adult fish are found off the southern Natal and Transkei coasts. The distribution of newly hatched fry has still to be documented. Catch records indicate that young fish of 0,5 to 1,5 kg are common in southern Cape waters during summer. Their virtual absence during the winter months may indicate seasonal migrations.

CAPTURE

The red steenbras is one of southern Africa's great angling fishes, but its abundance has been drastically reduced in the past three decades. The subject of many 'fishing stories', it fights long and hard, and even when exhausted and landed it remains aggressive and should be handled with great care, as its fearsomely armed jaws can inflict deep wounds. The liver of this species should not be eaten in excessive quantities, as it contains large amounts of Vitamin A, which can result in severe illness. This much-sought-after table fish generally takes a variety of baits, but is often inexplicably 'off the bite'. The red steenbras places the spearfishermen successful in landing it, amongst an elite few.

World angling record – 52,2 kg.
SA angling record – 52,2 kg.
SA spearfishing record – 45,4 kg.

SPECIFIC CATCH RESTRICTIONS

Protected species; closed season: 1 Sept to 30 Nov.

NAME DERIVATION

Petrus, stone; *rupestris,* living amongst rocks – both refer to the species' rocky habitat. Red steenbras, a reference to its colour, and its resemblance to the *steenbrasem,* a 'stone-loving' freshwater species occurring in Europe.

SIMILAR SPECIES

The large size, 11 dorsal fin spines and absence of molars are all important distinguishing features.

Polyamblyodon germanum

(Barnard, 1934)
Common name German
[Smith 183□27]

IDENTIFYING FEATURES

COLOUR, SHAPE AND SIZE
This fish is perpetually and wrongly identified as a bronze or copper bream. This is not surprising as, superficially, it bears a close resemblance to both these species. (The arrangement of the teeth, mentioned below, is the surest clue to correct identification). The German is deep-bodied, robust, and has a smooth upper profile. The forehead is steep. The body has a striking, overall bronzy sheen, but the forehead and cheeks are darker and most distinctive. The fins are dark, except for the pectorals which are sometimes blue. Can attain 50 cm.
EXTERNAL ANATOMY
The lateral line is distinct, and along it are arranged 69-72 series of scales. The fins are spiny and well developed, and include a single dorsal of 11 spines plus 11 or 12 rays; an anal of three spines plus ten or 11 rays; a strongly forked caudal; and pectorals that reach slightly beyond the level of the vent. Both jaws of the small mouth carry an outer row of canine teeth, about 40 in the upper jaw and 52 in the lower. Significantly, there are also about seven inner rows of molar teeth, a feature that helps to distinguish this fish from *Pachymetopon* species. The jaws do not reach a point below the eyes. The first gill arch carries 16-20 rakers.

NATURAL HISTORY

The German frequents deeper reefs, and the fact that it is not caught from the shore should also help to avoid confusing it with *Pachymetopon grande*.The outer teeth are well suited to nibbling at encrusting organisms such as tunicates, whereas the powerful molars within enable crabs, crayfish, shrimps and gastropod molluscs to be eaten. Also included in the diet are tiny fish, as well as small amounts of seaweed. Nothing is known of the reproductive biology of this species.

DISTRIBUTION

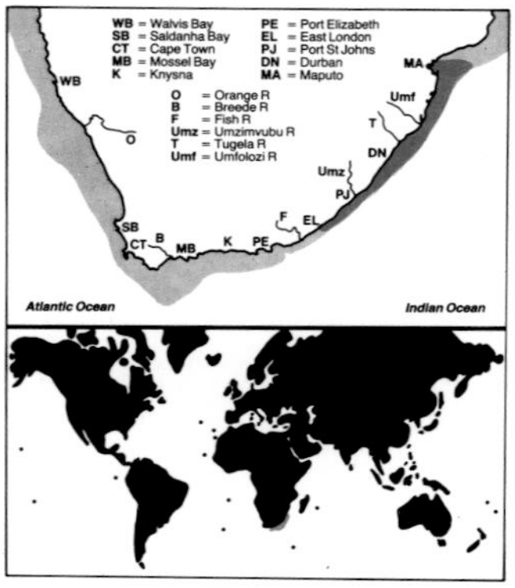

CAPTURE

German take most baits freely, and the majority of ski-boat anglers in Natal have caught this fish. Its flesh makes excellent eating. Spearfishermen also often bag this species, but the sparse fishing-record claims confirm the frequent misidentification of this fish.
SA angling record - 2,5 kg.

NAME DERIVATION

Polyamblyodon, many blunt teeth; *germanum,* sibling. German, derived from the scientific name which can also be translated as 'having the same parents', a reference to its close resemblance to *Pachymetopon grande.*

SPECIFIC CATCH RESTRICTIONS

None.

SIMILAR SPECIES

Easily distinguished from the closely related cristy *(Polyamblyodon gibbosum)* by its longer pectoral fin, which reaches to the vent. The German can be distinguished from the very similar bronze bream by its far more numerous teeth.

Polysteganus coeruleopunctatus

Klunzinger, 1870
Common name blueskin
[Smith 183□29]

IDENTIFYING FEATURES

COLOUR, SHAPE AND SIZE
This fairly deep-bodied fish has a smoothly convex snout, and is generally red above and pinkish-white below. The dorsal surface has a metallic blue sheen, and most of the upper body scales have iridescent blue spots, giving living specimens a remarkably vivid appearance. Attains 50 cm, but most fish are considerably smaller.

EXTERNAL ANATOMY
There are 52-56 series of moderate scales arranged along the lateral line, and only a small area on the forehead below the nostrils is naked. The fins are well developed, and include a single dorsal of 12 spines plus ten rays, an anal of three spines plus eight rays, and a moderately forked caudal. The jaws extend to a point below the eyes, and are armed with large canines, four in the upper and six in the lower. There are also several rows of smaller, conical teeth. The first gill arch has 15-18 lanceolate rakers. The eyes are relatively large.

Note: The blueskin is most distinctive, for it typifies a group of fishes that were originally placed in a separate family, the Denticidae. These are now a subfamily which includes the red steenbras, seventyfour, carpenter, Scotsman, santer and the blueskin itself. All share a number of distinguishing characteristics. Most obvious and important of these are the teeth which, unlike those of other sparids, comprise many large, outward-flaring canines. Molars, however, are lacking.

NATURAL HISTORY

During winter, the blueskin is quite common around reefs, as deep as 100 m. It is mainly a solitary species, and feeds primarily on crustaceans such as crabs. Details of its life cycle and general behaviour are not known, but its seasonal fluctuations would seem to indicate that migrations take place. The blueskin's large eyes appear to be a successful adaptation to the lower reaches of its habitat, where little light penetrates. The blueskin was first 'discovered' in the Red Sea. Today it is known to be widespread throughout the western Indian Ocean, but despite this extensive distribution, information pertaining to its biology is remarkably sparse.

DISTRIBUTION

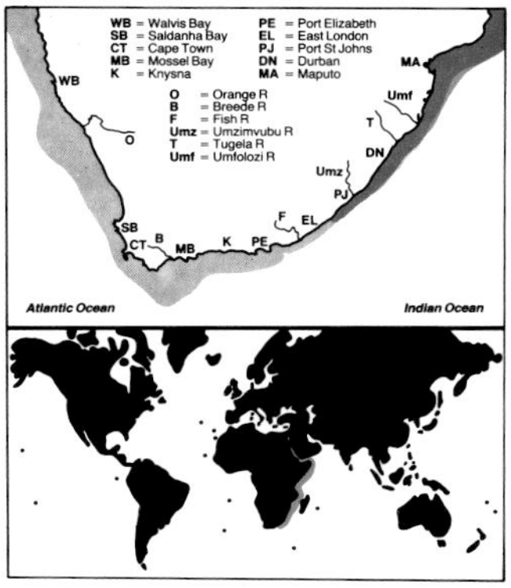

CAPTURE

The blueskin is a tasty species, and, though often caught by ski-boat and commercial line-boat fishermen, it is not a 'target', and most are merely identified as 'line fish'. It freely takes fish baits drifted over a reef. Few are speared by divers.

SA angling record – 4,5 kg.
SA spearfishing record – vacant.

SPECIFIC CATCH RESTRICTIONS

None.

NAME DERIVATION

Polysteganus, densely covered; *coeruleopunctatus,* blue spotted. Blueskin, a reference to its blue spots.

Note: Many fishermen will know this fish as the 'trawl soldier', an allusion to its preference for deeper water, and its similarity to the soldier or santer, *Cheimerius nufar.*

SIMILAR SPECIES

The blueskin is quite easily confused with a number of other species, though the blue-spotted scales are most distinctive. Notice that it is best distinguished from the santer by the absence of any distinctly elongate dorsal spines, and a proportionately larger eye.

Polysteganus praeorbitalis

(Günther, 1859)
Common name Worldwide – Scotsman
[Smith 183□31]

IDENTIFYING FEATURES

COLOUR, SHAPE AND SIZE

This is one of the larger Sparidae, and its body, though deep in front, tapers somewhat towards the tail. The snout is blunt, and the steep forehead gives the fish a rather long face. Colouration is basically pinkish to red, with several series of blue dots forming broken stripes along the sides. There is a blue streak running along the upper flanks and around the eyes. Attains 75 cm.

EXTERNAL ANATOMY

There are 59-63 series of medium-sized scales arranged along the lateral line, but the forehead below the level of the eyes is naked. Scales on the flanks are considerably bigger than those elsewhere, and the scaly sheaths at the bases of the soft dorsal and anal fins are exceptionally deep and sturdy. The fins are well developed, and include a single dorsal of 12 spines plus ten rays, an anal of three spines plus eight rays, and a forked caudal. The large mouth has four canines in the upper jaw, six in the lower, and rows of smaller, conical teeth. The jaws do not reach a point below the eyes. A total of 20-25 long, thin rakers occurs on the first gill arch.

NATURAL HISTORY

The Scotsman is predominantly a solitary species which haunts deep offshore reefs ranging from 20-100 m. This powerful predator feeds on large crabs, crayfish, a variety of reef fish and also, when plentiful, squid. Notwithstanding its solitary nature, small shoals do congregate during the winter breeding season. Sexual maturity is attained at approximately 35-40 cm, and spawning occurs off the Natal coast. The distribution of juveniles, however, is not known.

DISTRIBUTION

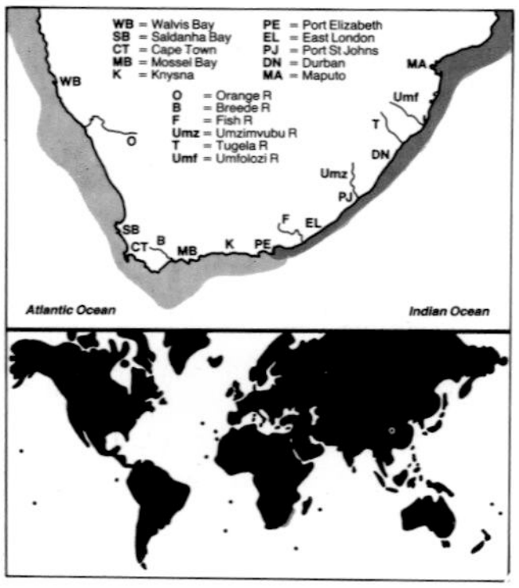

SPECIFIC CATCH RESTRICTIONS

Protected species; minimum legal size is 25 cm.

CAPTURE

Although it is not an uncommon species, large hauls of Scotsman are seldom made. Most ski-boaters regard this as a desirable catch, for though it readily takes fish baits, it is seldom landed because of its powerful, tackle-smashing fighting abilities. It is of moderate commercial value to Natal line-boat operators, mainly because of its esteemed flesh. The Scotsman is seldom landed by shore anglers, except where the sea-bed shelves steeply downwards, and they can cast into deeper water. Few spearfishermen dive deep enough to have any success.
SA angling record – 10,0 kg.
SA spearfishing record – 3,6 kg.

NAME DERIVATION

Polysteganus, densely covered (with scales); *praeorbitalis,* (a long head) in front of eyes. Scotsman, a reference to its hard, dogged fighting abilities.

SIMILAR SPECIES

The Scotsman is easily distinguished from other seabreams by its very steep forehead and noticeably small eye. It can, however, be confused with the emperors, though these have only ten dorsal spines.

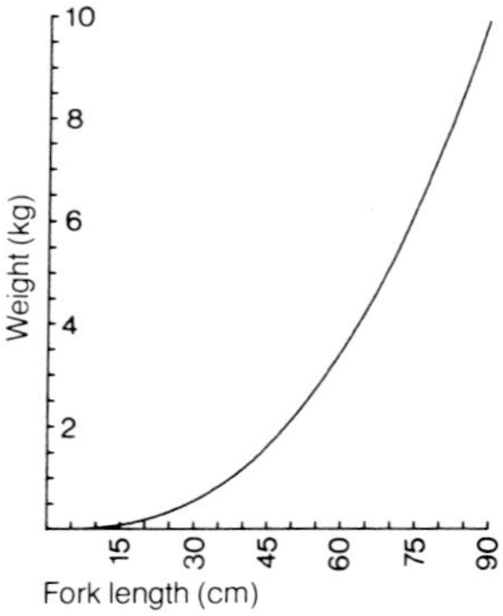

Polysteganus undulosus

(Regan, 1908)

Common name seventyfour

[Smith 183□32]

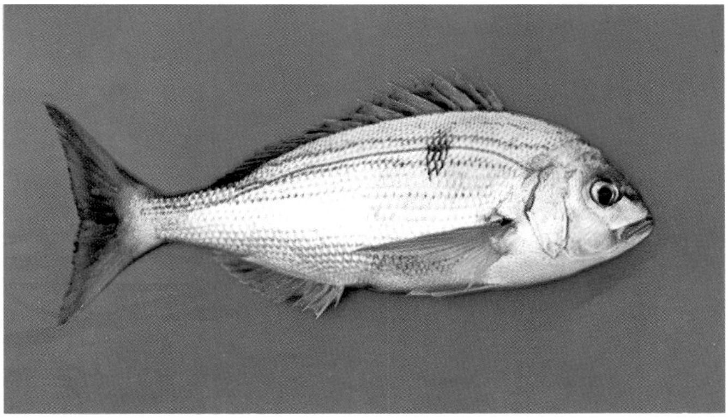

IDENTIFYING FEATURES

COLOUR, SHAPE AND SIZE

This moderately elongate fish has a smoothly convex upper profile. The overall body colour is pinkish-red above, with a white underside. The upper body has an iridescent, blue sheen, and there are 4-6 longitudinal, dotted, blue stripes along the flanks. A conspicuous and distinguishing black mark lies across the lateral line, immediately below the fifth and sixth dorsal spines. This mark is, however, absent in very small fish.

Note: If a dark patch is evident on the chin, the specimen is almost certainly a male. This is a rather unusual feature as very few Sparidae display external sexual differences. Can attain 100 cm.

EXTERNAL ANATOMY

There are 58-62 series of scales arranged along the lateral line, but the forehead below the nostrils is naked. The fins are well developed, and include a single dorsal of 12 spines plus ten rays, an anal of three spines plus eight or nine rays, and a large, slightly forked caudal. The smallish mouth has four canines in the upper jaw and six in the lower, as well as several rows of villiform teeth within. The first gill arch has 20-23 short rakers.

DISTRIBUTION

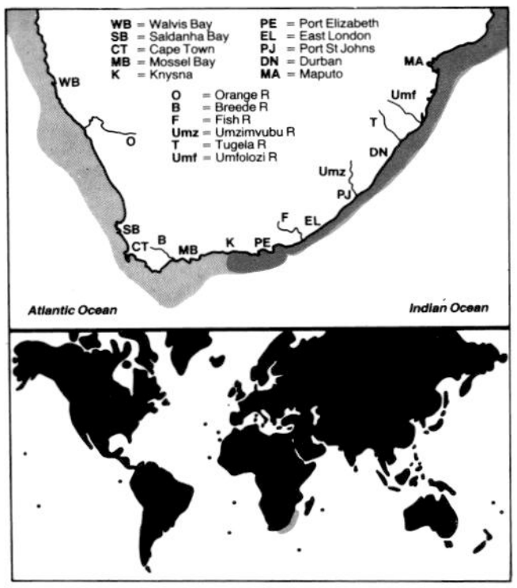

NATURAL HISTORY

The seventyfour frequents deep-water reefs and pinnacles to 200 m. Here, fairly dense shoals often form and move about the reef while feeding; primarily on a variety of fish, but also on squid and planktonic organisms such as pteropods and mantis shrimps. Sexual maturity is attained in the third year at an approximate length of 32-34 cm for males and 34-36 cm for females. Certain specific reefs, such as the Illovo Banks off the Natal coast, are spawning grounds, where large shoals congregate during winter and spring. During this period the 'ripe' fish are exceedingly vulnerable to over-exploitation, a fact which has probably accounted for their serious depletion over the past two decades.

CAPTURE

Experienced ski-boat and commercial anglers know just where and when to catch this highly esteemed and valuable table fish. Pilchard is usually the best bait, but even then catches are not guaranteed. In the past when more plentiful, it formed an important component of the East Coast commercial line-fishing industry. Its deep-water habitat is beyond the range of most shore anglers and spearfishermen.

World angling record – 16,0 kg.
SA angling record – 14,1 kg.
SA spearfishing record – vacant.

SPECIFIC CATCH RESTRICTIONS

Protected species; minimum legal size is 25 cm total length. Closed season; 1 Sept – 30 Nov.

NAME DERIVATION

Polysteganus, densely covered (with scales); *undulosus,* a reference to the undulating blue lines along its sides. Seventyfour, a reference to its alleged resemblance to a 'man-o'-war' with 74 gun-ports.

SIMILAR SPECIES

No other fish has the same body colours and conspicuous black mark on its flank.

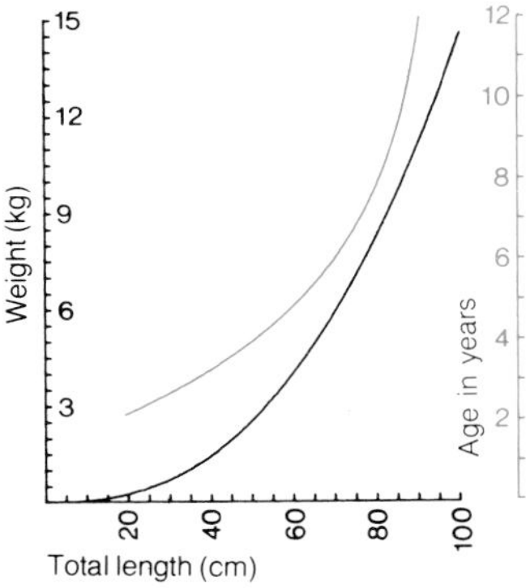

Porcostoma dentata

(Gilchrist & Thompson, 1908)
Common name Dane
[Smith 183□33]

IDENTIFYING FEATURES

COLOUR, SHAPE AND SIZE

This rather plump-bodied species is one of the smaller members of the Sparidae. The upper body surface is orange-red, but fades to an almost-white belly. There is a dark-purple band across the forehead joining the eyes. The orange-red colours are carried through onto the caudal fins, as well as the spiny sections of the dorsal and anal fins, whereas the pectorals, pelvics and the soft sections of the dorsal and anal fins are yellow. The outer edge of the caudal and anal fins are white, and there is a bright red spot on the pectoral axils. Can attain 30 cm, although most fish are smaller.

EXTERNAL ANATOMY

The body is covered with 71-73 almost-square scales arranged along the lateral line. The forehead and part of the pre-opercular flange are naked. The fins are well developed, and include a single dorsal of 13 spines plus 10-11 rays, an anal of three spines plus eight or nine rays, and a slightly forked caudal which has a stout peduncle. There are conspicuous forward-pointing canines in each jaw, four in the upper and six in the lower, as well as a number of molars and smaller teeth deep within the mouth. The 'hinges' of the jaws are completely concealed by the pre-orbital bones on the side of the head. The first gill arch has 17 or 18 short rakers.

NATURAL HISTORY

The Dane is a common species that forms loosely packed shoals over deeper reefs, especially in the vicinity of pinnacles or steep drop-offs, in waters ranging from 20-100 m in depth. The strong jaws and powerful teeth easily crush hard-shelled prey such as crabs, hermit crabs, polychaete worms and crinoids (feather stars). Mantis shrimps are also eaten in large quantities when available. During summer, and at certain specific localities, the Dane may be one of the most abundant species present over a reef. Little has been documented about its life history, but fish exceeding 15 cm in length are mature, and the peak spawning period is during spring.

DISTRIBUTION

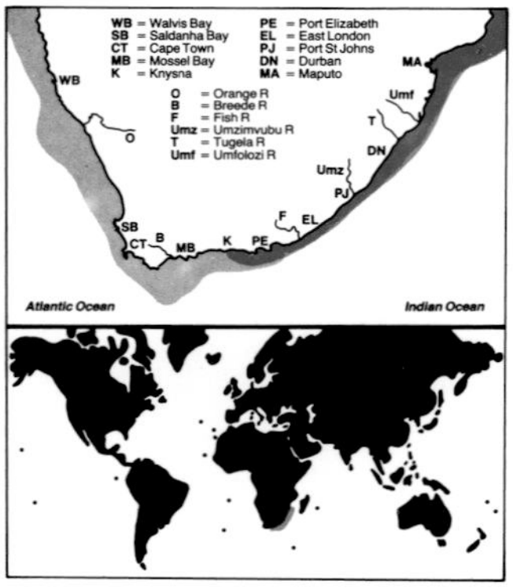

NAME DERIVATION

Porcostoma, pig-shaped, a reference to its plump body; *dentata,* a reference to its strong teeth. Dane, apparently this was a name spontaneously proposed by Mr. Alex Anderson, the pioneer of deep-sea angling in Natal who was, in fact, responsible for many of the local common names.

CAPTURE

The Dane is easily caught by ski-boat fishermen using fish baits. It is generally too small to be of commercial or spearfishing value. It is, nevertheless, a fine table fish.
SA angling record – 0,7 kg.
SA spearfishing record – vacant.

SPECIFIC CATCH RESTRICTIONS

None.

SIMILAR SPECIES

The Dane, with its rather plump body, is not easily confused with any other species. It is the only seabream with 13 dorsal spines, a dark stripe along the beginning of the lateral line, and a purple band across the forehead.

Pterogymnus laniarius

(Cuvier, 1830)
Common name panga
[Smith 183□34]

IDENTIFYING FEATURES

COLOUR, SHAPE AND SIZE
This moderately elongate fish is rosy-red overall, but has a white belly and a number of blue-green longitudinal stripes along the flanks. The fins are translucent pink or dusky. Can attain 45 cm.

EXTERNAL ANATOMY
The lateral line is conspicuous, and along it are arranged 55-60 series of ctenoid scales. The pre-opercular flange and the forehead between the eyes are naked. The fins are well developed, and include a dorsal of 12 spines plus ten rays, an anal of three spines plus eight rays, and a slightly forked caudal. Thick, fleshy lips surround the terminal mouth, and both jaws are armed with formidable canines, the outer pair in each jaw projecting outwards. These are followed by two rows of rather small molars. About 13 rakers occur on the first gill arch. *Note:* Although this species undoubtedly belongs to the Sparidae, there has in the past been some confusion about its precise classification. The panga least resembles the other seabreams because of its flaring canines and poorly developed molar teeth.

NATURAL HISTORY

The panga occurs mainly in deepish water over sandy and rocky bottoms, normally between 50 and 120 m in depth, and often in large shoals. This carnivore, with its fleshy lips, is well suited to feeding on sandy bottoms, where it preys on a wide variety of invertebrates. These include burrowing molluscs, crabs, brittlestars and polychaete worms. There is an extensive summer breeding season with fish spawning from October to May. Growth is slow and sexual maturity is only attained in its fifth year, corresponding to a length of 23-25 cm. Both males and females take a further five years to reach maximum size. The markings of the otoliths, or earstones, can be used to determine age, rather in the manner of reading the annual rings of trees. The panga undergoes sex reversal at about 36 cm total length, and as much as 30 per cent of the population may be bisexual at any one time. However, although both male and female reproductive organs are often present, it is unlikely that both are active simultaneously.

DISTRIBUTION

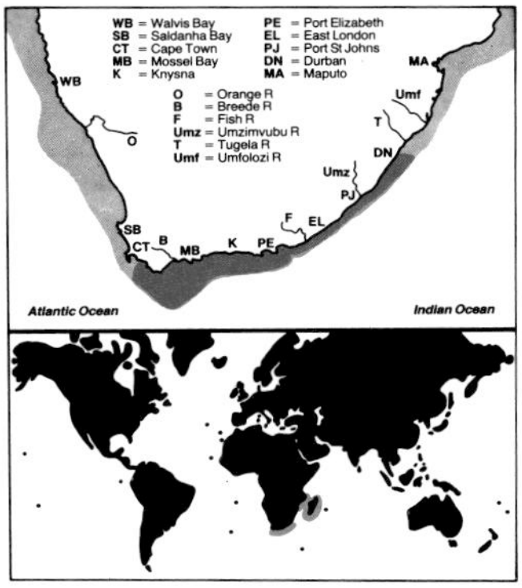

CAPTURE

The panga is very important to the trawling industry, especially in the coastal waters off Port Elizabeth. Ski-boat and line-boat anglers also often land panga, but the species is generally too small to be actively pursued. It is a fine food-fish.
SA angling record - 1,0 kg.

SPECIFIC CATCH RESTRICTIONS

None.

NAME DERIVATION

Pterogymnus, naked wing, a reference to the scaleless patch on the pre-operculum; *laniarius,* longitudinal stripes. Panga, derived from *pangarang,* a similar fish found in Malaya.

SIMILAR SPECIES

This species can be confused with several other seabreams, hence careful attention should be given to the identifying features described here.

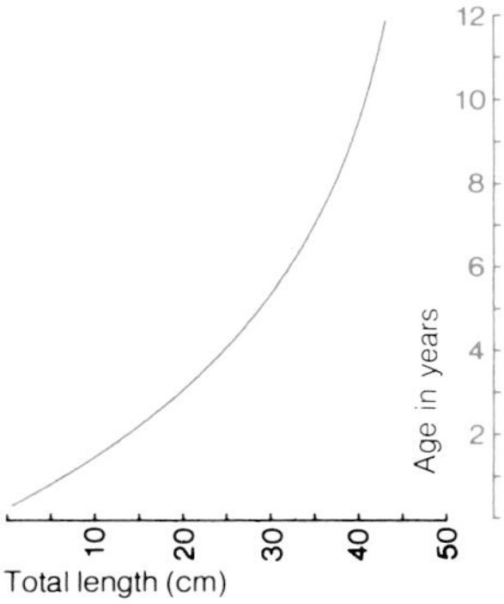

Rhabdosargus globiceps

(Cuvier, 1830)
Common name white stumpnose
[Smith 183□35]

IDENTIFYING FEATURES

COLOUR, SHAPE AND SIZE
This robust species has a steep head profile and a blunt snout. The body is generally silvery, with five or more dark, vertical crossbars. Some specimens may, however, be considerably darker in colour, but this probably depends on its environment. Attains 50 cm.
EXTERNAL ANATOMY
There are about 60 series of scales arranged along the lateral line, but the bridge between the eyes is naked. The fins are well developed, and include a single dorsal of 11 spines plus 11-13 rays, an anal of three spines plus ten or 11 rays, and a moderately forked caudal. The jaws of the terminal mouth each have four to eight rows of outer incisors, and several rows of strong molar teeth within. There are 7-9 rakers on the lower first gill arch.

DISTRIBUTION

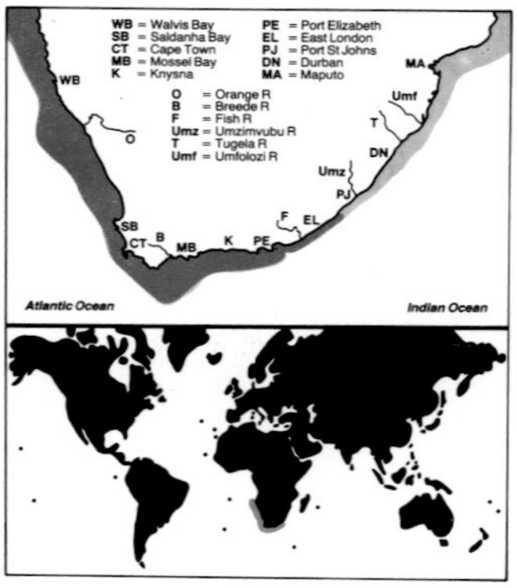

NATURAL HISTORY

The white stumpnose is a coastal species, often occurring in large shoals which range to depths of 60 m. Juveniles up to 15 cm in length are common in estuaries along the Cape coast, and in the sheltered areas of False Bay, especially at night. Adult white stumpnose are usually found over sandy sea-beds, but frequently near small reefs or rocky outcrops. The composition of the diet changes with size and age from omnivorous to exclusively carnivorous. Juveniles feed on filamentous algae, eelgrass, polychaete worms and small crustaceans such as mud-prawns and cracker-shrimps, while larger fish feed on crabs, bivalve molluscs, worms and other crustaceans. Isopod parasites often clog the mouth and about 25 per cent of landed specimens have intestinal worm infestations. Shoals migrate to warmer regions during winter, and spawning occurs close inshore during spring and summer. The fertilized eggs are known to float near the surface. Sexual maturity is attained in the third year, at a length of approximately 30 cm. As juveniles depend on estuaries as nursery areas, it is important that the degradation of these environments be prevented to ensure the long-term viability of this fish. As with other Sparidae, growth patterns on the otoliths may be used to determine age.

CAPTURE

The flesh of the white stumpnose is extremely tasty. It is a popular sport fish, and is best caught on very dark nights, both in estuaries and along the coast. A variety of baits is usually successful, including marine worms and shrimps. It is commercially exploited by line-boat and seine-net fishermen, especially around Kalk Bay.
SA angling record - 2,8 kg.
SA spearfishing record - 2,2 kg.

SPECIFIC CATCH RESTRICTIONS

Minimum legal size is 20 cm total length.

NAME DERIVATION

Rhabdosargus, striped bream; *globiceps,* round headed. White stumpnose, a reference to the stubby snout, and pale colour when compared to the red stumpnose, *Chrysoblephus gibbiceps.*

SIMILAR SPECIES

This fish is easily identified by the crossbars and absence of yellow colours.

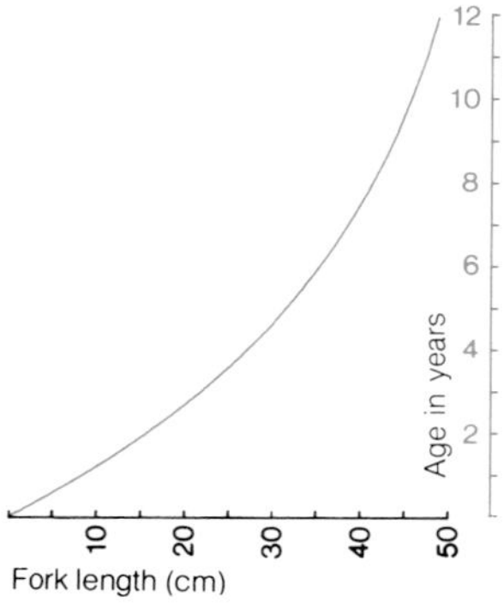

Rhabdosargus holubi

(Steindachner, 1881)
Common name Cape stumpnose
[Smith 183□36]

IDENTIFYING FEATURES

COLOUR, SHAPE AND SIZE
The Cape stumpnose is a rather deep-bodied, oval-shaped fish, with a rounded dorsal profile. The body has an overall silvery sheen, and a distinctive, lemon-yellow line along the middle of each side. The fins are dusky yellow. Juvenile specimens less than 5 cm in length are olive green, and have several vertical crossbars. This is the smallest of the stumpnose species, attaining 40 cm.

EXTERNAL ANATOMY
There are 55-60 series of scales arranged along the distinct lateral line, but the bridge between the eyes is naked. The fins are well developed, and include a dorsal of 11 spines plus 12 or 13 rays, an anal of three spines plus ten or 11 rays, and a moderately forked caudal. The compressed teeth in both jaws are distinctive, and, in younger fish, are clearly tricuspid. There are also several rows of molars and pharyngeal teeth within the mouth and gullet respectively. The lower first gill arch has seven or eight rakers.

DISTRIBUTION

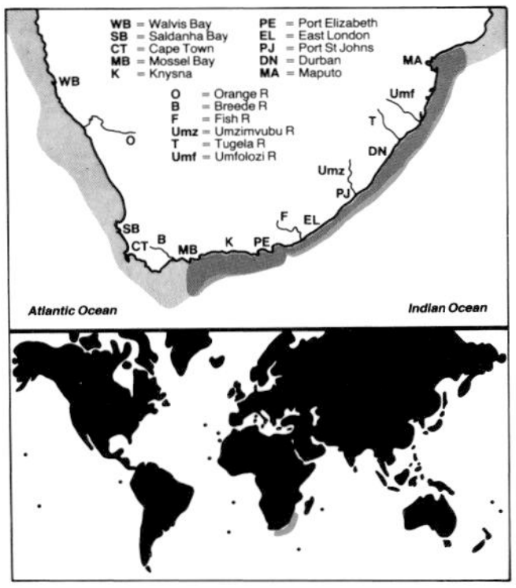

NATURAL HISTORY

The Cape stumpnose is most abundant within a specific range, which lies between that of the Natal stumpnose and the white stumpnose. Though common in shallow coastal waters and estuaries, recent observations indicate that this species is also plentiful around the deep reefs of the Natal coast. The young make extensive use of coastal lagoons as nursery areas, and have a great 'taste' for the eelgrass beds common in some unspoiled estuaries. Their specialized cutting teeth are well-suited to this grazing habit. The eelgrass is not fully digested, however, and is eaten mostly for the nutritious micro-organisms that attach themselves to these plants. Adult fish, however, feed mainly on small bivalve molluscs, shrimps and crabs. Sexual maturity is attained at a length of approximately 20 cm, and spawning takes place during winter along the Natal coast. With the onset of warm weather this species migrates southwards, and during summer it is more abundant in Cape waters. Because juvenile Cape stumpnose are dependent on estuaries as nurseries and feeding grounds, the spoiling of these environments could have a detrimental effect on future Cape stumpnose populations.

CAPTURE

This excellent table fish provides good sport for the light-tackle enthusiast. Worm or shrimp baits cast into gullies and river mouths will give the angler the best chance of success. The Cape stumpnose is not popular with spearfishermen. Nowhere is it exploited commercially.
SA angling record – 2,3 kg.

SPECIFIC CATCH RESTRICTIONS

Minimum legal size is 20 cm total length.

NAME DERIVATION

Rhabdosargus, striped bream; *holubi,* named after Dr Holub, an early German traveller in southern Africa. Cape stumpnose, a reference to the fish's blunt snout and its prevalence in Cape waters.

SIMILAR SPECIES

The lemon-yellow body stripe and tricuspid front teeth are distinctive.

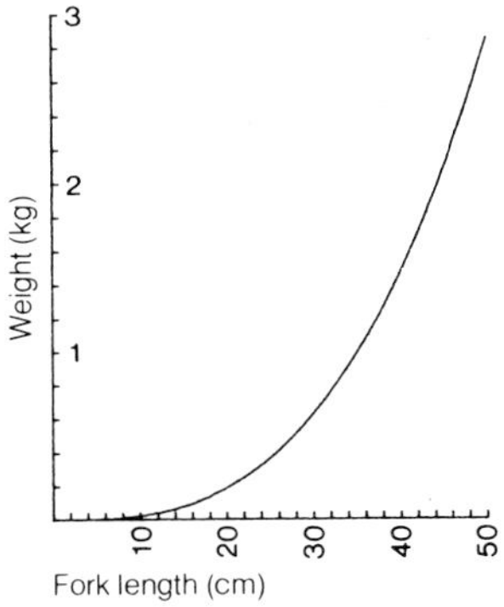

Rhabdosargus sarba

(Forsskål, 1775)
Common names SA - Natal stumpnose, yellowfin bream. Elsewhere - seabream
[Smith 183□37]

IDENTIFYING FEATURES

COLOUR, SHAPE AND SIZE

This deep-bodied species has a rounded dorsal profile. It is silvery-grey overall, but the golden centre to each scale often gives the impression of longitudinal lines along the flanks. The belly, pelvic, pectoral and anal fins are all yellow, though this fades with age. The Natal stumpnose grows to 80 cm, but most measure less than 40 cm.

EXTERNAL ANATOMY

Scales are well developed, and are arranged in 56-64 series along the lateral line, but the bridge between the eyes is naked. The sturdy fins include a dorsal of 11 spines plus 12-13 rays, an anal of three spines plus 11 rays, and a slightly forked caudal. There is a distinct outer row of teeth in each jaw, and several rows of strong molars within. Pharyngeal grinding teeth occur in the gullet. The first gill arch carries 7-9 rakers on its lower limb.

DISTRIBUTION

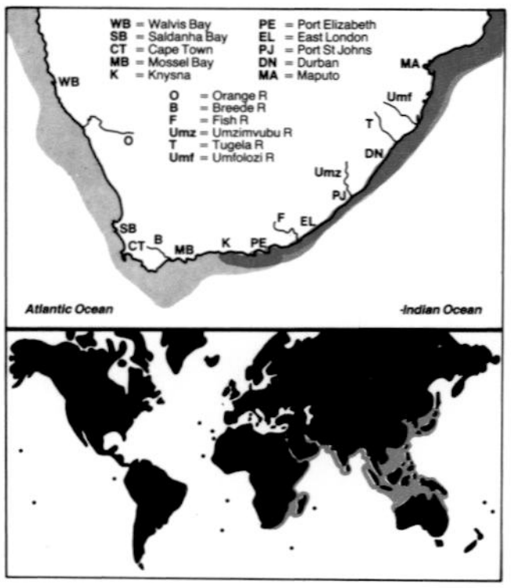

NATURAL HISTORY

Shallow, and often brackish waters around inshore reefs and sandy bays are the most common habitats of this species. Few individuals are found at depths greater then 50 m. Many also frequent estuaries. The summer months usually mark the period of peak abundance, and large shoals are often present at this time. The strong teeth and pharyngeal mill easily cope with the hardest of shellfish, and, not surprisingly, common food items include rock and sand mussels, oysters, clams, sand dollars, sea urchins and mole crabs (sea lice). Sexual maturity is attained at a length of 25 cm, but in common with many Sparidae, the Natal stumpnose often passes through a bisexual stage, when both male and female reproductive organs are present simultaneously. Spawning takes place during winter near river mouths. This ensures that many newly hatched juveniles are able to reach estuaries, where they shelter for their first year.

SPECIFIC CATCH RESTRICTIONS

Minimum legal size is 25 cm.

CAPTURE

In southern Africa, this species is only fished for sport, but elsewhere in the world, bottom trawls and gill-nets are used for commercial exploitation. Mussels, mole crabs (sea lice) and redbait are successful baits. The Natal stumpnose is best caught at night, close inshore and near a rocky ledge. Spearfishermen often bag larger specimens of this fine table fish over deeper reefs.

SA angling record - 7,7 kg.
SA spearfishing record - 6,4 kg.

NAME DERIVATION

Rhabdosargus, striped bream; *sarba,* meaning obscure. Natal stumpnose, a reference to the centre of its South African distribution, and to its blunt snout.

SIMILAR SPECIES

The pointed row of outer teeth, 11 anal rays, absence of crossbars, and moderate yellow colouration characterize *R. sarba.*

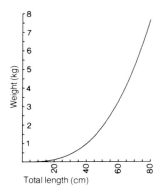

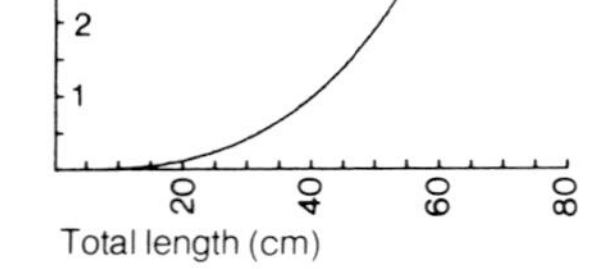

Rhabdosargus thorpei

Smith, 1979
Common name bigeye stumpnose
[Smith 183□38]

IDENTIFYING FEATURES

COLOUR, SHAPE AND SIZE
This deep-bodied species has a smoothly rounded profile and a somewhat blunt snout. The body has an overall silvery sheen, somewhat darker above and white below. There is a distinct, broad, golden band which runs from the chest along the entire underside, as well as a number of finer golden stripes along the flanks. The pelvic and anal fins are bright yellow.
Can attain 50 cm.

EXTERNAL ANATOMY
There are 55-60 series of scales arranged along the lateral line, but the forehead between the eyes is naked. The fins are well developed, and include a single dorsal of 11 spines plus 13 or 14 rays, an anal of three spines plus 11 or 12 rays, and a moderately forked caudal.
In each of the jaws, there is an outer row of incisors followed by numerous molars deeper within the mouth. Pharyngeal grinding plates occur in the throat. The first gill arch carries 15-20 rakers. The eyes are proportionately larger than those of other stumpnose species.
Note: The past confusion that reigned about the correct classification of the several South African *Rhabdosargus* species had been finally resolved by the late Prof. J.L.B. Smith. Mr. A.R. Thorpe then 'discovered' this species at Mbibi in Tongaland. Although now described by Prof. Margaret Smith as a new species, the name *R. auriventris* has also been applied to this fish.

NATURAL HISTORY

The bigeye stumpnose has a distribution similar to that of the Natal stumpnose, and often these two species occur together. This species ranges to slightly deeper water, as well as the outer edges of coral and rocky reefs. Its diet consists mainly of molluscs and crustaceans, most being crushed by the molars and pharyngeal mill. The remains of mussels, clams, barnacles, crabs and small crayfish have been found in the stomachs of landed specimens. Adults do not enter estuaries, but juveniles are quite common in Kosi Bay and other nearby tropical estuaries. Little is known of its life history.

DISTRIBUTION

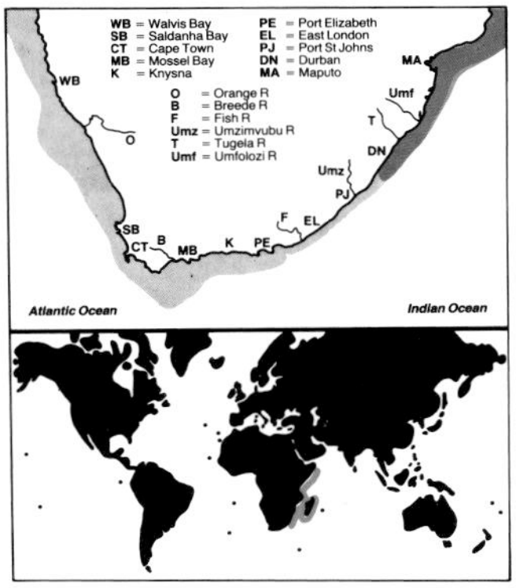

SPECIFIC CATCH RESTRICTIONS

None.

CAPTURE

The bigeye stumpnose is frequently caught by ski-boaters and by rock and surf anglers in Zululand. It is best caught on light tackle with mussel or crayfish bait, and, despite its small size, it is a good table fish.
SA angling record – 1,4 kg.
SA spearfishing record – vacant.

NAME DERIVATION

Rhabdosargus, striped bream; *thorpei,* after Mr. A.R. Thorpe who brought this species to the attention of Prof. Margaret Smith. Bigeye stumpnose, a reference to its large eyes and blunt snout.

SIMILAR SPECIES

The large eye and broad, golden band will positively identify this species.

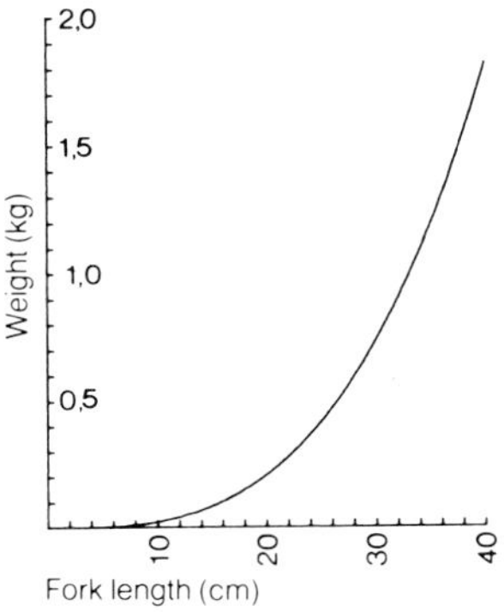

Sarpa salpa

(Linnaeus, 1758)
Common names SA - strepie, karanteen. Elsewhere - saupe
[Smith 183□39]

IDENTIFYING FEATURES

COLOUR, SHAPE AND SIZE
Though elongate, this species is somewhat plump-bodied, and has an overall silver sheen. Some 8-10 longitudinal, yellow stripes run from the gill covers to the tail. Attains 30 cm in length.

EXTERNAL ANATOMY
There are about 75 series of scales arranged along the lateral line, but the bridge between the eyes is naked. The fins are well developed, and include a single dorsal of 11 spines plus 14-16 rays, an anal of three spines plus 13-15 rays, and a forked caudal. Teeth in juveniles are pointed and conical, but in adults these are replaced by multi-cusped incisors. There are about 13 rakers on the first gill arch.

DISTRIBUTION

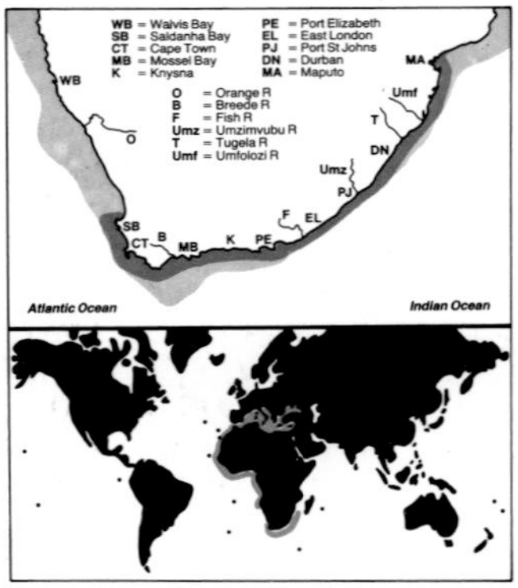

NATURAL HISTORY

This inshore species inhabits rocky regions, and generally prefers cooler water. During the day, feeding shoals can often be observed moving in and out of shallow water with the tides. Although the fry initially feed on planktonic animals, larger fish almost exclusively consume red seaweeds. This complete change of diet is facilitated by concommitant changes in anatomy; the pointed teeth of juveniles give way to sharp, cutting teeth more suited to a browsing habit, and the gut lengthens considerably to cope more efficiently with the high-bulk, low-energy, vegetarian diet. Small amounts of animal food in the form of hydrozoa and bivalve molluscs are also occasionally eaten.
As it is one of the most abundant herbivorous fishes in southern Africa, it is undoubtedly an important link in the foodweb. In Natal, where this species is most abundant during the winter months, spawning has been recorded amongst specimens exceeding 16 cm in length from April to September. Juveniles are tolerant of salinity changes, and make extensive use of southern Cape estuaries and shallow, sandy coastlines as development areas.
It is likely that the great southwards 'push' of the warm Agulhas Current plays an important role in this dispersal of fry down the coast to the Cape.

CAPTURE

The strepie is a tasty table fish, and, despite its small size, it is popular with anglers. It is frequently caught from breakwaters and rocky shores. It is also an excellent bait for larger fish, particularly if rigged live. The species has no spearfishing or commercial importance.
SA angling record - 1,3 kg.

SPECIFIC CATCH RESTRICTIONS

Open species; minimum legal size is 15 cm.

NAME DERIVATION

Sarpa, meaning obscure; *salpa,* a Latin name applied to certain food fishes. Strepie, Dutch/Afrikaans for striped. Karanteen, meaning obscure, probably of Mauritian origin.

SIMILAR SPECIES

Few will misidentify this fish, with its bright-yellow stripe, and absence of molar teeth.

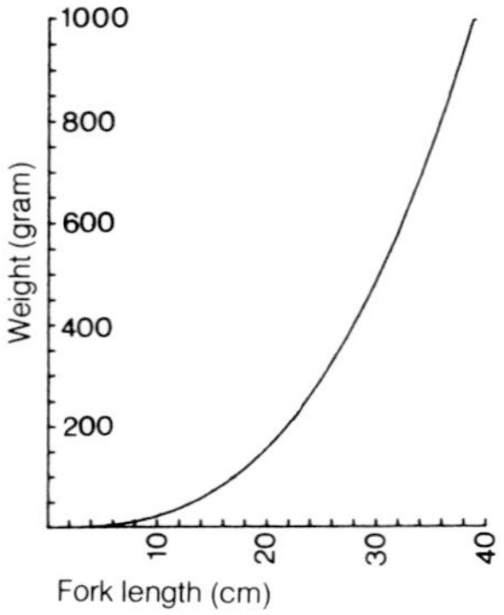

Sparodon durbanensis

(Castelnau, 1861)
Common names white musselcracker, brusher, white biskop
[Smith 183□40]

IDENTIFYING FEATURES

COLOUR, SHAPE AND SIZE

This robust, oval-bodied fish has a large head with a broad ridge between the eyes, and a blunt snout. The silvery body soon darkens after death. Juveniles have longitudinal stripes and orange fins. Can attain 120 cm.

EXTERNAL ANATOMY

The scales are firm and distinct, and are arranged in 58-61 series along the lateral line, but the bridge between the eyes is naked. The fins are well developed, and include a single dorsal of 11 spines plus 11-12 rays, an anal of three spines plus ten rays, and a slightly forked caudal. The mouth is surrounded by thick lips, and there are four prominent incisors in the front of each jaw, as well as several rows of large molars within. Some of these crushing teeth are distinctly bigger than others. The first gill arch carries about 13 short rakers. The eyes are rather small.

DISTRIBUTION

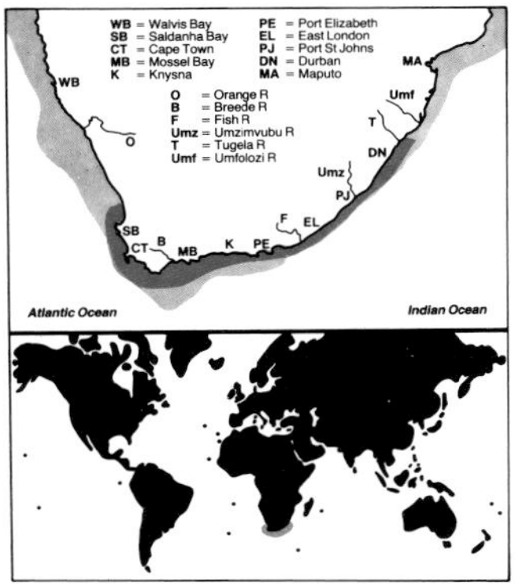

NATURAL HISTORY

The white musselcracker is found in coastal waters, especially along rocky shores. Underwater observations indicate that this species can vary its colour to blend with its immediate surroundings; hence white musselcrackers feeding on mussel beds aften tend to be much darker than those over a sandy bottom. Its large, flat teeth and powerful jaws are put to good use, as the black mussel forms its prime source of food. The diet is supplemented with sand mussels, gastropod molluscs, whelks, redbait, tube worms and sand dollars, as well as occasional crabs, crayfish and small fish. Juveniles feed on copepods, amphipods and mysids. Seasonal variations in abundance occur, and, during winter, it is more numerous along the East Coast, while during the summer it is more prolific along the South Coast. Despite these fluctuations, the musselcracker appears to be resident, for at least part of the year, within specific localities. This makes it vulnerable to heavy fishing pressure in these regions, but the establishment of marine reserves could circumvent this real danger. Though this fish is normally solitary, shoals occur during the breeding season, frequently just off sandy beaches. Spawning occurs during winter, spring and early summer along the entire Cape coast. The brightly coloured juveniles are common in intertidal rock pools.

CAPTURE

Large white musselcrackers are superb fighting fish, and, though much sought after by rock anglers, hooked specimens are not always landed, as they have the ability to literally 'bend hooks'. Crabs, crayfish, redbait and mussels are all successful baits. Because of its inshore habitat, it is seldom caught from ski-boats, but it is a favourite target for spearfishermen. The flesh of very large specimens may be rather coarse, but generally it is highly palatable, and the head is regarded by some as an especial delicacy.
SA angling record – 23,1 kg.
SA spearfishing record – 22,2 kg.

SPECIFIC CATCH RESTRICTIONS

None.

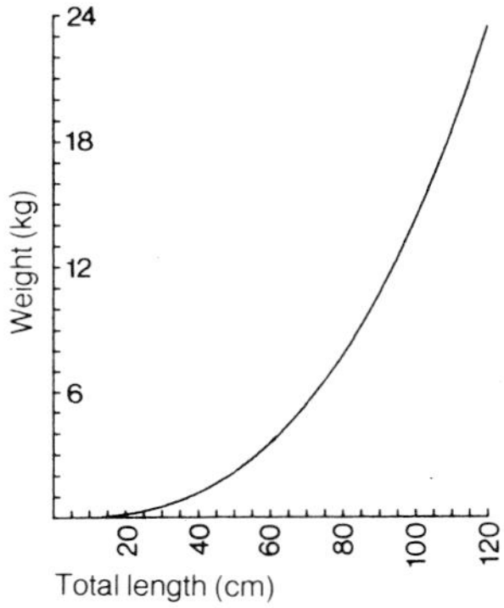

Spondyliosoma emarginatum

(Cuvier, 1830)
Common name steentjie
[Smith 183□41]

IDENTIFYING FEATURES

COLOUR, SHAPE AND SIZE
This small species has a fairly elongate body. Colours vary from brown to silvery-blue, but the belly is pale. There are about seven longitudinal, yellow lines along the flanks, and the scaleless forehead is dark brown. The fins are dusky to dark, and often marked with blue spots. Attains 30 cm but few exceed 25 cm.

EXTERNAL ANATOMY
The scales are rather small, and are arranged in 80-90 series along the lateral line. These cover most of the body, except for a naked patch on the bridge between the eyes and on the inter-operculum. The fins are well developed, and include a single dorsal of 11 spines plus 11-13 rays, an anal of three spines plus ten rays, and a moderately forked caudal. There are several rows of elongate teeth in each jaw, though the inner teeth tend to be rounded. The lower limb of the first gill arch carries 15-17 rakers.

DISTRIBUTION

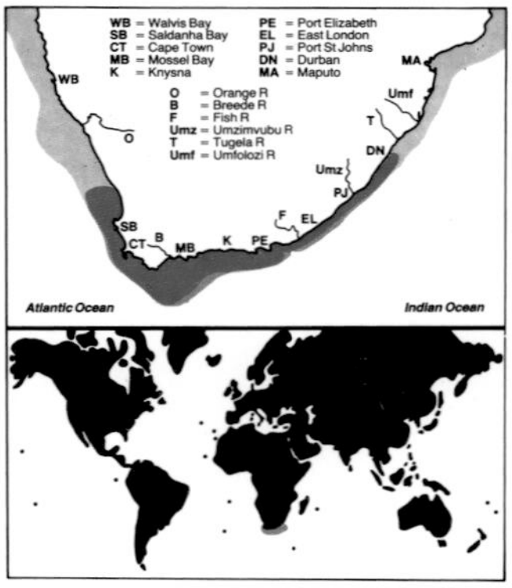

NATURAL HISTORY

The steentjie occurs in large shoals around, or just above reefs, varying in depth from 5-30 m. Despite occasional sorties into estuaries, it is not tolerant of low salinities. Its major source of food is redbait, supplemented by polychaete worms, small crabs and amphipods. It is possible that limited algal grazing also occurs. Seasonal fluctuations take place, and the steentjie is most abundant off the eastern Cape coast during autumn and off the southern Cape coast during spring and summer, when spawning has been recorded. Specimens exceeding 22 cm are sexually mature, and engage in a peculiar courtship display and breeding pattern that is most uncommon within the Sparidae. The male fish, which is more intensely marked and coloured, constructs a nest on a coarse, sandy bottom. This consists of a shallow, 50-cm-wide depression to which the female is enticed after a courtship chase. A clutch of eggs is then produced, and the nest is aggressively protected until the fry are hatched some days later.

CAPTURE

The steentjie is caught in large numbers by both commercial line-boat fishermen and sport anglers using a variety of baits including redbait and marine worms. Though used primarily as bait for larger gamefish, this species is becoming increasingly popular and important as a source of food.
SA angling record – vacant.
SA spearfishing record – vacant.

SPECIFIC CATCH RESTRICTIONS

Open species.

NAME DERIVATION

Spondyliosoma, a body with a jointed backbone; *emarginatum*, emarginate. Steentjie, an old Dutch/Afrikaans word meaning 'little stone', a reference to its size and rocky habitat.

SIMILAR SPECIES

The steentjie can be distinguished from the hottentot by a scaly sheath that covers the base of the soft dorsal and anal fins. It has a much smaller eye than that of the Fransmadam.

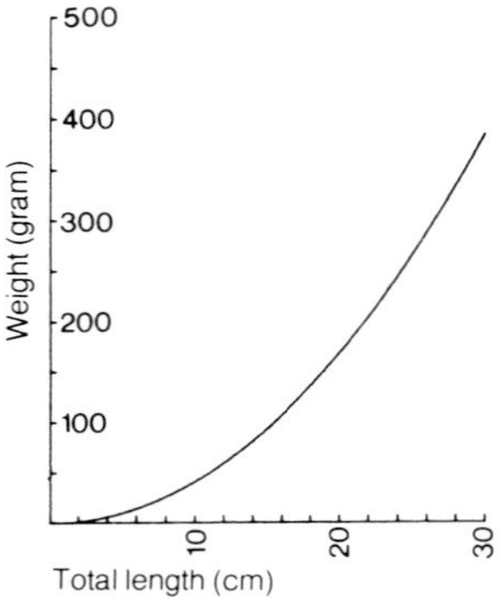

Sphyraena barracuda

(Walbaum, 1792)
Common name Worldwide - great barracuda
[Smith 224□3]

IDENTIFYING FEATURES

COLOUR, SHAPE AND SIZE

This large, robust fish is elongate and slightly compressed. Its snout is long and pointed. The overall body colour is grey with a silver and white underside. Smaller specimens have some 20 faint crossbars on the sides, whereas larger individuals display several obvious, inky blotches below the lateral line. Attains 165 cm.

EXTERNAL ANATOMY

Well-formed scales are arranged in 75-90 series along the lateral line, which is clearly visible as each of the scales overlying it has a distinct tubercle. There are two dorsal fins; the first comprises five strong spines, while the second has one spine plus eight or nine rays. The anal fin has one spine plus seven or eight rays. The caudal fin is broad and moderately forked. Both jaws of the large, widely gaping mouth bear a fearsome array of sharp teeth. The lower jaw projects slightly, giving the fish an undershot appearance. The first gill arch lacks rakers.

NATURAL HISTORY

This is the largest and most famous of the barracudas, and, though it occurs in shoals, solitary individuals are often observed gliding around coral reefs. It is a voracious feeder, and its prey includes a large variety of fish species. The diet varies according to age, with young barracuda feeding on anchovies and other small, shoaling fish, and adults eating either sluggish, reef fish, or faster, surface species such as kingfish, mullet and garfish. Solitary barracuda tend to feed on large, non-shoaling fish. Though adults normally show a preference for reef environments, the choice of habitat is also linked to age and size, with juveniles being more common in tropical mangrove areas and shallow estuaries. Sexual maturity is attained at a length of 50 cm or more, and spawning occurs during summer in the tropical waters of East Africa and the Seychelles. In their very early stages, juveniles are pelagic, and particularly sensitive to sudden changes in water temperature. Several well-documented cases exist in which the great barracuda has attacked humans. Despite this, however, the great barracuda can hardly be considered a 'maneater', and is only dangerous when provoked or molested.

DISTRIBUTION

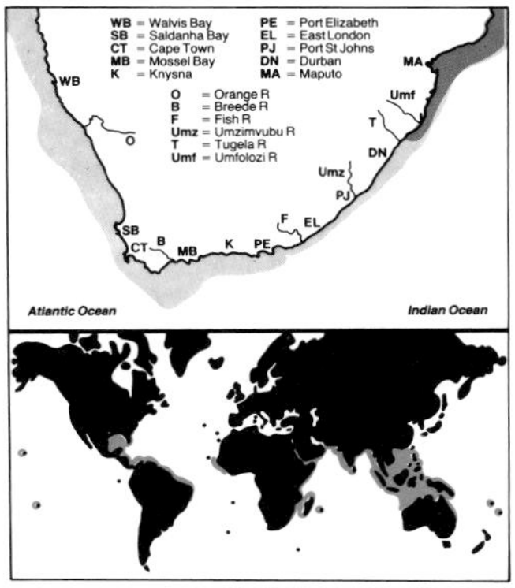

SPECIFIC CATCH RESTRICTIONS

None.

CAPTURE

The great barracuda can be caught on live bait or lures, usually from ski-boats, but also, occasionally, from the shore. Brave (or foolhardy) spearfishermen also hunt this fish successfully. The flesh is wholesome and, though held responsible for ciguatera poisoning on some tropical islands, is not known to be toxic in southern African waters.

World angling record – 38,8 kg.
SA angling record – 24,0 kg.
SA spearfishing record – 29,6 kg.

NAME DERIVATION

Sphyraena, an ancient name for a hammer; *barracuda*, a reference to the common name. Great barracuda, a reference to its size, and its Spanish-American name of unknown origin.

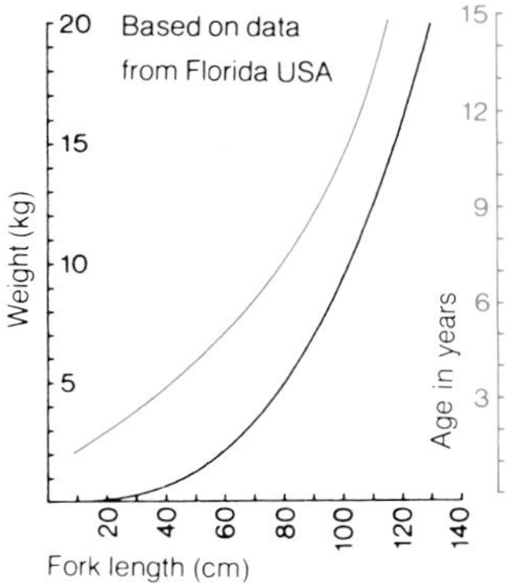

Sphyraena jello

Cuvier, 1829

Common names SA - pickhandle barracuda, seapike. Elsewhere - slender barracuda

[Smith 224□17]

IDENTIFYING FEATURES

COLOUR, SHAPE AND SIZE

This elongate fish is almost cylindrical in cross-section. Its body is silvery overall, but yellow-green above and white below. There are also about 20 vertical, dusky crossbars on the flanks. Can attain 100 cm.

EXTERNAL ANATOMY

The body is covered with small, but well-developed, cycloid scales arranged in 135-140 series along the lateral line. There are two widely separated dorsal fins, the first consisting of five spines, and the second of one spine plus nine rays. The anal fin comprises two spines plus eight rays, while the caudal is relatively large, and forked. The widely gaping mouth has a slightly projecting lower jaw. The long, sharp teeth are strongly flattened. The complete absence of gill rakers is characteristic.

DISTRIBUTION

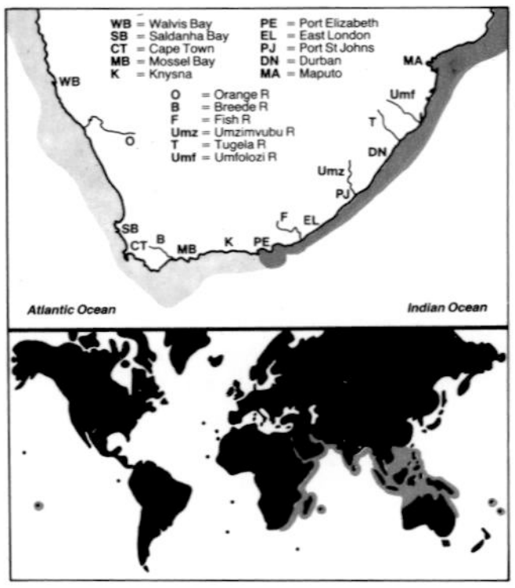

NATURAL HISTORY

The pickhandle barracuda is a fierce, predatory shoaling fish, which is generally confined to coastal reefs. Despite its size, this barracuda is remarkably inconspicuous in clear open water, a phenomenon often reported by skin divers. This characteristic camouflage is largely dependent on the fish's 'dappled' body colours, but is enhanced by its ability to 'freeze' in midwater. By melding so effectively with its environment, the barracuda probably remains undetected by potential prey - undoubtedly an important aspect of its hunting strategy. It feeds almost exclusively on fish, especially those species associated with coral and rocky reefs. Squid are also occasionally consumed. Migrating shoals of more than 50 tightly packed individuals are also often spotted. Little is known of this species' life history, though juveniles are preyed upon by king mackerel and dolphinfish around Durban.

SPECIFIC CATCH RESTRICTIONS

None.

CAPTURE

The pickhandle barracuda is caught by anglers using live bait, lures and sometimes fish fillets. Though not commercially exploited in southern African waters, it is of greater importance in tropical regions where traps may be used to make considerable hauls. Spearfishermen bag good numbers, especially when migrating shoals are encountered. Its flesh is of fair eating quality.

World angling record - 6,63 kg.

SA angling record - 16,8 kg.

SA spearfishing record - 16,0 kg.

NAME DERIVATION

Sphyraena, an ancient name for a hammer; *jello,* meaning obscure. Pickhandle barracuda, a reference to the fish's slender body, and to 'barracuda', a worldwide common name of unknown Spanish-American origin

SIMILAR SPECIES

Barracudas are never easy to identify, and may require careful scale and body measurements. However, the great barracuda, with its black blotches, and the pickhandle with its 20 crossbars, absence of gill rakers, and more than 130 scale series, are distinctive.

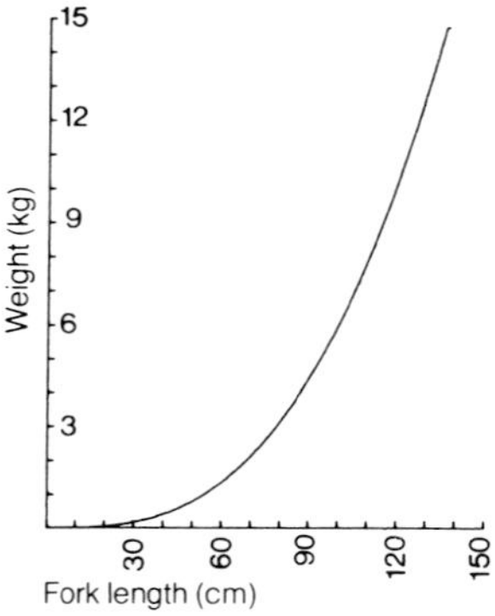

Saurida undosquamis

(Richardson, 1848)
Common names SA – largescale lizardfish. Elsewhere – brushtooth lizardfish, saury
[Smith 79□3]

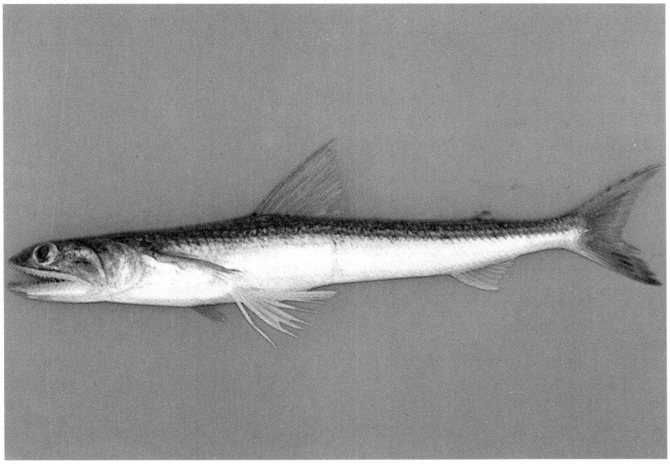

IDENTIFYING FEATURES

COLOUR, SHAPE AND SIZE

The elongate and cylindrical body of the largescale lizardfish is brown above and white below. A number of blotches occur along the flanks, and 4-7 black dots mark the upper lobe of the caudal fin. Live specimens seen underwater, however, may appear considerably more mottled. Attains 50 cm.

EXTERNAL ANATOMY

Distinct, cycloid scales cover the body except for the head. These scales are arranged in 45-52 series, with those overlying the lateral line being enlarged to form a distinctive ridge on either side of the body. Spines are lacking in the primitive fins. There are two dorsal fins; the first comprises 11 or 12 rays, while the second lacks rays and is made up of adipose tissue. The anal fin has 10-12 rays, and the caudal fin is strongly forked. Both pelvic fins have nine rays, the outer rays being only slightly shorter than the inner. The mouth is large, and the jaws extend almost to the gill covers. Numerous teeth occur in both jaws in addition to several rows on the palate. Most of these teeth can be folded inwards. Both eyes are covered with an adipose eyelid. There are approximately 70 small rakers on the first gill arch.

NATURAL HISTORY

This reptile-like fish is common over sandy areas near offshore reefs. Here it lies quite still on the sea-bed, only its eyes moving and focussing on the potential prey around it. The fish's mottled colouration blends well with its surroundings, and, while this certainly affords protection against predators, it also plays a role in feeding. Small fish, unaware of its presence, often stray very close, and are snatched in a sudden flurry, after which the lizardfish returns to its resting place on the sand. Feeding occurs during daylight only. Sexual maturity is attained at the age of two years and at a length of 24-25 cm, the ratio of males to females being 1:5. Spawning may then occur intermittently over long periods. Little is known of the whereabouts or distribution of the fry.

DISTRIBUTION

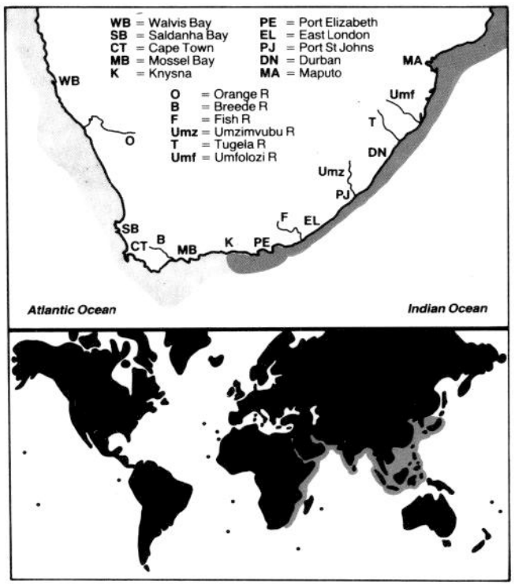

CAPTURE

With light tackle and small hooks, any number of these fish can be caught from a ski-boat. Though generally too small to be of importance, in the Far East they represent an important resource, and tons are eaten annually, mainly in the form of fish cakes. The largescale lizardfish is an important component of the natural diet of the king mackerel, and, as such, should be an excellent bait for this gamefish.

SPECIFIC CATCH RESTRICTIONS

None.

NAME DERIVATION

Saurida, lizard; *undosquamis*, large scales. Lizardfish, a reference to its superficial resemblance to this reptile.

SIMILAR SPECIES

While identification of the ten South African lizardfishes is not always a simple task, the largescale lizardfish can be immediately recognized by the black dots on its upper caudal fin.

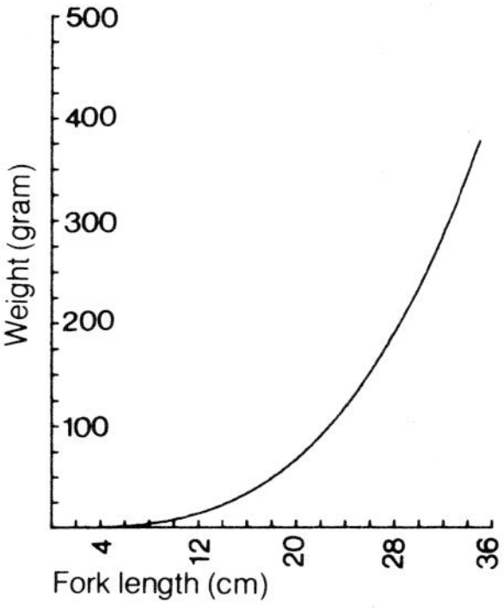

Terapon jarbua

(Forsskål, 1775)
Common names SA – thornfish, tigerfish. Elsewhere – jarbua therapon
[Smith 173□2]

IDENTIFYING FEATURES

COLOUR, SHAPE AND SIZE
This small fish, with its compressed, oblong body, is silvery overall, with three or four longitudinal, brown stripes along each flank. Several black blotches occur on the dorsal and caudal fins. Can attain 20 cm.
EXTERNAL ANATOMY
Small, but rough ctenoid scales cover the body, arranged in 70-100 series. The dorsal and anal spines are very robust and sharp. The dorsal fin has 11 or 12 spines preceding 9-11 soft rays, the anal consists of three spines plus 7-10 rays, and the caudal fin is slightly forked. There is also a strong, powerful spine on each gill cover. The mouth is slightly downward-slanting, and the jaws are set with bands of fine,villiform teeth. There are 13 -16 rakers on the lower first gill arch.

DISTRIBUTION

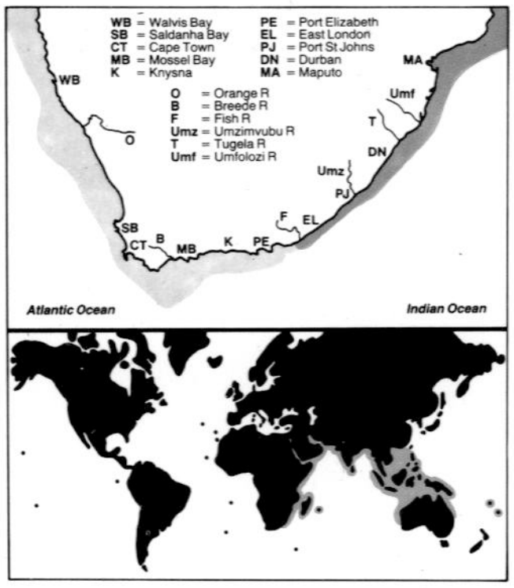

NATURAL HISTORY

The thornfish is most frequently found in brackish water, close to the shore. Young fish use estuaries as nursery areas, and some have been recorded in 100 per cent fresh water. Prey includes small crabs, shrimps and fish fry. The thornfish also exploits an additional, rather bizarre food source, for it removes and eats the scales of other live fish. As scales consist primarily of keratin (a protein), the thornfish is assured of an almost infinite supply of food. This fish displays cunning aspect to its feeding strategy. It hides in shallow depressions in the mud, and, when a suitable fish ventures close by, it rapidly stirs the soft sea-bed with its tail. This creates a cloud of fine mud, and when the unsuspecting victim approaches to investigate the disturbance, the thornfish rushes out from behind its 'smokescreen' to snatch its meal. Spawning occurs at sea during late spring. The swim bladder is sometimes used to produce a croaking sound, though the significance of this habit is unknown. An interesting aspect of the thornfish's defence strategy is that, when captured, it bends its body almost double to expose its body spines. This makes the fish most unpalatable, and too 'thorny' for predators to swallow, especially fish-eating birds.

CAPTURE

The thornfish is not generally regarded as an angling or food-fish. At times it persistently annoys anglers by nibbling at baits intended for other species, especially at St Lucia on the Zululand coast, where it has earned for itself the somewhat dubious title 'pest of St Lucia'.
In some parts of the Far East, thornfishes are considered palatable.
SA angling record – 0,6 kg.

SPECIFIC CATCH RESTRICTIONS

None.

NAME DERIVATION

Terapon, from *theraps*, meaning slave; *jarbua*, unknown, but probably of Arabic origin. Thornfish, a reference to its stout spines.

SIMILAR SPECIES

There are two similar thornfish species in southern African waters. While this species has curved body stripes, the closely related, but rarer, *T. theraps* has distinctly straight lines along each flank.

Amblyrhynchotes honckenii

(Bloch, 1795)
Common name Worldwide – evileyed puffer
[Smith 268□1]

IDENTIFYING FEATURES

COLOUR, SHAPE AND SIZE
The evileyed puffer resembles a robust and rather elongate blaasop. The dark-green upper flanks and dorsal surface are separated from the white underside by a broad, yellow band. Irregular, pale blotches mark the upper body and the head. The eyes are noticeably green. Can attain 30 cm.

EXTERNAL ANATOMY
Scales are lacking, and, though the mid-flank region is smooth, numerous small spines occur on the upper and lower sides. These spiky projections are not always very conspicuous, however, and are best seen under a magnifying glass. The fins are quite large, and the single dorsal and anal fins are located opposite one another. No spines occur in the fins, and the dorsal consists of eight or nine rays, while the anal has seven or eight rays. The caudal fin is large and truncate. As with other Tetraodontidae, the teeth are fused into a strong beak. Small, round gill openings precede the large pectoral fins. The lateral line is branched and extends onto the caudal peduncle. Unlike many common puffers, the members of this species do not have a raised fold of skin along the lower surface of the peduncle.

NATURAL HISTORY

The evileyed puffer is one of the most widely dispersed and best known of the marine fishes in southern Africa. It is particularly abundant in eastern and southern Cape waters. Shallow, sandy areas are favoured habitats, though it is also common around deeper reefs and in estuaries. This puffer is predominantly a bottom-dweller, and often buries itself beneath the sand with only its eyes protruding. From such 'ambush' positions, it darts out to snatch unsuspecting prey, including small crabs, slow-swimming fishes and various bottom-living invertebrates. The evileyed puffer is also an eager scavenger, and fishing sites, with their constant supply of discarded bait and offal, are regular haunts. Typically, the members of this species are able to inflate themselves to grotesque proportions if threatened or molested. As a defence strategy, this behaviour is often effective, as would-be predators are suddenly confronted with a much larger fish than the original target. Details of the life history are unknown, but juveniles are probably dispersed by sheltering beneath floating objects borne along by ocean currents.

SPECIFIC CATCH RESTRICTIONS

None.

CAPTURE

The bait-robbing evileyed puffer is the bane of the shore angler's life, many specimens being caught unintentionally. Though it may spoil angling on occasions, the practice, at many fishing sites, of slaughtering landed puffers, is unnecessary and not to be recommended. The flesh of this fish is at least as toxic as that of other Tetraodontidae and should never be eaten or fed to animals.

DISTRIBUTION

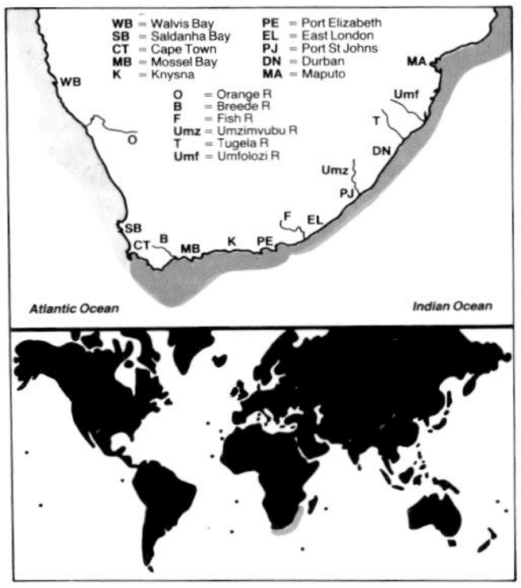

NAME DERIVATION

Amblyrhynchotes, blunt snouted; *honckenii*, origin unknown. Evileyed puffer, a reference to its 'evil', green eyes, and the ability to inflate itself.

SIMILAR SPECIES

The colour, shape and patterns shown here are distinctive. However, some confusion exists about the identification of this and the next species (see notes on page 376).

Chelonodon patoca

(Hamilton-Buchanan, 1822)
Common names SA – milkspotted puffer. Elsewhere – marbled toad
No Smith reference

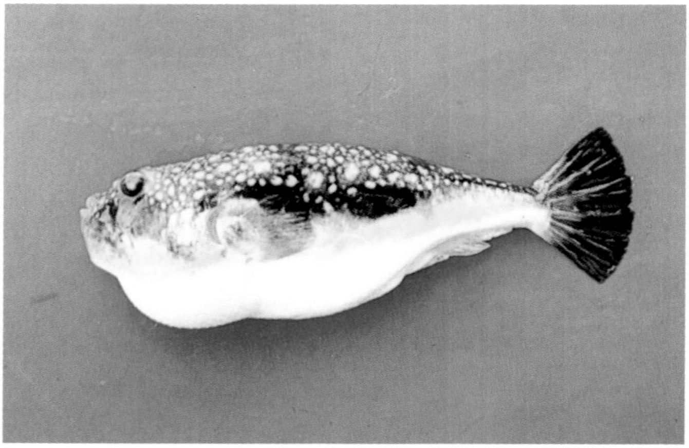

IDENTIFYING FEATURES

COLOUR, SHAPE AND SIZE
This robust puffer is slightly elongate, and tapers towards the tail. Its body colouration is complex. Basically it is brown above and white below with a silver streak along the sides, which is edged with bright yellow. The brown upper surface is marked with greenish spots, each being slightly smaller than the eye diameter. Three indistinct, but broad, dark saddles lie across the back. The fins are yellowish brown or translucent. Can attain 35 cm in some parts of the world, but does not exceed 15 cm in southern African waters.

EXTERNAL ANATOMY
True scales are lacking, but there are numerous small spines on the dorsal surface that extend as far back as the dorsal fin. These spines also occur on much of the belly. There is a single dorsal fin of 9-11 rays, and an anal of 8-10 rays. The caudal fin is slightly rounded. There are no pelvic fins. The small mouth is situated at the tip of the stubby snout, and is armed with a powerful beak comprising two bony plates in each jaw. The eyes bulge prominently, and in front of them is a pair of nostrils which have raised edges.

NATURAL HISTORY

The milkspotted puffer lives in shallow water, either over sandy bottoms near reefs, or in estuaries. On being approached by a diver or, presumably, any other potential danger, it invariably burrows beneath the sand, leaving only its eyes protruding. Although this fish is often thought to be primarily a scavenger, consuming only dead fish and crustacean moults, its ability to hide below the sand may well enable the fish to snatch unsuspecting prey. Browsing on sedentary worms and crustaceans is also known to occur. This species can inflate itself with water or air when attacked or molested, and will only 'subside' and swim away once the cause for alarm has passed.

DISTRIBUTION

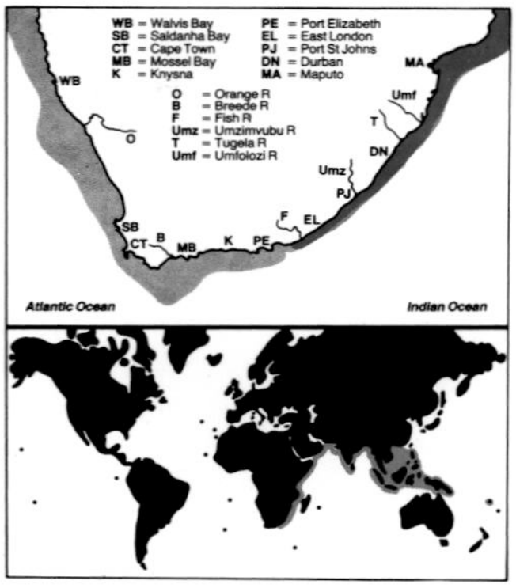

SPECIFIC CATCH RESTRICTIONS

None.

CAPTURE

As with the previous species, this fish is cursed by sport anglers. It often congregates near fishing spots, presumably attracted by the discarded bait. Here, it eagerly pounces on baits intended for other fish. It is never intentionally caught by anglers in southern Africa as its flesh, liver and skin are exceedingly toxic. Some Japanese gourmets, however, regard the carefully prepared flesh of this and other puffers as a delicacy.

NAME DERIVATION

Chelonodon, biting teeth; *patoca*, possibly a corruption of *patonce*, a cross having four arms radiating from the centre, an allusion to the pattern formed by the fused teeth. Milkspotted puffer, from the milky colouration of the spots on its round body.

SIMILAR SPECIES

There is considerable confusion about the true identity of this fish. Recent publications suggest that this species is in fact the evileyed puffer described on the previous page. However, while undoubtedly similar, there are many noticeable differences that suggest that the two are indeed distinct species. Until further scientific study has been conducted, the milkspotted puffer (*C. patoca*) is tentatively retained here.

Lagocephalus guentheri?

Ribiero, 1915
Common name SA - blackback blaasop
[Smith 268□19]

IDENTIFYING FEATURES

COLOUR, SHAPE AND SIZE
This elongate, but thickly set fish is dark olive-green above, silvery along the sides and has light-green cheeks. The belly is white, and the caudal fin lobes are tipped with white. Can attain 30 cm.

EXTERNAL ANATOMY
This fish lacks true scales, but there are small spines on the belly and head which become erect when the fish inflates. The spineless fins are much reduced and include a single dorsal of 12 rays, an anal of 10-14 rays, a lunate caudal and broad pectorals. At the base of each pectoral fin is a tiny gill opening. The small, terminal mouth contains two plate-like teeth which form a strong beak. The eight, paired rakers are difficult to expose. A fold of skin occurs along the lower edge of the sides and on the tail. The double lateral line is conspicuous on both sides of the body: one surrounds the eyes and the other runs along the flanks as far as the tail.

NATURAL HISTORY

This puffer is a shallow-water species, but it rarely enters estuaries, and solitary individuals are normally encountered over scattered reefs or around jetties and wharfs. It is essentially a scavenger, feeding on dead and floating matter. The powerful beak may, however, also be used to bite off chunks of encrusting organisms. If alarmed, threatened or provoked, this fish inflates itself almost to the point of bursting. By increasing its overall size in this manner, the fish 'suddenly' becomes too large for many predators. The inflating mechanism of this species and, indeed, puffers in general, has been the subject of research for many years. The process involves the gulping in of either water or air, depending on the medium in which the fish finds itself at the time of stress. Contrary to popular belief, the puffer does not come to the surface to inflate itself. Modified muscles in the throat facilitate the pumping action and once the special branch of the stomach, the diverticulum, is fully distended, pressure is maintained by the voluntary contraction of special sphincter muscles, and not by valve-like flaps as was previously supposed. Very little is known of its life history. The poisonous liver, gonads, intestines and skin of puffers appears to be another aspect of the general defence strategy of these fishes. Yet predators such as barracuda and dolphinfishes readily feed on them, hence the reasons for the presence of these nerve toxins is not altogether clear. Humans, however, are highly susceptible to the puffer's poisonous organs and skin, and, if eaten, rapid and violent death can ensue. Locomotion in this rather sluggish fish is largely dependent on the pectoral fins.

CAPTURE

Excluding the Japanese, few people intentionally fish for this species. It is, nevertheless, often landed as, much to the ire of anglers, it is quick to snatch bait intended for 'worthier' fish.
SA angling record - 0,9 kg.

SPECIFIC CATCH RESTRICTIONS

None.

DISTRIBUTION

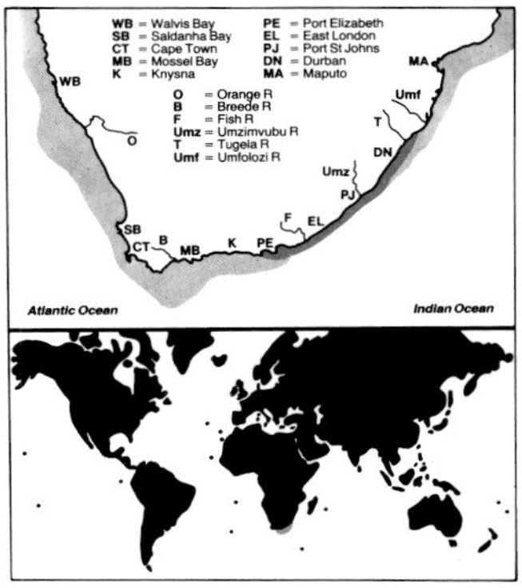

NAME DERIVATION

Lagocephalus, having a head like a hare; *guentheri,* after Guenther, a systematist for the British Museum at the turn of the centry. Blackback blaasop, reference to its colour and ability to inflate itself.

SIMILAR SPECIES

This blaasop was previously identified as *Gastrophysus spadiceus,* but this appears to be incorrect, as *G. spadiceus* has the entire caudal margin white. It is, therefore, tentatively named *L. guentheri,* a species also found in Brazil and Japan. The related smooth blaasop *(L. inermis)* can be identified by its more lunate caudal fin, and complete lack of spines on the back.

Chelidonichthys capensis

(Cuvier, 1829)
Common names Cape gurnard, Cape sea robin
[Smith 157□1]

IDENTIFYING FEATURES

COLOUR, SHAPE AND SIZE

The Cape gurnard is an elongate fish with a broad, flattened head encased in a bony shield. The tapering body is red overall with a white belly. Particularly striking are the pectoral axils, with their spectacular, blue-green and black markings. Can attain 70 cm.

EXTERNAL ANATOMY

Approximately 100 series of small scales are arranged along the lateral line. There is also a row of 3-25 bony plates on either side of the dorsal fin. Each plate is armed with a single spine. The breast is naked. The fins are well developed, and include a dorsal of eight or nine spines plus 15-17 rays, and a spineless anal of 14-16 rays. The large caudal fin is emarginate, and the pectorals are exceptionally large, each having three, separated, barbel-like rays. The small mouth is slightly underslung, and has very fine teeth in each jaw.

DISTRIBUTION

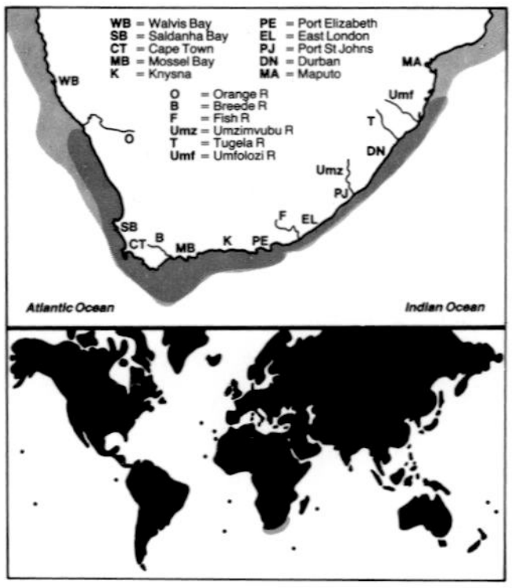

NATURAL HISTORY

The Cape gurnard is generally found in rather deep water, at least to 300 m. It is a bottom-dweller, and feeds extensively on the crustaceans of this region. It is particularly fond of crabs, which are selected with the assistance of the sensory, pectoral 'feelers'. Female fish appear to attain sexual maturity before males. Nevertheless, most fish are able to spawn in their fourth year, at a corresponding length of approximately 35 cm. Spawning occurs primarily during spring and early summer, but details of the breeding grounds and the dispersal of young are sparse. Studies have revealed that the Cape gurnard is quite probably of major ecological importance in the foodweb of the Algoa Bay region. There is some speculation about the significance of the large, brightly coloured pectoral fins, but it appears that they 'warn off' predators when suddenly exposed. The markings on these fins also resemble eyes, and this could serve to confuse predators as to the gurnard's size. The otoliths, or earstones, of this species have been used to determine age.

SPECIFIC CATCH RESTRICTIONS

None.

CAPTURE

The Cape gurnard is of considerable commercial significance, and is one of the six most important fish trawled off the eastern Cape coast. It is also caught by ski-boat and hand-line fishermen, but it is not regarded as a sport fish. Its flesh makes very good eating.
SA angling record - 3,2 kg.

NAME DERIVATION

Chelidonichthys, swallow-like fish; *capensis*, of the Cape, its main region of occurrence. Cape gurnard, derived from the old French word *gornart*, meaning 'to grunt', presumably a reference to the croaking noises made by this fish when captured.

SIMILAR SPECIES

The seven gurnard species found in southern Africa require detailed examination to determine identity. However, this common species can be positively identified by the pectoral fin markings and colours. The bluefin (*C. kumu*) is similar but has a large, bright-blue patch on each pectoral.

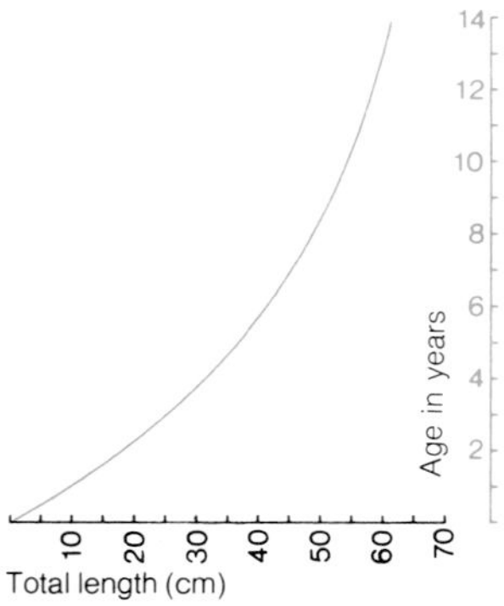

Trichiurus lepturus

Linnaeus, 1758

Common names SA – cutlassfish, ribbonfish, walla-walla. Elsewhere – cutlassfish, hairtail

[Smith 248□6]

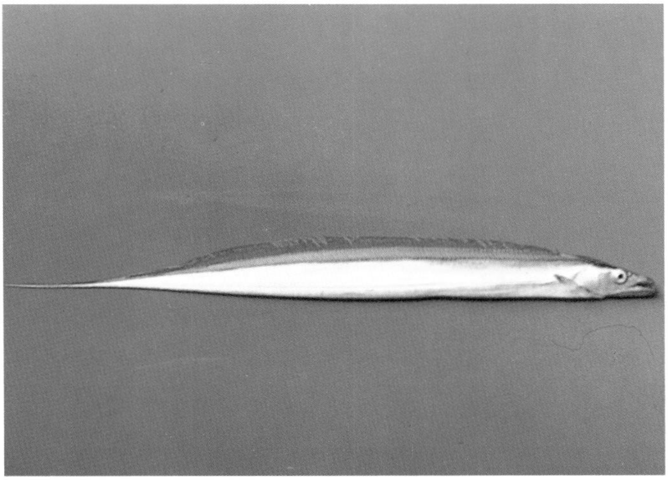

IDENTIFYING FEATURES

COLOUR, SHAPE AND SIZE

The highly compressed and elongate body of the cutlassfish tapers to a long, pointed tail. The overall colour is bright silver, with a bluish sheen on the upper body. Attains 200 cm.

EXTERNAL ANATOMY

Scales are absent, and the smooth skin readily loses its silvery coating after capture. The lateral line is conspicuous; it originates on the upper head and dips sharply downwards above the pectoral fin, before running horizontally towards the tail. The spines are poorly developed in the primitive fins. The single dorsal fin has three spines preceding 124-138 rays, while the anal has two inconspicuous spines followed by 105-110 rays. No pelvic fins occur, but short pectoral fins are present. The large, terminal mouth bears vicious, fang-like teeth, which have conspicuous barbs and sharp edges. The first gill arch has 16-24 rakers. The large eyes tend to bulge outwards. *Note:* Dissection reveals a very long, thin swim bladder.

NATURAL HISTORY

This wide ranging fish is generally confined to continental shelf waters, ranging from shallow sandy estuaries to depths of 300 m. During summer, its abundance increases in temperate waters. Feeding takes place in the half-light of dusk and dawn. Small, pelagic fish, especially anchovies, as well as small squid, prawns and mantis shrimps, are actively preyed upon. As with many carnivorous fishes, the stomach of the cutlassfish distends greatly during feeding, and sometimes the body weight is increased by as much as 25 per cent. Cutlassfishes are normally encountered in dense shoals, and, as such, are vulnerable to net capture. Spawning has been recorded off the Natal coast among specimens exceeding 70 cm. Females tend to be larger than males. Though populations in the Atlantic and Indian oceans show no variability, there is evidence to suggest that the mature fish from these two regions do not mingle past Cape Agulhas. The cutlassfish often assumes a vertical stance in the water, with its head pointing forward and its long body trailing downwards. The purpose of this distinctive behaviour is not known.

DISTRIBUTION

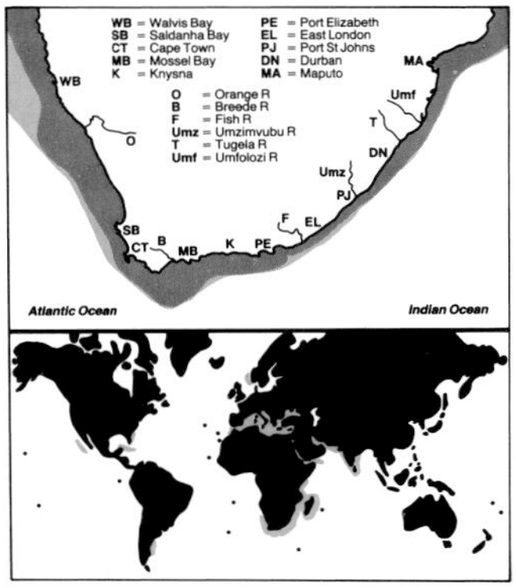

SPECIFIC CATCH RESTRICTIONS

None.

CAPTURE

This fish is easily caught by anglers using light tackle and small lures or surface baits. Once hooked, it fights gamely. There is a knack to cleaning this very bony fish, but it is worth the trouble, for the flesh is very tasty. It is not speared, but is trawled commercially in many parts of the world.

SA angling record – 2,4 kg.

NAME DERIVATION

Trichiurus, hair-like tail; *lepturus*, slender tail. Cutlassfish, a reference to its sword-like shape.

SIMILAR SPECIES

The pointed tail, absence of a pelvic fin, and barbed fangs will positively identify this species.

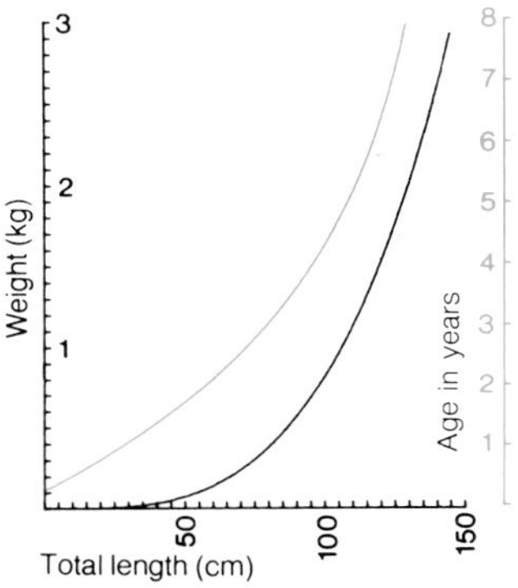

Zanclus canescens

(Linnaeus, 1758)
Common name Worldwide – Moorish idol
[Smith 244□1]

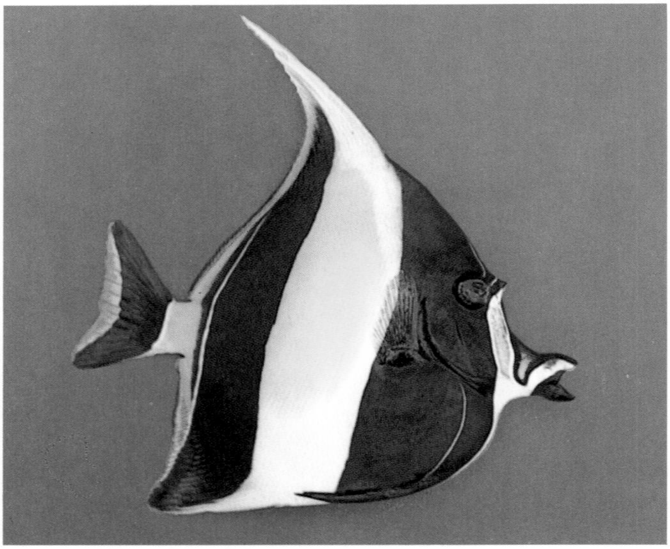

IDENTIFYING FEATURES

COLOUR, SHAPE AND SIZE
This unmistakable fish is strongly compressed and almost round, but the body depth is exaggerated by the extended dorsal and anal fins. A broad, central, white bar is flanked on either side by a broad, black bar, and together they cover much of the body. A large, yellow blotch overlies the central bar, while the black bars include a variable number of fine, vertical, blue lines. The face is black and white, with an orange saddle across the bridge of the pronounced snout. Can attain 22 cm in length.

EXTERNAL ANATOMY
The body is covered with numerous minute, ctenoid scales. The third of the six or seven dorsal spines is long and thread-like, and, if undamaged, can exceed the entire body length. There are 39-42 dorsal rays, and the anal fin comprises three spines plus 32 rays. The caudal fin is slightly concave. The small mouth has slightly protractile jaws which contain several rows of long brush-like teeth. Adult specimens normally have horn-like projections on the forehead.

NATURAL HISTORY

This exquisite little fish occurs in pairs or small groups over shallow, rocky or coral reefs. It especially favours the newly proclaimed St Lucia Marine Reserve, but, with the southward push of the warm Agulhas Current during summer, its distribution is extended further into Natal waters, with some specimens even occasionally reaching the eastern Cape. Most feeding occurs during daylight, and the specialized mouth makes it possible for this fish to feed on the algae and small invertebrates that shelter in cracks and crevices in the coral. This ability gives the Moorish idol a distinct advantage, as these food items are inaccessible, with a few exceptions, to other coral or rocky reef dwellers. Sponges are also an important food source. Breeding takes place during summer, and the transparent fry are pelagic, before adopting a bottom habitat at a length of 5 cm. Juveniles have been recorded at depths of 300 m in mid-ocean waters.

DISTRIBUTION

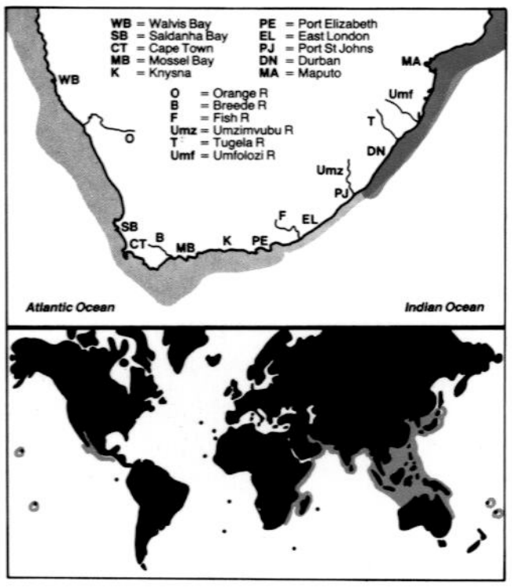

CAPTURE

Though much sought after by marine aquarists, the Moorish idol is not easily caught, and is only maintained in captivity with difficulty. It is not considered edible, and is best left undisturbed.

SPECIFIC CATCH RESTRICTIONS

None.

NAME DERIVATION

Zanclus, a sickle; *canescens*, turning grey or hoary. Moorish idol, a reference to its position of considerable reverence among certain Moslem populations.

SIMILAR SPECIES

While there is some resemblance to the coachman, *Heiniochus acuminatus* (Page 175), the large yellow mark on its flank, and the orange saddle across its snout make the Moorish Idol unmistakable.

Zeus faber

Linnaeus, 1758
Common name Worldwide - target John Dory
[Smith 138□5]

IDENTIFYING FEATURES

COLOUR, SHAPE AND SIZE
The oval-shaped body, which is exceedingly compressed, is dull greyish-green overall. The underside is somewhat paler. Most distinctive on each flank is the dark, round blotch located below the arched lateral line and just behind the pectorals. This mark is clearly surrounded by a lighter, almost silvery border. Can attain 75 cm.

EXTERNAL ANATOMY
This very smooth fish lacks scales, except for those that lie along the distinct and curved lateral line. The fins are well developed, and include a single dorsal of nine or ten very elongate spines plus 21-24 rays, an anal of four spines plus 20-22 rays, and a broadly rounded caudal. The pectoral fins are short, but the pelvics are fairly large. Along the base of the dorsal and anal fins is a row of bony plates, each carrying a number of sharp spines. Another distinctive characteristic is the very large mouth, which can be protruded to the most remarkable extent. Fine teeth occur in both jaws. The first gill arch has 10-15 rakers.

NATURAL HISTORY

Most John Dories are common in deep water, often at depths of 140-400 m. The members of this species, however, occasionally venture onto shallower coastal reefs, presumably to feed on the abundance of small fish in this region. Its method of hunting provides an excellent example of 'ambush tactics'. Its deep, clumsy body is unsuited to speeding after prey, and it has evolved a strategy far more suited to its awkward body proportions. The John Dory swims very slowly and head-on towards its intended meal, but because of its excessive 'thinness', it remains almost invisible to the victim. In this manner, the John Dory approaches to within a few centimetres of its prey. Then, with great rapidity, the jaws shoot forward and the prey is snatched and swallowed. Of further interest is its peculiar mode of forward propulsion. This is achieved by opposing beats of the anal and dorsal rays, and provides a striking contrast to the body and tail undulations of most other fishes. Spawning occurs over the continental shelf, mainly during summer, and the eggs drift just above the bottom.

CAPTURE

Large quantities of the target John Dory are landed in commercial trawl nets. However, though it is one of the tastiest of fish, most are discarded because of their unusual external appearance. Ski-boat anglers frequently catch this fish.
SA angling record - 2,7 kg.
SA spearfishing record - 2,6 kg.

NAME DERIVATION

Zeus, named after the Greek god; *faber,* a blacksmith. Target John Dory, 'target' refers to the 'bulls-eye' lateral marks, but the origin of 'John Dory' has numerous explanations. Some allege that it is derived from the Italian *janitore* meaning a doorkeeper, while others believe it to be a corruption of the Gascon name *Jan Doree.*

DISTRIBUTION

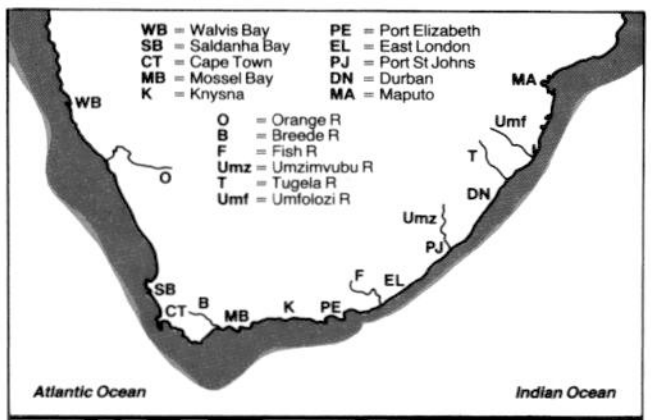

SPECIFIC CATCH RESTRICTIONS

None.

SIMILAR SPECIES

The related Cape dory (*Z. capensis)* has a fainter-black spot on or above the lateral line.

GLOSSARY
BIBLIOGRAPHY
INDEX

GLOSSARY

Many of the entries in the glossary are illustrated in the introductory pages to this book. For example, food organisms are illustrated on page 16, while line drawings setting out the anatomy of cartilaginous and bony fishes can be found in the 'Illustrated Outlines' on pages 25 to 27 and 65 to 67 respectively.

A

abdomen — belly.
acuminate — tapering to a point, e.g. as in fins.
acute — sharply pointed.
adipose — fatty tissue. Many fish have an adipose layer covering all or part of their eyes, or forming rayless fins.
aggregation — a group of fish not necessarily all swimming in the same direction, i.e. as opposed to a shoal.
air bladder — see swim bladder.
algae — a low form of aquatic plant-life.
amphipod — sometimes known as a sand hopper, a small crustacean which lacks a carapace.
alimentary canal — the gut.
anadromous — descriptive of fish which migrate from the sea to spawn in fresh water, as opposed to catadromous.
anal — region of the vent, or anal fin.
anal papilla — a fleshy projection at the anus; a secondary sex characteristic found in males of some fish species.
anterior — front or head region.
anus — the termination of the alimentary canal, through which faeces are excreted.
ascidian — a sessile, marine animal with a sac-like body, e.g. sea squirt or redbait
attenuated — slender, drawn out.
axil — the inner region of the fin base in paired fins, roughly corresponding to the human armpit.

B

backline — the row of breaking waves furthest from the shore.
barbel — a fleshy projection near the mouth, often used for taste or touch.
batoid — a flat cartilaginous fish, i.e. skates or rays.
benthic — bottom-living.

bicuspid — with two cusps or points, e.g. some teeth.
bony fishes — or teleosts, i.e. fishes with a true bone skeleton
brackish — a term applied to water that is neither completely fresh nor as salty as sea water.
branchial — the region of the gills.
branchiostegal — descriptive of bony rays supporting the lower gill covers.
breast — in most bony fishes, the area immediately below the pectoral fins.
Bryozoa — a group of minute marine animals.
buccal — the inside of the mouth.

C

caecum — a blind, sac-like appendage attached to the stomach of some fishes.
canine — a long, conical tooth usually used for grasping or piercing.
carapace — a rigid shield encasing the body, e.g. the shell of crabs
cartilage — gristle, firm elastic tissue that forms all or part of a vertebrate skeleton.
cartilaginous — (1) composed of gristle; (2) descriptive of fishes such as sharks, skates and rays, which lack true bony skeletons.
catadromous — descriptive of fish which migrate from fresh water to spawn at sea.
caudal fin — the unpaired fin at the tail of most fishes.
caudal peduncle — the narrow region that attaches the caudal fin to the body.
caudal notch — an indentation at the base of the caudal fin in sharks.
cephalic — the region of the head.
cephalopods — a class of molluscs, the members of which have distinct heads, e.g. squids and octopus
Cetacea — the order of marine mammals which includes whales and dolphins.
chin — the region below the lower jaw.
chumming — the practice of attracting fish or creating a feeding frenzy by deliberately placing quantities of aromatic food such as chopped fish in the water.
ciguatera — a fish toxin, dangerous to man, but only found in isolated tropical localities.
cilia — hair-like outgrowths from the skin.
circumtropical — throughout tropical regions.
claspers — rod-like, grooved processes attached to the pelvic fins of male sharks, skates, rays and guitarfishes. Used to transmit sperm during copulation.
commensalism — animals or plants of different species living in close association with one another and sharing a common food source. Such associations are not necessarily of mutual benefit.
compressed — flattened from side to side, e.g. the shape of some fish.
conglomerate — gathered into a mass, e.g. some fish eggs.
conical — cone-shaped, e.g. some teeth.
continental shelf — the shallow ledge forming the sea-bed that surrounds land masses, usually taken to the arbitrary depth of 200 m.
continental slope — that part of the sea-bed which slopes from the continental shelf to the much deeper abyss.
copepods — a sub-class of minute crustaceans; most are free-swimming, but some are parasitic.
corselet — a distinct region of scales, usually behind the pectoral fins in some fishes, especially Scombridae.
crepuscular — active at dusk and dawn.
crustaceans — a large group of mostly aquatic, invertebrate animals such as prawns, crabs and crayfish.
ctenoid — edged with minute spines, e.g. the scales of some fish.
cusp — a point, e.g. as in teeth.
cutaneous — pertaining to the skin.
cycloid — smoothly rounded, e.g. the shape of some fish scales.

D

deep-bodied — the shape of fishes where the height is great in relation to length.
demersal — living close to the sea-bed.
denticles — tooth-like projections such as the scales which completely cover the bodies of cartilaginous fishes.
dentine — the hard, calcium-based component that makes up teeth.
dentition — the characteristic arrangement of teeth.
depressed — flattened from top to bottom, e.g. the shape of some fishes such as rays and gurnards.
dermal — of the skin.
dermal denticles — tough, often tooth-like projections of the skin.
dextral — right-handed, e.g. soles with both eyes on their right sides. Opposite to sinistral.
diatoms — microscopic, unicellular algal plants with silica exoskeletons.
disc — the fused head and fin region of some depressed fishes, e.g. skates and rays.
disc width — the 'wingspan' of rays.
dorsal — pertaining to the upper or back region.
dorsal ridge — a tough fold of skin that runs along the upper body of some sharks.

E

East Coast — the coastline including the Transkei northward to Moçambique (see also 'South Coast', 'West Coast').
economic zone — see 'fisheries zone'.
ecosystem — a natural system of interacting organisms and their environment e.g. an estuary, a coral reef.
eelgrass — a flowering marine plant with long, thin leaves that occurs in estuaries and quiet bays.
elasmobranchs — cartilaginous fishes.
elongate — extended or drawn out, e.g. some fishes

where the body length is great in relation to height.
emarginate — slightly concave, e.g. the shape of some fins.
embedded — hidden within body tissue, e.g. some spines or scales.
embryo — a developing organism prior to hatching or birth.
epiphyte — a small plant that grows on the surface of other plants, but not parasitically, and only using the 'host' for support.
erectile — capable of being raised, e.g. the spines of some fishes.
estuary — that part of a river closest to the sea, where salinities fluctuate considerably.
euphausid — krill, a small, shrimp-like, pelagic crustacean.
euryhaline — the ability of an organism to tolerate wide-ranging salinities (see also 'stenohaline').
eutrophic — water enriched by organic matter.
exoskeleton — a rigid covering encasing the body, e.g. the cuticle of crustaceans.

F

falcate — sickle-shaped, e.g. some fins.
fecundity — reproductive potential, i.e. number of eggs produced.
feather — a fishing lure in which a combination of feathers, usually of selected colours, is intended to resemble a squid.
fermented fish — a traditional method of preparing fish in some eastern countries; done by allowing the whole animal to ferment in its own stomach juices, as well as by the action of micro-organisms.
filamentous — thread-like, e.g. some fins.
finlets — small, separate fins, situated behind the dorsal and anal fins.
fins — any of the firm appendages that are the organs of propulsion and balance in fishes and some other aquatic animals. Most fishes have paired fins (pelvic and pectoral) and unpaired fins (dorsal, anal and caudal), the former corresponding to the limbs of higher vertebrates.
fisheries zone — the coastal waters bordering a country, and within which the country has the exclusive right to fish and to manage fisheries. In terms of South Africa, this zone extends to the 200 nautical mile limit.
food chain — a continuum of organisms in which each is the food of one or more subsequent members of the chain.
foodweb — a system of inter-relating foodchains.
foraminifera — microscopic, unicellular animals with calcareous exoskeletons.
forehead — the curve of the head and the region between the eyes.
fork length — the length of a fish measured from the tip of the snout to the fork of the tail (see also 'total length').
fry — newly hatched juvenile fish.
fusiform — spindle-shaped, tapering at both ends, e.g. the body shape of some gamefish such as tuna and mackerel.

G

gamefish — a pelagic fish that is actively pursued by anglers because of its fighting ability.
genus — a group of closely related animal or plant species.
gill — the respiratory organ of fish and other aquatic animals.
gill arch — the bony arch to which the gill membranes and rakers are attached.
gill cover — or operculum, a plate, comprising several bones, protecting the gills of bony fishes.
gill opening — the opening behind the head, protected by the gill covers, through which exhaled water is passed.
gill rakers — the appendages on the gill arch that filter food from water passing through the gill chamber.
gizzard — a very muscular section of the digestive system that precedes the stomach.
gonads — reproductive organs, i.e. ovary or roe and testis or milt.
gravid — pregnant.
gregarious — descriptive of behaviour that, in fish, leads to the formation of groups or shoals.

H

habitat — the specific environment of an organism.
height (in fins, usually the dorsals) — the vertical distance from the tip of the fin to the body.
hermaphrodite — an organism possessing both male and female reproductive organs.
hydrozoa — small, often colonial, animals related to and resembling sea anemones.
hypersaline — water that has a salt concentration greater than the normal sea water average of 35 parts per thousand.
hypertonic — fluid with a higher concentration of dissolved salt than another fluid.
hypotonic — fluid with a lower dissolved salt concentration than another fluid.

I

Indo-Pacific — embracing the Indian and, usually, the eastern Pacific oceans.
incisors — front, cutting teeth.
interdorsal ridge (of sharks) — see 'dorsal ridge'.
interopercle — the lower bony plate of the gill cover.
interorbital — the region between the eyes.
intertidal zone — the shoreline between high and low water.
invertebrate — an animal without a backbone.
isopods — small crustaceans resembling woodlice.

J

jigging — the unsporting practice of intentionally foul-hooking fish with unbaited hooks.

K

keel — a flat, longitudinal ridge that occurs on either side of the caudal peduncle in some gamefishes and sharks.

krill — see 'euphausid'.

L

lanceolate — spear-shaped, tapering to a point, e.g. some scales, such as those of billfishes.

lanternfish — a deep-water fish, usually with large eyes and luminous organs.

lateral — on the side.

lateral line — a series of sensory tubercles forming a raised line along either side of the body of some fishes.

leptocephalus — the ribbon-like, transparent juvenile of eels and some primitive fishes.

line fish — all those fish that are readily caught on hook and line, but often inferring reef fishes of superior eating quality such as seventyfour, red steenbras, etc.

litter — the newly born young of a shark, skate or ray.

littoral — the tidal zone, i.e. that area between the highest and lowest spring tides.

longline — a continuous line or cord, sometimes 50 km long, with interspaced baited hooks and floats, set by commercial fishermen for the capture of large fish.

lunate — shaped like a crescent moon, e.g. some fins.

lure — a man-made device intended to resemble the natural prey of fishes (e.g. shrimp, squid or small baitfish) and used as an alternative to fresh bait.

M

mantis shrimp — see 'stomatopod'.

maxilla — the upper jaw.

megalopa — a free-swimming larval stage of crabs.

midwater — somewhere between the surface and the sea-bed.

milt — testis, i.e. sperm or 'soft or white roe', the reproductive parts of male fish.

modern (shark or fish) — a term generally used to describe a species for which no fossil records exist, therefore suggesting that it evolved in comparatively recent times.

molars — rounded, grinding teeth.

mole crabs (sea lice) — burrowing crustaceans often used as bait.

mollusc — an invertebrate animal, usually with an outer shell, e.g. mussels, perlemoen, cuttlefish.

morphology — the form or outer structure of organisms.

mucous — pertaining to tissue capable of producing mucus.

mucus — a viscous or slimy fluid secreted by the skin of many fishes.

multicuspid — with many points, e.g. some teeth.

mysid — a small, free-swimming, shrimp-like crustacean.

N

naked — without cover, e.g. scaleless.

nasal — the region of the nostrils.

nekton — all organisms that actively swim in the water column.

nematode — a thread-like roundworm, either parasitic or free-living.

nets

beach seine — a net, hanging from floats and having a central bag and equal-sized wings, that can be pulled in shallow water.

purse-seine — a large net, hanging from floats and having a central bag and wings, that can be retrieved or 'pursed' from a craft at sea.

gill — a net comprising pre-set panels of netting with a fixed mesh size. Fish swimming into them are caught by their gill covers, e.g. the anti-shark nets protecting Natal's bathing beaches.

trawl — a small net, often set in a gate-like frame, which is usually pulled over the sea-bed.

plankton — a microscopically-fine net, sock-like in shape, that is towed behind a craft to collect minute organisms for scientific purposes.

neuston — all animal or plant life that floats on or swims in surface waters.

niche — the place or position that an organism occupies in its environment.

nictitating membrane — a transparent fold of skin forming a protective inner eyelid. Occurs in some sharks, birds, reptiles and mammals.

O

offshore — a term loosely applied when describing fish that do not approach the coastline.

operculum — see 'gill cover'.

orbital horns — bony projections near the eyes in some fish, e.g. the Moorish idol.

organic — (1) derived from, relating to or characteristic of plants and animals; (2) matter that consists only of carbon compounds.

ostracods — minute crustaceans, often living in a paired shell.

otolith (or earstone) — a structure of calcium carbonate in the inner ear of vertebrates. The movement of otoliths, caused by changing body positions, stimulates sensory cells which register, with the brain, the animal's position relative to the pull of gravity, and thus enable it to maintain equilibrium.

outrigger — in fishing, a pole projecting from the side of a craft which allows the fisherman to troll his line further from the boat.

oviparous — producing young by laying egg cases in which the embryos continue to develop after being shed (see also 'ovoviviparous' and 'viviparous').

ovoviviparous — producing young from egg cases in which the embryos develop within the maternal body and are expelled at hatching (see also 'oviparous' and 'viviparous').

P

palate — the roof of the mouth.
pantropical — throughout tropical regions.
papilla — a fleshy projection.
parasite — an organism living on another and being nourished by it, sometimes, but not always, to the detriment of the host.
pavement teeth — the 'cobbled' arrangement of teeth in a number of cartilaginous fishes.
pectoral — the chest region where the pectoral fins usually attach to the body.
peduncle — see 'caudal peduncle'.
pelagic — living in the open sea, especially near the surface.
pelvic — the region, posterior to the belly, to which paired pelvic fins are attached.
pharyngeal — of the pharynx or gullet region.
photosynthesis — the process whereby plants, in the presence of light, can convert carbon dioxide and water into carbohydrates, with a simultaneous release of oxygen.
phyllosoma — one of the pelagic larval stages of rock lobsters and crayfish.
phytoplankton — the plant component of plankton (see also 'plankton' and 'zooplankton').
plankton — small animal or plant organisms suspended in the water column (see also 'phytoplankton' and 'zooplankton').
polychaete — a segmented marine worm with bristles.
polyps — anemone-like animals, e.g. corals and hydrozoa.
population dynamics — the study of animal populations.
pores — small pits or tubules, e.g. along the lateral line or on the chin.
portunid crab — see swimming crab.
posterior — hind region.
pre-operculum — a flat, falcate bone in bony fishes that lies below the eye and before the gill opening and forms part of the gill cover. Its rear edge is often sharply serrated.
produced — drawn out to a point.
prop-roots — in mangroves, adventitious aerial roots growing downward from the stem.
protractile — capable of being extended, e.g. some jaws.
protrusible — capable of projection, e.g. some jaws.
pteropod — a small, pelagic snail that swims with wing-like feet.
pungent — (1) an acrid taste or smell; (2) piercing or sharply pointed, e.g. a spine.
pup — a newly born shark, skate or ray.

R

rakers — see 'gill rakers'.
ray (fin) — a cartilaginous and jointed fin support.
reds — a general term for some 'red' reef fishes, but usually excluding the better quality line fish, e.g. slinger, soldier, dageraad, etc.
reticulated — resembling a network pattern.
rhomboid — diamond-shaped, e.g. some scales.
robust — thick set, i.e. the shape of some fishes.
roe — ovary or eggs.
rostrum — a projecting snout or beak.

S

salinity — salt content, e.g. sea water has 35 parts salt (sodium chloride) per 1 000 parts water.
salp — a transparent, planktonic animal belonging to a primitive chordate order.
sand dollar — a rather fragile, bottom-living echinoderm, also known as a sea pansy, related to the sea stars.
sand hopper — see 'amphipod'.
sashimi — a traditional Japanese dish in which sliced fish is dipped in a marinade and eaten raw.
scuba — acronym for 'Self Contained Underwater Breathing Apparatus', i.e. aqualungs.
scute — an external bony plate, often pointed, usually a modified scale.
sealice — see 'mole crab'.
seine net — see 'nets'.
sensory — capable of perceiving external stimuli.
serrate — notched or saw-like, e.g. some spines.
sessile — being attached, as in the case of mussels, and hence immobile.
shoal — a group of fish, with most of the members swimming in the same direction (see also 'aggregation').
sinistral — left-handed, e.g. some soles with both eyes on the left side. Opposite to dextral.
South Coast — the coastline from False Bay in the south-western Cape up to and including the eastern Cape (see also 'West Coast', 'East Coast').
spine — a sharp, unjointed projection, often a part of a fin.
spiracles — respiratory openings behind the eyes in some sharks and rays.
sport fish — any fish that is caught by anglers or spearfishermen for its sporting and recreational value.
standard length — the length of a fish from the tip of the snout to the base of the tail.
stenohaline — the inability of an organism to tolerate even slight fluctuations in salinity (see also 'euryhaline').
stomatopod — a shrimp-like crustacean that superficially resembles the praying mantis.
striated — marked by narrow lines.
swim bladder — a gas-filled sac situated below the backbone in many bony fishes, which enables them to remain at a desired depth.
swimming crab — a crab in which some or all of the legs have modified 'paddle-like' ends, which enable the animal to propel itself through the water column.

symbiosis — an association between two or more different organisms in which both or all members derive benefit.

synonymous — refers to all names that have been applied either correctly or incorrectly to the same species.

T

teleosts — see 'bony fishes'.

temperate — of mild temperature. In geography, usually the regions between the Tropic of Cancer and the Arctic circle, and the Tropic of Capricorn and the Antarctic circle. In fishes this infers that their distribution is principally confined to these regions.

terminal — at the extreme end.

thermocline — the distinct interface between warm, surface waters and cooler, deeper waters.

thoracic — pertaining to the chest region.

tooth formula — the typical and regular arrangement of teeth, especially those of sharks.

total length — the length of a fish measured from the tip of the snout to the tip of the tail. Where the caudal fin is forked, total length is measured from the tip of the snout to the tip of the longer lobe folded down (see also 'fork length').

trematodes — entirely parasitic flatworms, including tapeworms and flukes.

tricuspid — with three points, e.g. some teeth, especially those of the ragged tooth shark.

troll — to draw a baited line or lure through the water, often behind a boat.

truncate — almost square edged, e.g. the shape of some fins.

tubercle — a small, rounded projection on the surface of the body.

tunicates — a group of sedentary marine animals including ascidians.

turbid — descriptive of water which is cloudy or muddy, owing to the suspension of organic and inorganic matter.

type — the original specimen from which a species was described.

U

upwelling — a process whereby deeper, cold waters, rich in nutrient salts, rise to the surface as a result of the combined effects of wind, ocean currents, earth rotation and fluctuating water densities. This usually stimulates prolific growth of phytoplankton.

V

vent — the anus or cloaca of lower vertebrate animals.

ventral — pertaining to the lower region or underside of a fish.

vestigial — rudimentary.

vlei — an area of low marshy ground, usually the shallow upper reaches of a lake or region where rain water collects.

villiform — numerous, very fine projections, e.g. descriptive of some teeth.

viviparous — bearing live young after the development of an embryo or embryos within the maternal organism, e.g. in mammals and some reptiles and fishes (see also 'ovoviviparous' and 'oviparous').

vomer — a bony plate forming the front part of the roof of the mouth.

W

water column — the body of water between the sea-bed and the surface.

West Coast — the Atlantic coastline from Cape Point northwards (see also 'South Coast' and 'East Coast').

Y

yolk-sac — a sac containing the remains of the egg-yolk, often temporarily suspended from the underside of newly hatched fish.

Z

zoea — one of the pelagic larval stages of crabs.

zooplankton — the animal component of plankton (see also 'plankton' and 'phytoplankton').

BIBLIOGRAPHY

AHRENS, R.L., 1964. A preliminary report on the biology of the seventy-four *Polysteganus undulosus* (Regan) in Natal Waters. Unpublished M.Sc. thesis, University of Natal, Durban: 1-77.

ALLEN, G.R., 1972. The anemonefishes, their classification and biology. Neptune City, U.S.A., T.F.H.: 1-288.

ALLEN, G.R., 1980. Butterfly and angelfishes of the world. Vol. 2. New York, John Wiley: 148-252.

ALLYN, R., 1969. Florida fishes. St. Petersburg, Great Outdoors Publ.: 1-90.

BAIRD, D., 1970. Age and growth of the South African pilchard, *Sardinops ocellata. Invest. Rep Sea Fish. Branch (S. Afr.)*, (91): 1-16.

BAIRD, D., 1971. Seasonal occurrence of the pilchard, *Sardinops ocellata* on the east coast of South Africa. *Invest. Rep. Sea Fish. Branch (S. Afr.)*, (96): 1-19.

BAIRD, D., 1977. Age, growth and aspects of reproduction of the mackerel, *Scomber japonicus* in South African waters (Pisces: Scombridae). *Zool. Afr.*, **12**(2): 347-362.

BAIRD, D., 1978. Catch composition and population structure of the commercially exploited mackerel *Scomber japonicus*, 1954-1975. *Fish. Bull. S. Afr.*, **10**: 50-61.

BAMBER, R.C., 1915. Reports on the marine biology of the Sudanese Red Sea - The fishes. *J. Linn. Soc., Zool.*, **31**: 477-486.

BARNARD, K.H., 1925. A monograph of the marine fishes of South Africa. **21**(1-2): 1-1065.

BASS, A.J. and BALLARD, J.A.P., 1972. Buoyancy control in the shark *Odontaspis taurus* (Rafinesque). *Copeia, (3): 594-595.*

BASS. A.J., D'AUBREY, J.D. and KISTNASAMY, N.,

1973. Sharks of the east coast of southern Africa Part I. The genus *Carcharhinus* (Carcharhinidae). *Invest. Rep. oceanogr. Res. Inst.,* (33): 1-168.

BASS, A.J., D'AUBREY, J.D. and KISTNASAMY, N., 1975. Sharks of the east coast of southern Africa Part II. The families Scyliorhinidae and Pseudotriakidae. *Invest. Rep. oceanogr. Res. Inst.,* (37): 1-74.

BASS, A.J., D'AUBREY, J.D. and KISTNASAMY, N., 1975. Sharks of the east coast of southern Africa. Part III. The families Carcharhinidae (excluding *Carcharhinus* and *Mustelus*) and Sphyrnidae. *Invest. Rep. oceanogr. Res. Inst.,* (38): 1-100.

BASS, A.J., D'AUBREY, J.D. and KISTNASAMY, N., 1975. Sharks of the east coast of southern Africa. Part IV. The families Odontaspididae, Scapanorhynchidae, Isuridae, Cetorhinidae, Alopiidae, Orectolobidae and Rhiniodontidae. *Invest. Rep. oceanogr. Res. Inst.,* (39): 1-102.

BASS, A.J., D'AUBREY, J.D. and KISTNASAMY, N., 1975. Sharks of the east coast of southern Africa. Part V. The families Hexanchidae, Chlamydoselachidae, Heterodontidae, Pristiophoridae and Squatinidae. *Invest. Rep. oceanogr. Res. Inst.,* (43): 1-50.

BASS, A.J., D'AUBREY, J.D. and KISTNASAMY, N., 1976. Sharks of the east coast of southern Africa. Part VI. The families Oxynotidae, Squalidae, Dalatiidae and Echinorhinidae. *Invest. Rep. oceanogr. Res. Inst.,* (45): 1-103.

BEN-TUVIA, A., 1966. Red Sea fishes recently found in the Mediterranean. *Copeia,* (2): 254-274.

BEUMER, J.P., 1978. Feeding ecology of four fishes from a mangrove creek in north Queensland, Australia. *J. Fish Biol.,* **12**: 475-490.

BIDEN, C.L., 1930. Sea-angling fishes of the Cape (South Africa). London, Oxford Univ. Press: 1-303.

BIGELOW, H.B. and SCHROEDER, W.C., 1948. Fishes of the western North Pacific. Sharks. *Mem. Sears Fdn. mar. Res.,* (1): 59-576.

BLABER, S.J.M., 1974. Field studies of the diet of *Rhabdosargus holubi* (Pisces: Teleostei: Sparidae). *J. Zool. Lond.,* **173**: 407-417.

BLABER, S.J.M., 1974. The population structure and growth of juvenile *Rhabdosargus holubi* (Steindachner) (Teleostei: Sparidae) in a closed estuary. *J. Fish Biol.,* **6**: 455-460.

BLABER, S.J.M., 1977. The feeding ecology and relative abundance of mullet (Mugilidae) in Natal and Pondoland estuaries. *Biol. J. Linn. Soc.,* **9**: 259-275.

BLABER, S.J.M., 1979. The biology of filter feeding teleosts in Lake St Lucia, Zululand. *J. Fish Biol.,* **15**: 37-59.

BLABER, S.J.M. and WHITFIELD, A.K., 1977. The feeding ecology of juvenile mullet (Mugilidae) in south-east African estuaries. *Biol. J. Linn. Soc.,* **9**: 277-284.

BOTHA, L,. 1970. The growth of the Cape hake *Merluccius capensis. Invest. Rep. Sea Fish. Branch (S. Afr.),* (82): 1-9.

BRIGGS, J.C., 1960. Fishes of worldwide (circumtropical) distribution. *Copeia,* (3): 171-180.

BROWNELL, C.L., 1979. Stages in the early development of 40 marine fish species with pelagic eggs from the Cape of Good Hope. *Ichthyol. Bull. Rhodes Univ.* (40): 1-84.

BRUGER, G.E., 1974. Age, growth, food habits and reproduction of bonefish. *Albula vulpes,* in south Florida waters. *Fla. mar. Res. Publ.*, (3): 1-20.

BUDNICHENKO, V.A. and NOR, L.A., 1979. Some features of the growth of *Saurida undosquamis* and *S. tumbil* (Pisces: Synodontidae) in the Arabian Sea. *J. Ichthyol.* **18**(5): 750-755.

BURGESS, W. and AXELROD, H.R., *eds.,* 1972. Pacific marine fishes. v.I-3 by Fujio Yasuda and Yoshio Hiyama. Hong Kong. T.F.H. Publs.: 1-839.

BUXTON, C.D., 1984. Feeding biology of the Roman *Chrysoblephus laticeps* (pisces: Sparidae). *S. Afr. J. Mar. Sci.,* (2): 33-42.

BUXTON, C.D. and KOK, H.M., 1983. Notes on the diet of *Rhabdosargus holubi* (Steindachner) and *Rhabdosargus globiceps* (Cuvier) in the marine environment. *S. Afr. J. Zool.,* **18**(4): 406-408.

BUXTON, C.D. and SMALE, M.J., 1984. A preliminary investigation of the ichthyofauna of the Tsitsikamma Coastal National Park. *Koedoe,* (27): 13-24.

BUXTON, C.D., SMALE, M.J., WALLACE, J.H. and COCKCROFT, V.G., 1984. Inshore small-mesh trawling survey of the Cape south coast. Part 4. Contributions to the biology of some Teleostei and Chondrichthyes. *S. Afr. J. Zool.* **19**(3): 180-188.

CALDWALLER, P.D., 1975. Graphical fitting of the von Bertalanffy equation. *Nauri ORA.* **3**: 11-17.

CARCASSON, R.H., 1977. A field guide to the coral reef fishes of the Indian and West Pacific Oceans. London, Collins: 1-320.

CASEY, J.G., 1964. Angler's guide to sharks of the northeastern United States - Maine to Chesapeake Bay. *Circ. Bur. Sport Fish. Wildl.,* (179): 1-32.

CASTLE, P.H.J. and WILLIAMSON, G.R., 1975 Systematics and distribution of eels of the *Muraenesox* group (Anguilliformes: Muraenesocidae). A preliminary report and key. *Spec. Publ. J.L.B. Smith Inst. Ichthyol.,* (15): 1-9.

CASTERLIN, H.E. and REYNOLDS, W.W., 1979. Diet activity patterns of the smooth dogfish shark *Mustelus canis. Bull. mar. Sci.,* **29**(3): 440-442.

CAYRÉ, P., 1979. Détermination de l'âge de listaos. *Katsuwonus pelamis,* debarques a Dakar: note preliminaire. *Coll. Vol. Sc. Pap. ICCAT,* **8**: 196-200.

CHABANNE, J., 1971. La pêche à la traine sur la partie nord-ouest du plateau continental de Madagascar. *Bull. Madagascar.* (297): 1-23.

CHABANNE, J., 1972. Études sur la biologie de *Caranx ignobilis. Caranx sexfasciatus* et *Caranx melampygus* (Pisces: Carangidae) de la région de Nosy-Bé, Madagascar. *Doc. Sci. Cent. Nosy-Bé, ORSTOM,* (27): 1-42.

CHRISTENSEN, M.S., 1978. Trophic relationships in juveniles of three species of sparid fishes in the South African marine littoral. *Fish. Bull., U.S.* **76**(2): 389-402.

CLARK, J.R. and BUXTON, C.D., 1985. Notes on the diet of *Pterogymnus laniarius* (Cuvier) (Pisces: Sparidae). *S. Afr. J. Zool.* **20**(2): 68-71.

COETZEE, P.S., 1978. Aspects of the angling fishes of St Croix island with special reference to the biology of *Cheimerius nufar,* Ehrenberg, 1820 (Teleostei: Sparidae). Unpublished M.Sc. thesis, Univ. P.E.,: 1-215.

COLLETTE, B.B. and RUSSO, J.L., 1978. An introduction to the Spanish mackerels, genus *Scomberomorus.* Proc. Mackerel Colloquium,: (Ed. E.L. Nakamura): 3-16 (Gulf states Mar. Fish. Comm.).

CYRUS, D.P., 1980. The biology of Gerreidae (Bleeker 1859. Teleostei) in Natal estuaries. Unpublished M.Sc. thesis. Univ. Natal Dbn.: 1-178.

DAVIES, D.H., 1949. Preliminary investigations on the food of South African fishes: with notes on the general fauna of the area surveyed. *Investl. Rep. Fish. mar. biol. Surv. Div. Un. S. Afr.,* (11): 1-36.

DAVIS, W.P. and BIRDSONG, R.S., 1973. Coral reef fishes which forage in the water column. *Helgoländer wiss. Meeresunters.,* **24**: 292-306.

DAWSON, C.E., 1967. Contributions to the biology of the cutlassfish *(Trichiurus lepturus)* in the northern Gulf of Mexico. *Trans. Am. Fish Soc.,* **96**(2): 117-121.

DAY, F., 1878. reprint 1978: The fishes of India, v.I.

London, Dawson: 1-778.
DAY, J.H., FIELD, J.E. and PENRITH, M.J., 1970. The benthic fauna of False Bay, South Africa. *Trans. R. Soc. S. Afr.,* **39**(1): 1-108.
DE SYLVA, D.P., 1963. Systematics and life history of the great barracuda, *Sphyraena barracuda* (Walbaum). *Stud. Trop. Oceangr.* **1**: 1-179.
DE SYLVA, D.P., 1973. Barracudas (Pisces: Sphyraenidae) of the Indian Ocean and adjacent seas. A preliminary review of their systematics and ecology. *J. mar. biol. Ass. India.* **15**: 74-94.
DEVADOSS, P., 1969. Maturity and spawning in *Otolithes ruber* and *Johnius dussumierei* (C. & V.). *Indian J. Fish.,* 16(1/2): 117-128.
DE VILLIERS, G., 1976. Exploitation of harders along Southern African shores. *S. Afr. Shipp. News Fish. Ind. Rev.* **31**(4): 57-61.
DHAWAN, R.M., NAMBOOTHIRI, P.V.S. and GOPINATHAN, V.E., 1969. Results of trolling line operations in Goa waters during 1965-68. *Indian J. Fish.,* **16**(1/2): 181-187.
DRUZHININ, A.D., 1977. Some data on the spotted drepane *(Drepane punctata)* of the Andaman and Arabian seas. *Vopr. iktiol.* **17**(6): 945-950.
DRYDEN, D. 1979. Game fish Union of Africa list of open records 1980, Salisbury. Mardon.
FISHELSON, L., 1970. Protogynous sex reversal in the fish *Anthias squamipinnis* (Teleostei: Anthiidae) regulated by the presence or absence of a male fish. *Nature, Lond.,* **227**: 90-91.
FISHELSON, L., POPPER, D. and AVIDOR, A., 1974. Biosociology and ecology of pomacentrid fishes around the Sinai Peninsula (northern Red Sea). *J. Fish Biol.,* **6**: 119-133.
FISHER, W. and WHITEHEAD, P.J.P., *eds.,* 1974. FAO species identification sheets for fishery purposes. Eastern Indian Ocean and Western Central Pacific. Rome. FAO,: 4V.
FITCH, J.E. AND LAVENBERG, R.J., 1971. Marine food and game fishes of California. Berkeley. Univ. of Calif. Press: 1-179
FOWLER, H.W., 1923. Fishes from Madeira, Syria, Madagascar, and Victoria, Australia. *Proc. Acad. nat. Sci. Philad.,* **75**: 33-45.
FOWLER, H.W., 1925. Fishes from Natal, Zululand and Portuguese East Africa. *Proc. Acad. nat. Sci. Philad.,* **77**: 187-268.
FOWLER, H.W., 1949. The fishes of Oceania. Suppl. 3. *Mem. Bernice P. Bishop Mus.,* **12**(2): 37-186.
GARRATT, P.A., 1984. The biology and fishery of *Chrysoblephus puniceus* (Gilchrist and Thompson, 1917) and *Cheimerius nufar* (Ehrenberg, 1830), two offshore sparids in Natal waters. Unpublished M.Sc. thesis. University of Natal, Durban: 1-139.
GARRATT, P.A., 1985. The offshore linefishery of Natal. (I) Exploited population structures of the sparids, *Chrysoblephus puniceus* and *Cheimerius nufar. Invest. Rep. oceanogr. Res. Inst.,* (62): 1-18.
GARRATT, P.A., 1985. The offshore linefishery of Natal. (II) Reproductive biology of the sparids, *Chrysoblephus puniceus* and *Cheimerius nufar. Invest. Rep. oceanogr. Res. Inst.,* (63): 1-21.
GARRATT, P.A., 1985. The offshore linefishery of Natal. (III) Food and feeding of the sparids, *Chrysoblephus puniceus* and *Cheimerius nufar. Invest. Rep. oceanogr. Res. Inst.,* (64): 1-17.
GARRATT, P.A., 1986. Protogynous hermaphroditism in the slinger *Chrysoblephus puniceus* (Gilchrist and Thompson, 1917) (Teleostei: Sparidae). *J. Fish Biol.,* **28**(3): 297-306.
GELDENHUYS, N.D., 1973. Growth of the South African maasbanker *Trachurus trachurus* L. and age composition of the catches. 1950-1971. *Invest. Rep. Sea Fish. Branch (S. Afr.),* (101): 1-24.
GIBBS, R.H. and COLLETTE, B.B., 1959. On the identification, distribution and biology of the dolphins, *Coryphaena hippurus* and *C. equiselis. Bull. mar. Sci. Gulf Caribb.,* **9**(2): 117-152.
GIBBS, R.H. and COLLETTE, B.B., 1967. Comparative anatomy and systematics of the tunas, genus *Thunnus. Fish. Bull. U.S.,* **66**(1): 65-130.
GILCHRIST, J.D.F., 1902. History of the local names of Cape fish. *Trans. S. Afr. phil. Soc.* **11** (4): 207-232.
GOSLINE, W.A. and BROCK, V.E., 1960. Handbook of Hawaiian fishes. Honolulu, Univ. of Hawaii Press (Hawaii Univ. press): 1-372.
GREENWOOD, P.H., ROSEN, D.E., WEITZMAN, S.H. and MYERS, G.S., 1966. Phyletic studies of teleostean fishes, with a provisional classification of living forms. *Bull. Am. Mus. nat. Hist.,* **131**(4): 341-455.
GROSVENOR, M.B., 1965. Wondrous world of fishes. Washington, Nat. Geographic Soc.: 1-367.
GUBANOV, Ye P., 1979. The reproduction of some species of pelagic sharks from the equatorial zone of the Indian Ocean. *Ichthyol. Bull.,* **18**(5): 781-792.
GUDGER, E.W., 1919. On the use of sucking-fish for catching fish and turtles: studies in *Echeneis* or remora. III. *Am. Nat.,* **53**: 515-525.
HALSTEAD, B.W. and COURVILLE, D.A., 1965. Poisonous and venomous marine animals of the world, v.1: Invertebrates, v.2-3: Vertebrates. Washington, U.S. government printing office: 3V.
HARMAN, H.A.J., BLABER, S.J.M. and CYRUS, D.P. 1982. The biology and taxonomic status of an estuarine population of *Pranesius pinguis* (Lacèpéde) (Teleostei: Atherinidae) in south east Africa. *S. Afr. J. Zool.,* **17**(1): 15-23.
HARMELING-VIVIEN, M.L., 1976. Ichthyofauna de quelques récifs coralliens des Îles Maurice et la Réunion. *Bull. Maurit. Inst.,* **8**(11): 69-104.
HARRIS, T.F.W., 1978. Review of coastal currents in South African waters. *S. Afr. Natl. Sci. Programmes Rep.,* (30): 30-103.
HECHT, T., 1977. Contributions to the biology of the Cape gurnard, *Trigla capensis* (Pisces: Triglidae): age, growth and reproduction. *Zool. Afr.,* **12**(2): 373-382.
HECHT, T. and BAIRD, D., 1977. Contributions to the biology of the panga. *Pterogymnus laniarius* (Pisces: Sparidae): age, growth and reproduction. *Zool. Afr.,* **12**(2): 363-372.
HEEMSTRA, P.C., 1980. A revision of the zeid fishes (Zeiformes: Zeidae) of South Africa. *Ichthyol. Bull. Rhodes Univ.* (40): 1-18.
HOBSON, E.S., 1965. Diurnal-nocturnal activity of some inshore fishes in the Gulf of California. *Copeia,* (3): 291-302.
HOBSON, E.S., 1968. Predatory behaviour of some shore fishes in the Gulf of California. *Res. Rep. U.S. Fish. Wildl. Serv.,* (73): 1-92.
HOBSON, E.S., 1974. Feeding relationships of teleostean fishes on coral reefs in Kona, Hawaii. *Fish. Bull. U.S.,* **72** (4): 915-1031.
HOLDEN, M.J., 1974. Problems in the rational exploitation of elasmobranch populations and some suggested solutions. *In:* HARDEN-JONES, F.R. *ed.* Sea fisheries research. London. Paul Elek: 117-137.
HOWARD, J.K. and STARCK, W.A., 1975. Distribution and relative abundance of billfishes (Istiophoridae) of the Indian Ocean. *Stud. Trop. oceanogr.,* (13): 1-31.
I.G.F.A., 1980. 1980 World record game fishes. Fort Lauderdale.: 1-272.
JAMES, P.S.B.R., 1975. A systematic review of the fishes

of the family Leiognathidae. *J. mar. biol. Ass. India.* **17**(1): 138-172.

JOHANNES, R.E., 1978. Reproductive strategies of coastal marine fishes in the tropics. *Env. Biol. Fish.* **3**(1): 65-78.

JOLLEY, J.W., 1977. The biology and fishery of Atlantic sailfish *Istiophorous platypterus,* from southeast Florida. *Fla. mar. Res. Publ.,* (28): 1-31.

JONES, B.W. and VAN ECK, T.H., 1967. The Cape hake: its biology and the fishery. *S. Afr. Shipp. News Fish. Ind. Rev.,* **22**(11): 90-97.

JORDAN, D.S. and EVERMANN, B.W., 1896. (reprint 1963) The fishes of north and middle America. *Bull. U.S. natn. Mus.,* **1-4**: 1-3136. New Jersey. T.F.H.

JOSEPH, J., KLAWE, W. and MURPHY, P., 1980. Tuna and billfish - fish without a country. La Jolla I.A.T.T.C.: 1-45.

JOUBERT, C.S.W., 1981. Aspects of the biology of five species of inshore reef fishes on the Natal Coast, South Africa. *Invest. Rep. oceanogr. Res. Inst.,* (51): 1-100.

JOUBERT, C.S.W., 1981. A survey of shore anglers' catches at selected sites on the Natal Coast, South Africa. *Invest. Rep. oceanogr. Res. Inst.,* (52): 1-16.

JOUBERT, C.S.W. and HANEKOM, P.B., 1980. A study of feeding in some inshore reef fish of the Natal coast, South Africa. *S. Afr. J. Zool.* **15**(4): 260-274.

JOUBERT, I., 1980. The biology of *Blennius cristatus* L. and *Blennius cornutus* L. (Teleostei: Blennioidae) on a Natal reef. Unpublished M.Sc. thesis. University of Natal, Durban: 1-90.

KHALAF, K.T., 1961. The marine and freshwater fishes of Iraq, Baghdad. Ar-Rabitta: 11-64.

KIENER, A., 1961. Poissons Malgaches. *Bull. Madagascar.* (179-181): 1-117.

KIKAWA, S., 1962. Synopsis of biological data on bonito *Sarda orientalis* Temminck & Schlelgel. World Scientific meeting on the biology of tunas and related species. La Jolla, U.S.A. Species synopsis 3.

KLAUSEWITZ, W., 1969. Verleichend-taxonomische untersuchungen au Fishen der Gattung *Heniochus. Senckenberg. biol.,* **50**(1-2): 49-89.

KLAUSEWITZ, W., 1978. Zoogeography of the littoral fishes of the Indian Ocean, based on the distribution of the Chaetodontidae and Pomacanthidae. *Senckenberg, biol.,* **59**(1-2): 25-39.

KLIMAJ, A., 1978. Fishery Atlas of the south west African shelf. Bottom and pelagic catches. Springfield. N.M.F.S.: 1-173.

KLUNZINGER, C.B., 1870. Synopsis der Fische des Rothen Meeres. Theil 1. Percoiden, Mugiloiden. *Verh. zool. bot. Ges. Wien.* (20): 85-834.

KLUNZINGER, C.B., 1871. Synopsis der Fische des Rothen Meeres. Theil 2. Scomberoidei - Myliobatoidei. *Verh. zool. bot. Ges. Wien.* (21): 444-688.

KRISHNAMURTHY, K.N., 1968. Observations on the food of the sandwhiting *Sillago sihama* (Forsskål) from Pulicat Lake. *J. mar. biol. Ass. India,* **11**(1-2): 295-303

KUNGVANKIJ, P., 1973. Biological study of red snapper, *Lutjanus sanguineus.* [S.E.A. F.D.E.C. - S.C.S. - 73-S-16.] Singapore, *Fish Res. Dept.:* 1-19

KYUSHIN, K., 1977. Fishes of the Indian Ocean. Tokyo, Hiroshige Ehara: 1-392.

LAEVASTU, T. and ROSA, H., 1962. Distribution and relative abundance of tunas in relation to their environment. World Scientific meeting on the biology of tunas and related species. La Jolla, U.S.A. Inf. paper. 2.

LAVONDES, H. and RANDALL, J.E., 1978. Les noms de poissons Marquisiens. *J. Soc. Océanistes,* **34**(60): 79-112.

LANDAU, R., 1965. Determination of age and growth rate in *Euthynnus alleteratus* and *E. affinis* using vertebrae. *Rapp. P.-Reun. CIESMM,* **18**(2): 241-243.

LE GALL, J.-Y., 1974. Exposé synoptique des données biologiques sur le Germon *Thunnus alalunga,* de l'Océan Atlantique. *Synop. FAO Pêches.* (109): 1-70.

LENARZ, W.H., 1974. Length-weight relations for five eastern tropical Atlantic scombrids. *Fish. Bull. U.S.,* **72**(3): 849-851.

LOBEL, P.S. and JOHANNES, R.E., 1980. Nesting, eggs and larvae of triggerfishes (Balistidae). *Environ. Biol. Fish.,* **5**(3): 251-252.

LOUBENS, G., 1978. Biologie de quelques espèces de poisson du Lagon Néo-Calédonien. *Cah. ORSTOM (Océanogr.),* **16**(3-4): 263-283.

LUTHER, G., 1964. On the shedding of gill raker processes in grey mullets. *J. mar. biol. Ass. India,* **6**(2): 251-256.

LUTHER, G., 1966. On the little known fish, *Chirocentrus nudus* (Swainson) from the Indian seas and its comparison with *Chirocentrus dorab* (Forsskål). *J. mar. biol. Ass. India,* **8**(1): 193-201.

LYTHGOE, J. and LYTHGOE, G., 1971. Fishes of the sea. The coastal waters of the British Isles, Northern Europe and the Mediterranean. London. Blanford: 1-320.

MACNAE. W., 1968. A general account of the fauna and flora of mangrove swamps and forests in the Indo-west Pacific region. *Adv. Mar. Biol.,* (6): 73-270.

MACNAE, W. and KALK, M., *eds.* 1958. A natural history of Inhaca Island, Mocambique. Johannesburg. Wits Univ. Press: 1-163.

MARCHAND., J.M., 1935. The South African marine fishes of commercial and angling importance. *Fish. Bull. Un. S. Afr.,* (2): 1-160.

MARSHALL, T.C., 1964. Fishes of the Great Barrier Reef and coastal waters of Queensland, Sydney. Angus & Robertson: 1-566.

MASSON, H. and MARAIS, J.F.K., 1975. Stomach content analysis of mullet from the Swartkops estuary. *Zool. Afr.,* **10**(2): 193-207.

MATSUMOTO, W.N., 1967. Morphology and distribution of larval wahoo. *A. solandri* (Cuvier) in the central Pacific. *Fish. Bull. U.S.,* **66**(2): 299-322.

MAY, R.C., AKIYAMA, E.S. and SANTER, M.T., 1979. Lunar spawning of the threadfin *Polydactylus sexfilis,* in Hawaii. *Fish. Bull. U.S.,* **76**(4): 900-904.

McKAY, R.J., 1976. The fishes of the family Sillaginidae from India with a description of a new species. *J. mar. biol. Ass. India,* **18**(2): 375-385.

MEHL, J.A.P., 1969. Food of barracouta (Teleostei: Gempylidae) in eastern Cook Strait. *N.Z. J. Mar. Freshwat. Res.,* **3**(3): 389-393.

MEHL, J.A.P., 1973. Ecology, osmoregulation and reproductive biology of the white steenbras, *Lithognathus lithognathus* (Teleostei: Sparidae) *Zool. Afr.,* **8**(2): 157-230.

MERRETT, N.R., 1968. Weight-length relationships for certain scombroid fishes from the equatorial western Indian Ocean. *E. Afr. agric. For. J.,* **34**(2): 165-169.

MERRINER, J.V., 1971. Life history aspects of the tripletail *Lobotes surinamensis* (Chordata: Pisces: Lobotidae), in temperate waters. *ASB Bulletin*:46 .

MIGDALSKI, E.C., 1958. Angler's guide to the salt water game fishes: Atlantic and Pacific. New York, Ronald: 1-506.

MIKHAYLIN, S.V., 1976. Characteristics of the distribution of some members of the families Gempylidae and Trichiuridae in the waters of Southwest Africa. *J. Ichthyol.,* **16**(2): 319-323.

MORGANS, J.F.C., 1959. Three confusing species of serranid fish, one described as new, from East Africa. *Ann. Mag. nat. Hist. Ser. 13,* **1**: 642-656.

MUNRO, I.S.R., 1955. The marine and freshwater fishes

of Ceylon, Sydney, Halstead: 1-351.

MUNRO, I.S.R., 1958. The fishes of the New Guinea region. *Fish Bull. Papua.* (1): 1-1369.

MURCHISON, A.F. and MAGNUSON, J.J., 1966. Notes on coloration and behaviour of the common dolphin *Coryphaena hippurus. Pacif. Sci.,* **20**(4): 515-517.

MURTY, V.S., 1967. Notes on hyperostosis in the fish *Drepane punctata. J. mar. biol. Ass. India,* **9**(2): 323-326.

NAKAMURA, E.L. and MAGNUSON, J.J., 1965. Colouration of the scombrid fish. *Euthynnus affinis* (Cantor). *Copeia,* (2): 234-235.

NAKAMURA, H., 1969. Tuna distribution and migration. London, Fishing News: 1-76.

NARASIMHAM, K.A., 1976. Age and growth of ribbonfish *Trichiurus lepturus* Linnaeus. *Indian J. Fish,* **23**(1-2): 174-182.

NEPGEN, C.S. de V., 1975. The closed season for snoeking. *S. Afr. Shipp. News Fish. Ind. Rev.,* **30**(11): 57.

NEPGEN, C.S. de V., 1976. Die biologie van die hottentot *Pachymetopon blochii* (Val.) en die silvervis *Argyrozona argyrozona* (Val.) langs die Kaapse Suidweskus. *Tak seevisserye ondersoekverslag,* (105): 1-36.

NEPGEN, C.S. de V., 1979. Trends in the line fishery for snoek. *Thyrsites atun* off the south-western Cape, and in size composition, length-weight relationship and condition. *Fish. Bull. S. Afr.,* (12): 35-43.

NELSON, J.S., 1976. Fishes of the world. New York, Wiley: 1-416.

NIKOLSKY, G.V., 1963. The ecology of fishes. London, Academic Press: 1-352.

NOBLE, A., 1973. Food and feeding of the post larvae and juveniles of *Megalops cyprinoides* (Brouss.). *Indian J. Fish.,* **20**(1): 203-208.

NOBLE, A., 1974. Fishery and biology of the mackerel *Rastrelliger kanagurta* (Cuvier) at Cochin. *J. mar. biol. Ass. India,* **16**(3): 816-829.

NZIOKA, R.M., 1979. Observations on the spawning season of East African reef fishes. *J. Fish. Biol.,* **14**(4): 329-342.

OKADA, Y., 1966. Fishes of Japan. Tokyo, Uno Schoten: 1-458.

OKIYAMA, M., 1970. Studies on the early life history of the rainbow runner, *Elagatis bipinnulatus* (Quoy & Gaimard) in the Indo-Pacific Oceans. *Bull. Far Seas Fish. Res. Lab.,* (3): 167-186.

OLSEN, A.M., 1954. The biology, migration and growth rate of the school shark. *Galeorhinus australis* (MacLeay) in south-eastern Australian waters. *Aust. J. mar. Freshwat. Res.,* **5**: 353-410.

OTSU, T. and HANSEN, R.J., 1961. Sexual maturity and spawning of the albacore in the Central South Pacific. Pacific tuna biology conference. Honolulu, Paper VII-2.

PAYNE, A.I.L., 1977. Stock differentiation and growth of the southern African kingklip *Genypterus capensis. Invest. Rep. Sea Fish. Branch (S. Afr.),* (113): 1-32.

PEARCE, A.F., 1977. The shelf circulation of the east coast of South Africa. *N.R.I.O. Stellenbosch Prof. Res. Ser.,* (1): 1-220.

PENRITH, M.J., 1967. The fishes of Tristan da Cunha, Gough Island and the Vema seamount. *Ann. S. Afr. Mus.,* **48**(22): 523-549.

PENRITH, M.J., 1972. The behaviour of reef-dwelling sparid fishes. *Zool. Afr.,* **7**(1): 43-48.

PENRITH, M.J., 1972. Sex reversal in the sparid fish *Chrysoblephus laticeps. Koedoe.,* **15**: 135-139.

PENRITH, M.J., 1976. Distribution of shallow water marine fishes around southern Africa. *Cimbebasia,* **4**(7): 138-154.

PENRITH, M.J., 1978. An annotated check-list of the inshore fishes of Southern Angola. *Cimbebasia,* (4)**1**(11): 179-190.

PETERS, W.C.H., 1855. Uebersicht der in Mossambique beobachteten Seefische. *Arch. Naturgesch. 21 Jahrg.* 1: 234-282.

PILLAI, P.K.M., 1972. Fecundity and spawning habits of some silverbellies. *Indian J. Fish.* **19**(1-2): 196-199.

PILLAI, P.P. and HONMA, M., 1978. Seasonal and areal distribution of the pelagic sharks taken by the tuna longline in the Indian Ocean. *Bull. Far Seas Fish. Res. Lab.* (16): 33-49.

PILLAI, P.P. and UEYANAGI, S., 1978. Distribution and biology of the striped marlin *Tetrapturus audax* (Philippi) taken by the longline fishery in the Indian Ocean. *Bull. Far Seas Fish. Res. Lab.,* (16): 9-32.

PLAYFAIR, R.L. and GÜNTHER, A.L.G., 1866. The fishes and Zanzibar. London, John van Voorst.

POLLEN, F.L., 1874. Les pêches à Madagascar et ses dépendances. *In:* POLLEN, P.L. and VAN DAM, D.C. Recherches sur la fauna de Madagascar et ses dépendances d'après les decouvertes de Francois. Pt. 4.

RANDALL, J.E., 1961. A contribution to the biology of the convict surgeonfish of the Hawaiian islands. *Acanthurus triostegus sandvicensis. Pacif. Sci.,* **15**(2): 215-272.

RANDALL, J.E. and CALDWELL, D.K., 1970. Clarification of the species of the butterflyfish genus *Forcipiger. Copeia,* (4): 727-731.

RANDALL, J.E. and EMERY, A.R., 1971. On the resemblance of the young of the fishes *Platax pinnatus* and *Plectorhynchus chaetodontoides* to flatworms and nudibranchs. *Zoologica.,* **56**:115-119.

RANDALL, J.E., ALLEN, G.R. and SMITH-VANIZ, F.W., 1978. Illustrated identification guide to commercial fishes. Rome, FAO, FI:DP/RAB/71/278/3: 1-221.

RANGARAJAN, K., 1971. Maturity and spawning of the snapper, *Lutianus kasmira* (Forsskål) from the Andaman sea. *Indian J. Fish.,* **18**(1-2): 114-125.

RANGARAJAN, K., 1973. Length-weight relationship in the snapper *Lutianus kasmira. Indian J. Fish.,* **20**(1): 205-208.

RAO, A.V., 1968. Observations on the food and feeding habits of *Gerres oyena* (Forsskål) and *Gerres filamentosus* (Cuvier) from the Pulicat Lake with notes on the food of allied species. *J. mar. biol. Ass. India.,* **10**(2): 332-346.

RAO, A.V., 1970. Observations on the larval ingress of the milkfish. *Chanos chanos* (Forsskål) into the Pulicat Lake. *J. mar. biol. Ass. India.,* **13**(2): 249-257.

REED, W., 1964. Red sea fishes of Sudan. Khartoum, Min. Animal Res.: 1-112.

REINTJIES, J.W., 1974. Five spot herring *Hilsa kelee* and other marine clupeoid resources of South India. *J. mar. biol. Ass. India,* **6**(2): 523-527.

RICHARDS, C.E., 1967. Age, growth and fecundity of the cobia. *Rachycentron canadum,* from Chesapeake Bay and adjacent mid Atlantic waters. *Trans. Am. Fish. Soc.,* **96**(3): 343-350.

ROBERTSON, D.R., 1972. Social control of sex reversal in a coral reef fish. *Science,* **177**: 1007-1009.

ROBINS, C.R., BAILEY, R.M., BOND, C.E., BROOKER, J.R., LACHNER, E.A., LEA., R.N. and SCOTT, W.B., 1980. A list of common and scientific names of fishes from the United States and Canada, 4th ed. *Spec. Publ. Am. Fish. Soc.,* (12): 1-174.

ROBINSON, R., 1916. History of local names of some South African fishes. *Mar. biol. Rep., C.T.:* **(3)**: 62-68.

ROBINSON, R. and DUNN, J.S., 1923. Salt water angling in South Africa, Durban, Robinson: 1-315.

ROEDEL, P.M., 1953. Common ocean fishes of the Californian coast. *Bull. Dep. Fish. Game St. Calif.* (91): 1-184.

ROSE, C.D. and HASSLER, W.W., 1968. Age and growth of the dolphin, *Coryphaena hippurus* (Linnaeus) in North Carolina waters. *Trans. Am. Fish. Soc.,* **97**(3): 271-276.

ROSSOUW, G.J., 1983. The biology of the sandshark *Rhinobatus annulatus,* in Algoa Bay with notes on other elasmobranchs. Unpublished Ph.D. thesis. University of Port Elizabeth, Port Elizabeth: 1-180.

SALE, P.F., 1968. Influence of cover availability on depth preference of the juvenile manini, *Acanthurus triostegus sandvicensis. Copeia,* (4): 802-807.

SCHULTZ, L.P., HERALD, E.S., LACHNER, E.A., WELANDER, A.D. and WOODS, L.P., 1953. Fishes of the Marshall and Marianas Islands. v.1. *Bull. U.S. natn. Mus.,* (202): 1-685.

SESHAPPA, E., 1969. The problem of age-determination in the Indian mackerel. *Rastrelliger kanagurta,* by means of scales and otoliths. *Indian J. Fish.,* **16**(1-2): 14-28.

SHOMURA, R.S. and WILLIAMS, F. *eds,* 1974. Proceedings of the international billfish symposium *Kailua-kona, Hawaii, 9-12 Aug. 1972.* Pt.2. Review and contributed papers. *NOAA Tech. Rep. NMFS (Spec. Sci. Rep.-Fish Ser.),* 675: 1-335.

SHOMURA, R.S. and WILLIAMS, F. *eds,* 1975. Proceedings of the international billfish symposium, *Kailua-kona, Hawaii,* 9-12 Aug. 1972. Pt. 3. Species synopses. *NOAA Tech. Rep. NMFS (Spec. Sci. Rep.-Fish. Ser.).* 675: 1-159.

SILAS, E.G. and DAWSON, E., 1959. On the concealing behaviour of the tigerfish, *Therapon jarbua* (Forsskål). *J. mar. biol. Ass. India,* (1): 252-253.

SKILLMAN, R.A. AND YOUNG, M.Y., 1976. Von Bertalanffy growth curves for striped marlin, *Tetrapturus audax,* and blue marlin, *Makaira nigricans,* in the central north Pacific Ocean. *Fish. Bull. U.S.,* **74**(3): 553-566.

SMALE, M.J., 1983. Resource partitioning by top predatory teleosts in the Eastern Cape coastal waters (South Africa). Unpublished Ph.D. thesis, Rhodes University, Grahamstown: 1-285.

SMITH, D.G., 1979. Guide to the Leptocephali (Elopiformes, Anguilliformes and Notacanthiformes) *NOAA Tech. Rep. NMFS Circular,* 424: 1-39.

SMITH, J.L.B., 1938. The South African fishes of the families Sparidae and Denticidae. *Trans. R. Soc. S. Afr.,* **26**(3): 225-305.

SMITH, J.L.B., 1949. The Sea Fishes of Southern Africa, Cape Town, CNA: 1-580.

SMITH, J.L.B., 1959. Serioline fishes (yellowtails: amberjacks) from the western Indian Ocean. *Ichthyol. Bull. Rhodes Univ.,* (15): 255-261.

SMITH, J.L.B., 1962. The sparid genus Lithognathus Swainson, 1938, with a description of an interesting new species. *S. Afr. J Sci.,* **58**: 109-114.

SMITH, J.L.B., 1965. New records and descriptions of fishes from Southwest Africa. *Occas. Pap. J.L.B. Smith Inst. Ichthyol.,* (3): 13-23.

SMITH, J.L.B., 1966. Interesting fishes from South Africa. *Occas Pap. J.L.B. Smith Inst. Ichthyol.,* (8): 83-95.

SMITH, J.L.B., 1967. Studies in carangid fishes, 3: The genus *Trachinotus* Lacepede, in the western Indian Ocean. *Occas. Pap. J.L.B. Smith Inst. Ichthyol.,* (14): 150-166.

SMITH, J.L.B., 1968. Studies in carangid fishes, 4. The identity of *Scomber sansun* Forsskål 1775. *Occas. Pap. J.L.B. Smith Inst. Ichthyol.,* (15): 173-184.

SMITH, J.L.B., 1969. Ichthyological bulletins (1-20), 1956-1961. *J.L.B. Smith Inst. Ichthyol.: 1-356.*

SMITH, J.L.B., 1970. Studies in carangid fishes, 5. The genus *Chorinemus* Cuvier, 1831 in the western Indian Ocean. *Occas. Pap. J.L.B. Smith Inst. Ichthyol.,* (17): 217-228.

SMITH, J.L.B., 1973. Ichthyological bulletins (21-32), 1961-1966. *J.L.B. Smith Inst. Ichthyol.:* 357-682.

SMITH, J.L.B. and SMITH, M.M., 1963. The fishes of Seychelles. Grahamstown, Rhodes Univ.: 1-215.

SMITH, J.L.B. and SMITH, M.M., 1966. Fishes of the Tsitsikama coastal National Park. Jhb., Swan: 1-161.

SMITH, M.M. *(ed),* 1969. J.L.B. Smith Ichthyological papers 1931-1943, vols 1 & 2. Grahamstown, Rhodes Univ.: 1-576.

SMITH, M.M., 1970. Endemism in South African marine fishes. Oceanography in South Africa - 1970. SANCOR symposium, *Durban, 4-6 Aug. 1970.* (H3): 1-11. Unpublished paper.

SMITH, M.M., 1975. Common and scientific names of the fishes of southern Africa. I. Marine fishes. *Spec. Publ. J.L.B. Smith Inst. Ichthyol.,* (14): 1-178.

SMITH, M.M., 1979. *Rhabdosargus thorpei,* a new sparid from South Africa, with a key to the species of *Rhabdosargus. Copeia,* (4): 702-709.

SMITH, M.M., 1980. A review of the South African Cheilodactylid fishes (Pisces: Perciformes) with descriptions of two new species. *Ichthyol. Bull., J.L.B. Smith Inst. Ichthyol.,* (42): 1-15.

SMITH, M.M. & HEEMSTRA, P.C., *eds.,* 1986. Smiths' Sea Fishes. Macmillan, Johannesburg: 1-1047.

SMITH-VANIZ, F.W. and STAIGER, J.C., 1973. Comparative revision of *Scomberoides, Oligaplites, Parona* and *Hypacanthus* with comments on the phylogenetic position of *Campogramma* (Pisces: Carangidae): *Proc. Calif. Acad. Sci.,* **34**(13): 185-256.

SPRINGER, V.E. and SMITH-VANIZ, W.F., 1972. Mimetic relationships involving fishes of the family Blenniidae. *Smithson. Contrib. Zool.,* (112): 1-36.

SQUIRE, J.L. AND SMITH, S.E., 1977. Anglers guide to the United States Pacific coast. Seattle, U.S. Dept. Commerce, NOAA. NMFS: 1-139.

SREENIVASAN, P.V., 1976. Records of six species of carangids from the southwest coast of India. *Indian J. Fish.,* **23**(1-2): 41-56.

STEBBINGS, R.C. and KALK, M., 1961. Observations on the natural history of the mud-skipper, *Perioptha1mus sobrinus, Copeia,* (1): 18-27.

STRASSBURG, D.W., 1962. Pelagic stages of *Zanclus canescens* from Hawaii. *Copeia,* (4): 844.

SUAU, P., 1970. Contribucion al estudio de la biologia de *Lithognathus (= Pagellus) mormyrus* L. (Peces espáridos. *Investigacion pesq.,* (34): 237-265.

SUSEELAN, C. and SOMASEKHARAN NAIR. K.V., 1969. Food and feeding habits of the demersal fishes off Bombay. *Indian J. Fish.,* **16**(1-2): 56-74.

SUZUKI, Z., 1971. Comparison of growth parameters estimated for the yellowfin tuna in the Pacific Ocean. *Bull. Far Seas Fish. Res. Lab.,* (5): 89-105.

TAKAHASHI, M. and MORI, K., 1973. Studies on relative growth in body parts compared in *Coryphaena hippurus* and *C. equiselis,* and notes on gonadal maturation in the latter species. *Bull. Far Seas Fish. Res. Lab.,* (8): 73-113.

TALBOT, F.H., 1955. Notes on the biology of the white stumpnose, *Rhabdosargus globiceps* (Cuvier), and on the fish fauna of the Klein River estuary. *Trans. R. Soc. S. Afr.,* **34**(3): 387-407.

TALBOT, F.H., 1960. Notes on the biology of the Lutjanidae (Pisces) of the East African coast, with special reference to *L. bohar* (Forsskål). *Ann. S. Afr. Mus.,* **45**(5): 549-573.

TALBOT, F.H. and WILLIAMS, F., 1956. Sexual colour differences in *Caranx ignobilis* (Forsk.). *Nature,* Lond., **178**: 934.

TALBOT, F.H. and PENRITH, M.J., 1968. The tunas of the genus *Thunnus* in South African waters. *Ann. S. Afr.*

Mus., **52**: 1-41.
TARBITT, J., 1980. Demersal trawling in Seychelles waters. Fish. *Bull. Fish. Div. Seychelles,* (4): 1-84.
TORTONESE, E., 1956. Fauna d'Italia: 2. Leptocardia, Ciclostomata, Selachii. Bologna, Calderina: 1-334.
TREWAVAS, E., 1977. The sciaenid fishes (croakers or drums) of the Indo-west-Pacific. *Trans zool. Soc. Lond.,* **33**: 1-541.
TSUKAHARA, H., 1962. Biology of the cutlassfish, *Trichiurus lepturus* Linnaeus: 2. age and growth. *Rec. oceanogr. wks Japan,* (6): 57-64.
UCHIDA, R.N., 1981. Synopsis of the biological data on frigate tuna. *Auxis thazard* and bullet tuna, *A. rochei. NOAA Tech. Rep. NMFS Circular 436, NMFS/S 124.*
VAN BRUGGEN, A.C., 1965. Records and observations in the Port Elizabeth Oceanarium in 1960 *Zool. Gert.,* **31**: 184-202.
VAN DER ELST, R.P., 1976. Game fish of the east coast of southern Africa: 1. The biology of the elf *Pomatomus saltatrix* (Linnaeus) in the coastal waters of Natal. *Invest. Rep oceanogr. Res. Inst.,* (44): 1-59.
VAN DER ELST, R.P., 1978. The St Lucia sport fishery - a 21 year catch analysis. Oceanographic Research Institute. Durban: 1-16. Unpublished report.
VAN DER ELST, R.P., 1979. The marine sport fishery of Maputaland. *In:* BRUTON, M.N. and COOPER, K.H., Studies on the ecology of Maputaland. Grahamstown, *J.L.B. Smith Inst. Ichthyol.,* Rhodes Univ.: 188-197.
VAN DER ELST, R.P., 1979. A proliferation of small sharks in the Natal shorebased sport fishery. *Environ. Biol. Fish.* **4**(4): 349-362.
VAN DER ELST, R.P. and WALLACE, J.H., 1976. Identification of the juvenile mullet of the east coast of South Africa. *J. Fish. biol.,* **9**(4): 371-374.
VAN DER WESTHUIZEN, H.C. and MARAIS, J.F.K., 1977. Stomach content analyses of *Pomadasys commersonni* from the Swartkops Estuary. *Zool. Afr.,* **12**: 500-504.
VON WESTERNHAGEN, H. 1973. The natural food of the rabbitfish *Siganus oramin* and *S. striolata. Mar. Biol.,* **22**: 367-370.
VON WESTERNHAGEN, H., 1974. Observations on the natural spawning of *Alectis indicus* (Rüppell) and *Caranx ignobilis* (Forsk.) (Carangidae). *J. Fish Biol.,* **6**: 513-516.
WALLACE, J.H., 1967. The batoid fishes of the east coast of southern Africa: I. Sawfishes and guitarfishes. *Invest. Rep. oceanogr. Res. Inst.,* (15): 1-32.
WALLACE, J.H., 1967. The batoid fishes of the east coast of southern Africa: II. Manta, eagle, duckbill, cownose, butterfly and sting rays. *Invest. Rep. oceanogr. Res. Inst.,* (16): 1-56.
WALLACE, J.H., 1967. The batoid fishes of the east coast of southern Africa: III. Skates and electric rays. *Invest. Rep. oceanogr. Res. Inst.,* (17): 1-62.
WALLACE, J.H., 1975. The estuarine fishes of the East Coast of South Africa. I Species composition and length distribution in the estuarine and marine environments. II Seasonal abundance and migrations. *Invest. Rep. oceanogr. Res. Inst.,* (40): 1-72.
WALLACE, J.H., 1975. The estuarine fishes of the East Coast of South Africa. III Reproduction. *Invest. Rep. oceanogr. Res. inst.,* (41): 1-51.
WALLACE, J.H. and SCHLEYER, M.H., 1979. Age determination in two important species of South African angling fishes, the kob *(Argyrosomus hololepidotus* Lacep.) and the spotted grunter *(Pomadasys commersonni* Lacep.). *Trans. R. Soc. S. Afr.,* **44**: 15-26.
WALLACE, J.H. and VAN DER ELST, R.P., 1975. The estuarine fishes of the East Coast of South Africa. IV Occurrence of juveniles in estuaries. V Biology, estuarine dependence and status. *Invest. Rep. oceanogr. Res. Inst.,* (42): 1-63.
WHEELER, A., 1978. Key to the fishes of northern Europe. London, Warne: 1-380.
WHEELER, J.F.G. and OMMANNEY, F.D., 1953. Report on the Mauritius-Seychelles fisheries survey - 1948-1949. *Fish. Publ. London,* (3): 1-148.
WILLIAMS, F., 1958. Fishes of the family Carangidae in British East African waters. *Ann. Mag. nat. Hist.,* **13**(1): 369-430.
WILLIAMS, F., 1959. The barracudas (genus *Sphyraena)* in British East African waters. *Ann. Mag. nat. Hist.,* **13**(2): 92-128.
WILLIAMS, F., 1962. The scombroid fishes of East Africa. Symposium on scombroid fishes - part 1. Mandapam, India.: 107-164.
WILLIAMS, F., 1962. Synopsis of biological data on little tuna *Euthynnus affinis* (Cantor) 1850 (Indian Ocean). World scientific meeting on the biology of tunas and related species. FAO, Rome: Species synopsis (5): 13 pp.
WILLIAMS, F., 1965. Further notes on the biology of East African pelagic fishes of the families Carangidae and Sphyraenidae. *E. Afr. agric. For. J.,* **31**(2): 141-168.
WILLIAMS, F. and VENKATATAMANI, V.K., 1978. Notes on Indo-Pacific carangid fishes of the genus *Carangoides* Bleeker. 1. The *Carangoides malabaricus* group. *Bull. Mar. Sci.,* **28**(3): 501-511.
YABUTA, Y. and YUKINAWA, M., 1961. Age and growth of yellowfin tuna. Pacific tuna biology conference, Honolulu: Unpublished report.
YESAKI, M., 1979. Rainbow runner: A latent oceanic resource? *Mar. Fish. Rev.,* **41**(8): 1-6.
YOSHIDA, H.O., 1979. Synopsis of biological data on tunas of the genus *Euthynnus. NOAA Tech. Rep. NMFS. Circular 429, NMFS/S 122:* 1-57.
YOSHIDA, H.O., 1980. Synopsis of biological data on bonitos of the genus *Sarda. NOAA Tech. Rep. NMFS/S 118.*
ZOUTENDYK, P., 1973. The biology of the Agulhas sole, *Austroglossus pectoralis,* I. Environment and trawling grounds. *Trans. R. Soc. S. Afr.,* **40**(5): 349-366.
ZOUTENDYK, P., 1974. The biology of the Agulhas sole, *Austroglossus pectoralis,* 2. Age and growth. *Trans. R. Soc. S. Afr.,* **41**(1): 33-41.
ZOUTENDYK, P., 1974. The biology of the Agulhas sole, *Austroglossus pectoralis,* 3. Length-weight relationships. *Trans. R. Soc. Afr.,* **41**(2): 99-110.

INDEX

A

B

C

Q

R

S